Talaro's Foundations in
Microbiology
Basic Principles

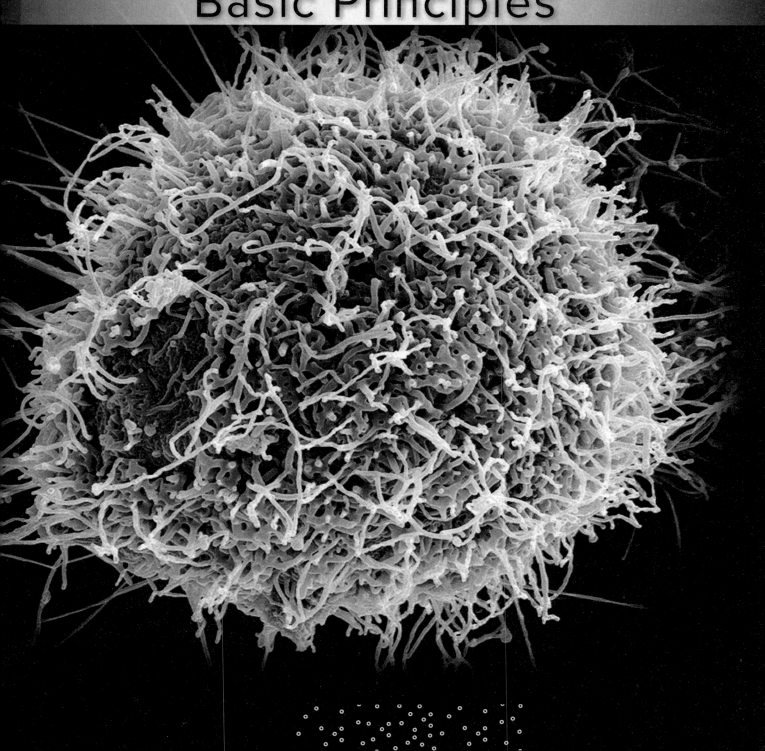

Talaro's Foundations in Microbiology

Basic Principles

Eleventh Edition

McGraw Hill

Barry Chess

FOUNDATIONS IN MICROBIOLOGY BASIC PRINCIPLES

ISBN 978-1-260-57538-5
MHID 1-260-57538-1

Cover Image: *Filamentous Ebola virus particles (colored blue) budding from a chronically-infected VERO E6 cell (colored yellow). Callista Images/Getty Images*

mheducation.com/highered

Brief Contents

Barry Chess has taught microbiology at Pasadena City College for more than 20 years. Prior to that, while studying at the California State University and the University of California, he conducted research into the expression of genes involved in the development of muscle and bone.

At PCC, beyond his usual presence in the microbiology laboratory and lecture hall, Barry has taught majors and non-majors biology, developed a course in human genetics, helped to found a biotechnology program on campus, and regularly supervises students completing independent research projects in the life sciences. Of late, his interests focus on innovative methods of teaching that lead to greater student success. He has written and reviewed cases for the National Center for Case Study Teaching in Science and contributed to the book *Science Stories You Can Count On: 51 Case Studies with Quantitative Reasoning in Biology*. Barry has presented papers and talks on the effective use of case studies in the classroom, the use of digital tools to enhance learning, and for several years served as a scientific advisor for the American Film Institute.

In addition to *Foundations in Microbiology*, Barry is the author of *Laboratory Applications in Microbiology, A Case Study Approach*, now in its fourth edition. He is a member of the American Association for the Advancement of Science, the American Society for Microbiology, and the Skeptics Society. When not teaching or writing, he spends as much time as possible with water; skiing atop it in winter and diving beneath it in summer. Barry was profiled in the book *What Scientists Actually Do*, where he was illustrated as a young girl with pigtails, about to stick a fork into an electrical outlet.

Barry Chess

Callista Images/Getty Images

The eleventh edition marks the first time that Kathy Talaro has been absent from this book. In creating *Foundations in Microbiology* she revolutionized how we teach the subject, and every other text in the field uses methods, ideas, and examples that Kathy pioneered. Personally, Kathy has been a friend and mentor for more than 20 years. By stepping away, Kathy will once again have the opportunity to wonder at the microbes around her, without having to simultaneously worry about what needs to be cut from Chapter 17.

 are used in the sections below.

FOR INSTRUCTORS

You're in the driver's seat.

Want to build your own course? No problem. Prefer to use our turnkey, prebuilt course? Easy. Want to make changes throughout the semester? Sure. And you'll save time with Connect's auto-grading too.

65%
Less Time Grading

Laptop: McGraw-Hill; Woman/dog: George Doyle/Getty Images

They'll thank you for it.

Adaptive study resources like SmartBook® 2.0 help your students be better prepared in less time. You can transform your class time from dull definitions to dynamic debates. Find out more about the powerful personalized learning experience available in SmartBook 2.0 at **www.mheducation.com/highered /connect/smartbook**

Make it simple, make it affordable.

Connect makes it easy with seamless integration using any of the major Learning Management Systems— Blackboard®, Canvas, and D2L, among others—to let you organize your course in one convenient location. Give your students access to digital materials at a discount with our inclusive access program. Ask your McGraw-Hill representative for more information.

Padlock: Jobalou/Getty Images

Solutions for your challenges.

A product isn't a solution. Real solutions are affordable, reliable, and come with training and ongoing support when you need it and how you want it. Our Customer Experience Group can also help you troubleshoot tech problems— although Connect's 99% uptime means you might not need to call them. See for yourself at **status .mheducation.com**

Checkmark: Jobalou/Getty Images

FOR STUDENTS

Effective, efficient studying.

Connect helps you be more productive with your study time and get better grades using tools like SmartBook 2.0, which highlights key concepts and creates a personalized study plan. Connect sets you up for success, so you walk into class with confidence and walk out with better grades.

Study anytime, anywhere.

Download the free ReadAnywhere app and access your online eBook or SmartBook 2.0 assignments when it's convenient, even if you're offline. And since the app automatically syncs with your eBook and SmartBook 2.0 assignments in Connect, all of your work is available every time you open it. Find out more at **www.mheducation.com/readanywhere**

"I really liked this app—it made it easy to study when you don't have your text-book in front of you."

- Jordan Cunningham, Eastern Washington University

No surprises.

The Connect Calendar and Reports tools keep you on track with the work you need to get done and your assignment scores. Life gets busy; Connect tools help you keep learning through it all.

Calendar: owattaphotos/Getty Images

Learning for everyone.

McGraw-Hill works directly with Accessibility Services Departments and faculty to meet the learning needs of all students. Please contact your Accessibility Services office and ask them to email accessibility@mheducation.com, or visit **www.mheducation.com/about/accessibility** for more information.

Save time with auto-graded assessments. Gather powerful performance data.

McGraw-Hill Connect for *Talaro's Foundations in Microbiology* provides online presentation, assignment, and assessment solutions, connecting your students with the tools and resources they'll need to achieve success.

Homework and Assessment

With **Connect for *Talaro's Foundations in Microbiology*,** you can deliver auto-graded assignments, quizzes, and tests online. Choose from a robust set of interactive questions and activities using high-quality art from the textbook and animations. Assignable content is available for every Learning Outcome in the book and is categorized according to the **ASM Curriculum Guidelines.** As an instructor, you can edit existing questions and author entirely new ones.

Significant faculty demand for content at higher Bloom's levels led us to examine assessment quality and consistency of our Connect content, to develop a scientific approach to systemically increase critical-thinking levels, and develop balanced digital assessments that promote student learning. The increased challenge at higher Bloom's levels will help the student grow intellectually and be better prepared to contribute to society.

Detailed Reports

Track individual student performance—by question, by assignment, or in relation to the class overall—with detailed grade reports. Integrate grade reports easily with your Learning Management Systems (LMS).

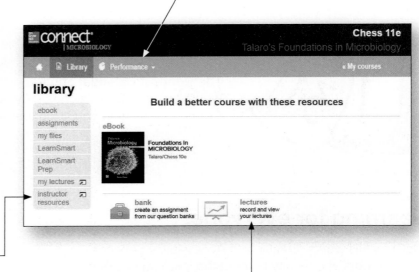

Instructor Resources

Customize your lecture with tools such as PowerPoint® presentations, animations, and editable art from the textbook. An instructor's manual for the text saves you time in developing your course.

Lecture Capture

McGraw-Hill Tegrity® records and distributes your class lecture with just a click of a button. Students can view anytime, anywhere via computer or mobile device. Indexed as you record, students can use keywords to find exactly what they want to study.

Learn more at connect.mheducation.com

Integrated and Adaptive Tools

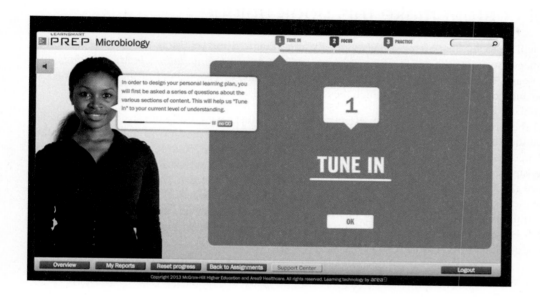

LearnSmart® Prep is an adaptive learning tool that prepares students for college-level work in microbiology. LearnSmart Prep individually identifies concepts the student does not fully understand and provides learning resources to teach essential concepts so he or she enters the classroom prepared. Data-driven reports highlight areas where students are struggling, helping to accurately identify weak areas.

SmartBook 2.0 is the adaptive learning solution that is personalized to individual student needs, continually adapting to pinpoint knowledge gaps and focus learning on concepts requiring additional study. For instructors, SmartBook 2.0 provides greater control over course content and performance data—most importantly, students are better prepared, so instructors can focus on advanced instruction for a more dynamic class experience.

Download the ReadAnywhere App to study anytime, anywhere!

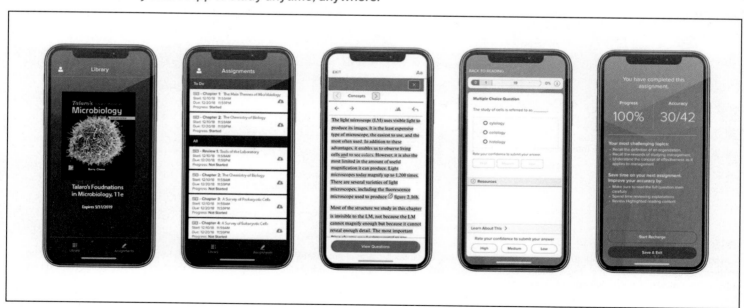

Art and organization of content make this book unique

You always hope that the current revision will be easier, that after 11 editions and 30 years you've finally managed to create the perfect book. But, of course, that's never the case. Crafting a truly useful learning tool for students takes time and dedication. Every line of text and every piece of art is scrutinized for instructional usefulness, placement, and pedagogy, and then reexamined with each revision. In this eleventh edition, the author has gone through the book page by page, with more depth than ever before, to make sure it maintains its instructional quality, superior art program, currency, and engaging writing style. Since the first edition, the goals of this book have been to explain complex topics clearly and vividly, and to present the material in a straightforward manner that students can understand. The eleventh edition continues to meet these goals with the most digitally integrated, up-to-date, and pedagogically important revision yet. More than a compendium of facts, figures, and photographs, *Foundations in Microbiology* tells a story of microorganisms, of people, and of the myriad ways in which they interact.

An effective textbook must be carefully constructed to place art where it makes the most sense in the flow of the narrative; create process figures that break down complex processes into their component parts; and provide explanations that are clear, concise, and correctly targeted to the reader, with pedagogical tools that help all types of learners. Hopefully, the time and effort put into this revision shows, so that when the pieces come together, the result is an expertly crafted learning tool—a story of the microbial world.

A strong art program is a defining quality of an effective textbook. Complex biological processes can be disassembled into their component parts, allowing understanding to take place one step at a time. Working closely with scientific illustrators, Barry Chess ensures that *Foundations in Microbiology* has an art program that allows difficult concepts to come to life.

Chapter-Opening Case Studies

Each chapter opens with a two-page introduction. On the left is a synopsis of the chapter's contents, while the right side contains the first part of the Case Study, which has been carefully chosen to exhibit microbiology in real-world situations. Line art and micrographs are all part of the chapter-opening pages to help students see the big picture and grasp the relevance of the material they're about to study. Questions appearing after the chapter opener serve as prompts to the most important aspects of the case, providing students with touchstones to lean on as they learn. The chapter concludes with the second part of the Case Study, which resolves the microbiological (and occasionally social, political, and economic) aspects of the case. Once again, questions follow, helping students to reinforce their newfound knowledge, and use it to develop a more inquisitive view of the broader world.

CASE STUDY Part 1 | **When a Body Can't Get Out of Its Own Way**

Certain combinations of **signs** and **symptoms** are guaranteed to garner the attention of an emergency room physician, because they signal a serious, **emergent situation**. So, when a young woman seen by emergency room doctors displayed **tachypenea** (rapid breathing), a depressed level of consciousness, and **fever**, she was immediately admitted to the hospital for further examination. She also exhibited low blood pressure, had not passed any urine that day, and had a blueish tinge to her fingers and toes, a clinical presentation compatible with **sepsis**. Sepsis is a serious complication of infection that occurs when chemicals released by the body trigger an overwhelming inflammatory response. Without rapid, aggressive treatment, sepsis can quickly lead to death.

Laboratory tests were also consistent with sepsis, as the patient had a **low platelet count** and a decreased number of infection-fighting **leukocytes**. Elevated levels of C-reactive protein indicated widespread inflammation throughout the body, while blood tests showed damage to the liver and kidneys, along with intravascular coagulation. Sepsis was causing her body to shut down.

The patient, though only 15 years old, was no stranger to the hospital. She had been diagnosed with **systemic lupus erythematosus (SLE**, or simply lupus) at the age of 6 and had an extensive medical history. Lupus is an autoimmune disorder in which the body's immune system attacks itself by producing **antibodies** against the nuclei of its own cells. **Inflammation** due to lupus can affect the skin, joints, kidneys, liver, heart, and lungs, with symptoms ranging from mild to severe, and fluctuating greatly over time. In less than 9 years, the patient had already experienced nephritis, pancreatitis, hemolytic anemia, and arterial hypertension, all due to a particularly aggressive form of the disease. Her lupus was being treated with corticosteroids along with multiple **immunosuppressive drugs**, including methotrexate and cyclophosphamide. She was last seen at the hospital 3 months previously, where she displayed no clinical manifestations of SLE.

A chest X-ray was unremarkable, while a computed tomography (CT) scan revealed sinusitis, likely not enough to cause the symptoms seen in the patient. *Streptococcus pneumoniae* was cultured from both the blood, indicating a **systemic infection**, and cerebrospinal fluid, indicating **meningitis**. *Streptococcus pneumoniae* is a gram-positive, heavily **encapsulated** bacterium, commonly responsible for infections of the sinuses, lungs, blood, and meninges. An MRI (magnetic resonance imaging) scan was performed, the results of which were remarkable not for what was seen, but for what was absent. The patient did not have a spleen.

- *Inflammation is normally part of what line of defense?*

- *If the immune system functioned properly, what type of white blood cell would be increased in number in this case?*

To continue the Case Study, go to Case Study Part 2 at the end of the chapter.

Plush Studios/Blend Images LLC

Illustrated to Increase Understanding

The author's experience and talent transform difficult concepts

Truly instructional artwork has always been a hallmark feature of *Foundations in Microbiology*, and the eleventh edition of the book continues to set the standard. Common sense, backed by many decades of research, have shown that when abstract concepts are explained using scientifically accurate illustrations, understanding is increased. Powerful artwork that paints a conceptual picture for students is more important than ever for today's visual learners. *Foundations in Microbiology*'s art program combines vivid colors, multidimensionality, and self-contained narrative to help students study the challenging concepts of microbiology.

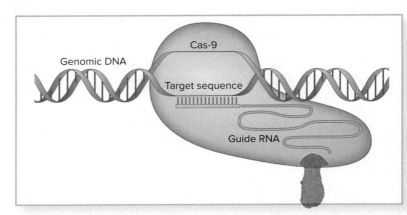

Process Figures

Process figures break down difficult concepts to more clearly illustrate their component parts. Each step is clearly numbered, making the entire process easy to follow for all types of learners. A distinctive icon identifies each process figure and, when needed, the accompanying legend provides additional explanation.

Clinical photos help students visualize

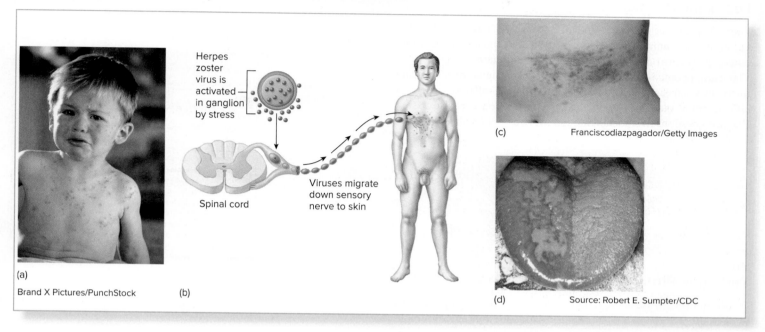

Herpes zoster virus is activated in ganglion by stress

Spinal cord

Viruses migrate down sensory nerve to skin

(a)

Brand X Pictures/PunchStock

(b)

(c) Franciscodiazpagador/Getty Images

(d) Source: Robert E. Sumpter/CDC

Modern Processes

Microbial diagnostics are not what they were 20 years ago. Automated diagnostics, rapid tests, and Point-of-Care testing are featured throughout the text.

MS detector

TOF

Laser

Sample

Matrix

MALDI-TOF sample plate

m/z Profile (Match to Database)

Protein/DNA and matrix

⚙ Process Figure 22.4 **MALDI-TOF identification of a fungal sample.** (**1**) Sample of an unknown fungus is combined with a volatile matrix and applied to a metal plate. (**2**) A laser beam heats the sample and matrix, converting them to gas and ionizing DNA and protein molecules in the sample. (**3**) The ions move through a time-of-flight tube, where they are separated by size, as small ions move across the tube faster than larger ones. (**4**) The mass-to-charge ratio (m/z) for each ion is displayed as a spectrum, which is compared to the spectrum produced by other fungi (contained in a database) to determine identification.
(inset): BENPOL/Shutterstock

Learn and Practice

Succinctly answering every student's "What do I need to know?" question, each numbered section in the book opens with learning outcomes (Learn) and closes with assessment questions (Practice). The learning outcomes are tightly correlated to digital materials and instructors can easily measure student learning in relation to the specific learning outcomes used in their course. You can also assign Practice questions to students through McGraw-Hill's Connect.

6.1 Overview of Viruses

Learn

1. Indicate how viruses were discovered and characterized.
2. Describe the unique characteristics of viruses.
3. Discuss the origin and importance of viruses.

Practice SECTION 13.1

1. Describe the significant relationships that humans have with microbes.
2. Explain what is meant by *microbiota* and *microbiome* and summarize their importance to humans.
3. Differentiate between contamination, colonization, infection, and disease, and explain some possible outcomes in each.
4. How are infectious diseases different from other diseases?
5. Outline the general body areas that are sterile and those regions that harbor normal resident microbiota.
6. Differentiate between transient and resident microbes.
7. Explain the factors that cause variations in the microbiota of the newborn intestine and the vaginal tract.

Pathogen Profiles

Pathogen Profiles are abbreviated snapshots of the major pathogens in each disease chapter. The pathogen is featured in a micrograph, along with a description of the microscopic morphology, means of identification, habitat information, and virulence factors. Artwork displays the primary infections/disease, as well as the organs and systems primarily impacted. New to the eleventh edition, each Pathogen Profile also includes a System Profile that presents the pathogen in relation to organs systems affected.

Pathogen Profile #1 *Staphylococcus aureus*

Microscopic Morphology Gram-positive cocci in irregular clusters; nonmotile; non–spore-forming. May form biofilm infections on catheters and other indwelling devices.

Identified By Growth on high-salt (7.5% NaCl or more) media, Gram reaction, and arrangement. Fermentation of sugars distinguishes *Staphylococcus* from *Micrococcus*; catalase production distinguishes *Staphylococcus* from *Streptococcus*. Coagulase production distinguishes *S. aureus* from other species of *Staphylococcus*. Commercially available rapid identification tests rely on antibody-coated latex beads that bind specifically with *S. aureus*.

Source: Janice Carr/CDC

Habitat Carried by 20% to 60% of healthy persons in the nostrils, skin, nasopharynx, and intestine. Very resistant to harsh environmental conditions and routinely present on fomites.

Virulence Factors *S. aureus* possesses enzymes that destroy host tissue (hyaluronidase), digest blood clots (staphylokinase), colonize oily skin (lipase), and resist the effects of penicillin (penicillinase). Toxins (leukocidins) destroy neutrophils and macrophages, lyse red blood cells (hemolysins), and cause damage throughout the body (enterotoxins, exfoliative toxins, toxic shock syndrome toxin).

Primary Infections/Disease Local cutaneous infections include folliculitis, furuncles, and carbuncles, as well as bullous impetigo. Systemic infections include osteomyelitis, pneumonia, and endocarditis. A rare cause of meningitis. Diseases due to *S. aureus* toxins include food intoxication, scalded skin syndrome, and toxic shock syndrome.

Control and Treatment Control of healthcare–associated infection relies on careful hygiene and adequate cleansing of surgical incisions and burns; isolation of persons with open lesions; and barring of *S. aureus* carriers from sensitive areas such as operating rooms and nurseries. Special concern is paid to the strains known as MRSA, which have high levels of drug resistance. Community-acquired infections are controlled through disinfection of shared environments and equipment. Treatment involves intensive chemotherapy, often with multiple antimicrobics. The problem of MRSA strains requires antimicrobial susceptibility testing to select a correct chemotherapeutic agent. Many cutaneous lesions require perforation and drainage prior to antimicrobic therapy.

System Profile

System	Skin/Skeletal	Nervous/Muscle	Cardiovascular/Lymphatic/Systemic	Gastrointestinal	Respiratory
Disease	1. Boils, carbuncles 2. Impetigo 3. Scalded skin syndrome 4. Osteomyelitis	Meningitis	1. Endocarditis 2. Toxic shock syndrome	Food intoxication	Pneumonia

Pathogen Profile #2 *Morbillivirus (measles virus)*

Microscopic Morphology Enveloped virus, 100 to 200 nm in diameter, containing a nonsegmented, single-stranded RNA genome.

Identified By Clinical presentation, especially the appearance of a maculopapular rash and Koplik's spots, which are indicative of measles. Serological testing that reveals measles-specific IgM antibodies early in the course of the disease or a rising IgG titer when comparing acute and convalescent samples confirms a diagnosis of measles.

Source: Cynthia Goldsmith/CDC

Habitat Humans are the only natural reservoir for *Morbillivirus*.

Virulence Factors Syncytium formation.

Primary Infections/Disease Early symptoms of measles (rubeola) include sore throat, dry cough, headache, conjunctivitis, lymphadenitis, and fever, followed by oral lesions called Koplik's spots and a maculopapular rash over most of the body. The most serious complication is subacute sclerosing panencephalitis (SSPE), a progressive neurological disease resulting in coma and death. Less serious complications include secondary bacterial infections such as pneumonia and otitis media.

Control and Treatment The MMR (measles, mumps, rubella) vaccine has greatly reduced the incidence of measles, with deaths in the United States being extremely rare. Worldwide, the disease still claims about 89,000 lives each year. Treatment of measles centers on reducing fever, suppressing cough, and replacing lost fluids. In some cases, secondary bacterial infections may be treated with antibiotics, and children may receive vitamin A supplements.

System Profile

System	Skin/Skeletal	Nervous/Muscle	Cardiovascular/Lymphatic/Systemic	Gastrointestinal	Respiratory	Urogenital
Disease	Measles	Subacute sclerosing panencephalitis				

Pedagogy created to promote active learning

Clinical Connections

Clinical Connections boxes, found throughout the book, provide students with concrete examples of the central role microbiology plays in the health care environment. Generally no longer than half a page, each feature creates a link for students between microbiological theory and clinical practice. Each Clinical Connections box ends with a question requiring students to use knowledge from the chapter to analyze or evaluate real-life problems.

CLINICAL CONNECTIONS

The Immunological Benefits of Breast-Feeding

An advertising slogan from the past claims that cow's milk is "nature's most nearly perfect food." One could go a step farther and assert that human milk is nature's *perfect* food for young humans. Clearly, it is loaded with essential nutrients, not to mention being available on demand from a readily portable, hygienic container that does not require refrigeration or warming. But there is another and perhaps even greater benefit. During lactation, the breast becomes a site for the proliferation of lymphocytes that produce IgA antibodies that protect the mucosal surfaces from local invasion by microbes. The very earliest secretion of the breast, a thin, yellow milk called **colostrum**, is very high in these antibodies. They form a protective coating in the gastrointestinal tract of a nursing infant that guards against infection by a number of enteric pathogens (*Escherichia coli*, *Salmonella*, poliovirus, rotavirus). Protection at this level is especially critical because an infant's own antibodies and natural intestinal barriers are not yet developed. As with immunity in utero, the necessary antibodies will be donated only if the mother herself has active immunity to the microbe through a prior infection or vaccination.

A critical benefit of breast-feeding that has not been given adequate credit is the connection between nursing, the breast microbiome, and the neonatal microbiome. For many years, milk was

International symbol for breast feeding
Lukasz Stefanski/Shutterstock

thought to be sterile unless the mother's breasts were infected. Now we know from studies on the human microbiome that breast milk and tissues harbor a diverse bacterial community that is distinct from that of the skin or the mouth. This discovery acknowledges that, in addition to its nutritional and immunological support, breast milk is an important early source of microbes that populate the newborn intestine and other body sites. A related function of the breast microbiome could be to supply bacterial stimuli for the continuing development of the baby's immune system.

For a number of years, the ready availability of artificial formulas and the changing lifestyles of women have reduced the incidence of breast-feeding. According to UNICEF, only about 38% of mothers worldwide breast-feed their babies for 6 months or more. Where adequate hygiene and medical care prevail, bottle-fed infants get through the critical period with few problems because the foods given them are relatively free of pathogens and they have received protection against some childhood infections in utero. Mothers in developing countries with untreated water supplies or poor medical services are strongly discouraged from using prepared formulas, because they can actually inoculate the baby's intestine with pathogens from the formula. Millions of neonates suffer from severe and life-threatening diarrhea that could have been prevented by sustained breast-feeding. The use of formula has been so damaging to infant health that the World Health Organization issued an *International Code on the Marketing of Breast Milk Substitutes*, discouraging the use of formula in the developing world.

Explain the reasons donated antibodies (either placental or in breast milk) are only a temporary protection.

Quick Search

This feature reminds students that videos, animations, and pictorial displays that provide further information on the topic are just a click away using their smartphone, tablet, or computer. This integration of learning via technology helps students become more engaged and empowered in their study of the featured topic.

> **Quick Search**
>
> Search the Web using the phrase "Bacterial Pathogen Pronunciation Station" for help in correctly pronouncing some common scientific names.

> **Quick Search**
>
> To compare the types of movement seen in eukaryotes, find videos using the search words *amoebic*, *flagellate*, and *ciliate movement* on YouTube.

Footnotes

Footnotes provide the reader with additional information about the text content.

4. A mnemonic device to keep track of this is *LEO* says *GER: Lose E*lectrons *O*xidized; *G*ain *E*lectrons *R*educed.

Combination Figures

Line drawings combined with photos give students two perspectives: the realism of photos and the explanatory clarity of illustrations. The authors chose this method of presentation often to help students comprehend difficult concepts.

(mold on bread): Richard Hutchings/McGraw-Hill Education; (mold): Mitroshkin/Getty Images; (Rhizopus sporangia and zygote): Richard Gross/McGraw-Hill Education

Illustrated Tables

Illustrated tables provide quick access to information. Horizontal contrasting lines set off each entry, making them easy to read.

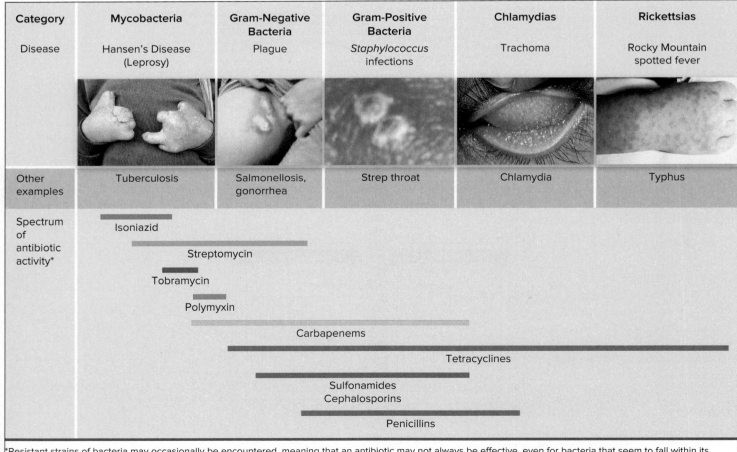

Category	Mycobacteria	Gram-Negative Bacteria	Gram-Positive Bacteria	Chlamydias	Rickettsias
Disease	Hansen's Disease (Leprosy)	Plague	*Staphylococcus* infections	Trachoma	Rocky Mountain spotted fever
Other examples	Tuberculosis	Salmonellosis, gonorrhea	Strep throat	Chlamydia	Typhus

Spectrum of antibiotic activity*

Isoniazid
Streptomycin
Tobramycin
Polymyxin
Carbapenems
Tetracyclines
Sulfonamides
Cephalosporins
Penicillins

*Resistant strains of bacteria may occasionally be encountered, meaning that an antibiotic may not always be effective, even for bacteria that seem to fall within its spectrum of action.

(Tuberculosis): NikomMaelao Production/Shutterstock; (Salmonellosis): *Source:* CDC; (Strep throat): McGraw-Hill Education *Source:* Susan Lindsley/CDC; (Chlamydia): Susan Lindsley is the source for Chlamydia (Typhus): *Source:* CDC

New to this edition, *Clinic Cases* are short case studies that typically focus on a single aspect of a chapter. They provide relevance for lessons learned and easily serve as collaborative warm-up activities.

CLINIC CASE

If Only We Could Give You a Mutation The patient, Timothy Ray Brown, presented to doctors in Berlin with overwhelming fatigue. Used to 20 miles a day on his bicycle back and forth to work, he was suddenly unable to make the one-mile ride to a restaurant near his office. Diagnosed with the human immunodeficiency virus (HIV) 10 years earlier, Brown had been keeping the virus in check with a combination of AZT and protease inhibitors. He was in good health and had a life expectancy about the same as someone uninfected by the virus. Doctors in Berlin diagnosed Brown with anemia (unrelated to his HIV) and provided blood transfusions to increase the number of circulating erythrocytes. An oncologist performed a bone marrow biopsy, and less than a week after his initial symptoms, Brown was diagnosed with acute myeloid leukemia (AML), a cancer of the bone marrow.

After several failed rounds of chemotherapy, doctors brought up the idea of a bone marrow transplant, a treatment for leukemia in which the bone marrow, both cancerous and healthy, is destroyed and new, healthy bone marrow is transplanted into the body. Brown's doctor wanted to go one step further though, and proposed a treatment that would, perhaps, cure Brown of his HIV at the same time.

To enter cells of the immune system, the human immunodeficiency virus must first bind to a cell surface receptor protein known as CCR-5. Approximately 1% of the population has a mutation in both copies of their CCR-5 gene (called CCR-5 delta 32, or CCR-5 Δ32) that creates a stop codon. HIV cannot use these mutant proteins to enter the cell and is therefore unable to replicate. If a bone marrow donor with the CCR-5 Δ32 mutation could be found, perhaps Brown's AML and HIV could be cured simultaneously.

As luck would have it, Brown is of northern European descent and the CCR-5 Δ32 mutation is most commonly found in that group as well. An appropriate donor was found that possessed the mutation and Brown underwent transplant on February 6, 2007, the same day he stopped taking his anti-HIV medication. A second transplant, from the same donor, was required in 2008, but in more than 10 years, Brown has shown no signs of his HIV progressing, leaving him the first person cured of HIV infection.

Δ32 refers to a 32-base-pair deletion in the CCR-5 gene. Besides a deletion mutation and nonsense mutation, what other type of mutation was created in the gene?

CLINIC CASE

Plague Is Not an Opportunistic Infection, Unless... The patient was Malcolm Casadaban, a 60-year-old professor at the University of Chicago who was well known for his work with *Yersinia pestis*, the bacterium that causes bubonic plague. A primary pathogen responsible for the death of more than 100 million people in the 1300s, outbreaks of plague were still seen from time to time, and Casadaban was working to develop a vaccine to protect against the disease. But even plague researchers get the flu from time to time, and this is what compelled Dr. Casadaban to visit his primary care physician.

Not surprisingly, given his occupation, the first question the doctor asked was, "Do you work with *Yersinia pestis*?" Casadaban assured his doctor that he worked exclusively with an attenuated strain of the bacterium that required excess iron—more than was normally found in the human body—to reproduce. While it grew well in the lab, there was no chance this strain could cause disease. Assured that he wasn't dealing with the "Black Death," the doctor diagnosed a viral infection and sent Dr. Casadaban home with instructions to rest. Three days later, he returned to the hospital, very sick, and soon thereafter died.

An autopsy revealed the supposedly innocuous strain of *Yersinia pestis* in his system, but the researcher's demise remained a mystery. How could such a weakened strain of *Yersinia pestis* cause death? Analysis of the doctor's blood finally solved the puzzle. Unbeknownst to him, Dr. Casadaban suffered from hemochromatosis, a genetic disorder in which people accumulate high levels of iron in their blood. This excess of iron allowed the usually iron-starved *Yersinia pestis* to assume its original virulence. Dr. Casadaban's condition increased his susceptibility to a single bacterial species, the one he had been working with for years.

Drugs meant to reduce stomach acid (to combat heartburn) may make the patient more susceptible to infection by bacteria that pass through the gastrointestinal tract. How is this situation similar to what happened to Dr. Casdaban?

Pedagogy designed for varied learning styles

The end-of-chapter material for the eleventh edition has been carefully planned and updated to promote active learning and provide review for different learning styles and levels of Bloom's Taxonomy.

Chapter Summary with Key Terms

A brief outline of the chapter's main concepts is provided for students, with important terms highlighted. Key terms are also included in the glossary at the end of the book.

Chapter Summary with Key Terms

3.1 Methods of Microbial Investigation
A. Microbiology as a science is very dependent on a number of specialized laboratory techniques.
 1. Initially, a specimen must be collected from a source, whether environmental or patient.
 2. **Inoculation** of a **medium** with the specimen is the first step in **culturing.**
 3. **Incubation** of the medium with the microbes under the right conditions creates a **culture** with visible growth.
 4. **Isolation** of the microbes in the sample into discrete, separate **colonies** is one desired goal.
 5. **Inspection** begins with macroscopic characteristics of the culture and continues with microscopic analysis.
 6. **Information gathering** involves acquiring additional data from physiological, serological, and genetic tests.
 7. **Identification** correlates the key characteristics that can pinpoint the actual species of microbe.

End-of-Chapter Questions

Questions are divided into two levels.

 Assess Your Knowledge

Level I. These questions require a working knowledge of the concepts in the chapter and the ability to recall and understand the information you have studied.

 Application, Analysis, Evaluation, and Synthesis

Level II. These problems go beyond just restating facts and require higher levels of understanding and an ability to interpret, problem solve, transfer knowledge to new situations, create models, and predict outcomes.

The consistent layout of each chapter allows students to develop a learning strategy and gain confidence in their ability to master the concepts, leading to success in the class!

Developing a Concept Inventory

Students can assess their knowledge of basic concepts by answering these questions and looking up the correct answers in appendix D. In addition, SmartBook allows for students to quiz themselves interactively using these questions.

Developing a Concept Inventory

Select the correct answer from the answers provided. For questions with blanks, the statement.

1. An example/examples of a nonspecific chemical barrier to infection is/are
 a. unbroken skin c. cilia in respiratory tract
 b. lysozyme in saliva d. all of these
2. Which nonspecific host defense is associated with the trachea?
 a. lacrimation c. desquamation

Case Study Analysis

These questions provide a quick check of concepts covered by the Case Study and allow instructors to assess students on the Case Study material.

Case Study Analysis

1. Small intestinal bacterial overgrowth (known by its acronym, SIBO) is a condition similar to gut fermentation syndrome. SIBO occurs when an overabundance of bacteria, rather than yeast, in the small intestine ferment carbohydrates. What product would be produced in the gut of someone suffering from SIBO?

On the Test

On the Test questions cover material from the chapter that may appear on the TEAS (Test of Essential Academic Skills) or NCLEX (National Council Licensure Exam). Written in the style seen on each exam, these questions help students forge a link between the chapter contents and two of the most important exams they'll take in the future.

On the Test

These questions will help to prepare you to successfully answer similar questi NCLEX (National Council Licensure Examination).

1. The nurse gives a primigravida (first pregnancy) client an injection of RhoGAM during the 28th week of her pregnancy. Why was the nurse required to take this action?
 a. The mother was Rh-negative while the father was Rh-positive.
 b. The mother was Rh-positive while the father was Rh-negative.
 c. The mother was O-negative while the father was Ab-positive.
 d. Both the mother and father were Rh-positive.

Writing Challenge

Writing Challenge questions are suggested as a writing experience. Students are asked to compose a one- or two-paragraph response using the factual information learned in the chapter.

Writing Challenge

For each question, compose a one- or two-paragraph answer that includes the questions can also be used for writing-challenge exercises.

1. Discuss the relationship of
 a. anabolism to catabolism
 b. ATP to ADP
 c. glycolysis to fermentation
 d. electron transport to oxidative phosphorylation

Concept Mapping

Concept Mapping activities have been designed for each chapter, and an introduction to concept mapping can be found on Connect.

Concept Mapping

On Connect you can find an Introduction to Concept Mapping that provides guidance for working with concept maps, along with concept-mapping activities for this chapter.

Critical Thinking

Using the facts and concepts they just studied, students must reason and problem solve to answer these specially developed questions. Questions do not have a single correct answer and thus open doors to discussion and application.

Critical Thinking

Critical thinking is the ability to reason and solve problems using facts and concepts. These questions can be approached from a number of angles and, in most cases, they do not have a single correct answer.

1. a. What is the main clinical strategy in preventing gas gangrene?
 b. Why does it work?
2. a. Why is it unlikely that diseases such as tetanus and botulism will ever be completely eradicated?
 b. Name some bacterial diseases in this chapter that could be completely eradicated and explain how.
3. Why is the cause of death similar in tetanus and botulism?
4. a. Why does botulinum toxin not affect the senses?
 b. Why does botulism not commonly cause intestinal symptoms?
5. Account for the fact that boiling does not destroy botulism spores but

8. What would be the likely consequence of diphtheria infection alone without toxemia?
9. How can one tell that acne involves an infection?
10. Do you think the spittoons of the last century were effective in controlling tuberculosis? Why or why not?
11. a. Provide an explanation for the statement that TB is a "family disease."
 b. What, if anything, can be done about multidrug-resistant tuberculosis?
 c. Explain an important rationale for *not* administering BCG vaccine in the United States to the general public.

Visual Assessment

1. From **chapter 3, figure 3.18b.** Which bacteria have a well-developed capsule: "*Klebsiella*" or "*S. aureus*"? Defend your answer.

Kathy Park Talaro

Visual Assessment

Visual Assessment questions take images and concepts learned in other chapters and ask students to apply that knowledge to concepts covered in the current chapter.

Changes to *Foundations in Microbiology, Eleventh Edition*

Global Changes to the Eleventh Edition

- Chapter-opening pages include a content outline, helping to emphasize the chapter organization.
- Clinic Cases appear in every chapter to highlight important topics.
- End-of-chapter questions in the style of the TEAS and NCLEX exams have been added.

Chapter-Specific Changes

Chapter 1
- New introduction to viruses and prions
- Clinic Case concerning *Microcystis* poisoning
- Discussion concerning the changing nature of infectious disease and microbial roles in noninfectious disease
- Ten new photographs

Chapter 2
- New Case Study on lactose intolerance
- Clinic Case illustrating the pH-dependent germination of *Clostridium botulinum*
- Six new photos and illustrations

Chapter 3
- New Case Study concerning the laboratory diagnosis of *Salmonella* Typhi
- Clarified discussion of fluorescence microscopy
- Clinic Case concerning anthrax infection in New York City
- Discussion of unculturable microorganisms
- Nineteen new photographs and illustrations

Chapter 4
- New Case Study concerning biofilm formation within dental equipment
- Process figure on biofilm formation
- Discussion of capsules, biofilms, and quorum sensing
- Clinic Case concerning gas gangrene in an IV drug user
- Twelve new photographs and illustrations

Chapter 5
- New Case Study concerning *Amanita phalloides* (death cap mushroom) poisoning
- Discussion of the eukaryotic cytoskeleton has been clarified
- Eukaryotic classification has been updated to reflect the latest findings
- Clinic Case concerning paralytic shellfish poisoning
- Clinic Case involving roundworm infection of a toddler
- Twenty-seven new photographs and illustrations

Chapter 6
- New Case Study dealing with bacteriophage therapy
- Clinic Case examining a monkeypox infection in Wisconsin
- Discussion of persistent viral infections
- Clinic Case concerning an incident of variant Creutzfeldt-Jakob disease
- Nine new photographs and illustrations

Chapter 7
- New Case Study concerning *Vibrio vulnificus* infection related to a recent tattoo
- Clinic Case concerning *Vibrio parahaemolyticus* infections related to warming oceans
- Modified discussion concerning associations between microbes
- Eleven new photographs and illustrations

Chapter 8
- New Case Study on auto-brewery syndrome
- Clinic Case on the use of ethanol as an antidote to methanol poisoning
- Clarified discussion of electron carriers
- Discussion of glycolysis has been clarified, and reactions are divided into "first five" and "second five"
- Four new photographs and illustrations

Chapter 9
- New Case Study concerning the 14th known case of vancomycin-resistant *Staphylococcus aureus*
- Clarified discussion of DNA structure and replication, transcription and translation, and mutations
- Clinic Case on the use of a bone marrow donor carrying a CCR-5 mutation being used to cure the recipient's HIV
- Six new photographs and illustrations

Chapter 10
- New Case Study on the use of genetically engineered mosquitoes to reduce Zika virus infection
- Discussion of genetic engineering, restriction enzymes, and electrophoresis
- Discussion of transcriptomics, proteomics, metagenomics, and metabolomics
- Updated discussion on the potential benefits of GMOs
- Clinic Case discussing the use of modified bacteria as a treatment for phenylketonuria
- Discussion of the CRISPR/Cas-9 system for editing DNA
- Discussion of gene therapy used to correct blindness due to Leber congenital amaurosis
- Clinic Case concerning the use of familial DNA fingerprinting to identify the Grim Sleeper serial killer
- Nine new photographs and illustrations

Chapter 11
- New Case Study concerning infection linked to improper disinfection of duodenoscopes at UCLA
- Clarified discussion of sterilization with regard to prions
- Clinic Case concerning a case of botulism due to inadequate processing of commercially canned chili
- Clinic Case concerning the use of ultraviolet light to disinfect the water in an interactive fountain
- Seven new photographs and illustrations

Chapter 12
- New Case Study illustrating the side effects of fluoroquinolone antibiotics
- Terminology has been added, updated, and clarified throughout the chapter
- New drugs used to cure hepatitis C and prevent replication of influenza are discussed
- Expanded discussion of new HIV drugs used to fight existing infection or as pre-exposure prophylactics
- The relationship between biofilms and drug resistance is now part of the chapter
- A feature on clinical testing of antimicrobics is included in the chapter
- A Clinic Case concerning the use of intentional drug interaction to treat a drug overdose has been added
- Nineteen new photographs and illustrations

Chapter 13
- The role of viruses as normal microbiota is addressed
- Clinic Case concerning a plague researcher who dies from infection with an attenuated strain of *Yersinia pestis*
- Clinic Case concerning an MRSA outbreak in a newborn nursery
- Disease statistics have been updated throughout the chapter
- The discussion of epicurves has been clarified
- Twenty-one new photographs and illustrations

Chapter 14
- New Case Study concerning autosplenectomy related to lupus
- Clarified discussion of the body's interconnections with regard to the immune system
- Clinic Case exploring an occurrence of trichinellosis resistant to freezing

- Clarified discussion of hematopoiesis and the role of natural killer cells
- Nine new photographs and illustrations

Chapter 15
- New Case Study regarding an incident of necrotizing fasciitis
- Figures used to clarify the genetics of antibody generation, and the activation of T cells
- Expanded discussion of T helper 17 cells, T regulatory cells, Gamma-Delta T cells, natural killer cells, and natural killer T cells
- New figure explaining the outcomes of antibody binding of antigen
- Updated discussion on the use of monoclonal antibodies

- Clinic Case following an outbreak of measles in Minnesota
- Clarified discussion of hematopoiesis and the role of natural killer cells
- Fifteen new photographs and illustrations

Chapter 16
- New Case Study following a case of anti-NMDAR encephalitis, an autoimmune disease resulting in severe neurologic changes
- Updated information concerning the development of food allergies and treatments for severe allergic reactions
- Clinic Case following four cases of transplant-transmitted infection
- Seven new photographs and illustrations

Chapter 17
- New Case Study following a case of meningitis due to lymphocytic choriomenigitis virus
- New discussions of fluorescent in-situ hybridization, pulsed-field gel electrophoresis, and whole genome sequencing
- Clinic Case concerning misidentification of a bacterial isolate as a potential bioterrorism agent
- Clarified discussion of ELISA
- Eight new photographs and illustrations

Acknowledgments

The biggest lies are told before the marriage, after the hunt, and during the election.

—*Otto von Bismarck*

And the biggest lie of all may be "I write a book." Because writing a book is most definitely a team sport. And thank-you's are owed to the rest of the team.

Beginning of course with microbiology itself, a subject whose ever-changing nature means that after just a few years, a book begins to look antiquated, irrelevant, even silly. A few editions ago, there was little thought given to Zika virus, probiotics, or the microbiome, topics of great import today. So the first thanks go to the science itself and those who spend their days (and nights, and weekends) coaxing answers from the smallest of organisms.

To the students, instructors, and colleagues who've used the book, sent an email, suggested a change, or simply walked up with book in hand and a quizzical expression which said "Huh?," thank you. Your suggestions have never once fallen upon deaf ears, and you've helped me to hopefully make this edition better than the last. A special shout-out to to Anna Oller of the University of Central Missouri and Elizabeth Co of Boston University, who reviewed the chapters on host defenses.

More thanks to the people who really know how to write a book and can cogently discuss typefaces, obtain permissions, and corral writers: the editorial and production staff at McGraw-Hill Education. For the eleventh edition, I have been fortunate to work with product developer Krystal Faust (anyone tasked to develop me deserves thanks) and brand manager Lauren Vondra (anyone tasked to manage me…). Marketing manager Jim Connely, project manager Ann Courtney, content licensing specialist Lorraine Buzcek, designer Jessica Cuevas, copyeditor Nicole Schlutt, and, in what is only a slight exaggeration, a cast of thousands. When I say I couldn't have done it without them, realize that in the absence of these people, you'd be, at best, holding my coffee-stained notes in your hands.

Despite the careful work of all these people, typos, errors, and oversights may make it to the printed page. These errors belong solely to me. If you find an error or wish to make other comments, feel free to contact the publisher, sales representative, or myself (barry.chess.micro@gmail.com). Enjoy.

—*Barry Chess*

When you awoke this morning, the coating you felt on your teeth was a bacterial biofilm. For every human cell of your body, at least three cells are not human. Remember the time you didn't get smallpox, polio, and measles. How about that safe water? Enjoy yogurt? Cheese? Bread? Beer? Have I made my point?

Microbiology is often the very essence of "Out of sight, out of mind," but it is my sincere hope that this book can change that. For most of you, this course is a required prerequisite for your chosen career, but microbiology is so much more than that. From before we're born until after we die, we have an intimate association with all manner of microorganisms, and the goal of this book is to make these relationships more familiar. Which organisms are dangerous? Beneficial? Useful? Along the way, there will be Greek terminology, a little chemistry, and some math. Sorry.

As you use this book, please *use* this book, it was designed solely with you in mind. Study the photographs, look up unfamiliar words, answer the questions, make the information yours. Without even being aware of it, you'll gain a greater understanding of not only the world around you, but the world within you. Not a bad way to spend some time.

—*Barry Chess*

Contents

CHAPTER 7

Microbial Nutrition, Ecology, and Growth 192

Source: Eric Erbe/Chris Pooley, USDA-ARS

CHAPTER 8

An Introduction to Microbial Metabolism: The Chemical Crossroads of Life 226

Ingram Publishing/Alamy Stock Photo

CHAPTER 9

An Introduction to Microbial Genetics 266

Source: Janice Carr/CDC

CHAPTER 10

Genetic Engineering: A Revolution in Molecular Biology 304

Akil Rolle-Rowan/Shutterstock

CHAPTER 11

Physical and Chemical Agents for Microbial Control 334

Tadaki crew/Shutterstock

CHAPTER 12

Drugs, Microbes, Host— The Elements of Chemotherapy 368

Scott J. Ferrell/Congressional Quarterly/Getty Images

CHAPTER **13**

Microbe-Human Interactions: Infection, Disease, and Epidemiology 406

Igormakarov/Shutterstock

CHAPTER **14**

An Introduction to Host Defenses and Innate Immunities 448

Science Photo Library/ Alamy Stock Photo

The Main Themes of Microbiology

In This Chapter...

A frozen white wasteland, a toxic soup. Two fairly common descriptions of an environment so harsh—cold, toxic, or lacking nutrients—that no life can survive. Lake Whillans, a small, shallow lake trapped beneath half a mile of ice, certainly fits that description. Located 640 kilometers from the South Pole, Lake Whillans is completely encased in ice and sits at a slant, pressed against the side of a hill far below the icy surface. As heat from the core of the earth melts the bottom of the Antarctic ice sheet, a few milliliters of liquid water are added to the lake each year.

Subglacial lakes like Lake Whillans were discovered only in the late 1990s when ice-penetrating radar and satellite measurements allowed researchers to see through the dense ice sheets that cover the polar regions of the planet. The next phase of the project was—as has been the case as long as humans have been exploring their environments—to determine what, if anything, lived in the newly discovered area. Although the immediate instinct would be to drill through the ice and sample the water in the lake, **microbial ecologists** realized that sampling Lake Whillans was not terribly different from performing surgery on a human patient; **aseptic techniques** would have to be followed so that external microbes were not allowed to contaminate the lake. Drilling equipment was **sterilized** using a combination of ultraviolet light and hydrogen peroxide, the same techniques routinely used in hospitals and laboratories, and the water used to bore through the ice was filtered to remove even the smallest microorganisms. When the drill penetrated the last of the ice, it entered the lake, which at −0.5°C was several degrees warmer than the Antarctic surface.

Over the next few days, until the drilling hole froze shut, scientists and graduate students collected 30 liters of water and several sediment samples from the lake.

Study of those samples, which continues today, reveals that Lake Whillans hosts a vibrant ecosystem. **DNA analysis** revealed nearly 4,000 different **microbial species,** and each milliliter of lake water contained more than 130,000 cells, comparable to what one finds in the deepest oceans. The biggest difference between life in Lake Whillans and ecosystems found on the surface of the planet is the lack of sunlight. In terrestrial lakes, **photosynthetic microorganisms** use the energy in sunlight to convert dissolved carbon dioxide into sugars. Because sunlight can't penetrate the half mile of ice covering Lake Whillans, many of the microbes in the lake derive energy from the oxidation of iron, sulfur, or ammonium compounds, a strategy used by some deep-sea bacteria. If it turns out, as many scientists believe, that the microorganisms in Lake Whillans supply minerals and nutrients to the surrounding ocean, then this small, dark, cold, invisible lake may have a tremendous effect on the ecosystem surrounding it. Not bad for a frozen wasteland.

■ *One of the environmental pressures microorganisms from Lake Whillans had to adapt to was the ability to grow in very cold temperatures. What were several other environmental challenges these microbes faced?*

■ *What fields of microbiology were used to initially study these microbes, and what fields could be involved in the further study of the isolated cells?*

To continue this Case Study, go to Case Study Part 2 at the end of the chapter.

(methane bubbles arise from the sea floor) Source: NOAA Okeanos Explorer Program, 2013 ROV Shakedown and Field Trials in the U.S. Atlantic Canyons.

1.1 The Scope of Microbiology

 Learn

1. Define *microbiology* and *microorganisms,* and identify the major organisms included in the science of microbiology.

2. Name and define the primary fields included in microbiological studies.

As we observe the natural world, teeming with life, we cannot help but be struck by its beauty and complexity. But for every feature that is visible to the naked eye, there are millions of other features that are concealed from our sight by their small size. This microscopic universe is populated by a vast microbial menagerie that is equally beautiful and complex. To sum up the presence of microbes in one word, they are **ubiquitous.*** They are found in all natural habitats and most of those that have been created by humans. As scientists continue to explore remote and unusual environments, the one kind of entity they always find is microbes. These exist deep beneath the polar ice caps, in the ocean to a depth of 7 miles, in hot springs and thermal vents, in toxic waste dumps, and even in the clouds.

Microbiology is a specialized area of biology that deals with tiny life forms that are not readily observed without magnification, which is to say they are **microscopic.*** These microscopic organisms are collectively referred to as **microorganisms, microbes,*** or several other terms, depending upon the purpose. Some people call them "germs" or "bugs" in reference to their role in infection and disease, but those terms have other biological meanings and perhaps place undue emphasis on the disagreeable reputation of microorganisms. The major groups of microorganisms included in this study are **bacteria, viruses, fungi, protozoa, algae,** and **helminths** (parasitic worms). As we will see in subsequent chapters, each group exhibits a distinct collection of biological characteristics. The nature of microorganisms makes them both easy and difficult to study. Easy, because they reproduce so rapidly and can usually be grown in large numbers in the laboratory. Difficult, because we can't observe or analyze them without special techniques, especially the use of microscopes (see chapter 3).

Microbiology is one of the largest and most complex of the biological sciences because it integrates subject matter from many diverse disciplines. Microbiologists study every aspect of microbes—their genetics, their physiology, characteristics that may be harmful or beneficial, the ways they interact with each other and the environment, and their uses in industry and agriculture.

In fact, many areas of the field have become so specialized that a microbiologist may spend an entire career focused on a single subspecialty, a few of which are:

- Bacteriology—the study of bacteria; small, single-celled prokaryotic organisms

- Mycology—the study of fungi; eukaryotic organisms that include both microscopic (molds and yeasts) and larger members like mushrooms, puffballs, and truffles
- Protozoology—the study of protozoa; a group of mostly single-celled eukaryotes
- Virology—the study of viruses; noncellular particles that parasitize cells
- Parasitology—the study of parasites; traditionally including pathogenic protozoa, helminth worms, and certain insects
- Phycology or algology—the study of simple photosynthetic eukaryotes, the algae; ranging from single-celled forms to large seaweeds
- Morphology—the study of the detailed structure of microorganisms
- Physiology—investigation of organismal metabolism at the cellular and molecular levels
- Taxonomy—the classification, naming, and identification of microorganisms
- Microbial genetics and molecular biology—the study of the genetic material and biochemical reactions that make up a cell's metabolism
- Microbial ecology—the interrelationships between microbes and the environment; the roles of microorganisms in nutrient cycles and natural ecosystems

Studies in microbiology have led to greater understanding of many general biological principles. For example, the study of microorganisms established universal concepts concerning the chemistry of life, systems of inheritance, and the global cycles of nutrients, minerals, and gases. **Table 1.1** describes just a few of the occupations included within the greater field of microbiology.

1.2 General Characteristics of Microorganisms and Their Roles in the Earth's Environments

 Learn

3. Describe the basic characteristics of prokaryotic cells and eukaryotic cells and their evolutionary origins.

4. State several ways that microbes are involved in the earth's ecosystems.

5. Describe the cellular makeup of microorganisms and their size range, and indicate how viruses differ from cellular microbes.

The Origins and Dominance of Microorganisms

For billions of years, microbes have shaped the development of the earth's habitats and influenced the evolution of other life forms. It is understandable that scientists searching for life on other planets first look for signs of microorganisms.

The fossil record uncovered in ancient rocks and sediments points to bacteria-like cells having existed on earth for at least

* *ubiquitous* (yoo-bik′-wih-tis) L. *ubique,* everywhere, and *ous,* having. Being, or seeming to be, everywhere at the same time.
* *microscopic* (my″-kroh-skaw′-pik) Gr. *mikros,* small, and *scopein,* to see.
* *microbe* (my′-krohb) Gr. *mikros,* small, and *bios,* life.

TABLE 1.1	A Sampling of Fields and Occupations in Microbiology

Medical Microbiology, Public Health Microbiology, and Epidemiology

Medical microbiology, which studies the effects of microorganisms on human beings, remains the most well-known branch of microbiology. The related fields of public health and epidemiology monitor and control the spread of diseases in communities. Some of the institutions charged with this task are the U.S. Public Health Service (USPHS) and the Centers for Disease Control and Prevention (CDC). The CDC collects information and statistics on diseases from around the United States and publishes it in *The Morbidity and Mortality Weekly Report* (see chapter 13).

A parasite specialist examines leaf litter for the presence of black-legged ticks—the carriers of Lyme disease.
Source: Scott Bauer/USDA

Immunology

This branch studies the complex web of protective substances and reactions caused by invading microbes and other harmful entities. It includes such diverse areas as blood testing, vaccination, and allergy (see chapters 15, 16, and 17).

A CDC virologist examines cultures of influenza virus that are used in producing vaccines. This work requires high-level biohazard containment.
Source: James Gathany/CDC

Biotechnology, Genetic Engineering, and Industrial Microbiology

These branches revolve around the idea that microorganisms can be used to derive a desired product, from beer to vaccines. Biotechnology focuses on the natural abilities of microbes, while genetic engineering involves the deliberate alteration of the genetic makeup of organisms to create novel microbes, plants and animals with unique behaviors and physiology. Industrial microbiology is the science of scaling up these processes to produce large quantities of a desired product (see chapters 10 and 27).

A technician tests the effectiveness of microorganisms in the production of new sources of energy.
Source: Lawrence Berkeley National Laboratory

Agricultural Microbiology

This branch is concerned with the relationships between microbes and domesticated plants and animals. Plant specialists focus on plant diseases, soil fertility, and nutritional interactions. Animal specialists work with infectious diseases and other interactions between animals and microorganisms.

Microbiologists from the U.S. Food and Drug Administration collect soil samples to detect animal pathogens.
Source: Black Star/Steve Yeater for FDA

Food Microbiologists

These scientists are concerned with the impact of microbes on the food supply, including such areas as food spoilage, food-borne diseases, and production.

A U.S. Department of Agriculture technician observes tests for the presence of *Escherichia coli* in foods.
Source: Keith Weller/USDA

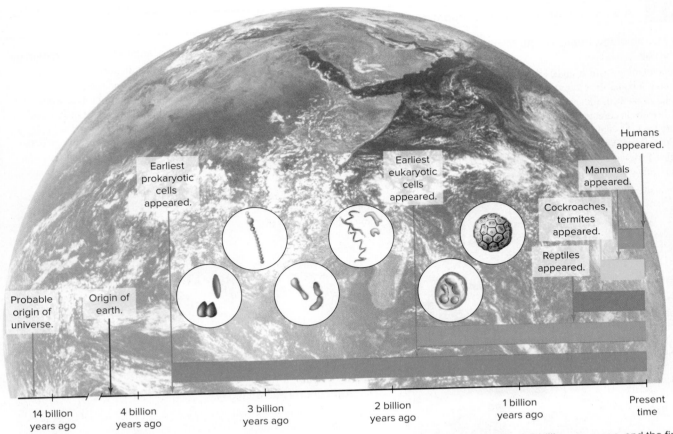

Humans appeared.

Mammals appeared.

Earliest prokaryotic cells appeared.

Earliest eukaryotic cells appeared.

Cockroaches, termites appeared.

Reptiles appeared.

Probable origin of universe.

Origin of earth.

| 14 billion years ago | 4 billion years ago | 3 billion years ago | 2 billion years ago | 1 billion years ago | Present time |

Figure 1.1 Evolutionary time line. The first simple prokaryotes appeared on earth approximately 3.5 billion years ago, and the first eukaryotes arose about 2 billion years ago. Although these appearances seem abrupt, hundreds of millions of years of earth's history passed while they were evolving to these stages. The fossil record for these periods is incomplete because many of the earliest microbes were too delicate to fossilize.
Source: NASA

3.5 billion years **(figure 1.1).** Early microorganisms of this type dominated the earth's life forms for the first 2 billion years. These ancient cells were small and simple, and lacked specialized internal structures to carry out their functions. The genetic material of these cells was not bound into a separate compartment called a nucleus or "karyon." The term assigned to cells and microbes of this type is **prokaryotic,*** meaning "before the nucleus." About 1.8 billion years ago, there appeared in the fossil record a more complex cell, which had developed a nucleus and various specialized internal structures called **organelles.*** These types of cells and organisms are defined as **eukaryotic*** in reference to their "true" nucleus. **Figure 1.2** compares the two cell types and includes some examples of viruses for comparison. In chapter 5 we will learn more about the origins of eukaryotic cells—they didn't arise suddenly out of nowhere; they evolved over millennia from prokaryotic cells through an intriguing process called endosymbiosis. The early eukaryotes, probably similar to algae and protozoa, started lines of evolution that eventually gave rise to fungi, plants, and multicellu-lar animals such as worms and insects. You can see from figure 1.1 how long that took! The bacteria preceded even the earliest animals by about 3 billion years. This is a good indication that humans are not likely to, nor should we try to, eliminate microorganisms from our environment. Having existed for eons, they are absolutely essential for maintaining the planet's life-giving characteristics.

The Cellular Organization of Microorganisms

As a general rule, prokaryotic cells are smaller than eukaryotic cells, and in addition to lacking a nucleus, they lack organelles, which are structures in cells bound by one or more membranes. Examples of organelles include the mitochondria and Golgi complexes, and several others, which perform specific functions such as transport, feeding, energy release and use, and synthesis. Prokaryotes perform similar functions, but they lack dedicated organelles to carry them out (figure 1.2).

The body plan of most microorganisms consists of a single cell or clusters of cells **(figure 1.3).** All prokaryotes are microorganisms, and they include the bacteria and archaea. Only some of the eukaryotes are microorganisms: primarily algae, protozoa, molds and yeasts (types of fungi), and certain animals such as worms and arthropods. Not all members of these last two groups are micro-

* *prokaryotic* (proh″-kar-ee-ah′-tik) Gr. *pro,* before, and *karyon,* nucleus.
* *organelles* (or-gan′-elz) Gr. *organa,* tool, and *ella,* little.
* *eukaryotic* (yoo″-kar-ee-ah′-tik) Gr. *eu,* true or good, and *karyon,* nucleus.

(a) **Basic cell types**

Prokaryotic cell

Flagellum
Chromosome
Ribosomes

Cell wall
Cell membrane

Eukaryotic cell showing selected organelles

Nucleus
Ribosomes
Cell membrane

Flagellum
Mitochondria

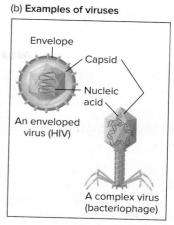

(b) **Examples of viruses**

Envelope
Capsid
Nucleic acid

An enveloped virus (HIV)

A complex virus (bacteriophage)

Figure 1.2 **Basic structure of cells and viruses. (a)** Comparison of a prokaryotic cell and a eukaryotic cell. These cell types and viruses are discussed in more detail in chapters 4, 5, and 6. **(b)** Two examples of viruses.

Bacteria: *Mycobacterium tuberculosis,* a rod-shaped cell (15,500×).

Reproductive structures

Fungi: *Histoplasma capsulatum,* with lollipop-like reproductive structures (750×). This agent is the cause of Ohio Valley fever.

Algae: *Micrasterias truncata* (750×), one of the predecessors of modern-day plants.

A single virus particle

Virus: *Herpes simplex,* the cause of cold sores (100,000×).

Protozoa: A protozoan, *Oxytricha trifallax* bearing tufts of cilia that function like tiny legs (3,500×).

Helminths: Roundworms of *Trichinella spiralis* coiled in the muscle of a host (250×). This worm causes trichinellosis.

Figure 1.3 **The six basic types of microorganisms.** Organisms are not shown at the same magnifications; approximate magnification is provided. To see these microorganisms arrayed more accurately to scale, look for them in figure 1.4.
(bacteria): *Source:* Janice Carr/CDC; (fungi): *Source:* Dr. Libero Ajello/CDC; (algae): Lebendkulturen.de/Shutterstock; (virus): *Source:* Dr. Erskine Palmer/CDC; (protozoa): *Source:* National Human Genome Research Institute; (helminths): *Source:* CDC

scopic, but certain members are still included in the study of microbiology because worms can be involved in infections and may require a microscope to identify them. Some arthropods such as fleas and ticks may also be carriers of infectious diseases. Additional coverage on cell types and microorganisms appears in chapters 4 and 5.

Noncellular Pathogenic Particles—Viruses and Prions

Viruses are well-studied in microbiology, as they are the most common microbes on earth and are responsible for diseases ranging from the common cold to AIDS, but they are not cells. Rather, viruses are small particles composed of a small amount of hereditary material, surrounded by a protein coat, and are so simple that most biologists don't consider them to be alive (primarily because they are incapable of replication on their own).

Prions—a contraction of the words *proteinaceous infectious particle*—are even simpler than viruses, consisting solely of protein. The very existence of prions was doubted until the late twentieth century, but they are now recognized as the causative agent of transmissible spongiform encephalopathies, a group of invariably fatal diseases, including mad cow disease and its human counterpart Creutzfeld-Jakob disease. Both viruses and prions will be examined in greater depth in chapter 6.

Microbial Dimensions: How Small Is Small?

When we say that microbes are too small to be seen with the unaided eye, what sorts of dimensions are we talking about? This concept is best visualized by comparing microbial groups with some organisms of the macroscopic world and also with the molecules and atoms of the molecular world (**figure 1.4**). The dimensions of macroscopic organisms are usually given in centimeters (cm) and meters (m), whereas those of most microorganisms fall within the range of micrometers (μm) and, sometimes, nanometers (nm) and millimeters (mm). The size range of most microbes extends from the smallest viruses, measuring around 10 nm and actually not much bigger than a large molecule, to protozoans measuring 3 to 4 mm and visible with the naked eye.

Microbial Involvement in Energy and Nutrient Flow

The microbes in all natural environments have lived and evolved there for billions of years. We do not yet know all of their roles, but it is likely they are vital components of the structure and function of these ecosystems.

Microbes are deeply involved in the flow of energy and food through the earth's ecosystems.[1] Most people are aware that plants carry out **photosynthesis,** which is the light-fueled conversion of carbon dioxide to organic material, accompanied by the formation of oxygen. But microorganisms were photosynthesizing long be-

Metric Chart			
Length	Symbol	Log No.	Multiplier
meter	m	10^0	1×
millimeter	mm	10^{-3}	0.001×
micrometer	μm	10^{-6}	0.000,001×
nanometer	nm	10^{-9}	0.000,000,001×
angstrom	Å	10^{-10}	0.000,000,000,1×
picometer	pm	10^{-12}	0.000,000,000,001×

Figure 1.4 **The sizes of the smallest organisms and objects.** Even though they are all very small, they still display extensive variations in size. This illustration organizes the common measurements used in microbiology, along with examples of organisms or items that fall into these measurement ranges. The scale includes macroscopic, microscopic, ultramicroscopic, and atomic dimensions. Most microbes we study measure somewhere between 100 micrometers (μm) and 10 nanometers (nm) overall. The examples are more or less to scale within a size zone but not between size zones.
(flea): Cosmin Manci/Shutterstock; (roundworm): *Source:* CDC; (algae): Lebendkulturen.de/Shutterstock; (protozoan): *Source:* National Human Genome Research Institute; (mold spores): Dr. Lucille K. Georg/CDC; (spirochete): *Source:* CDC; (rods, cocci): *Source:* Janice Carr/CDC; (herpesvirus): *Source:* Jeff Hageman, M.H.S./Janice Carr/CDC

fore the first plants appeared. In fact, they were responsible for changing the atmosphere of the earth from one without oxygen to one with oxygen. Today, photosynthetic microorganisms (including algae) account for more than 50% of the earth's photosynthesis, contributing the majority of the oxygen to the atmosphere (**figure 1.5a**).

1. Ecosystems are communities of living organisms and their surrounding environment.

CLINIC CASE

Toxic Treatments Like over 100,000 of his Brazilian countrymen (and over half a million people in the United States), Arnaldo Luis Gomes suffered from kidney failure and depended on dialysis to keep him alive. Three days a week he visited a clinic in the city of Caruaru and spent 4 hours tethered to a machine that cleansed the toxins from his blood. On this day, however, he knew something was wrong. His head hurt, his stomach ached, and the whites of his eyes began to turn yellow with jaundice, a sure sign that his liver was failing. Despite the best efforts of his doctors, 2 hours later he was dead from toxic hepatitis. Over the next 3 days, more than 100 patients had similar symptoms.

The culprit was identified as *Microcystis*, a type of algae which produces a powerful liver toxin. Unlike most bacterial contamination, water containing high levels of *Microcystis* cannot be made safe by boiling; only removal of the algae can guarantee safety. An investigation revealed that inadequate filtration of water from a local reservoir allowed the use of toxin-laden water in the clinic, eventually killing 46 clients.

Brazil is not the only place where toxic algae is a health concern. Toledo, Ohio—which gets its drinking water from Lake Erie—typically has several days each summer when tap water is unsafe to drink due to high levels of *Microcystis*. A combination of abundant sunlight from long summer days and agricultural runoff into Lake Erie promote the growth of algae to dangerous levels in the lake, which is exactly what happened in Brazil.

Speculate on why algae blooms, like the ones in Toledo, typically occur in summer.

Another process that helps keep the earth in balance is the process of biological **decomposition** and nutrient recycling. Decomposition involves the breakdown of dead matter and wastes into simple compounds that can be directed back into the natural cycles of living things (**figure 1.5*b***). If it were not for multitudes of bacteria and fungi, many chemical elements would become locked up and unavailable to organisms. In the long-term, microorganisms are greatly responsible for the structure and content of the soil, water, and atmosphere. For example:

- Earth's temperature is regulated by "greenhouse gases," such as carbon dioxide and methane, that create an insulation layer in the atmosphere and help retain heat. A significant proportion of these gases is produced by microbes living in the environment and in the digestive tracts of animals.
- Recent estimates propose that, based on weight and numbers, up to 50% of all organisms exist within and beneath the earth's crust in soil, rocks, and even the frozen Antarctic (**figure 1.5*c***). It is increasingly evident that this enormous underground community of microbes is a major force in weathering, mineral extraction, and soil formation.
- Bacteria and fungi live in complex associations with plants. They assist the plants in obtaining nutrients and water and may protect them against disease. Microbes form similar interrelationships with animals, notably as residents of numerous bodily sites.

(a)

(b)

5 µm

(c)

Figure 1.5 A microscopic wonderland. (a) A summer pond is heavily laden with surface scum that reveals several different types of green algae called desmids (*Micrasterias rotata*, 600×). **(b)** A rotting tomato being invaded by a fuzzy forest of mold. The fungus is *Botrytis,* a common decomposer of tomatoes and grapes (250×). **(c)** Tunneling through an ice sheet in Antarctica, one of the coldest places on earth (−35°C), to access hidden microbes. Here we see a red cyanobacterium, *Nostoc* (3,000×), that has probably been frozen in suspended animation there for 3,000 years. Like the example discussed in the chapter-opening case study, this environment may serve as a model for what may one day be discovered on other planets.
(a): *Source:* Lynn Betts, USDA Natural Resources Conservation Service; (a, inset): Lebendkulturen.de/Shutterstock; (b & b, inset): Kathy Park Talaro; (c): *Source:* Ames Research Center/NASA; (c, inset): Image courtesy of the Priscu Research Group, Montana State University, Bozeman

 Practice SECTIONS 1.1–1.2

1. Define what is meant by the term *microorganism* and outline the important contributions microorganisms make to the earth's ecosystems.

2. Describe five different ways in which humans exploit microorganisms for our benefit.

3. Identify the groups of microorganisms included in the scope of microbiology, and explain the criteria for including these groups in the field of microbiology.

4. Observe figure 1.3 and place the microbes pictured there in a size ranking, going from smallest to largest. Use the magnification as your gauge.

5. Construct a table that displays all microbial groups based on what kind of cells they have or do not have.

6. Explain this statement: Microorganisms—we need to live with them because we can't live without them.

1.3 Human Use of Microorganisms

 Learn

6. Discuss the ways microorganisms can be used to create solutions for environmental problems and industrial products.

The incredible diversity and versatility seen in microbes make them excellent candidates for solving human problems. By accident or choice, humans have been using microorganisms for thousands of years to improve life and even to further human progress. Yeasts, a type of microscopic fungi, cause bread to rise and ferment sugar to make alcoholic beverages. Historical records show that households in ancient Egypt kept moldy loaves of bread to apply directly to wounds and lesions, which was probably the first use of penicillin! The manipulation of microorganisms to make products in an industrial setting is called **biotechnology.*** One newer application of this process uses farmed algae to extract a form of oil (biodiesel) to be used in place of petroleum products **(figure 1.6*a*)**.

Genetic engineering is a newer area of biotechnology that manipulates the genetics of microbes, plants, and animals for the purpose of creating new products and genetically modified organisms. One powerful technique for designing new organisms is termed **recombinant DNA.** This technology makes it possible to deliberately alter DNA[2] and to switch genetic material from one organism to another. Bacteria and fungi were some of the first organisms to be genetically engineered, because their relatively simple genetic material is readily manipulated in the laboratory. Recombinant DNA technology has unlimited potential in terms of medical, industrial, and agricultural uses. Microbes can be engineered to synthesize desirable proteins such as drugs, hormones, and enzymes (see table 1.1).

* *biotechnology* (by′-oh-tek-nol″-oh-gee) The use of microbes or their products in the commercial or industrial realm.

2. DNA, or deoxyribonucleic acid, the chemical substance that comprises the genetic material of organisms.

(a)

(b)

Figure 1.6 **Microbes at work. (a)** A scientist from the National Oceanic and Atmospheric Agency (NOAA) demonstrates a series of biodiesel reactors that culture single-celled algae (inset 750×) as a source of oil. This new "green" renewable energy source looks very promising. **(b)** Biotechnology meets bioremediation. Scientists at Pacific Northwest National Laboratories (PNNL) test the capacity of two newly discovered bacteria—*Shewanella* (green) and *Synechococcus* (yellow) (1,000×)—to reduce and detoxify radioactive waste. The process, carried out in large bioreactors, could speed the cleanup of hazardous nuclear waste deposits.
(a): *Source:* Christopher Botnick/NOAA; (a, inset): Yuuji Tsukii, Protist Information Server; (b & b, inset): *Source:* Pacific Northwest National Laboratory.

Among the genetically unique organisms that have been designed by bioengineers are bacteria that contain a natural pesticide, yeasts that produce human hormones, pigs that produce hemoglobin, and plants that are resistant to disease (see table 1.1). The techniques have also paved the way for characterizing human genetic material and diseases.

Another way of tapping into the unlimited potential of microorganisms is the relatively new science of **bioremediation.*** This process introduces microbes into the environment to restore stability or to clean up toxic pollutants. Bioremediation is required to control the massive levels of pollution that result from human activities. Microbes have a surprising capacity to break down chemicals that would be harmful to other organisms. Agencies and companies have developed microbes to handle oil spills and detoxify sites contaminated with heavy metals, pesticides, and even radioactive wastes (**figure 1.6***b*). The solid waste disposal industry is focusing on methods for degrading the tons of garbage in landfills, especially plastics and paper products. One form of bioremediation that has been in use for some time is the treatment of water and sewage. With clean freshwater supplies dwindling worldwide, it will become even more important to find ways to reclaim polluted water.

1.4 Microbial Roles in Infectious Diseases

 Learn

7. Review the roles of microorganisms as parasites and pathogens that cause infection and disease.

8. Define what is meant by emerging and reemerging diseases.

It is important to remember that the large majority of microorganisms are relatively harmless, have quantifiable benefits to humans and the environment, and in many cases are essential to life as we know it. They are free living and derive everything they need to survive from the surrounding environment. Much of the time they form cohesive communities with other organisms, sharing habitat and nutrients. Examples include the natural partnerships that are found in symbioses and biofilms.[3]

Some microbes have adapted to a non–free-living lifestyle called parasitism. A **parasite** lives in or on the body of a larger organism called the **host** and derives most of its sustenance from that host. A parasite's actions generally damage the host through infection and disease. Another term that can be used to specify this type of microbe is **pathogen.***

Humanity is plagued by nearly 2,000 different pathogens that can cause various types of disease. Infectious diseases still devastate human populations worldwide, despite significant strides in understanding and treating them. The most recent estimates from the World Health Organization (WHO) point to around 10 billion infections of all types across the world every year. There are more infections than people because many people acquire more than one infection. Infectious diseases are also among the most common causes of death in much of humanity, and they still kill a significant percentage of the U.S. population. The worldwide death toll from infections is about 13 million people per year, and 90% of the deaths are caused by just

* *biōremediation* (by′-oh-ree-mee-dee-ay″-shun) *bios,* life; *re,* again; *mederi,* to heal. The use of biological agents to remedy environmental problems.

3. A biofilm is a complex network of microbes and their secretions that form in most natural environments, discussed further in chapter 4.

* *pathogen* (path′-oh-jen) Gr. *pathos,* disease, and *gennan,* to produce. Disease-causing agents.

TABLE 1.2	Worldwide Morbidity and Mortality of Common Diseases*	
Disease	**New Cases per Year**	**Deaths per Year**
Influenza	3–5 million cases of severe illness	250,000–500,000
Typhoid fever	21,000,000	200,000
Measles	20,000,000	145,700
HIV/AIDS	2,300,000	1,500,000
Dengue fever	96,000,000	22,000
Shigellosis	80,000,000–165,000,000	600,000
Viral hepatitis (A and B)	380,000,000	1,280,000
Malaria	200,000,000	627,000
Tuberculosis	9,000,000**	1,500,000

*Estimates from most recent CDC and World Health Organization statistics.

**As many as 2,000,000,000 people are believed to carry the tuberculosis bacterium, most as long-term carriers.

Source: Data from World Health Organization.

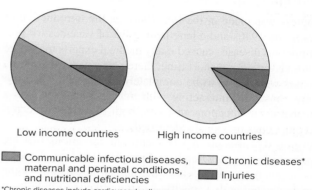

Low income countries High income countries

■ Communicable infectious diseases, maternal and perinatal conditions, and nutritional deficiencies ■ Chronic diseases* ■ Injuries

*Chronic diseases include cardiovascular diseases, cancers, chronic respiratory disorders, diabetes, neuropsychiatric and sense organ disorders, musculoskeletal disorders, digestive diseases, genitourinary diseases, congenital abnormalities, and skin diseases. Most of them are not associated with a single infectious agent.

Figure 1.7 **The burden of infectious disease.** As the average income of a country increases, the risk of death from infectious disease decreases dramatically. Chronic diseases, many of which occur later in life, take a much greater toll in developed countries.

six infectious agents. **Table 1.2** illustrates the toll of some common infectious diseases, while **figure 1.7** compares the causes of death between countries that differ significantly in socioeconomic levels. It is quite evident which world inhabitants suffer the most from infectious diseases. **Table 1.3** displays the number of people affected by what are commonly known as neglected tropical diseases (NTDs), a collection of conditions that thrive among the world's poorest populations and receive far too little attention. Most NTDs are easily treatable with drugs or preventable with vaccines.

Those hardest hit are residents in countries where access to adequate medical care is lacking. One-third of the earth's 7 billion inhabitants live on less than $1 per day, are malnourished, are not fully immunized, and have no access to drugs. Take the case of malaria, caused by a microorganism transmitted by mosquitoes, which kills 1 to 2 million people every year worldwide. Currently the most effective way for citizens of developing countries to avoid

TABLE 1.3	Neglected Tropical Diseases
Disease	**Number of Cases**
Ascariasis	1,000,000,000
Hookworm infection	700,000,000
Onchocerciasis (river blindness)	37,000,000
Lymphatic filariasis	120,000,000
Schistosomiasis	240,000,000
Trachoma	40,000,000
Trichuriasis	800,000,000

Figure 1.8 The *Aedes aegypti* mosquito is the vector for several emerging viral diseases. In this female mosquito, feeding on her photographer, blood can clearly be seen within the fascicle (feeding apparatus) and filling the distended abdomen of the mosquito. Because this species is found throughout the Americas, it is thought to be only a matter of time before the Zika, dengue, and chikungunya viruses are well established in the United States. *Source:* Frank Hadley Collins, Dir. Center for Global Health and Infectious Diseases; University of ND/CDC

infection is to sleep under a bed net, because the mosquitoes are most active in the evening. Yet even this inexpensive solution is beyond the reach of people in many developing countries who cannot afford the $3 to $5 for nets to protect their family. Fortunately for many countries in the malaria zone, several international organizations have collaborated to provide special insecticide-treated nets that can help lower the rate of infections.

The Changing Specter of Infectious Diseases

Great progress was made in the mid-1900s as the introduction of antibiotics in the 1940s and a lengthening list of vaccines for preventing numerous diseases caused many medical experts to declare a premature victory. For a short time, there was a sense that infectious diseases were going to be completely manageable. Because humans are constantly interacting with microbes, we serve as a handy incubator for infectious diseases, both those newly recognized and older ones previously identified.

Emerging diseases are newly identified conditions that are being reported in increasing numbers. Since 1980, at least 87 novel infectious agents have arisen within the human population. Some have been associated with a specific location, like the Ebola fever virus, named for the Ebola River, near which the disease was first seen, while other diseases are **pandemic,** meaning they spread across continents (human immunodeficiency virus, HIV, provides a perfect example). Still others cause **zoonoses,** which are infectious diseases native to animals that can be transmitted to humans. One recent example is chikungunya virus, spread by mosquitoes to humans and other mammals. This virus traveled from the Caribbean to Florida in 2014. It is unclear how fast the virus will spread throughout the United States, as conditions become less favorable to the life cycle of mosquitoes as one moves north. Even more recently, Zika virus, which is spread by the same type of mosquito, **(figure 1.8)** has been detected within the United States.

Reemerging diseases are older, well-known diseases that are increasing in occurrence. Among the most common reemerging infectious diseases are tuberculosis (TB), influenza, malaria, cholera, and hepatitis B. Tuberculosis, which has been known since ancient times, still causes 8 million new infections and kills 1 million to 2 million people every year. As you will see, numerous factors play a part in the tenaciousness of infectious diseases, but fundamental to all of them is the formidable capacity of microbes to adapt to alterations in the individual, community, and environment.

Altogether, government agencies are keeping track of more than 100 emerging and reemerging infectious diseases. Reemerging diseases demonstrate just how difficult it is to eradicate microbes and the diseases they cause, even though we are aware of them and often have drugs and vaccines to combat them. Only smallpox has been eliminated, although we are very close to eradicating polio. In fact, we continue to experience epidemics of childhood diseases that are usually preventable with vaccines. A prime example is measles—considered eliminated from the United States in 2000—which has reemerged as vaccination rates have declined.

A major contributing factor in the spread of disease is our increased mobility and travel, especially by air—an infected person can travel around the world before showing any symptoms of infection, carrying the infectious agent to many far-flung locations and exposing populations along the way, who in turn can infect their contacts. A second factor is the spread of diseases by vectors, living organisms such as fleas, ticks, or mosquitoes. Emerging viruses like chikungunya, dengue, and Zika are all spread by the *Aedes* mosquito, which is so aggressive it routinely follows people indoors to partake of a blood meal (figure 1.8). Other significant effects involve our expanding population and global food-growing practices. As we continue to encroach into new territory and wild habitats, there is potential for contact with emerging pathogens, as has been seen with Ebola fever, Lyme disease, and hantavirus pulmonary syndrome. Our agricultural practices can unearth microbes that were lying dormant or hidden. A bacterium carried in the intestine of domestic cattle, *Escherichia coli* O157:H7, the agent of a serious kidney disease, has been associated with hundreds of thousands of infections from food and water contaminated with cattle feces. Mass-produced fresh food can also travel around the world, infecting people along the way. Several large outbreaks of salmonellosis, shigellosis, and listeriosis have been traced to contaminated dairy, poultry products, and vegetables.

* *zoonosis* (zoh″-uh-noh′-sis) Gr. *zoion*, animal, and *nosos*, disease. Any disease indigenous to animals transmissible to humans.

The incredible resistance of microbes also contributes to their continued spread. The emergence of drug-resistant "superbugs" has become a massive problem in medicine. Some forms of *Staphylococcus aureus* (MRSA) and *Mycobacterium tuberculosis* are resistant to so many drugs that there are few, and sometimes no, treatment choices left. As hard as we may try to manage microbes, we keep coming up against a potent reality, a sentiment summed up by the renowned microbiologist Louis Pasteur over 130 years ago when he declared, "Microbes will have the last word."

Microbial Roles in Noninfectious Disease

One of the most eye-opening discoveries has been that many diseases once considered noninfectious probably do involve microbial infection. Most scientists expect that, in time, a majority of chronic conditions will be linked to microbial agents. The most famous of these is gastric ulcers, now known to be caused by a bacterium called *Helicobacter* (see chapter 21). Diseases as disparate as type 1 diabetes, obsessive-compulsive disorder, and coronary artery disease have been linked to chronic infections with microorganisms. Even the microbiome, the collection of microorganisms we all carry with us even when healthy, has been shown to have a much greater effect on our health than was previously thought. Recent studies have linked changes in the microbiome population to metabolic syndrome, a collection of health conditions including high cholesterol, hypertension, high blood sugar levels, and excess fat, all of which can raise the risk of heart disease, stroke, and diabetes.

It seems that the golden age of microbiological discovery, during which all of the "obvious" diseases were characterized and cures or preventions were devised for them, should more accurately be referred to as the first golden age. We're now discovering the roles of microorganisms in hidden but slowly destructive diseases. These include female infertility caused by *Chlamydia* infection and malignancies such as liver cancer (hepatitis viruses) and cervical cancer (human papillomavirus). In fact, epidemiologists analyzing statistics on world cancer have estimated that one in six cancers can be associated with an infectious agent.

Another important development in infectious disease trends is the increasing number of patients with weakened defenses who are kept alive for extended periods. We are becoming more susceptible to infectious disease precisely because of advances in medicine. People are living longer and sick people are staying alive much longer than in the past, creating a population far more susceptible to what we might call "garden-variety" microbes.

Practice SECTIONS 1.3–1.4

7. Describe several ways the beneficial qualities of microbes greatly outweigh microbes' roles as infectious agents.

8. Look up in the index some of the diseases shown in table 1.2 and determine which ones could be prevented by vaccines or cured with drugs. Are there other ways (besides vaccines) to prevent any of these?

9. Distinguish between emerging and reemerging infectious diseases and explain what factors contribute to their development.

1.5 The Historical Foundations of Microbiology

Learn

9. Outline the major events in the history of microbiology, including the major contributors to the early development of microscopy, medical advances, aseptic techniques, and the germ theory of disease.

10. Explain the main features of the scientific method, and differentiate between inductive and deductive reasoning and between hypothesis and theory.

If not for the extensive interest, curiosity, and devotion of thousands of microbiologists over the last 300 years, we would know little about the microscopic realm that surrounds us. Many of the discoveries in this science have resulted from the prior work of men and women who toiled long hours in dimly lit laboratories with the crudest of tools. Each additional insight, whether large or small, has added to our current knowledge of life forms and processes. This section summarizes the prominent discoveries made in the past 300 years: microscopy, the rise of the scientific method, and the development of medical microbiology, including the germ theory and the origins of modern microbiological techniques. The table "Significant Events in Microbiology," found in **Online Appendix 2,** summarizes some of the pivotal events in microbiology from its earliest beginnings to the present.

The Development of the Microscope: Seeing Is Believing

It is likely that from the very earliest history, humans noticed that when certain foods spoiled, they became inedible or caused illness and yet other "spoiled" foods did no harm and even had enhanced flavor. Even several centuries ago, there was already a sense that diseases such as the black plague and smallpox were caused by some sort of transmissible matter. But the causes of such phenomena were obscure because the technology to study them was lacking. Consequently, they remained cloaked in mystery and regarded with superstition—a trend that led even well-educated scientists to believe in spontaneous generation (**1.1 Making Connections**).

True awareness of the widespread distribution of microorganisms and some of their characteristics was finally made possible by the development of the first microscopes. These devices revealed microbes as discrete entities sharing many of the characteristics of larger, visible plants and animals. Several early scientists fashioned magnifying lenses and microscopes, but these lacked the optical clarity needed for examining bacteria and other small, single-celled organisms. The most careful and exacting observations awaited the simple single-lens microscope hand-fashioned by **Antonie van Leeuwenhoek,** a Dutch linen merchant and self-made microbiologist.

During the late 1600s in Holland, Leeuwenhoek used his early lenses to examine the thread patterns of the draperies and upholstery he sold in his shop. Between customers, he retired to

the workbench in the back of his shop, grinding glass lenses to ever-finer specifications. He could see with increasing clarity, but after a few years he became interested in things other than thread counts. He took rainwater from a clay pot, smeared it on his specimen holder, and peered at it through his finest lens. He found "animals appearing to me ten thousand times more than those which may be perceived in the water with the naked eye."

Quick Search

Search for "Through van Leeuwenhoek's Eyes: Microbiology in a Nutshell" on YouTube to watch a video inspired by Leeuwenhoek's world

He didn't stop there. He scraped plaque from his teeth, and from the teeth of volunteers who had never cleaned their teeth in their lives, and took a close look at that. He recorded: "In the said matter there were many very little living animalcules, very prettily a-moving Moreover, the other animalcules were in such enormous numbers, that all the water . . . seemed to be alive." Leeuwenhoek started sending his observations to the Royal Society of London, and eventually he was recognized as a scientist of great merit.

Leeuwenhoek constructed more than 250 small, powerful microscopes that could magnify up to 300 times **(figure 1.9).** Considering that he had no formal training in science and that he was the first person ever to faithfully record this strange new world, his descriptions of bacteria and protozoa (which he called "animalcules") were astute and precise. Because of Leeuwenhoek's extraordinary contributions to microbiology, he is sometimes considered the father of bacteriology and protozoology.

From the time of Leeuwenhoek, microscopes became more complex and improved, with the addition of refined lenses, a condenser, finer focusing devices, and built-in light sources. The prototype of the modern compound microscope, in use from about the mid-1800s, was capable of magnifications of 1,000 times or more, largely because it had two sets of lenses for magnification. Even our modern laboratory microscopes are not greatly different in basic structure and function from those early microscopes. The technical characteristics of microscopes and microscopy are a major focus of chapter 3.

The Scientific Method and the Search for Knowledge

The research that led to acceptance of biogenesis provides us with one example of the early development of science-based thought. Over the next few sections we will glimpse other important milestones in the development of the scientific method, such as vaccination, germ theory, asepsis, and Koch's postulates. The impact of science is so pervasive that you may not realize how much of our everyday life is built upon applications of the scientific method. Vaccines, antibiotics, space travel, computers, medical diagnosis, and DNA testing exist primarily because of the work of thousands of scientists doing objective observations and collecting evidence that is measurable, can be expressed quantitatively, and is subject to critical analysis.

The information obtained through the scientific method is explanatory and predictive. It aims to explain how and why phenomena occur and to predict what is expected to happen under known conditions.

Lens
Specimen holder
Focus screw
Handle

(a)

(b)

Figure 1.9 **Leeuwenhoek's microscope. (a)** A brass replica of a Leeuwenhoek microscope and how it is held (inset). **(b)** Early illustrations of bacterial cells from a sample of milk, magnified about 300×. These drawings closely resemble those Leeuwenhoek made of his animalcules.
(a): Kathy Park Talaro; (a, inset): Pasadena City College/Kathy Park Talaro

How do scientists apply the scientific method? In the **deductive reasoning** approach, a scientist uses general observations of some phenomenon to develop a set of facts to explain that phenomenon—that is, they *deduce* the facts that can account for what they have observed. This early explanation is considered a **hypothesis,** and however tentative it may start out, it is still based on scientific thought rather than subjective beliefs that come from superstition or myth. A valid hypothesis will allow for experimentation and testing and can be shown to be false. An example of a workable

1.1 MAKING CONNECTIONS

The Fall of Superstition and the Rise of Microbiology

For thousands of years, people believed that certain living things arose from vital forces present in nonliving or decomposing matter. This ancient idea, known as **spontaneous generation,** was continually reinforced as people observed that meat left out in the open soon "produced" maggots, that mushrooms appeared on rotting wood, that rats and mice emerged from piles of litter, and that other magical phenomena occurred. Though some of these early ideas seem quaint and ridiculous in light of modern knowledge, we must remember that, at the time, mysteries in life were accepted and the scientific method was not widely practiced.

Even after single-celled organisms were discovered during the mid-1600s, the idea of spontaneous generation persisted. Some scientists assumed that microscopic beings were an early stage in the development of more complex ones.

Over the subsequent 200 years, scientists waged an experimental battle over the two hypotheses that could explain the origin of simple life forms. Some tenaciously clung to the idea of **abiogenesis*** which embraced spontaneous generation. On the other side were advocates of **biogenesis,*** saying that living things arise only from others of their same kind. There were serious proponents on both sides, and each side put forth what appeared on the surface to be plausible explanations of why their evidence was more correct. Gradually the abiogenesis hypothesis was abandoned as convincing evidence for biogenesis continued to mount. The following series of experiments were among the most important in finally tipping the balance.

Some of the important variables to be considered in testing the hypotheses were the effects of nutrients, air, and heat and the presence of preexisting life forms in the environment. One of the first people to test the spontaneous generation theory was **Francesco Redi** of Italy. He conducted a simple experiment in which he placed meat in a jar and covered the jar with fine gauze. Flies gathering at the jar were blocked from entering and thus laid their eggs on the outside of the gauze. The maggots subsequently developed without access to the meat, indicating that maggots were the offspring of flies and did not arise from some "vital force" in the meat. This and related experiments laid to rest the idea that more complex animals such as insects and mice developed through abiogenesis, but it did not convince many scientists of the day that simpler organisms could not arise in that way.

The Frenchman **Louis Jablot** reasoned that even microscopic organisms must have parents, and his experiments with infusions (dried hay steeped in water) supported that hypothesis. He divided an infusion that had been boiled to destroy any living things into two containers: a heated container that was closed to the air and a heated container that was freely open to the air. Only the open vessel developed microorganisms, which he presumed had entered in air laden with dust. Regrettably, the validation of biogenesis was temporarily set back by **John Needham,** an Englishman who did similar experiments using mutton gravy. His results were in conflict with Jablot's because both his heated and unheated test containers teemed with microbes. Unfortunately, his experiments were

done before the realization that heat-resistant microbes are not usually killed by mere boiling. Apparently Jablot had been lucky; his infusions were sterile.

Then, in the mid-1800s, the acclaimed microbiologist **Louis Pasteur** entered the arena. He had recently been studying the roles of microorganisms in the fermentation of beer and wine, and it was clear to him that these processes were brought about by the activities of microbes introduced into the beverage from air, fruits, and grains. The methods he used to discount abiogenesis were simple yet brilliant.

Pasteur's Experiment

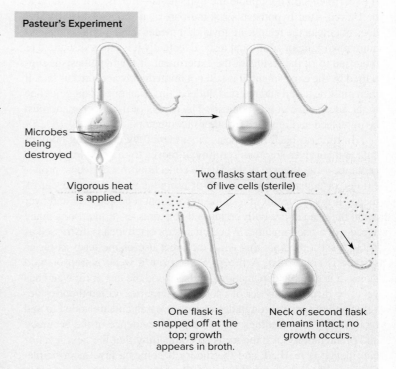

Microbes being destroyed

Vigorous heat is applied.

Two flasks start out free of live cells (sterile)

One flask is snapped off at the top; growth appears in broth.

Neck of second flask remains intact; no growth occurs.

To further clarify that air and dust were the source of microbes, Pasteur filled flasks with broth and fashioned their openings into elongate, swan-neck–shaped tubes. The flasks' openings were freely open to the air but were curved so that gravity would cause any airborne dust particles to deposit in the lower part of the necks. He heated the flasks to sterilize the broth and then incubated them. As long as the flask remained intact, the broth remained sterile, but if the neck was broken off so that dust fell directly down into the container, microbial growth immediately commenced.

Pasteur summed up his findings, "For I have kept from them, and am still keeping from them, that one thing which is above the power of man to make; I have kept from them the germs that float in the air, I have kept from them life."

What type of microorganisms were likely responsible for the misleading results of John Needham's experiment and were absent in Jablot's and Pasteur's experiments?

* *abiogenesis* (ah-bee″-oh-jen′-uh-sis) L. *a,* without, *bios,* life, and *genesis,* beginning.
* *biogenesis* (by-oh-jen-uh-sis) to begin with life.

hypothesis based on deduction might be the speculation that a disease such as hemophilia is an inheritable condition. This would pave the way for specific experiments that test for the influence of genetics. A nonworkable hypothesis would be that hemophilia is caused by a curse placed on the royal family of England. Because supernatural beliefs cannot be tested, they can never be subjected to the rigors of the scientific method.

With **inductive reasoning,** one applies specific observations to develop a general explanation. This method is often used in the early phases of evaluation and can formulate a generalization to be tested deductively. In the previous example, induction might begin with the observation of a family in which several people have hemophilia, and this may lead to the general idea that it is inheritable.

A lengthy process of experimentation, analysis, and testing eventually leads to conclusions that either support or refute the hypothesis. If experiments do not uphold the hypothesis—that is, if it is found to be flawed—the hypothesis or some part of it is reconsidered. This does not mean the results are invalid; it means the hypothesis may require reworking or additional tests. Eventually it is either discarded or modified to fit the results of the experiment. If the hypothesis is supported by the experiment, it is still not immediately accepted as fact. It then must be tested and retested. Indeed, this is an important guideline in the acceptance of a hypothesis. The results of the experiment must be published and repeated by other investigators.

In time, as each hypothesis is supported by a growing body of data and survives rigorous scrutiny, it moves to the next level of acceptance—the **theory.** A theory is a collection of statements, propositions, or concepts that explains or accounts for a natural event. A theory is not the result of a single experiment repeated over and over again but is an entire body of ideas that expresses or interprets many aspects of a phenomenon. When an unsupported idea is dismissed as being "just a theory," this is an incorrect use of the term as far as science is concerned. A theory is far from a weak notion or wild guess. It is a viable explanation that has stood the test of time and has yet to be disproved by serious scientific inquiries. Often theories develop and progress through decades of research and are added to and modified by new findings. At some point, evidence of the accuracy and predictability of a theory is so compelling that the next level of confidence is reached, and the theory becomes a **law,** or principle. For example, the **germ theory of disease** has been so thoroughly tested that it has clearly passed into the realm of law.

Science and its hypotheses and theories must progress along with technology. As advances in instrumentation allow new, more detailed views of living phenomena, old theories may be reexamined and altered and new ones proposed. Scientific knowledge is accumulative, and it must have built-in flexibility to accommodate new findings. It is for these reasons that scientists do not take a stance that theories are absolutely proved.

Figure 1.10 provides a summary of the scientific method in action using Edward Jenner's monumental discovery of vaccines. What is remarkable about Jenner's work is that he was the first to use scientific thought to construct a rigorous experimental model to inoculate people against disease, and he carried it through to its completion. It is also remarkable that he did this knowing nothing about viruses or even microbes. He worked out the concept of safely conferring artificial immunity long before there was any understanding of the immune system.

The Development of Medical Microbiology

Early experiments on the sources of microorganisms led to the profound realization that microbes are everywhere: Not only are air and dust full of them, but the entire surface of the earth, its waters, and all objects are inhabited by them. This discovery led to immediate applications in medicine. Thus the seeds of medical microbiology were sown in the middle to latter half of the nineteenth century with the introduction of the first practical vaccine; the germ theory of disease; and the resulting use of sterile, aseptic, and pure culture techniques.

Jenner and the Introduction of Vaccination

We saw in figure 1.10 how the English physician and scientist **Edward Jenner** modeled the scientific method. His experiments ultimately gave rise to the first viable method to control smallpox by inoculating patients with a closely related disease agent. It is often said of Jenner that his discovery saved more lives than any other in history. His work marked the beginning of an era of great scientific achievement—one that produced some of the most far-reaching developments in microbiology and medicine.

The Discovery of Spores and Sterilization

Following Pasteur's inventive work with infusions (1.1 Making Connections), it was not long before English physicist **John Tyndall** provided the initial evidence that some of the microbes in dust and air have very high heat resistance and that particularly vigorous treatment is required to destroy them. Later, the discovery and detailed description of heat-resistant bacterial endospores by **Ferdinand Cohn,** a German botanist, clarified why heat would sometimes fail to completely eliminate all microorganisms. The modern sense of the word **sterile,** meaning completely free of all infectious agents, including endospores, viruses, and prions, had its beginnings here (see chapter 11). The capacity to sterilize objects and materials is an absolutely essential part of microbiology, medicine, dentistry, and some industries.

The Development of Aseptic Techniques

From earliest history, humans experienced a vague sense that "unseen forces" or "poisonous vapors" emanating from decomposing matter could cause disease. As the study of microbiology became more scientific and the invisible was made visible, the fear of such mysterious vapors was replaced by the knowledge, and sometimes even the fear, of "germs." About 130 years ago, the first studies by **Robert Koch** clearly linked a microscopic organism with a specific disease. Since that time, microbiologists have conducted a continuous search for disease-causing agents.

At the same time that abiogenesis was being hotly debated, a few budding microbiologists began to suspect that microorganisms could cause not only spoilage and decay but also infectious diseases. It occurred to these rugged individualists that even the human body itself was a source of infection. **Dr. Oliver Wendell Holmes,** an American physician, observed that mothers who gave birth at home experienced fewer infections than did mothers who gave birth in the hospital, and the Hungarian **Dr. Ignaz Semmelweis** showed quite clearly that women became infected in the maternity ward after examinations by physicians coming directly from the autopsy room.

Observations/ information gathering

1. Dr. Jenner observed that cows had a form of pox similar to smallpox. Jenner also noted that milkmaids acquired cowpox only on the hands, and they appeared to be immune to smallpox.

Formation of Jenner's hypothesis

2. Jenner deduced that the cowpox was closely related to smallpox and could possibly be used on patients to provide protection similar to that of the milkmaids he had seen.

Testing the hypothesis, experiment I

3. Jenner took scrapings from cowpox blisters on the hand of a milkmaid and inoculated them into a boy who had not had smallpox. He developed minor symptoms but remained healthy.

Testing the hypothesis, experiment II

4. After a few weeks, the child was exposed twice to the pus from an active smallpox lesion. He did not acquire smallpox and appeared to have immune protection.

Reproducibility of results

5. Jenner went on to inoculate 23 other test subjects with cowpox. For the first time, he used lesions from one child to inoculate another. All subjects remained protected from smallpox.

Publishing of results; other medical testing

6. Jenner wrote a paper detailing his experiment. He called his technique *vaccination*, from the Latin *vacca* for cow. Other local English physicians began to vaccinate patients with some success.

Vaccination theory becomes widespread

7. Over the next 100 years vaccination was brought to the rest of the world through local programs. Scientists used Jenner's methods to develop vaccines for other pathogens. The theory of artificial immunity became well established.

Smallpox is eradicated from the world.

8. A massive vaccination campaign was aimed to reduce cases and to stamp out the disease completely. Billions of doses given over a decade reduced smallpox to zero. The last cases occurred in 1977, and in 1979 the disease was declared eradicated.

Figure 1.10 **Edward Jenner and the saga of the smallpox vaccine.** Jenner's work documents the first attempt based on the scientific method to control an infectious disease—smallpox. This disease was characterized by raised skin blisters called pox, and it often caused severe damage to organs. Throughout its long history this deadly disease decimated many populations worldwide, until 1977, when the last cases were reported.

The English surgeon **Joseph Lister** took notice of these observations and was the first to introduce **aseptic* techniques** aimed at reducing microbes in a medical setting and preventing wound infections. Lister's concept of asepsis was much more limited than our modern precautions. It mainly involved disinfecting the hands and the air with strong antiseptic chemicals, such as phenol, prior to surgery. It is hard for us to believe, but as recently as the late 1800s surgeons wore street clothes in the operating room and had little idea that hand washing was important. Lister's techniques and the application of heat for sterilization became the bases for microbial control by physical and chemical methods, which are still in use today.

The Discovery of Pathogens and the Germ Theory of Disease

Two ingenious founders of microbiology, **Louis Pasteur** of France **(figure 1.11)** and **Robert Koch** of Germany, introduced techniques that are still used today. Pasteur made enormous contributions to

* *aseptic* (ay-sep′-tik) Gr. *a*, no, and *sepsis*, decay or infection. These techniques are aimed at reducing pathogens and do not necessarily sterilize.

Figure 1.11 **Photograph of Louis Pasteur (1822–1895), the father of microbiology.** Few microbiologists can match the scope and impact of Pasteur's contributions to the science of microbiology. Pixtal/age fotostock

our understanding of the roles of microorganisms in many aspects of medicine and industry. He developed two vaccines (rabies and anthrax) and clarified the actions of microbes in wine and beer fermentation. He invented pasteurization and completed some of the first studies showing that human diseases could arise from infection. These studies, supported by the work of other scientists, became known as the **germ theory of disease.** Pasteur's contemporary, Koch, established *Koch's postulates,* a series of proofs that verified the germ theory and could establish whether an organism was pathogenic and which disease it caused (see chapter 13). Around 1875 Koch used this experimental system to show that anthrax is caused by a bacterium called *Bacillus anthracis.* So useful were his postulates that the causative agents of 20 other diseases were discovered between 1875 and 1900, and even today they serve as a basic premise for establishing a link between pathogens and diseases. It is not an overstatement to say that Koch and his colleagues invented many of the techniques that are described in chapter 3: inoculation, isolation, media, maintenance of pure cultures, and preparation of specimens for microscopic examination. Other highlights in this era of discovery are presented in later chapters on microbial control (see chapter 11) and vaccination (see chapter 15).

 Practice SECTION 1.5

10. Outline the most significant discoveries and events in microscopy, culture techniques, and other methods of handling or controlling microbes.

11. Differentiate between a hypothesis and a theory. If someone says a scientific explanation is "only a theory," what do they really mean?

12. Is the germ theory of disease actually a law, and why?

13. Why was the abandonment of the spontaneous generation theory so significant?

1.6 Taxonomy: Organizing, Classifying, and Naming Microorganisms

Learn

11. Define *taxonomy* and its supporting terms *classification, nomenclature, identification,* and *phylogenetic.*

12. Explain how the levels of a taxonomic scheme relate to each other. Give the names of the levels, and place them in a hierarchy.

13. Describe the goals of nomenclature and how the binomial system is structured. Know how to correctly write a scientific name.

Students just beginning their microbiology studies are often dismayed by the seemingly endless array of new, unusual, and sometimes confusing names for microorganisms. Learning microbial **nomenclature*** is very much like learning a new language, and occasionally its demands may be a bit overwhelming. But paying attention to proper microbial names is just like following a baseball game: You cannot tell the players apart without a program! Your understanding and appreciation of microorganisms will be greatly improved by learning a few general rules about how they are named.

The formal system for organizing, classifying, and naming living things is **taxonomy.*** This science originated more than 250 years ago when **Carl von Linné** (also known as Linnaeus; 1701–1778), a Swedish botanist, laid down the basic rules for taxonomic categories, or **taxa.** Von Linné realized early on that a system for recognizing and defining the properties of living things would prevent chaos in scientific studies by providing each organism with a unique name and an exact "slot" in which to catalog it. This classification would then serve as a means for future identification of that same organism and permit workers in many biological fields to know if they were indeed discussing the same organism. The von Linné system has served well in categorizing the 2 million or more different types of organisms that have been discovered since that time.

The primary concerns of taxonomy are classification, nomenclature, and identification, which together help to keep the tens of million of species on earth organized. Like grouping photos on your phone, many options exist to catalogue organisms, but the most useful is to group individuals together based on a common evolutionary history and shared genetic features, a so-called **phylogenetic** system. **Classification** is an orderly arrangement of organisms into groups that indicate evolutionary relationships

* *nomenclature* (noh′-men-klay″-chur) L. *nomen,* name, and *clare,* to call. A system of naming.
* *taxonomy* (tacks-on″-uh-mee) Gr. *taxis,* arrangement, and *nomos,* name.

and history. **Nomenclature** is the system of assigning names to the various taxonomic rankings of each microbial species. **Identification** is the process of using the specific characteristics and capabilities of an organism to determine its exact identity and placement in taxonomy. A survey of some general methods of identification appears in chapter 3.

The Levels of Classification

The main taxa, or groups, in a classification scheme are organized into several descending ranks called a **hierarchy.** It begins with **domain,** which is a giant, all-inclusive category based on a unique cell type, and ends with **species,*** the smallest and most specific taxon. All the members of a domain share only one or a few general characteristics, whereas members of a species share the majority of their characteristics. The order of taxa between the top and bottom levels is, in descending order: **domain, kingdom, phylum*** or **division,**[4] **class, order, family, genus,*** and **species.** Thus, each domain may be subdivided into a series of kingdoms, each kingdom is made up of several phyla, each phylum contains several classes, and so on. In some cases, additional levels can be imposed immediately above (super) or below (sub) a taxon, giving us such categories as superphylum and subclass.

To illustrate how this hierarchy works, we compare the taxonomic breakdowns of a human and a common pond protozoan **(figure 1.12).** Humans and protozoa belong to the same domain (Eukarya) but are placed in different kingdoms. To emphasize just how broad the category kingdom is, think about the fact that humans belong to the same kingdom as jellyfish. Of the several phyla within this kingdom, humans are in the Phylum Chordata, but even a phylum is rather all-inclusive, considering that humans share it with other vertebrates, as well as with creatures called sea squirts. The next level, Class Mammalia, narrows the field considerably by grouping only those vertebrates that have hair and suckle their young. Humans belong to the Order Primates, a group that also includes apes, monkeys, and lemurs. Next comes the Family Hominoidea, containing only humans and apes. The final levels are our genus, *Homo* (all races of modern and ancient humans), and our species, *sapiens* (meaning wise). Notice that for both the human and the protozoan, the categories become less inclusive and the individual members more closely related and similar in overall appearance. Other examples of classification schemes are provided in sections of chapters 4 and 5 and in several later chapters. A superior source for the taxonomic breakdown of microbes is Wikipedia. Go there to search the scientific name of any species, and its taxonomy will be shown in a box on the upper-right portion of the first page.

We need to remember that all taxonomic hierarchies are based on the judgment of scientists with certain expertise in a particular group of organisms and that not all other experts may agree with the system being used. Consequently, no taxa are permanent to any degree; they are constantly being revised and refined as new information becomes available or new viewpoints become prevalent. Our primary aim in introducing taxonomy is to present an organizational tool that helps you keep track of the various microbial groups and recognize their major categories. For the most part our emphasis will remain on the higher-level taxa (phylum, class) and genus and species.

Assigning Scientific Names

Many larger organisms are known by a common name suggested by certain dominant features. For example, a bird species may be called a yellow-bellied sapsucker, or a flowering plant, a sunflower. Some species of microorganisms (especially pathogens) are also sometimes designated by informal names, such as the gonococcus (*Neisseria gonorrhoeae*) or the TB bacillus (*Mycobacterium tuberculosis*), but this is not the usual practice. If we were to adopt common names such as the "little yellow coccus" (for *Micrococcus luteus**) or the "club-shaped diphtheria bacterium" (for *Corynebacterium diphtheriae**), the terminology would become even more cumbersome and challenging than scientific names. Even worse, common names are notorious for varying from region to region, even within the same country. A decided advantage of standardized nomenclature is that it provides a universal language that enables scientists from all countries on the earth to freely exchange information.

The **scientific name,** also known as the **specific epithet,** is assigned by using a **binomial** (two-name) **system** of nomenclature. The scientific name is always a combination of the generic (genus) name followed by the species name. The generic part of the scientific name is capitalized, and the species part begins with a lowercase letter. Both should be italicized (or underlined if italics are not available), as follows:

Histoplasma capsulatum or **Histoplasma capsulatum**

Because other taxonomic levels are not italicized and consist of only one word, one can always recognize a scientific name. An organism's scientific name is sometimes abbreviated to save space, as in *H. capsulatum,* but only if the genus name has already been stated. The source for nomenclature is usually Latin or Greek. If other languages such as English or French are used, the endings of these words are revised to have Latin endings.

An international group oversees the naming of every new organism discovered, making sure that standard procedures have been followed and that there is not already an earlier name for the organism or another organism with that same name. The inspiration for names is extremely varied and often rather imaginative. Some species have been named in honor of a microbiologist who originally discovered the microbe or who has made outstanding contributions to the field. Other names may designate a characteristic of the microbe (shape, color), a location where it was found, or a

* *species* (spee′-sheez) L. *specere,* kind. In biology, this term is always in the plural form.

* *phylum* (fy′-lum) pl. phyla (fye′-luh) Gr. *phylon,* race.

4. The term *phylum* is used for protozoa, animals, bacteria, and fungi. Division is for algae and plants.

* *genus* (jee′-nus) pl. genera (jen′-er-uh) L. birth, kind.

* *micrococcus luteus* Gr. *micros,* small, and *kokkus,* berry, and L. *luteus,* yellow.

* *corynebacterium diphtheriae* Gr. *coryne,* club, *bacterion,* little rod, and *diphtheriae,* the causative agent of the disease diphtheria.

Domain: Eukarya (All eukaryotic organisms)

Kingdom: Animalia

Sea squirt Lemur Sea star

Phylum: Chordata

Class: Mammalia

Order: Primates

Family: Hominoidea

Genus: *Homo*

Species: *sapiens*
Scientific name: *Homo sapiens*

(a)

Domain: Eukarya (All eukaryotic organisms)

Kingdom: Protista
 Includes
 protozoa
 and algae

Phylum: Ciliophora
 Protozoa with cilia
 Covered by flexible
 pellicle
 Contain two types
 of nuclei

Class: Oligohymenophora
 Single, rapidly
 swimming cells
 Regular rows of cilia
 Distinct ciliated oral
 groove

Order: Peniculida
 Uniform dense cilia
 dispersed over cell
 Oral cilia are peniculae
 Trichocysts in outer
 membrane

Family: Parameciidae
 Cells round to elongate
 Rotate while swimming
 Deep oral grooves

Genus: *Paramecium*
 Ovoid, cigar- and foot-shaped cells

Species: *caudatum*
 Cells elongate, cylindrical
 Blunt at one end and tapered to a
 point at the other
Scientific name: *Paramecium caudatum*

(b)

Figure 1.12 **Sample taxonomy.** Two organisms belonging to Domain Eukarya, traced through their taxonomic series. **(a)** Modern humans, *Homo sapiens.* **(b)** A common protozoan, *Paramecium caudatum.*

disease or symptom that it causes. Some examples of scientific names and origins are:

1. ***Histoplasma capsulatum*** Gr. *histo,* tissue, *plasm,* to form, and L. *capsula,* small sheath. A fungus that causes Ohio Valley fever.

2. ***Trichinella spiralis*** Gr. *trichos,* hair, *ella,* little, and L. *spira,* coiled. The nematode worm that causes the food-borne infection trichinellosis.

3. ***Shewanella oneidensis*** Named for British bacteriologist J. M. Shewan and Lake Oneida, New York, where it was discovered. This is a remarkable species that can bioremediate radioactive metals in contaminated waste sites.

4. ***Bordetella pertussis*** After Jules Bordet, a Belgian microbiologist who discovered this bacterium, and L. *per,* severe, and *tussis,* cough. This is the cause of pertussis, or whooping cough.

1. *Source:* Dr. Libero Ajello/CDC; **2.** *Source:* CDC

3. *Source:* Rizlan Bencheikh and Bruce Arey, Environmental Molecular Sciences Laboratory, DOE Pacific Northwest National Laboratory; **4.** *Source:* CDC

When you encounter the name of a microorganism in the chapters ahead, it is helpful to take the time to sound it out one syllable at a time and repeat until it seems familiar. You are much more likely to remember the names that way—and they will become part of the new language you will be learning.

> **Quick Search**
> Search the Web using the phrase "Bacterial Pathogen Pronunciation Station" for help in correctly pronouncing some common scientific names.

 Practice SECTION 1.6

14. Differentiate between taxonomy, classification, and nomenclature.
15. What is the basis for a phylogenetic system of classification?
16. Explain the binomial system of nomenclature and give the correct order of taxa, going from most general to most specific.
17. Explain some of the benefits of using scientific names for organisms.

1.7 The Origin and Evolution of Microorganisms

 Learn

14. Discuss the fundamentals of evolution, evidence used to verify evolutionary trends, and the use of evolutionary theory in the study of organisms.
15. Explain the concepts behind the organization of the two main trees of life, and indicate where the major groups of microorganisms fall on these trees.
16. Explain the bases for classification, taxonomy, and nomenclature.
17. Recall the order of taxa and the system of notation used in creating scientific names.

All Life Is Related and Connected Through Evolution

As we indicated earlier, *taxonomy,* the classification of biological species, is a system used to organize all of the forms of life. In biology today, there are different methods for deciding on taxonomic categories, but they all rely on the history and relatedness of organisms. The natural relatedness between groups of living things is called their **phylogeny.** Biologists can apply their knowledge of phylogenetic relationships to develop a system of taxonomy.

To understand how organisms originate, we must understand some fundamentals of **evolution.** You have no doubt heard comments that dismiss evolution as "only a theory" as though there remain significant problems with its acceptance. But you have also learned that a scientific theory is a highly documented and well-established concept. The body of knowledge that has accumulated

over hundreds of years regarding the process of evolution is so significant that scientists from all disciplines consider evolution to be a fact. It is an important theme that underlies all of biology, including microbiology. Put simply, the scientific principle of evolution states that living things change gradually over time. The process of evolution is selective: Those changes that most favor the survival of a particular organism or group of organisms tend to be retained, and those that are less beneficial to survival tend to be lost. The great naturalist Charles Darwin labeled this process natural selection. We do not have the space here to present a detailed analysis of evolutionary theories, but the occurrence of evolution is supported by a tremendous amount of evidence from the fossil record and from the study of **morphology** (structure), **physiology** (function), and **genetics** (inheritance). Evolution accounts for the millions of different species on the earth and their adaptation to its many and diverse habitats.

Evolution is founded on two premises: (1) that all new species originate from preexisting species through inheritance of traits and (2) that closely related organisms have similar features because they evolved from common ancestral forms. Usually evolution progresses toward greater complexity, and evolutionary stages range from simple, less evolved forms that are close to an ancestral organism to more complex, evolved forms that have advanced beyond the ancestral forms. Regardless of their evolutionary history, all species presently residing on the earth are modern, but some have arisen more recently in evolutionary history than others.

Traditionally we present the history of life, or phylogeny, in the form of branching trees that are designed to show the origins of various life forms (**figures 1.13** and **1.14**). At the base are the oldest ancestral forms (somewhat like roots), and the trunk indicates the progression of major lines that emerge through selection. Branches split off the main trunk as further selection and modification occur. With this arrangement, more closely related organisms appear nearer to each other on the tree. Any tree of life is nothing more than a system for classifying organisms, and the characteristics used for the process are specified by the person or group creating the tree. Classifying organisms alphabetically (aardvark, acinetobacter, aloe, antelope) or by size (giant redwood, blue whale . . .) are equally valid strategies. However, the most scientifically useful classification schemes group organisms according to their biological characteristics, using the tree to display the evolutionary relationships between organisms.

Systems for Presenting a Universal Tree of Life

The earliest classification schemes assigned every living thing to either the Plant Kingdom or the Animal Kingdom, even though many organisms were a poor fit for either. As knowledge grew concerning cellular structure, means of acquiring nutrients, and how organisms moved about, Robert Whittaker developed a five-kingdom system (figure 1.13) in the 1960s that remained the standard for many years. Individual members of the five kingdoms—the **monera, fungi, protists, plants,** and **animals**—were easily distinguished from one another using techniques common to most laboratories during the mid-twentieth century.

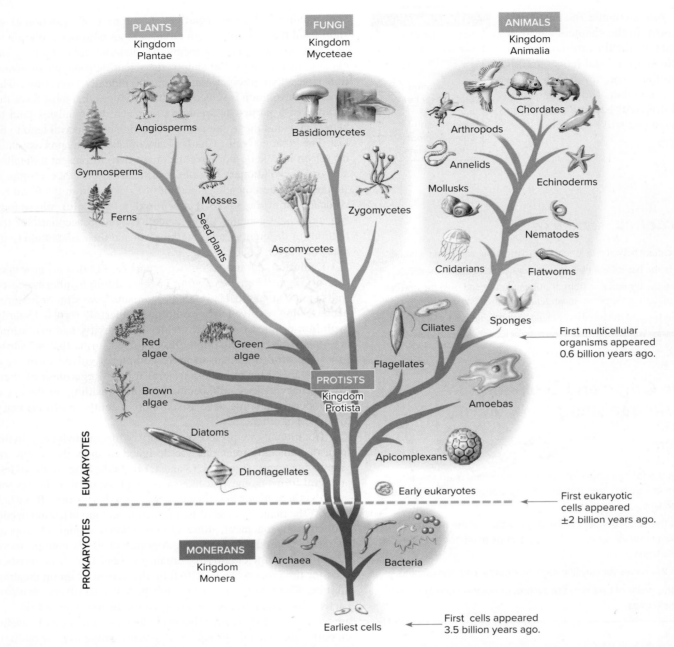

Figure 1.13 **Traditional Whittaker system of classification.** In this system, kingdoms are based on cell structure and type, the nature of body organization, and nutritional type. Bacteria and Archaea (monerans) have prokaryotic cells and are unicellular. Protists have eukaryotic cells and are simple unicellular and colonial organisms. They can be photosynthetic (algae), or they can feed on other organisms (protozoa). Fungi are eukaryotic cells with unicellular or multicellular bodies; they have cell walls and are not photosynthetic. Plants have eukaryotic cells, are multicellular, have cell walls, and are photosynthetic. Animals have eukaryotic cells, are multicellular, do not have cell walls, and derive nutrients from other organisms.

By the late twentieth century, the manner in which organisms were studied was undergoing a dramatic change. The techniques of molecular biology allowed scientists to examine the structure and function of individual genes and to clarify the relationships between organisms based on similarities in their genetic material, rather than simply shared characteristics. Using these new molecular methods, Carl Woese and George Fox proposed a classification system that some have likened to a shrub of life rather than a tree

(figure 1.14). In this system, organisms are most broadly classified as belonging to one of three domains. The members of the **Domain Bacteria** have prokaryotic cells and are what most people think of as traditional bacterial species. The **Domain Eukarya** contains all of the organisms that display a eukaryotic cell structure and includes the Kingdom Protista, Kingdom Fungi, Kingdom Plantae, and Kingdom Animalia. Members of the **Domain Archaea** also possess prokaryotic cells, but these cells are so distinct from those

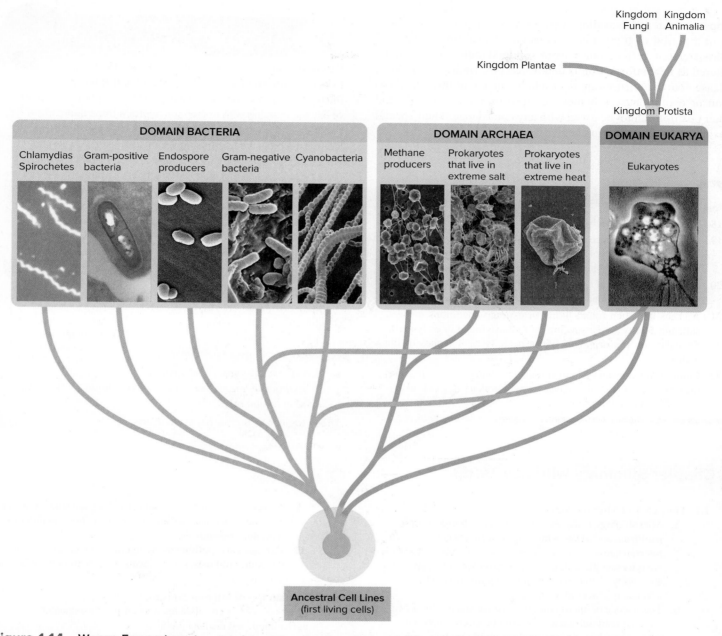

Figure 1.14 **Woese-Fox system.** A system for representing the origins of cell lines and major taxonomic groups as proposed by Carl Woese and colleagues. They propose three distinct cell lines placed in superkingdoms called domains. We know little about the earliest cells, called progenotes, except that they were prokaryotic. Lines of these early primitive cells gave rise to the Domains Bacteria and Archaea. Molecular evidence indicates that the Archaea started the branch that would eventually become the Domain Eukarya. Notice that two early bacterial lines contributed to the evolution of the Eukarya. Selected representatives of the domains are included. The traditional eukaryotic kingdoms are still present with this system (see figure 1.13). Further details of classification systems are covered in chapters 4 and 5.
(1): *Source:* CDC; (2): *Source:* Dr. Balasubr Swaminathan & Peggy Hayes, photo by Elizabeth White/CDC; (3): *Source:* Laura Rose & Janice Haney Carr/CDC; (4): *Source:* CDC/Janice Haney Carr; (5): Steve Gschmeissner/Getty Images; (6, 7): *Source:* Maryland Astrobiology Consortium, NASA and STScI; (8): *Source:* From Stand Genomic Sci. 2011 July 1;4(3): 381-392 doi: 10.4056/sigs.2014648; (9): *Source:* CDC-DPDx

found in the Bacteria and the Eukarya that they have been placed in a domain of their own. Most members of the Domain Archaea are characterized by their ability to live in extreme environments or produce novel metabolic by-products. Some species thrive in water near undersea volcanic vents that has been heated to near boiling or in concentrations of salt as high as 35%, while others produce methane gas as a by-product of their metabolism.

Still newer classification systems, revolving around six or seven kingdoms, have been proposed, but are not yet widely accepted. The Woese-Fox system still represents the most accurate relationship between organisms. In any event, the classification scheme ultimately chosen does not affect the presentation of most microbes because we tend to discuss them at the genus and species level. But be aware that biological taxonomy—and more

important, our understanding of the early evolution of organisms—is in a period of transition. It is essential that any methods of classification reflect our current understanding and can be altered as new information is uncovered (see figure 4.27). Also, please note that viruses are *not* included in any of the classification or evolutionary schemes, because they are not cells and their position cannot be given with any confidence. Their special taxonomy is discussed in chapter 6.

Practice SECTION 1.7

18. Define what is meant by the term *evolution*.

19. Explain how the process of evolution is responsible for the millions of different species on the earth and their adaptation to its many and diverse habitats. Cite examples in your answer.

20. Looking at the tree of life (figure 1.13), determine to which kingdom or kingdoms humans are most closely related.

21. Archaea are often found living in extreme conditions of heat, salt, and acidity, which are similar to those found in early earth. Speculate on the origin of life, especially as it relates to the archaea.

22. Compare the domain system with the five-kingdom system. Does the newer system change the basic idea of prokaryotes and eukaryotes? What is the third cell type?

CASE STUDY Part 2

If Lake Whillans is a frozen wasteland, then Pitch Lake is a toxic soup. Located in Trinidad and Tobago, Pitch Lake is the world's largest asphalt lake—a hot, toxic pool of oily tar, teeming with poisonous hydrocarbons and carbon dioxide—and another environment seemingly too hostile for life to exist. So it was surprising when scientists studying tiny water droplets trapped in the oil discovered vibrant communities of microorganisms, many of which were adapted to life in extreme conditions. Furthermore, chemical analysis of the oil surrounding the water droplets indicated that the microorganisms inside were degrading the oil, using it as a source of energy and producing methane gas as an end product, a process known as methanogenesis.

- *The organisms found in Pitch Lake degrade oil as a way to supply themselves with energy. How could humans use this same biodegradation to benefit our own environment?*

- *Methane is the most predominant component of natural gas. How could methanogenesis be of value to humans?*

These topics are further explored in chapter 7.

Quick Search

To view a video of the expedition to Lake Whillans, search the Internet for "Antarctica's Secret Garden."

Chapter Summary with Key Terms

1.1 The Scope of Microbiology

A. **Microbiology** is the study of **bacteria, viruses, fungi, protozoa,** and **algae,** which are collectively called **microorganisms,** or microbes. In general, microorganisms are **microscopic** and, unlike **macroscopic** organisms, which are readily visible, they require magnification to be adequately observed or studied.

B. The science of microbiology is diverse and has branched out into many subsciences and applications. Important subsciences include **immunology, epidemiology,** public health, food, dairy, aquatic, and industrial microbiology.

1.2 General Characteristics of Microorganisms and Their Roles in the Earth's Environments

Microbes live in most of the world's habitats and are indispensable for normal, balanced life on earth. They play many roles in the functioning of the earth's ecosystems.

A. Microbes are **ubiquitous.**

B. There are many kinds of relationships between microorganisms and humans; most are beneficial, but a few are harmful.

C. Microbes are involved in nutrient production and energy flow. Algae and certain bacteria trap the sun's energy to produce food through **photosynthesis.**

D. Other microbes are responsible for the breakdown and recycling of nutrients through **decomposition.** Microbes are essential to the maintenance of the air, soil, and water.

E. Microbial cells are either the small, relatively simple, nonnucleated **prokaryotic** variety or the larger, more complex **eukaryotic** type that contain a **nucleus** and **organelles.**

F. **Viruses** are microbes but not cells. They are smaller in size and infect their prokaryotic or eukaryotic hosts in order to reproduce themselves.

G. **Parasites** and **pathogens** are microorganisms that invade the bodies of **hosts,** often causing damage through infection and disease.

1.3 Human Use of Microorganisms

Microbes have been called upon to solve environmental, agricultural, and medical problems.

A. **Biotechnology** applies the power of microbes to the manufacture of industrial products, foods, and drugs.

B. Microbes form the basis of **genetic engineering** and **recombinant DNA** technology, which alter genetic material to produce new products and modified life forms.

C. In **bioremediation,** microbes are used to clean up pollutants and wastes in natural environments.

1.4 Microbial Roles in Infectious Diseases

A. Nearly 2,000 microbes are **pathogens** that cause infectious diseases that result in high levels of mortality and morbidity (illness). Many infections are **emerging,** meaning that they are newly identified pathogens gaining greater prominence. Many older diseases are reemerging.

B. **Zoonoses** are infectious diseases native to animals and that also can be transmitted to humans.

C. Some diseases previously thought to be noninfectious may involve microbial infections (e.g., *Helicobacter*, causing gastric ulcers).

D. An increasing number of individuals have weak immune systems, which makes them more susceptible to infectious diseases.

1.5 The Historical Foundations of Microbiology

A. Microbiology as a science is about 300 years old. Hundreds of contributors have provided discoveries and knowledge to enrich our understanding.

B. With his simple microscope, van Leeuwenhoek discovered organisms he called animalcules. As a consequence of his findings and the rise of the **scientific method,** the notion of **spontaneous generation,** or **abiogenesis,** was eventually abandoned for **biogenesis.** The scientific method develops rational **hypotheses** and **theories** that can be tested. Theories that withstand repeated scrutiny become **laws** in time.

C. Early microbiology blossomed with the conceptual developments of **sterilization, aseptic techniques,** and the **germ theory of disease.** Prominent scientists from this period include Robert Koch, Louis Pasteur, and Joseph Lister.

1.6 Taxonomy: Organizing, Classifying, and Naming Microorganisms

A. **Taxonomy** is a hierarchical scheme for the **classification, identification,** and **nomenclature** of organisms, which are grouped in categories called **taxa,** based on features ranging from general to specific.

B. Starting with the broadest category, the taxa are **domain, kingdom, phylum** (or **division**), **class, order, family, genus,** and **species.** Organisms are assigned **binomial scientific names** consisting of their genus and species names.

1.7 The Origin and Evolution of Microorganisms

A. All life on earth **evolved** from simple cells appearing in ancient oceans about 3.5 billion years ago.

B. Evolutionary change occurs when the environment places pressure on organisms that selects for the survival of those with more adaptive inheritable traits.

C. All new species are the products of preexisting species, and their ancestry may be traced by examining fossils, morphology, physiology, genetics, and other scientific forms of investigation.

D. The records of **phylogeny** are displayed in the form of a tree of life that shows organisms' relatedness.

E. One classification scheme is based on a five-kingdom organization developed by Whittaker that includes:
1. Kingdom Prokaryotae (Monera), containing eubacteria and archaea;
2. Kingdom Protista, containing primitive unicellular microbes such as algae and protozoa;
3. Kingdom Myceteae, containing the fungi;
4. Kingdom Animalia, containing animals; and
5. Kingdom Plantae, containing plants.

F. A newer classification scheme for living things is based on the genetic structure of their ribosomes. This Woese-Fox system recognizes three **Domains: Archaea,** simple prokaryotes that often live in extreme environments; **Bacteria,** typical prokaryotes; and **Eukarya,** all types of eukaryotic organisms.

Assess Your Knowledge

Level I. These questions require a working knowledge of the concepts in the chapter and the ability to recall and understand the information you have studied.

Developing a Concept Inventory

Select the correct answer from the answers provided. For questions with blanks, choose the combination of answers that most accurately completes the statement.

1. Which of the following is not considered a microorganism?
 a. archaeon
 b. bacterium
 c. protozoan
 d. mushroom

2. An area of microbiology that is concerned with the occurrence of disease in human populations is
 a. immunology
 b. parasitology
 c. epidemiology
 d. bioremediation

3. Which process involves the deliberate alteration of an organism's genetic material?
 a. bioremediation
 b. biotechnology
 c. decomposition
 d. recombinant DNA

4. A prominent difference between prokaryotic and eukaryotic cells is the
 a. larger size of prokaryotes
 b. lack of pigmentation in eukaryotes
 c. presence of a nucleus in eukaryotes
 d. presence of a cell wall in prokaryotes

5. Which of the following parts was absent from Leeuwenhoek's microscopes?
 a. focusing screw
 b. lens
 c. specimen holder
 d. condenser

6. Abiogenesis refers to the
 a. spontaneous generation of organisms from nonliving matter
 b. development of life forms from preexisting life forms
 c. development of aseptic technique
 d. germ theory of disease

7. A hypothesis can be defined as
 a. a belief based on knowledge
 b. knowledge based on belief
 c. a scientific explanation that is subject to testing
 d. a theory that has been thoroughly tested

8. Which early microbiologist was most responsible for developing standard microbiology laboratory techniques?
 a. Ignaz Semmelweiss
 b. Robert Koch
 c. Carl von Linné
 d. John Tyndall

9. Which scientist is most responsible for finally laying the theory of spontaneous generation to rest?
 a. Joseph Lister
 b. Robert Koch
 c. Francesco Redi
 d. Louis Pasteur

10. When a hypothesis has been thoroughly supported by long-term study and data, it is considered
 a. a law c. a theory
 b. a speculation d. proved

11. Which is the correct order of the taxonomic categories, going from most specific to most general?
 a. domain, kingdom, phylum, class, order, family, genus, species
 b. division, domain, kingdom, class, family, genus, species
 c. species, genus, family, order, class, phylum, kingdom, domain
 d. species, family, class, order, phylum, kingdom

12. By definition, organisms in the same _____ are more closely related than are those in the same _____.
 a. order, family c. family, genus
 b. class, phylum d. phylum, division

13. Which of the following are prokaryotic?
 a. bacteria
 b. archaea
 c. protists
 d. both a and b

14. Order the following items by size, using numbers: 1 = smallest and 8 = largest.
 3 _____ human immunodeficiency virus (HIV)
 7 _____ protozoan
 4 _____ rickettsia
 2 _____ protein
 8 _____ worm
 5 _____ coccus-shaped bacterium
 _____ spirochete
 _____ atom

15. Which of the following is not an emerging infectious disease?
 a. avian influenza c. common cold
 b. Lyme disease d. West Nile fever

16. How would you categorize a virus?
 a. as prokaryotic
 b. as eukaryotic
 c. as an archaeon
 d. none of these choices
 Explain your choice for question 16.

Case Study Analysis

1. Many of the bacteria in Lake Whillans derive energy from the oxidation of chemical compounds. What might have made this necessary?
 a. exceedingly low temperatures
 b. a lack of sunlight
 c. the size of the bacterial populations they found
 d. a lack of fresh water

2. How was the number of different species in Lake Whillans determined?
 a. counting individual cells
 b. analyzing the DNA recovered from the samples

 c. growing the cells and then classifying them according to their structural characteristics
 d. measuring the concentration of cells in each milliliter of lake water

3. Do you think scientists working at Pitch Lake were at a great risk of infection from the organisms growing in the lake? Explain.

On the Test

These questions will help to prepare you to successfully answer similar questions you'll see on the TEAS (Test of Essential Academic Skills) and NCLEX (National Council Licensure Examination).

1. The nurse in an emergency department is reviewing discharge instructions with a client. The client asks for clarification of a zoonosis with regard to the type of illness. What is the **best** response by the nurse?
 a. A zoonosis refers to any viral disease.
 b. A zoonosis is any disease that can be successfully treated with antibiotics.
 c. A zoonosis is a disease typically found in animals but that can infect humans.
 d. A zoonosis is a disease caused by a eukaryotic parasite.

Writing Challenge

For each question, compose a one- or two-paragraph answer that includes the factual information needed to completely address the question. Practice questions can also be used for writing-challenge exercises.

1. What does it mean to say microbes are ubiquitous?

2. What is meant by diversity with respect to organisms?

3. What events, discoveries, or inventions were probably the most significant in the development of microbiology and why?

4. Explain how microbiologists use the scientific method to develop theories and explanations for microbial phenomena.

5. Explain how microbes are classified into groups according to evolutionary relationships, provided with standard scientific names, and identified by specific characteristics.

6. a. What are some of the sources for "new" infectious diseases?
 b. Comment on the sensational ways in which some media portray the dangers of infectious diseases.

Concept Mapping

On Connect you can find an Introduction to Concept Mapping that provides guidance for working with concept maps, along with concept-mapping activities for this chapter.

 ## Application, Analysis, Evaluation, and Synthesis

Level II. These problems go beyond just restating facts and require higher levels of understanding and an ability to interpret, problem solve, transfer knowledge to new situations, create models, and predict outcomes.

Critical Thinking

Critical thinking is the ability to reason and solve problems using facts and concepts. These questions can be approached from a number of angles and, in most cases, they do not have a single correct answer.

1. What do you suppose the world would be like if there were cures for all infectious diseases and a means to destroy all microbes? What characteristics of microbes would prevent this from happening?

2. How would you describe the types of scientific reasoning in the various experiments for supporting and denying spontaneous generation?

3. Give the technical name of a microbiologist who researches or works with protozoa in a termite's gut, bacteria that live in volcanoes, the tapeworms of dogs, molds that cause food poisoning, emerging viral diseases, the metabolism of bacteria that live in acid swamps, and the classification of *Paramecium*.

4. Name the six most common infectious agents on earth and the four microbes that cause the highest rates of cancer.

5. What is the ultimate way that microbes will, as Pasteur said, have the "last word"?

6. Can you develop a scientific hypothesis and means of testing the cause of stomach ulcers? (Are they caused by an infection? By too much acid? By a genetic disorder?)

7. Construct the scientific name of a newly discovered species of bacterium using your name or the name of a pet, a place, or a unique characteristic. Be sure to use proper notation and endings.

Visual Assessment

Use the following pattern to construct an outline of the scientific reasoning that was involved in developing the germ theory of disease similar to figure 1.10.

Observations

↓

Hypothesis

↓

Testing the Hypothesis

↓

Establishment of Theory

↓

Accepted Principle

Source: NOAA Okeanos Explorer Program, 2013 ROV Shakedown and Field Trials in the U.S. Atlantic Canyons.

CHAPTER 2

The Chemistry of Biology

In This Chapter...

On the seventh floor of a large medical center, Megyn Chang, a high school junior, is providing a nurse with her medical history. She initially called for an appointment because over the last 8 weeks she'd had a variety of **digestive issues,** including **abdominal cramps, diarrhea, bloating, gas,** and **nausea.** Megyn at first felt that her stomach upset could be related to a **lack of sleep.** Since the school year began 6 months ago, she has been enrolled in an AP physics class and the increased studying has led to many late nights. She also mentions that she's been more stressed than usual because . . . physics. Since joining a study group 2 months ago, she has gotten more sleep and suffered less **stress** and had hoped that she would start feeling better, but if anything, her stomach problems seem to be getting worse. And she says, jokingly, "I'm also broke and addicted to mocha lattes, since my study group meets in a coffee house three times a week!"

Megyn's doctor enters the exam room, and after a few minutes of small talk (including some sympathy about AP physics), begins to review her chart. He says that he's almost certain that Megyn is suffering from **lactose intolerance,** an inability to digest lactose (milk sugar). He explains that as an infant, Megyn, like nearly everyone else on earth, produced an enzyme called lactase in the cells lining her small intestine. The lactase enzyme **catalyzed** the breakdown of the **disaccharide** lactose to the **monosaccharides glucose** and **galactose.** The two monosaccharides were then absorbed by cells of the small intestine and quickly entered the bloodstream, where they were used to power reactions throughout the body. Lactase levels are typically high at birth but decline sharply as one grows older, beginning at about 2 years of age.

"By the age of 16," the doctor explains, "you probably produce very little lactase, and are unable to digest anything beyond miniscule amounts of lactose." Undigested lactose, which is not absorbed by the small intestine, instead passes intact into the large intestine, where it is **metabolized** by a wide variety of bacteria, producing hydrogen, carbon dioxide, and methane as by-products, leading to bloating, flatulence, and nausea. The doctor says that he'd like to analyze Megyn's **breath** to confirm the diagnosis.

In the neonatal intensive care unit (NICU) of the same hospital, a pediatric **gastroenterologist** is examining Alex, a 3-week-old male born 6 weeks premature, weighing 5 pounds 4 ounces at birth. Initially healthy, Alex has since lost over half a pound, and his pediatrician has determined that Alex is showing signs of **failure to thrive.** One obvious problem is that Alex has frequent **bloating** and **diarrhea** shortly after he **nurses.** The gastroenterologist orders a **stool acidity test** to check for lactose intolerance.

- *Enzymes are typically composed of what type of biomolecule?*

- *Where do acids fall on the pH scale?*

To continue the Case Study, go to Case Study Part 2 at the end of the chapter.

(latte): Cathy Yeulet/amenic181/123RF

2.1 Atoms: Fundamental Building Blocks of All Matter in the Universe

 Learn

1. Describe the properties of atoms and identify the relationships of the particles they contain.
2. Characterize elements and their isotopes.
3. Explain the differences between atomic number, mass number, and atomic weight.
4. List the major elements associated with life.
5. Describe electron orbitals and energy shells and how they are filled.

The universe is composed of an infinite variety of substances existing in gaseous, liquid, and solid states. All such tangible materials that occupy space and have mass are called **matter.** The organization of matter—whether air, rocks, or bacteria—begins with individual building blocks called atoms. An **atom** is defined as the smallest particle that cannot be subdivided into smaller substances without losing its properties. Even in a science dealing with very small things, an atom's minute size is striking; for example, an oxygen atom is only 0.0000000013 mm (0.0013 nm) in diameter, and 1 million of them in a cluster would barely be visible to the naked eye.

Although scientists have not directly observed the detailed structure of an atom, the exact composition of atoms has been well established by extensive physical analysis using sophisticated instruments. In general, an atom derives its properties from a combination of subatomic particles called **protons** (p^+), which are positively charged; **neutrons** (n^0), which have no charge (are neutral); and **electrons** (e^-), which are negatively charged. Protons and neutrons are similar to one another in both mass and volume, while each is about 2,000 times as heavy as an electron. The protons and neutrons make up a central core, or atomic **nucleus,**[1] that is surrounded by one or more electrons **(figure 2.1).** The nucleus makes up the larger mass (weight) of the atom, whereas the electron region, sometimes called the "electron cloud," accounts for the greater volume. To get a perspective on proportions, consider this: If an atom were the size of a football stadium, the nucleus would be

1. Be careful not to confuse the nucleus of an atom with the nucleus of a cell.

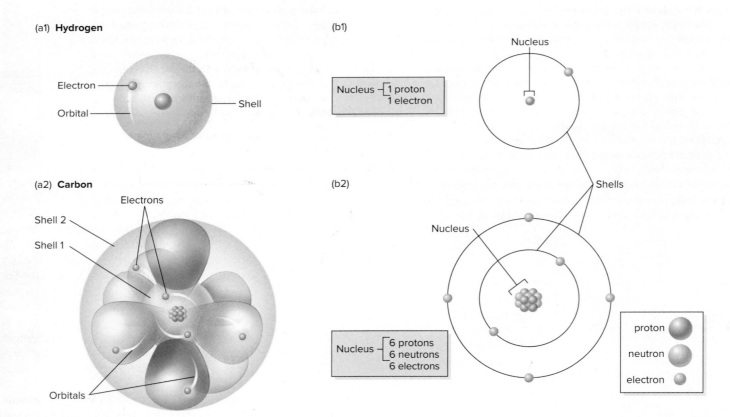

Figure 2.1 **Models of atomic structure.** Three-dimensional models of hydrogen and carbon that approximate their actual structure. The atomic nucleus is surrounded by electrons that travel within orbitals and occur in energy levels called shells. **(a1)** Hydrogen has just one orbital and one shell. **(a2)** Carbon has four orbitals and two shells. The outermost orbitals are most accurately portrayed as sets of lobe-shaped pairs rather than circles or spheres. **(b1, 2)** Simple models of hydrogen and carbon are not strictly accurate representations of atomic structure but are designed as a quick reference to the numbers and arrangements of shells and electrons and the numbers of protons and neutrons in the nucleus. (Not to scale.)

about the size of a marble! The stability of atomic structure is largely maintained by

- the mutual attraction of the protons and electrons (opposite charges attract each other) and
- the exact balance of proton number and electron number, which causes the opposing charges to cancel each other out.

At least in theory, then, isolated intact atoms do not carry a charge.

Different Types of Atoms: Elements and Their Properties

All atoms share the same fundamental structure. All protons are identical, all neutrons are identical, and all electrons are identical. But when these subatomic particles come together in specific, varied combinations, unique types of atoms called **elements** result. Each element is a pure substance that has a characteristic atomic structure and predictable chemical behavior. To date, 118 elements have been described. Ninety-four of them are naturally occurring, and the rest were artificially produced by manipulating the particles in the nucleus. By convention, an element is assigned a distinctive name with an abbreviated shorthand symbol. The elements essential to life, often called bioelements, are outlined in **table 2.1.** In some form or another, they make up the matter of all earth's organisms and viruses. Microorganisms have a particularly important relationship with most of these elements. This is due to the roles microbes play in the cycling processes that maintain the elements in forms usable by other organisms.

The vast majority of life forms require only about 20 of the 94 naturally occurring elements. The other 70 or so are not critical to life, and a number of them, such as arsenic and uranium, can be highly toxic to cells. As we will see in chapter 7, microbes have some incredible "survival skills" that enable them to occupy extreme habitats containing large amounts of these elements. The word that describes such a microbe is **extremophile.*** For additional information on the functions of elements and the involvement of microbes in their recycling, look ahead to table 7.1.

Quick Search

Find Carl Sagan's engaging overview of "The Chemical Elements" on YouTube.

The Major Elements of Life and Their Primary Characteristics

The unique properties of each element result from the numbers of protons, neutrons, and electrons it contains, and each element can be identified by certain physical measurements.

Each element is assigned an **atomic number (AN)** based on the number of protons it has. The atomic number is a valuable measurement because an element's proton number does not vary, and knowing it automatically tells you the usual number of electrons (recall that a neutral atom has an equal number of protons and electrons). Another useful measurement is the **mass number (MN),** equal to the number of protons and neutrons. If one knows the mass number and the atomic number, it is possible to determine the number of neutrons by subtraction. Hydrogen is a unique element because its

TABLE 2.1	Chemical Characteristics of Major Elements of Life			
Element	**Atomic Symbol***	**Atomic Number**	**Atomic Mass****	**Ionized Forms (see section 2.3)**
Calcium	Ca	20	40.08	Ca^{2+}
Carbon	C	6	12.01	CO_3^{2-}
Carbon˙	C-14	6	14.0	
Chlorine	Cl	17	35.45	Cl^-
Cobalt	Co	27	58.93	Co^{2+}, Co^{3+}
Copper	Cu	29	63.54	Cu^+, Cu^{2+}
Hydrogen	H	1	1.00	H^+
Hydrogen˙	H-3	1	3.01	
Iodine	I	53	126.9	I^-
Iodine˙	I-131	53	131.0	
Iron	Fe	26	55.84	Fe^{2+}, Fe^{3+}
Magnesium	Mg	12	24.30	Mg^{2+}
Manganese	Mn	25	54.93	Mn^{2+}, Mn^{3+}
Nitrogen	N	7	14.0	NO_3^- (nitrate)
Oxygen	O	8	15.99	
Phosphorus	P	15	31.97	PO_4^{3-} (phosphate)
Phosphorus˙	P-32	15	32	
Potassium	K	19	39.10	K^+
Sodium	Na	11	22.99	Na^+
Sulfur	S	16	32.06	SO_4^{-2} (sulfate)
Zinc	Zn	30	65.38	Zn^{2+}

*Based on the Latin name of the element. The first letter is always capitalized; if there is a second letter, it is always lowercased.

**The atomic mass or weight is equal to the average mass number for the isotopes of that element.

˙An isotope of the element.

common form has only one proton, one electron, and no neutron, making it the only element with the same atomic and mass number.

Isotopes are variant forms of the same element that differ in the number of neutrons and thus have different mass numbers. These multiple forms occur naturally in certain proportions. Carbon, for example, exists primarily as carbon 12 with 6 neutrons (MN = 12); but a small amount (about 1%) consists of carbon 13 with 7 neutrons and carbon 14 with 8 neutrons. Although isotopes have virtually the same chemical properties, some of them have unstable nuclei that spontaneously release energy in the form of radiation. Such *radioactive isotopes* play a role in a number of research and medical applications. Because they emit detectable energy, they can be used to trace the position of key atoms or molecules in chemical reactions, they are tools in diagnosis and treatment, and they are even applied in sterilization procedures (see chapter 11).

Another important measurement of an element is its **atomic mass** or **atomic weight.*** This is given as the average mass numbers of all isotopic forms (table 2.1). You will notice that this number

* *extremophile* (ex-tree′-moh-fyl″) A microbe that can live in very severe conditions that would be harmful to other organisms.

* *Mass and weight* are not technically the same, but as long as we are dealing with an unchanging gravitational force (for instance, as long as everything takes place on earth), the two values are identical.

may not come out even, because most elements have several isotopes and differing proportions of them.

Electron Orbitals and Shells

The structure of an atom can be envisioned as a central nucleus surrounded by a cloud of electrons that constantly spin at exceedingly high speed within confined pathways surrounding the nucleus (see figure 2.1). The pathways taken by electrons are called **orbitals,** which are not actual objects or exact locations but represent volumes of three-dimensional space in which an electron is likely to be found. The position of an electron at any one instant is dictated by its energy level, or **shell,** proceeding from the lower-level energy electrons nearest the nucleus to the higher-energy electrons in the outer shells.

Electrons fill the orbitals and shells in *pairs,* starting with the shell nearest the nucleus:

- The first shell contains 1 orbital and a maximum of 2 electrons.
- The second shell has 4 orbitals and up to 8 electrons.

- The third shell, with nine orbitals, can hold up to 18 electrons.
- The fourth shell, with 16 orbitals, contains up to 32 electrons.

The number of orbitals and shells and how completely they are filled depend on the number of electrons, so that each element will have a unique pattern. For example:

- Helium (AN = 2) has only a filled first shell of 2 electrons.
- Oxygen (AN = 8) has a filled first shell and a partially filled second shell of 6 electrons.
- Magnesium (AN = 12) has a filled first shell, a filled second shell, and a third shell that has only one filled orbital, so is nearly empty.

As we will see, the chemical properties of an element are controlled mainly by the distribution of electrons in the outermost shell. **Figure 2.2** presents various simplified models of atomic structure and electron maps, superimposed over a partial display of the periodic table of elements.

Figure 2.2 **Examples of biologically important atoms.** Featured element boxes contain information on symbol, atomic number, atomic mass, and electron shell patterns. Simple models show how the shells are filled by electrons as the atomic numbers increase. Chemists depict elements in shorthand form (red Lewis structures) that indicate only the outermost electrons, because these are the electrons involved in chemical bonds. The background shows the position of these elements in the periodic table.

 Practice SECTION 2.1

1. How are the concepts of an atom and an element related? What causes elements to differ from one another?
2. What are the subatomic particles and how do they contribute to the structure and character of atoms?
3. How are mass number and atomic number derived? What is the atomic mass or weight?
4. What is distinctive about isotopes of elements, and why are they important?
5. Why is an isolated atom electrically neutral?
6. Describe the concept of the atomic nucleus, electron orbitals, and shells.

2.2 Bonds and Molecules

Learn

6. Explain how elements make chemical bonds to form molecules and compounds.
7. State the relationship among an atom, a molecule, and a compound.
8. Identify the differences between covalent, ionic, and hydrogen bonds.
9. Summarize the concepts of valence, polarity, and diatomic elements.
10. Describe ionization and distinguish between anions and cations.
11. Compare oxidation and reduction and their effects.

Most elements do not exist naturally in pure, uncombined form but are bound together as molecules and compounds. A **molecule*** is a distinct chemical substance that results from the combination of two or more atoms. A few of them, such as oxygen (O_2), hydrogen (H_2), and nitrogen (N_2), consist of two atoms of the same element and are referred to as diatomic. But most molecules—for example, carbon dioxide (CO_2) and water (H_2O)—contain two or more different elements and are more appropriately termed **compounds.** So compounds are one major type of molecule. Other examples of compounds are biological molecules such as proteins, sugars, and fats.

When atoms bind together in molecules, they lose the properties of the atom and take on the properties of the combined substance. In the same way that an atom has an atomic weight, a molecule has a **formula mass** or **molecular weight**[2] (MW), which is calculated from the sum of all of the atomic masses of the atoms it contains.

Chemical bonds of molecules are created when two or more atoms share, donate (lose), or accept (gain) electrons (**figure 2.3**). This capacity for making bonds, termed **valence,*** is determined by the number of electrons that an atom has to lose or share with other atoms during bond formation. The valence electrons determine the degree of reactivity and the types of bonds an element can make. Elements with a filled outer orbital are relatively nonreactive because they have no extra electrons to share with or donate to other atoms. For example, helium has one filled shell, with no tendency either to give up electrons or to take them from other elements, making it a stable, inert (nonreactive) gas. Elements with partially filled outer orbitals are less stable and are more apt to form some sort of bond.

Many chemical reactions are based on the tendency of atoms with unfilled outer shells to gain greater stability by achieving, or at least approximating, a filled outer shell. For example, an atom (such as oxygen) that can accept two additional electrons will bond readily with atoms (such as hydrogen) that can share or donate electrons. We explore some additional examples of the basic types of bonding in the following section.

In addition to reactivity, the number of electrons in the outer shell dictates the number of chemical bonds an atom can make. For instance, hydrogen can bind with one other atom, oxygen can bind with up to two other atoms, and carbon can bind with four.

* *valence* (vay′-lents) L. *valentia,* strength. The binding qualities of an atom dictated by the number of electrons in its outermost shell.

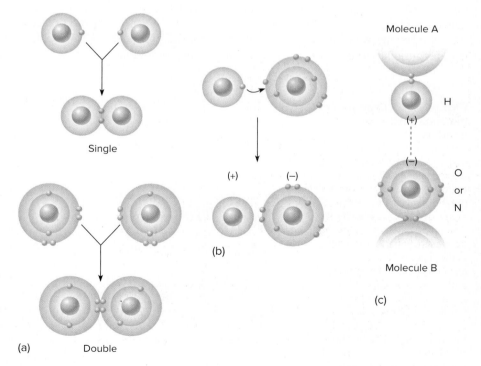

Single

(a) Double

(b)

(+) (−)

Molecule A

H
(+)

(−)

O or N

Molecule B

(c)

Figure 2.3 **General representation of three types of bonding. (a)** Covalent bonds, both single and double. **(b)** Ionic bond. **(c)** Hydrogen bond. Note that hydrogen bonds are represented in models and formulas by dotted lines, as shown in (c).

* *molecule* (mol′-ih-kyool) L. *molecula,* little mass.

2. Biologists prefer to use this term.

Covalent Bonds: Molecules with Shared Electrons

Covalent bonds form between atoms with valences that suit them to sharing electrons rather than to donating or receiving them. A simple example is hydrogen gas (H_2), which consists of two hydrogen atoms. A hydrogen atom has only a single electron, but when two of them combine, each will bring its electron to orbit about both nuclei, thereby approaching a filled orbital (2 electrons) for both atoms and thus creating a single covalent bond **(figure 2.4a)**. Covalent bonding also occurs in oxygen gas (O_2), but with a difference. Because each atom has 2 electrons to share in this molecule, the combination creates two pairs of shared electrons, also known as a double covalent bond **(figure 2.4b)**. The majority of the molecules associated with living things are composed of single and double covalent bonds between the most common biological elements (carbon, hydrogen, oxygen, nitrogen, sulfur, and phosphorus), which are discussed in more depth in chapter 7. A slightly more complex pattern of covalent bonding is shown for methane gas (CH_4) in **figure 2.4c**.

Polarity in Molecules

Electronegativity refers to the tendency of an atom or molecule to attract electrons. When atoms of different electronegativity form covalent bonds, the electrons will not be shared equally and will be pulled toward the more electronegative atom. This force causes one end of a molecule to assume a partial negative charge and the other end to assume a partial positive charge. A molecule with such an unequal distribution of charges is termed **polar** and shows polarity—meaning it has positive and negative poles.

Observe the water molecule shown in **figure 2.5** and note that, because the oxygen atom is larger and has more protons than

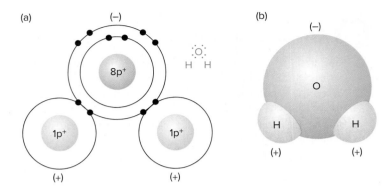

Figure 2.5 **Polar molecule. (a)** A simple model and **(b)** a three-dimensional model of a water molecule indicate the polarity, or unequal distribution, of electrical charge, which is caused by the pull of the shared electrons toward the oxygen side of the molecule.

the hydrogen atoms, it will have a stronger attraction for the shared electrons than the hydrogen atoms have. Because the electrons will spend more time near the oxygen, it will express a partial negative charge. The electrons are less attracted to the hydrogen orbitals, causing the positive charge of the hydrogen's single proton to dominate. The polar nature of water plays an important role in a number of biological reactions, which are discussed later. Polarity is a significant property of many large molecules in living systems and greatly influences both their reactivity and their structure.

When covalent bonds are formed between atoms that have the same or similar electronegativity, the electrons are shared equally between the two atoms. Because of this balanced distribution, no part of the molecule has a greater attraction for the electrons. This sort of electrically neutral molecule is termed **nonpolar**. Examples of nonpolar molecules are oxygen, methane (see figure 2.4), and lipids (see figure 2.20).

Figure 2.4 **Examples of molecules with covalent bonding. (a)** A hydrogen molecule is formed when two hydrogen atoms share their electrons and form a single bond. **(b)** In a double bond, the outer orbitals of two oxygen atoms overlap and permit the sharing of 4 electrons (one pair from each) and the saturation of the outer orbital for both. **(c)** Simple, three-dimensional, and working models of methane. Note that carbon has 4 electrons to share and hydrogens each have 1, thereby completing the shells for all atoms in the compound and creating four single bonds. Note that (a) and (b) also show the formation of diatomic molecules.

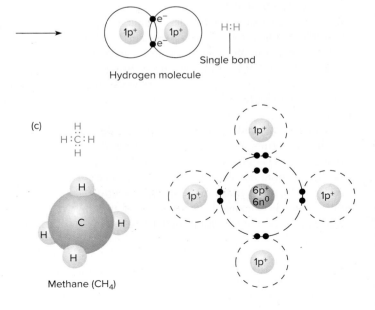

Ionic Bonds: Electron Transfer among Atoms

In reactions that form **ionic bonds,** electrons are transferred completely from one atom to another and are not shared. These reactions invariably occur between atoms with complementary valences. This means that one atom has an unfilled outer shell that can readily accept electrons and the other atom has an unfilled outer shell that will readily give up electrons. A striking example is the reaction that occurs between sodium (Na) and chlorine (Cl). Elemental sodium is a soft, lustrous metal so reactive that it can burn flesh, and molecular chlorine is a very poisonous yellow gas. But when the two are combined, they form sodium chloride[3] (NaCl)—the familiar nontoxic table salt—a compound with properties quite different from either parent element **(figure 2.6).**

How does this transformation occur? Sodium has 11 electrons (2 in shell one, 8 in shell two, and only 1 in shell three), so it is 7 short of having a complete outer shell. Chlorine has 17 electrons (2 in shell one, 8 in shell two, and 7 in shell three), making it 1 short of a complete outer shell. When these two atoms come together, the sodium atom will readily donate its single valence electron and the chlorine atom will avidly receive it. The reaction is slightly more involved than a single sodium atom's combining with a single chloride atom, but the details do not negate the fundamental reaction as described here. The outcome of this reaction is a solid crystal complex that interlinks millions of sodium and chloride atoms (figure 2.6c, d). The binding of Na^+ and Cl^- exists in three dimensions. Each Na is surrounded by 6 Cls and vice versa. Their charges balance out, and no single molecule of NaCl is present.

Ionization: Formation of Charged Particles

Compounds with intact ionic bonds are electrically neutral, but they can produce charged particles when dissolved in a liquid called a solvent. This phenomenon, called **ionization,** occurs when the ionic bond is broken and the atoms dissociate (separate) into unattached, charged particles called **ions (figure 2.7).** To illustrate what imparts a charge to ions, let us look again at the reaction between sodium and chlorine. When a sodium atom reacts with chlorine and loses 1 electron, the sodium is left with 1 more proton than electrons. This imbalance produces a positively charged sodium ion (Na^+). Chlorine, on the other hand, has gained 1 electron and now has 1 more electron than protons, producing a negatively charged ion (Cl^-). Positively charged ions are termed **cations,*** and negatively charged ions are termed **anions.*** Substances such as salts, acids, and bases that release ions when dissolved in water are termed **electrolytes** because their charges enable them to conduct an electrical current.

(a)

Na

11p+
12n⁰

Sodium atom (Na)

Cl:

17p+
18n⁰

Chlorine atom (Cl)

(b) :Na:Cl: ⟶ [Na]⁺ [Cl]⁻

(c)

Sodium Chloride

(d)

Figure 2.6 Ionic bonding between sodium and chlorine.
(a) During the reaction, sodium loses its single outer orbital electron to chlorine, thereby filling chlorine's outer shell. **(b)** Simple model of ionic bonding. **(c)** Sodium and chloride ions form large molecules, or crystals, in which the two atoms alternate in a definite, regular, geometric pattern. **(d)** Note the cubic nature of NaCl crystals at the macroscopic level.
(d): Vladislav Gajic/Shutterstock

3. In general, when a salt is formed, the ending of the name of the negatively charged ion is changed to -ide.

* *cation* (kat′-eye-on) A positively charged ion that migrates toward the negative pole, or cathode, of an electrical field.
* *anion* (an′-eye-on) A negatively charged ion that migrates toward the positive pole, or anode.

Because particles with the same charge repel each other and those with opposite charges attract each other, ions interact electrostatically with other ions and polar molecules. Such interactions are important in many cellular chemical reactions, in the formation of solutions, and in the reactions microorganisms have with dyes.

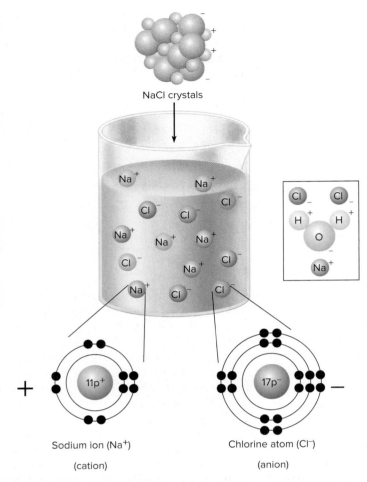

Figure 2.7 **Ionization.** When NaCl in the crystalline form is added to water, the ions are released from the crystal as separate charged particles (cations and anions) into solution. (See also figure 2.12.) In this solution, Cl⁻ ions are attracted to the hydrogen component of water, and Na⁺ ions are attracted to the oxygen (box).

Hydrogen Bonding

Some types of bonding do not involve sharing, losing, or gaining electrons but instead are due to attractive forces between nearby molecules or atoms. One such bond is a **hydrogen bond,** a weak electrostatic force that forms between a hydrogen covalently bonded to one molecule and an oxygen or nitrogen atom on the same molecule or on a different molecule. This phenomenon occurs because a hydrogen atom in a covalent bond tends to be positively charged. Thus, it can attract a nearby negatively charged atom and form an easily disrupted bridge with it. This type of bonding is usually represented in molecular models with a dotted line. A simple example of hydrogen bonding occurs between water molecules **(figure 2.8).** More extensive hydrogen bonding is partly responsible for the structure and stability of proteins and nucleic acids, as you will see later on.

Weak molecular interactions similar to hydrogen bonds that play major roles in the shape and function of biological molecules are **van der Waals forces.** The basis for these interactions is also an attraction of two regions on atoms or molecules that are opposite in charge, but van der Waals forces can occur between nearly any

Figure 2.8 **Hydrogen bonding in water.** Because of the polarity of water molecules, the negatively charged oxygen end of one water molecule is weakly attracted to the positively charged hydrogen end of an adjacent water molecule.

types of molecules and not just those containing hydrogen, oxygen, and nitrogen. These forces come into play whenever the electrons in molecules move about their orbits and become unevenly distributed. This unevenness leads to short-term "sticky spots" in the molecule—some positively charged and others negatively charged. When such regions are located close together, their opposite charges pull them together. These forces can hold even large molecules together because of the cumulative effects of numerous sites of interaction. They not only function between molecules but may occur within different regions of the same large molecule. Van der Waals forces are a significant factor in protein folding and stability (see figure 2.24, steps 3 and 4).

Electron Transfer and Oxidation-Reduction Reactions

The metabolic work of cells, such as synthesis, movement, and digestion, revolves around energy exchanges and transfers. The management of energy in cells is almost exclusively dependent on chemical rather than physical reactions, because most cells are far too delicate to operate with heat, radiation, and other more potent forms of energy. The outer-shell electrons are readily portable and easily manipulated sources of energy. It is in fact the movement of electrons from molecule to molecule that accounts for most energy exchanges in cells. Fundamentally, then, cells must have a supply of atoms that can gain or lose electrons if they are to carry out life processes.

The phenomenon in which electrons are transferred from one atom or molecule to another is termed an **oxidation-reduction** (shortened to **redox**) **reaction.** The term *oxidation* includes any reaction that causes an atom to lose electrons. Because all redox reactions occur in pairs, it follows that *reduction* is the result of a different atom gaining these same electrons. Keep in mind that because electrons are being added during reduction, the atom that receives them will become more negative; and that is the meaning of *reduction* in this context.

To analyze the phenomenon, let us again review the production of NaCl but from a different standpoint. When these two atoms, called the redox pair, react to form sodium chloride, a sodium atom gives up an electron to a chlorine atom. During this reaction, sodium is oxidized because it loses an electron, and chlorine is reduced because it gains an electron **(figure 2.9)**. With this system, an atom such as sodium that can donate electrons and thereby reduce another atom is a **reducing agent.** An atom that can receive extra electrons and thereby oxidize another molecule is an **oxidizing agent.** You may find this concept easier to keep straight if you think of redox agents as partners: The reducing partner gives its electrons away and is oxidized; the oxidizing partner receives the electrons and is reduced.[4]

Redox reactions are essential to many of the biochemical processes discussed in chapter 8. In cellular metabolism, electrons are frequently transferred from one molecule to another as described here. In other reactions, oxidation and reduction occur with the transfer of a hydrogen atom (a proton and an electron) from one compound to another.

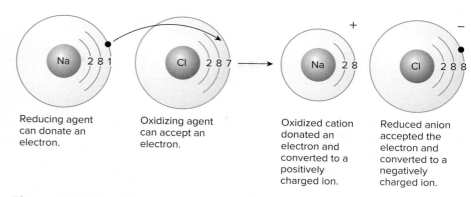

Figure 2.9 Simplified diagram of the exchange of electrons during an oxidation-reduction reaction. Numbers indicate the total electrons in that shell.

Reducing agent can donate an electron.

Oxidizing agent can accept an electron.

Oxidized cation donated an electron and converted to a positively charged ion.

Reduced anion accepted the electron and converted to a negatively charged ion.

 Practice SECTION 2.2

7. Explain how the concepts of molecules and compounds are related.
8. Distinguish between the general reactions in covalent, ionic, and hydrogen bonds.
9. Which kinds of elements tend to make covalent bonds?
10. Distinguish between a single and a double bond.
11. Define *polarity* and explain what causes it.
12. Which kinds of elements tend to make ionic bonds?
13. Differentiate between an anion and a cation, using examples.
14. Differentiate between oxidation and reduction, and between an oxidizing agent and a reducing agent, using examples.

2.3 Chemical Reactions, Solutions, and pH

Learn

12. Classify different forms of chemical shorthand and types of reactions.

13. Explain solutes, solvents, and hydration.

14. Differentiate between hydrophilic and hydrophobic.

15. Describe the pH scale and how it was derived; define *acid, base,* and *neutral levels.*

Formulas, Models, and Equations

The atomic content of molecules can be represented by a few convenient formulas. We have already been using the molecular formula, which concisely gives the atomic symbols and the number of the atoms involved in subscripts (CO_2, H_2O). More complex molecules such as glucose ($C_6H_{12}O_6$) can also be symbolized this way, but this formula is not unique, because fructose and galactose also share it. Molecular formulas are useful, but they only summarize the atoms in a compound; they do not show the position of bonds between atoms. For this purpose, chemists use structural formulas illustrating the relationships of the atoms and the number and types of bonds **(figure 2.10)**. Other structural models present the three-dimensional appearance of a molecule, illustrating the orientation of atoms (differentiated by color codes) and the molecule's overall shape **(figure 2.11)**. Many complex molecules such as proteins are now represented by computer-generated images (see figure 2.24, step 4).

Molecules, including those in cells, are constantly involved in **chemical reactions,** leading to changes in the composition of the matter they contain. These changes generally involve the breaking and making of bonds and the rearrangement of atoms. The chemical substances that start a reaction and that are changed by the reaction are called the **reactants.** The substances that result from the reaction are called the **products.** Keep in mind that all of the matter in any reaction is retained in some form, and the same types and numbers of atoms going into the reaction will be present in the products. Chemists and biologists use shorthand to summarize the content of a reaction by means of a **chemical equation.** In an equation, the reactant(s) are on the left of an arrow and the product(s) are on the right. The number of atoms of each element must be balanced on either side of the arrow. Note that the numbers of reactants and products are indicated by a coefficient in front of the formula (no coefficient means 1). We have already reviewed the reaction with sodium and chloride, which would be shown with this equation:

$$2Na + Cl_2 \rightarrow 2NaCl$$

Most equations do not give the details or even exact order of the reaction but are meant to keep the expression a simple overview of the process being shown. Some of the common reactions in organisms are syntheses, decompositions, and exchanges.

4. A mnemonic device to keep track of this is *LEO* says *GER: Lose Electrons Oxidized; Gain Electrons Reduced.*

(a) | Molecular formulas | H_2 | O_2 | H_2O | CO_2 | CH_4 |

Figure 2.10 **Comparison of molecular and structural formulas. (a)** Molecular formulas provide a brief summary of the elements in a compound. **(b1)** Structural formulas clarify the exact relationships of the atoms in the molecule, depicting single bonds by a single line and double bonds by two lines. **(b2)** In structural formulas of organic compounds, cyclic or ringed compounds may be completely labeled, or **(b3)** they may be presented in a shorthand form in which carbons are assumed to be at the angles and attached to hydrogens. See figure 2.17 for structural formulas of three sugars with the same molecular formula, $C_6H_{12}O_6$.

In a **synthesis* reaction,** the reactants bond together in a manner that produces an entirely new molecule (reactant A plus reactant B yields product AB). An example is the production of sulfur dioxide, a by-product of burning sulfur fuels and an important component of smog:

$$S + O_2 \rightarrow SO_2$$

Some synthesis reactions are not such simple combinations. When water is synthesized, for example, the reaction does not really involve one oxygen atom combining with two hydrogen atoms, because elemental oxygen exists as O_2 and elemental hydrogen exists as H_2. A more accurate equation for this reaction is:

$$2H_2 + O_2 \rightarrow 2H_2O$$

In **decomposition reactions,** the bonds on a single reactant molecule are permanently broken to release two or more product

Figure 2.11 **Three-dimensional, or space-filling, model of DNA.** Each element is represented by a unique color. Note the helical twist of the molecule for which DNA is famous.
Molekuul/SPL/Age Fotostock

molecules. A simple example can be shown for the common chemical hydrogen peroxide:

$$2H_2O_2 \rightarrow 2H_2O + O_2$$

During **exchange reactions,** the reactants trade portions between each other and release products that are combinations of the two:

$$AB + XY \rightleftharpoons AY + XB$$

This type of reaction occurs between an acid and a base when they react to form water and a salt:

$$HCl + NaOH \rightarrow NaCl + H_2O$$

The reactions in biological systems can be reversible, meaning that reactants and products can be converted back and forth. These reversible reactions are symbolized with a double arrow, each pointing in opposite directions, as in the exchange reaction shown earlier. Whether a reaction is reversible depends on the proportions of these compounds, the difference in energy state of the reactants and products, and the presence of **catalysts** (substances that increase the rate of a reaction). Additional reactants coming from another reaction can also be indicated by arrows that enter or leave at the main arrow:

$$X + Y \xrightarrow{\;\;C} XYD$$

Solutions: Homogeneous Mixtures of Molecules

A **solution** is a mixture of one or more substances called **solutes** uniformly dispersed in a dissolving medium called a **solvent.** An important characteristic of a solution is that the solute cannot be separated by filtration or settling. The solute can be gaseous, liquid, or solid, and the solvent is usually a liquid. Examples of solutions are salt or sugar dissolved in water and iodine dissolved in alcohol. In general, a solvent will dissolve a solute only if it has similar electrical characteristics as indicated by the rule of solubility, expressed simply as "like dissolves like." For example,

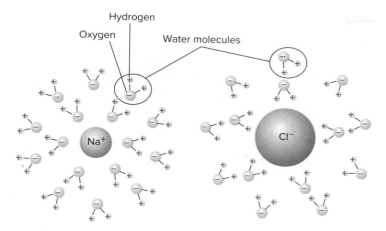

Figure 2.12 **Hydration spheres formed around ions in solution.** In this example, a sodium cation attracts the negatively charged region of water molecules, and a chloride anion attracts the positively charged region of water molecules. In both cases, the ions become surrounded by spherical layers of specific numbers and arrangements of water molecules.

water is a polar molecule and will readily dissolve an ionic solute such as NaCl, yet a nonpolar solvent such as benzene will not dissolve NaCl.

Water is the most common solvent in natural systems, having several characteristics that suit it to this role. The polarity of the water molecule causes it to form hydrogen bonds with other water molecules, but it can also interact readily with charged or polar molecules.

When ionic solutes such as NaCl crystals are added to water, the Na^+ and Cl^- are released into solution. Dissolution occurs because Na^+ is attracted to the negative pole of the water molecule and Cl^- is attracted to the positive poles. In this way, they are drawn away from the crystal separately into solution. As it leaves, each ion becomes **hydrated,** which means that it is surrounded by a sphere of water molecules **(figure 2.12).** Molecules such as salt or sugar that attract water to their surface are termed **hydrophilic.*** Nonpolar molecules, such as benzene, that repel water are considered **hydrophobic.*** A third class of molecules, such as the phospholipids in cell membranes, are considered **amphipathic*** because they have both hydrophilic and hydrophobic properties.

Because most biological activities take place in aqueous (water-based) solutions, the concentration of these solutions can be very important (see chapter 7). The **concentration** of a solution expresses the amount of solute dissolved in a certain amount of solvent. It can be figured by percentage or molarity. Percentage is the ratio of solute in solution expressed as some combination of weight or volume.

A common way to calculate concentration by percentage is to use the weight of the solute, measured in grams (g), dissolved in a

specified volume of solvent, measured in milliliters (ml). For example, dissolving 3 g of NaCl in the amount of water to produce 100 ml of solution is a 3% solution; dissolving 30 g in water up to 100 ml of solution produces a 30% solution; and dissolving 3 g in 1,000 ml (1 liter) produces a 0.3% solution.

A frequent way to express concentration of biological solutions is by its molar concentration, or *molarity* (M). A standard molar solution is obtained by dissolving 1 *mole*, defined as the molecular weight of the compound in grams, in 1 L (1,000 ml) of solution. To make a 1 M solution of sodium chloride, we would dissolve 58 g of NaCl to give 1 L of solution; a 0.1 M solution would require 5.8 g of NaCl in 1 L of solution.

Acidity, Alkalinity, and the pH Scale

Another factor with far-reaching impact on living things is the concentration of acidic or basic solutions in their environment. To understand how solutions become acidic or basic, we must look again at the behavior of water molecules. Hydrogens and oxygen tend to remain bonded by covalent bonds, but under certain conditions, a water molecule may dissociate. This occurs when a single hydrogen atom breaks away as an ionic H^+, or **hydrogen ion,** leaving the remainder of the molecule in the form of an OH^-, or **hydroxide ion.** The H^+ ion is positively charged because it is essentially a hydrogen that has lost its electron; the OH^- is negatively charged because it remains in possession of that electron. Ionization of water is constantly occurring, but in pure water containing no other ions, H^+ and OH^- are produced in equal amounts, and the solution remains neutral. By one definition, a solution is considered **acidic** when one of its components (an acid) releases excess hydrogen ions.[5] A solution is **basic** when a component (a base) releases excess hydroxide ions, so that there is no longer a balance between the two ions. Another term used interchangeably with basic is **alkaline.**

To measure the acid and base concentrations of solutions, scientists use the **pH** scale, a graduated numerical scale that ranges from 0 (the most acidic) to 14 (the most basic). This scale is a useful standard for rating the relative acid or base content of a substance. Use **figure 2.13** to familiarize yourself with the pH readings of some common substances. It is not an arbitrary scale but actually a mathematical derivation based on the negative logarithm of the concentration of H^+ ions in moles per liter (symbolized as $[H^+]$) in a solution, represented as:

$$pH = -\log[H^+]$$

Acidic solutions have a greater concentration of H^+ than OH^-, starting with pH 0, which contains 1.0 moles H^+/liter. Each of the subsequent whole-number readings in the scale reduces the $[H^+]$ by tenfold:

- pH 1 contains [0.1 moles H^+/L].
- pH 2 contains [0.01 moles H^+/L].
- Continuing in the same manner up to pH 14, which contains [0.00000000000001 moles H^+/L].

* *hydrophilic* (hy-droh-fil´-ik) Gr. *hydros,* water, and *philos,* to love.
* *hydrophobic* (hy-droh-fob´-ik) Gr. *phobos,* fear.
* *amphipathic* (am´-fy-path´-ik) Gr. *amphi,* both.

5. Actually, it forms a hydronium ion (H_3O^+), but for simplicity's sake we will use the notation H^+.

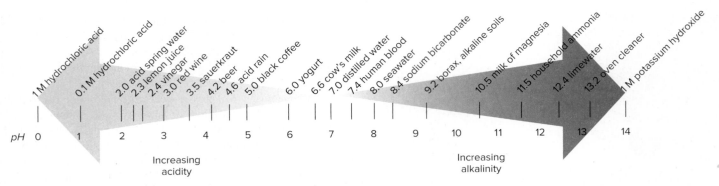

Figure 2.13 **The pH scale.** Shown are the relative degrees of acidity and alkalinity and the approximate pH readings for various substances.

TABLE 2.2		Hydrogen Ion and Hydroxide Ion Concentrations at a Given pH	
Moles/L of Hydrogen Ions	Logarithm	pH	Moles/L of OH$^-$
1.0	10^0	0	10^{-14}
0.1	10^{-1}	1	10^{-13}
0.01	10^{-2}	2	10^{-12}
0.001	10^{-3}	3	10^{-11}
0.0001	10^{-4}	4	10^{-10}
0.00001	10^{-5}	5	10^{-9}
0.000001	10^{-6}	6	10^{-8}
0.0000001	10^{-7}	7	10^{-7}
0.00000001	10^{-8}	8	10^{-6}
0.000000001	10^{-9}	9	10^{-5}
0.0000000001	10^{-10}	10	10^{-4}
0.00000000001	10^{-11}	11	10^{-3}
0.000000000001	10^{-12}	12	10^{-2}
0.0000000000001	10^{-13}	13	10^{-1}
0.00000000000001	10^{-14}	14	10^0

These same concentrations can be represented more manageably by exponents:

- pH 2 has an [H$^+$] of 10^{-2} moles.
- pH 14 has an [H$^+$] of 10^{-14} moles **(table 2.2).**

It is evident that the pH units are derived from the exponent itself. Even though the basis for the pH scale is [H$^+$], it is important to note that as the [H$^+$] in a solution decreases, the [OH$^-$] increases in direct proportion. At midpoint—pH 7 or **neutrality**—the concentrations are exactly equal and neither predominates, this being the pH of pure water previously mentioned.

In summary, the pH scale can be used to rate or determine the degree of acidity or alkalinity of a solution. On this scale, a pH below

7 is acidic, and the lower the pH, the greater the acidity; a pH above 7 is basic, and the higher the pH, the greater the alkalinity. Incidentally, although pHs are given here in even whole numbers, more often pH readings are given in decimal form; for example, pH 4.5 or 6.8 (acidic) and pH 7.4 or 10.2 (basic). Because of the damaging effects of very concentrated acids or bases, most cells operate best under neutral, weakly acidic, or weakly basic conditions (see chapter 7).

Aqueous solutions containing both acids and bases may be involved in **neutralization** reactions, which give rise to water and other neutral by-products. For example, when equal molar solutions of hydrochloric acid (HCl) and sodium hydroxide (NaOH, a base) are mixed, the reaction proceeds as follows:

$$HCl + NaOH \rightarrow H_2O + NaCl$$

Here the acid and base ionize to H$^+$ and OH$^-$ ions, which form water, and other ions, Na$^+$ and Cl$^-$, which form sodium chloride. Any product other than water that arises when acids and bases react is called a salt. Many of the organic acids (such as lactic and succinic acids) that function in **metabolism*** are available as the acid and the salt form (such as lactate, succinate), depending on the conditions in the cell (see chapter 8).

Practice SECTION 2.3

15. Review the types of chemical reactions and the general ways they can be expressed in equations.

16. Define *solution*, *solvent*, and *solute*.

17. What properties of water make it an effective biological solvent, and how does a molecule like NaCl become dissolved in it?

18. What is molarity? Tell how to make a 1 M solution of Mg$_3$(PO$_4$)$_2$ and a 0.1 M solution of CaSO$_4$.

19. What determines whether a substance is an acid or a base? Briefly outline the pH scale.

* *metabolism* (muh-tab′-oh-lizm) A general term referring to the totality of chemical and physical processes occurring in the cell.

CLINIC CASE

I've Eaten So Much I Can't Move The sudden onset of neurological symptoms is guaranteed to get the attention of health care professionals, so when a patient visited the emergency room of Kingston City Hospital suffering from double vision, slurred speech, a diminished gag reflex, and muscle weakness severe enough that he was unable to stand without assistance, doctors took note. Descending flaccid paralysis, like that displayed by the patient, is one of the primary symptoms of botulism, an often-fatal form of food poisoning. Botulism can occur when cells of *Clostridium botulinum* grow and produce potent neurotoxins. One of the reasons botulism is not widespread is that cells of the bacterium (which are common in soil) will only grow when the pH is above 4.6 and oxygen is absent.

The patient had eaten several pieces of garlic bread at a dinner party he hosted 2 days before his symptoms appeared. He prepared the bread by mixing raw, chopped garlic with margarine and spreading the mixture onto pita bread. Laboratory testing of the garlic revealed *Clostridium botulinum* cells and the botulinum neurotoxin. The garlic itself had been prepared (commercially) by chopping raw garlic and combining it with extra-virgin olive oil. The pH of the garlic was found to be 5.7, high enough to allow for growth of the bacterium, while the olive oil prevented the entry of oxygen, creating an anaerobic environment. Thanks to the quick work of doctors, botulinum antitoxin, and a mechanical ventilator to assist the patient's breathing, he was able to leave the hospital after a 29-day stay.

The U.S. Food and Drug Administration responded to this case by requiring foods like garlic, that are raw and packaged in oil, to be acidified with citric, propionic, or similar acids, to a pH of 4.6 or lower (you likely have food manufactured this way in your refrigerator right now).

Taking antacids may significantly increase the risk of becoming infected with certain gastrointestinal pathogens like *Vibrio cholerae*. Speculate on why this is.

2.4 The Chemistry of Carbon and Organic Compounds

 Learn

16. Describe the chemistry of carbon and the difference between inorganic and organic compounds.
17. Identify functional groups and give some examples.
18. Define *macromolecule, polymer,* and *monomer.*

So far our main focus has been on the characteristics of atoms, ions, and small, simple substances that play diverse roles in the structure and function of living things. These substances are often lumped together in a category called **inorganic chemicals.** A chemical is usually inorganic if it does not contain *both* carbon and hydrogen. Examples of inorganic chemicals include H_2O, O_2, NaCl (sodium chloride), $Mg_3(PO_4)_2$ (magnesium phosphate), $CaCO_3$ (calcium carbonate), and CO_2 (carbon dioxide). In reality, the biology of living organisms depends on the chemistry of **organic compounds.** The minimum requirement for a compound to be considered organic is that it contains a basic framework of carbon bonded to hydrogens. Organic molecules vary in complexity from the simplest, methane (CH_4; see figure 2.4c), which has a molecular weight of 16, to certain antibody molecules (produced by an immune reaction) that have a molecular weight of nearly 1 million and are among the most complex molecules on earth. Most organic chemicals in cells contain other elements such as oxygen, nitrogen, and phosphorus in addition to the carbon and hydrogen.

The role of carbon as the fundamental element of life can best be understood if we look at its chemistry and bonding patterns. The valence of carbon makes it an ideal atomic building block to form the backbone of organic molecules; it has 4 electrons in its outer orbital to be shared with other atoms (including other carbons) through covalent bonding. As a result, it can form stable chains containing thousands of carbon atoms and still has bonding sites available for forming covalent bonds with numerous other atoms. Carbon forms bonds that are linear, branched, or ringed, and it can form four single bonds, two double bonds, or one triple bond **(figure 2.14)**. Several unique kinds of molecules are made of pure carbon alone. You may be familiar with diamonds and graphite.

Nanotechnologists—scientists specializing in the practical uses of molecule-sized structures—have focused their attention on two related systems, liposomes and fullerenes **(figure 2.15)**. Both are hollow, carbon-based structures that seem well-suited to the precise delivery of drugs within the body. The greatest success has been with liposomes, which consist of a lipid bilayer similar to a cell membrane. They can carry a variety of drugs in their core and readily fuse with the membrane of the cell they are targeting, immediately delivering their contents directly into the cytoplasm. Fullerenes are an unusual group of molecules that consist only of carbon bonded to other carbons, forming a lattice network that can assume several configurations, including **buckyballs*** and nanotubes. These molecules can also have drugs loaded into their cores and be directed toward specific cells or organs, but they are not broken down in the body and can remain in place significantly longer than traditional drug carriers. They are being tested as a means of treating cancers with radioactive isotopes and delivering antiviral drugs into infected cells.

Functional Groups of Organic Compounds

One important advantage of carbon's serving as the molecular skeleton for living things is that it is free to bind with a variety of

* *Buckyballs* were named for Buckminster Fuller, the inventor of the geodesic dome, to which the carbon structure bears a striking resemblance.

Figure 2.14 The versatility of bonding in carbon. In most compounds, each carbon makes a total of four bonds. **(a)** Single, double, and triple bonds can be made with other carbons, oxygen, and nitrogen; single bonds are made with hydrogen. Simple electron models show how the electrons are shared in these bonds. **(b)** Multiple bonding of carbons can give rise to long chains, branched compounds, and ringed compounds, many of which are extraordinarily large and complex.

special molecular groups or accessory molecules called **functional groups.** Functional groups help define the chemical class of certain groups of organic compounds and confer unique reactive properties on the whole molecule **(table 2.3).** Because each type of functional group behaves in a distinctive manner, reactions of an organic compound can be predicted by knowing the kind of functional group or groups it carries. Many synthesis, decomposition, and transfer reactions rely upon functional groups such as R—OH or R—NH$_2$. The R designation on a molecule is shorthand for remainder, and its placement in a formula indicates that the group attached at that site varies from one compound to another.

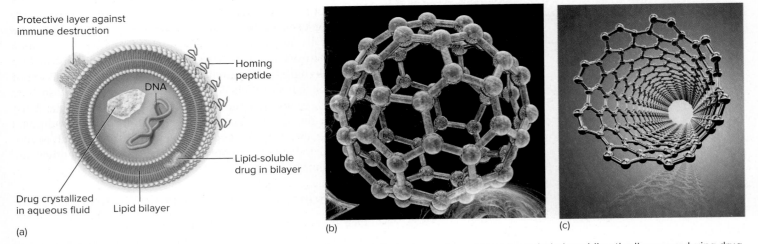

Figure 2.15 (a) Diagram of a liposome is shown carrying drugs and displaying surface molecules to help in guiding the liposome during drug delivery. **(b)** Structure of a buckyball indicates its "soccer ball" appearance of hexagonal carbons. **(c)** Model of a nanotube displaying the hollow interior, which could be used to precisely deliver drugs or biomolecules to cells.
(b): Laguna Design/Science Photo Library/Alamy Stock Photo; (c): Miriam Maslo/Science Photo Library/Alamy Stock Photo

TABLE 2.3	Representative Functional Groups and Organic Compounds That Contain Them	
Formula of Functional Group	**Name**	**Can Be Found In**
R* —[O — H]	Hydroxyl	Alcohols, carbohydrates
R — C (=O) OH	Carboxyl	Fatty acids, proteins, organic acids
R — C (H, H) [NH₂]	Amino	Proteins, nucleic acids
R — C (=O) O — R	Ester	Lipids
R — C (H, H) SH	Sulfhydryl	Cysteine (amino acid), proteins
R — C (=O) H	Carbonyl, terminal end	Aldehydes, polysaccharides
R — C (=O) — C —	Carbonyl, internal	Ketones, polysaccharides
R — O — P (=O) — OH (OH)	Phosphate	DNA, RNA, ATP

*The R designation on a molecule is shorthand for remainder, and its placement in a formula indicates that what is attached at that site varies from one compound to another.

Organic Macromolecules: Superstructures of Life

The compounds of life fall into the realm of **biochemistry.** Biochemicals are organic compounds produced by (or that are components of) living things, and they include four main families: carbohydrates, lipids, proteins, and nucleic acids **(table 2.4).** The compounds in these groups are assembled from smaller molecular subunits, or building blocks, and because they are often very large compounds, they are termed **macromolecules.** All macromolecules except lipids are formed by polymerization, a process in which repeating subunits termed **monomers*** are bound into chains of various lengths termed **polymers.*** For example, amino acids (monomers), when arranged in a chain, form proteins (polymers). The large size and complex, three-dimensional shapes of macromolecules enable them to function as structural components, molecular messengers, energy sources, enzymes (biochemical catalysts), nutrient stores, and sources of genetic information. In section 2.5 and in later chapters, we consider numerous concepts relating to the roles of macromolecules in cells. Table 2.4 will also be a useful reference when you study metabolism in chapter 8.

 Practice SECTION 2.4

20. What atoms must be present in a molecule for it to be considered organic?
21. Name several inorganic compounds.
22. What characteristics of carbon make it ideal for the formation of organic compounds?
23. What are functional groups?
24. Differentiate between a monomer and a polymer. How are polymers formed?

2.5 Molecules of Life: Carbohydrates

 Learn

19. Define *carbohydrate* and know the functional groups that characterize carbohydrates.
20. Distinguish among mono-, di-, and polysaccharides, and describe how their bonds are made.
21. Discuss the functions of carbohydrates in cells.

The term **carbohydrate** originates from the way that most members of this chemical class resemble combinations of carbon and water. Carbohydrates can be generally represented by the formula $(CH_2O)_n$, in which *n* indicates the number of units that combine to make the finished carbohydrate. The basic structure of a simple carbohydrate monomer is a backbone of carbon bound to two or more hydroxyl groups. Because they also have either an aldehyde or a ketone group, they are often designated as *polyhydroxy* **aldehydes** or **ketones (figure 2.16).** In simple terms, a sugar such as glucose is an aldehyde with a terminal carbonyl group bonded to a hydrogen and another carbon. Fructose sugar is a ketone with a carbonyl group bonded between two carbons.

Carbohydrates exist in a great variety of configurations. The common term *sugar* (**saccharide***) refers to a simple carbohydrate,

* *monomer* (mahn′-oh-mur) Gr. *mono*, one, and *meros*, part.
* *polymer* (pahl′-ee-mur) Gr. *poly*, many; also the root for polysaccharide, polypeptide, and polynucleotide.
* *saccharide* (sak′-uh-ryd) Gr. *sakcharon*, sweet.

TABLE 2.4 Macromolecules and Their Functions

Macromolecule	Description/Basic Structure	Examples/Notes
Carbohydrates		
Monosaccharides	3- to 7-carbon sugars	Glucose, fructose / Sugars involved in metabolic reactions; building block of disaccharides and polysaccharides
Disaccharides	Two monosaccharides	Maltose (malt sugar) / Composed of two glucoses; an important breakdown product of starch
		Lactose (milk sugar) / Composed of glucose and galactose
		Sucrose (table sugar) / Composed of glucose and fructose
Polysaccharides	Chains of monosaccharides	Starch, cellulose, glycogen / Cell wall, food storage
Lipids		
Triglycerides	Fatty acids + glycerol	Fats, oils / Major component of cell membranes; storage
Phospholipids	Fatty acids + glycerol + phosphate	Membranes
Waxes	Fatty acids, alcohols	Mycolic acid / Cell wall of mycobacteria
Steroids	Ringed structure	Cholesterol, ergosterol / Membranes of eukaryotes and some bacteria
Proteins		
Polypeptides	Amino acids in a chain bound by peptide bonds	Enzymes; part of cell membrane, cell wall, ribosomes, antibodies / Metabolic reactions; structural components
Nucleic acids	Nucleotides, composed of pentose sugar + phosphate + nitrogenous base	Purines: adenine, guanine; Pyrimidines: cytosine, thymine, uracil
Deoxyribonucleic acid (DNA)	Contains deoxyribose sugar and thymine, not uracil	Chromosomes; genetic material of viruses / Inheritance
Ribonucleic acid (RNA)	Contains ribose sugar and uracil, not thymine	Ribosomes; mRNA, tRNA / Expression of genetic traits
Adenosine triphosphate (ATP)	Contains adenine, ribose sugar, and 3 phosphate groups	A high-energy compound that gives off energy to power reactions in cells

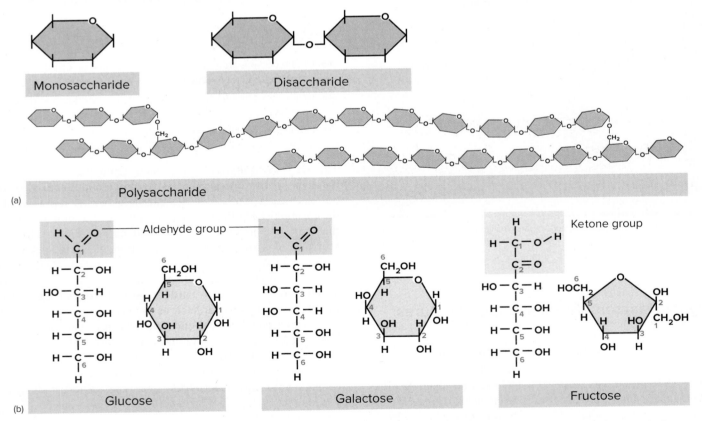

Figure 2.16 Common classes of carbohydrates. (a) Major saccharide groups, named for the number of sugar units each contains. (b) Three hexoses with the same molecular formula ($C_6H_{12}O_6$) and different structural formulas. Both linear and ring models are given. The linear form emphasizes aldehyde and ketone groups, although in solution the sugars exist in the ring form. Note that the carbons are numbered in red so as to keep track of reactions within and between monosaccharides.

such as a monosaccharide or a disaccharide, that has a sweet taste. A **monosaccharide** is a simple polyhydroxy aldehyde or ketone molecule containing from 3 to 7 carbons; a **disaccharide** is a combination of two monosaccharides; and a **polysaccharide** is a polymer of five or more monosaccharides bound in linear or branched chain patterns (figure 2.16). Monosaccharides and disaccharides are specified by combining a prefix that describes some characteristic of the sugar with the suffix -**ose.** For example, **hexoses** are composed of 6 carbons, and **pentoses** contain 5 carbons. **Glucose** (Greek for sweet) is the most common and universally important hexose; the most frequently encountered form of glucose is often referred to as dextrose. **Fructose** is named for fruit (one of its sources); and xylose, a pentose, derives its name from the Greek word for wood. Disaccharides are named similarly: **lactose** (Latin for milk) is an important component of milk; **maltose** means malt sugar; and **sucrose** (French for sugar) is common table sugar or cane sugar.

The Nature of Carbohydrate Bonds

The subunits of disaccharides and polysaccharides are linked by means of **glycosidic bonds,** in which carbons (each is assigned a number) on adjacent sugar units are bonded to the same oxygen atom like links in a chain **(figure 2.17).** For example:

- Maltose is formed when the number 1 carbon on a glucose bonds to the oxygen on the number 4 carbon on a second glucose.
- Sucrose is formed when glucose and fructose bind oxygen between their number 1 and number 2 carbons.
- Lactose is formed when glucose and galactose connect by their number 1 and number 4 carbons.

This bond is formed by one carbon giving up its OH group and the other (the one contributing the oxygen to the bond) losing the H from its OH group. Because a water molecule is produced, this

Figure 2.17 **Glycosidic bond in three common disaccharides. (a)** Formation of the 1,4 bond between two α glucoses to produce maltose. **(b)** Formation of the 1,2 bond between glucose and fructose to produce sucrose. **(c)** A 1,4 bond between a galactose and glucose produces lactose. Note that all three dehydration synthesis reactions release water.

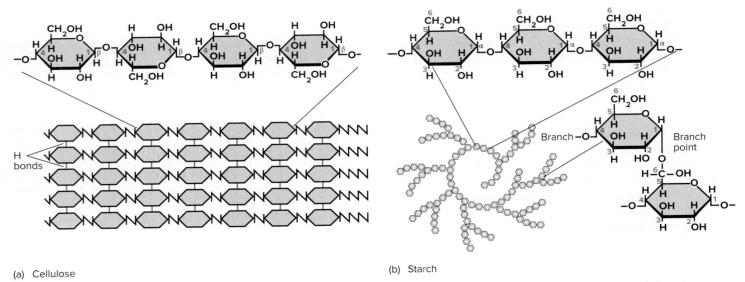

(a) Cellulose

(b) Starch

Figure 2.18 Polysaccharides. (a) Cellulose is composed of β-glucose bonded in 1,4 bonds that produce linear, lengthy chains of polysaccharides that are H-bonded along their length. This accounts for fibrous support structures of plants. **(b)** Starch is also composed of glucose polymers, in this case α glucose. The main structure is amylose bonded in a 1,4 pattern, with side branches of amylopectin bonded by 1,6 bonds. The entire molecule is compact and granular.

reaction is known as **dehydration synthesis,** a process common to most polymerization reactions (see proteins, section 2.7). Three polysaccharides (starch, cellulose, and glycogen) are structurally and biochemically distinct, even though all are polymers of the same monosaccharide—glucose. The basis for their differences lies primarily in the exact way the glucose molecules are bound together, which greatly affects the characteristics of the end product **(figure 2.18).** The synthesis and breakage of each type of bond require a specialized catalyst called an enzyme (see chapter 8).

The Functions of Carbohydrates in Cells

Carbohydrates are the most abundant biological molecules in nature. They play numerous roles in cell structure, adhesion, and metabolism.

Polysaccharides typically contribute to structural support and protection and serve as nutrient and energy stores. The cell walls in plants and many microscopic algae derive their strength and rigidity from **cellulose,** a long, fibrous polymer (figure 2.18*a*). Because of this role, cellulose is probably one of the most common organic substances on the earth, yet it is digestible only by certain bacteria, fungi, and protozoa that produce the enzyme cellulase. These microbes, called decomposers, play an essential role in breaking down and recycling plant materials (see figure 7.2). Some bacteria secrete slime layers of a glucose polymer called *dextran.* This substance causes a sticky layer to develop on teeth that leads to plaque, described later in chapter 21.

Other structural polysaccharides can be conjugated (chemically bonded) to amino acids, nitrogen bases, lipids, or proteins. **Agar,** a polysaccharide indispensable for preparing solid culture media, is a natural component of certain seaweeds. It is a complex polymer of galactose and sulfur-containing carbohydrates.

Chitin, a polymer of glucosamine (a sugar with an amino functional group), is a major compound in the cell walls of fungi and the exoskeletons of insects. **Peptidoglycan*** is one special class of compounds in which polysaccharides (glycans) are linked to peptide fragments (a short chain of amino acids). This molecule provides the main source of structural support to the bacterial cell wall. The cell wall of gram-negative bacteria also contains **lipopolysaccharide,** a complex of lipid and polysaccharide responsible for symptoms such as fever and shock (see chapters 4 and 13).

The outer surface of many cells has a delicate "sugar coating" composed of polysaccharides bound in various ways to proteins (the combination is called mucoprotein or glycoprotein). This structure, called the **glycocalyx,*** functions in attachment to other cells or as a site for *receptors*—surface molecules that receive and respond to external stimuli. Small sugar molecules account for the differences in human blood types, and carbohydrates are a component of large protein molecules called antibodies. Some viruses have glycoproteins on their surface for binding to and invading their host cells.

Polysaccharides are usually stored by cells in the form of glucose polymers, such as **starch** (figure 2.18*b*) or **glycogen,** that are readily tapped as a source of energy and other metabolic needs. Because a water molecule is required for breaking the bond between two glucose molecules, digestion is also termed **hydrolysis.*** Starch is the primary storage food of green plants, microscopic algae, and some fungi; glycogen (animal starch) is a stored carbohydrate for animals and certain groups of bacteria and protozoa.

* *peptidoglycan* (pep-tih-doh-gly′-kan).
* *glycocalyx* (gly″-koh-kay′-lix) Gr. *glycos,* sweet, and *calyx,* covering.

2.6 Molecules of Life: Lipids

 Learn

22. Define *lipid, triglyceride, phospholipid, fatty acid,* and *cholesterol.*

23. Describe how an ester bond is formed.

24. Discuss the major functions of lipids in cells.

The term **lipid,** derived from the Greek word *lipos,* meaning fat, is not a chemical designation but an operational term for a variety of substances that are not soluble in polar solvents such as water (recall that oil and water do not mix) but will dissolve in nonpolar solvents such as benzene and chloroform. This property occurs because the substances we call lipids contain relatively long or complex C—H (hydrocarbon) chains that are nonpolar and thus hydrophobic. The main groups of compounds classified as lipids are triglycerides, phospholipids, steroids, and waxes.

Important storage lipids are the **triglycerides,** a category that includes fats and oils. Triglycerides are composed of a single molecule of glycerol bound to three **fatty acids (figure 2.19). Glycerol** is a 3-carbon alcohol[6] with three OH groups that serve as binding sites. Fatty acids are long-chain, unbranched hydrocarbon molecules with a carboxyl group (COOH) at one end that is free to bind to the glycerol. The bond that forms between the —OH group and the —COOH is defined as an **ester bond** (figure 2.19*a*). The hydrocarbon portion of a fatty acid can vary in length from 4 to 24 carbons and, depending on the fat, it may be *saturated* or *unsaturated.* A saturated fatty acid has all of the carbons in the chain bonded to hydrogens with single bonds. Fatty acids having at least one carbon—carbon double bond are considered unsaturated (figure 2.19*b*). Fats that contain such fatty acids are described with these terms as well. The structure of fatty acids is what gives fats and oils (liquid fats) their greasy,

6. Alcohols are hydrocarbons containing an —OH functional group.

Figure 2.19 Synthesis and structure of a triglyceride. (a) Because a water molecule is released at each ester bond, this is another form of dehydration synthesis. The jagged lines and R symbol represent the hydrocarbon chains of the fatty acids, which are commonly very long. **(b)** Structural models of two kinds of fatty acids. (top) A saturated fatty acid has long, straight chains that readily pack together. (bottom) An unsaturated fatty acid has at least one double bond and cannot pack densely due to the bends in the long chain caused by the double bonds. **(c)** Three-dimensional models of triglycerides containing saturated (top) and unsaturated fatty acids (bottom). Which of these two fats is an oil and which one is solid?

insoluble nature. In general, solid fats (such as butter) are more saturated, and oils (or liquid fats) are less saturated.

In most cells, triglycerides are stored for long-term use in concentrated form as droplets or globules. When the ester linkage is acted on by digestive enzymes called lipases, the fatty acids and glycerol are freed to be used in metabolism. Fatty acids are a superior source of energy, yielding twice as much per gram as other storage molecules (starch). Soaps are K^+ or Na^+ salts of fatty acids whose qualities make them excellent grease removers and cleaners (see chapter 11).

Membrane Lipids

The **phospholipids** serve as a major structural component of cell membranes. Although phospholipids also contain glycerol and fatty acids, they differ significantly from triglycerides. Phospholipids contain only two fatty acids attached to the glycerol, and the third glycerol binding site holds a phosphate group. The phosphate is in turn bonded to an alcohol, which varies from one phospholipid to another **(figure 2.20a)**. This class of lipids has a hydrophilic region from the charge on the phosphoric acid–alcohol "head" of the molecule and a hydrophobic region that corresponds to the long,

uncharged "tail" (formed by the fatty acids). When exposed to an aqueous solution, the charged heads are attracted to the water phase, and the nonpolar tails are repelled from the water phase **(figure 2.20b)**. This property causes lipids to naturally assume single and double layers (bilayers), which contribute to their biological significance in membranes. When two single layers of polar lipids come together to form a double layer, the outer hydrophilic face of each single layer will orient itself toward the solution, and the hydrophobic portions will become immersed in the core of the bilayer. A standard model of membrane structure has the lipids forming a continuous bilayer. Embedded at numerous sites in this bilayer are various-sized globular proteins **(figure 2.21)**. Some proteins are situated only at the surface; others extend fully through the entire membrane. Membranes are dynamic and constantly changing because the lipid phase is in motion and many proteins can migrate freely about. This fluidity is essential to such activities as engulfment of food and discharge or secretion by cells. The structure of the lipid phase provides an impenetrable barrier that accounts for the selective permeability and transport of molecules. Membrane proteins function in receiving molecular signals (receptors), in binding and transporting nutrients, and as enzymes, topics to be discussed in chapters 7 and 8.

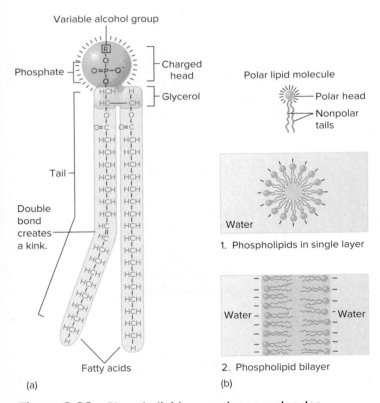

(a)
(b)

Figure 2.20 Phospholipids—membrane molecules.
(a) A model of a single molecule of a phospholipid. The phosphate-alcohol head lends a charge to one end of the molecule; its long, trailing hydrocarbon chain is uncharged. **(b)** Phospholipids in water-based solutions become arranged (1) in single layers called micelles, with the charged head oriented toward the water phase and the hydrophobic nonpolar tail buried away from the water phase, or (2) in double-layered systems with the hydrophobic tails sandwiched between two hydrophilic layers.

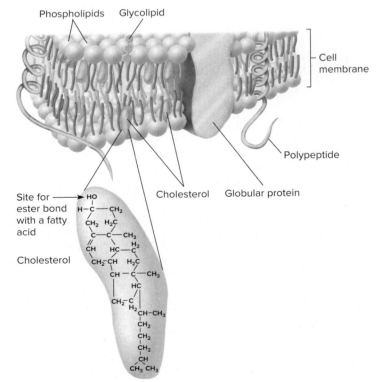

Figure 2.21 Cutaway view of a membrane with its bilayer of lipids. The primary lipid is phospholipid; however, cholesterol is inserted in some membranes. Other structures are protein and glycolipid molecules. Cholesterol can become esterified with fatty acids at its OH^- group, imparting a polar quality similar to that of phospholipids.

Miscellaneous Lipids

Steroids are complex ringed compounds commonly found in cell membranes and animal hormones. The best known of these is the sterol (meaning a steroid with an OH group) called **cholesterol** (figure 2.21). Cholesterol reinforces the structure of the cell membrane in animal cells and in an unusual group of cell-wall–deficient bacteria called the mycoplasmas (see chapter 4).

The cell membranes of fungi also contain a unique sterol, called ergosterol. *Prostaglandins* are fatty acid derivatives found in trace amounts that function in inflammatory and allergic reactions, blood clotting, and smooth muscle contraction. Chemically, a *wax* is an ester formed between a long-chain alcohol and a saturated fatty acid. The resulting material is typically pliable and soft when warmed but hard and water-resistant when cold. Among living things, fur, feathers, fruits, leaves, human skin, and insect exoskeletons are naturally waterproofed with a coating of wax. Bacteria that cause tuberculosis and leprosy produce a wax that contributes to their pathogenicity.

 Practice SECTIONS 2.5–2.6

25. What is the structure of carbohydrates and glycosidic bonds?
26. Differentiate between mono-, di-, and polysaccharides, and give examples of each.
27. What are some of the functions of polysaccharides in cells?
28. Draw simple structural molecules of triglycerides and phospholipids to compare their differences and similarities. What is an ester bond?
29. Describe the interaction of water, lipids, and proteins in a cell membrane.

2.7 Molecules of Life: Proteins

 Learn

25. Describe the structures of peptides and polypeptides and how their bonds form.

26. Characterize the four levels of protein structure and describe the pattern of folding.

27. Summarize some of the essential functions of proteins.

Figure 2.22 **Structural formulas of selected amino acids.** The basic structure common to all amino acids is shown in blue type; and the variable group, or R group, is placed in a colored box.

The predominant organic molecules in cells are **proteins,** a fitting term adopted from the Greek word *proteios,* meaning first or prime. To a large extent, the structure, behavior, and unique qualities of each living thing are a consequence of the proteins they contain. To best explain the origin of the special properties and versatility of proteins, we must examine their general structure.

The building blocks of proteins are **amino acids,** which exist in 20 different naturally occurring forms. **Figure 2.22** provides examples of several common amino acids. See **Appendix A** for a table that shows all 20. Various combinations of these amino acids account for the nearly infinite variety of proteins. Amino acids have a basic skeleton consisting of a carbon (called the α carbon) linked to an amino group (NH_2), a carboxyl group (COOH), a hydrogen atom (H), and a variable R group. The variations among the amino acids occur at the R group, which is different in each amino acid and imparts the unique characteristics to the molecule and to the proteins that contain it. A covalent bond called a **peptide bond** forms between the amino group on one amino acid and the carboxyl group on another amino acid. As a result of peptide bond formation, it is possible to produce molecules varying in length from two amino acids to chains containing thousands of them.

Figure 2.23 The formation of peptide bonds in a tetrapeptide. Each time two amino acids bond to one another, a molecule of water is created via a dehydration reaction.

Various terms are used to denote the nature of compounds containing peptide bonds. **Peptide*** usually refers to a molecule composed of short chains of amino acids, such as a dipeptide (two amino acids), a tripeptide (three), and a tetrapeptide (four) **(figure 2.23)**. A **polypeptide** contains an unspecified number of amino acids but usually has more than 20 and is often a smaller subunit of a protein. A protein is the largest of this class of compounds and usually contains a minimum of 50 amino acids. It is common for the terms *polypeptide* and *protein* to be used interchangeably, though not all polypeptides are large enough to be considered proteins. In chapter 9, we will see that protein synthesis is not just a random connection of amino acids; it is directed by information provided in DNA.

Protein Structure and Diversity

The reason proteins are so varied and specific is that they do not function in the form of a simple straight chain of amino acids (called the primary structure). A protein has a natural tendency to assume more complex levels of organization, called the secondary, tertiary, and quaternary structures **(process figure 2.24).**

The **primary (1°) structure** of a protein is simply the sequence of each amino acid in the polypeptide chain. Proteins vary extensively in the exact order, type, and number of amino acids, and it is this quality that gives rise to the unlimited diversity in protein form and function.

A polypeptide does not remain in its primary state, but instead spontaneously arranges itself into a higher level of complexity called its **secondary (2°) structure.** The secondary structure arises from numerous hydrogen bonds occurring between the C=O and N—H groups of amino acids located near one another in the primary sequence. This bonding causes the whole chain to coil or fold into regular patterns. The coiled spiral form is called the α helix, and the folded, accordion form is called the β-pleated sheet. Polypeptides ordinarily will contain both types of configurations.

Once a chain has assumed the secondary structure, it goes on to form yet another level of folding and compacting—the **tertiary**

(3°) structure. This structure arises through additional intrachain[7] forces and bonds between various parts of the α helix and β-pleated sheets. The chief actions in creating the tertiary structure are additional hydrogen bonds between charged functional groups, van der Waals forces between various parts of the polypeptide, and covalent disulfide bonds. The disulfide bonds occur between sulfur atoms on the amino acid **cysteine,*** and these bonds confer a high degree of stability to the overall protein structure. The result is a complex, three-dimensional protein that is now the completed functional state in many cases.

The most complex proteins assume a **quaternary (4°) structure,** in which two or more polypeptides interact to form a large, multiunit protein. The polypeptide units form loose associations based on weak van der Waals and other forces. The polypeptides in proteins with quaternary structure can be the same or different. The arrangement of these individual polypeptides tends to be symmetrical and will dictate the exact form of the finished protein (figure 2.24, step 4).

The most important outcome of bonding and folding is that each different type of protein develops a unique shape, and its surface displays a distinctive pattern of pockets and bumps. As a result, a protein can react only with molecules that complement or fit its particular surface features. Such a degree of specificity can provide the functional diversity required for many thousands of different cellular activities. **Enzymes** serve as the catalysts for all chemical reactions in cells, and nearly every reaction requires a different enzyme (see chapter 8). **Antibodies** are complex glycoproteins with specific regions of attachment for bacteria, viruses, and other microorganisms. Certain bacterial toxins (poisonous proteins) react with only one specific organ or tissue. Proteins embedded in the cell membrane have reactive sites restricted to a certain nutrient. Some proteins function as *receptors* to receive stimuli from the environment.

The functional, three-dimensional form of a protein is termed the *native state,* and if it is disrupted by some means, the protein is said to be *denatured.* Such agents as heat, acid, alcohol, and some disinfectants disrupt (and thus denature) the stabilizing intrachain bonds and cause the molecule to become nonfunctional, as described in chapter 11.

Practice SECTION 2.7

30. Describe the basic structure of an amino acid and the formation of a peptide bond.
31. Differentiate between a peptide, a polypeptide, and a protein.
32. Explain what causes the various levels of structure of a protein molecule.
33. What functions do proteins perform in a cell?

7. **Intra**chain means within the chain; **inter**chain would be between two chains.

* *peptide* (pep′-tyd) Gr. *pepsis,* digestion.

* *cysteine* (sis′-tuh-yeen) Gr. *kystis,* sac. An amino acid first found in urine stones.

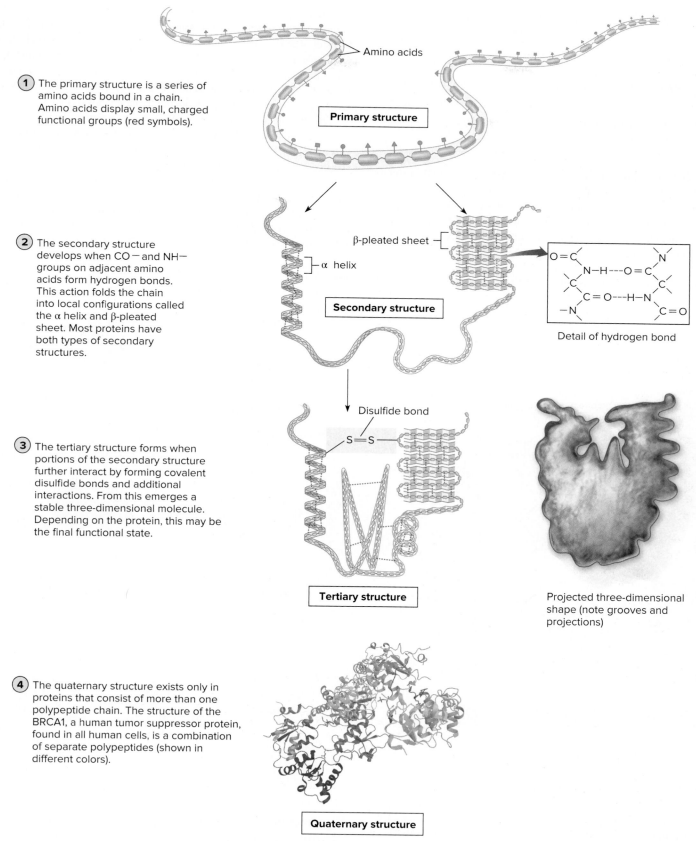

① The primary structure is a series of amino acids bound in a chain. Amino acids display small, charged functional groups (red symbols).

Amino acids

Primary structure

② The secondary structure develops when CO— and NH— groups on adjacent amino acids form hydrogen bonds. This action folds the chain into local configurations called the α helix and β-pleated sheet. Most proteins have both types of secondary structures.

β-pleated sheet

α helix

Secondary structure

Detail of hydrogen bond

③ The tertiary structure forms when portions of the secondary structure further interact by forming covalent disulfide bonds and additional interactions. From this emerges a stable three-dimensional molecule. Depending on the protein, this may be the final functional state.

Disulfide bond

S═S

Tertiary structure

Projected three-dimensional shape (note grooves and projections)

④ The quaternary structure exists only in proteins that consist of more than one polypeptide chain. The structure of the BRCA1, a human tumor suppressor protein, found in all human cells, is a combination of separate polypeptides (shown in different colors).

Quaternary structure

Process Figure 2.24 Formation of structural levels in a protein. Red dashed lines indicate H bonds.

(4): ibreakstock/Shutterstock

2.8 Nucleic Acids: A Program for Genetics

 Learn

28. Identify a nucleic acid and differentiate between DNA and RNA.

29. Describe the structures of nucleotides and list the nitrogen bases.

30. Explain how the DNA code may be copied, and describe the basic functions of RNA.

The nucleic acids, **deoxyribonucleic acid (DNA)*** and **ribonucleic acid (RNA)***, were originally isolated from the cell nucleus. Shortly thereafter, they were also found in other parts of nucleated cells, in cells with no nuclei (bacteria), and in viruses. The universal occurrence of nucleic acids in all known cells and viruses emphasizes their important roles as informational molecules. DNA, the master

* *deoxyribonucleic* (dee-ox″-ee-ry″-boh-noo-klay′-ik).
* *ribonucleic* (ry″-boh-noo-klay′-ik) It is easy to see why the abbreviations are used!

instruction manual of cells, contains a coded genetic program with detailed and specific instructions for each organism's heredity. It transfers the details of its program to RNA, "helper" molecules responsible for carrying out DNA's instructions and translating the DNA program into proteins that can perform life functions. For now, let us briefly consider the structure and some functions of DNA, RNA, and a close relative, adenosine triphosphate (ATP).

Both nucleic acids are polymers of repeating units called **nucleotides,*** each of which is composed of three smaller units: a **nitrogenous base,** a pentose (5-carbon) sugar, and a *phosphate* **(figure 2.25a).** The nitrogenous base is a cyclic compound that comes in two forms: *purines* (two rings) and *pyrimidines* (one ring). There are two types of purines—**adenine (A)** and **guanine (G)**—and three types of pyrimidines—**thymine (T), cytosine (C),** and **uracil (U) (figure 2.26).** A characteristic that differentiates DNA from RNA is that DNA contains all of the nitrogenous bases

* *nucleotide* (noo′-klee-oh-tyd) From *nucleus* and *acid*.

(a) A nucleotide, composed of a phosphate, a pentose sugar, and a nitrogenous base (either A, T, C, G, or U) is the monomer of both DNA and RNA.

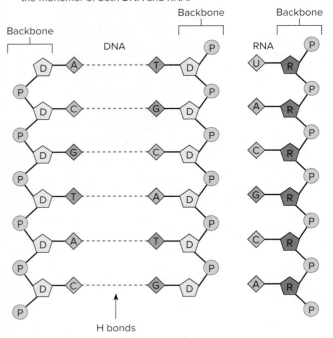

(b) In DNA, the polymer is composed of alternating deoxyribose (D) and phosphate (P) with nitrogenous bases (A, T, C, G) attached to the deoxyribose. DNA almost always exists in pairs of strands, oriented so that the bases are paired across the central axis of the molecule.

(c) In RNA, the polymer is composed of alternating ribose (R) and phosphate (P) attached to nitrogenous bases (A, U, C, G), but it is usually a single strand.

Figure 2.25 The general structure of nucleic acids.

(a) **Pentose sugars**

Deoxyribose

Ribose

(b) **Purine bases**

Adenine (A)

Guanine (G)

(c) **Pyrimidine bases**

Thymine (T)

Cytosine (C)

Uracil (U)

Figure 2.26 The sugars and nitrogenous bases that make up DNA and RNA. (a) DNA contains deoxyribose, and RNA contains ribose. **(b)** A and G purine bases are found in both DNA and RNA. **(c)** Pyrimidine bases are found in both DNA and RNA, but T is found only in DNA, and U is found only in RNA.

except uracil, and RNA contains all of the nitrogenous bases except thymine. The nitrogenous base is covalently bonded to the sugar *ribose* in RNA and *deoxyribose* (because it has one fewer oxygen than ribose) in DNA. Phosphate (PO_4^{3-}), a derivative of phosphoric acid (H_3PO_4), provides the final covalent bridge that connects sugars in series. Thus, the backbone of a nucleic acid strand is a chain of alternating phosphate-sugar-phosphate-sugar molecules, and the nitrogenous bases branch off the side of this backbone **(figure 2.25b, c).**

The Double Helix of DNA

DNA is a huge molecule formed by two very long polynucleotide (meaning that it consists of many nucleotides joined together) strands linked along their length by hydrogen bonds between complementary

> **Quick Search**
> Look for the video "Assembly of DNA" on YouTube.

pairs of nitrogenous bases. The term *complementary* means that the nitrogenous bases pair in matched sets according to this pattern: Adenine ordinarily pairs with thymine, and cytosine with guanine. The bases are attracted in this way because each pair has oxygen, nitrogen, and hydrogen atoms positioned precisely to favor the formation of hydrogen bonds between them **(figure 2.27).**

For ease in understanding the structure of DNA, it is sometimes compared to a ladder, with the sugar-phosphate backbone representing the rails and the paired nitrogenous bases representing the steps. The flat ladder is useful for understanding basic components and orientation, but in reality DNA exists in a three-dimensional arrangement called a *double helix*. A better analogy may be a spiral staircase. In this model, the two strands (helixes or helices) coil together, with the sugar-phosphate forming outer ribbons, and the paired bases sandwiched between them (figure 2.27). As is true of protein, the structure of DNA is intimately related to its function. DNA molecules are usually extremely long, a feature that satisfies a requirement for storing genetic information in the sequence of base pairs the molecule contains. The hydrogen bonds between pairs can be disrupted when DNA is being copied, and the fixed complementary base pairing is essential to maintain the genetic code.

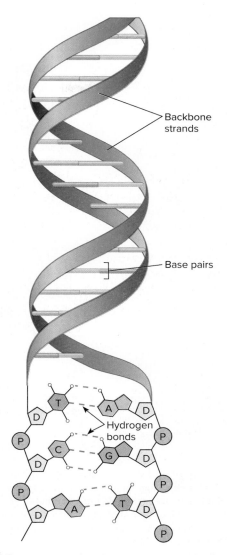

Figure 2.27 **A structural representation of the double helix of DNA.** At the bottom are the details of hydrogen bonds between the nitrogenous bases of the two strands.

Making New DNA: Passing on the Genetic Message

The biological properties of cells and viruses are ultimately programmed by a master code composed of nucleic acids. This code is in the form of DNA in all cells and many viruses; a number of viruses are based on RNA alone. Regardless of the exact genetic makeup, both cells and viruses can continue to exist only if they can duplicate their genetic material and pass it on to subsequent generations. **Figure 2.28** summarizes the main steps in this process in cells.

During its division cycle, the cell has a mechanism for making a copy of its DNA by **replication,*** using the original strand as a pattern. Note that replication is guided by the double-stranded nature of DNA and the precise pairing of bases that create the

master code. Replication requires the separation of the double strand into two single strands by an enzyme that helps to split the hydrogen bonds along the length of the molecule. This event exposes the base code and makes it available for copying. Complementary nucleotides are used to synthesize new strands of DNA that adhere to the pairing requirements of A—T and C—G. The end result is two separate double strands with the same order of bases as the original molecule. With this type of replication, each new double strand contains one of the original single strands from the starting DNA.

RNA: Organizers of Protein Synthesis

Like DNA, RNA is a polynucleotide that consists of a long chain of nucleotides. However, RNA is a single strand containing ribose sugar instead of deoxyribose and uracil instead of thymine (see figure 2.25). Several functional types of RNA are formed

* *replication* (reh″-plih-kay′-shun) A process that makes an exact copy.

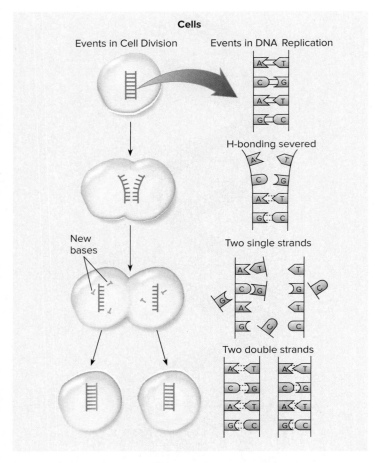

Figure 2.28 **Simplified view of DNA replication in cells.** The DNA in the cell's chromosome must be duplicated as the cell is dividing. This duplication is accomplished through the separation of the double DNA strand into two single strands. New strands are then synthesized using the original strands as guides to assemble the correct new complementary bases.

Figure 2.29 **Model of an ATP molecule, the chemical form of energy transfer in cells. (a)** Structural formula: The wavy lines connecting the phosphates represent bonds that release large amounts of energy when broken. **(b)** Ball-and-stick model shows the arrangement of atoms in three dimensions.

using the DNA template through a replication-like process. Three major types of RNA are important for protein synthesis. Messenger RNA (mRNA) is a copy of a gene from DNA that provides instructions for the order of amino acids; transfer RNA (tRNA) is a carrier that delivers the correct amino acids during protein synthesis; and ribosomal RNA (rRNA) is a major component of ribosomes, which are the sites of protein synthesis. More information on these important processes is presented in chapter 9.

ATP: The Energy Molecule of Cells

A relative of RNA involved in an entirely different cell activity is **adenosine triphosphate (ATP).** ATP is a nucleotide containing adenine, ribose, and three phosphates rather than just one **(figure 2.29).** It belongs to a category of high-energy compounds (also including guanosine triphosphate, GTP) that give off energy when the bond is broken between the second and third (outermost) phosphate. The presence of these high-energy bonds makes

it possible for ATP to release and store energy for cellular chemical reactions. Breakage of the bond of the terminal phosphate releases energy to do cellular work and also generates adenosine diphosphate (ADP). ADP can be converted back to ATP when the third phosphate is restored, thereby serving as an energy depot. Carriers for oxidation-reduction activities (nicotinamide adenine dinucleotide [NAD], for instance) are also derivatives of nucleotides (see chapter 8).

Practice SECTION 2.8

34. Describe a nucleotide and a polynucleotide, and compare and contrast the general structure of DNA and RNA.

35. Name the two purines and the three pyrimidines.

36. What are the functions of RNA?

37. What is ATP, and how does it function in cells?

 CASE STUDY **Part 2**

The doctor ordered a hydrogen breath test and explained that Megyn would have to—after consuming a drink containing lactose—breathe into a plastic bag every 15 minutes for the next 2 hours. The gases expelled into the bag were analyzed, and increased levels of hydrogen, indicative of lactose intolerance, were detected.

Megyn's case underscores the importance of a good patient history; her doctor was probably able to correctly diagnose lactose intolerance prior to any physical exam. While 15% of people of northern European ancestry are lactose intolerant, upwards of 90% of those of Asian descent have the condition and can show symptoms whenever they ingest more than small amounts of lactose. Without even being aware of it, Megyn had limited her exposure to lactose her entire life, being raised in a family where milk was not the beverage of choice, and never developing a taste for yogurt or ice cream, for example. The doctor noted that Megyn's symptoms worsened not when she began the dreaded physics class, but rather when she joined the study group and commenced her three-times-a-week mocha latte habit. Although there is no cure for lactose intolerance, her doctor prescribed a switch to black coffee, and while Megyn couldn't go that far, she found that mocha lattes made with almond milk (which contains no lactose) caused her symptoms to subside.

While adolescents and adults may have no crucial need for milk sugar, evolution has dictated that newborns leave the womb able to digest lactose, a principal component of breast milk. In the womb, however, lactase is not produced in large quantities until the last few weeks of gestation. Alex, born 6 weeks premature, was also suffering from lactose intolerance, and the same fermentative reactions occurring in Megyn's colon were taking place in Alex's, causing the same bloating, pain, and flatulence. Additionally, the presence of lactose in the large intestine was drawing water into the colon via osmosis, causing diarrhea. Lactose in the colon is fermented by enteric bacteria, producing lactic acid as a by-product and lowering the pH of the stool. A stool acidity test revealed that Alex's stool had a pH of 5.3, below the value of 5.5 which indicates excessive sugar in the colon. Fortunately, during the newborn period, the production of lactase can be induced by continuing to supply lactose. Alex was fed a combination of breast milk and low-lactose formula, which struck a balance between inducing lactose production and avoiding symptoms of lactose intolerance. Over the next few weeks, his ability to tolerate lactose improved dramatically.

■ Lactose intolerance is common, but glucose intolerance is virtually unheard of. Why do you think this is so?

■ While some people manage their lactose intolerance by simply avoiding the sugar, others take a pill containing lactase when they ingest lactose-rich foods. Can you think of a good reason to treat lactose intolerance as opposed to simply avoiding lactose?

To learn more about lactose intolerance, visit the National Institute of Diabetes and Digestive and Kidney Diseases at http://niddk.nih.gov.

Chapter Summary with Key Terms

2.1 Atoms: Fundamental Building Blocks of All Matter in the Universe
 A. Atomic Structure and Elements
 1. All **matter** in the universe is composed of minute particles called **atoms**—the simplest form of matter not divisible into a simpler substance by chemical means. Atoms are composed of smaller particles called **protons, neutrons,** and **electrons.**
 2. a. Protons are positively (+) charged, neutrons are without charge, and electrons are negatively (−) charged.
 b. Protons and neutrons form the **nucleus** of the atom.
 c. Electrons orbit the nucleus in energy shells.
 3. Atoms that differ in numbers of the protons, neutrons, and electrons are elements. **Elements** can be described by **mass number (MN),** equal to the number of protons and neutrons it has, and **atomic number (AN),** the number of protons in the nucleus, and each is known by a distinct name and symbol. Elements may exist in variant forms called **isotopes.** The **atomic mass or atomic weight** is equal to the average of the isotope mass numbers.

2.2 Bonds and Molecules
 A. Atoms interact to form **chemical bonds** and **molecules.** If the atoms combining to make a molecule are different elements, then the substance is termed a **compound.**
 1. The type of bond is dictated by the electron makeup of the outer orbitals (**valence**) of the atoms. Bond types include:
 a. **Covalent bonds,** with shared electrons. The molecule is formed by one atom sharing its electrons with another atom; the balance of charge will be **polar** if unequal or **nonpolar** if equally shared/electrically neutral.
 b. **Ionic bonds,** where one atom transfers its electron(s) to another atom that can come closer to filling up its outer orbital. Dissociation of these compounds leads to the formation of charged **cations** and **anions.**
 c. **Hydrogen bonds** involve weak attractive forces between hydrogen (+ charge) and nearby oxygens and nitrogens (− charge).
 d. **Van der Waals forces** are also weak interactions between polarized zones of molecules such as proteins.

B. An **oxidation** is a loss of electrons and a **reduction** is a gain of electrons. A substance that causes an oxidation by taking electrons is called an **oxidizing agent,** and a substance that causes a reduction by giving electrons is called a **reducing agent.**

2.3 Chemical Reactions, Solutions, and pH

A. Chemicals termed **reactants** can interact in a way to form different compounds termed **products.** Examples of reactions are synthesis and decomposition.

B. A **solution** is a combination of a solid, liquid, or gaseous chemical (the **solute**) dissolved in a liquid medium (the **solvent**). Water is the most common solvent in natural systems.

C. Ionization of water leads to the release of hydrogen ions (H^+) and hydroxyl (OH^-) ions. The **pH** scale expresses the concentration of H^+ such that a pH of less than 7.0 is considered **acidic,** and a pH of more than that, indicating fewer H^+, is considered **basic (alkaline).**

2.4 The Chemistry of Carbon and Organic Compounds

A. **Biochemistry** is the study of molecules that are found in living things. Most of these substances are **organic** compounds, which consist of carbon and hydrogen covalently bonded in various combinations. Some are **inorganic** compounds that are composed of elements other than C and H.

B. Functional groups are small accessory molecules bonded to many organic compounds that impart unique characteristics.

C. **Macromolecules** are very large organic compounds and are generally assembled from single units called **monomers** by polymerization. Molecules of life fall into basic categories of carbohydrates, lipids, proteins, and nucleic acids.

2.5 Molecules of Life: Carbohydrates

A. **Carbohydrates** are composed of carbon, hydrogen, and oxygen and contain aldehyde or ketone groups.
1. **Monosaccharides** such as glucose are the simplest carbohydrates with 3 to 7 carbons; these are the monomers of carbohydrates.
2. **Disaccharides** such as lactose consist of two monosaccharides joined by **glycosidic bonds.**
3. **Polysaccharides** such as **starch** and **peptidoglycan** are chains of five or more monosaccharides.

2.6 Molecules of Life: Lipids

A. **Lipids** contain long hydrocarbon chains and are not soluble in polar solvents such as water due to their nonpolar, hydrophobic character. Common components of fats are **fatty acids,** elongate molecules with a carboxylic acid group. Examples are **triglycerides, phospholipids,** sterols, and waxes.
1. The cell membrane is formed from a bilayer of lipids.

2.7 Molecules of Life: Proteins

A. **Proteins** are highly complex macromolecules that are crucial in most, if not all, life processes.
1. **Amino acids** are the basic building blocks of proteins. They all share a basic structure of an amino group, a carboxyl group, an R group, and hydrogen bonded to a carbon atom. There are 20 different R groups, which define the basic set of 20 amino acids, found in all life forms.
2. A **peptide** is a short chain of amino acids bound by **peptide bonds:** a **protein** contains at least 50 amino acids.
3. The structure of a protein is very important to its function. This is described by the **primary structure** (the chain of amino acids), the **secondary structure** (formation of α helixes and β-sheets due to hydrogen bonding within the chain), **tertiary structure** (cross-links, especially disulfide bonds, between secondary structures), and **quaternary structure** (formation of multisubunit proteins). The incredible variation in shapes is the basis for the diverse roles proteins play as **enzymes, antibodies,** receptors, and structural components.

2.8 Nucleic Acids: A Program for Genetics

A. **Nucleotides** are the building blocks of nucleic acids. They are composed of a **nitrogen base,** a pentose sugar, and a phosphate. Nitrogen bases are ringed compounds: **adenine (A), guanine (G), cytosine (C), thymine (T),** and **uracil (U).** Pentose sugars may be deoxyribose or ribose, depending on the type of nucleic acid.

B. **Deoxyribonucleic acid (DNA)** is a polymer of nucleotides that occurs as a double-stranded helix with hydrogen bonding between pairs of bases on the helices. It has all of the bases except uracil, and the pentose sugar is deoxyribose. DNA is the master code for a cell's life processes and must be transmitted to the offspring through **replication.**

C. **Ribonucleic acid (RNA)** is a polymer of nucleotides where the sugar is ribose and **uracil** is the replacement base for thymine. It is almost always found single-stranded and is used to express the DNA code into proteins.

D. **Adenosine triphosphate (ATP)** is a nucleotide with 3 phosphates that serves as the energy molecule in cells.

 ## Assess Your Knowledge

Level I. These questions require a working knowledge of the concepts in the chapter and the ability to recall and understand the information you have studied.

Developing a Concept Inventory

Select the correct answer from the answers provided. For questions with blanks, choose the combination of answers that most accurately completes the statement.

1. The smallest unit of matter with unique characteristics is
 a. an electron
 b. a molecule
 c. an atom
 d. a proton

2. The _____ charge of a proton is exactly balanced by the _____ charge of a(n) _____.
 a. negative, positive, electron
 b. positive, neutral, neutron
 c. positive, negative, electron
 d. neutral, negative, electron

3. Electrons move around the nucleus of an atom in pathways called
 a. shells
 b. orbitals
 c. circles
 d. rings

4. Which parts of an element do not vary in number?
 a. electrons
 b. neutrons
 c. protons
 d. All of these vary.

5. If a substance contains two or more elements of different types, it is considered
 a. a compound
 b. a monomer
 c. a molecule
 d. organic

6. Bonds in which atoms share electrons are defined as _____ bonds.
 a. hydrogen
 b. ionic
 c. double
 d. covalent

7. A hydrogen bond can form between _____ adjacent to each other.
 a. two hydrogen atoms
 b. two oxygen atoms
 c. a hydrogen atom and an oxygen atom
 d. negative charges

8. An atom that can donate electrons during a reaction is called
 a. an oxidizing agent
 b. a reducing agent
 c. an ionic agent
 d. an electrolyte

9. In a solution of NaCl and water, NaCl is the _____ and water is the _____.
 a. acid, base
 b. base, acid
 c. solute, solvent
 d. solvent, solute

10. A solution with a pH of 2 _____ than a solution with a pH of 8.
 a. has less H^+
 b. has more H^+
 c. has more OH^-
 d. is less concentrated

11. Fructose is a type of
 a. disaccharide
 b. monosaccharide
 c. polysaccharide
 d. amino acid

12. Bond formation in polysaccharides and polypeptides is accompanied by the removal of a
 a. hydrogen atom
 b. hydroxyl ion
 c. carbon atom
 d. water molecule

13. The monomer unit of polysaccharides such as starch and cellulose is
 a. fructose
 b. glucose
 c. ribose
 d. lactose

14. A phospholipid contains
 a. three fatty acids bound to glycerol
 b. three fatty acids, a glycerol, and a phosphate
 c. two fatty acids and a phosphate bound to glycerol
 d. three cholesterol molecules bound to glycerol

15. Proteins are synthesized by linking amino acids with _____ bonds.
 a. disulfide
 b. glycosidic
 c. peptide
 d. ester

16. The amino acid that accounts for disulfide bonds in the tertiary structure of proteins is
 a. tyrosine
 b. glycine
 c. cysteine
 d. serine

17. DNA is a hereditary molecule that is composed of
 a. deoxyribose, phosphate, and nitrogen bases
 b. deoxyribose, a pentose, and nucleic acids
 c. sugar, proteins, and thymine
 d. adenine, phosphate, and ribose

18. What is meant by the term *DNA replication?*
 a. synthesis of nucleotides
 b. cell division
 c. interpretation of the genetic code
 d. the exact copying of the DNA code into two new molecules

19. Proteins can function as
 a. enzymes
 b. receptors
 c. antibodies
 d. all of these

20. RNA plays an important role in what biological process?
 a. replication
 b. protein synthesis
 c. lipid metabolism
 d. water transport

Case Study Analysis

1. Lactose is a simple carbohydrate. Which other molecules are carbohydrates? (Select all that apply.)
 a. glucose
 b. starch
 c. amino acids
 d. glycogen

2. Bacteria known as coliforms ferment lactose and produce acid and gas as by-products. Where in the body would you expect to find coliforms?
 a. stomach
 b. small intestine
 c. large intestine
 d. esophagus

3. SIBO (small intestinal bacterial overgrowth) is a disorder where bacteria from the large intestine move into the distal portion of the small intestine, where they are not normally found. How do you think a person with SIBO would be affected?

On the Test

These questions will help to prepare you to successfully answer similar questions you'll see on the TEAS (Test of Essential Academic Skills) and NCLEX (National Council Licensure Examination).

1. An atom with an unfilled outer electron shell may be stabilized by
 a. gaining a proton from a nearby atom
 b. donating a neutron to another atom
 c. sharing electrons with another atom
 d. moving an electron from a filled inner shell to an unfilled outer shell

2. Proteins are composed of small subunits called
 a. nucleic acids
 b. transfer RNAs
 c. ribosomes
 d. amino acids

Writing Challenge

For each question, compose a one- or two-paragraph answer that includes the factual information needed to completely address the question. Practice questions can also be used for writing-challenge exercises.

1. Explain this statement: "All compounds are molecules, but not all molecules are compounds." Give an example.

2. What causes atoms to form chemical bonds? Why do some elements not bond readily?

3. Why are some covalent molecules polar and others nonpolar?

4. Explain why some elements are diatomic.

5. Exactly what causes the charges to form on atoms in ionic bonds?

6. Why are hydrogen bonds relatively weak?

7. What kind of substances will be expected to be hydrophilic and hydrophobic, and what makes them so?

8. How can a neutral salt be formed from acids and bases?

9. a. What characteristic of phospholipids makes them essential components of cell membranes?
 b. How are saturated and unsaturated fatty acids different?
 c. Why is the hydrophilic end of phospholipids attracted to water?

10. What makes the amino acids distinctive, and how many of them are there?

11. Why is DNA called a double helix?

12. Describe what occurs in a dehydration synthesis reaction.

13. How is our understanding of microbiology enhanced by a knowledge of chemistry?

Concept Mapping

On Connect you can find an Introduction to Concept Mapping that provides guidance for working with concept maps, along with concept-mapping activities for this chapter.

 ## Application, Analysis, Evaluation, and Synthesis

Level II. These problems go beyond just restating facts and require higher levels of understanding and an ability to interpret, problem solve, transfer knowledge to new situations, create models, and predict outcomes.

Critical Thinking

Critical thinking is the ability to reason and solve problems using facts and concepts. These questions can be approached from a number of angles and, in most cases, they do not have a single correct answer.

1. The "octet rule" in chemistry helps predict the types of bonds that atoms will form. In general, an atom will be most stable if it fills its outer shell of 8 electrons. Atoms with fewer than 4 valence electrons tend to donate electrons and those with more than 4 valence electrons tend to accept additional electrons; those with exactly 4 can do both. Using this rule, determine what category each of the following elements falls into: N, S, C, P, O, H, Ca, Fe, and Mg. (You will need to work out the valence of the atoms.)

2. Predict the kinds of bonds that occur in ammonium (NH_3), phosphate (PO_4), disulfide (S—S), and magnesium chloride ($MgCl_2$). (Use simple models, such as those in figure 2.4.)

3. Work out the following problems:
 a. Will an H bond form between H_3C—CH═O and H_2O? Draw a simple figure to support your answer.
 b. Draw the following molecules and determine which are polar: Cl_2, NH_3, CH_4.
 c. What is the pH of a solution with a concentration of 0.00001 moles/ml (M) of H^+?
 d. What is the pH of a solution with a concentration of 0.00001 moles/ml (M) of OH^-?
 e. Draw the atomic structure of magnesium and predict what kinds of bonds it will make.
 f. What kind of ion would you expect magnesium to make on the basis of its valence?

4. Distinguish between polar and ionic compounds.

5. Is galactose an aldehyde or a ketone sugar?

6. a. How many water molecules are released when a triglyceride is formed?
 b. How many peptide bonds are in a hexapeptide?

7. Observe figure 2.27 and explain why adenine forms hydrogen bonds only with thymine and why cytosine forms them only with guanine.

8. For a and b, explain your choice.
 a. Is butter an example of a saturated or an unsaturated fat?
 b. Is olive oil an example of a saturated or an unsaturated fat?
 c. Explain why sterols like cholesterol can add "stiffness" to membranes that contain them.

Visual Assessment

1. Explain why the oil does not evenly disperse through the water?

Narcisopa/Shutterstock

2. Using figure 2.18 as your basis for comparison, speculate which type of molecule is being shown and give a reason for the microscopic appearance seen here.

50 μm

Courtesy of Professor Robert J. Linhardt, Rensselaer Polytechnic Institute

CHAPTER

3

Tools of the Laboratory:
Methods of Studying Microorganisms

In This Chapter...

3.1 Methods of Microbial Investigation

3.2 The Microscope: Window on an Invisible Realm
- Magnification and Microscope Design
- Variations on the Optical Microscope
- Electron Microscopy

3.3 Preparing Specimens for Optical Microscopes
- Fresh, Living Preparations
- Fixed, Stained Smears

3.4 Additional Features of the Six "I"s
- Inoculation, Growth, and Identification of Cultures
- Isolation Techniques
- Identification Techniques

3.5 Media: The Foundations of Culturing
- Types of Media
- Physical States of Media
- Chemical Content of Media
- Media to Suit Every Function

(burrito): John E. Kelly/Getty Images; (Bacillus species Malachite Green spore stain):
Source: Larry Stauffer/Oregon State Public/CDC; (Isolating bacteria - streak plate): Kathy Park Talaro;
(urinary pathogen culture): Kathy Park Talaro

CASE STUDY Part 1

Would You Like Salsa and Typhoid with Your Burrito?

Typhoid fever is caused by infection with *Salmonella enterica*, serovar Typhi—often shortened to *Salmonella* Typhi—the most worrisome **strain** of *Salmonella*. Rare in the United States, *Salmonella* Typhi is **endemic** in many countries, where it is responsible for 22 million infections and 200,000 deaths each year. Of the 5,700 cases of typhoid fever reported yearly in the United States, nearly all are seen in people who have recently travelled internationally. Humans are the only **reservoir** for *Salmonella* Typhi, and the bacterium may be **transmitted** when feces from an infected person contacts food or water.

Typhoid fever is classified as a **notifiable disease,** meaning that diagnosed infections are reported to state and local health departments, who in turn report the information to the Centers for Disease Control and Prevention. On September 11, 2015, a single case of typhoid fever was reported to the Colorado Department of Public Health and Environment (CDPHE). Because this patient had recently returned from a trip abroad, the infection was at first thought to be travel-associated, but when a second case was identified, in a patient with no recent travel, the CDPHE initiated an investigation with three goals: 1) to determine whether these cases represented part of a larger **outbreak,** 2) to identify common **exposure** sources, and 3) to stop **transmission** of the bacterium.

The patients first displayed symptoms—fever, headache, constipation, chills, myalgia (pain), and malaise (fatigue)—on September 2 and 20, respectively, and initial questioning revealed no immediate epidemiological link; the patients did not know one another, and lived 6 miles apart. Investigators questioned each patient using the **Salmonella National Hypothesis Generating Questionnaire,** a lengthy survey with questions including past travel, recent meals, hospital stays, and animal contact. Examination of credit card receipts, frequent-buyer cards, and social media interactions revealed that the two patients had fresh produce purchases from the same grocery store and had six common restaurant exposures. On October 19, CDPHE was notified of a third person who had tested positive for *Salmonella* Typhi infection, with symptoms beginning September 15. An investigation similar to that used for the first two cases was undertaken and revealed that all three patients had eaten at the same Mexican restaurant where food was prepared from fresh ingredients, the only **epidemiological link** between all three cases.

- *What specimens do you think investigators collected in this case?*

- *Why would isolation be so important in a case like this?*

To continue the Case Study, go to Case Study Part 2 at the end of the chapter.

(Salmonella typhimurium): Moredun Animal Health LTD/Science Photo Library/Alamy Stock Photo

3.1 Methods of Microbial Investigation

 Learn

1. Explain what unique characteristics of microorganisms make them challenging subjects for study.
2. Briefly outline the processes and purposes of the six types of procedures that are used in handling, maintaining, and studying microorganisms.

Biologists studying large organisms like animals and plants can, for the most part, immediately see and differentiate their experimental subjects from the surrounding environment and from one another. They can use their senses of sight, smell, hearing, and even touch to detect and evaluate identifying characteristics and to keep track of growth and developmental changes.

Because microbiologists cannot rely as much as other scientists on senses other than sight, they are confronted by some unique problems. First, most habitats (such as the soil and the human mouth) harbor microbes in complex associations. It is often necessary to separate the organisms from one another so they can be identified and studied. Second, to maintain and keep track of such small research subjects, microbiologists usually will need to grow them under artificial conditions. A third difficulty in working with microbes is that they are not visible to the naked eye. This, coupled with their wide distribution, means that undesirable ones can be inconspicuously introduced into an experiment, where they may cause misleading results.

To deal with the challenges of their tiny and sometimes elusive targets, microbiologists have developed several procedures for investigating and characterizing microorganisms. These techniques can be summed up succinctly as the **six "I"s: inoculation, incubation, isolation, inspection, information gathering,** and **identification (table 3.1, figure 3.1).** Depending on the purposes of the particular investigator, these may be performed in different combinations and orders, but together they serve as the major tools of the microbiologist's trade. As novice microbiologists, most of you will be learning some basic microscope, inoculation, culturing, and identification techniques. Many professional researchers use more advanced investigation and identification techniques that may not even require growth or absolute isolation of the microbe in culture. If you examine the example from the Case Study in chapter 1, you will notice that the researchers used only some of the 6 "I"s, whereas the case study in this chapter includes all of them in some form.

The first four sections of this chapter cover some of the essential concepts that revolve around the six "I"s, but not necessarily in the exact order presented in table 3.1. Microscopes are so important to microbiological inquiry that we start out with the subject of microscopes, magnification, and staining techniques. This is followed by culturing procedures and media.

Quick Search

Watch "A Tour of the Microbiology Lab" on YouTube to see the daily work performed there.

 Practice SECTION 3.1

1. Name the notable features of microorganisms that have created a need for the specialized tools of microbiology.
2. In one sentence each, define what is involved in each of the six "I"s.

TABLE 3.1	An Overview of Microbiology Techniques	
Technique	**Process Involves**	**Purpose and Outcome**
Inoculation	Placing a sample into a container of medium that supplies nutrients for growth and is the first stage in culturing	To increase visibility; makes it possible to handle and manage microbes in an artificial environment and begin to analyze what the sample may contain
Incubation	Exposing the inoculated medium to optimal growth conditions, generally for a few hours to days	To promote multiplication and produce the actual culture. An increase in microbe numbers will provide the higher quantities needed for further testing
Isolation	Methods for separating individual microbes and achieving isolated colonies that can be readily distinguished from one another macroscopically*	To make additional cultures from single colonies to ensure they are pure; that is, containing only a single species of microbe for further observation and testing
Inspection	Observing cultures macroscopically for appearance of growth and microscopically for appearance of cells	To analyze initial characteristics of microbes in samples. Stains of cells may reveal information on cell type and morphology.
Information gathering	Testing of cultures using procedures that analyze biochemical and enzyme characteristics, immunologic reactions, drug sensitivity, and genetic makeup	To provide specific data and generate an overall profile of the microbes. These test results and descriptions will become key determinants in the last category, identification.
Identification	Analysis of collected data to help support a final determination of the types of microbes present in the original sample; this is accomplished in a variety of ways	This lays the groundwork for further research into the nature and roles of these microbes; it can also provide numerous applications in infection diagnosis, food safety, biotechnology, and microbial ecology

*Observable to the unaided or naked eye. This term usually applies to the cultural level of study.

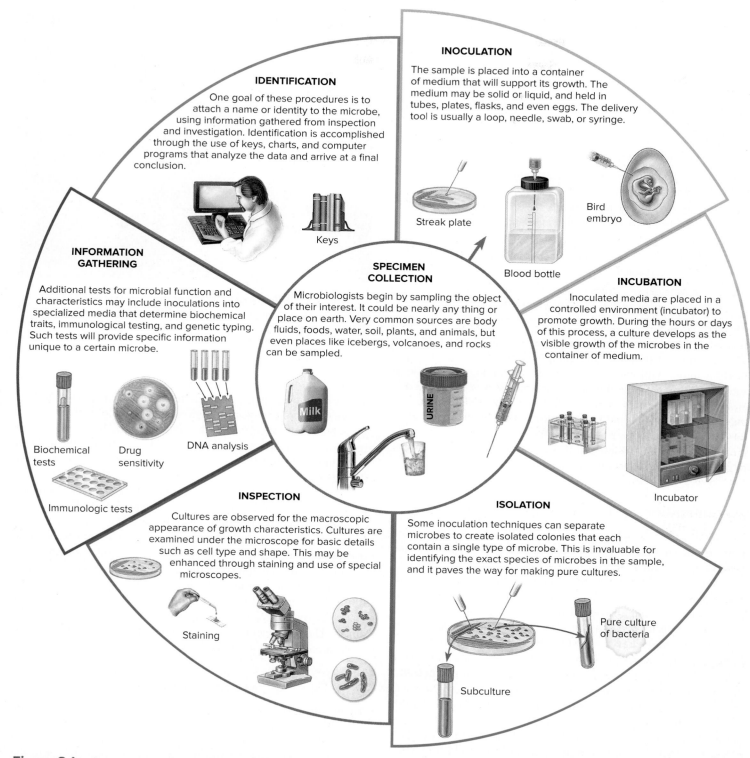

Figure 3.1 **An overview of some general laboratory techniques carried out by microbiologists.** The six "I"s. Procedures start at the central "hub" of specimen collection and flow from there to inoculation, incubation, inspection, and so on. But not all steps are always performed, nor do they necessarily proceed in exactly this order. Some investigators go directly from sampling to microscopic inspection, or from sampling to DNA testing. Others may require only inoculation and incubation on special media or test systems. See table 3.1 for a brief description of each procedure, its purpose, and intended outcome.

3.2 The Microscope: Window on an Invisible Realm

 Learn

3. Describe the basic plan of an optical microscope, and differentiate between magnification and resolution.

4. Explain how the images are formed, along with the role of light and the different powers of lenses.

5. Indicate how the resolving power is determined and how resolution affects image visibility.

6. Differentiate between the major types of optical microscopes, their illumination sources, image appearance, and uses.

7. Describe the operating features of electron microscopes and how they differ from optical microscopes in illumination source, magnification, resolution, and image appearance.

8. Differentiate between transmission and scanning electron microsopes in image formation and appearance.

Imagine **Leeuwenhoek**'s excitement and wonder when he first viewed a drop of rainwater and glimpsed an amazing microscopic world teeming with unearthly creatures. Beginning microbiology students still experience this sensation, and even experienced microbiologists remember their first view. The microbial existence is indeed another world, but it would remain largely uncharted without an essential tool: the microscope. Your efforts in exploring microbes will be more meaningful if you understand some essentials of **microscopy*** and specimen preparation.

Magnification and Microscope Design

The two key characteristics of a reliable microscope are **magnification,*** the ability to make objects appear enlarged, and **resolving power,** the ability to show detail.

A discovery by early microscopists that spurred the advancement of microbiology was that a clear glass sphere could act as a lens to magnify small objects. Magnification in most microscopes results from a complex interaction between visible light waves and the curvature of the lens. When a beam or ray of light transmitted through air strikes and passes through the convex surface of glass, it experiences some degree of **refraction,*** defined as the bending or change in the angle of the light ray as it passes through a medium such as a lens. The greater the difference in the composition of the two substances the light passes between, the more pronounced the refraction. When an object is placed a certain distance from the spherical lens and illuminated with light, an optical replica, or **image,** of it is formed by the refracted light. Depending upon the size and curvature of the lens, the image appears enlarged to a particular degree, which is called its power of magnification and is usually identified with a

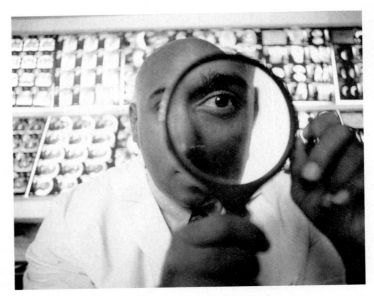

Figure 3.2 **Effects of magnification.** Demonstration of the magnification and image-forming capacity of clear glass "lenses." Given a proper source of illumination, a magnifying glass can deliver 2 to 10 times magnification.
John Foxx/Getty Images

number combined with × (read "times"). This behavior of light is evident if one looks through an everyday object such as a glass ball or a magnifying glass (**figure 3.2**). It is basic to the function of all optical, or light, microscopes, though many of them have additional features that define, refine, and increase the size of the image.

The first microscopes were **simple,** meaning they contained just a single magnifying lens and a few working parts. Examples of this type of microscope are a magnifying glass, a hand lens, and Leeuwenhoek's basic little tool shown earlier in figure 1.9a. Among the refinements that led to the development of today's **compound (two-lens) microscope** were the addition of a second magnifying lens system, a lamp in the base to give off visible light and **illuminate*** the specimen, and a special lens called the **condenser** that converges or focuses the rays of light to a single point on the object. The fundamental parts of a modern compound light microscope are illustrated in **figure 3.3a.**

Principles of Light Microscopy

To be most effective, a microscope should provide adequate magnification, resolution, and clarity of image. Magnification of the object or specimen by a compound microscope occurs in two phases. The first lens in this system (the one closest to the specimen) is the objective lens, and the second (the one closest to the eye) is the ocular lens, or eyepiece (**figure 3.3b**). The objective forms the initial image of the specimen, called the **real image.** When the real image is projected to the plane of the eyepiece, the ocular lens magnifies it to produce a second image,

* *microscopy* (mye-kraw′-skuh-pee) Gr. The science that studies microscope techniques.
* *magnification* (mag′-nih-fih-kay″-shun) L. *magnus,* great, and *ficere,* to make.
* *refraction* (ree-frakt′, ree-frak′-shun) L. *refringere,* to break apart.

* *illuminate* (ill-oo′-mih-nayt) L. *illuminatus,* to light up.

the **virtual image.** The virtual image is the one that will be received by the eye and converted to a retinal and visual image. The magnifying power of the objective alone usually ranges from 4× to 100×, and the power of the ocular alone ranges from 10× to 20×. The total power of magnification of the final image formed by the combined lenses is a product of the separate powers of the two lenses:

Power of Objective ×	*Usual Power* =	*Total*
	of Ocular	*Magnification*
4× scanning objective	10× =	40×
10× low-power objective	10× =	100×
40× high dry objective	10× =	400×
100× oil immersion objective	10× =	1,000×

(a) (b)

Figure 3.3 **(a) Light pathway and image formation in light microscopes.** Light formed by the lamp is directed through the lamp filter and into the opening of the iris diaphragm; the condenser gathers the light rays and focuses them into a single point on the specimen; an enlarged image of the specimen—the real image—is next formed by the objective lens. This image is not seen but is projected into the ocular lens, which forms a final level of magnification called the virtual image. This image is observed in the field of view by the eye and perceived by the brain. Note that the lenses reverse the image and flip it upside down. **(b) The main parts of a microscope.** This is a compound light microscope with two oculars (binocular) for viewing. Such microscopes usually have four objective lenses, a mechanical stage to move the specimen, a condenser, an iris diaphragm, and a built-in light source (lamp).
(b): Barry Chess

Microscopes are equipped with a nosepiece holding three or more objectives that can be rotated into position as needed. The power of the ocular usually remains constant for a given microscope. Depending on the power of the ocular, the total magnification of standard light microscopes can vary from 40× with the lowest-power objective (called the scanning objective) to 2,000×[1] with the highest-power objective (the oil immersion objective).

Resolution: Distinguishing Magnified Objects Clearly In addition to magnification, a microscope must have adequate **resolution,** or **resolving power.** Resolution defines the capacity of an optical system to distinguish two adjacent objects or points from one another. For example, at a distance of 25 cm (10 in), the lens in the human eye can resolve two small objects as separate points just as long as the two objects are no closer than 0.2 mm apart. The eye examination given by optometrists is in fact a test of the resolving power of the human eye for various-size letters read at a distance of 20 feet. Because microorganisms are extremely small and usually very close together, they will not be seen with clarity or any degree of detail unless the microscope's lenses can resolve them.

A simple equation in the form of a fraction expresses the main mathematical factors that influence the expression of resolving power.

$$\text{Resolving power (RP)} = \frac{\text{Wavelength of light in nm}}{2 \times \text{Numerical aperture of objective lens}}$$

From this equation, it is evident that the resolving power is a function of the wavelength of light that forms the image, along with certain characteristics of the objective. The light source for optical microscopes consists of a band of colored wavelengths in the visible spectrum. The shortest visible wavelengths are in the violet-blue portion of the spectrum (400 nm), and the longest are in the red portion (750 nm). Because the wavelength must pass between the objects that are being resolved, shorter wavelengths (in the 400–500 nm range) will provide better resolution **(figure 3.4).**

The other factor influencing resolution is the **numerical aperture (NA),** a mathematical constant derived from the physical structure of the lens. This number represents the angle of light produced by refraction and is a measure of the quantity of light gathered by the lens. Each objective has a fixed numerical aperture value ranging from 0.1 in the lowest-power lens to approximately 1.25 in the highest-power (oil immersion) lens. Lenses with higher NAs provide better resolving power because they increase the angle of refraction and widen the cone of light entering the lens. For the oil immersion lens to arrive at its maximum resolving capacity, a drop of oil must be inserted between the tip of the lens and the specimen on the glass slide. Because immersion oil has the same optical qualities as glass, it prevents refractive loss that normally occurs as peripheral light passes from the slide into the air; this property effectively increases the numerical aperture **(figure 3.5).** There is an absolute limitation to resolution in optical microscopes, which can be demonstrated by calculating

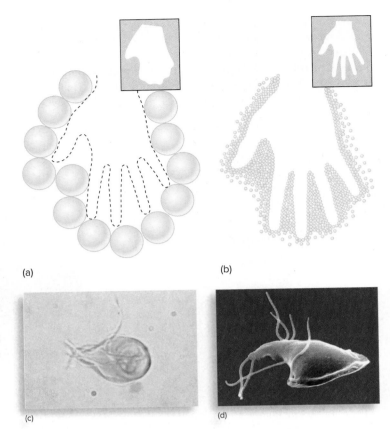

(a) (b)

(c) (d)

Figure 3.4 Effect of wavelength on resolution. A simple model demonstrates how the wavelength influences the resolving power of a microscope. Here, an outline of a hand represents the object being illuminated, and two different-sized beads represent the wavelengths of light. **(a)** The longer waves are too large to penetrate between the finer spaces, and they produce a fuzzy, undetailed image. **(b)** Shorter waves are small enough to enter small spaces and produce a much more detailed image that is recognizable as a hand. **(c)** The longer waves used by the light microscope produce an indistinct image of the protozoan parasite *Giardia.* **(d)** The much shorter waves of electrons used by the scanning electron microscope produce an image of the same organism with far greater detail.
(c): *Source:* Dr. Mae Melvin/CDC; (d): *Source:* Dr. Stan Erlandsen; Dr. Dennis Feely/CDC

the resolution of the oil immersion lens using a blue-green wavelength of light:

$$\text{RP} = \frac{500 \text{ nm}}{2 \times 1.25}$$
$$= 200 \text{ nm (or } 0.2 \text{ } \mu\text{m)}$$

In practical terms, this calculation means that the oil immersion lens can resolve any cell or cell part as long as it is at least 0.2 μm in diameter and that it can resolve two adjacent objects as long as they are no closer than 0.2 μm **(figure 3.6).** In general, organisms that are 0.5 μm or more in diameter are readily seen. This includes fungi and protozoa and some of their internal structures, and most bacteria. However, a few bacteria and most viruses are too small to be resolved by the optical microscope and require electron microscopy. The factor that most limits the clarity of a microscope's image is its resolving power. Even if a light microscope were designed to magnify several

1. Some microscopes are equipped with 20× oculars or special annuli that can double their magnification.

Figure 3.5 **Workings of an oil immersion lens.** To maximize its resolving power, an oil immersion lens (the one with highest magnification) must have a drop of oil placed at its tip. This transmits a continuous cone of light from the condenser to the objective, thereby increasing the amount of light and, consequently, the numerical aperture. Without oil, some of the peripheral light that passes through the specimen is scattered into the air or onto the glass slide; this scattering decreases resolution.

thousand times, its resolving power could not be increased, and the image it produced would be enlarged but blurry.

Despite this limit, small improvements to resolution are possible. One is to utilize blue light, keeping the wavelength at the shortest possible value. Another comes from maximizing the numerical aperture. That is the effect of adding oil to the immersion lens, which effectively increases the NA from 1.25 to 1.4 and improves the resolving power to 0.17 μm.

Variations on the Optical Microscope

Optical microscopes that use visible light can be described by the nature of their **field of view,** or **field,** which is the circular area

observed through the ocular lens. With special adaptations in lenses, condensers, and light sources, four special types of microscopes can be described: bright-field, dark-field, phase-contrast, and interference. A fifth type of optical microscope, the fluorescence microscope, uses ultraviolet radiation as the illuminating source, and a sixth, the confocal microscope, uses a laser beam. Each of these microscopes is adapted for viewing specimens in a particular way, as described in the next sections and summarized in **table 3.2.** Refer back to figure 1.4 for size comparisons of microbes and molecules.

Bright-Field Microscopy

The bright-field microscope is the most widely used type of light microscope. A bright-field microscope forms its image when light is transmitted through the specimen. The specimen, being denser and more opaque than its surroundings, absorbs some of this light, and the rest of the light is transmitted directly up through the ocular into the field. As a result, the specimen will produce an image that is darker than the surrounding brightly illuminated field. The bright-field microscope is a multipurpose instrument that can be used for both live, unstained material and preserved, stained material. The bright-field image is compared with that of other microscopes in table 3.2.

Dark-Field Microscopy

A bright-field microscope can be adapted as a dark-field microscope by adding a special disc called a *stop* to the condenser. The stop blocks all light from entering the objective lens except peripheral light that is reflected off the sides of the specimen itself. The resulting image is brightly illuminated specimens surrounded by a dark (black) field (table 3.2). The most effective use of dark-field microscopy is to visualize living cells that would be distorted by drying or heat or that cannot be stained with the usual methods. It

Figure 3.6 **Effect of resolution on image visibility.** Comparison of objects that would not be resolvable versus those that would be resolvable under oil immersion at 1,000× magnification. Note that in addition to differentiating two adjacent things, good resolution means being able to observe an object with clarity.

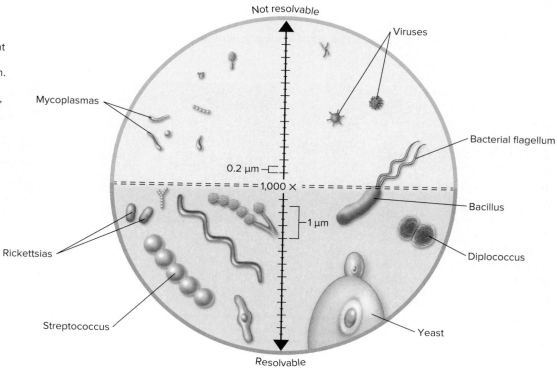

TABLE 3.2 **Comparisons of Types of Microscopy**

A. Comparative Images from Optical Microscopes

The subject here is amoeba examined at 400× with four types of microscopes. Notice the differences in the appearance of the field and the degree of detail shown in the four methods.

I. Microscopes with visible light illumination
Maximum effective magnification = 1,000× to 2,000×*.
Maximum resolution = 0.2 μm.

Bright-field microscope

Common multipurpose microscope for live and preserved stained specimens; specimen is dark, field is white; provides fair cellular detail.

Dark-field microscope

Best for observing live, unstained specimens; specimen is bright, field is black; provides outline of specimen with reduced internal cellular detail.

Phase-contrast microscope

Used for live specimens; specimen is contrasted against gray background; excellent for internal cellular detail.

Differential interference contrast microscope

Provides very detailed, highly contrasting, three-dimensional images of live specimens.

B. Modifications of Optical Microscopes with Specialized Functions

II. Microscopes with ultraviolet or laser beam illumination
Maximum effective magnification = 1,000× to 2,000×*.
Maximum resolution = 0.2 μm**.

Fluorescent microscope

Cells of *Yersinia pestis*, the bacterium responsible for plague, viewed at 1,500×. Ultraviolet light is used to illuminate the specimen. Antibodies labeled with fluorescent dyes emit visible light only if the antibody recognizes and binds to the cell. The specificity of this technique makes it a superior diagnostic tool.

Confocal microscope

Paramecium, 1,500×, stained by fluorescent dyes, and scanned by a laser beam, form multiple images that are combined into a three-dimensional image. Confocal microscopes may utilize visible or ultraviolet light. Note the fine detail of cilia and organelles.

C. Electron Microscopes Image Objects with a Beam of Electrons

III. Microscopes use a beam of electrons
Maximum effective magnification TEM = 1,000,000×.
Maximum effective magnification SEM = 650,000×.
Maximum resolution TEM = 0.5 nm.
Maximum resolution SEM = 10 nm.

Transmission electron microscope (TEM)

Influenza virus particle viewed with a transmission electron microscope (TEM). This type of microscope provides the best resolution and can be used to view the internal structure of cells and viruses.

Colorized transmission electron microscope image

Colorized version of the same TEM image. Electron microscopes produce only black-and-white images, but these are often artificially colored, with the aid of a computer.

Scanning electron microscope (SEM)

Artificially colorized scanning electron microscope (SEM) image of Middle East respiratory syndrome Coronavirus (MERS CoV) viral particles (colored yellow) on the surface of a eukaryotic cell (colored blue). The electron beam scans over the surface of the cell to produce a three-dimensional image.

*The 2,000× maximum is achieved through the use of a 20× ocular or 2× annulus.
**Three chemists recently developed a super-resolved fluorescent microscope that can resolve to 50 nm (0.05 μm).

(A1–2): Lisa Burgess/McGraw-Hill Education; (A3): Stephen Durr; (A4): micro_photo/Getty Images; (B1): *Source:* Dr. Sherif Zaki; Dr. Kathi Tatti; Elizabeth White/CDC; (B2): Anne Fleury; (C1–C2): *Source:* Cynthia Goldsmith/CDC; (C3): *Source:* National Institute of Allergy and Infectious Diseases (NIAID)/CDC

can outline the organism's shape and permit rapid recognition of swimming cells that may appear in fresh specimens, but it does not reveal fine internal details.

Phase-Contrast and Interference Microscopy

If similar objects made of clear glass, ice, and transparent plastic are immersed in the same container of water, an observer would have difficulty telling them apart because they have similar optical properties. In the same way, internal components of a live, unstained cell also lack sufficient contrast to be distinguished readily. The phase-contrast microscope contains devices that transform the subtle changes in light waves passing through the specimen into differences in light intensity. For example, denser cell parts such as organelles alter the pathway of light to a greater extent than less dense regions such as the cytoplasm, creating contrast. The amount of internal detail visible by this method is greater than by either bright-field or dark-field methods (table 3.2). The phase-contrast microscope is most useful for observing intracellular structures such as bacterial spores, granules, and organelles, as well as the locomotor structures of eukaryotic cells.

Like the phase-contrast microscope, the **differential interference contrast (DIC)** microscope provides a detailed view of unstained, live specimens by manipulating the light. But this microscope has additional refinements that can add contrasting colors to the image. DIC microscopes produce extremely well-defined images that are often vividly colored and appear three-dimensional (table 3.2).

Scanning Confocal Microscopes

Simple optical microscopes may be unable to form a clear image at higher magnifications, because samples are often too thick for conventional lenses to focus all levels of cells simultaneously. This is especially true of larger cells with complex internal structures. Instead of using traditional illumination, *scanning confocal microscopes* use a laser beam of light to scan various depths in the specimen and deliver a sharp image, focusing on just a single plane. This produces an image that is a high-definition "slice" of a sample. A computer is then used to assemble the slices into a high-resolution, three-dimensional image. It is most often used on flourescent-stained specimens, but it can also be used to visualize live unstained cells and tissues (table 3.2).

Fluorescence Microscopy

The fluorescence microscope utilizes ultraviolet light as opposed to visible light. When a sample is suspected of containing a specific microorganism, antibodies—immunological proteins that recognize and bind to specific cells or viruses—are added to the sample. Antibodies, which are chemically bound to a fluorescent dye, will attach themselves to the sample if it is recognized. The fluorescent microscope then bombards the sample with ultraviolet light, causing the bound antibodies to fluoresce, converting invisible ultraviolet light to visible light. Depending on the dye used, specimens produce intense blue, yellow, green, orange, or red images against a dark field. Fluorescent antibodies can be used to identify the causative agents in such diseases as syphilis, chlamydia, trichomoniasis, herpes, and influenza. **Figure 3.7** displays the results of a fluorescent antibody technique used to highlight the spirochete of syphilis. Fluorescent microscopy

Figure 3.7 Fluorescent staining of a sample of *Treponema pallidum,* the causative agent of syphilis. The specific fluorescent antibodies that attach only to the pathogen and fluoresce a bright green make it a valuable diagnostic stain. Note the spiral nature of the cells (1,000×).
Source: Russell/CDC

can be handy for locating specific microbes in complex mixtures because only those cells targeted by the technique will fluoresce.

Electron Microscopy

If conventional light microscopes are our windows on the microscopic world, then the electron microscope (EM) is our window on the tiniest details of that world. Unlike light microscopes, the electron microscope forms an image with a beam of electrons that can be made to travel in wavelike patterns when accelerated to high speeds. These waves are 100,000 times shorter than the waves of visible light. Knowing that resolving power is a function of wavelength makes it evident that the RP fraction and number will become very small. Indeed, it is possible to resolve atoms with an electron microscope, even though the practical resolution for most biological applications is approximately 0.5 nm. The degree of resolution allows magnification to be extremely high—usually between 5,000× and 1,000,000× for biological specimens and up to 5,000,000× in some applications. Its capacity for magnification and resolution makes the EM an invaluable tool for studying the finest structure of cells and viruses. If not for electron microscopes, our understanding of biological structure and function would still be in its early theoretical stages.

In fundamental ways, the electron microscope is similar to the optical microscope. It employs components analogous to those in light microscopy **(table 3.3)**. For instance, it magnifies in stages by means of two lens systems, and it has a condensing lens, a specimen holder, and a focusing apparatus. Otherwise, the two types have numerous differences (table 3.3). An electron gun aims its beam through a vacuum to ring-shaped electromagnets that focus this beam on the specimen. Specimens must be pretreated with chemicals or dyes to increase contrast and usually cannot be observed in a live state. The enlarged image is displayed on a viewing screen or photographed for further study rather than being observed directly through an eyepiece. Because images produced

TABLE 3.3	Comparison of Light Microscopes and Electron Microscopes	
Characteristic	**Light or Optical**	**Electron (Transmission)**
Useful magnification	2,000×*	1,000,000× or more
Maximum resolution	200 nm (0.2 μm)	0.5 nm
Image produced by	Light rays	Electron beam
Image focused by	Glass objective lens	Electromagnetic objective lenses
Image viewed through	Glass ocular lens	Fluorescent screen
Specimen placed on	Glass slide	Copper mesh
Specimen may be alive	Yes	Usually not
Specimen requires special stains or treatment	Depends on technique	Yes
Shows natural color	Yes	No

*This maximum requires a 20× ocular.

by electrons lack color, electron micrographs (a micrograph is a photograph of a microscopic object) are always shades of black, gray, and white. The color-enhanced micrographs have computer-added color.

Two general forms of EM are the **transmission electron microscope (TEM)** and the **scanning electron microscope (SEM)** (see table 3.2). Transmission electron microscopes are the method of choice for viewing the detailed structure of cells and viruses. This microscope produces its image by transmitting electrons through the specimen. Because electrons cannot readily penetrate thick preparations, the specimen must be stained or coated with metals that will increase image contrast and sectioned into extremely thin slices (20–100 nm thick). The electrons passing through the specimen travel to the fluorescent screen and display a pattern or image. The darker and lighter areas of the image correspond to more and less dense parts on the specimen **(figure 3.8a).** The TEM can also be used to produce negative images and shadow casts of whole microbes (see figure 6.3).

The scanning electron microscope provides some of the most dramatic and realistic images in existence. This instrument can create an extremely detailed three-dimensional view of all things biological—from dental plaque to tapeworm heads. To produce its images, the SEM bombards the surface of a whole, metal-coated specimen with electrons while scanning back and forth over it. A shower of electrons deflected from the surface is picked up with great accuracy by a sophisticated detector, and the electron pattern is displayed as an image on a monitor screen. The contours of the specimens resolved with scanning electron micrography are very revealing and often surprising. Areas that look smooth and flat with the light microscope display intriguing surface features with the SEM **(figure 3.8b).** Improved technology has continued to refine electron microscopes and to develop variations on the basic plan. Some inventive relatives of the EM are the scanning probe microscope and atomic force microscope.

Practice SECTION 3.2

3. Differentiate between the concepts of magnification, refraction, and resolution and explain how they contribute to the clarity of an image.
4. Briefly explain how an image is made and magnified.
5. On the basis of the formula for resolving power, explain why a smaller RP value is preferred to a larger one, and explain what it means in practical terms if the resolving power is 1.0 μm.
6. What adjustments can improve a microscope's resolution?
7. Compare bright-field, dark-field, phase-contrast, confocal, and fluorescence microscopy as to field appearance, specimen appearance, light source, and uses.
8. Compare and contrast the optical compound microscope with the electron microscope.
9. Why is the resolution so superior in the electron microscope?
10. Compare the way that the image is formed in the TEM and the SEM.

(a)

(b)

Figure 3.8 Micrographs from two types of electron microscopes. (a) Colorized TEM image of the H1N1 influenza virus, displaying its internal contents. This was a new strain of virus first observed in 2009. **(b)** Colorized SEM image of two methicillin-resistant *Staphylococcus aureus* (MRSA) bacteria in the process of being phagocytized by a human neutrophil.
(a, b): *Source:* National Institute of Allergy and Infectious Diseases (NIAID)/CDC

3.3 Preparing Specimens for Optical Microscopes

 Learn

9. Explain the basic differences between fresh and fixed preparations for microscopy and how they are used.

10. Define *dyes* and describe the basic chemistry behind the process of staining.

11. Differentiate between negative and positive staining, giving examples.

12. Distinguish between simple, differential, and structural stains, including their applications.

13. Describe the process of Gram staining and how its results can aid the identification process.

A specimen for optical microscopy is generally prepared by mounting a sample on a suitable glass slide that sits on the stage between the condenser and the objective lens. The manner in which a slide specimen, or mount, is prepared depends upon (1) the condition of the specimen, either in a living or preserved state; (2) the aims of the examiner, whether to observe overall structure, identify the microorganisms, or see movement; and (3) the type of microscopy available, whether it is bright-field, dark-field, phase-contrast, or fluorescence.

Fresh, Living Preparations

Live samples of microorganisms are used to prepare **wet mounts** so that they can be observed as near to their natural state as possible. The cells are suspended in a suitable fluid (water, broth, saline) that temporarily maintains viability and provides space and a medium for locomotion. A wet mount consists of a drop or two of the culture placed on a slide and overlaid with a cover glass. Although this preparation is quick and easy to make, it has certain disadvantages. The cover glass can damage larger cells, and the slide is very susceptible to drying and can contaminate the handler's fingers.

A more satisfactory alternative is the **hanging drop slide** (below) made with a special concave (depression) slide, an adhesive or sealant, and a coverslip from which a small drop of sample is suspended. These types of short-term mounts provide a true assessment of the size, shape, arrangement, color, and motility of cells. Even greater cellular detail can be observed with phase-contrast or interference microscopy.

Fixed, Stained Smears

A more permanent mount for long-term study can be obtained by preparing fixed, stained specimens. The smear technique, developed by Robert Koch more than 100 years ago, consists of spreading onto a slide a thin film made from a liquid suspension of cells and air-drying it. Next, the air-dried **smear** is usually heated gently by a process called **heat fixation** that simultaneously kills the specimen and secures it to the slide. Fixation also preserves various cellular components in a natural state with minimal distortion. Some types of fixation are performed with chemicals such as alcohol and formalin.

The unstained cells of a fixed smear are indistinct and require staining to create contrast and make biological features stand out. Staining is any procedure that applies colored chemicals called dyes to specimens. Dyes impart a color to cells or cell parts by becoming affixed to them through a chemical reaction. In general, they are classified as **basic** (cationic) **dyes,** which have a positive charge, or **acidic** (anionic) **dyes,** which have a negative charge.

Negative Versus Positive Staining

Two basic types of staining technique are used, depending upon how a dye reacts with the specimen (summarized in **table 3.4**). Most procedures involve a **positive stain,** in which the dye actually sticks to cells and gives them color. A **negative stain,** on the other hand, is just the reverse. The dye does not color the specimens but

TABLE 3.4	Comparison of Positive and Negative Stains	
	Positive Staining	**Negative Staining**
Appearance of cell	Colored by dye	Clear and colorless
Background	Not stained (generally white)	Stained (dark gray or black)
Dyes employed	Basic dyes: Crystal violet, Methylene blue, Safranin, Malachite green	Acidic dyes: Nigrosin, India ink
Subtypes of stains	Several types: Simple stain; Differential stains: Gram stain, Acid-fast stain, Spore stain; Structural stains: One type of capsule stain, Flagella stain, Spore stain, Granules stain, Nucleic acid stain	Few types: Capsule, Spore, Negative stain of *Bacillus anthracis,* showing its capsule

(bottom): *Source:* Larry Stauffer, Oregon State Public Health Laboratory/CDC

dries around its outer boundary, forming a silhouette. Nigrosin (a blue-black dye) and India ink (a black suspension of carbon particles) are the dyes most commonly used for negative staining. The cells themselves do not stain because these dyes are negatively charged and are repelled by the negatively charged surface of the cells. The value of negative staining is its relative simplicity and the reduced shrinkage or distortion of cells, as the smear is not heat fixed. A quick assessment can thus be made regarding cellular size, shape, and arrangement. Negative staining is also used to accentuate the capsule that surrounds certain bacteria and yeasts **(figure 3.9)**.

Staining Reactions of Dyes

Because many microbial cells lack contrast, it is necessary to use dyes to observe their detailed structure and identify them. Dyes are colored compounds carrying double-bonded groups such as C═O, C═N, and N═N. When these groups are illuminated, they emit

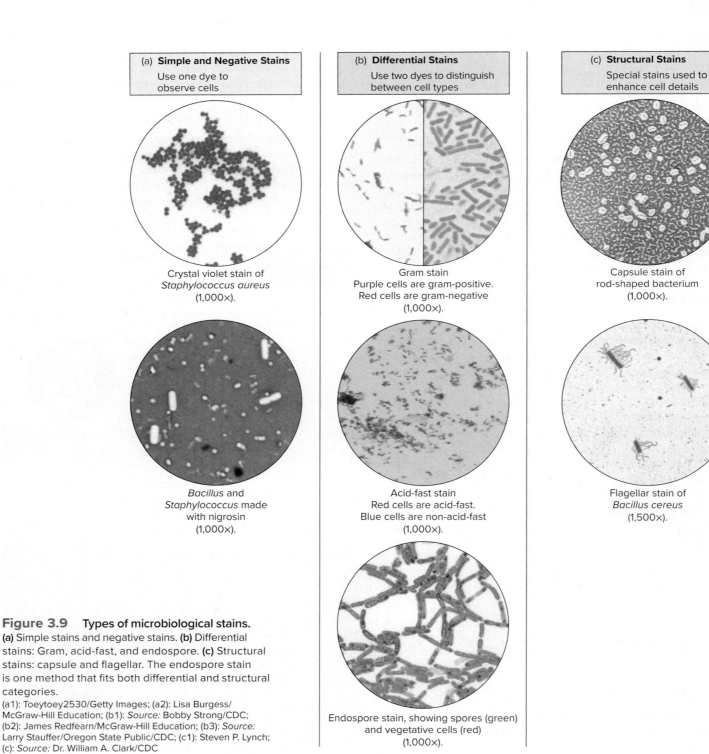

(a) **Simple and Negative Stains**	(b) **Differential Stains**	(c) **Structural Stains**
Use one dye to observe cells	Use two dyes to distinguish between cell types	Special stains used to enhance cell details

Crystal violet stain of *Staphylococcus aureus* (1,000×).

Bacillus and *Staphylococcus* made with nigrosin (1,000×).

Gram stain
Purple cells are gram-positive.
Red cells are gram-negative
(1,000×).

Acid-fast stain
Red cells are acid-fast.
Blue cells are non-acid-fast
(1,000×).

Capsule stain of
rod-shaped bacterium
(1,000×).

Flagellar stain of
Bacillus cereus
(1,500×).

Endospore stain, showing spores (green)
and vegetative cells (red)
(1,000×).

Figure 3.9 Types of microbiological stains.
(a) Simple stains and negative stains. **(b)** Differential stains: Gram, acid-fast, and endospore. **(c)** Structural stains: capsule and flagellar. The endospore stain is one method that fits both differential and structural categories.
(a1): Toeytoey2530/Getty Images; (a2): Lisa Burgess/ McGraw-Hill Education; (b1): *Source:* Bobby Strong/CDC; (b2): James Redfearn/McGraw-Hill Education; (b3): *Source:* Larry Stauffer/Oregon State Public/CDC; (c1): Steven P. Lynch; (c): *Source:* Dr. William A. Clark/CDC

specific colors. The color-bearing portion of the dye, termed a **chromophore,** has a charge that attracts it to certain cell parts bearing the opposite charge.

Basic dyes carry a positively charged chromophore and are attracted to negatively charged cell components (nucleic acids and proteins). Because bacteria contain large amounts of negatively charged substances, they stain readily with basic dyes such as methylene blue, crystal violet, fuchsin, and safranin.

The chromophores of acidic dyes have a negative charge and therefore bind to areas of a cell carrying a positive charge. One example is eosin, a red dye used to stain blood cells. Because bacterial cells have numerous acidic substances and carry a slightly negative charge on their surface, they tend to repel acidic dyes. Acidic dyes such as nigrosin and India ink can still be used successfully on bacteria using the negative stain method (table 3.4). With this technique, the dye settles around the cell and creates a dark background.

Simple Versus Differential Staining Positive staining methods are classified as simple, differential, or structural (see figure 3.9). **Simple stains** require only a single dye and an uncomplicated procedure, while **differential stains** use two different-colored dyes, called the *primary dye* and the *counterstain,* to distinguish between cell types or parts. These staining techniques tend to be more complex, sometimes requiring additional chemical reagents to produce the desired reaction.

Most simple staining techniques take advantage of the ready binding of bacterial cells to dyes like malachite green, crystal violet, basic fuchsin, and safranin. Simple stains cause all cells in a smear to appear more or less the same color, regardless of type, but they can still reveal characteristics such as shape, size, and arrangement. A simple stain with methylene blue is often used to stain granules in bacteria such as *Corynebacterium*, which can be a factor in identification.

Types of Differential Stains An effective differential stain uses dyes of contrasting color to clearly emphasize differences between two cell types or cell parts. Common combinations are red and purple, red and green, or pink and blue. Differential stains can also pinpoint other characteristics, such as the size, shape, and arrangement of cells. Typical examples include Gram, acid-fast, and endospore stains. Some staining techniques (spore, capsule) fall into more than one category.

Gram staining is a 130-year-old method named for its developer, **Hans Christian Gram.** Even today, it is an important diagnostic staining technique for bacteria. It permits ready differentiation of major categories based upon the color reaction of the cells: **gram-positive,** which are stained purple, and **gram-negative,** which are stained red (figure 3.9*b*). This difference in staining quality is due to structural variations found in the cell walls of bacteria. The Gram stain is the basis of several important bacteriologic topics, including bacterial taxonomy, cell wall structure, identification, and drug therapy. Gram staining is discussed in greater detail in **3.1 Making Connections.**

The **acid-fast stain** is another commonly used differential stain. This stain originated as a specific method to detect *Mycobac-*

> **Quick Search**
>
> Search the Internet for "Microbiology Bytes: The Gram Stain" to see a demonstration of this technique.

terium tuberculosis in specimens. These bacterial cells have compounds in their outer wall that hold fast (tightly) to the dye (carbol fuchsin) used in the acid-fast stain, even when washed with a solution containing a combination of acid and alcohol (figure 3.9*b*). After staining, acid-fast bacteria appear pink, while non–acid-fast bacteria are blue in color. This stain is used for other medically important mycobacteria such as the Hansen's disease (leprosy) bacillus and for *Nocardia,* an agent of lung or skin infections (see chapter 19).

The **endospore stain** (spore stain) is similar to the acid-fast method in that a dye is forced by heat into resistant survival cells called spores or endospores formed in response to adverse conditions. This stain is designed to distinguish between spores and the vegetative cells that make them (figure 3.9*b*). Of significance in medical microbiology are the gram-positive, spore-forming members of the genus *Bacillus* (the cause of anthrax) and *Clostridium* (the cause of botulism and tetanus)—dramatic diseases of universal fascination that we examine more thoroughly in later chapters.

CLINIC CASE

There Are No Goats in New York City The patient, a resident of New York City, had travelled to Pennsylvania to take part in a show featuring traditional African drumming and dancing. While there, he collapsed and was admitted to a local hospital where he reported experiencing shortness of breath, dry cough, and malaise over the previous 3 days. The flu in the middle of February is hardly unusual, but when a chest X-ray revealed bilateral infiltrates and pleural effusions—suggesting anything from pneumonia to tuberculosis to lung cancer—doctors knew something serious was occurring. Over the next few days the patient's respiratory status continued to worsen, and on February 17, microbiological examination of blood cultures revealed gram-positive, endospore-forming bacteria that were identified as *Bacillus anthracis,* the bacterium responsible for anthrax.

Anthrax is rare in the United States, and is almost always associated with animals like sheep or goats, who may carry endospores of the bacterium on their skin. Those most at risk for anthrax include ranchers and shepherds, not dancers from New York City. Further investigation revealed that the patient had purchased four goat hides from his village on the Ivory Coast of Africa, which he took home to New York to fashion into Djembe drum heads. This required that the hides be soaked in water and then scraped with a sharp blade to produce a drumhead of uniform thickness, a process that filled the air of his small, unventilated workspace with tiny bits of goat skin. And anthrax bacillus.

After a month in the hospital, and a thorough decontamination of his apartment, the patient was released, after recovering from the first case of naturally occurring anthrax in the United States in 18 years.

An endospore stain was obviously important to the diagnosis of the patient in this case. Why would an endospore stain of samples from his apartment also be important?

3.1 MAKING CONNECTIONS

The Gram Stain: A Grand Stain

In 1884, Hans Christian Gram discovered a staining technique that could be used to make bacteria in infectious specimens more visible. His technique consisted of timed, sequential applications of crystal violet (the primary dye), Gram's iodine (IKI, the mordant), an alcohol rinse (decolorizer), and a contrasting counterstain—usually, the red dye, safranin. This color choice provides differentiation between bacteria that stain purple, called gram-positive, and those that stain red, called gram-negative.

Although these staining reactions involve an attraction of the cell to a charged dye, it is important to note that the terms *gram-positive* and *gram-negative* are used to indicate not the electrical charge of cells or dyes, but whether or not a cell retains the primary dye-iodine complex after decolorization. There is nothing specific in the reaction of gram-positive cells to the primary dye or in the reaction of gram-negative cells to the counterstain. The different results in the Gram stain are due to differences in the structure of the cell wall and how it reacts to the series of reagents applied to the cells.

In the first step, crystal violet stains cells in a smear all the same purple color. The second step is the mordant—Gram's iodine. The mordant causes the dye to form large crystals that get trapped by the meshwork of the cell wall. Because this layer in gram-positive cells is thicker, the entrapment of the dye is far more extensive in them than in gram-negative cells. Application of alcohol in the third step dissolves lipids in the outer membrane of the gram-negative cells, which removes the dye from them. By contrast, the crystals of dye tightly embedded in the gram-positive bacteria are relatively inaccessible and resistant to removal. Because gram-negative bacteria are colorless after decolorization, their presence is demonstrated by applying the counterstain safranin in the final step.

This staining method remains an important basis for bacterial classification and identification. It permits differentiation of four major

Step	Microscopic Appearance of Cell		Chemical Reaction in Cell (very magnified view)	
	Gram (+)	Gram (−)	Gram (+)	Gram (−)
1 Crystal violet (primary dye)				Both cell walls stain with the dye.
2 Gram's iodine (mordant)			Dye crystals trapped in cell	No effect of iodine
3 Alcohol (decolorizer)			Crystals remain in cell.	Outer wall is weakened; cell loses dye.
4 Safranin (red dye counterstain)			Red dye has no effect.	Red dye stains the colorless cell.

categories based upon color reaction and shape: gram-positive rods, gram-positive cocci, gram-negative rods, and gram-negative cocci (see table 4.4). The Gram stain can also be a practical aid in diagnosing infection and in guiding drug treatment. For example, Gram staining a fresh urine or throat specimen can point to a preliminary cause of infection, and in some cases it is possible to begin drug therapy on the basis of this stain. Even in this day of elaborate and expensive medical technology, the Gram stain remains an important and unbeatable first tool in diagnosis.

Could the Gram stain be used to diagnose the flu? Why or why not?

Structural stains are used to emphasize special cell parts such as capsules, endospores, and flagella that are not revealed by conventional staining methods. Capsule staining is a method of observing the microbial capsule, an unstructured protective layer surrounding the cells of some bacteria and fungi. Because the capsule does not react with most stains, it is often negatively stained with India ink, or it may be demonstrated by special positive stains. The fact that not all microbes exhibit capsules is a useful feature for identifying pathogens. One example is *Cryptococcus,* which causes a serious fungal meningitis in AIDS patients.

Flagellar staining is a method of revealing flagella, the tiny, slender filaments used by bacteria for locomotion. Because the width of bacterial flagella lies beyond the resolving power of the light microscope, in order to be seen, they must be enlarged by

depositing a coating on the outside of the filament and then staining it. The presence, number, and arrangement of flagella can be helpful in identification of bacteria (figure 4.4).

Practice SECTION 3.3

11. List the various staining methods and briefly characterize each.
12. Explain what happens in positive staining to cause the reaction in the cell.
13. Explain what happens in negative staining that causes the final result.
14. For a stain to be considered differential, what must it do?
15. Outline the main differential stains and how they are used.

3.4 Additional Features of the Six "I"s

 Learn

14. Define *inoculation, media,* and *culture,* and describe sampling methods and instruments and what aspects must be controlled.

15. Describe three basic techniques for isolation, including tools, media, incubation, and outcome.

16. Explain what an isolated colony is and indicate how it forms.

17. Differentiate between a pure culture, subculture, mixed culture, and contaminated culture. Define *contaminant.*

18. What kinds of data are collected during information gathering?

19. Describe some of the processes involved in identifying microbes from samples.

Inoculation, Growth, and Identification of Cultures

To cultivate, or **culture,*** microorganisms, one introduces a tiny sample (the inoculum) into a container of **medium*** (pl. media), which provides an environment in which they multiply. This process is called **inoculation.*** The observable growth that later appears in or on the medium is known as a culture. The nature of the sample being cultured depends on the objectives of the analysis. Clinical specimens for determining the cause of an infectious disease are obtained from body fluids (blood, cerebrospinal fluid), discharges (sputum, urine, feces), or diseased tissue. Samples subject to microbiological analysis can include nearly any natural material. Some common ones are soil, water, sewage, foods, air, and inanimate objects. The important concept of media will be covered in more detail in section 3.5.

Some Special Requirements of Culturing

Inherent in these practices are the implementation of **sterile, aseptic,** and **pure culture**[2] techniques. Contamination during inoculation is a constant problem, so sterile techniques (media, transfer equipment) help ensure that only microbes that came from the sample are present. Another concern is the possible release of infectious agents from cultures into the environment, which is prevented by aseptic techniques. Many of these techniques revolve around keeping species in the pure culture form for further study, identification, or biotechnology applications.

* *culture* (kul'-chur) Gr. *cultus,* to tend or cultivate. It can be used as a verb or a noun.

* *medium* (mee'-dee-um) pl. media; L. middle.

* *inoculation* (in-ok"-yoo-lay'-shun) L. *in,* and *oculus,* eye.

2. *Sterile* means the complete absence of viable microbes; *aseptic* refers to prevention of infection; *pure culture* refers to growth of a single species of microbe.

Isolation Techniques

Certain **isolation** techniques are based on the concept that if an individual bacterial cell is separated from other cells and provided adequate space on a nutrient surface, it will grow into a discrete mound of cells called a **colony (figure 3.10).** Because it arises from a single cell or cluster of cells, an isolated colony consists of just one species. Proper isolation requires that a small number of cells be inoculated into a relatively large volume or over an expansive area of medium. It generally requires the following materials: a medium that has a relatively firm surface (see the description of agar in section 3.5) contained in a clear, flat covered plate called a *Petri dish,* and inoculating tools.

In the **streak plate method,** a small droplet of sample is spread with a tool called an **inoculating loop** over the surface of the medium according to a pattern that gradually thins out the sample and separates the cells spatially over several sections of the plate **(figure 3.11a, b).** Because of its ease and effectiveness, the streak plate is the method of choice for most applications.

In the **loop dilution,** or **pour plate, technique,** the sample is inoculated, also with a loop, into a series of cooled but still liquid agar tubes so as to dilute the number of cells in each successive tube in the series **(figure 3.11c, d).** Inoculated tubes are then plated out (poured) into sterile Petri dishes and are allowed to solidify (harden). The number of cells per volume has decreased so that cells have ample space to form separate colonies in the second or third plate. One difference between this and the streak plate method

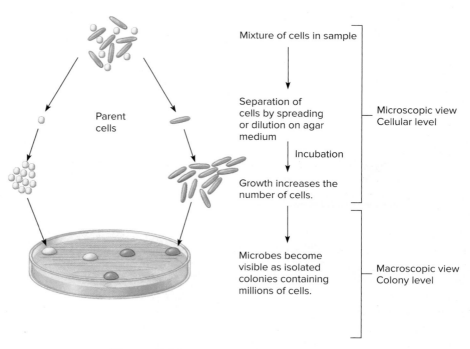

Figure 3.10 Isolation technique. Stages in the formation of an isolated colony, showing the microscopic events and the macroscopic result. Separation techniques such as streaking can be used to isolate single cells. After numerous cell divisions, a macroscopic mound of cells, or a colony, will be formed. This is a relatively simple yet successful way to separate different types of bacteria in a mixed sample.

is that in this technique, some of the colonies will develop deep in the medium itself and not just on the surface.

With the **spread plate technique,** a small volume of liquid from a diluted sample is pipetted onto the surface of the medium and spread around evenly by a sterile spreading tool (sometimes called a "hockey stick"). As with the streak plate, cells are spread over a large surface area so that they can form individual colonies **(figure 3.11e, f).**

Once a container of medium has been inoculated, it is **incubated** in a temperature-controlled chamber (incubator) to encourage microbial growth. Although microbes have adapted to growth at temperatures ranging from freezing to boiling, the usual temperatures used in laboratory propagation fall between 20°C and 40°C. Incubators can also control the content of atmospheric gases such as oxygen and carbon dioxide that may be required for the growth of certain microbes. During the incubation period (ranging from a few hours to several weeks), the microbe multiplies and produces a culture with macroscopically observable growth. Microbial growth in a liquid medium materializes as cloudiness, sediment, a surface scum, or colored pigment. Growth on solid media may take the form of a spreading mat or separate colonies.

Note: This method works best if the spreading tool (usually an **inoculating loop**) is resterilized (flamed) after each of steps 1–3.

Loop containing sample

1 2 3 4

(a) **Steps in a Streak Plate;** this one is a four-part or quadrant streak.

(b)

Loop containing sample

1 2 3

1 2 3

(c) **Steps in Loop Dilution;** also called a pour plate or serial dilution.

(d)

"Hockey stick"

1 2

(e) **Steps in a Spread Plate**

(f)

Figure 3.11 Methods for isolating bacteria. (a) Steps in a quadrant streak plate and **(b)** resulting isolated colonies of bacteria. **(c)** Steps in the loop dilution method and **(d)** the appearance of plate 3. **(e)** Spread plate and **(f)** its result. Techniques in (a) and (c) use a loopful of culture, whereas **(e)** starts with a prediluted sample.

(b, d, f): Kathy Park Talaro

In some ways, culturing microbes is analogous to gardening. Cultures are formed by "seeding" tiny plots (media) with microbial cells. Extreme care is taken to exclude weeds (contaminants). A pure culture is a container of medium that grows only a single known species or type of microorganism (**figure 3.12c**). This type of culture is most frequently used for laboratory study, because it allows the precise examination and control of one microorganism by itself. (Instead of the term *pure culture,* some microbiologists prefer the synonymous term *axenic culture.*) A standard method for preparing a pure culture is based on the **subculture** technique for making a second-level culture. A tiny sample of cells from a well-isolated colony is transferred into a separate container of media and incubated.

A **mixed culture** (**figure 3.12a**) is a container that holds two or more easily differentiated species of microorganisms, not unlike a garden plot containing both carrots and onions. A **contaminated culture** (**figure 3.12b**) has had **contaminants** (unwanted microbes of uncertain identity) introduced into it, like weeds into a garden. Because contaminants have the potential for disrupting experiments and tests, special procedures have been developed to control them, as you will no doubt witness in your own laboratory.

Identification Techniques

How does one determine what sorts of microorganisms have been isolated in cultures? Certainly microscopic appearance can be valuable in differentiating the smaller, simpler prokaryotic cells from the larger, more complex eukaryotic cells. Appearance can often be used to identify eukaryotic microorganisms to the level of genus or species because of their more distinctive appearance.

Bacteria are generally not as readily identifiable by these methods because very different species may appear quite similar. For them, we must include other techniques, some of which characterize their cellular metabolism. These methods, called **biochemical tests,** can determine fundamental chemical characteristics such as nutrient requirements, products given off during growth, presence of enzymes, and mechanisms for deriving energy. **Figure 3.13a** provides an example of a multiple-test, miniaturized system for obtaining biochemical characteristics. These tests are discussed in more depth in chapter 17 and in chapters that cover identification of pathogens.

By compiling macroscopic and microscopic traits together with the results of biochemical and physiological testing a complete picture of the microbe can be developed. A traditional pathway in bacterial identification uses flowcharts, also known as keys, that apply the results of tests to a selection process (**figure 3.13b**). The top of the key provides a general category from which to begin a series of branching points, usually into two pathways at each new junction. The points of separation are based on having a positive or negative result for each test. Following the pathway that fits the characteristics leads to an end point where a name for an organism is given. This process of "keying out" the organism can simplify the identification process. In some cases, identification requires testing the isolated culture against known antibodies (immunologic testing) or inoculating a suitable laboratory animal. More and more, diagnostic tools are available that analyze genetic characteristics and can detect microbes based on their DNA or RNA (see chapters 10 and 17).

Practice SECTION 3.4

16. Clarify what is involved in inoculation, growth, and contamination.

17. Name two ways that pure, mixed, and contaminated cultures are similar and two ways that they differ from each other.

18. Explain what is involved in isolating microorganisms and why it may be necessary to do this.

19. Compare and contrast three common laboratory techniques for separating bacteria in a mixed sample.

20. Describe how an isolated colony forms.

21. Explain why an isolated colony and a pure culture are not the same thing.

Figure 3.12 Various states of cultures. (a) A mixed culture of *Micrococcus luteus* and *Escherichia coli* can be readily differentiated by their colors. **(b)** This plate of *Serratia marcescens* was overexposed to room air and has developed a large white colony. Because this intruder is not desirable and not identified, the culture is now contaminated. **(c)** Tubes containing pure cultures of *E. coli* (white), *M. luteus* (yellow), and *S. marcescens* (red) made by subculturing isolated colonies.
(a–c): Kathy Park Talaro

(a)

(b)

(c)

Figure 3.13 Rapid mini test system and identification key for bacterial isolates. (a) A test system for common gram-negative rods uses 20 small wells of media, which are inoculated with a pure culture and incubated. A certain combination of positive and negative reactions (tabulated on the data sheet seen in the photograph) allows identification of an unknown isolate. **(b)** A sample of a key that uses test data (positive or negative reactions) to guide identification of genera and species related to *N. meningitidis*.
(a): John Watney/Science Source

(a)

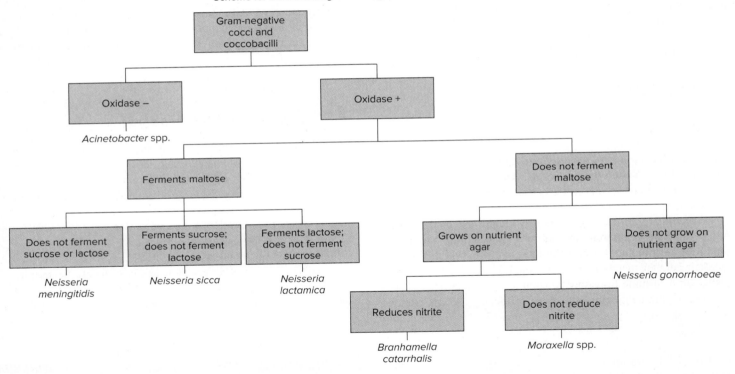

(b)

3.5 Media: The Foundations of Culturing

 Learn

20. Explain the importance of media for culturing microbes in the laboratory.

21. Name the three general categories of media, based on their inherent properties and uses.

22. Compare and contrast liquid, solid, and semisolid media, giving examples.

23. Analyze chemically defined and complex media, describing their basic differences and content.

24. Describe functional media; list several different categories, and explain what characterizes each type of functional media.

25. Identify the qualities of enriched, selective, and differential media; use examples to explain their content and purposes.

26. Explain what it means to say that microorganisms are not culturable.

27. Describe live media and the circumstances that require it.

A major stimulus to the rise of microbiology in the late 1800s was the development of techniques for growing microbes out of their natural habitats and in pure form in the laboratory. This milestone enabled the close examination of a microbe and its morphology,

physiology, and genetics. It was evident from the very first that for successful cultivation, the microorganisms being cultured had to be provided with all of their required nutrients in an artificial medium.

Some microbes require only a very few simple inorganic compounds for growth; others need a complex list of specific inorganic and organic compounds. This tremendous diversity is evident in the types of media that can be prepared. At least 500 different types of media are used in culturing and identifying microorganisms. Culture media are contained in test tubes, flasks, or Petri dishes, and they are inoculated by such tools as loops, needles, pipettes, and swabs. Media are extremely varied in nutrient content and consistency, and can be specially formulated for a particular purpose.

For an experiment to be properly controlled, sterile technique is necessary. This means that the inoculation must start with a sterile medium and inoculating tools with sterile tips must be used. Measures must be taken to prevent introduction of nonsterile materials, such as room air and fingers, directly into the media.

Types of Media

Most media discussed here are designed for bacteria and fungi, though algae and some protozoa can be propagated in media. Viruses can only be cultivated in live host cells. Media fall into three general categories based on their properties: physical state, chemical composition, and functional type (table 3.5).

Physical States of Media

Liquid media are defined as water-based solutions that do not solidify at temperatures above freezing and that tend to flow freely when the container is tilted (figure 3.14). These media, termed **broths,** milks, or infusions, are made by dissolving various solutes in distilled water. Growth occurs throughout the container and can then present a dispersed, cloudy, or flaky appearance. A common laboratory medium, *nutrient broth,* contains beef extract and partially digested proteins dissolved in water. Other examples of liquid media are methylene blue milk and litmus milk that contain

(a)

(b)

Figure 3.14 Sample liquid media. (a) Liquid media tend to flow freely when the container is tilted. Urea broth is used to show a biochemical reaction in which the enzyme urease digests urea and releases ammonium. This raises the pH of the solution and causes the dye to become increasingly pink. Left: uninoculated broth, pH 7; right: positive, pH 8.0. **(b)** Presence-absence broth is for detecting the presence of fecal bacteria in water samples. It contains lactose and bromcresol purple dye. As some fecal bacteria ferment lactose, they release acidic substances. This lowers the pH and changes the dye from purple to yellow (right is *Escherichia coli*). Nonfermenters such as *Pseudomonas* (left) grow but do not change the pH (purple color indicates neutral pH). (a): Lisa Burgess/McGraw-Hill Education; (b): Kathy Park Talaro

whole milk and dyes. Fluid thioglycollate is a slightly viscous broth used for determining patterns of growth in oxygen (see figure 7.11).

At ordinary room temperature, **semisolid media** have a thicker consistency (figure 3.15) because they contain just enough of a solidifying agent (agar or gelatin) to thicken them without producing a firm substrate. Semisolid media are used to determine the motility of bacteria and to localize a reaction at a specific site. Motility test medium and sulfur indole motility (SIM) medium both contain a small amount (0.3% to 0.5%) of agar. In both cases, the medium is stabbed carefully in the center with an inoculating needle and later observed for the pattern of growth around the stab line. In addition to motility, SIM can test for physiological characteristics used in identification (hydrogen sulfide production and indole reaction).

Solid media provide a firm surface on which cells can form discrete colonies (see figure 3.11.) and are advantageous for isolating and culturing bacteria and fungi. They come in two forms: liquefiable and nonliquefiable. Liquefiable solid media, sometimes called reversible solid media, contain a solidifying agent that changes its physical properties in response to temperature. By far the most widely used and effective of these agents is **agar,** a polysaccharide isolated from the red alga *Gelidium*. The benefits of agar are numerous. It is solid at room temperature, and it

| TABLE 3.5 | Three Categories of Media Classification | | |
|---|---|---|
| **Physical State (Medium's Normal Consistency)** | **Chemical Composition (Type of Chemicals Medium Contains)** | **Functional Type (Purpose of Medium)*** |
| 1. Liquid | 1. Synthetic (chemically defined) | 1. General purpose |
| 2. Semisolid | | 2. Enriched |
| 3. Solid (can be converted to liquid) | 2. Nonsynthetic (complex; not chemically defined) | 3. Selective |
| | | 4. Differential |
| | | 5. Anaerobic growth |
| 4. Solid (cannot be liquefied) | | 6. Specimen transport |
| | | 7. Assay |
| | | 8. Enumeration |

*Some media can serve more than one function. For example, a medium such as brain-heart infusion is general purpose and enriched, mannitol salt agar is both selective and differential, and blood agar is both enriched and differential.

(a)

1 2 3 4

(b)

Figure 3.15 **Sample semisolid media. (a)** Semisolid media have more body than liquid media but are softer than solid media. They do not flow freely and have a soft, clotlike consistency. **(b)** Sulfur indole motility (SIM) medium. When this medium is stabbed with an inoculum, the appearance of growth around the stab line can be used to determine nonmotility (2) or motility (3). Tube 1 is a control that has not been inoculated, and tube 4 shows a black precipitate that occurs around the stab when H_2S gas has been produced.
(a–b): Kathy Park Talaro

microbes and will melt at room and warmer temperatures, leaving a liquid. Agar and gelatin media are illustrated in **figure 3.16.**

Nonliquefiable solid media do not melt. They include materials such as rice grains (used to grow fungi), cooked meat media (good for anaerobes), and egg or serum media that are permanently coagulated or hardened by moist heat.

(a)

(b)

Figure 3.16 **Solid media that are reversible to liquids.**
(a) Media containing 1%–5% agar are solid and do not move when containers are tilted or inverted. Because they are reversibly solid, they can be liquefied with heat, poured into a different container, and resolidified. **(b)** Nutrient gelatin contains enough gelatin (12%) to take on a solid consistency. The top tube shows it as a solid. The bottom tube indicates what happens when it is warmed or when microbial enzymes digest the gelatin and liquefy it.
(b): Kathy Park Talaro

melts (liquefies) at the boiling temperature of water (100°C or 212°F). Once liquefied, agar does not resolidify until it cools to 42°C (108°F), so it can be inoculated and poured in liquid form at temperatures (45°C to 50°C) that will not harm the microbes or the handler (body temperature is about 37°C or 98.6°F). Agar is flexible and moldable, and it provides a basic matrix to hold moisture and nutrients. Another useful property is that it is not readily digestible and thus not a nutrient for most microorganisms.

Any medium containing 1% to 5% agar usually has the word *agar* in its name. *Nutrient agar* is a common one. Like nutrient broth, it contains beef extract and peptone, as well as 1.5% agar by weight. Many of the examples covered in the section on functional categories of media contain agar.

Although gelatin is not nearly as satisfactory as agar, it will create a reasonably solid surface in concentrations of 10% to 15%. The main drawback for gelatin is that it can be digested by some

Chemical Content of Media

Media with a **chemically defined** composition are termed **synthetic.** Such media contain pure chemical nutrients that vary little from one source to another and have a molecular content specified by means of an exact formula. Synthetic media come in many forms. Some media, such as minimal media for fungi, contain nothing more than a few salts and amino acids dissolved in water. Others contain dozens of precisely measured ingredients **(table 3.6A).** Such standardized and reproducible media are most useful in research and cell culture. But they can only be used when the exact nutritional needs of the test organisms are known. For example, a medium developed to grow the parasitic protozoan *Leishmania* required 75 different chemicals.

If even one component of a given medium is not chemically definable, the medium is a **nonsynthetic, or complex,**[3] **medium (table 3.6B).** The composition of this type of medium cannot be described by an exact chemical formula. Substances that can make it nonsynthetic are extracts from animal or plant tissues, including ground-up cells and secretions. Other examples are blood, serum, meat extracts, infusions, milk, soybean digests, and peptone. Peptone is a partially digested protein, rich in amino acids, that is often used as a carbon and nitrogen source. Nutrient broth, blood agar, and MacConkey agar, though different in function and appearance, are all complex nonsynthetic media. They present a rich mixture of nutrients for microbes with complex nutritional needs.

Tables 3.6A and 3.6B provide a practical comparison of the two categories, based on media used to grow *Staphylococcus aureus.* Every substance in medium A is known to a very precise degree. The dominant substances in medium B are macromolecules that contain unknown (but potentially required) nutrients. Both A and B will satisfactorily grow the bacteria. (Which one would you rather make?)

Media to Suit Every Function

Microbiologists have many types of media at their disposal, with new ones being devised all the time. Depending upon what is added, a microbiologist can fine-tune a medium for nearly any purpose.

General-purpose media are designed to grow a broad spectrum of microbes that do not have special growth requirements. As a rule, these media are nonsynthetic (complex) and contain a mixture of nutrients that could support the growth of a variety of bacteria and fungi. Examples include nutrient agar and broth, brain-heart infusion, and trypticase soy agar (TSA). TSA is a complex medium that contains partially digested milk protein (casein), soybean digest, NaCl, and agar.

An **enriched medium** contains complex organic substances such as blood, serum, hemoglobin, or special **growth factors** that must be provided to certain species in order for them to grow.

| TABLE 3.6A | Chemically Defined Synthetic Medium for Growth and Maintenance of Pathogenic *Staphylococcus aureus* |

0.25 Grams Each of These Amino Acids	0.5 Grams Each of These Amino Acids	0.12 Grams Each of These Amino Acids
Cystine	Arginine	Aspartic acid
Histidine	Glycine	Glutamic acid
Leucine	Isoleucine	
Phenylalanine	Lysine	
Proline	Methionine	
Tryptophan	Serine	
Tyrosine	Threonine	
	Valine	

Additional ingredients

0.005 mole nicotinamide ⎤
0.005 mole thiamine
0.005 mole pyridoxine ⎬ —Vitamins
0.5 micrograms biotin ⎦
1.25 grams magnesium sulfate
1.25 grams dipotassium hydrogen phosphate ⎤
1.25 grams sodium chloride ⎬ —Salts
0.125 grams iron chloride ⎦

Ingredients are dissolved in 1,000 milliliters of distilled water and buffered to a final pH of 7.0.

| TABLE 3.6B | Brain-Heart Infusion Broth: A Complex, Nonsynthetic Medium for Growth and Maintenance of Pathogenic *Staphylococcus aureus* |

27.5 grams brain-heart extract, peptone extract
2 grams glucose
5 grams sodium chloride
2.5 grams disodium hydrogen phosphate
Ingredients are dissolved in 1,000 milliliters of distilled water and buffered to a final pH of 7.0.

Growth factors are organic compounds such as vitamins or amino acids that microbes cannot synthesize themselves. Bacteria that require growth factors and complex nutrients are termed **fastidious.** Blood agar, which is made by adding sterile animal blood (usually from sheep) to a sterile agar base **(figure 3.17a)** is widely employed to grow fastidious streptococci and other pathogens. Pathogenic *Neisseria* and *Yersinia* species are often subcultured on chocolate agar, which is made by heating blood agar and does not contain chocolate—it just has that appearance **(figure 3.17b).**

Selective and Differential Media

Some of the cleverest and most inventive media recipes belong to the categories of selective and differential media. These media are

3. *Complex* means that the medium has large molecules such as proteins, polysaccharides, lipids, and other chemicals that can vary greatly in exact composition.

TABLE 3.7	Examples of Selective Media, Agents, and Functions	
Medium	**Selective Agent**	**Used For**
Mannitol salt agar	7.5% NaCl	Isolation of *Staphylococcus aureus* from infectious material
Enterococcus faecalis broth	Sodium azide, tetrazolium	Isolation of fecal enterococci
Phenylethanol agar (PEA)	Phenylethanol chloride	Isolation of staphylococci and streptococci
Tomato juice agar	Tomato juice, acid	Isolation of lactobacilli from saliva
MacConkey agar (MAC)	Bile, crystal violet	Isolation of gram-negative enterics
Eosin-methylene blue agar (EMB)	Bile, dyes	Isolation of coliform bacteria in specimens
Salmonella/Shigella (SS) agar	Bile, citrate, brilliant green	Isolation of *Salmonella* and *Shigella*
Sabouraud's agar (SAB)	pH of 5.6 (acid) inhibits bacteria	Isolation of fungi

designed for special microbial groups, and they have extensive applications in isolation and identification. They can permit, in a single step, the preliminary identification of a genus or even a species.

A **selective medium** (table 3.7) contains one or more agents that inhibit the growth of a certain microbe or microbes (call them A, B, and C) but not another (D). This difference favors, or *selects,* microbe D and allows it to grow by itself. Selective media are very important in primary isolation of a specific type of microorganism from samples containing mixtures of different species—for example, feces, saliva, skin, water, and soil. They hasten isolation by suppressing the unwanted background organisms and allowing growth of the desired ones.

Bile salts, a component of feces, inhibit most gram-positive bacteria while permitting many gram-negative rods to grow. Media for isolating intestinal pathogens (EMB agar, MacConkey agar,

Hektoen enteric [HE] agar) contain bile salts as a selective agent. Dyes such as methylene blue and crystal violet also inhibit certain gram-positive bacteria. The opposite effect can be achieved by using a different selective agent. Mannitol salt agar (MSA) contains a high concentration of NaCl (7.5%) that is inhibitory to most human pathogens, but not to the gram-positive bacteria in the genus *Staphylococcus,* which grow well and consequently can be amplified in mixed samples. Other agents that have selective properties are antimicrobial drugs and acid. Some selective media contain strongly inhibitory agents to favor the growth of a pathogen that would otherwise be overlooked because of its low numbers in a specimen. Selenite and brilliant green dye are used in media to isolate *Salmonella* from feces, and sodium azide is used to isolate enterococci from water and food.

Differential media grow several types of microorganisms but are designed to bring out visible differences among those microorganisms. Differences show up as variations in colony size or color, in media color changes, or in the formation of gas bubbles and precipitates (table 3.8). These variations come from the types of chemicals contained in the media and the ways that microbes react to them (figure 3.18a). For example, if microbe X metabolizes a certain substance not used by organism Y, then X will cause a visible change in the medium and Y will not. The simplest differential media show two reaction types, such as a color change in some colonies but not in others. Several newer forms of differential media contain artificial substrates called chromogens that release a wide variety of colors, each tied to a specific microbe. **Figure 3.18b** shows the result from a urine culture containing six different bacteria. Other chromogenic agar is available for identifying *Staphylococcus, Listeria,* and pathogenic yeasts.

Dyes are effective differential agents because many of them are pH indicators that change color in response to the production of an acid or a base. For example, MacConkey agar contains neutral red, a dye that is yellow when neutral and pink or red when acidic (figure 3.18c). A common intestinal bacterium such as *Escherichia coli* that produces acid when it metabolizes the lactose in the medium develops red to pink colonies, and one such as *Salmonella* that does not produce acid remains its natural color (off-white). Some fermentation broths also contain phenol red to indicate changes in pH associated with breakdown of sugars into acids (figure 3.19).

Growth of *Streptococcus pyogenes* showing beta hemolysis

(a) (b)

Figure 3.17 **Examples of enriched media. (a)** A blood agar plate growing the pathogenic bacterium *Streptococcus pyogenes,* which is the cause of strep throat and scarlet fever. Note that this medium can also differentiate among colonies by the types of hemolysis they display. Observe the colonies with clearly defined zones (beta hemolysis) and others with less defined zones (alpha hemolysis). **(b)** A culture of *Yersinia pestis* on chocolate agar, which gets its brownish color from cooked blood and does not produce hemolysis. It is used to grow fastidious pathogens like this notorious agent of bubonic plague.
(a): *Source:* Richard R. Facklam, Ph.D/CDC; (b): Kathy Park Talaro

TABLE 3.8	Examples of Differential Media	
Medium	Substances That Facilitate Differentiation	Differentiates
Blood agar (BAP)	Intact red blood cells (RBC)	Types of RBC damage (hemolysis)
Mannitol salt agar (MSA)	Mannitol and phenol red	Species of *Staphylococcus*
Hektoen enteric (HE) agar*	Bromthymol blue, acid fuchsin, sucrose, salicin, thiosulfate, ferric ammonium citrate, and bile	*Salmonella, Shigella,* and other lactose nonfermenters from fermenters; H_2S reactions are also observable
MacConkey agar (MAC)	Lactose, neutral red	Bacteria that ferment lactose (lowering the pH) from those that do not
Eosin-methylene blue (EMB)	Lactose, eosin, methylene blue	Same as MacConkey agar
Urea broth	Urea, phenol red	Bacteria that hydrolyze urea to ammonia and increase the pH
Sulfur indole motility (SIM)	Thiosulfate, iron	H_2S gas producers; motility; indole formation
Triple-sugar iron agar (TSIA)	Triple sugars, iron, and phenol red dye	Fermentation of sugars, H_2S production
XLD agar	Lysine, xylose, iron, thiosulfate, phenol red	Can differentiate *Enterobacter, Escherichia, Proteus, Providencia, Salmonella,* and *Shigella*

*Contains dyes and bile to inhibit gram-positive bacteria.

(a) 1 2 3 4 5 6

(b)

Figure 3.18 Media that differentiate multiple characteristics of bacteria. (a) Triple sugar iron agar (TSIA) inoculated on the surface and stabbed into the thicker region at the bottom (butt). This medium contains three sugars, phenol red dye to indicate pH changes (bright yellow is acid, various shades of red, basic), and iron salt to show H_2S gas production. Reactions are (1) uninoculated; (2) acid production throughout; (3) no reaction; (4) acid production in the butt only; (5) acid production throughout with H_2S precipitation (black precipitate) in the butt; (6) alkaline reaction with H_2S precipitation. **(b)** A medium developed for culturing and identifying the most common urinary pathogens. CHROMagar Orientation™ uses color-forming reactions to distinguish at least seven species and permits rapid identification and treatment. In the example, the bacteria were streaked so as to spell their own names. Which bacterium was probably used to write the name at the top? **(c)** On MacConkey agar, bacteria that ferment lactose produce red colonies, while those that cannot ferment the sugar produce colonies much lighter in color. (see text).
(a, c): Lisa Burgess/McGraw-Hill Education; (b): Kathy Park Talaro

(c)

Figure 3.19 Carbohydrate fermentation in broths. This medium is designed to show fermentation (acid production) using phenol red broth and gas formation by means of a small, inverted Durham tube for collecting gas bubbles. The tube on the left is an uninoculated negative control; the center tube is positive for acid (yellow) and gas (open space); the tube on the right shows growth but neither acid nor gas.
Harold J. Benson

A single medium can be classified in more than one category depending on the ingredients it contains. MacConkey and EMB media **(figure 3.20),** for example, appear in table 3.7 (selective media) and table 3.8 (differential media). Blood agar is both enriched and differential. Media companies have developed selective-differential media for numerous common pathogens, which makes it possible to identify them with a single streak plate. We will see examples of some of these media in later chapters.

Miscellaneous Media

A **reducing medium** contains a substance (thioglycollic acid or cystine) that absorbs oxygen or slows the penetration of oxygen in a medium, thus reducing its availability. Reducing media are important for growing anaerobic bacteria or for determining oxygen requirements of isolates. Carbohydrate fermentation media contain sugars that can be fermented (converted to acids) and a pH indicator to show this reaction (see figure 3.19a). Media for other biochemical reactions that provide the basis for identifying bacteria and fungi are presented in several later chapters.

Transport media are used to maintain and preserve specimens that have to be held for a period of time before clinical analysis or to sustain delicate species that die rapidly if not held under stable conditions. Stuart's and Amie's transport media contain buffers and absorbants to prevent cell destruction but will not support growth. **Assay media** are used by technologists to test the effectiveness of antimicrobial drugs (see chapter 12) and by drug manufacturers to assess the effect of disinfectants, antiseptics, cosmetics, and preservatives on the growth of microorganisms. Enumeration media are used by industrial and environmental microbiologists to count the numbers of organisms in milk, water, food, soil, and other samples.

Obligate Parasites and Unculturable Microorganisms

Some microbes, including viruses, rickettsias, and a few bacteria, will only grow on live cells or animals. These obligate parasites have unique requirements that must be provided by living animals such as rabbits, guinea pigs, mice, or bird embryos. Such animals can be an indispensable aid for studying, growing, and identifying microorganisms.

Other microbes go a step further and thwart almost any attempt to culture them. These microorganisms, termed **viable but nonculturable,** or **VBNC,** may describe upwards of 99% of the microbes in the environment. It was only through the advent of nonculturing tools—principally various

Figure 3.20 Media with both selective and differential properties. EMB agar is commonly used to detect enteric bacteria in food and dairy products. The inclusion of the dyes eosin and methylene blue (which give the medium its name) allows the medium to act both selectively and differentially at the same time. Gram-negative bacteria that do not ferment the sugar lactose will grow on the medium, producing clear or slightly colored growth (*Salmonella* Typhimurium, left and *Pseudomonas aeruginosa,* top). Gram-negative bacteria that do ferment lactose will produce much darker growth, sometimes with a green metallic sheen (*Escherichia coli,* right). The growth of gram-positive bacteria (*Staphylococcus aureus,* bottom) is almost completely inhibited (i.e., selected against).
Lisa Burgess/McGraw-Hill Education

forms of genetic testing—that scientists became able to identify microbes by analyzing their DNA alone. These were the techniques used to study the bacteria isolated from Lake Whillans (see the Case Study in chapter 1).

The human microbiome likely includes many viable but non-culturable microbes, and these organisms may play a role in diseases long thought to be noninfectious, just as many oral microbes always thought of as innocuous are now known to play a role in cancer and heart disease. In chapter 13, we will explore some of the findings from the Human Microbiome Project, a comprehensive study of the microbial content of several body sites. One important finding was the numerous roles many resident organisms have in developing and maintaining the immune system.

Practice SECTION 3.5

22. Describe the main purposes of media, and compare the three categories based on physical state, chemical composition, and usage.

23. Differentiate among the ingredients and functions of enriched, selective, and differential media.

24. Explain the two principal functions of dyes in media.

25. Why are some bacteria difficult to grow in the laboratory? Relate this to what you know so far about the nutrients that are added to media.

26. What conditions are necessary to cultivate viruses in the laboratory?

CASE STUDY **Part 2**

Inspections performed within the restaurant revealed no deficiencies regarding hand hygiene or food handling. Proper handwashing, especially after using the restroom, is crucial in interrupting outbreaks caused by microbes like *Salmonella*, that spread via the oral-fecal route. Restaurant administrators cooperated with the investigation, supplying the names of all food handlers, who were given paid time off to be interviewed and examined.

Because no employees were symptomatic, investigators presumed they were searching for a carrier, someone infected with a pathogen who doesn't display signs or symptoms of disease. As the normal microbiome of the human gut contains many hundreds of different species of bacteria, isolating one particular species can be a daunting task. Samples were obtained from the rectum of each employee, and pure culture techniques were used to isolate and identify *Salmonella* Typhi in a single food handler. This employee reported having travelled 15 years previously to a country where typhoid fever was endemic, but had not been ill and had not had contact with any ill persons. The worker was excluded from food service work and treated with the antibiotic azithromycin for 28 days. After three consecutive stool specimens (obtained at least 1 month apart) tested negative for *Salmonella* Typhi, the employee was allowed to return to work, where his job had been held open for him.

■ How could flies (which cannot be infected by *Salmonella* Typhi) act to spread disease in this case?

■ How would selective media be especially useful, given the type of bacterium involved in the outbreak?

For more information on *Salmonella* and the diseases it causes, see chapter 20 and log on to http://www. cdc.gov /salmonella/index.html.

Chapter Summary with Key Terms

3.1 Methods of Microbial Investigation

A. Microbiology as a science is very dependent on a number of specialized laboratory techniques.

1. Initially, a specimen must be collected from a source, whether environmental or patient.

2. **Inoculation** of a **medium** with the specimen is the first step in **culturing.**

3. **Incubation** of the medium with the microbes under the right conditions creates a **culture** with visible growth.

4. **Isolation** of the microbes in the sample into discrete, separate **colonies** is one desired goal.

5. **Inspection** begins with macroscopic characteristics of the culture and continues with microscopic analysis.

6. **Information gathering** involves acquiring additional data from physiological, serological, and genetic tests.

7. **Identification** correlates the key characteristics that can pinpoint the actual species of microbe.

3.2 The Microscope: Window on an Invisible Realm

A. Optical, or light, microscopy depends on lenses that **refract** light rays, drawing the rays to a focus to produce a magnified image.

1. A simple microscope consists of a single magnifying lens, whereas a compound microscope relies on two lenses: the ocular lens and the objective lens.

2. The total power of magnification is calculated as the product of the ocular and objective magnifying powers.

3. **Resolution,** or the **resolving power,** is a measure of a microscope's capacity to make clear images of very small objects. Resolution is improved with shorter wavelengths of illumination and with a higher **numerical aperture** of the lens. Light microscopes are limited by resolution to magnifications around 2,000×.

4. Modifications in the lighting or the lens system give rise to the bright-field, dark-field, phase-contrast, interference, fluorescence, and confocal microscopes.

B. Electron microscopy depends on electromagnets that serve as lenses to focus electron beams. A **transmission electron microscope (TEM)** projects the electrons through prepared sections of the specimen, providing detailed structural images of cells, cell parts, and viruses. A **scanning electron microscope (SEM)** is more like dark-field microscopy, bouncing the electrons off the surface of the specimen to detectors.

3.3 Preparing Specimens for Optical Microscopes

A. Specimen preparation in optical microscopy varies according to the specimen, the purpose of the inspection, and the type of microscope being used.

 1. Wet mounts and hanging drop mounts permit examination of the characteristics of live cells, such as motility, shape, and arrangement.
 2. Fixed mounts are made by drying and heating a film of the specimen called a smear. This is then stained using dyes to permit visualization of cells or cell parts.

B. Staining uses either **basic** (cationic) **dyes** with positive charges or **acidic** (anionic) **dyes** with negative charges. The surfaces of microbes are negatively charged and attract basic dyes. This is the basis of **positive staining**. In **negative staining**, the microbe repels the dye and it stains the background. Dyes may be used alone and in combination.

 1. **Simple stains** use just one dye and highlight cell morphology.
 2. **Differential stains** require a primary dye and a contrasting counterstain in order to distinguish cell types or parts. Important differential stains include the **Gram stain, acid-fast stain,** and the endospore stain.
 3. **Structural stains** are designed to bring out distinctive characteristics. Examples include capsule stains and flagellar stains.

3.4 Additional Features of the Six "I's"

A. Inoculation of media followed by incubation produces visible growth in the form of **cultures.**

B. Techniques with solid media in Petri dishes provide a means of separating individual microbes by producing **isolated colonies.**

 1. With the **streak plate,** a loop is used to thin out the sample over the surface of the medium.

2. With the **loop dilution** (pour plate), a series of tubes of liquified solid media is used to dilute the sample.
3. The **spread plate** method evenly distributes a tiny drop of inoculum over the surface of an agar plate.
4. Isolated colonies can be **subcultured** for further testing at this point. The goal is a **pure culture,** in most cases, or a **mixed culture. Contaminated cultures** can ruin correct analysis and study.

3.5 Media: The Foundations of Culturing

A. Artificial media allow the growth and isolation of microorganisms in the laboratory and can be classified by their physical state, chemical composition, and functional types. The nutritional requirements of microorganisms in the laboratory may be simple or complex.

B. Physical types of media include those that are **liquid,** such as **broths** and milks; those that are **semisolid;** and those that are solid. Solid media may be liquefiable, containing a solidifying agent such as **agar** or gelatin.

C. Chemical composition of a medium may be completely **chemically defined,** thus **synthetic. Nonsynthetic,** or **complex,** media contain ingredients that are not completely definable.

D. Functional types of media serve different purposes, often allowing biochemical tests to be performed at the same time. Types include **general-purpose, enriched, selective,** and **differential media.**

 1. Enriched media contain **growth factors** required by microbes.
 2. Selective media permit the growth of desired microbes while inhibiting unwanted ones.
 3. Differential media bring out visible variations in microbial growth.
 4. Others include anaerobic (reducing), assay, and enumeration media. Transport media are important for conveying certain clinical specimens to the laboratory.

E. In certain instances, microorganisms have to be grown in cell cultures or host animals.

F. The majority of microorganisms found in the environment may not be culturable at all using current techniques. **Viable but nonculturable (VBNC)** microbes are generally only detected through the presence of the DNA.

 ## Assess Your Knowledge

Level I. These questions require a working knowledge of the concepts in the chapter and the ability to recall and understand the information you have studied.

Developing a Concept Inventory

Select the correct answer from the answers provided. For questions with blanks, choose the combination of answers that most accurately completes the statement.

1. Which of the following is not one of the six "I's"?
 a. inspection d. incubation
 b. identification e. inoculation
 c. illumination

2. The term *culture* refers to the _____ growth of microorganisms in _____.
 a. rapid, an incubator c. microscopic, the body
 b. macroscopic, media d. artificial, colonies

3. A mixed culture is
 a. the same as a contaminated culture
 b. one that has been adequately stirred
 c. one that contains two or more known species
 d. a pond sample containing algae of a single species

4. Agar is superior to gelatin as a solidifying agent because agar
 a. does not melt at room temperature
 b. solidifies at 75°C
 c. is not usually decomposed by microorganisms
 d. both a and c

5. The process that most accounts for magnification is
 a. a condenser c. illumination
 b. refraction of light rays d. resolution

6. A subculture is a
 a. colony growing beneath the media surface
 b. culture made from a contaminant
 c. culture made in an embryo
 d. culture made from an isolated colony

7. Resolution is _____ with a longer wavelength of light.
 a. improved c. not changed
 b. worsened d. not possible

8. A real image is produced by the
 a. ocular c. condenser
 b. objective d. eye

9. A microscope that has a total magnification of 1,500× when using the oil immersion objective has an ocular of what power?
 a. 150× c. 15×
 b. 1.5× d. 30×

10. The specimen for an electron microscope is always
 a. stained with dyes c. killed
 b. sliced into thin sections d. viewed directly

11. Motility is best observed with a
 a. hanging drop preparation c. streak plate
 b. negative stain d. flagellar stain

12. Bacteria tend to stain more readily with cationic (positively charged) dyes because bacteria
 a. contain large amounts of alkaline substances c. are neutral
 b. contain large amounts of acidic substances d. have thick cell walls

13. The primary difference between a TEM and SEM is in
 a. magnification capability
 b. colored versus black-and-white images
 c. preparation of the specimen
 d. type of lenses

14. A fastidious organism must be grown on what type of medium?
 a. general-purpose medium c. synthetic medium
 b. differential medium d. enriched medium

15. What type of medium is used to maintain and preserve specimens before clinical analysis?
 a. selective medium c. enriched medium
 b. transport medium d. differential medium

16. Which of the following is NOT an optical microscope?
 a. dark-field c. atomic force
 b. confocal d. fluorescent

17. **Multiple Matching.** For each type of medium, select all descriptions that fit. For media that fit more than one description, briefly explain why this is the case.
 _____ mannitol salt agar a. selective medium
 _____ chocolate agar b. differential medium
 _____ MacConkey agar c. chemically defined (synthetic)
 _____ nutrient broth medium
 _____ brain-heart infusion broth d. enriched medium
 _____ Sabouraud's agar e. general-purpose medium
 _____ triple-sugar iron agar f. complex medium
 _____ SIM medium g. transport medium

Case Study Analysis

1. The restaurant at the center of the outbreak was identified through questioning ill persons, looking at credit card receipts, examining social media posts, etc. Under which of the six "I"s would such epidemiological investigation be placed?
 a. inoculation d. isolation
 b. incubation e. information gathering
 c. inspection f. identification

2. *Salmonella-Shigella* agar contains yeast extract to promote bacterial growth and bile salts to inhibit the growth of gram-positive bacteria. It also contains lactose and phenol red (a pH indicator) that cause lactose fermenting bacteria to produce pink colonies and lactose non-fermenters to produce white colonies. This medium would be classified as (Select all that apply.)
 a. general purpose
 b. synthetic
 c. selective
 d. differential
 e. liquid

3. Of the three isolation techniques discussed in this chapter, which one(s) would have been appropriate to isolate bacteria in this case? Explain your reasoning.

On the Test

These questions will help to prepare you to successfully answer similar questions you'll see on the TEAS (Test of Essential Academic Skills) and NCLEX (National Council Licensure Examination).

1. Media used to detect the fermentation of lactose is prepared using an excess of
 a. DNA c. lipids
 b. carbohydrates d. protein

2. What is the total magnification of a specimen being viewed under the microscope using a 10× ocular lens and a 45× objective lens?
 a. 45× c. 55×
 b. 1000× d. 450×

Writing Challenge

For each question, compose a one- or two-paragraph answer that includes the factual information needed to completely address the question. Practice questions can also be used for writing-challenge exercises.

1. a. When buying a microscope, what features are most important to check for?
 b. What is probably true of a $20 microscope that claims to magnify 1,000×?
2. How can one obtain 2,000× magnification with a 100× objective?
3. Differentiate between microscopic and macroscopic methods of observing microorganisms, citing a specific example of each method.
4. Describe the steps of the Gram stain, and explain how it can be an important diagnostic tool for infections.

5. Describe the steps you would take to isolate, cultivate, and identify a microbial pathogen from a urine sample.
6. Trace the pathway of light from its source to the eye, explaining what happens as it passes through the major parts of the microscope.
7. Evaluate the following preparations in terms of providing information on microbial size, shape, motility, and differentiation: spore stain, negative stain, simple stain, hanging drop slide, and Gram stain.

Concept Mapping

On Connect you can find an Introduction to Concept Mapping that provides guidance for working with concept maps, along with concept-mapping activities for this chapter.

Application, Analysis, Evaluation, and Synthesis

Level II. These problems go beyond just restating facts and require higher levels of understanding and an ability to interpret, problem solve, transfer knowledge to new situations, create models, and predict outcomes.

Critical Thinking

Critical thinking is the ability to reason and solve problems using facts and concepts. These questions can be approached from a number of angles and, in most cases, they do not have a single correct answer.

1. A certain medium has the following composition:

Glucose	15 g
Yeast extract	5 g
Peptone	5 g
KH_2PO_4	2 g
Distilled water	1,000 ml

 a. Tell what chemical category this medium belongs to, and explain why this is true.
 b. How could you convert *Staphylococcus* medium (table 3.6A) into a nonsynthetic medium?

2. a. Name four categories that blood agar fits.
 b. Name four differential reactions that TSIA shows.
 c. Observe figure 3.15. Suggest what causes the difference in growth pattern between nonmotile and motile bacteria.

 d. Explain what a medium that is both selective and differential does, using figure 3.20.

3. a. What kind of medium might you make to selectively grow a bacterium that lives in the ocean?
 b. One that lives in the human stomach?
 c. Why are intestinal bacteria able to grow on media containing bile?

4. Go back to section 1.2 and observe the six micrographs in figure 1.3. See if you can tell what kind of microscope was used to make the photograph, based on magnification and appearance.

5. Since the dyes for the Gram stain are not specific to the bacteria they stain, what mistakes in the procedure could cause an incorrect result?

Visual Assessment

1. Examine figure 3.11*a, b* (shown here). If you performed the quadrant streak plate method using a broth culture that had 10× fewer cells than the broth used in the culture shown, which quadrant might you expect to yield isolated colonies? Explain your answer.

2. Using the three categories of media classification listed in table 3.5, classify the SIM media seen in figure 3.15 as to physical state, chemical composition, and functional type.

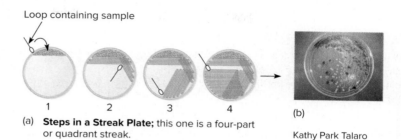

Loop containing sample

1 2 3 4

(a) **Steps in a Streak Plate;** this one is a four-part or quadrant streak.

(b)

Kathy Park Talaro

A Survey of Prokaryotic Cells and Microorganisms

In This Chapter...

On September 13, 2015, the Georgia Department of Public Health was notified of a cluster of ***Mycobacterium abscessus* infections,** all requiring hospitalization. The patients—20 in the initial cluster—had an average age of 7 years and had all undergone **pulpotomy** treatment at the same pediatric dentistry practice. Pulpotomy, sometimes referred to as a baby root canal, involves the removal of decay and **diseased pulp** from a deciduous (baby) tooth. The inside of the tooth is filled with protective material and the tooth is then covered with a stainless steel crown. The procedure is done to preserve the deciduous tooth so that space remains available for the permanent tooth. Although typically very safe, soft tissue—with its attendant **blood vessels and nerves**—is exposed during the procedure and the risk of **infection** is greater than that seen in the filling of cavities.

The story was essentially the same for each of the children. Several weeks after undergoing pulpotomy treatment, the child began to complain of **pain, swelling,** and **redness** around the tooth, with many also seeing blood when they brushed. Upon examination, infection was evident and *Mycobacterium abscessus* was isolated from the **infected tissues.** Each infection was combatted with long-term **antibiotic therapy,** along with **surgery** to remove infected teeth, gum tissue, and in some cases, jawbone.

A few months later, and 2,200 miles to the west, a virtually identical outbreak occurred in Anaheim, California. The Orange County Health Agency (OCHA) ordered a local pediatric dental group to stop using water for procedures after 68 pulpotomy patients were hospitalized with serious infections. Dr. Eric Handler, the health officer for Orange County, ordered the dental practice to completely **replace the water system** and equipment that could harbor the bacterium. The clinic followed the mandate of the OCHA and replaced equipment that could possibly have contributed to the outbreak. In December 2016, only a few months after the equipment was replaced, the clinic was ordered to close after *M. abscessus* was again detected in the water system. In April 2017, the clinic reopened after installing equipment that relied on **sterile, bottled water** for procedures like pulpotomies. Several months later, after the bacterium appeared once again, the clinic closed permanently.

To continue the Case Study, go to Case Study Part 2 at the end of the chapter.

(tooth filling) Szasz-Fabian Jozsef/Shutterstock

4.1 Basic Characteristics of Cells and Life Forms

 Learn

1. Describe the fundamental characteristics of cells.
2. Identify the primary properties that define life and living things.

There is a universal biological truth that the basic unit of life is the cell, whether the organism is a bacterium whose entire body is just a single cell or an elephant made up of trillions of cells. Regardless of their origins, all cells share a few common characteristics. They tend to assume cubical, spherical, or cylindrical shapes and have a **cell membrane** that encases an internal matrix called the **cytoplasm.** All cells have one or more chromosomes containing DNA. They all also possess ribosomes for protein synthesis and exhibit highly complex chemical reactions. As we learned in chapter 1, all cells discovered thus far are classified into one of two fundamentally different groups: the small, seemingly simple **prokaryotic cells** and the larger, structurally more complicated **eukaryotic cells.**

Eukaryotic cells are found in animals, plants, fungi, and protists. They contain a number of complex internal parts called **organelles** that perform useful functions for the cell. By convention, organelles are defined as cell components enclosed by membranes that carry out specific activities involving metabolism, nutrition, and synthesis. Organelles also partition the eukaryotic cell into smaller compartments. The most visible organelle is the nucleus, a roughly spherical mass surrounded by a double membrane that contains the DNA of the cell. Other organelles include the Golgi apparatus, endoplasmic reticulum, vacuoles, and mitochondria (all discussed in chapter 5).

Prokaryotic cells are found only in the bacteria and archaea. Sometimes it may seem that prokaryotes are the microbial "have-nots," because, for the sake of comparison, they are described by what they lack. They have no nucleus or other organelles. This apparent simplicity is misleading, because the fine structure of prokaryotes can be complex. Overall, prokaryotic cells can engage in nearly every activity that eukaryotic cells can, and many can function in ways that eukaryotes cannot.

We start this chapter with a description of the characteristics that impart the essence of life to cells, followed by a look at prokaryotic cell anatomy and a survey of major groups of prokaryotes. In chapter 5, we will do a similar survey of the eukaryotic world. After you have studied the cells as presented in this chapter and chapter 5, refer to table 5.2, which summarizes the major differences between prokaryotic and eukaryotic cells.

What Is Life?

Biologists have long debated over universal characteristics we see in organisms that are solid indicators of life or of being alive. What does a cell do that sets it apart from a nonliving entity? One of the first things that often comes to mind is the ability to move or to grow. Unfortunately, taken individually, these are not life signs.

After all, inanimate objects can move and crystals can grow. There is probably no single property that we can hold up as the ultimate indicator of life. In fact, defining life requires a whole collection of behaviors and properties that even the simplest organisms will have. First and foremost on this list would be a self-contained and highly organized unit to carry out the activities of life, namely a **cell.** It is the cell that is the staging area for these life-supporting phenomena: heredity, reproduction, growth, development, metabolism, responsiveness, and transport **(figure 4.1).**

- **Heredity** is the transmission of an organism's **genome*** to the next generation by chromosomes, which carry DNA, the molecular blueprint of life.
- **Reproduction** involves the generation of offspring necessary to continue a species's line of evolution. All organisms manifest asexual reproduction, with one cell simply dividing into two new cells by fission or mitosis. Many organisms also display sexual reproduction, involving the union of sex cells from two parents.
- **Growth** has two general meanings in microbiology. In the usual sense, it means an increase in size of a population through reproduction. In another case, it refers to the enlargement of a single organism during maturation.
- **Development** includes all changes over the life span of an organism that complete the full expression of its genome.
- **Metabolism** encompasses the thousands of chemical reactions that all cells need to function. Generally, these reactions either synthesize new cell components or release energy that drives cellular activities. Both types of metabolism are supported and regulated by unique molecules of life called **enzymes.**
- **Responsiveness** is the capacity of cells to interact with external factors through irritability, communication, or movement. Cells demonstrate irritability by receiving and reacting to stimuli such as light and chemicals from their environment. They may also communicate with other cells by sending or receiving signals. Some cells show self-propulsion or motility using specialized locomotor structures.
- **Transport** is a system for controlling the flow of materials. This includes carrying nutrients and water from the external environment into the cell's interior. Without these raw materials, metabolism would cease. Cells also secrete substances, or expel waste, in the reverse direction. Movement of this type is the work of the cell membrane, which functions as the gatekeeper for cellular activities. Together, all of these life properties provide microorganisms with the capacity to adapt and evolve.

One of the main reasons viruses are generally considered nonliving is that they are not cellular. Even if one argues that they are tiny units somewhat like cells and that they do show some traits of life such as heredity, development, and evolution, they do not display these characteristics independent of their living host cell. Outside of their host, they lack most other features of life we just described and are inactive and inert. We will return to this discussion about viruses in chapter 6.

* *genome* (jee'-nohm) The complete set of chromosomes and genes of an organism.

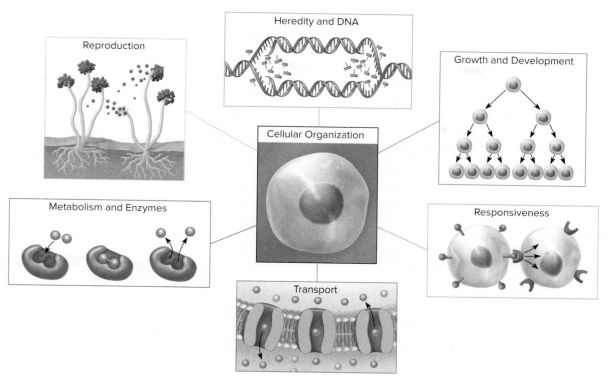

Figure 4.1 **A summary of the major life-defining properties.** The cell is central to the collective activities that are synonymous with being alive.

Practice SECTION 4.1

1. Outline the primary indicators of life.
2. Name several general characteristics that could be used to define the prokaryotes.

4.2 Prokaryotic Profiles: The Bacteria and Archaea

Learn

3. Describe the generalized anatomy of bacterial cells.

4. Distinguish among the types of external cell appendages.

5. Describe the structure and position of bacterial flagella and axial filaments and their attachment patterns.

6. Explain how flagella influence motility and motile behavior.

7. Discuss the structure and functions of pili and fimbriae.

8. Define *glycocalyx,* and describe its different forms and functions.

In chapter 1, we introduced the two major types of prokaryotic cells: the bacteria and the archaea. As the first type of cells on earth, prokaryotic cells have an evolutionary history that dates back over 3.5 billion years. At present we cannot know the precise nature

of these first cells, but many microbiologists speculate that they would be similar to present-day archaea living on sulfur compounds in deep, hot oceanic vents (see figure 4.33), extreme habitats they continue to dominate 3.5 billion years later. Bacteria evolved over the same time frame as archaea and share a similar ancient history. Biologists have estimated that these two domains still account for at least half of the total mass of life forms on earth. The fact that these organisms have endured for so long in such a variety of habitats indicates cellular structure and function that are incredibly versatile and adaptable. The general structural plan of a prokaryotic cell can be represented with this flowchart:

Structures that are essential to the functions of all prokaryotic cells include a cell membrane, cytoplasm, ribosomes, and one, or occasionally more, chromosomes. The majority of bacteria also have a cell wall and some form of surface coating or glycocalyx. Specific structures that are found in some, but not all, bacteria are flagella, pili, fimbriae, a capsule or slime layer, an S layer, cytoskeleton, inclusions, microcompartments, endospores, and intracellular membranes.

The Structure of a Generalized Bacterial Cell

Prokaryotic cells appear featureless and two-dimensional when viewed with an ordinary microscope, but this is only because of their small size. Higher magnification provides increased insight into their intricate and often complex structure (see figures 4.18 and 4.28 in later sections). The descriptions of prokaryotic structure, except where otherwise noted, refer to the **bacteria,** a category of prokaryotes with peptidoglycan in their cell walls. **Figure 4.2** shows a three-dimensional illustration of a generalized (rod-shaped) bacterial cell with most of the structures from the flowchart. As we survey the principal anatomical features of this cell, we begin with the outer cell structures and proceed to the internal contents. In sections 4.6 and 4.7, we will cover prokaryotic taxonomy, discuss the differences between bacteria and archaea, and introduce the major characteristics of archaea.

Cell Extensions and Surface Structures

Bacteria often bear accessory **appendages** sprouting from their surfaces. Appendages can be divided into two major groups: those that provide motility (flagella and axial filaments) and those that provide attachment sites or channels (fimbriae and pili).

Flagella—Bacterial Propellers

The prokaryotic **flagellum*** is responsible for bacterial motility, or self-propulsion. It allows a cell to swim freely through an aqueous habitat. The bacterial flagellum is composed of three distinct parts: the filament, the hook (sheath), and the basal body **(figure 4.3).** The **filament** is a helical structure composed of a protein called flagellin. It is approximately 20 nm in diameter and varies from 1 to 70 μm in length. It is inserted into a curved, tubular hook. The hook is anchored to the cell by the **basal body,** a stack of rings firmly anchored through the cell wall to the cell membrane. The hook and its filament are free to rotate 360°—like a tiny propeller. This is in contrast to the flagella of eukaryotic cells, which undulate back and forth.

One can generalize that all spirilla, about half of the bacilli, and a small number of cocci are flagellated (these bacterial shapes are shown in figure 4.23). Flagella vary both in number and arrangement according to two general patterns: (1) In a **polar** arrangement, the flagella are attached at one or both ends of the cell. Three subtypes of this pattern are **monotrichous,*** the only group with a single flagellum; **lophotrichous,*** posessing small bunches or tufts of flagella emerging from the same site; and **amphitrichous,***

posessing flagella at both poles of the cell. (2) In a **peritrichous*** arrangement, flagella are dispersed over the surface of the cell **(figure 4.4).**

The presence of motility is one piece of information used in the laboratory identification of various groups of bacteria. Special stains or electron microscope preparations must be used to see the arrangement, because flagella are too minute to be seen in live preparations with a light microscope. Often it is sufficient to know simply whether a bacterial species is motile. One way to detect motility is to stab a tiny mass of cells into a soft (semisolid) medium in a test tube (see figure 3.15). Growth spreading rapidly through the entire medium is indicative of motility. Alternatively, cells can be observed microscopically with a hanging drop slide. A truly motile cell will flit, dart, or wobble around the field, making some progress, whereas one that is nonmotile jiggles about in one place but makes no progress.

Flagellar Responses Flagella often function as more than just a locomotor device. They are sensory appendages that can detect and respond to environmental signals. When the signal is of a chemical nature, the behavior is called **chemotaxis.*** Positive chemotaxis is movement of a cell in the direction of a favorable chemical stimulus (usually a nutrient); negative chemotaxis is movement away from a repellent (potentially harmful) compound.

The flagellum can guide bacteria in a certain direction because the system for detecting chemicals is linked to the mechanisms that drive the flagellum. Located in the cell membrane are clusters of receptors[1] that bind specific molecules coming from the immediate environment. The attachment of sufficient numbers of these molecules transmits signals to the flagellum and sets it into rotary motion. If several flagella are present, they become aligned and rotate as a group **(figure 4.5).** As a flagellum rotates counterclockwise, the cell itself swims in a smooth, linear direction toward the stimulus; this action is called a *run*. Runs are interrupted at various intervals by *tumbles* caused by the flagellum reversing its direction. This makes the cell stop and change its course. It is believed that attractant molecules inhibit tumbles, increase the length of runs, and permit progress toward the stimulus **(figure 4.6).** Repellents cause numerous tumbles, allowing the bacterium to redirect itself away from the stimulus. Some photosynthetic bacteria exhibit *phototaxis,* a type of movement in response to light rather than chemicals.

A few pathogenic bacteria use their flagella to invade the surface of mucous membranes during infections. *Helicobacter pylori,* the agent of gastric ulcers, bores through the stomach lining, and *Vibrio cholerae,* the cause of cholera, penetrates the small intestine with the help of its flagellum.

Periplasmic Flagella

Corkscrew-shaped bacteria called **spirochetes*** show a wormlike or serpentine mode of locomotion caused by two or more long, coiled threads, the periplasmic flagella or **axial filaments.** A periplasmic flagellum is a type of internal flagellum that is enclosed in

* *flagellum* (flah-jel′-em) pl. flagella; L., a whip.
* *monotrichous* (mah″-noh-trik′-us) Gr. *mono,* one, and *tricho,* hair.
* *lophotrichous* (lo″-foh-trik′-us) Gr. *lopho,* tuft or ridge.
* *amphitrichous* (am″-fee-trik′-us) Gr. *amphi,* on both sides.

* *peritrichous* (per″-ee-trik′-us) Gr. *peri,* around.
* *chemotaxis* (ke″-moh-tak′-sis) Gr. *chemo,* chemicals, and *taxis,* an ordering or arrangement.

1. Cell surface molecules that bind specifically with other molecules.
* *spirochete* (spy′-roh-keet) Gr. *speira,* coil, and *chaite,* hair.

In All Bacteria

Cell (cytoplasmic) membrane—A thin sheet of lipid and protein that surrounds the cytoplasm and controls the flow of materials into and out of the cell pool.

Bacterial chromosome or nucleoid—Composed of condensed DNA molecules. DNA contains the genetic information of the cell and codes for all proteins.

Ribosomes—Tiny particles composed of protein and RNA that are the sites of protein synthesis.

Cytoplasm—Water-based solution filling the entire cell.

In Some Bacteria

S layer—Monolayer of protein used for protection and/or attachment.

Fimbriae—Fine, hairlike bristles extending from the cell surface that help in adhesion to other cells and surfaces.

Outer membrane—Extra membrane similar to cell membrane but also containing lipopolysaccharide. Controls flow of materials, and portions of it are toxic to mammals when released.

Cell wall—A semirigid casing that provides structural support and shape for the cell.

Actin cytoskeleton—Long fibers of proteins that encircle the cell just inside the cell membrane and contribute to the shape of the cell.

Pilus—An appendage used for drawing another bacterium close in order to transfer DNA to it.

Capsule (tan coating)—A coating or layer of molecules external to the cell wall. It serves protective, adhesive, and receptor functions. It may fit tightly or be very loose and diffuse. Also called slime layer and glycocalyx.

Inclusion/Granule—Stored nutrients such as fat, phosphate, or glycogen deposited in dense crystals or particles that can be tapped into when needed.

Bacterial microcompartments—Protein-coated packets used to localize enzymes and other proteins in the cytoplasm.

Plasmid—Small, double stranded DNA molecule containing extra genes.

Flagellum—Specialized appendage attached to the cell by a basal body that holds a long, rotating filament. The movement pushes the cell forward and provides motility.

In Some Bacteria (not shown)

Endospore (not shown)—Dormant body formed within some bacteria that allows for their survival in adverse conditions.

Intracellular membranes (not shown)

Figure 4.2 **Structure of a typical bacterial cell.** Cutaway view of a rod-shaped bacterium, showing major structural features.

Figure 4.3 **Details of the flagellar basal body and its position in the cell wall.** The hook, rings, and rod function together as a tiny device that rotates the filament 360°. **(a)** Structure in gram-negative cells. **(b)** Structure in gram-positive cells.

(a) — 22 nm — (b)

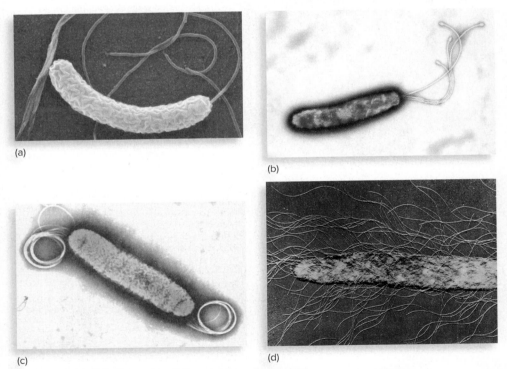

(a)

(b)

(c)

(d)

Figure 4.4 **Electron micrographs depicting types of flagellar arrangements.** **(a)** Monotrichous flagellum on the pathogen *Vibrio cholerae* (10,000×). Note its highly textured glycocalyx. **(b)** Lophotrichous flagella on *Helicobacter pylori, a cause of stomach ulcers* (14,000×). **(c)** Unusual flagella on *Aquaspirillum* are amphitrichous and coil up into tight loops (7,500×). **(d)** *Proteus mirabilis* exhibits peritrichous flagella (10,000×).

(a): *Source:* Louisa Howard/Dartmouth Electron Microscope Facility; (b): Heather Davies/Science Source; (c): From: W.J. Strength and N.R. Krieg", "Flagellar activity in an aquatic bacterium", "*Can. J. Microbiol.* May 1971, 17:1133-1137, Fig. 5. Reproduced by permission of the National Research Council of Canada"; (d): PTP/Phototake

Nonflagellar Appendages: Fimbriae and Pili

The structures termed **fimbria*** and **pili*** both refer to common bacterial surface appendages that are involved in interactions with other cells but do not provide locomotion, except for some specialized pili. Some microbiologists use the terms interchangeably, but we will refer to the smaller common appendages as fimbriae and the ones with specialized functions as pili.

Fimbriae are small, bristlelike fibers emerging from the surface of many types of bacterial cells (**figure 4.8**). Their exact composition varies, but most of them contain protein. Fimbriae have an inherent tendency to stick to each other and to surfaces. They may be responsible for the mutual clinging of cells that leads to biofilms and other thick aggregates of cells on the surface of liquids and for the microbial colonization of inanimate solids such as rocks and glass. Some pathogens can colonize and infect host tissues because of a tight adhesion between their fimbriae and epithelial cells. For example, *Escherichia coli* colonizes the intestine and begins its invasion of tissues by this means. Mutant forms of these pathogens that lack fimbriae are unable to cause infections.

Pili come in several varieties. A versatile form, called the Type IV pilus, is found only in gram-negative bacteria. This structure is a flexible tube made of the protein pilin. Bacteria with pili participate in a mating

the space between the outer sheath and the cell wall peptidoglycan (**figure 4.7**). The filaments curl closely around the spirochete coils yet are free to contract and impart a twisting or flexing motion to the cell. This form of locomotion must be seen in live spirochetes to be truly appreciated (see Quick Search, section 4.5).

* *fimbria* (fim′-bree-ah) pl. fimbriae; L., a fringe.
* *pilus* (py′-lus) pl. pili; L., hair.

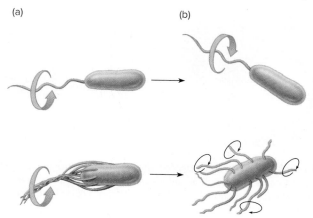

Figure 4.5 **The operation of flagella and the mode of locomotion in bacteria with polar and peritrichous flagella.** **(a)** Runs. When a polar flagellum rotates in a counterclockwise direction, the cell swims forward in runs. In peritrichous forms, all flagella sweep toward one end of the cell and rotate as a single group. **(b)** Tumbles. When the flagellum reverses direction and rotates clockwise, the cell stops and tumbles. Peritrichous flagella also reverse direction and cause the cell to lose coordination and stop.

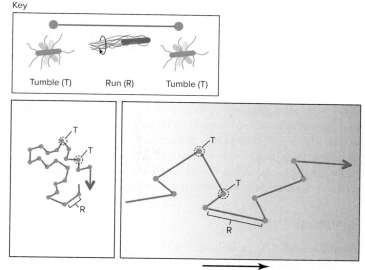

Key

Tumble (T) Run (R) Tumble (T)

(a) **No attractant or repellent** (b) **Gradient of attractant concentration**

Figure 4.6 **Chemotaxis in bacteria. (a)** A cell moves via a random series of short runs and tumbles when there is no attractant or repellent. **(b)** The cell spends more time on runs as it gets closer to an attractant.

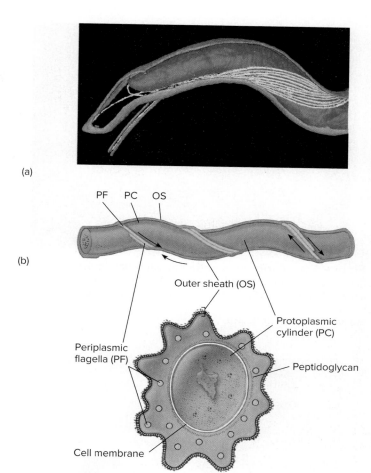

(a)

PF PC OS

(b)

Outer sheath (OS)

Protoplasmic cylinder (PC)

Periplasmic flagella (PF)

Peptidoglycan

Cell membrane

(c)

Figure 4.7 **The orientation of periplasmic flagella on the spirochete cell. (a)** Section through *Borrelia burgdorferi,* the spirochete of Lyme disease. The micrograph has been colorized to indicate the periplasmic flagella (yellow), the outer sheath (blue), and the protoplasmic cylinder (pink). **(b)** Longitudinal view with major cell parts labeled. **(c)** Cross section, indicating the position of the flagella with respect to other cell parts. Contraction of the filaments imparts a spinning and undulating pattern of locomotion.
(a): Courtesy of Dr. Misha Kudryashev and Dr. Friedrich Frischknecht, Mol Microbiol, 2009 Mar; 71(6):1415-34.

process termed **conjugation,**[2] which uses the pilus (also called a sex pilus) as a connector for transferring DNA from a donor cell to a recipient **(figure 4.9).** This role of pili is discussed further in chapter 9.

Type IV pili are a major contributor to the infectiousness of *Neisseria gonorrhoeae,* the agent of gonorrhea, by providing a mechanism for binding to the epithelial cells of the reproductive tract. Type IV pili

found in *Pseudomonas* bacteria carry out a remarkable sort of twitching motility. Cells can slide in jerking movements over moist surfaces by extending and then retracting pili in a repetitive motion. Microbiologists have found that this mechanism is every bit as complex and regulated as the flagellar mode of locomotion.

Quick Search
This remarkable motility may be observed on YouTube by searching for "type IV pili twitching motility."

Bacterial Surface Coatings: The S Layer and Glycocalyx

Because bacteria are frequently exposed to severe environmental conditions, they have evolved outer layers that exist solely to protect the cell. The first of these is the **S layer,** which consists of thousands of copies of a single protein linked together to form a strong, tight covering surrounding the cell. Interestingly, the S layer is only

2. Although the term *mating* is sometimes used for this process, it is not a form of reproduction.

Figure 4.8 **Form and function of bacterial fimbriae.**
Several cells of pathogenic *Escherichia coli* covered with numerous fibers called fimbriae (30,000×). Note also the dark blue masses, which are chromosomes.
Eye of Science/Science Source

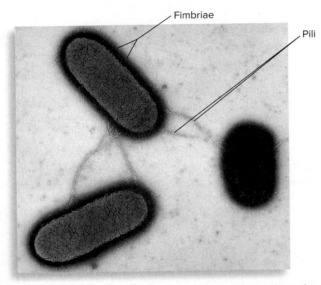

Figure 4.9 **Three bacteria in the process of conjugating.**
Clearly evident are the sex pili forming mutual conjugation bridges between a donor (upper cell) and two recipients (two lower cells). Fimbriae can also be seen on the donor cell.
L. Caro/SPL/Science Source

produced when a bacterium finds itself in a hostile environment, one of the reasons that discovery of the S layer is fairly recent event. Bacteria growing in the welcoming conditions of a laboratory—pure culture, nutritious broth, no competition—had no reason to produce the protective layer. Recent research has shown that many bacterial species, including pathogens like *Clostridium difficile* and *Bacillus anthracis,* produce S layers under harsh conditions. The S layer also allows for the attachment of cells to an underlying substrate, a key step in the initiation of infection.

A second layer, typically produced under all environmental conditions, is the **glycocalyx,** which consists of repeating polysaccharide units, and may include protein. Like the S layer, glycocalyces help the cell to adhere to surfaces in the environment.

Figure 4.10 **Types of glycocalyces seen through cutaway views of cells. (a)** The slime layer is a loose structure that is easily washed off. **(b)** The capsule is a thick, structured layer that is not readily removed.

Glycocalyces differ among bacteria in thickness, organization, and chemical composition. Some bacteria are covered with a loose shield called a **slime layer** that protects them from dehydration and loss of nutrients, as well as serving in adhesion **(figure 4.10*a*).** Other bacteria produce **capsules,** which are bound more tightly to the cell than a slime layer and have a thick gummy consistency that gives a prominently sticky (mucoid) character to the colonies of most encapsulated bacteria **(figure 4.11).**

Capsules are formed by many pathogenic bacteria, including *Streptococcus pneumoniae* (a cause of pneumonia), *Haemophilus influenzae* (one cause of meningitis), and *Bacillus anthracis* (the cause of anthrax). Encapsulated bacterial cells generally have greater pathogenicity because capsules protect the bacteria against white blood cells called phagocytes. Phagocytes are a natural body defense that can engulf and destroy foreign cells, which helps to prevent infection. The capsule blocks the phagocytes from attaching to, engulfing, and killing bacteria. By escaping phagocytosis, the bacteria are free to multiply and infect body tissues. Encapsulated bacteria that mutate to nonencapsulated forms usually lose their pathogenicity.

Biofilms

Microbes rarely live in isolation. More often, they cling together in complex masses called **biofilms.** The formation of these living layers is a universal phenomenon that all of us have observed—the scum that builds up in toilet bowls, on shower stalls, even the plaque on teeth. Biofilms are cooperative associations among several microbial groups (bacteria, fungi, algae, and protozoa) as well as plants and animals. Substrates favorable to biofilm development have a moist, thin layer of organic material like polysaccharides or glycoproteins deposited on their exposed surface. This sticky texture attracts primary colonists, usually bacteria, which attach, multiply, and begin to lay down a sticky matrix which may include fimbriae, pili, slime layers, or capsules. As more cells become attracted to the developing community, the biofilm evolves, undergoing specific adaptations to the habitat in which it forms. At some point, despite being firmly attached to a substrate, cells within a biofilm can break away and disperse to other habitats, initiating the process of biofilm formation in a new location **(process figure 4.12).**

A fascinating behavior of biofilms is **quorum sensing**, which occurs when individual species alter the expression of their genes to cooperate with other cells in the biofilm. For instance, one species

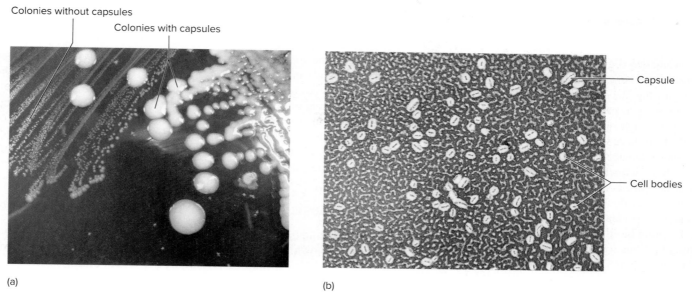

Colonies without capsules

Colonies with capsules

Capsule

Cell bodies

(a)

(b)

Figure 4.11 Appearance of encapsulated bacteria. (a) Small, discrete, unencapsulated colonies of *Streptococcus mutans* are dwarfed by the much larger, mucoid, encapsulated colonies of *Klebsiella pneumoniae.* Even at the macroscopic level, the moist, slimy character of the capsule is evident. **(b)** A capsule stain reveals the microscopic appearance of a large, well-developed capsule (the clear "halo" around the cells) of an unidentified, rod-shaped bacterium (1,000×).

(a): Barry Chess; (b): Steven P. Lynch

(a)

(b)

⚙ **Process Figure 4.12 Formation of a biofilm. (a) (1)** Planktonic cells attach to surface. **(2), (3)** Extracellular matrix of polysaccharides, glycoproteins, pili, fimbriae, slime layers, and capsules is produced as cells become permanently attached to the underlying surface. **(4)** The biofilm continues to grow both through cell division and the recruitment of new cells. **(5)** Dispersion allows cells to leave the biofilm and colonize other areas. **(b)** Scanning electron micrograph of a biofilm on the surface of a tooth (6,000×).

(b): Steve Gschmeissner/Science Photo Library/Getty Images

may synthesize a growth factor while another provides protection against an antibiotic. Bacterial cells routinely express different genes when growing alone—so-called **planktonic growth**—than they do when growing as part of a biofilm. In this way, the biofilm behaves more like a single organism than a collection of individual species.

Biofilms have serious medical implications as they are inclined to colonize damaged tissues like heart valves or hard surfaces like teeth. They routinely form on indwelling medical devices, including IUDs, catheters, shunts, and gastronomy tubes. Treating these infections is difficult, due to the thick, protective nature of the biofilm and the presence of antibiotic-resistant cells, which may protect the entire biofilm. A great deal of work is currently focused on battling biofilms (on industrial surfaces and within the body), at a cost of more than $13 billion annually in the United States.

Practice SECTION 4.2

3. What other microbial groups besides bacteria have prokaryotic cells?

4. Describe the structure of a flagellum and how it operates. What are the four main types of flagellar arrangements?

5. How does the flagellum dictate the behavior of a motile bacterium? Differentiate between flagella and periplasmic flagella.

6. Differentiate between the structure and functions of pili and fimbriae.

7. Explain the position of the glycocalyx.

8. How do slime layers and capsules differ in structure and function?

9. How can a capsule or slime layer be detected even at the level of a colony?

10. Explain how the bacterial glycocalyx and certain surface appendages contribute to biofilm formation.

4.3 The Cell Envelope: The Outer Boundary Layer of Bacteria

Learn

9. Explain the concept of the cell envelope, and describe its structure.

10. Outline the structure and functions of cell walls, and explain the role of peptidoglycan.

11. Contrast the major structure of gram-positive and gram-negative cell walls.

12. Summarize how gram-positive and gram-negative cells differ in their reactions.

13. Relate the characteristics of other types of cell walls and wall-free cells.

14. Describe the structure of the cell membrane, and explain several of its major roles in bacterial cells.

The majority of bacteria have a chemically complex external covering, termed the cell envelope, that encloses the cytoplasm. It is composed of two main layers: the cell wall and the cell membrane. These layers are stacked together and often tightly bound into a unit like the outer husk and casings of a coconut. Although each envelope layer performs a distinct action, together they act as a single unit required for a cell's normal function and integrity.

Basic Types of Cell Envelopes

Long before the detailed anatomy of bacteria was even remotely known, a Danish physician named **Hans Christian Gram** developed a staining technique, the **Gram stain**,[3] which is commonly used to delineate two different groups of bacteria known as the gram-positive bacteria and the gram-negative bacteria. You may wish to review this stain, described in 3.1 Making Connections.

The extent of the differences between gram-positive and gram-negative bacteria is evident in the physical appearance of their cell envelopes (**figure 4.13**). In **gram-positive** cells, a microscopic section reveals two layers: the thick cell wall, composed primarily of peptidoglycan (defined in the next section), and the cell membrane. A similar section of a gram-negative cell envelope shows three layers: an outer membrane, a thin peptidoglycan layer, and the cell membrane. The reactions of the Gram stain are the result of these basic differences. The thick

3. This text follows the American Society for Microbiology style, which calls for capitalization of the terms *Gram stain* and *Gram staining* and lowercase treatment of gram-negative and gram-positive, except in headings.

Peptidoglycan ————

Cell membrane ————

Cell membrane ————

Peptidoglycan ————

Periplasmic space ————

Outer membrane ————

(a) (b)

Figure 4.13 **Comparative views of the envelopes of gram-positive and gram-negative cells. (a)** A section through a gram-positive cell wall/membrane with an interpretation of the main layers visible (92,000×). **(b)** A section through a gram-negative cell wall/membrane with an interpretation of its three sandwich-style layers (90,000×). (a): Courtesy of Newcastle University Electron Microscopy Unit; (b): *Source:* Cynthia Goldsmith and Melissa Bell/CDC

TABLE 4.1	Comparison of Gram-Positive and Gram-Negative Cell Walls	
Characteristic	**Gram-Positive**	**Gram-Negative**
Number of major layers	One	Two
Chemical composition	Peptidoglycan Teichoic acid Lipoteichoic acid Mycolic acids and polysaccharides*	Lipopolysaccharide (LPS) Lipoprotein Peptidoglycan Porin proteins
Overall thickness	Thicker (20–80 nm)	Thinner (8–11 nm)
Outer membrane	No	Yes
Periplasmic space	Narrow	Extensive
Permeability to molecules	More penetrable	Less penetrable

*In some cells.

peptidoglycan of the gram-positive cell traps the crystal violet-mordant complex and makes it inaccessible to the decolorizer, leaving the cells purple. Gram-negative cell walls are thinner, and the crystal violet is relatively easy to remove with the decolorizer. In addition, the alcohol dissolves the outer membrane of the cell, which increases this loss of dye. These factors create a colorless cell that will stain with a red counterstain. **Table 4.1** provides a summary of the major similarities and differences between the wall types.

Structure of Cell Walls

The cell wall accounts for a number of important bacterial characteristics. In general, it helps determine the shape of a bacterium, and it also provides the kind of strong structural support necessary to keep a bacterium intact despite constant changes in environmental conditions. The cell walls of most bacteria gain their relative strength and stability from a unique macromolecule called **peptidoglycan (PG).** This compound is composed of a repeating framework of long **glycan*** chains cross-linked by short peptide fragments **(figure 4.14).** The amount and exact composition of peptidoglycan vary among the major bacterial groups.

Because many bacteria live in aqueous habitats with a low solute concentration, they are constantly absorbing excess water by osmosis. Were it not for the structural support of the peptidoglycan in the cell wall, they would rupture from internal pressure. Several types of drugs used to treat infection (penicillin, cephalosporins) are effective because they target the peptide cross-links in the peptidoglycan, thereby disrupting its integrity. With their cell walls incomplete or missing, such cells have very little protection from **lysis.*** Lysozyme, an enzyme contained in tears and saliva, provides a natural defense against certain bacteria by hydrolyzing the bonds in the glycan chains and causing the wall to break down. Chapters 11 and 12 provide more information on the actions of antimicrobial chemical agents and drugs.

The Gram-Positive Cell Wall

The bulk of the gram-positive cell wall is a thick, homogeneous sheath of peptidoglycan ranging from 20 to 80 nm in thickness. It also contains tightly bound acidic polysaccharides, including teichoic acid directly attached to the peptidoglycan and lipoteichoic acid **(figure 4.15).** Cell wall **teichoic acid** is a polymer of ribitol or glycerol and phosphate embedded in the peptidoglycan sheath. Lipoteichoic acid is similar in structure but is attached to the lipids in the plasma membrane. These molecules appear to function in cell wall maintenance, enlargement during cell division, and binding of some pathogens to tissues. The cell wall of gram-positive bacteria is loosely adherent to the cell membrane, but at their junction lies a small compartment called the **periplasmic*** **space.** This is analogous to the larger space in gram-negatives, but it has different functions. It is a site for temporary storage of enzymes that have been released by the cell membrane. More recent studies have found that this space serves as the major site for peptidoglycan synthesis.

The Gram-Negative Cell Wall

The gram-negative cell wall is more complex in morphology because it is composed of an **outer membrane (OM)** and a thinner shell of peptidoglycan (see figures 4.13 and 4.15). The outer membrane is somewhat similar in construction to the cell membrane, except that it contains specialized types of **lipopolysaccharides (LPS)** and **lipoproteins.** Lipopolysaccharides consist of lipid molecules bound to polysaccharides. The lipids form the matrix of the top layer of the OM, and the polysaccharide strands project from the lipid surface. The lipid portion may become toxic when it is released during infections. Its role as an endotoxin is described in chapter 13. The polysaccharides give rise to the somatic (O) antigen in gram-negative pathogens and can be used in identification. They may also function as receptors and interfere with host defenses.

Two types of proteins are located in the OM. The **porins** are inserted in the upper layer of the outer membrane. They have some regulatory control over molecules entering and leaving the cell. Many qualities of the selective permeability of gram-negative bacteria to bile, disinfectants, and drugs are due to the porins. Some structural proteins are also embedded in the upper layer of the OM. The bottom layer of the outer membrane is similar to the cell membrane in its overall structure and is composed of phospholipids and lipoproteins.

The bottom layer of the gram-negative wall is a single, thin (1–3 nm) sheet of peptidoglycan. Although it acts as a somewhat

* *glycan* (gly′-kan) Gr., sugar. These are large polymers of simple sugars.
* *lysis* (ly′-sis) Gr., to loosen. A process of cell destruction, as occurs in bursting.

* *periplasmic* (per″-ih-plaz′-mik) Gr. *peri*, around, and *plastos*, the fluid substances of a cell.

(a) The peptidoglycan of a cell wall is a huge, three-dimensional latticework that is actually one giant molecule which surrounds and supports the cell.

(b) The molecular pattern of peptidoglycan consists of alternating glycans (NAG and NAM) bound together in long strands. The NAG stands for *N*-acetyl glucosamine, and the NAM stands for *N*-acetyl muramic acid. Adjacent muramic acid molecules on parallel chains are bound by a cross-linkage of peptides (brown spheres).

(c) An enlarged view of the links between the NAM molecules. Tetrapeptide chains branching off the muramic acids connect by amino acid interbridges. The amino acids in the interbridge can vary or may be lacking entirely. It is this linkage that provides rigid yet flexible support to the cell.

Figure 4.14 Structure of peptidoglycan component of cell walls.

chemistry shows that they do not fit the descriptions for typical gram-negative or gram-positive cells. For example, the cells of *Mycobacterium* and *Nocardia* contain peptidoglycan and stain gram-positive, but the bulk of their cell wall is composed of unique types of lipids. One of these is a very-long-chain fatty acid called *mycolic acid,* or cord factor, that contributes to the pathogenicity of this group. The thick, waxy nature imparted to the cell wall by these lipids is also responsible for a high degree of resistance to certain chemicals and dyes. Such resistance is the basis for the **acid-fast stain** used to diagnose tuberculosis and leprosy. In this stain, hot carbol fuchsin dye becomes tenaciously attached (is held fast) to these cells so that an acid-alcohol solution will not remove the dye.

The Cell Wall and Infections

Variations in cell wall anatomy contribute to several differences between the two cell types besides staining reactions. The outer membrane contributes an extra barrier in gram-negative bacteria that makes them more impervious to some antimicrobic chemicals, such as dyes and disinfectants, so they are generally more difficult to inhibit or kill than gram-positive bacteria. One exception is for alcohol-based compounds, which can dissolve the lipids in the outer membrane, removing this extra layer of protection from gram-negative cells. Treating infections caused by gram-negative bacteria often involves different drugs than gram-positive infections, because of the special requirement that the drugs must cross the outer membrane.

The cell wall, or its parts, can also interact with human tissues and contribute to disease. The lipopolysaccharides have been referred to as endotoxins because they stimulate fever and shock in gram-negative infections such as meningitis and typhoid fever. Proteins attached to the outer portion of the cell wall of several gram-positive species, including *Corynebacterium diphtheriae* (the agent of diphtheria) and *Streptococcus pyogenes* (the cause of strep throat), also have toxic properties. The lipids in the cell walls of certain *Mycobacterium* species are harmful to human cells as well. Because most macromolecules in the cell walls are foreign to humans, they stimulate antibody production by the immune system (see chapter 15).

rigid protective structure, as previously described, its thinness gives gram-negative bacteria a relatively greater flexibility and sensitivity to lysis. There is a well-developed periplasmic space above and below the peptidoglycan. This space in gram-negative bacteria is a site of many metabolic reactions related to synthesis and transport of proteins, actions of enyzmes, and energy release.

Atypical Cell Walls

Several bacterial groups lack the cell wall structure of gram-positive or gram-negative bacteria, and some bacteria have no cell wall at all. Although these exceptional forms can stain positive or negative in the Gram stain, examination of their fine structure and

Figure 4.15 **A comparison of the detailed structure of gram-positive and gram-negative cell envelopes and walls.**

Mycoplasmas and Other Cell Wall–Deficient Bacteria

Mycoplasmas are bacteria that naturally lack a cell wall. Although other bacteria require an intact cell wall to prevent the bursting of the cell, the mycoplasma cell membrane contains sterols that make it resistant to lysis. These extremely tiny bacteria range from 0.1 to 0.5 μm in size. They range in shape from filamentous to coccus or doughnut-shaped. This property of extreme variations in shape is a type of **pleomorphism.*** Mycoplasmas are found in many habitats, including plants, soil, and animals. The most important medical species is *Mycoplasma pneumoniae* **(figure 4.16),** which adheres to the epithelial cells in the lung and causes an atypical form of pneumonia (sometimes referred to as walking pneumonia) in humans.

Some bacteria that ordinarily have a cell wall can lose it during part of their life cycle. These wall-deficient forms are referred to as **L forms** or L-phase variants (for the Lister Institute, where they were discovered). L forms arise naturally from a mutation in the wall-forming genes, or they can be induced artificially by treatment with a chemical such as lysozyme or penicillin that disrupts the cell wall. When a gram-positive cell loses its cell wall completely, it becomes a **protoplast,*** a fragile cell bounded only by a membrane that is highly susceptible to lysis. A gram-negative cell that

Figure 4.16 **Scanning electron micrograph of *Mycoplasma pneumoniae* (10,000×).** Cells exhibit extreme variation in shape due to the lack of a cell wall.
Courtesy of Dr. Heinrich Lünsdorf, HZI

loses the peptidoglycan layer of its cell wall generally retains its outer membrane, leaving a less fragile but nevertheless weakened **spheroplast.*** Evidence points to a role for L forms in certain chronic infections.

* *pleomorphism* (plee″-oh-mor′-fizm) Gr. *pleon,* more, and *morph,* form or shape. The tendency for cells of the same species to vary to some extent in shape and size.
* *protoplast* (proh′-toh-plast) Gr. *proto,* first, and *plastos,* formed.

* *spheroplast* (sfer′-oh-plast) Gr. *sphaira,* sphere.

Cell Membrane Structure

A layer in the cell envelope appearing just beneath the cell wall is the **cell,** or **cytoplasmic, membrane,** a very thin (5–10 nm), flexible sheet structured as one complete sheath around the cytoplasm. In general composition, it is a lipid bilayer with proteins embedded to varying degrees **(figure 4.17).** This configuration, first proposed by S. J. Singer and G. L. Nicolson, is called the **fluid mosaic model.** The model describes a membrane as a continuous bilayer formed by lipids with the polar heads oriented toward the outside and the nonpolar tails toward the center of the membrane. Embedded at numerous sites in this bilayer are proteins of various sizes. Peripheral proteins are situated only at the surface and are readily removed. Integral proteins extend fully through the entire membrane and are often fixed in place. The configurations of the inner and outer sides of the membrane can be quite different because of the variations in protein shape and position.

Membranes are dynamic and constantly changing because the lipid phase is in motion, which allows some proteins to migrate to specific locations where they are needed. This fluidity is essential to such activities as cell enlargement and discharge or secretion by cells. The structure of the lipid phase provides an impenetrable barrier to many substances. This property accounts for the selective permeability and capacity to regulate transport of molecules. Bacterial cell membranes contain primarily phospholipids (making up about 30%–40% of the membrane mass) and proteins (contributing 60%–70%). Major exceptions to this description are the membranes of mycoplasmas, which contain high amounts of sterols—rigid lipids that stabilize and reinforce the membrane—and the membranes of archaea, which contain unique branched hydrocarbons rather than fatty acids. Look back to figure 2.21 to observe the eukaryotic membrane structure, which is very similar to bacteria, except for the presence of cholesterol in the eukaryotic variety.

Although bacteria lack complex internal membranous organelles, some members develop stacked layers of internal membranes that carry out physiological processes related to energy and synthesis. These membranes are usually an outgrowth of the cell membrane extending into the cytoplasm, which can increase the membrane surface area available for these reactions. Examples of cells with internal membranes are cyanobacteria, whose thylakoid membranes are the sites of photosynthesis. Even eukaryotic mitochondria, considered bacterial in origin, function by means of a series of internal membranes.

Functions of the Cell Membrane

Because bacteria have none of the eukaryotic organelles, the cell membrane provides a site for energy reactions, nutrient processing, and synthesis. The most important function of the cell membrane, however, is to act as a barrier between the inside and outside of the cell, regulating **transport**—the passage of nutrients into the cell and the discharge of wastes. Although water and small uncharged molecules can diffuse across the membrane unaided, the membrane is a **selectively permeable** structure with special carrier mechanisms for the passage of most molecules (see chapter 7). The glycocalyx and cell wall can bar the passage of large molecules, but they are not the primary transport apparatus. The cell membrane is also involved in **secretion,** or the release of metabolic products into the extracellular environment.

The membranes of bacteria are an important site for a number of metabolic activities. For example, most enzymes that handle the energy reactions of respiration reside in the cell membrane (see chapter 8). Enzyme structures located in the cell membrane also help synthesize structural macromolecules to be incorporated into the cell envelope and appendages. Other products (enzymes and toxins) are secreted by the membrane into the extracellular environment.

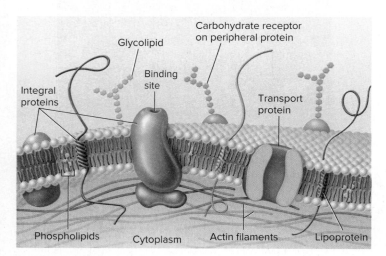

Figure 4.17 Cell membrane structure. A generalized version of the fluid mosaic model of a cell membrane indicates a bilayer of lipids with proteins embedded to some degree in the lipid matrix. Molecules attached to the proteins provide surface features for cell responsiveness and binding. This structure explains many characteristics of membranes, including flexibility, permeability, specificity, and transport.

Labels in figure: Carbohydrate receptor on peripheral protein; Glycolipid; Binding site; Integral proteins; Transport protein; Phospholipids; Cytoplasm; Actin filaments; Lipoprotein

Practice SECTION 4.3

11. Compare the basic structure of the cell envelopes of gram-positive and gram-negative bacteria.

12. Explain the function of peptidoglycan and give a simple description of its structure.

13. What happens to a cell when its peptidoglycan is disrupted or removed?

14. How does the precise structure of the cell walls differ between gram-positive and gram-negative bacteria?

15. What other properties besides staining are different in gram-positive and gram-negative bacteria?

16. What is the periplasmic space, and what is its function?

17. Describe the medical impact of the cell walls of gram-negative and gram-positive bacteria.

18. Describe the structure of the cell membrane, and explain why it is considered selectively permeable.

19. List five essential functions that the cell membrane performs in bacteria.

4.4 Bacterial Internal Structure

 Learn

15. List the contents of the cell cytoplasm.

16. Describe features of the bacterial chromosome and plasmids.

17. Characterize the bacterial ribosomes and cytoskeleton.

18. Describe inclusion bodies and granules, and explain their importance to cells.

19. Describe the life cycle of endospore-forming bacteria, including the formation and germination of endospores.

20. Discuss the resistance and significance of endospores.

Contents of the Cell Cytoplasm

The cell membrane surrounds a complex solution referred to as **cytoplasm,** or cytoplasmic matrix. This chemical "pool" is a prominent site for many of the cell's biochemical and synthetic activities. Its major component is water (70%–80%), which serves as a solvent for a complex mixture of nutrients, including sugars, amino acids, and other organic molecules and salts. The components of this pool serve as building blocks for cell synthesis or as sources of energy. The cytoplasm also holds larger, discrete bodies such as the chromosome, ribosomes, granules, and actin strands.

Bacterial Chromosomes and Plasmids: The Sources of Genetic Information

The hereditary material of most bacteria exists in the form of a single circular strand of DNA designated the **bacterial chromosome,** although a few bacteria have multiple or linear chromosomes. By definition, bacteria do not have a true nucleus. Their DNA is not enclosed by a nuclear membrane but instead is aggregated in a central area of the cell called the **nucleoid.** The chromosome is an extremely long molecule of DNA that is tightly coiled to fit inside the cell compartment and divided into genetic units (genes) that carry information required for bacterial maintenance and growth **(figure 4.18).**

Although the bacterial chromosome contains all the genetic material a cell needs to survive, many bacteria contain additional genetic elements called **plasmids.** Plasmids are generally small, circular pieces of DNA that exist independently within the cytoplasm, although at times they may become integrated into the much larger bacterial chromosome. During bacterial reproduction, they are duplicated and passed on to offspring. Although plasmids are not essential for survival, they often carry genes that confer favorable traits on the bacterial cell, such as toxin production or resistance to certain antibiotics (see chapter 9). Because they can be readily manipulated in the laboratory and transferred from one bacterial cell to another, plasmids are an important component of modern genetic engineering techniques.

Ribosomes: Sites of Protein Synthesis

Every bacterial cell contains tens of thousands of **ribosomes,** which are made of RNA and protein. When viewed even by very high

Figure 4.18 Bacterial cells stained to highlight their chromosomes. The individual cocci of *Deinococcus radiodurans* contain one or more prominent bodies that are the chromosomes or nucleoids (1,200×). Some cells are in the process of dividing. Notice how much of the cell's space the chromosomes (light blue bodies) occupy.
Courtesy of Michael J. Daly

magnification, ribosomes show up as fine, spherical specks dispersed throughout the cytoplasm that often occur in chains (polysomes). Many are also attached to the cell membrane. Chemically, a ribosome is a combination of a special type of RNA called ribosomal RNA, or rRNA (about 60%), and protein (40%).

One method of characterizing ribosomes is by S, or Svedberg,[4] units, which rate the molecular sizes of various cell parts that have been spun down and separated by molecular weight and shape in a centrifuge. Denser structures sediment faster and are assigned a higher S rating. Combining this method of analysis with high-resolution electron microscopy has revealed that the prokaryotic ribosome, which has an overall rating of 70S, is actually composed of two smaller subunits **(figure 4.19).** They fit together to form a miniature "factory" where protein synthesis occurs. We examine the more detailed functions of ribosomes in chapter 9.

Inclusions: Structures within the Cell

Although prokaryotic cells lack organelles, they do possess compartmentalized structures within the cytoplasm that perform a variety of functions. For example, most bacteria are exposed to severe shifts in the availability of food. During periods of nutrient abundance, some can compensate by storing nutrients as **inclusion bodies,** or **inclusions,** of varying size, number, and content. As the environmental source of these nutrients becomes depleted, the bacterial cell can mobilize its own storehouse as required. Some inclusion bodies contain condensed, energy-rich organic substances, such as glycogen and poly β-hydroxybutyrate (PHB), within special single-layered membranes **(figure 4.20a).** Gas vesicles are a unique

4. Named in honor of T. Svedberg, the Swedish chemist who developed the ultracentrifuge in 1926.

Ribosome (70S)

Large subunit (50S)

Small subunit (30S)

Figure 4.19 A model of a prokaryotic ribosome, showing the small (30S) and large (50S) subunits, both separate and joined.

type of inclusion found in some aquatic bacteria that provide buoyancy and flotation. Other inclusions, also called **granules,** contain crystals of inorganic compounds and are not enclosed by membranes. Sulfur granules of photosynthetic bacteria and polyphosphate granules of *Corynebacterium* and *Mycobacterium* are of this type. The latter are an important source of building blocks for nucleic acid and ATP synthesis. They have been termed **metachromatic granules** because they stain a contrasting color (red, purple) in the presence of methylene blue dye.

A second type of inclusion does far more than simply store nutrients for later use. **Microcompartments** are polyhedral (many-sided) packets formed by proteins bound together in compact units **(figure 4.20b).** The microcompartment encloses one or more enzymes along with the reactants needed for a specific metabolic

process. The best-understood microcompartment is the carboxysome, found in many cyanobacteria and other photosynthetic bacteria. It is the storage site of the enzyme responsible for CO_2 fixation, the process of converting CO_2 into organic compounds like sugar.

Perhaps the most remarkable cell granule is involved neither in nutrition nor in metabolism but rather in navigation. Magnetotactic bacteria contain crystalline particles of iron oxide (magnetosomes) that have magnetic properties **(figure 4.20c).** These granules occur in a variety of bacteria living in oceans and swamps. Their primary function is to orient the cells in the earth's magnetic field, somewhat like a compass. It is thought that magnetosomes direct these bacteria into locations with favorable oxygen levels or nutrient-rich sediments.

The Bacterial Cytoskeleton

Like eukaryotes, prokaryotic cells contain a cytoskeleton.[5] Protein polymers running throughout the cell play a crucial role in defining cell shape, along with aiding the processes of cell division, motility, and partitioning of cellular structures like DNA and microcompartments. Some cytoskeletal proteins are analogous to the actin, tubulin, and intermediate filament proteins found in eukaryotes, while others are unique to bacterial cells **(figure 4.21).**

Bacterial Endospores: An Extremely Resistant Life Form

Ample evidence indicates that the anatomy of bacteria helps them adjust rather well to adverse habitats. But of all microbial structures, nothing can compare to the bacterial **endospore** (or simply spore) for withstanding hostile conditions and facilitating survival. Endospores are dormant bodies produced by *Bacillus, Clostridium,* and several other bacterial genera. These bacteria have a two-phase life cycle that

5. An intracellular framework of fibers and tubules that bind and support eukaryotic cells.

(a) (b) (c)

Figure 4.20 Bacterial inclusion bodies. (a) Large, dark particles of polyhydroxybutyrate are deposited in an insoluble, concentrated form that provides an ample, long-term supply of that nutrient (32,500×). **(b)** Rendering of a bacterial microcompartment. The outer protein shell (blue) encloses the enzymes (green) required for a specific metabolic process. **(c)** A section through *Aquaspirillum* reveals a chain of tiny iron magnets (magnetosomes = MP). These unusual bacteria use these inclusions to orient within their habitat (123,000×).
(a): Kwangshin Kim/Science Source; (c): D. Balkwill and D. Maratea

Actin filaments

Figure 4.21 **Bacterial cytoskeleton of *Bacillus*.** Fluorescent stain of fibers appears as fine helical ribbons wound inside the cell. The inset provides a three-dimensional interpretation of its structure.
Rut Carballido-Lopez/I.N.R.A. Jouy-en-Josas, Laboratoire de Génétique Microbienne

shifts between a **vegetative cell** (**process figure 4.22, step 1**) and an endospore (process figure 4.22, step 8). The vegetative cell is the metabolically active and growing phase. When exposed to certain environmental signals, it forms an endospore by a process termed **sporulation.** The spore exists in an inert, resting condition that is capable of extreme resistance and long-term survival. The common shortening of the word *endospore* to *spore* has the potential to lead to confusion. Be sure not to confuse endospores—bacterial protective structures—with fungal spores, which are primarily reproductive structures.

Endospore Formation and Resistance

The major stimulus for endospore formation is the depletion of nutrients, especially amino acids. Once this stimulus has been received by the vegetative cell, it converts to a committed sporulating cell called a **sporangium.** Complete transformation of a vegetative cell into a sporangium and then into an endospore requires 6 to 12 hours in most spore-forming species. Process figure 4.22 illustrates some major physical and chemical events in this process.

Bacterial endospores are the hardiest of all life forms, capable of withstanding extremes in heat, drying, freezing, radiation, and

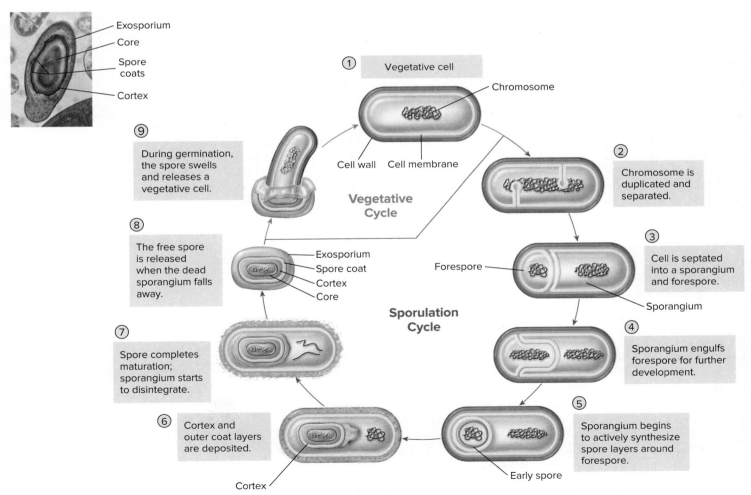

Exosporium
Core
Spore coats
Cortex

① Vegetative cell
Chromosome

Cell wall Cell membrane

Vegetative Cycle

② Chromosome is duplicated and separated.

③ Cell is septated into a sporangium and forespore.

Forespore

Sporangium

④ Sporangium engulfs forespore for further development.

⑤ Sporangium begins to actively synthesize spore layers around forespore.

Early spore

⑥ Cortex and outer coat layers are deposited.

Cortex

⑦ Spore completes maturation; sporangium starts to disintegrate.

Sporulation Cycle

⑧ The free spore is released when the dead sporangium falls away.

Exosporium
Spore coat
Cortex
Core

⑨ During germination, the spore swells and releases a vegetative cell.

⚙ **Process Figure 4.22** **A typical sporulation cycle from the active vegetative cell to release and germination.** This process takes, on average, about 10 hours. Inset is a high magnification (10,000×) cross section of a single spore showing the dense protective layers that surround the core with its chromosome.
(photo): SJ Jones, CJ Paredes, B Tracy, N Cheng, R Sillers, RS Senger, ET Papoutsakis, "The transcriptional program underlying the physiology of clostridial sporulation", Genome Biol, 2008. 9:R114.

chemicals that would readily kill ordinary cells. Their survival under such harsh conditions is due to several factors. The heat resistance of spores has been linked to their high content of calcium and *dipicolinic acid,* although the exact role of these chemicals is not yet clear. We know, for instance, that heat destroys cells by inactivating proteins and DNA and that this process requires a certain amount of water in the protoplasm. Because the deposition of calcium dipicolinate in the endospore removes water and leaves the endospore very dehydrated, it is less vulnerable to the effects of heat. It is also metabolically inactive and highly resistant to damage from further drying. The thick, impervious cortex and spore coats provide additional protection against radiation and chemicals.

The longevity of bacterial spores verges on immortality! One record describes the isolation of viable endospores from a fossilized bee that was 25 million years old. More recently, microbiologists unearthed a viable endospore from a 250-million-year-old salt crystal. Initial analysis of this ancient microbe indicates it is a species of *Bacillus* that is genetically different from known species.

The Germination of Endospores

After lying in a state of inactivity, endospores can be revitalized when favorable conditions arise. The breaking of dormancy, or **germination,** happens in the presence of water and a specific germination agent. Once initiated, it proceeds to completion quite rapidly (1½ hours). Although the specific germination agent varies among species, it is generally a small organic molecule, such as an amino acid or an inorganic salt. This agent stimulates the formation of hydrolytic (digestive) enzymes by the endospore membranes. These enzymes digest the cortex and expose the core to water. As the core rehydrates and takes up nutrients, it begins to grow out of the endospore coats. In time it reverts to a fully active vegetative cell, resuming the vegetative cycle (process figure 4.22).

Although most spore-forming bacteria are relatively harmless, several bacterial pathogens are spore-formers. In fact, some aspects of the diseases they cause are related to the persistence and resistance of their spores. Endospores of *Bacillus anthracis*, the agent of anthrax, are classified as a high-level bioterrorism agent. The genus *Clostridium* includes even more pathogens, including *C. tetani*, the cause of tetanus (lockjaw), and *C. perfringens*, the cause of gas gangrene. When the spores of these species are embedded in a wound that contains dead tissue, they can germinate, grow, and release potent toxins. Another toxin-forming species, *C. botulinum*, is the agent of botulism, a deadly form of food poisoning. These diseases are discussed further in chapter 19.

Because they inhabit soil and dust, endospores are a constant intruder where sterility and cleanliness are important. They resist ordinary cleaning methods that use boiling water, soaps, and disinfectants, and they frequently contaminate cultures and media. Hospitals and clinics must take precautions to guard against the potential harmful effects of endospores in wounds. Endospore destruction is a particular concern of the food-canning industry. Several endospore-forming species cause food spoilage or poisoning. Ordinary boiling (100°C) will usually not destroy such spores, so canning is carried out in pressurized steam at 120°C for 20 to 30 minutes. Such rigorous conditions ensure that the food is sterile and free from viable bacteria.

 CLINIC CASE

Just Say No When a 39-year-old man arrived at an emergency room complaining of severe pain, tenderness, and swelling in his upper shoulder and chest area, doctors diagnosed cellulitis caused by an infection and prescribed antibiotics. However, the patient's symptoms worsened, with severe inflammation and edema through much of the chest and one arm. The affected areas felt spongy to the touch, with blisters on the surface of the skin, and increasing areas of tissue death (necrosis). Drainage from the lesions contained pus and had a foul odor. Gram stains of tissue and fluid samples revealed varied cell types indicative of a mixed infection. Further questioning revealed that the patient was an IV drug user who had most recently mixed heroin and cocaine with tap water and injected it into his arm with a nonsterile needle.

The patient was diagnosed with clostridial myonecrosis, also known as gas gangrene, caused by *Clostridium perfringens*, an anaerobic, gram-positive bacillus, which is widespread in soil, dust, and mucous membranes of the GI tract. Ordinarily noninvasive, endospores of *Clostridium perfringens* can enter the body through lacerations or skin-piercing injuries—in this case, nonsterile water injected with an unclean needle—and germinate in the anoxic tissue. Other bacteria growing in the wound (as evidenced by the mixed result in the Gram stain) use up the available oxygen, contributing to a local anaerobic environment. Gas produced by the growth of *Clostridium* forces apart muscle fibers and contributes to the spongy feel of the infected area. This, along with bubbles on the surface of the skin, tissue destruction, and a foul odor, are all hallmarks of clostridial infection.

The patient was treated with antibiotics, surgical debridement of necrotic tissue, and spent several sessions in a hyperbaric oxygen chamber, along with physical therapy and treatment for drug addiction.

What is the importance of surgical debridement and hyperbaric oxygen therapy in this case?

Practice SECTION 4.4

20. Compare the functions of the bacterial chromosome (nucleoid) and plasmids.

21. What is unique about the structure of bacterial ribosomes, what is their function, and where are they located?

22. Compare and contrast the structure and function of inclusions and granules.

23. What are metachromatic granules, and what do they contain?

24. Describe the way endospores are formed, their structure, and their importance in the life cycle.

25. Explain why an endospore is not considered a reproductive body.

26. Why are spores so difficult to destroy?

4.5 Bacterial Shapes, Arrangements, and Sizes

 Learn

21. Describe the shapes of bacteria and their possible variants.

22. Identify several arrangements of bacteria and how they are formed.

23. Outline the size ranges among bacteria and in comparison to other organisms.

For the most part, bacteria function as independent single-celled, or unicellular, organisms. Although it is true that an individual bacterial cell can live in concert with others in colonies or biofilms, each one is fully capable of carrying out all necessary life activities, such as reproduction, metabolism, and nutrient processing, unlike the more specialized cells of a multicellular organism.

Bacteria exhibit considerable variety in shape, size, and colonial arrangement. It is convenient to describe most bacteria by one of three general shapes as dictated by the configuration of the cell wall **(figure 4.23).** If the cell is spherical or ball-shaped, the bacterium is

Key to Micrographs

(a) *Staphylococcus aureus* (10,000×) (b) *Legionella pneumophila* (6,500×) (c) *Vibrio cholerae* (13,000×) (d) *Aquaspirillum* (7,500×)

(e) *Borrelia burgdorferi* (10,000×) (f) *Streptomyces* species (1,000×)

Figure 4.23 Common bacterial shapes. Drawings show examples of shape variations for cocci, rods, vibrios, spirilla, spirochetes, and branching filaments. Below each shape is a micrograph of a representative example.

(a): *Source:* Jeff Hageman, M.H.S./Janice Carr/CDC; (b): *Source:* Janice Haney Carr/CDC; (c): BSIP SA/Alamy Stock Photo; (d): *Source:* Photo by De Wood, digital colorization by Chris Pooley, USDA-ARS; (e): *Source:* Janice Haney Carr/CDC; (f): *Source:* Dr. David Berd/CDC

TABLE 4.2	Comparison of the Two Spiral-Shaped Bacteria				
	Overall Appearance Helical or Spiral Forms	Mode of Locomotion	Number of Helical Turns	Gram Reaction (Cell Wall Type)	Examples of Important Types
Spirilla	Rigid helix Spirilla Richard Gross/McGraw-Hill Education	Polar flagella; cells swim by rotating around like corkscrews; do not flex; have one to several flagella; can be in tufts	Varies from 1 to 20	Gram-negative	Most are nonpathogenic. One species, *Spirillum minor*, causes rat bite fever.
Spirochetes	Flexible helix Spirochete Stephen Durr	Periplasmic flagella within sheath; cells flex; can swim by rotation or by creeping on surfaces; have 2 to 100 periplasmic flagella	Varies from 3 to 70	Gram-negative	*Treponema pallidum*, cause of syphilis; *Borrelia* and *Leptospira*, important pathogens

described as a **coccus.*** Cocci can be perfect spheres, but they also can exist as oval, bean-shaped, or even pointed variants.

A cell that is cylindrical (longer than wide) is termed a rod, or **bacillus.*** There is also a genus called *Bacillus,* named for its rod shape. As might be expected, rods are also quite varied in their actual form. Depending on the bacterial species, they can be blocky, spindle-shaped, round-ended, long and threadlike (filamentous), or even clubbed or drumstick-shaped. When a rod is short and plump, it is called a **coccobacillus;** if it is gently curved, it is a **vibrio.***

A bacterium with the shape of a curviform or spiral-shaped cylinder is called a **spirillum,*** a rigid helix, twisted twice or more along its axis (like a corkscrew). Another spiral cell mentioned earlier in conjunction with periplasmic flagella is the **spirochete,** a more flexible form that resembles a spring. Refer to **table 4.2** for a comparison of other features of the two helical bacterial forms. Because bacterial cells look two-dimensional and flat with traditional staining and microscope techniques, they are best observed using a scanning electron microscope to emphasize their striking three-dimensional forms (figure 4.23).

It is common for cells of a single species to show **pleomorphism*** **(figure 4.24).** This is due to individual variations in cell wall structure caused by nutritional or slight hereditary differences. For example, although the cells of *Corynebacterium diphtheriae* are generally considered rod-shaped, in culture they display club-shaped, swollen, curved, filamentous, and coccoid variations. Pleomorphism reaches an extreme in the mycoplasmas, which entirely lack cell walls and thus display extreme variations in shape (see figure 4.16).

Bacterial cells can also be categorized according to **arrangement,** or style of grouping. The main factors influencing the arrangement of a particular cell type are its pattern of division and how the cells remain attached afterward. The greatest variety in arrangement occurs in cocci

> **Quick Search**
> To appreciate their differences, look for "Spirochetes that Cause Lyme Disease" and "Motile Spirilla" on YouTube.

Figure 4.24 Pleomorphism and other morphological features of *Corynebacterium*. Cells are irregular in shape and size (800×). This genus typically exhibits a palisades arrangement, with cells in parallel array (inset). Close examination will also reveal darkly stained metachromatic granules.
Source: Dr. P.B. Smith/CDC

(figure 4.25). They may exist as singles, in pairs **(diplococci*),** in **tetrads** (groups of four), in irregular clusters (both **staphylococci*** and **micrococci**), or in chains of a few to hundreds of cells **(streptococci).** An even more complex grouping is a cubical packet of 8, 16, or more cells called a **sarcina.*** These different coccal groupings are the result of the division of a coccus in a single plane, in two perpendicular planes, or in several intersecting planes; after division, the resultant daughter cells remain attached.

* *coccus* (kok′-us) pl. cocci (kok′-seye) Gr. *kokkos,* berry.
* *bacillus* (bah-sil′-lus) pl. bacilli (bah-sil′-eye) L. *bacill,* small staff or rod.
* *vibrio* (vib′-ree-oh) L. *vibrare,* to shake.
* *spirillum* (spy-ril′-em) pl. spirilla; L. *spira,* a coil.
* *pleomorphism* (plee″-oh-mor′-fizm) Gr. *pleon,* more, and *morph,* form or shape.

* *diplococci* (dih-plo-kok-seye) Gr. *diplo,* double.
* *staphylococci* (staf″-ih-loh-kok′-seye) Gr. *staphyle,* a bunch of grapes.
* *sarcina* (sar′-sin-uh) L. *sarcina,* a packet.

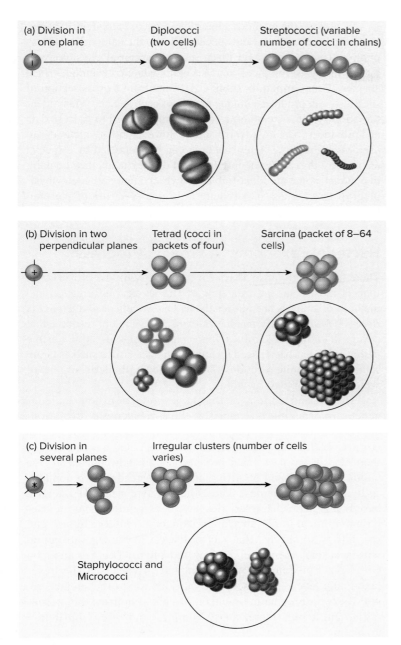

Figure 4.25 Arrangement of cocci resulting from different planes of cell division. (a) Division in one plane produces diplococci and streptococci. (b) Division in two planes at right angles produces tetrads and packets. (c) Division in several planes produces irregular clusters.

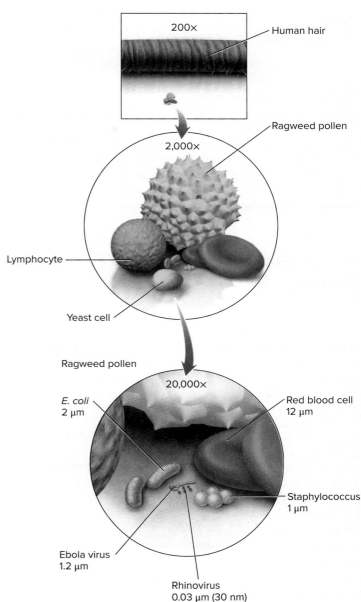

Figure 4.26 The dimensions of bacteria. The sizes of bacteria range from those just barely visible with light microscopy (0.2 µm) to those measuring a thousand times that size. Cocci measure anywhere from 0.5 to 3.0 µm in diameter; bacilli range from 0.2 to 2.0 µm in diameter and from 0.5 to 20 µm in length. Note the range of sizes as compared with eukaryotic cells and viruses. Comparisons are given as average sizes.

Bacilli are less varied in arrangement because they divide only in the transverse plane (perpendicular to the axis). They occur either as single cells, as a pair of cells with their ends attached (**diplobacilli**), or as a chain of several cells (**streptobacilli**). A **palisades*** arrangement, typical of the

> **Quick Search**
> For a fascinating comparison of the size of microscopic structures, search for "Size and Scale" on YouTube.

corynebacteria, is formed when the cells of a chain remain partially attached by a small hinged region at the ends. The cells tend to fold (snap) back upon each other, forming a row of cells oriented side by side (see figure 4.24). The reaction can be compared to the behavior of boxcars on a jackknifed train, and the result looks superficially like an irregular picket fence. Spirilla are occasionally found in short chains, but spirochetes rarely remain attached after division. Comparative sizes of typical cells are presented in **figure 4.26.**

* *palisades* (pal´-ih-saydz) L. *pale,* a stake. A fence made of a row of stakes.

 Practice SECTION 4.5

27. Classify bacteria according to their basic shapes.

28. How are spirochetes and spirilla different?

29. What are vibrios and coccobacilli?

30. Describe pleomorphism, and give examples of bacteria with this trait.

31. What is the difference between the use of the shape bacillus and the name *Bacillus*? *Staphylococcus* and staphylococcus?

32. Rank the size ranges of bacteria according to shape, and compare bacterial size with viruses and eukaryotic cells.

4.6 Classification Systems of Prokaryotic Domains: Archaea and Bacteria

 Learn

24. Describe the purposes of classification and taxonomy in the study of prokaryotes.

25. Summarize characteristics used to classify bacteria.

26. Outline a basic system of bacterial taxonomy.

27. Explain the species and subspecies levels for bacteria.

Classification systems serve both practical and academic purposes. They aid in differentiating and identifying unknown species in medical and applied microbiology. They are also useful in organizing bacteria and as a means of studying their relationships and evolutionary origins. Since classification was first initiated around 200 years ago, several thousand species of bacteria and archaea have been identified, named, and catalogued.

Tracing the origins of and evolutionary relationships among bacteria has not been an easy task. As a rule, tiny, relatively soft organisms do not form fossils very readily. Several times since the 1960s, however, scientists have discovered billion-year-old fossils of prokaryotes that look very much like modern bacteria.

One of the questions that has plagued taxonomists is: What characteristics are reliable indicators of closeness in ancestry? Early bacteriologists found it convenient to classify bacteria according to shape, variations in arrangement, growth characteristics, and habitat. However, as more species were discovered and as techniques for studying their biochemistry were developed, it soon became clear that similarities in cell shape, arrangement, and staining reactions do not automatically indicate relatedness. Even though gram-negative rods look alike, there are hundreds of different species with highly significant differences in biochemistry and genetics. If we attempted to classify them on the basis of Gram stain and shape alone, we could not assign them to a more specific level than class. Newer classification schemes depend more on genetic and molecular characteristics than appearance under the microscope.

In general, the methods a microbiologist uses to identify bacteria to the level of genus and species fall into the categories of morphology (microscopic and macroscopic), bacterial physiology or biochemistry, serological analysis, and genetic techniques (see chapter 17 and **appendix table C.1**). Data from a cross section of such tests can produce a unique profile of each species. Many identification systems are automated and computerized to process data and provide a "best fit" identification. However, not all methods are used on all bacteria. A few bacteria can be identified by a special technology that analyzes only the kind of fatty acids they contain; in contrast, some are identifiable by a Gram stain and a few physiological tests; others may require a diverse spectrum of morphological, biochemical, and genetic analyses.

Bacterial Taxonomy: A Work in Progress

There is no single official system for classifying the prokaryotes. Indeed, most plans are in a state of flux as new information and methods of analysis become available. One widely used reference is *Bergey's Manual of Systematic Bacteriology,* a major resource that covers all known prokaryotes. In the past, the classification scheme in this guide has been based mostly on characteristics such as Gram stain and metabolic reactions. This is called a **phenetic,** or phenotypic, method of classification.

The second edition of this large collection now includes genetic information that clarifies the **phylogenetic** (evolutionary) history and relationships of the thousands of known species **(figure 4.27).** This change has redefined our presentation of their classification, so that prokaryotes are now placed in five major subgroups and 25 different phyla instead of two domains split into four divisions. The Domains Archaea and Bacteria based on genetic characteristics have been retained, but the bacteria of clinical importance are no longer as closely aligned, and the 250 or so species that cause disease in humans are found within seven or eight of the revised phyla. The grouping by Gram reaction remains significant but primarily at the lower taxonomic levels. This being an introduction to the subject, we will follow a pragmatic organization that simplifies the presentation and avoids increasingly complex and often conflicting taxonomy.

The major categories of this revised taxonomic scheme are presented in **table 4.3,** which provides a brief survey of characteristics of the major taxonomic groups, along with examples of representative members (A–O). For a complete version of the major taxonomic groups and genera, go to **appendix table C.2.**

A Diagnostic Scheme for Medical Use

Many medical microbiologists prefer an informal working system that outlines the major families and genera **(table 4.4).** This scheme uses the phenotypic qualities of bacteria in identification. It is restricted to bacterial disease agents and depends less on nomenclature. It also divides the bacteria into gram-positive, gram-negative, and those without cell walls and then subgroups them according to cell shape, arrangement, and certain physiological traits such as oxygen usage: *Aerobic* bacteria use oxygen

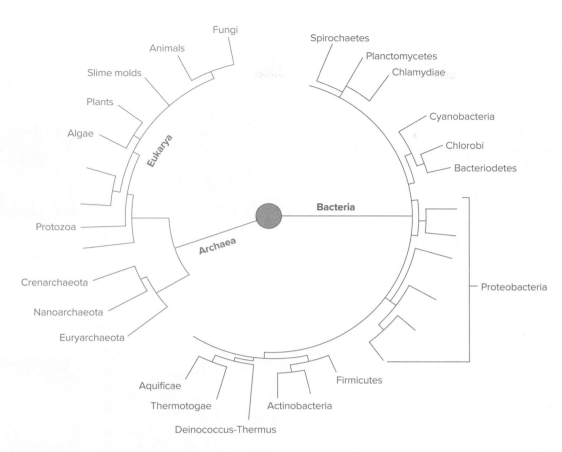

Figure 4.27 **A master classification scheme based on ribosomal analysis.** This pattern displays the major phyla within Domains Bacteria and Archaea. Branches indicate the origins of each group, and their relative positions estimate ancestral relationships. Major groups of Domain Eukarya are shown here for comparison.

in metabolism; *anaerobic* bacteria do not use oxygen in metabolism; and facultative bacteria may or may not use oxygen. Further tests not listed on the table would be required to separate closely related genera and species. Many of these are included in later chapters on specific bacterial groups.

Species and Subspecies in Bacteria

Among most organisms, the **species** level is a distinct, readily defined, and natural taxonomic category. In animals, for instance, a species is a distinct type of organism that can produce viable offspring only when it mates with others of its own kind. This definition does not work for bacteria primarily because they do not exhibit a typical mode of sexual reproduction. They can accept DNA from unrelated forms, and they can also alter their genetic makeup by a variety of mechanisms. Thus, it is necessary to use a modified definition for a bacterial species. Theoretically, it is a collection of bacterial cells, all of which share an overall similar pattern of traits, in contrast to other groups whose pattern differs significantly. Although the boundaries that separate two closely related species in a genus can be somewhat arbitrary, this definition still serves as a method to separate the bacteria into various kinds that can be cultured and studied.

Because the individual members of given species can show variations, microbiologists refer to subcategories within species like **subspecies, strain,** or **type.** Imagine, for example, breeds of dogs; poodles and Great Danes are both members of the same species but are clearly different. Similarly, there are pigmented and nonpigmented strains of *Serratia marcescens* and flagellated and nonflagellated strains of *Pseudomonas fluorescens.* A **serotype** refers to representatives of a species that have surface molecules different than other members of the species, and that can be identified using antibodies.

Practice SECTION 4.6

33. What general characteristics are used to classify bacteria?

34. What are the most useful characteristics for categorizing bacteria into phyla?

35. Explain some of the ways species level in bacteria is defined, and name at least three ways bacteria are classified below the species level.

TABLE 4.3 Overview of a Classification System for Prokaryotes Based on *Bergey's Manual,* 2nd Edition (see appendix table C.2 for a full outline.)

Volume 1 Domain Archaea Includes prokaryotes with unusual morphology, ecology, and modes of nutrition. Many of the known members are adapted to a habitat with extremes of temperature (hyperthermophiles), salt (halophiles), acidity (acidophiles), pressure, or lack of oxygen (anaerobic), and sometimes combinations of these. The domain has great ecological importance due to its actions in biogeochemical cycling. More coverage can be found in section 4.7.

Phylum Crenarchaeota Members depend on sulfur for growth and may inhabit hot and acidic sulfur pools and vents. Some species have adapted to cold habitats. See examples in **figures A** and 4.33.

Phylum Nanoarchaeota A newly discovered group of extremely small archaea found in salt mines and caves (see 4.1 Making Connections).

Phylum Euryarchaeota The largest and best-studied group of archaea; members' adaptations include methane production (methanogens), high saline or salt (halobacteria or halophiles), high temperature (thermophiles), and reduction of sulfur compounds. An example is *Methanocaldococcus* (**figure B**).

A. Unidentified thermophilic crenarchaeotes isolated from a deep-sea thermal vent at 160°F (71°C). *Source:* West Coast and Polar Regions Undersea Research Center, UAF/NOAA

B. *Methanocaldococcus*—a hyperthermophile inhabiting hydrothermal vents at near-boiling temperature. *Source:* Maryland Astrobiology Consortium, NASA and STScI

Volume 1 Domain Bacteria I This domain contains deeply branching and photosynthetic bacteria that are considered the oldest evolutionary lines still in existence. It contains a wide diversity of prominent bacteria, including photosynthesizers (cyanobacteria), thermophiles, radiation-resistant bacteria, halophiles, and sulfur metabolizers.

Phylum Aquificae This group contains small thermophilic rods that inhabit underwater volcanoes.

Phylum Thermotogae A phylum similar to Aquificae; includes thermophilic halophiles that live in deep-sea vents. An example is *Desulfurobacterium* (**figure C**).

Phylum Chlorobi Also known as green sulfur bacteria, this phylum consists of anaerobic bacteria that live in the muddy layers of lakes and ponds, where they photosynthesize and metabolize sulfides.

Phylum Deinococcus-Thermus A small phylum of extremophiles whose members range from being highly radiation- and desiccation-resistant cocci that live in soil and fresh water to rods that live in very hot aquatic habitats, such as hot springs and pools. *Deinococcus* can be seen in figure 4.18.

Phylum Cyanobacteria Very ubiquitous photosynthetic bacteria found in aquatic habitats, soil, and often associated with plants, fungi, and other organisms; blue-green, green, yellow, red, and orange in color. An example is *Gloeotrichia* (**figure D;** see section 4.7 for more coverage).

C. *Desulfurobacterium*—a tiny anaerobic, halophilic rod that reduces sulfur compounds. *Source:* From M. Goker et al, "Complete genome sequence of the thermophilic sulfur-reducer *Desulfurobacterium thermolithotrophum* type strain (BSA^T) from a deep-sea hydrothermal vent", "SIGS, 2011, 5:3, Fig. 2"

D. *Gloeotrichia*—a cyanobacterium that forms colonies of radiating filaments that float in lakes and ponds. *Source:* Barry H. Rosen, Ph. D/USGS

Volume 2 Domain Bacteria II This domain, along with the phyla that are covered in volumes 3, 4, and 5, contains bacteria that have the greatest medical impact.

Phylum Proteobacteria This phylum contains five classes representing an extremely varied cross section of over 2,000 identified species of bacteria. Though all share the characteristic of a gram-negative cell wall, the group contains bacteria with a wide range of adaptations, shapes, habitats, and ecology. Medically significant members include the obligately parasitic rickettsias; *Neisseria;* enterics such as *Escherichia coli* and *Salmonella; Vibrio* species; and other bacteria that live in the intestinal tracts of animals. The myxobacteria have the unique characteristic of being the only bacteria that can aggregate into multicellular structures (see figure 4.30; see also **figures E, F,** and **G** for examples).

E. A *Rickettsia rickettsii* cell (cause of Rocky Mountain spotted fever) being engulfed by a host cell. *Source:* Dr. Edwin P. Ewing, Jr./CDC

F. *Escherichia coli* O157:H7—a food-borne pathogen. *Source:* Janice Carr/CDC

G. A vibrio-shaped thermophile, *Desulfovibrio,* living in a pond biofilm. *Source:* Pacific Northwest National Laboratory

TABLE 4.3 *(continued)*

Volume 3 Phylum Firmicutes This collection of mostly gram-positive bacteria is characterized by having a low G + C content* (less than 50%). The three classes in the phylum display significant diversity, and a number of the members are pathogenic. Endospore-forming genera include *Bacillus* and *Clostridium.* Other important pathogens are found in genera *Staphylococcus* and *Streptococcus.* Although they lack a cell wall entirely, mycoplasmas (see figure 4.16) have been placed with the Firmicutes because of their genetic relatedness. (See **figures H** and **I.**)

H. *Bacillus anthracis*—SEM micrograph showing the rod-shaped cells next to a red blood cell.
Source: Arthur Friedlander

I. *Streptococcus pneumoniae*—image displays the diplococcus arrangement of this species.
Source: Janice Carr/CDC

Volume 4 Phylum Actinobacteria This taxonomic category includes the high G + C (over 50%) gram-positive bacteria. Members of this small group differ considerably in life cycles and morphology. Prominent members include the branching filamentous Actinomycetes, the spore-bearing Streptomycetes, *Corynebacterium* (see figure 4.24), *Mycobacterium,* and *Micrococcus.* (See **figures J** and **K.**)

J. *Streptomyces* species—common soil bacteria; often the source of antibiotics.
Source: Dr. David Berd/CDC

K. *Mycobacterium tuberculosis*—the bacillus that causes tuberculosis.
Source: Janice Carr/CDC

Volume 5 This represents a mixed assemblage of nine phyla, all of which are gram-negative but otherwise widely varied. The following is a selected array of examples.

Phylum Chlamydiae Another group of obligate intracellular parasites that reproduce inside host cells. These are among the smallest of bacteria, with a unique mode of reproduction. Several species cause diseases of the eyes, reproductive tract, and lungs. An example is *Chlamydia* (**figure L**).

Phylum Spirochetes These bacteria are distinguished by their shape and mode of locomotion. They move their slender, twisted cells by means of periplasmic flagella. Members live in a variety of habitats, including the bodies of animals and protozoans, fresh and marine water, and even muddy swamps. Important genera are *Treponema* (**figure M**) and *Borrelia* (see figure 4.23*e*).

Phylum Planctomycetes This group lives in fresh and marine water habitats and reproduces by budding. Many have a stalk that they use to attach to substrates. A unique feature is having a membrane around their DNA and special compartments enclosed in membranes. This has led to the speculation that they are similar to an ancestral form that gave rise to eukaryotes. An example is *Gemmata* (**figure N**).

Phylum Bacteriodetes These are widely distributed gram-negative anaerobic rods inhabiting soil, sediments, and water habitats, and frequently found as normal residents of the intestinal tracts of animals. They may be grouped with related Phyla Fibrobacteres and Chlorobi. Several members play an important role in the function of the human gut and some are involved in oral and intestinal infections. An example is *Bacteroides* (**figure O**).

L. View of an infected host cell revealing a vacuole containing *Chlamydia* cells in various stages of development. *Source:* N. Borel et al, "Mixed infections with Chlamydia and porcine epidemic diarrhea virus - a new in vitro model of chlamydial persistence", *BMC Microbiology* 2010, 10:201, Fig. 3a.

M. *Treponema pallidum*—spirochetes that cause syphilis.
Source: Joyce Ayers/CDC

N. *Gemmata*—view of a budding cell through a fluorescent microscope (note the large blue nucleoid). *Source:* K-C Lee, R Webb, JA Fuerst, "The cell cycle of the planctomycete Gemmata obscuriglobus with respect to cell compartmentalization", "BMC Cell Biol. 2009; 10:4, Fig 3i. NCBI"

O. *Bacteroides* species—may cause intestinal infections.
Source: V.R. Dowell/CDC

*G + C base composition. The overall percentage of guanine and cytosine in DNA is a general indicator of relatedness because it is a trait that does not change rapidly. Bacteria with a significant difference in G + C percentage are less likely to be genetically related. This classification scheme is partly based on this percentage.

TABLE 4.4 Important Families and Genera of Pathogenic Bacteria, with Notes on Some Diseases*

I. Bacteria with gram-positive cell wall structure (Phyla Firmicutes and Actinobacteria)

A. Cocci in clusters or packets that are aerobic or facultative

Family Staphylococcaceae:
Staphylococcus (members cause boils, skin infections)

B. Cocci in pairs and chains that are facultative

Family Streptococcaceae:
Streptococcus (species cause strep throat, dental caries)

C. Anaerobic cocci in pairs, tetrads, irregular clusters

Family Peptococcaceae: *Peptococcus, Peptostreptococcus* (involved in wound infections)

D. Spore-forming rods

Family Bacillaceae: *Bacillus* (anthrax), *Clostridium* (tetanus, gas gangrene, botulism)

E. Non-spore-forming rods

Family Lactobacillaceae:
Lactobacillus, Listeria (food infection), *Erysipelothrix* (erysipeloid)

Family Propionibacteriaceae:
Propionibacterium (involved in acne)

Family Corynebacteriaceae:
Corynebacterium (diphtheria)

Family Mycobacteriaceae:
Mycobacterium (tuberculosis, leprosy)

Family Nocardiaceae:
Nocardia (lung abscesses)

Family Actinomycetaceae:
Actinomyces (dental infections)

Family Streptomycetaceae:
Streptomyces (important source of antibiotics)

II. Bacteria with gram-negative cell wall structure (Phyla Proteobacteria, Bacteriodetes, Fusobacterium, Spirochaetes, Chlamydiae)

F. Aerobic cocci

Family Neisseraceae: *Neisseria* (gonorrhea, meningitis)

G. Aerobic coccobacilli

Family Moraxellaceae: *Moraxella, Acinetobacter*

H. Anaerobic cocci

Family Veillonellaceae: *Veillonella* (dental disease)

I. Aerobic rods

Family Pseudomonadaceae:
Pseudomonas (pneumonia, burn infections)

Miscellaneous rods (different families):
Brucella (undulant fever), *Bordetella* (whooping cough), *Francisella* (tularemia), *Coxiella* (Q fever), *Legionella* (Legionnaires' disease)

J. Facultative rods and vibrios

Family Enterobacteriaceae:
Escherichia, Edwardsiella, Citrobacter, Salmonella (typhoid fever), *Shigella* (dysentery), *Klebsiella, Enterobacter, Serratia, Proteus, Yersinia* (one species causes plague)

Family Vibronaceae: *Vibrio* (cholera, food infection)

Family Campylobacteraceae: *Campylobacter* (enteritis)
Family Helicobacteraceae: *Helicobacter* (ulcers)

Miscellaneous genera:
Flavobacterium, Haemophilus (meningitis), *Pasteurella* (bite infections), *Streptobacillus*

K. Anaerobic rods
Family Bacteroidaceae:
Bacteroides, Fusobacterium (anaerobic wound and dental infections)

L. Helical and curviform bacteria
Family Spirochaetaceae: *Treponema* (syphilis), *Borrelia* (Lyme disease), *Leptospira* (kidney infection)

M. Obligate and facultative intracellular bacteria
Family Rickettsiaceae: *Rickettsia* (Rocky Mountain spotted fever)
Family Anaplasmataceae:
Ehrlichia (human ehrlichosis)

Family Chlamydiaceae:
Chlamydia (sexually transmitted infection)
Family Bartonellaceae:
Bartonella (trench fever, cat scratch disease)

III. Bacteria with no cell walls (Class Mollicutes)

Family Mycoplasmataceae: *Mycoplasma* (pneumonia), *Ureaplasma* (urinary infection)

*Details of pathogens and diseases in later chapters.

4.7 Survey of Prokaryotic Groups with Unusual Characteristics

 Learn

28. Differentiate various groups of photosynthetic bacteria.
29. Characterize the types of obligate intracellular bacteria.
30. Summarize the basic characteristics of archaea.
31. Compare Domain Archaea with Domains Bacteria and Eukarya.
32. Explain archaeal adaptations that place them in the category of extremophiles.

So far in our introduction to the bacterial world, we have covered a rich variety of members with exceptional modes of living and behaving. And yet we are still in the early phases of discovery. Investigations of unexplored areas of the earth continue to surprise and instruct us about the adaptations and importance of these remarkable organisms. Doing justice to such incredible diversity would require more space than we can set aside in an introductory textbook, but in this section we have selected some of the more prominent and unusual groups to present. In this minisurvey, we consider some medically important groups and some representatives of bacteria living free in the environment that are ecologically important. Many of the bacteria mentioned here do not have the morphology typical of bacteria discussed previously, and in a few cases, they are vividly different **(4.1 Making Connections).**

Free-Living Nonpathogenic Bacteria

Photosynthetic Bacteria

The nutrition of many bacteria is heterotrophic; this means that the bacteria feed primarily off nutrients from other organisms. Photosynthetic bacteria, however, are independent cells that contain special light-trapping pigments and can use the energy of sunlight to synthesize all required nutrients from simple inorganic compounds. The two general types of photosynthetic bacteria are those that produce oxygen during photosynthesis and those that produce some other substance, such as sulfur granules or sulfates.

Cyanobacteria: Microbial Marvels

Cyanobacteria, gram-negative **phototrophic*** bacteria in the Phylum Cyanobacteria, are among the most dominant microorganisms on earth, with a long list of significant contributions to the planet. They are ancient in origin, probably having existed in some form for around 3 billion years. We can still find remnants of these early cells in fossil biofilms called stromatolites **(figure 4.28***b***1, 2).** Many evolutionary microbiologists theorize that because cyanobacteria were the very first photosynthesizers, they were responsible for converting the atmosphere from anaerobic to aerobic through their production of oxygen, which made it possible for the evolution of

aerobic eukaryotes. Other contributions they have made to eukaryotic evolution include the chloroplasts of algae and plants. When chloroplasts are subjected to genetic analysis, it turns out that they are close relatives of some of the oldest groups of cyanobacteria, and probably arose through endosymbiosis (see chapter 5). So the green color of a forest or a field of corn actually comes from these tiny bacteria that became a part of photosynthetic eukaryotes billions of years ago. The earth would be an entirely different place if it were not for these microorganisms.

Cyanobacteria are very diverse in distribution and morphology. They flourish in every type of aquatic environment, whether ocean, hot springs, or Antarctic ice, and they can also survive in a wide range of terrestrial habitats. Because of this widespread distribution, they are huge contributors to worldwide productivity. Two species of cyanobacteria alone—*Prochlorococcus* and *Trichodesmium*—account for 30% to 40% of biomass formation and 50% of oxygen production through photosynthesis in the oceans. They are also one of a few groups of microbes that can convert nitrogen gas (N_2) into ammonium (NH_4^+) that can be used by plants, making them essential players in the nitrogen cycle.

Their structure and arrangement are varied, from coccoid, rodlike, and spiral-shaped cells, with arrangements in filaments, clusters, and sheets, usually surrounded by a gelatinous sheath **(figure 4.28***a***, 2).** Although their primary photosynthetic pigments include green chlorophyll *b* and the bluish pigment phycocyanin, they may take on shades of yellow, orange, and red derived from other pigments.

Within an individual cell are found extensive specialized membranes called **thylakoids,** the locations of pigments and the sites of photosynthesis. They also have gas vesicles that keep the cells suspended high in the water column to facilitate photosynthesis. Cyanobacteria periodically overgrow in aquatic environments to form blooms that are harmful to fish and other inhabitants, and some produce toxins that could cause illness if ingested, but they are generally not medically important.

Green and Purple Sulfur Bacteria

The green and purple bacteria are also photosynthetic and contain pigments. They differ from the cyanobacteria in having a different type of chlorophyll called *bacteriochlorophyll* and by not giving off oxygen as a product of photosynthesis. They live in sulfur springs, freshwater lakes, and swamps that are deep enough for the anaerobic conditions they require yet where their pigment can still absorb wavelengths of light **(figure 4.29).** These bacteria are named for their predominant colors, but they can also develop brown, pink, purple, blue, and orange coloration. Both groups utilize sulfur compounds (H_2S, S) in their metabolism.

Gliding, Fruiting Bacteria

The gliding bacteria are a mixed collection of gram-negative bacteria in Phylum Proteobacteria that live in water and soil. The name is derived from the tendency of members to glide over moist surfaces. The gliding property evidently involves rotation of filaments or fibers just under the outer membrane of the cell wall.

* *phototropic* literally "to feed with light."

4.1 MAKING CONNECTIONS

Redefining Bacterial Size

Microbiologists keep being reminded how far we are from having a complete assessment of the bacterial world, mostly because the world is so large and bacteria are so small. There seem to be frequent reports of exceptional bacteria discovered in places like the deep-ocean volcanoes or Antarctic ice. Among the most remarkable are giant and dwarf bacteria.

Big Bacteria Break Records

In 1985 biologists discovered a new bacterium living in the intestine of surgeonfish that at the time was a candidate for the *Guinness Book of World Records*. The large cells, named *Epulopiscium fishelsoni* ("guest at a banquet of fish"), measure around 100 µm in length, although some specimens were as large as 300 µm. This record was broken when a marine microbiologist discovered an even larger species of bacteria living in ocean sediments near the African country of Namibia. These gigantic cocci are arranged in strands that look like pearls and contain hundreds of golden sulfur granules, inspiring their name, *Thiomargarita namibia* ("sulfur pearl of Namibia") (see photo). The size of the individual cells ranges from 100 up to 750 µm (0.75 mm), and many are large enough to see with the naked eye. By way of comparison, if the average bacterium were the size of a mouse, *Thiomargarita* would be as large as a blue whale!

These bacteria are found in such large numbers in the sediments that it is thought that they are essential to the ecological cycling of H_2S and other substances in this region, converting them to less toxic substances.

Miniature Microbes—Are They for Real?

At the other extreme, microbiologists are being asked to reevaluate the lower limits of bacterial size. Up until now it has been generally accepted that the smallest cells on the planet are some form of mycoplasma with dimensions of 0.2 to 0.3 µm, which is right at the limit of resolution with light microscopes. A new controversy is brewing over the discovery of tiny cells that look like dwarf bacteria but are 10 times smaller than mycoplasmas and 100 times smaller than the average bacterial cell. These minute cells have been given the name **nanobacteria** or **nanobes** (Gr. *nanos,* one-billionth).

Nanobacteria-like forms were first isolated from blood and serum samples. The tiny cells appear to grow in culture, have cell walls, and contain protein and nucleic acids, but their size range is only from 0.05 to

Thiomargarita namibia—giant cocci. Approximately how many times larger is Thiomargarita than the nanobe shown on the right?
Heide N. Schulz/Max Planck Institue for Marine Microbiology

Three-dimensional micrograph of an ARMAN measuring about 0.25 µm across. These are fully functioning cells with a tiny nucleoid (yellow) and a small number of ribosomes (blue dots).
©Banfield & Comolli

0.2 µm. Similar nanobes have been extracted by minerologists studying deposits in the ocean at temperatures up to 170°C. Many geologists are convinced that these nanobes are real cells, that they are probably similar to the first microbes on earth, and that they play a strategic role in the development of the earth's crust.

Microbiologists have been more skeptical. Experts have postulated that the minimum cell size to contain a functioning genome and reproductive and synthetic machinery is approximately 0.14 µm, which means that some of the nanobes could be artifacts or bits of larger cells that have broken free. It seems that the archaea may be the ultimate definers of smallness in prokaryotes. Microbiologists exploring acid mines in California have discovered ultrasmall archaea living in pink biofilms. These extremophiles, called ARMAN, are at the lower limits of size, between 100 and 400 nm. They are real cells, complete with a tiny genome and a reduced number of ribosomes, and are perhaps the first indisputable nanobes. Additional studies are needed to test this curious question of nanobes and possibly to answer some questions about the origins of life on earth and elsewhere in the universe.

What are some of the adaptations that a giant *Thiomargarita* would require for its survival?

They do not have flagella. Several morphological forms exist, including slender rods, long filaments, cocci, and some miniature, tree-shaped fruiting bodies. Probably the most intriguing and exceptional members of this group are the slime bacteria, or myxobacteria. What sets the myxobacteria apart from other bacteria is the complexity and advancement of their life cycle. During this cycle, the vegetative cells respond to chemotactic signals by swarming together and differentiating into a many-celled, colored structure called the fruiting body, making it one of the few bacteria that can generate a multicellular body form **(figure 4.30).** The fruiting body

is a survival structure that makes spores by a method very similar to that of certain fungi. These fruiting structures are often large enough to be seen with the unaided eye on tree bark and plant debris.

Unusual Forms of Medically Significant Bacteria

Most bacteria are free-living or parasitic forms that can metabolize and reproduce by independent means. Two groups of bacteria—the rickettsias and chlamydias—have adapted to living inside host cells.

(a1)

(a2)

Stromatolite
(b1)

10 μm

(b2)

Figure 4.28 **Cyanobacterial characteristics. (a)** Striking colors and arrangements of cells. **(1)** *Trichodesmium* is one of the dominant planktonic forms on earth. **(2)** *Merismopedia* displays a slimy sheath around its regular packets of cells. **(b)** Ancient signs of cyanobacteria. **(1)** A sectioned stromatolite displays layers of a cyanobacterial biofilm laid down over a billion years ago. **(2)** A microfossil of a billion-year-old filament found in Siberian fossils.

(a1): ©Angelicque E. White; (a2): Courtesy Jason Oyadomari; (b1): Richard Behl, California State University, Long Beach; (b2): J. William Schopf/UCLA

Figure 4.29 **Photosynthetic bacteria.** Purple-colored masses in a fall pond contain a concentrated bloom of purple sulfur bacteria (inset, 1,500×). The pond also harbors a mixed population of algae (green clumps).
Kathy Park Talaro; (inset): David J. Patterson

Vegetative growth

Aggregate

Fruiting

Fruiting body

Myxospore

Figure 4.30 **Life cycle of *Myxococcus.*** This multicellular bacterium goes through several developmental stages in response to environmental signals.

Because they cannot function without some essential factors from the host, they are considered **obligate intracellular parasites.**

Rickettsias

Rickettsias[6] are distinctive, tiny, gram-negative bacteria (**figure 4.31**). Although they have somewhat typical morphology, they are atypical in their life cycle and other adaptations. Most are pathogens that alternate between a mammalian host and blood-sucking arthropods,[7] such as fleas, lice, or ticks. Rickettsias cannot survive or multiply outside a host cell and cannot carry out metabolism completely on their own, so they are closely attached to their hosts. Several important human diseases are caused by rickettsias. Among these are Rocky Mountain spotted fever, caused by *Rickettsia rickettsii* (transmitted by ticks), and endemic typhus, caused by *Rickettsia typhi* (transmitted by lice). It is worth noting, in advance of chapter 5, that the mitochondrion, a eukaryotic organelle, is a close genetic relative to rickettsias, indicating an evolutionary link between them.

Chlamydias

Bacteria of the genera *Chlamydia* and *Chlamydophila,* termed **chlamydias,** are similar to the rickettsias in that they require host cells for growth and metabolism. But they are not closely related to

6. Named for Howard Ricketts, a physician who first worked with these organisms and later lost his life to typhus.

7. An arthropod is an invertebrate with jointed legs, such as an insect, tick, or spider.

Rickettsial cells Nucleus of cell

Figure 4.31 **Transmission electron micrograph of** *Rickettsia conorii* **inside its host cell (100,000×).** This species causes tick-borne Mediterranean fever.
Source: From C. Rovery, P. Brouqui, D. Raoult, "Questions on Mediterranean Spotted Fever a Century after Its Discovery", "Emerging Infectious Diseases, 14(9), September 2008, Fig. 2. CDC "

them and are not transmitted by arthropods. Because of their tiny size and obligately parasitic lifestyle, they were at one time considered a type of virus (see table 4.3L). Species that carry the greatest medical impact are *Chlamydia trachomatis,* the cause of both a severe eye infection (trachoma) that can lead to blindness and one of the most common sexually transmitted diseases, and *Chlamydophila pneumoniae,* an agent in lung infections.

Diseases caused by rickettsias and chlamydias are described in more detail in the infectious disease chapters.

Archaea: The Other Prokaryotes

The discovery and characterization of novel prokaryotic cells that have unusual anatomy, physiology, and genetics changed our views of microbial taxonomy and classification (see chapter 1 and table 4.3).

These single-celled, simple organisms, called **archaea,** or **archaeons,** are considered a third cell type in a separate superkingdom (the Domain Archaea). We include them in this chapter because they are prokaryotic in general structure and they do share many bacterial characteristics. But evidence is accumulating that they are more closely related to Domain Eukarya than to bacteria. For example, archaea and eukaryotes share a number of ribosomal RNA sequences that are not found in bacteria, and their protein synthesis and ribosomal subunit structures are similar. **Table 4.5** outlines selected points of comparison of the three domains.

Other ways in which the archaea differ significantly from other cell types are that certain genetic sequences are found only in their ribosomal RNA. Their cell walls are also quite different, being composed of polysaccharide or protein and lacking peptidoglycan, and some lack cell walls altogether (see figure 4.33). It is likely that the archaea are the most ancient of all life forms and have retained characteristics of the first cells that originated on the earth nearly 4 billion years ago. The early earth is thought to have contained a hot, anaerobic "soup" with sulfuric gases and salts in abundance. Many of the present-day archaea occupy the remaining habitats on the earth that have some of the same extreme conditions. For this reason they are considered **extremophiles,** or **hyperextremophiles,** meaning that they "love" the most extreme habitats on earth. Although it was once thought that archaea were almost exclusively relegated to these extreme environments, we now know that archaea are found in a broad variety of habitats (including the human body). As a general rule, archaea are difficult or impossible to culture using current techniques, and we are only aware of many of them through the detection of their genetic information.

Metabolically the archaea exhibit nearly incredible adaptations to what would be deadly conditions for other organisms. Many of these hardy microbes are living in severe combinations of extremes as well—for instance, high acidity and high temperature, high salt and alkalinity, low temperature and high pressure. Included in this group are methane producers, hyperthermophiles, extreme halophiles, and sulfur reducers.

TABLE 4.5	Comparison of Three Cellular Domains		
Characteristic	Bacteria	Archaea	Eukarya
Cell type	Prokaryotic	Prokaryotic	Eukaryotic
Chromosomes	Single, or few, circular	Single, circular	Several, linear
Types of ribosomes	70S	70S but structure is similar to 80S	80S
Unique ribosomal RNA signature sequences	+	+	+
Number of RNA sequences shared with Eukarya	One	Three	
Protein synthesis similar to Eukarya	−	+	
Presence of peptidoglycan in cell wall	+	−	−
Cell membrane lipids	Fatty acids with ester linkages	Long-chain, branched hydrocarbons with ether linkages	Fatty acids with ester linkages
Sterols in membrane	− (some exceptions)	−	+

Members of the group called **methanogens** can convert CO_2 and H_2 into methane gas (CH_4) through unusual and complex pathways. These archaea are common inhabitants of anaerobic mud and the bottom sediments of lakes and oceans. Some are even found in the oral cavity and large intestine of humans. The gas they produce in aquatic habitats collects in swamps and may become a source of fuel. Methane may also contribute to the "greenhouse effect," which maintains the earth's temperature and can contribute to global warming.

Other types of archaea—the **extreme halophiles**—require salt to grow and may have such a high salt tolerance that they can multiply in sodium chloride solutions (36% NaCl) that would destroy most cells. They exist in the saltiest places on the earth—inland seas, salt lakes, and salt mines. They are not particularly common in the ocean because the salt content is not high enough to support them. Many of the "halobacteria" use a red pigment to synthesize ATP in the presence of light. These pigments are responsible for "red herrings," the color of the Red Sea, and the red color of salt ponds **(figure 4.32)**.

Archaea adapted to growth at very low temperatures are described as **psychrophiles** (loving cold temperatures); those growing at very high temperatures are **hyperthermophiles**

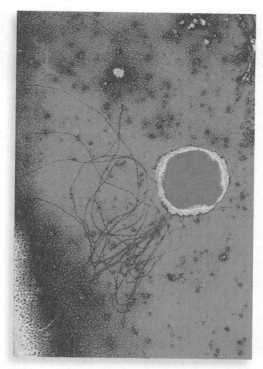

Figure 4.33 **The hottest life forms on earth.** A colorized transmission electron micrograph of strain 121. This member of Domain Archaea was isolated from an undersea thermal vent off the coast of Washington State. This organism thrives in habitats above the temperature of boiling water and can even survive being autoclaved. Derek Lovley/Kazem Kashefi/Science Source

(loving very high temperatures). Hyperthermophiles flourish at temperatures between 80°C and 121°C (21°C above boiling) and cannot grow at 50°C. They live in volcanic waters and soils and submarine vents, and are often salt- and acid-tolerant as well **(figure 4.33)**. Researchers sampling sulfur vents in the deep ocean discovered thermophilic archaea flourishing at temperatures up to 250°C—which is 150° above the temperature of boiling water! Not only were these archaea growing prolifically at this high temperature, but they were also living at 265 atmospheres of pressure. (On the earth's surface, pressure is about 1 atmosphere.) For additional discussion of the unusual adaptations of archaea, see chapter 7.

(a)

5 μm

(b)

Figure 4.32 **Halophiles around the world. (a)** An aerial view of a salt pond at San Francisco Bay, California. The archaea that thrive in this warm, highly saline habitat produce brilliant red, pink, and orange pigments. **(b)** A sample taken from a saltern in Australia viewed by fluorescence microscopy (1,000×). Note the range of cell shapes (cocci, rods, and squares) found in this community. (a): *Source:* NASA Johnson Space Center/ISS007E8738; (b): Courtesy Dr. Mike Dyall-Smith, University of Melbourne

Practice SECTION 4.7

36. Discuss several ways in which bacteria are medically and ecologically important.

37. Name two main groups of obligate intracellular parasitic bacteria and explain why these groups can't live independently.

38. Explain the characteristics of archaea that indicate that they constitute a unique domain of living things that is neither bacterial nor eukaryotic.

39. What is meant by the terms *extremophile* and *hyperextremophile*?

40. Describe the three major archaeal lifestyles and adaptations to extreme habitats.

CASE STUDY Part 2

Mycobacterium abscessus is a common inhabitant of water, soil, and dust, and has been responsible for previous outbreaks in acupuncture and cosmetic surgery clinics. Like other nontuberculous mycobacterium (NTM), *M. abscessus* is tolerant of commonly used disinfectants and is regularly found in plumbing systems and tap water. It is known to replicate and form biofilms within the dental unit waterline that supplies water to drills and other dental accessories. The American Dental Association and the manufacturer of the dental unit used in this case recommend flushing waterlines to begin each day and after each patient, along with chemical treatment of water used in the equipment, and routine testing of water quality. The equipment in the Georgia dental clinic used untreated tap water, and no routine testing was done to monitor water quality.

Water samples obtained from each of the seven dental stations within the clinic were tested and found to contain an average of 91,333 colony-forming units (CFU) per ml, far above the 500 CFU/ml recommended as a maximum by the Centers for Disease Control. DNA profiling of *M. abscessus* isolated from the dental units matched the profile seen in bacteria taken from patients, indicating that the dental units were indeed the source of infection.

■ Some dental units are designed so that chemical disinfectants may be easily added to the water system. Why might this level of attention still not be enough to prevent infections like those seen in this case?

■ One recommendation made in this case was to eliminate loops in waterline tubing that could retain water. How would this lower the risk of infection?

Chapter Summary with Key Terms

4.1 Basic Characteristics of Cells and Life Forms
 A. All living things are composed of cells, which are complex collections of macromolecules that carry out living processes. All cells must have the minimum structure of an outer **cell membrane, cytoplasm,** a **chromosome,** and **ribosomes.**
 B. Cells can be divided into two basic types: **prokaryotes** and **eukaryotes.**
 1. Prokaryotic cells are the basic structural unit of bacteria and archaea. They lack a nucleus or organelles. They are highly successful and adaptable single-cell life forms.
 2. Eukaryotic cells contain a membrane-surrounded nucleus and a number of organelles that function in specific ways. A wide variety of organisms, from single-celled protozoans to humans, are composed of eukaryotic cells.
 3. Viruses are not generally considered living or cells, and rely on host cells to replicate.
 C. Cells show the basic essential characteristics of life. Parts of cells and macromolecules do not show these characteristics independently.
 1. The primary life indicators are heredity, reproduction, growth, metabolism, responsiveness, and transport.

4.2 Prokaryotic Profiles: The Bacteria and Archaea
 A. Prokaryotes consist of two major groups, the bacteria and the archaea. Life on earth would not be possible without them.
 B. Prokaryotic cells lack the membrane-surrounded organelles and nuclear compartment of eukaryotic cells but are still complex in their structure and function. All prokaryotes have a cell membrane, cytoplasm, ribosomes, and a chromosome.
 C. **Appendages:** Some bacteria have projections that extend from the cell.
 1. **Flagella** and internal **axial filaments** found in spirochetes are used for motility.
 2. **Fimbriae** function in adhering to the environment; pili can be involved in adhesion, movement, and genetic exchange.

 3. The **S layer** is a monolayer of proteins present in some bacterial species.
 4. The **glycocalyx** may be a slime layer or a capsule.
 5. Prokaryotic organisms may exist in biofilms, communities where cells of multiple species are enmeshed in an extracellular matrix and work cooperatively.

4.3 The Cell Envelope: The Outer Boundary Layer of Bacteria
 A. Most prokaryotes are surrounded by a protective envelope that consists of the cell wall and the cell membrane.
 B. The wall is relatively rigid due to **peptidoglycan.**
 C. Structural differences give rise to **gram-positive** and **gram-negative cells,** as differentiated by the **Gram stain.**
 1. Gram-positive bacteria contain a thick wall composed of peptidoglycan and teichoic acid in a single layer.
 2. Gram-negative bacteria have a thinner, two-layer cell wall with an **outer membrane,** a thin layer of **peptidoglycan,** and a well-developed **periplasmic space.**
 3. Wall structure gives rise to differences in staining, toxicity, and effects of drugs and disinfectants.
 4. The **cell** or **cytoplasmic membrane** is a flexible sheet that surrounds the cytoplasm. It is composed of a bilayer of lipids with attached proteins. It is a multifunctional structure involved in transport, synthesis, and energy reactions.

4.4 Bacterial Internal Structure
 The cell cytoplasm contains some or all of the following internal structures in bacteria: the **chromosome(s)** condensed in the **nucleoid; ribosomes,** which serve as the sites of protein synthesis and are 70S in size; extra genetic information in the form of **plasmids;** storage structures known as **inclusions, granules,** and **microcompartments;** a **cytoskeleton** which helps give the bacterium its shape; and in some bacteria an **endospore,** which is a highly resistant structure for survival, not reproduction.

4.5 Bacterial Shapes, Arrangements, and Sizes

 A. Most bacteria are unicellular and are found in a great variety of shapes, arrangements, and sizes. General shapes include **cocci**, **bacilli**, and helical forms such as **spirilla** and **spirochetes.** Some show great variation within the species in shape and size and are **pleomorphic.** Other variations include **coccobacilli, vibrios,** and filamentous forms.

 B. Prokaryotes divide by binary fission and do not utilize mitosis. Various **arrangements** result from cell division and are termed **diplococci, streptococci, staphylococci, tetrads,** and **sarcina** for cocci; bacilli may form pairs, chains, or **palisades.**

 C. Variant members of bacterial species are called strains and types.

4.6 Classification Systems of Prokaryotic Domains: Archaea and Bacteria

 A. An important taxonomic system is standardized by *Bergey's Manual of Systemic Bacteriology*, which presents the prokaryotes in five major groups, as organized by volume.

4.7 Survey of Prokaryotic Groups with Unusual Characteristics

 A. Several groups of bacteria have unusual adaptations and life cycles.

 1. Medically important bacteria: **Rickettsias** and **chlamydias** are within the gram-negative group but are small **obligate intracellular parasites** that replicate within cells of the hosts they invade.

 2. Nonpathogenic bacterial groups: The majority of bacterial species are free-living and not involved in disease. Unusual groups include photosynthetic bacteria such as **cyanobacteria,** which provide oxygen to the environment, and the green and purple bacteria.

 B. **Archaea** share many characteristics with bacteria but vary in certain genetic aspects and structures such as the cell wall and ribosomes.

 1. Many are **extremophiles,** adapted to extreme environments similar to the earliest of earth's inhabitants.

 2. They are not considered medically important but are of ecological and potential economic importance.

 Assess Your Knowledge

Level I. These questions require a working knowledge of the concepts in the chapter and the ability to recall and understand the information you have studied.

Developing a Concept Inventory

Select the correct answer from the answers provided. For questions with blanks, choose the combination of answers that most accurately completes the statement.

1. Which structure is not a component of all cells?
 a. cell wall
 b. cell membrane
 c. genetic material
 d. ribosomes

2. Viruses are not considered living things because
 a. they are not cells
 b. they cannot reproduce by themselves
 c. they lack metabolism
 d. All of these are correct.

3. Which of the following is not found in all bacterial cells?
 a. cell membrane
 b. a nucleoid
 c. ribosomes
 d. cytoskeleton

4. The major locomotor structures in bacteria are
 a. flagella
 b. pili
 c. fimbriae
 d. cilia

5. Pili are appendages in _____ bacteria that serve as a means of _____.
 a. gram-positive, genetic exchange
 b. gram-positive, attachment
 c. gram-negative, genetic exchange
 d. gram-negative, protection

6. An example of a glycocalyx is
 a. a capsule
 b. pili
 c. outer membrane
 d. a cell wall

7. Which of the following is a primary bacterial cell wall function?
 a. transport
 b. motility
 c. support
 d. adhesion

8. Which of the following is present in both gram-positive and gram-negative cell walls?
 a. an outer membrane
 b. peptidoglycan
 c. teichoic acid
 d. lipopolysaccharides

9. Metachromatic granules are concentrated _____ found in _____.
 a. fat, *Mycobacterium*
 b. dipicolinic acid, *Bacillus*
 c. sulfur, *Thiobacillus*
 d. polyphosphate, *Corynebacterium*

10. Which of the following prokaryotes lacks cell walls?
 a. rickettsias
 b. mycoplasmas
 c. *Mycobacterium*
 d. archaea

11. The LPS layer in gram-negative cell walls releases _____ that cause _____.
 a. enzymes, pain
 b. endotoxins, fever
 c. techoic acid, inflammation
 d. phosphates, lysis

12. Bacterial endospores function in
 a. reproduction
 b. survival
 c. protein synthesis
 d. storage

13. An arrangement in packets of eight cells is described as a _____.
 a. micrococcus
 b. diplococcus
 c. tetrad
 d. sarcina

14. The major difference between a spirochete and a spirillum is
 a. presence of flagella
 b. the presence of twists
 c. the nature of motility
 d. size

15. Which phylum contains bacteria with a gram-positive cell wall?
 a. Proteobacteria
 c. Firmicutes
 b. Chlorobi
 d. Spirochetes

16. To which taxonomic group do cyanobacteria belong?
 a. Domain Archaea
 c. Domain Bacteria
 b. Phylum Actinobacteria
 d. Phylum Fusobacteria

17. Which stain is used to distinguish differences between the cell walls of medically important bacteria?
 a. simple stain
 c. Gram stain
 b. acridine orange stain
 d. negative stain

18. The first living cells on earth would most likely resemble which of these?
 a. a cyanobacterium
 c. a gram-positive cell
 b. an endospore former
 d. an archaeon

Case Study Analysis

1. Which bacterial structure is most directly involved in the formation of a biofilm?
 a. cytoskeleton
 c. ribosome
 b. glycocalyx
 d. cell wall

2. The regulation of gene expression in a biofilm is referred to as
 a. induction
 c. apoptosis
 b. imprinting
 d. quorum sensing

3. Biofilms are a leading cause of artificial joint infection, yet when a biofilm forms on a joint, blood tests rarely show evidence of infection. Why is this?

On the Test

These questions will help to prepare you to successfully answer similar questions you'll see on the TEAS (Test of Essential Academic Skills) and NCLEX (National Council Licensure Examination).

1. Which feature is found in all prokaryotic cells?
 a. cell membrane
 b. endospores
 c. flagella
 d. nucleus

2. Cell membranes are composed principally of
 a. DNA and protein
 b. phospholipids and DNA
 c. protein and phospholipids
 d. carbohydrates and proteins

Writing Challenge

For each question, compose a one- or two-paragraph answer that includes the factual information needed to completely address the question. Practice questions can also be used for writing-challenge exercises.

1. Label the parts on the bacterial cell featured here and write a brief description of its function.

2. Discuss the collection of properties that are used to define life and the prokaryotic cell structures that are involved in carrying out these life processes.

3. Describe the basic process of biofilm formation.

4. What leads microbiologists to believe the archaea are more closely related to eukaryotes than to bacteria?

5. What is required to kill endospores? How do you suppose archaeologists were able to date some spores as being thousands (or millions) of years old?

Concept Mapping

On Connect you can find an Introduction to Concept Mapping that provides guidance for working with concept maps, along with concept-mapping activities for this chapter.

 # Application, Analysis, Evaluation, and Synthesis

Level II. These problems go beyond just restating facts and require higher levels of understanding and an ability to interpret, problem solve, transfer knowledge to new situations, create models, and predict outcomes.

Critical Thinking

Critical thinking is the ability to reason and solve problems using facts and concepts. These questions can be approached from a number of angles and, in most cases, they do not have a single correct answer.

1. Using clay, demonstrate how cocci can divide in several planes and show the outcome of this division. Show how the arrangements of bacilli occur, including palisades.

2. Using a corkscrew and a spring to compare the flexibility and locomotion of spirilla and spirochetes, explain which cell type is represented by each object.

3. Under the microscope, you see a rod-shaped cell that is swimming rapidly forward.
 a. What do you automatically know about that bacterium's structure?
 b. Propose another function of flagella besides locomotion.

4. Name an acid-fast bacterium and explain what characteristics make this bacterium different from other gram-positive bacteria.

5. a. Name a bacterial group that uses chlorophyll to photosynthesize.
 b. Describe the two major groups of photosynthetic bacteria and how they are similar and different.

6. Propose a hypothesis to explain how bacteria and archaea could have, together, given rise to eukaryotes.

7. Explain or illustrate exactly what will happen to the cell wall if the synthesis of the interbridge is blocked by penicillin.

8. Ask your lab instructor to help you make a biofilm and examine it under the microscope. One possible technique is to suspend a glass slide in an aquarium for a few weeks, then carefully air-dry, fix, and Gram stain it. Observe the diversity of cell types.

Visual Assessment

1. From chapter 3, figure 3.18b. Which bacteria have a well-developed capsule: "*Klebsiella*" or "*S. aureus*"? Defend your answer.

Kathy Park Talaro

2. What is it about *Clostridium* cells that makes them stain unevenly, producing the appearance seen in the photo below?

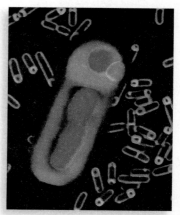

Courtesy of Kit Pogliano and Mark Sharp/UCSD

A Survey of Eukaryotic Cells and Microorganisms

Vegan, organic, locally sourced. For a 26-year-old woman in the San Francisco Bay Area, there was nothing not to like when she was offered a basket of freshly harvested wild mushrooms. The woods of the Bay Area had been especially wet and warm over the past few weeks, and wild mushrooms were plentiful. The woman grilled the mushrooms and served them for dinner to her family (husband and 18-month-old daughter) along with her sister and a girlfriend.

The sister was the first to visit the emergency room, complaining of nausea, vomiting, diarrhea, and abdominal cramps. She was diagnosed with simple gastroenteritis and discharged after receiving IV fluids and an antiemetic medication to lessen her nausea. The following day, she returned to the emergency room with worsening symptoms. By this time, everyone who had eaten the previous night's dinner was ill. Nausea, diarrhea, and vomiting had begun about 9 hours after dinner, and the mother, father, and child were seen by emergency room physicians by hour 20. All five patients displayed elevated levels of creatine kinase and liver enzymes, indicating dehydration and liver failure, respectively.

Liver failure following consumption of wild mushrooms is not a difficult mystery to solve, but to be sure, a local mycologist was called in to examine some of the uncooked mushrooms, which were quickly identified as *Amanita phalloides*, commonly known as the "death cap." The mystery was lessened by the fact that 14 cases of *A. phalloides* poisoning were seen in the Bay Area over a 2-week period, and doctors were well aware of an abundant toxic mushroom crop.

Amatoxins, three types of which are found in *Amanita* mushrooms, are responsible for 90% of the deaths related to mushroom poisoning. The toxins are heat stable and therefore unaffected by cooking. Once ingested, they are quickly absorbed by liver cells where they bind to RNA polymerase, halting intracellular protein synthesis and resulting in the death of liver cells. Amanitin is highly toxic, with a lethal dose being as little as 0.1 mg/kg of body weight, meaning that a 150-pound person need only ingest 7 mg, about half a mushroom. *Amanita* mushroom poisoning has a fatality rate approaching 20%.

- *To which kingdom do mushrooms belong?*
- *From the point of view of the organism, what purpose do mushrooms serve?*

To continue the Case Study, go to Case Study Part 2 at the end of the chapter.

(Amanita mushroom): Jorgen Bausager/Getty Images

5.1 The History of Eukaryotes

 Learn

1. Describe the evolutionary history of eukaryotic cells.
2. Provide a theory regarding how eukaryotic cells originated and how multicellularity came to be.
3. List the eukaryotic groups and their body plans.

Using evidence from ancient sediments, paleontologists estimate that the earliest eukaryotic cells first evolved around 2 billion years ago. Other intriguing evidence comes from fossilized cells discovered in shale deposits from China and Russia that are 600 million to nearly a billion years old. It is remarkable how much they resemble modern-day algae or protozoa (**figure 5.1**).

When biologists began to focus on the possible origins of these cells, they turned to an analysis of modern cells, and from these studies emerged convincing evidence that eukaryotic cells evolved from prokaryotic cells through a process of **endosymbiosis.** According to the endosymbiotic theory, eukaryotic cells arose when a much larger prokaryotic cell engulfed smaller prokaryotic cells, which began to live and reproduce inside the larger cell rather than being destroyed. As the smaller cells took up permanent residence, they came to perform specialized functions for the larger cell, such as food synthesis and oxygen utilization, that enhanced the larger cell's versatility and survival. Over time the cells evolved into a single functioning entity, and the relationship became obligatory; some of the smaller cells had become **organelles,** the distinguishing feature of eukaryotic cells (**figure 5.2**). The structure of these early cells was so versatile that eukaryotic microorganisms soon spread out into available habitats and adopted greatly diverse styles of living.

Figure 5.1 Ancient eukaryotic protists discovered in fossilized rocks. (a) A cell preserved in Siberian shale deposits dates from 850 million to 950 million years ago. **(b)** A disclike cell was recovered from a Chinese rock dating 590 million to 610 million years ago. Both cells are relatively simple, with (a) showing chloroplast-like bodies that would be found in an alga. Example (b) has a cell wall with spines, very similar to the modern alga *Pediastrum*.
(a and b): Andrew H. Knoll

A larger prokaryotic cell, possibly an archeon, containing a flexible outer envelope and folded internal membranes.

A smaller prokaryotic cell, related to modern rickettsias, that can live intracellularly.

Membrane forms around the DNA, creating a primitive nucleus.

The larger cell engulfs the smaller one; smaller one survives and remains surrounded by the vacuolar membrane.

Smaller bacterium becomes a permanent resident of its host's cytoplasm; it multiplies and is passed on during cell division. It utilizes aerobic metabolism and increases energy availability for the host.

Early endoplasmic reticulum

Early mitochondria

Ancestral eukaryotic cell develops additional membrane pouches that become the endoplasmic reticulum and Golgi apparatus.

Ancestral cell

Photosynthetic bacteria (ancient cyanobacteria) are also engulfed; they develop into chloroplasts.

Chloroplast

Cell wall

Many protozoa, animals

Some groups of algae, higher plants

Figure 5.2 A possible model for evolution of eukaryotic organisms according to the endosymbiotic theory. A large archaeal cell with its flexible envelope engulfs a smaller bacterial cell. Folds in the archaeal cell membrane wrap around the chromosome to form a nuclear envelope, The engulfed bacterial cell forges a metabolic relationship with the archeon, making use of archaeal molecules and contributing energy through aerobic respiration. Evolution of a stable mutualistic existence would maintain both cell types and create the eukaryotic cell and its organelles.

TABLE 5.1	Eukaryotic Organisms Studied in Microbiology	
Unicellular, a Few Colonial	**May Be Unicellular, Colonial, or Multicellular**	**Multicellular Except Reproductive Stages**
Protozoa	Fungi, Algae	Helminths (parasitic worms) Arthropods (animal vectors of diseases)

Much of the evidence supporting the endosymbiotic theory concerned the similarity between the organelles of modern eukaryotic cells and the structure of bacteria. In many ways the mitochondrion of eukaryotic cells behaves as a tiny cell within a cell. It is capable of independent division, contains a circular chromosome with bacterial DNA sequences, and has ribosomes that are clearly prokaryotic. Mitochondria also have bacterial membranes and can be inhibited by drugs that affect only bacteria. In a similar vein, genetic studies indicate that chloroplasts likely originated from endosymbiotic cyanobacteria that provided their host cells with a built-in feeding mechanism. Evidence is seen in protists, such as *Paulinella chromatophora,* that harbor specialized chloroplasts with cyanobacterial origins. The endosymbiotic theory is so well accepted that bacteriologists have placed both mitochondria and chloroplasts on the family tree of bacteria. In fact, the closest relative of mitochondria are rickettsias, which are also obligate intracellular bacteria!

The first primitive eukaryotes were probably single-celled, independent microorganisms, but over time some forms began to cluster in permanent groupings called colonies. With further evolution, some of the cells within colonies became *specialized,* or adapted to perform a particular function advantageous to the whole colony, such as locomotion, feeding, or reproduction. Complex multicellular organisms evolved as individual cells in the organism lost the ability to survive apart from the intact colony. Although a multicellular organism is composed of many cells, it is more than just a disorganized assemblage of cells like a colony. Rather, it is composed of distinct groups of cells that cannot exist independently of the rest of the body. Within a multicellular organism, groupings of cells that have a specific function are termed *tissues,* and groups of tissues make up *organs.*

Looking at modern eukaryotic organisms, we find examples of many levels of cellular complexity **(table 5.1).** All protozoa, as well as numerous algae and fungi, are unicellular. Truly multicellular organisms are found only among plants and animals and some of the fungi (mushrooms) and algae (seaweeds). Only certain eukaryotes are traditionally studied by microbiologists—primarily the protozoa, the microscopic algae and fungi, and animal parasites, or helminths.

5.2 Form and Function of the Eukaryotic Cell: External Structures

 Learn

4. Describe the plan of a basic eukaryotic cell and organelles, and indicate the structures all cells possess and those found only in some groups.

5. Describe the types of eukaryotic locomotor appendages.
6. Differentiate the structure and functions of flagella and cilia, and the types of cells that possess them.
7. Define the *glycocalyx* for eukaryotic cells and list its basic functions.
8. Characterize the cell wall and membrane of eukaryotic cells.

The cells of eukaryotic organisms are so varied that no one member can serve as a typical example, so a composite structure of a eukaryotic cell is depicted in **figure 5.3.** No single type of microbial cell would contain all structures represented. It is evident that the organelles impart much greater complexity and compartmentalization compared to a prokaryotic cell. Differences among fungi, protozoa, algae, and animal cells are introduced in later sections.

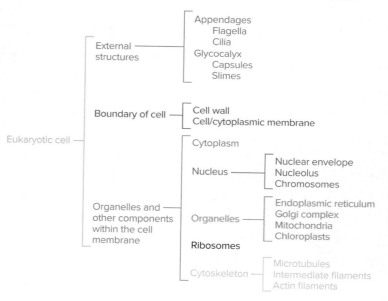

The flowchart shown here maps the structural organization of a eukaryotic cell. Compare this outline to the one found in chapter 4.

In general, eukaryotic microbial cells have a cytoplasmic membrane, nucleus, mitochondria, endoplasmic reticulum, Golgi apparatus, vacuoles, cytoskeleton, and glycocalyx. A cell wall, locomotor appendages, and chloroplasts are found only in some groups. In the following sections, we cover the microscopic structure and functions of the eukaryotic cell. As with the prokaryotes, we begin on the outside **(table 5.2)** and proceed inward through the cell.

Locomotor Appendages: Cilia and Flagella

Motility allows a microorganism to locate life-sustaining nutrients and to migrate toward positive stimuli such as sunlight; it also permits avoidance of harmful substances and stimuli. Locomotion by means of flagella is common in protozoa, algae, and a few fungal and animal cells. Cilia are found only in protozoa and animal cells.

In All Eukaryotes

Lysosome | Golgi apparatus | Mitochondrion | Intermediate filament | Microtubule | Actin filaments

Cell membrane

Nuclear membrane with pores

Nucleus

Nucleolus

Rough endoplasmic reticulum with ribosomes

Smooth endoplasmic reticulum

Flagellum | Chloroplast | Centrioles | Cell wall | Glycocalyx

In Some Eukaryotes

Figure 5.3 **Overview of composite eukaryotic cell.** This drawing represents all structures associated with eukaryotic cells, but no microbial cell possesses all of them. See figures 5.16, 5.23, and 5.25 for examples of individual cell types.

Although they share the same name, the **flagella** of eukaryotes are much different from those of prokaryotes. The eukaryotic flagellum is thicker (by a factor of 10), has a much different construction, and is covered by an extension of the cell membrane. A

TABLE 5.2	Function of External and Boundary Structures of the Eukaryotic Cell
Cilia and flagella	Cell movement
Glycocalyx	Adherence to surfaces; development of biofilms and mats; protection
Cell wall	Structural support and shape
Cytoplasmic membrane	Selective permeability; cell-cell interactions; adhesion to surfaces; signal transduction

flagellum is a long, sheathed cylinder containing regularly spaced hollow tubules—**microtubules**—that extend along its entire length **(figure 5.4b).** A cross section reveals nine pairs of closely attached microtubules surrounding a single central pair. This scheme, called the 9 + 2 arrangement, is a typical pattern of flagella and cilia **(figure 5.4a).** The nine pairs are linked together and anchored to the pair in the center. This architecture permits the microtubules to slide past each other, whipping the flagellum back and forth. Although details of this process are too complex to discuss here, it involves expenditure of energy and a coordinating mechanism in the cell membrane. Flagella can move the cell by pushing it forward like a fishtail or by pulling it by a lashing or twirling motion **(figure 5.4c).** The placement and number of flagella can be useful in identifying flagellated protozoa and certain algae.

(a)

(b)

(c) Whips back and forth and pushes in snakelike pattern

Twiddles the tip

Lashes, grabs the substrate, and pulls

Figure 5.4 **The structure of cilia and flagella. (a)** A cross section through a protozoan cilium reveals the typical 9 + 2 arrangement of microtubules seen in both cilia and flagella. **(b)** Longitudinal section through a cilium, showing the lengthwise orientation of the microtubules and the basal body (bb) from which they arise. Note the membrane that surrounds the cilium that is an extension of the cell membrane and shows that it is indeed an organelle. **(c)** Locomotor patterns seen in flagellates.
(a and b): Courtesy of Richard Allen

Cilia are very similar in overall architecture to flagella, but they are shorter and more numerous (some cells have several thousand). They are found only in certain protozoa and animal cells. In the ciliated protozoa, the cilia occur in rows over the cell surface, where they beat back and forth in regular oarlike strokes **(figure 5.5)** and provide rapid motility. On some cells, cilia also function as feeding and filtering structures.

> **Quick Search**
> To compare the types of movement seen in eukaryotes, find videos using the search words *amoebic, flagellate,* and *ciliate movement* on YouTube.

The Glycocalyx

Most eukaryotic microbes have a **glycocalyx,** an outermost boundary that comes into direct contact with the environment. This structure is usually composed of polysaccharides and appears as a network of fibers, a slime layer, or a capsule much like the glycocalyx of prokaryotes. From its position as the exposed cell layer, the glycocalyx serves a variety of functions. Most prominently, it promotes adherence to environmental surfaces and the development of biofilms and mats. It also serves important receptor and communication functions and offers some protection against environmental changes.

The nature of the layer beneath the glycocalyx varies among the several eukaryotic groups. Fungi and most algae have a thick, rigid cell wall surrounding a cell membrane. Protozoa, a few algae, and all animal cells lack a cell wall and are encased primarily by a cell membrane.

Form and Function of the Eukaryotic Cell: Boundary Structures

The Cell Wall

The cell walls of fungi and algae are rigid and provide structural support and shape, but they are different in chemical composition from prokaryotic cell walls. Fungal cell walls have a thick, inner

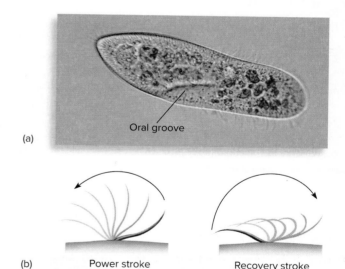

(a)

(b) Power stroke Recovery stroke

Figure 5.5 **Locomotion in ciliates. (a)** A common ciliate, a *Paramecium* has regular rows of cilia over its surface and within its oral groove and gullet for capturing and transporting food. **(b)** Cilia beat in coordinated waves, driving the cell forward and backward. The pattern of ciliary movement is like a swimmer's arms, with a power forward stroke and a repositioning stroke.
(a): Nancy Nehring/Getty Images

layer of polysaccharide fibers composed of chitin or cellulose and a thin outer layer of mixed glycans. The cell walls of algae are quite varied in chemical composition. Substances commonly found in various algal cell walls include various forms of sugar, such as cellulose, pectin,[1] and mannan,[2] along with minerals such as silicon dioxide and calcium carbonate.

1. A polysaccharide composed of galacturonic acid subunits.

2. A polymer of the sugar known as mannose.

The Cytoplasmic Membrane

The cytoplasmic (cell) membrane of eukaryotic cells is a typical bilayer of phospholipids in which protein molecules are embedded (see figures 2.21 and 4.17). In addition to phospholipids, eukaryotic membranes contain *sterols* of various kinds. Sterols are different from phospholipids in both structure and behavior, as you may recall from chapter 2. Their relative rigidity confers stability on eukaryotic membranes. This strengthening feature is extremely important in cells that lack a cell wall. Cytoplasmic membranes of eukaryotes are functionally similar to those of prokaryotes, serving as selectively permeable barriers in transport. Eukaryotic cell membranes are rich in membrane-bound proteins and carbohydrates, which are responsible for interactions between cells, adhesion to surfaces, secretion of products made within the cell, and communication between the cell and its environment (signal transduction).

Practice SECTIONS 5.1–5.2

1. Briefly explain how the eukaryotic cell could have evolved from prokaryotic ones.
2. Which kingdoms of the five-kingdom system contain eukaryotic microorganisms?
3. How do unicellular, colonial, and multicellular organisms differ from each other? Give examples of each type.
4. How are flagella and cilia similar? How are they different?
5. Which eukaryotic cells have a cell wall?
6. What are the functions of the glycocalyx, cell wall, and membrane?

5.3 Form and Function of the Eukaryotic Cell: Internal Structures

Learn

9. Describe the structure of the nucleus and its outstanding features.
10. Outline the stages in cell division and mitosis.
11. Describe the structure of the two types of endoplasmic reticulum and their functions.
12. Identify the parts of the Golgi apparatus, and explain its basic actions and uses in the cell.
13. Summarize the stages in processing by the nucleus, endoplasmic reticulum, and Golgi apparatus involved in synthesis, packaging, and export.
14. Describe the structure of a mitochondrion, and explain its importance and functions.
15. Describe the structure of chloroplasts, and explain their importance and functions.
16. Discuss features of eukaryotic ribosomes.
17. Indicate the basic structure of the cytoskeleton, and explain its main features and functions.

The Nucleus: The Control Center

The **nucleus** is a large compact body that is the most prominent organelle of eukaryotic cells. It is separated from the cell cytoplasm by an external boundary called a **nuclear envelope** or membrane. The envelope has a unique architecture. It is composed of two parallel membranes separated by a narrow space, and it is perforated with small, regularly spaced openings, or pores, at sites where the two membranes unite **(figure 5.6)**. The pores are structured to serve as

Nuclear envelope

Nuclear pore

Nucleolus

Chromatin

Endoplasmic reticulum

(a)

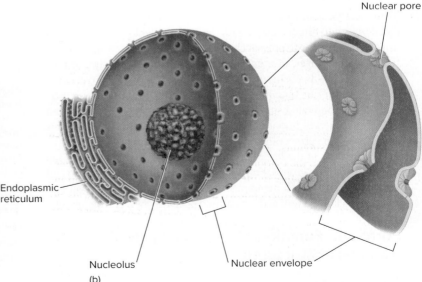

Nuclear pore

Endoplasmic reticulum

Nucleolus

(b)

Nuclear envelope

Figure 5.6 The nucleus. (a) Electron micrograph section of an interphase nucleus, showing its most prominent features. **(b)** Cutaway three-dimensional view of the relationships of the nuclear envelope, pores, and endoplasmic reticulum.

(a): Don W. Fawcett/Science Source

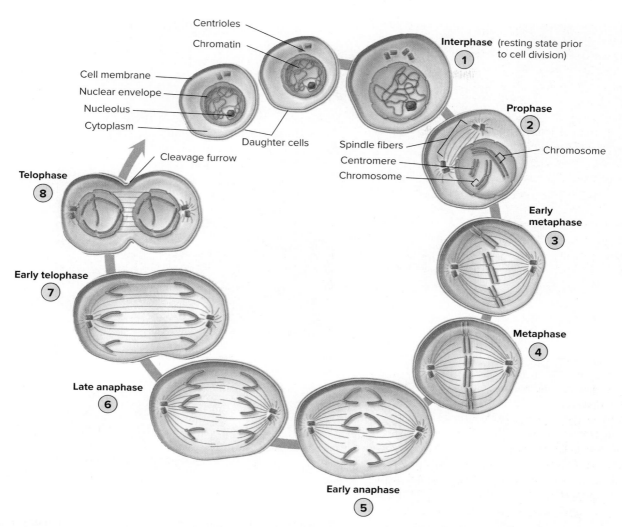

Centrioles

Chromatin

Cell membrane

Nuclear envelope

Nucleolus

Cytoplasm

Daughter cells

Interphase (resting state prior to cell division)
(1)

Prophase
(2)

Spindle fibers

Centromere

Chromosome

Chromosome

Early metaphase
(3)

Metaphase
(4)

Cleavage furrow

Telophase
(8)

Early telophase
(7)

Late anaphase
(6)

Early anaphase
(5)

⚙ **Process Figure 5.7** **Changes in the cell and nucleus during mitosis of a eukaryotic cell. (1)** Before mitosis (at interphase), chromosomes are visible only as chromatin. **(2)** As mitosis proceeds (early prophase), chromosomes take on a fine, threadlike appearance as they condense, and the nuclear membrane and nucleolus are temporarily disrupted. **(3)–(4)** By metaphase, the chromosomes are fully visible as X-shaped structures. The shape is due to duplicated chromosomes attached at a central point, the centromere. **(5)–(6)** Spindle fibers attach to these and facilitate the separation of individual chromosomes during anaphase. **(7)–(8)** Telophase completes chromosomal separation and division of the cell proper into daughter cells.

selective passageways for molecules to migrate between the nucleus and cytoplasm. The main body of the nucleus consists of a matrix called the nucleoplasm and a granular mass, the **nucleolus.** The nucleolus is the site of ribosomal RNA synthesis and a collection area for ribosomal subunits. The subunits are transported through the nuclear pores into the cytoplasm for final assembly into ribosomes.

A prominent feature of the nucleoplasm in stained preparations is a network of dark fibers known as **chromatin** because of its attraction for dyes. Chromatin consists primarily of DNA, along with many small proteins called **histones. Chromosomes,** the large structures within the nucleus of eukaryotic cells that contain the genetic information of the cell, are composed of chromatin. In nondividing cells, the chromosomes within the nucleus are not readily visible because they are long, linear DNA molecules bound in varying degrees to histone proteins, and are far too fine to be resolved as distinct structures without extremely high magnification. During **mitosis,** however, when the duplicated chromosomes are separated

equally into daughter cells, the chromosomes themselves become readily visible as discrete bodies **(process figure 5.7).** This appearance arises when the DNA becomes highly condensed by forming coils and supercoils around the histones to prevent the chromosomes from tangling as they are separated into new cells. This process is described in more detail in chapter 9.

Although we correctly view the nucleus as the primary genetic center, it does not function in isolation. As we show in the next three sections, it is closely tied to cytoplasmic organelles that perform elaborate cell functions.

Endoplasmic Reticulum: A Passageway and Production System for Eukaryotes

The **endoplasmic reticulum (ER)** is an interconnected network of membranous, hollow sacs that synthesize and transport cell substances **(figure 5.8a).** Originating from, and continuous with, the

Figure 5.8 **The origin and structures of the rough endoplasmic reticulum (RER) and Golgi apparatus. (a)** Schematic view of the origin of the endoplasmic reticulum from the outer membrane of the nuclear envelope. **(b)** Three-dimensional projection of the RER. **(c)** Detail of the orientation of a ribosome on the RER membrane. Proteins are collected within the RER cisternae and distributed through its network to other destinations. **(d)** The flattened layers of the Golgi apparatus receive protein-carrying transport vesicles from the RER, process their contents, and transport condensing vesicles to sites of various cellular functions.

outer membrane of the nuclear envelope, the ER serves as a passageway for materials between the nucleus and the cytoplasm. It also provides significant compartmentalization for numerous cell activities. The two types of endoplasmic reticulum are the **rough endoplasmic reticulum (RER)** and the **smooth endoplasmic reticulum (SER).** These two ER networks are similar in origin and are directly connected to each other, but they differ in some aspects of structure and function.

The RER consists of parallel, flattened sacs called **cisternae,*** and it appears "rough" in electron micrographs because its outer surface is studded with ribosomes **(figure 5.8b).** This architecture ties in with its role in synthesis of proteins, which are collected in the lumen **(figure 5.8c)** of the cisternae and processed for further transport to

the Golgi apparatus **(figure 5.8d).** The SER lacks ribosomes and is more tubular in structure (see figures 5.3 and 5.8a). Although it communicates with the RER and also transports molecules within the cell, it has specialized functions. Most important among them are the synthesis of nonprotein molecules such as lipids, and detoxification of metabolic waste products and other toxic substances.

Golgi Apparatus: A Packaging Machine

The **Golgi**[3] **apparatus,** also called the **Golgi complex** or **body,** is the site in the cell that collects proteins and and packages them for transport to their final destinations. It is a discrete organelle

* *cisternae* (siss-tur'-nee) sing. cisterna; L., *cisterna,* reservoir.

3. *Golgi* (gol'-jee) Named for C. Golgi, an Italian histologist who first described the apparatus in 1898.

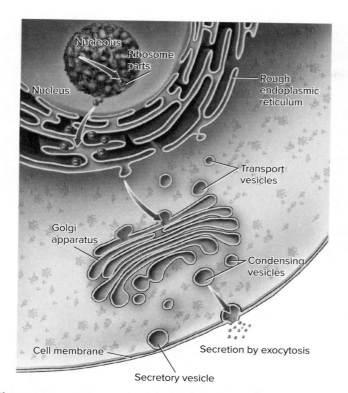

Figure 5.9 The synthesis and transport machine. Function requires cooperation and interaction among the system of organelles. The nucleolus provides a constant supply of ribosomes that travel through the nuclear pores to the RER. Once in place, ribosomes synthesize proteins that are assembled by the RER into vesicles and moved to the nearby Golgi. Finished vesicles leave the Golgi after processing and migrate to the cell membrane. From there they may be secreted (as here) or act internally.

consisting of layers of flattened, disc-shaped sacs also called cisternae, giving an appearance of a stack of pita breads. These sacs have outer limiting membranes and cavities like those of the endoplasmic reticulum, but they do not form a continuous network (figure 5.8d). This organelle is always closely associated with the endoplasmic reticulum both in its location and function. At a site where it borders on the Golgi apparatus, the endoplasmic reticulum buds off tiny membrane-bound packets of protein called **transport vesicles** that are picked up by the forming face of the Golgi apparatus. Once in the complex itself, the proteins are further modified for transport by the addition of polysaccharides and lipids. The final action of this apparatus is to pinch off finished **condensing vesicles** that will be conveyed to organelles such as lysosomes or transported outside the cell as **secretory vesicles (figure 5.9).**

Nucleus, Endoplasmic Reticulum, and Golgi Apparatus: Nature's Assembly Line

As the keeper of the eukaryotic genetic code, the nucleus ultimately governs and regulates all cell activities. But because the nucleus remains fixed in a specific cellular site, it must direct these activities through a structural and chemical network (figure 5.9). This network includes ribosomes, which originate in the nucleus, and the rough endoplasmic reticulum, which is continuously connected with the nuclear envelope.

Initially, a segment of the genetic code of DNA containing the instructions for producing a protein is copied into RNA and passed out through the nuclear pores directly to the ribosomes on the endoplasmic reticulum. Here, specific proteins are synthesized from the RNA code and deposited in the lumen (space) of the endoplasmic reticulum. Details of this process are covered in chapter 9. After being transported to the Golgi apparatus, the protein products are chemically modified and packaged into **vesicles*** that can be used by the cell in a variety of ways. Some of the vesicles contain enzymes to digest food inside the cell; other vesicles are secreted to digest materials outside the cell; and yet others are important in the enlargement and repair of the cell wall and membrane.

A **lysosome*** is one type of vesicle originating from the Golgi apparatus that contains a variety of enzymes. Lysosomes are involved in intracellular digestion of food particles and in protection against invading microorganisms. They also participate in digestion and removal of cell debris in damaged tissue.

Other types of vesicles include **vacuoles,*** which are membrane-bound sacs containing fluids or solid particles to be digested, excreted, or stored. They are formed in phagocytic cells (certain white blood cells and protozoa) in response to food and other substances that have been engulfed. The contents of a food vacuole are digested through the merger of the vacuole with a lysosome. This merged structure is called a phagosome **(figure 5.10)**. Other types of vacuoles are used in storing reserve food such as fats and glycogen. Protozoa living in freshwater habitats regulate osmotic pressure by means of contractile vacuoles, which regularly expel excess water that has diffused into the cell (discussed in section 7.3).

Mitochondria: Energy Generators of the Cell

None of the cellular activities of the genetic assembly line could proceed without a constant supply of energy, the bulk of which is generated in most eukaryotes by **mitochondria.*** When viewed with light microscopy, mitochondria appear as tiny round or elongated particles scattered throughout the cytoplasm. Higher magnification reveals that a mitochondrion consists of a smooth, continuous outer membrane that forms the external contour and an inner, folded membrane nestled neatly within the outer membrane **(figure 5.11)**. The folds on the inner membrane, called **cristae,*** vary in exact structure among eukaryotic cell types. Plant, animal, and fungal mitochondria have lamellar cristae folded into shelflike layers. Those of algae and protozoa are tubular, fingerlike projections or flattened discs.

The cristae membranes hold the enzymes and electron carriers of aerobic respiration. This is an oxygen-using process that extracts chemical energy contained in nutrient molecules and stores it in the form of high-energy molecules, or ATP. More detailed functions of mitochondria are covered in chapter 8. The spaces around the cristae are filled with a chemically complex fluid called the **matrix,*** which holds ribosomes, DNA, and a pool of enzymes and other

* *vesicle* (ves′-ik-l) L. *vesios,* bladder. A small sac containing fluid.
* *lysosome* (ly′-soh-sohm) Gr. *lysis,* dissolution, and *soma,* body.
* *vacuole* (vak′-yoo-ohl) L. *vacuus,* empty. Any membranous space in the cytoplasm.
* *mitochondria* (my″-toh-kon′-dree-uh) sing. mitochondrion; Gr. *mitos,* thread, and *chondrion,* granule.
* *cristae* (kris′-te) sing. crista; L. *crista,* a comb.
* *matrix* (may′-triks) L. *mater,* mother or origin.

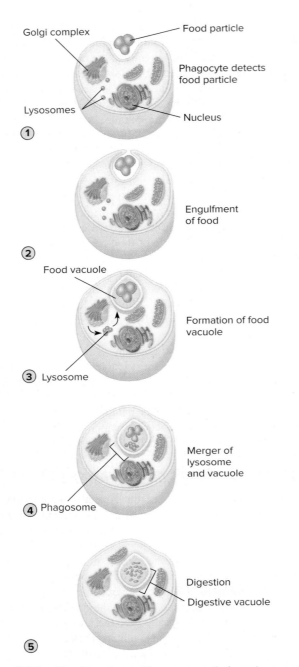

Figure 5.10 **The functions of lysosomes during phagocytosis.**

(a)

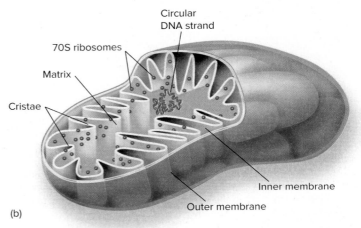

(b)

Figure 5.11 **General structure of a mitochondrion. (a)** An electron micrograph of a cross section. In most cells, mitochondria are elliptical or spherical, or occasionally filament-like. **(b)** A cutaway three-dimensional illustration details the double membrane structure and the extensive foldings of the inner membrane.
(a): Keith R. Porter/Science Source

compounds involved in the metabolic cycle. Mitochondria (along with chloroplasts) are unique among organelles in that they divide independently of the cell, contain circular strands of DNA, and have prokaryote-sized 70S ribosomes. The presence of 70S ribosomes in eukaryotic organelles like mitochondria (and, as seen in the next section, chloroplasts) is one of the strongest pieces of evidence for the endosymbiotic theory discussed in section 5.1.

Chloroplasts: Photosynthesis Machines

Chloroplasts are remarkable organelles found in algae and plant cells that are capable of converting the energy of sunlight into chemical energy through photosynthesis. The photosynthetic role

of chloroplasts makes them important primary producers of organic nutrients upon which all other organisms (except certain bacteria and archaea) ultimately depend. Another important photosynthetic product of chloroplasts is oxygen gas. Although chloroplasts resemble mitochondria, chloroplasts are larger, contain special pigments, and are much more varied in shape. Be reminded that chloroplasts are thought to have originated from intracellular cyanobacteria and resemble them in many ways.

There are differences among various algal chloroplasts, but most are generally composed of two membranes, one enclosing the other. The smooth, outer membrane completely covers an inner membrane folded into small, disclike sacs called **thylakoids** that are stacked upon one another into **grana.** These structures carry the green pigment chlorophyll and sometimes additional pigments as well. Surrounding the thylakoids is a ground substance called the **stroma* (figure 5.12).** The role of the photosynthetic pigments is

* *stroma* (stroh′-mah) Gr. *stroma,* mattress or bed.

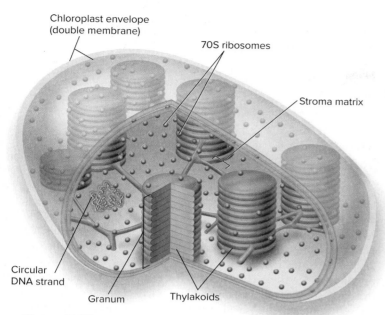

Figure 5.12 **Details of an algal chloroplast.** An artist's three-dimensional rendition of a chloroplast and its major features.

to absorb and transform solar energy into chemical energy, which is then used during reactions in the stroma to synthesize carbohydrates. We further explore some important aspects of photosynthesis in chapters 7 and 8.

Ribosomes: Protein Synthesizers

In an electron micrograph of a eukaryotic cell, ribosomes are numerous, tiny particles that give a "dotted" appearance to the cytoplasm. Ribosomes are distributed in two ways: Some are scattered freely in the cytoplasm (supported by the cytoskeleton), whereas

others are bound to the surface of the rough endoplasmic reticulum, as previously described. Multiple ribosomes are often found arranged in short chains called polyribosomes (polysomes). The basic structure of eukaryotic ribosomes is similar to that of prokaryotic ribosomes, described in chapter 4. Both are composed of large and small subunits of ribonucleoprotein (see figure 5.8). By contrast, however, the ribosomes of eukaryotes (except in the mitochondria and chloroplasts) are of the larger 80S variety that is a combination of 60S and 40S subunits. As in the prokaryotes, eukaryotic ribosomes are the staging areas for protein synthesis.

The difference between bacterial (70S) and eukaryotic (80S) ribosomes is important in antibiotic treatment of bacterial infections. Because the goal of antibacterial treatment is to harm bacterial cells without injuring cells of the (eukaryotic) host, differences between the two types of cells offer an inviting target. Antibiotics like tetracycline and erythromycin both interfere with prokaryotic ribosomes, but not with eukaryotic ribosomes, allowing physicians to treat bacterial infections with relatively few side effects.

The Cytoskeleton: A Support Network

The region encased by the cell membrane is called the cytoplasm, and it is within this region that cellular organelles are housed and metabolic and synthetic activities take place. The cytoplasm is traversed by a flexible framework of molecules called the **cytoskeleton (figure 5.13).** This framework has several functions, including anchoring organelles, moving RNA and vesicles, and permitting shape changes and movement in some cells. The three main types of cytoskeletal elements are actin filaments, intermediate filaments, and microtubules. **Actin filaments** are long, thin protein strands about 8 nm in diameter. Found throughout the cell but especially just inside the cell membrane, actin filaments are responsible for cellular movements such as contraction, pinching during cell division, and formation of cellular extensions. **Microtubules** are long,

Actin filaments (microfilaments) are composed of actin subunits and are about 8 nm in diameter.

(a)

(b)

Figure 5.13 **A model of the cytoskeleton. (a)** Depicted is the relationship between actin filaments, microtubules, microfilaments, and organelles. (Not to scale.) **(b)** The cytoskeleton of a eukaryotic muscle precursor cell is highlighted by fluorescent dyes. Actin filaments are stained green, and the nucleus is blue.

(b): Alex Ritter, Jennifer Lippincott Schwartz, Gillian Griffiths/National Institutes of Health

TABLE 5.3	Function of Internal Structures within the Eukaryotic Cell
Nucleus	Genetic center of the cell; repository of DNA; synthesis of RNA
Nucleolus	Ribosomal RNA synthesis; ribosome construction
Endoplasmic reticulum	Transport of materials; lipid synthesis
Golgi apparatus	Packaging and modification of proteins prior to secretion
Lysosomes	Intracellular digestion
Vacuoles	Temporary storage and transport; digestion (food vacuoles); regulation of osmotic pressure (water vacuoles)
Mitochondria	Energy production using the Krebs cycle, electron transport, and oxidative phosphorylation
Chloroplast	Conversion of sunlight into chemical energy through photosynthesis
Ribosomes	Protein synthesis
Cytoskeleton	Composed of microfilaments and microtubules; provides cell structure and movement; anchors organelles

hollow tubes about 25 nm in diameter, composed of protein subunits of tubulin. Microtubules maintain the shape of eukaryotic cells when they don't have cell walls, and serve to transport substances from one part of the cell to another. The spindle fibers that attach and separate chromosomes during mitosis are microtubules. Cilia and flagella, as discussed earlier, also depend on microtubules for function (see figure 5.4). **Intermediate filaments,** as their name suggests, are intermediate in size between the other two elements, appearing as ropelike structures about 10 nm in diameter. Their main role is the structural reinforcement of the cell and of organelles, for instance, supporting ribosomes and mitochondria. The internal structures of a eukaryotic cell are summarized in **table 5.3.**

Practice SECTION 5.3

7. In what ways does the nucleus function like the "brain" of the cell?
8. Explain how ribosomes and the nucleolus are related.
9. How does the nucleus communicate with the cytoplasm?
10. Compare and contrast the smooth ER, the rough ER, and the Golgi apparatus in structure and function.
11. Compare the structures and functions of the mitochondrion and the chloroplast.
12. What makes the mitochondrion and chloroplast unique among the organelles?
13. Describe some of the ways that organisms use lysosomes.
14. For what reasons would a cell need a "skeleton"?

5.4 Eukaryotic-Prokaryotic Comparisons and Taxonomy of Eukaryotes

Learn

18. Compare and contrast prokaryotic cells, eukaryotic cells, and viruses.

19. Outline the basics of eukaryotic taxonomy.

20. Explain what is meant by the term *protist,* and outline the types of organisms belonging to this designation.

Now that we have introduced the major characteristics of eukaryotic cells, in this section we will summarize these characteristics and compare and contrast them with prokaryotic cells (see chapter 4), especially from the standpoints of structure, physiology, and other traits **(table 5.4).** We have included viruses for the purposes of summarizing the biological characteristics of all microbes and to show you just how much viruses differ from cells. We will explore this fascinating group of microbes in chapter 6.

Overview of Taxonomy

Exploring the origins of eukaryotic cells with molecular techniques has both clarified and muddied our view of the relationships among organisms in Domain Eukarya. Historically, easily observed characteristics—cell type, the presence or absence of flagella, means of gathering nutrition—were used to classify organisms. More recently, the use of molecular biology techniques to examine these organisms has shown us that many of our past assumptions about evolutionary history were incorrect. As our understanding of the true relationship between organisms improves, we are left in the unenviable position of knowing that our current system is not entirely correct, but not knowing exactly *how* it is incorrect.

The current hierarchy divides the Domain Eukarya into five **supergroups,** a level between domain and kingdom. Each supergroup is further divided into kingdoms; a simplified version of this hierarchy is seen in **figure 5.14.** This system retains some of the traditional kingdoms, while others have been fragmented. The one group that has created the greatest challenge in establishing reliable relationships is **Kingdom Protista**—the protists. In the past, any simple eukaryotic cell that lacked multicellular structure or cell specialization had been placed into the Kingdom Protista generally as an alga (photosynthetic) or protozoan (nonphotosynthetic). Although exceptions had always arisen with this classification scheme—notably multicellular algae and the photosynthetic protozoans—most eukaryotic microbes had been readily accommodated in the Kingdom Protista as traditionally presented. Newer genetic data reveal that the organisms we call protists may be as different from each other as plants are different from animals. They are highly complex organisms that are likely to have evolved from a number of separate ancestors.

Of course, while microbiologists prefer to set up taxonomic systems that reflect true relationships based on all valid scientific

TABLE 5.4	A General Comparison of Prokaryotic and Eukaryotic Cells and Viruses			
Function or Structure	Characteristic*	Prokaryotic Cells	Eukaryotic Cells	Viruses**
Genetics	Nucleic acids	+	+	+
	True nucleus	−	+	−
	Nuclear envelope	−	+	−
	Nucleoid	+	−	−
Reproduction	Mitosis	−	+	−
	Production of sex cells	+/−	+	−
	Binary fission	+	+	−
Biosynthesis	Independent	+	+	−
	Golgi apparatus	−	+	−
	Endoplasmic reticulum	−	+	−
	Ribosomes	+***	+	−
Respiration	Enzymes	+	+	−
	Mitochondria	−	+	−
Photosynthesis	Pigments	+/−	+/−	−
	Chloroplasts	−	+/−	−
Motility/locomotor structures	Flagella	+/−***	+/−	−
	Cilia	−	+/−	−
Shape/protection	Cell membrane	+	+	−
	Cell wall	+/−***	+/−	− (have capsids instead)
	Capsule	+/−	+/−	−
Size (in general)		0.5–3 µm****	2–100 µm	< 0.2 µm

*+ means most members of the group exhibit this characteristic; − means most lack it; +/− means some members have it and some do not.

**Viruses cannot participate in metabolic or genetic activity outside their host cells.

***The prokaryotic type is structurally very different.

****Much smaller and much larger bacteria exist; see 4.1 Making Connections.

Figure 5.14 **Phylogenetic organization of the Domain Eukarya.** Molecular data divides eukaryotic organisms into five supergroups. This simplified tree does not include all members of each supergroup.

data, from the point of view of a survey of all eukaryotic microorganisms, we feel the term *protist* still has merit and will continue to use it for any eukaryote that is not a fungus, animal, or plant. A final note about taxonomy: No one system is perfect or permanent. Let your instructor guide you as to which one is satisfactory for your course.

With the general structure of the eukaryotic cell in mind, let us next examine the range of adaptations that this cell type has undergone. The following sections contain a general survey of the principal eukaryotic microorganisms—fungi, protists, and parasitic worms—while also introducing elements of their structure, life history, classification, identification, and importance. A survey of diseases associated with some of these microbes is found in chapters 22 and 23.

5.5 The Kingdom Fungi

 Learn

21. Describe the basic characteristics of the Kingdom Fungi in terms of general types of cells and organisms, structure, and nutrition.

22. Differentiate between characteristics of yeasts and of molds, and define fungal spores.

23. Classify types of fungal spores and explain their functions.

24. Discuss the main features of fungal classification and representative examples of each group.

25. Explain how fungi are identified.

26. Discuss the importance of fungi in ecology, agriculture, commerce, and medicine.

The position of the **fungi*** in the biological world has been debated for many years. They were originally classified with the green plants (along with algae and bacteria), and later they were placed in a group with algae and protozoa (the Protista). Even at that time, however, many microbiologists were struck by several unique qualities of fungi that warranted placement into a separate kingdom. Confirmation of their status by genetic testing eliminated any question that they belong in a kingdom of their own.

* *fungi* (fun′-jy) sing. fungus; Gr. *fungos,* mushroom.

The **Kingdom Fungi** is filled with organisms of great variety and complexity that have survived on earth for approximately 650 million years. About 100,000 species are known, although experts estimate a count much higher than this—perhaps as high as 1.5 million. For practical purposes, mycologists divide the fungi into two groups: the *macroscopic fungi* (mushrooms, puffballs, gill fungi) and the *microscopic fungi* (molds, yeasts). Although the majority of fungi are either unicellular or colonial, a few complex forms such as mushrooms and puffballs are considered multicellular.

Chemical traits of fungal cells include the possession of a polysaccharide, **chitin,** in their cell walls and a sterol, ergosterol, in their cell membranes. Cells of the microscopic fungi exist in two basic morphological types: hyphae and yeasts. **Hyphae*** are long, thread-like cells that make up the bodies of filamentous fungi, or **molds (figure 5.15).** A **yeast** cell is distinguished by its round to oval shape and by its mode of asexual reproduction. It grows swellings on its surface called buds, which then become separate cells **(figure 5.16a).** Some species form a **pseudohypha,*** a chain of yeasts formed when buds remain attached in a row **(figure 5.16c);** because of its manner of formation, it is not a true hypha like that of molds. Although some fungal cells exist only in a yeast form and others occur primarily as hyphae, a few, called **dimorphic,*** can take either form, depending upon growth conditions, such as

* *hyphae* (hy′-fuh) pl. hyphae (hy′-fee); Gr. *hyphe,* a web.
* *pseudohypha* (soo″-doh-hy′-fuh) pl. pseudohyphae; Gr. *pseudo,* false, and *hyphe,* a web.
* *dimorphic* (dy-mor′-fik) Gr. *di,* two, and *morphe,* form.

(a)

(b)

Septum

Septa

Septate hyphae
Septum with pores
Nucleus

As in *Penicillium*

(c)

Nonseptate hyphae
Nuclei

As in *Rhizopus*

Figure 5.15　Macroscopic and microscopic views of molds. (a) A container of food (left too long in the refrigerator) has developed a miniature forest of mold colonies. Note the various textures of mycelia and the array of color differences due to spores. **(b)** Close-up of hyphal structure (1,200×). **(c)** Basic structural types of hyphae. The septate hyphae develop small pores that allow communication between cells. Nonseptate hyphae lack septa and are single, long multinucleate cells.
(a): Kathy Park Talaro; (b): Dr. Judy A. Murphy, San Joaquin Delta College, Department of Microscopy, Stocton, CA

Figure 5.16 (a) Fungal (Yeast) Cell

Bud

Bud scar

Ribosomes

Mitochondrion

Endoplasmic reticulum

Nucleus

Nucleolus

Cell wall

Cell membrane

Golgi apparatus

Storage vacuole

(a)

Fungal (Yeast) Cell

(b)

Bud

Nucleus

Bud scars

(c)

Pseudohypha

Figure 5.16 Microscopic morphology of yeasts. (a) General structure of a yeast cell, representing major organelles. Note the presence of a cell wall and lack of locomotor organelles. **(b)** Scanning electron micrograph of *Saccharomyces cerevisciae,* common baker's yeast (3000×). **(c)** Formation and release of yeast buds and pseudohypha (a chain of budding yeast cells).
(b): Science Photo Library/Alamy Stock Photo

changing temperature. This variability in growth form is particularly characteristic of some pathogenic molds.

Fungal Nutrition

All fungi are **heterotrophic.*** They acquire nutrients from a wide variety of organic sources or **substrates (figure 5.17).** Most fungi are **saprobes,*** meaning that they obtain these substrates from the

* *heterotrophic* (het-ur-oh-tro'-fik) Gr. *hetero,* other, and *troph,* to feed. A type of nutrition that relies on an organic nutrient source.
* *saprobe* (sap'-rohb) Gr. *sapros,* rotten, and *bios,* to live. Also called saprotroph or saprophyte.

(a)

(b)

Figure 5.17 Nutritional sources (substrates) for fungi.
(a) *Penicillium notatum* mold, a very common decomposer of citrus fruit, is known for its velvety texture and typical blue-green color. Microscopic inset shows the brush arrangement of *Penicillium* phialospores (220×), the asexual phase. **(b)** The appearance of athlete's foot, an infection caused by *Trichophyton rubrum.* The inset is a 1,000× magnification revealing its hyphae (blue) and conidia (brown).
(a): Kathy Park Talaro; (a: inset): Natures Geometry/Alamy Stock Photo;
(b): carroteater/Getty Images; (b: inset): *Source:* Dr. Libero Ajello/CDC

remnants of dead plants and animals in soil or aquatic habitats. Fungi can also be parasites on the bodies of living animals or plants, although very few fungi absolutely require a living host. In general, the fungus penetrates the substrate and secretes enzymes that reduce it to small molecules that can be absorbed. Fungi have enzymes for digesting an incredible array of substances, including feathers, hair, cellulose, petroleum products, wood, even rubber. It is likely that every naturally occurring organic material on the earth can be attacked by some type of fungus. Some fungi have developed into normal residents of plants called endophytes or associate with photosynthetic microbes (algae or cyanobacteria) to form an unusual hybrid organism called a **lichen,** an important participant in the formation of soil.

The medical and agricultural impact of fungi is extensive. A number of species cause **mycoses** (fungal infections) in animals, and thousands of species are important plant pathogens. Over the last several years, a newly recognized fungal pathogen, *Pseudogymnoascus destructans,* has decimated bats in 33 states, with some populations reduced by as much as 80%. Though many people might at first not be concerned by losses in the bat population, bats are the primary predator of insects, and the agricultural damage from unsuppressed insect populations has been estimated at up to $50 billion per year in the United States.

Fungi frequently share human living quarters, especially in locations that provide ample moisture and nutrients. Often their presence is harmless and limited to a film of mildew on shower stalls or in other moist environments, but in some cases, these indoor fungi can be the source of medical problems. Such common fungi as *Aspergillus, Cladosporium,* and *Stachybotrys* can release airborne spores and toxins that, when inhaled, cause a spectrum of symptoms sometimes referred to as "sick building syndrome." The usual source of harmful fungi is the presence of chronically water-damaged walls, ceilings, and other building materials that have come to harbor these fungi. People exposed to these houses or buildings report symptoms that range from skin rash, flulike reactions, sore throat, and headaches to fatigue, diarrhea, allergies, and immune suppression.

Organization of Microscopic Fungi

The cells of most microscopic fungi grow in loose associations or colonies. The colonies of yeasts are much like those of bacteria in that they have a soft, uniform texture and appearance. The colonies of filamentous fungi are noted for the striking cottony, hairy, or velvety textures that arise from their microscopic organization and morphology. The woven, intertwining mass of hyphae that makes up the body or colony of a mold is called a **mycelium.***

Although hyphae contain the usual eukaryotic organelles, they also have some unique organizational features. In most fungi, the hyphae are divided into segments by cross walls, or **septa,** and such hyphae are referred to as septate (see figure 5.15*c*). The nature of the septa varies from solid partitions with no communication between the compartments to partial walls with small pores that allow the flow of organelles and nutrients between adjacent compartments. Nonseptate hyphae consist of one long, continuous cell *not* divided

into individual compartments by cross walls. With this construction, the cytoplasm and organelles move freely from one region to another, and each hyphal element can have several nuclei (see figure 5.15*c*).

Hyphae can also be classified according to their particular function. Vegetative hyphae (mycelia) are responsible for the visible mass of growth that appears on the surface of a food source and penetrates it to digest and absorb nutrients. During the development of a fungal colony, the vegetative hyphae give rise to structures called reproductive, or fertile, hyphae that branch off vegetative mycelium. These hyphae are responsible for the production of fungal reproductive bodies called spores, discussed next. Other specializations of hyphae are illustrated in **figure 5.18.**

Reproductive Strategies and Spore Formation

Fungi have many complex and successful reproductive strategies. Most can propagate by the simple outward growth of existing hyphae or by fragmentation, in which a separated piece of mycelium can generate a whole new colony. But the primary reproductive mode of fungi involves the production of various types of **spores.** Do not confuse fungal spores with the extremely resistant, nonreproductive bacterial endospores. Fungal spores function not only in

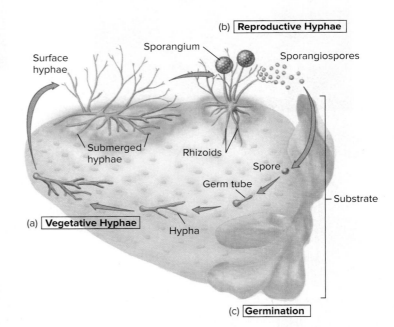

Figure 5.18 **Functional types of hyphae using the mold Rhizopus as an example. (a)** Vegetative hyphae are those surface and submerged filaments that digest, absorb, and distribute nutrients from the substrate. This species also has special anchoring structures called rhizoids. **(b)** Later, as the mold matures, it sprouts reproductive hyphae that produce asexual spores called sporangiospores. **(c)** During the asexual life cycle, the free mold spores settle on a substrate and send out germ tubes that elongate into hyphae that produce an extensive mycelium. So prolific are the fungi that a single colony of mold can easily contain 5,000 spore-bearing structures. If each of these released 2,000 single spores, and if every spore were able to germinate, we would soon find ourselves in a sea of mycelia. Most spores do not germinate, but enough are successful to keep the numbers of fungi and their spores very high in most habitats.

* *mycelium* (my'-see-lee-yum) pl. mycelia; Gr. *mykes,* root word for fungus.

multiplication but also in survival (providing genetic variation) and dissemination. Because of their compactness and relatively light weight, fungal spores are dispersed widely through the environment by air, water, and living things. Upon encountering a favorable substrate, a spore will germinate and produce a new fungus colony in a very short time (figure 5.18).

The fungi exhibit such a marked diversity in spores that they are largely classified and identified by their spores and spore-forming structures. Although there are some elaborate systems for naming and classifying spores, we present only a basic overview of the principal types. The most general subdivision is based on the way the spores arise. Asexual spores are the products of mitotic division of a single parent cell, and sexual spores are formed through a process involving the fusing of two parental nuclei followed by meiosis.

Asexual Spore Formation

On the basis of the nature of the reproductive hypha and the manner in which the spores originate, there are two subtypes of asexual spore **(figure 5.19):**

1. **Sporangiospores** (figure 5.19*a*) are formed by successive cleavages within a saclike head called a **sporangium,*** which

is attached to a stalk, the sporangiophore. These spores are initially enclosed but are released when the sporangium ruptures. Some sporangiospores are the end result of the sexual phase of the life cycle, as seen in figure 5.20.

2. **Conidia*** (conidiospores) are free spores not enclosed by a spore-bearing sac (figure 5.19*b*). They develop either by pinching off the tip of a special fertile hypha or by segmentation of a preexisting vegetative hypha. Conidia are the most common asexual spores, and they occur in these forms:

arthrospore (ar′-thro-spor) Gr. *arthron,* joint. A rectangular spore formed when a septate hypha fragments at the cross walls.
chlamydospore (klam-ih′-doh-spor) Gr. *chlamys,* cloak. A spherical conidium formed by the thickening of a hyphal cell. It is released when the surrounding hypha fractures, and it serves as a survival or resting cell.
blastospore. A spore produced by budding from a parent cell that is a yeast or another conidium; also called a bud.
phialospore (fy′-ah-lo-spor) Gr. *phialos,* a vessel. A conidium budded from the mouth of a vase-shaped spore-bearing cell called a phialide or *sterigma*, leaving a small collar.

* *sporangium* (spo-ran′-jee-um) pl. sporangia; Gr. *sporos,* seed, and *angeion,* vessel.

* *conidia* (koh-nid′-ee-uh) sing. conidium; Gr. *konidion,* a particle of dust.

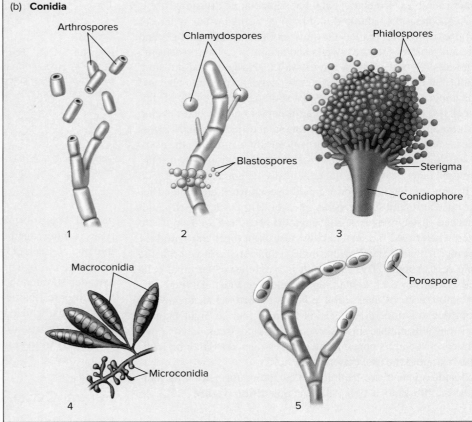

Figure 5.19 Types of asexual mold spores. (a) Sporangiospores: (1) *Absidia,* (2) *Syncephalastrum,* (table 5.5) **(b)** Conidia: (1) arthrospores (e.g., *Coccidioides*), (2) chlamydospores and blastospores (e.g., *Candida albicans*), (3) phialospores (e.g., *Aspergillus,* table 5.5), (4) macroconidia and microconidia (e.g., *Microsporum,* table 5.5), and (5) porospores (e.g., *Alternaria*).

microconidium and *macroconidium*. The smaller and larger conidia formed by the same fungus under varying conditions. Microconidia are one-celled, and macroconidia have two or more cells.

porospore. A conidium that grows out through small pores in the spore-bearing cell; some are composed of several cells.

Sexual Spore Formation

Because fungi can propagate successfully by producing millions of asexual spores, it is natural to wonder about the survival potential of sexual spores. The answer lies in important variations that occur when fungi of different genetic makeup combine their genetic material. As in plants and animals, a union of genes from two parents creates offspring with combinations of genes different from that of either parent. The offspring from such a union can have slight variations in form and function that are potentially advantageous to the adaptation and evolution of their species.

The majority of fungi produce sexual spores at some point. The nature of this process varies from the simple fusion of fertile hyphae of two different strains to a complex union of differentiated male and female structures and the development of special fruiting bodies. We consider the three most common sexual spores: zygospores, ascospores, and basidiospores. These spore types provide an important basis for classifying the major fungal divisions.

Zygospores* are sturdy diploid spores formed when hyphae of two opposite strains (called the plus and minus strains) fuse and create a diploid zygote that swells and becomes covered by strong, spiny walls **(figure 5.20).** When its wall is disrupted and moisture and nutrient conditions are suitable, the zygospore germinates and forms a mycelium that gives rise to a sporangium. Meiosis of diploid cells of the sporangium results in haploid nuclei that develop into sporangiospores. Both the sporangia and the sporangiospores that arise from sexual processes are outwardly identical to the asexual type, but because the spores arose from the union of two separate fungal parents, they are not genetically identical.

In general, haploid spores called **ascospores*** are created inside a special fungal sac, or **ascus** (pl. asci) **(figure 5.21).** Although details can vary among types of fungi, the ascus and ascospores are formed when two different strains or sexes join together to produce offspring. In many species, the male sexual organ fuses with the female sexual organ. The end result is a number of terminal cells called *dikaryons,* each containing a diploid nucleus. Through differentiation, each of these cells enlarges to form an ascus, and its diploid nucleus undergoes meiosis to form four to eight haploid nuclei that will mature into ascospores. A ripe ascus breaks open and releases the ascospores. Some species form an elaborate fruiting body to hold the asci (inset, figure 5.21).

Basidiospores* are haploid sexual spores formed on the outside of a club-shaped cell called a **basidium (figure 5.22).** In

Figure 5.20 Formation of zygospores in *Rhizopus stolonifer*. Sexual reproduction occurs when two mating strains of hyphae grow together, fuse, and form a mature diploid zygospore. Germination of the zygospore involves production of a haploid sporangium that looks just like the asexual one shown in figure 5.19, but the individual spores contain genes from two different parents. So, in this case, the sporangiospores are the result of sexual recombination.
(mold on bread): Richard Hutchings/McGraw-Hill Education; (mold): Mitroshkin/Getty Images; (Rhizopus sporangia and zygote): Richard Gross/McGraw-Hill Education

general, spore formation follows the same pattern of two mating types coming together, fusing, and forming terminal cells with diploid nuclei. Each of these cells becomes a basidium, and its nucleus produces, through meiosis, four haploid nuclei. These nuclei are extruded through the top of the basidium, where they develop into basidiospores. Notice the location of the basidia along the gills in mushrooms, which are often dark from the spores they contain. It may be a surprise to discover that the fleshy part of a mushroom is actually a fruiting body designed to protect and help disseminate its sexual spores.

Fungal Classification

It is often difficult for microbiologists to assign logical and useful classification schemes to microorganisms that also reflect their evolutionary relationships. This difficulty is due to the fact that the organisms do not always perfectly fit the neat categories made for

* *zygospore* (zy′-goh-spor) Gr. *zygon,* yoke, to join.
* *ascospore* (as′-koh-sporz) Gr. *ascos,* a sac.
* *basidiospore* (bah-sid′-ee-oh-sporz) Gr. *basidi,* a pedestal.

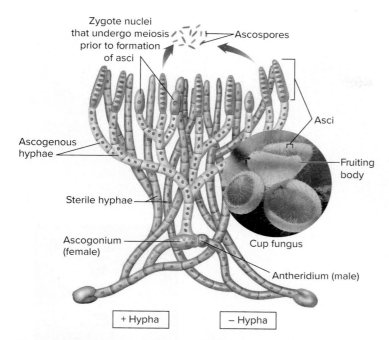

Zygote nuclei that undergo meiosis prior to formation of asci

Ascospores

Asci

Ascogenous hyphae

Fruiting body

Sterile hyphae

Cup fungus

Ascogonium (female)

Antheridium (male)

+ Hypha

– Hypha

Figure 5.21 **Production of ascospores in a cup fungus.** Inset shows the cup-shaped fruiting body of *Cookeina tricholoma* that houses the asci. Raindrops falling into the fruiting body help to disperse the spores.
(inset): Worraket/Shutterstock

them, and even experts cannot always agree on the nature of the categories. The fungi are no exception, and there are several ways to classify them. For our purposes, we adopt a classification scheme with a medical mycology emphasis, in which Kingdom Fungi is subdivided into several phyla based upon the type of sexual reproduction, hyphal structure, and genetic profile. **Table 5.5** outlines the major phyla, their characteristics, and typical members.

Fungi that Produce Only Asexual Spores (Imperfect)

From the beginnings of fungal classification, any fungus that lacked a sexual state was called "imperfect" and was placed in a catchall category, the Fungi Imperfecti. A species would remain classified in that category until its sexual state was described. Gradually many species were found to make sexual spores, and they were assigned to the taxonomic grouping that best fit those spores. In other cases they have been reassigned because genetic analysis indicated they belonged to an established phylum, usually to Ascomycota.

Fungal Identification and Cultivation

Fungi are identified in medical specimens by first being isolated on special types of media and then being observed macroscopically and microscopically. Examples of media for cultivating fungi are cornmeal, blood, and Sabouraud's agar. The latter medium is useful in isolating fungi from mixed samples because of its low pH, which inhibits the growth of bacteria but not of most fungi. Because the fungi are classified into general groups by the presence and type of sexual spores, it would seem logical to identify them in the same way, but sexual spores are rarely, if ever, demonstrated in the laboratory setting. As a result, the asexual spore-forming structures and spores are usually used to identify organisms to the level of genus and species. Other characteristics that contribute to identification are hyphal type, colony texture and pigmentation, physiological characteristics, and genetic makeup.

Fungi in Medicine, Nature, and Industry

Nearly all fungi are free-living and do not require a host to complete their life cycles. Even among those fungi that are pathogenic, most human infection occurs through accidental contact with an environmental source such as soil, water, or dust. Humans are generally quite resistant to fungal infection, except for two main types of fungal pathogens: the primary

Basidiocarp (cap)

Young mushroom (button)

Gill

Mycelium

Basidia

Above ground

Below ground

Basidiospores

FERTILIZATION

Basidiospores vary in genetic makeup.

(−) Mating strain

(+) Mating strain

(−)

(+)

Germination of mating strains

Figure 5.22 **The cycle of sexual spore formation in basidiomycota.** A mushroom is one example to observe formation of the sexual spores. Following mating between parental hyphae underground, the mycelium gives rise to the fruiting body that we commonly identify as a mushroom. Under the cap are gills bearing club-shaped basidia which form and release basidiospores. Because they are genetically different, these basidiospores produce different parental hyphae that begin the cycle again.
(Blewit mushroom): IT Stock/age fotostock

TABLE 5.5	A Survey of Fungal Groups, Characteristics, and Representative Members

Phylum I—Zygomycota (also Zygomycetes)

- Sexual spores: zygospores
- Asexual spores: mostly sporangiospores, some conidia
- Hyphae are usually nonseptate; if septate, the septa are complete
- Most species are free-living saprobes; some are animal parasites
- Can be obnoxious contaminants in the laboratory, food spoilage agents, and destructive to crops
- Examples of common molds: *Rhizopus,* a black bread mold; *Mucor; Absidia; Circinella* (**figure A**, *Syncephalastrum,* and **figure B**, *Circinella*)

A. *Syncephalastrum,* a common inhabitant of soil and plants (400×).
Dennis Kunkel Microscopy, Inc./Phototake

B. A beautiful mold, *Circinella* is known for its curved sporangiophore (500×).
Kathy Park Talaro

Phylum II—Ascomycota (also Ascomycetes)

- Sexual spores: most produce ascospores in asci
- Asexual spores: many types of conidia, formed at the tips of conidiophores
- Hyphae with porous septa
- Examples: This is by far the largest phylum. Members vary from macroscopic mushrooms to microscopic molds and yeasts.
 - *Penicillium* is one source of antibiotics (see figure 5.17).
 - *Aspergillus* is a common airborne mold that may be involved in respiratory infections and toxicity (**figure C**).
 - *Saccharomyces* is a yeast used in making bread and beer (**figure D**).
 - Includes many human and plant pathogens, such as *Pneumocystis (carinii) jiroveci,* a pathogen of AIDS patients.
 - *Histoplasma* is the cause of Ohio Valley fever (see figure 1.3).
 - *Trichophyton* is one cause of ringworm, which is a common name for certain fungal skin infections that often grow in a ringed pattern (see figure 22.18).
 - *Coccidioides immitis* is the cause of Valley fever; *Candida albicans* is the cause of various yeast infections; and *Stachybotrys* is a toxic mold.

C. *Aspergillus fumigatus,* displaying its flowery conidial heads (600×).
Source: CDC

D. Scanning electron micrograph of *Candida* pseudohyphae (4000×).
Steve Gschmeissner/Science Photo Library/Getty Images

Phylum III—Basidiomycota (also Basidiomycetes)

Many members are familiar macroscopic forms such as mushrooms and puffballs, but this phylum also includes a number of microscopic plant pathogens called rusts and smuts that attack and destroy major crops, This has extensive impact on agriculture and global food production.

- Sexual reproduction by means of basidia and basidiospores
- Asexual spores: conidia
- Incompletely septate hyphae
- Some plant parasites and one human pathogen
- Fleshy fruiting bodies are common.
- Examples: mushrooms (**figure E**), puffballs, bracket fungi, and plant pathogens (rusts and smuts)
- The one human pathogen, the yeast *Cryptococcus neoformans,* causes an invasive systemic infection in several organs, including the skin, brain, and lungs (**figure F**).

E. Fly Agaric (*Amanita muscaria*) sprouting from the forest floor. The mushroom is both toxic and hallucinogenic.
Tinke Hamming/Ingram Publishing

F. *Cryptococcus neoformans*—a yeast that causes cryptococcosis (400×). Note the capsule around each cell.
Source: Dr Leanor Haley/CDC

Phylum IV—Chytridimycota

Members of this phylum are unusual, primitive fungi commonly called **chytrids.*** Their cellular morphology ranges from single cells to clusters and colonies. They generally do not form hyphae or yeast-type cells. The one feature that most characterizes them is the presence of special flagellated spores, called zoospores and gametes. Most chytrids are saprobic and free-living in soil, water, and decaying matter. A significant number are parasites of plants, animals, and other microbes (**figure G**), but they are not known to cause human disease. They are known to be serious frog pathogens, often responsible for destroying whole populations in some habitats.

G. Parasitic chytrid fungi. The filamentous diatom *Chaetoceros* is attacked by flagellated chytrids that dissolve and destroy their host (400×).
Joyce E. Longcore, University of Maine

* *chytrid* (kit´-rid) Gr. *chytridion,* little pot.

TABLE 5.6	Major Fungal Infections of Humans	
Degree of Tissue Involvement and Area Affected	Name of Infection	Name of Causative Fungus
Superficial (not deeply invasive)		
Outer epidermis	Tinea versicolor	*Malassezia furfur*
Epidermis, hair, and dermis can be attacked	Dermatophytosis, also called tinea or ringworm of the scalp, body, feet (athlete's foot), toenails	*Microsporum, Trichophyton,* and *Epidermophyton*
Mucous membranes, skin, nail	Candidiasis, or yeast infection	*Candida albicans**
Systemic (deep; organism enters lungs; can invade other organs)		
Lung	Coccidioidomycosis (San Joaquin Valley fever)	*Coccidioides immitis*
	North American blastomycosis (Chicago disease)	*Blastomyces dermatitidis*
	Histoplasmosis (Ohio Valley fever)	*Histoplasma capsulatum*
	Cryptococcosis (torulosis)	*Cryptococcus neoformans*
Lung, skin	Paracoccidioidomycosis (South American blastomycosis)	*Paracoccidioides brasiliensis*

*This fungus can cause severe, invasive systemic infections in patients with cancer, AIDS, or other debilitating diseases.

pathogens, which can infect even healthy persons, and the opportunistic pathogens, which attack persons who are already weakened in some way.

Mycoses (fungal infections) vary in the way the agent enters the body and the degree of tissue involvement **(table 5.6)**. The list of opportunistic fungal pathogens has been increasing in the past few years because of newer medical techniques that keep immunocompromised patients alive. Even so-called harmless species found in the air and dust around us may be able to cause opportunistic infections in patients who already have AIDS, cancer, or diabetes.

Fungi are involved in other medical conditions besides infections. Fungal cell walls give off chemical substances that can cause allergies. The toxins produced by poisonous mushrooms can induce neurological disturbances and even death. The mold *Aspergillus flavus* synthesizes a potentially lethal poison called aflatoxin,[4] which is the cause of a disease in domestic animals that have eaten grain contaminated with the mold and is also a cause of liver cancer in humans.

4. From aspergillus, flavus, toxin.

Fungi pose an ever-present economic hindrance to the agricultural industry. A number of species are pathogenic to field plants such as corn and grain, and fungi also rot fresh produce during shipping and storage. It has been estimated that as much as 40% of the yearly fruit crop is consumed not by humans but by fungi.

On the beneficial side, however, fungi play an essential role in decomposing organic matter and returning essential minerals to the soil. They form stable associations with plant roots (mycorrhizae) that increase the ability of the roots to absorb water and nutrients. Industry has tapped the biochemical potential of fungi to produce large quantities of antibiotics, alcohol, organic acids, and vitamins. Some fungi are eaten or used to impart flavorings to food. The yeast *Saccharomyces* produces the alcohol in beer and wine and the gas that causes bread to rise. Blue cheeses, soy sauce, and cured meats derive their unique flavors from the actions of fungi.

 Practice SECTIONS 5.4–5.5

15. Review the major differences and similarities between prokaryotic and eukaryotic cells.
16. Compare the structures of yeast and hyphal cells and differentiate between yeasts and molds.
17. Tell how fungi obtain nutrients and in what habitats one would expect to find them.
18. Describe the two main types of asexual fungal spores and how they are formed. Name several types of conidia.
19. Describe the three main types of sexual spores, and construct a simple diagram to show how each is formed.
20. Explain general features of fungal classification, give examples of the four fungal phyla, and describe their structure and significance.
21. Define the term *mycosis* and explain the levels of invasion of the body by fungi.

5.6 Survey of Protists: Algae

Learn

27. Discuss the major characteristics of algae, and explain how they are classified.
28. Describe several ways that algae are important microorganisms.

Even though the terms *algae* and *protozoa* do not have taxonomic status, they are still scientifically useful. These are terms, like *protist* (which, you should recall, we previously defined as any eukaryote that is not a fungus, animal, or plant) that provide a shorthand label for certain eukaryotes. Microbiologists use such general terms to reference organisms that possess a collection of predictable characteristics. For example, protozoa are considered unicellular eukaryotic protists that lack tissues and share similarities in cell structure, nutrition, life cycles, and biochemistry. They are all microorganisms, and most of them are motile. Algae are eukaryotic

protists, usually unicellular or colonial, that photosynthesize with chlorophyll *a.* They lack vascular systems for transport and have simple reproductive structures.

The Algae: Photosynthetic Protists

The **algae** are a group of photosynthetic organisms most readily recognized by their larger members, such as seaweeds and kelps. In addition to being beautifully colored and diverse in appearance, they vary in length from a few micrometers to 100 meters. Algae occur in unicellular, colonial, and filamentous forms, and the larger forms can possess tissues and simple organs. Examples of algal forms are shown in **figure 5.23** and **table 5.7.** An algal cell exhibits most of the organelles (figure 5.23*a*). The most noticeable of these are the chloroplasts, which

> **Quick Search**
>
> Find the video "Brink: Algae to Oil" on the Science Channel to learn about a new source of "green" products.

contain, in addition to the green pigment chlorophyll, a number of other pigments that create the yellow, red, and brown coloration of some groups.

Algae are widespread inhabitants of fresh and marine waters. They are one of the main components of the large floating community of microscopic organisms called **plankton.** In this capacity, they play an essential role in aquatic food webs and contribute significantly to the oxygen content of the atmosphere through photosynthesis. One of the most prevalent groups on earth are single-celled *diatoms* (figure 5.23*b*). These beautiful algae have silicate cell walls and golden pigment in their chloroplasts.

Animal tissues would be rather inhospitable to algae, so algae are rarely infectious. One exception, *Prototheca,* is an unusual nonphotosynthetic alga associated with skin and subcutaneous infections in humans and animals.

The primary medical threat from algae is due to a type of food poisoning caused by the toxins of marine algae such as dinoflagellates. Overgrowth of these algae result in a harmful algae bloom, or

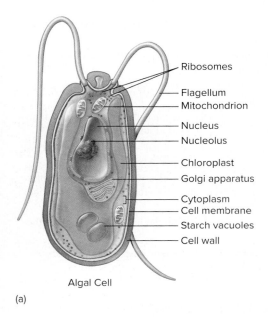

Ribosomes
Flagellum
Mitochondrion
Nucleus
Nucleolus
Chloroplast
Golgi apparatus
Cytoplasm
Cell membrane
Starch vacuoles
Cell wall

Algal Cell

(a)

Diatoms

(b)

(c)

(d)

Figure 5.23 **Representative algae. (a)** Structure of *Chlamydomonas,* a motile green alga. **(b)** Silica cell wall (frustule) of a diatom, *Arachnoidiscus* sp. (800×). Tiny holes in the frustule allow for the exchange of nutrients, waste products, and gases with the surrounding environment. **(c)** *Micrasterias truncata,* a green alga composed of two mirror-image semi-cells connected by a narrow isthmus. Each semi-cell contains a single large chloroplast (750×). **(d)** An algal bloom of dinoflagellates in Puget Sound.

(b): Science Photo Library/Alamy Stock Photo; (c): Lebendkulturen.de/Shutterstock; (d): Don Paulson Photography/Purestock/Alamy Stock Photo

TABLE 5.7	Summary of Algal Characteristics					
Supergroup	Division/ Common Name	Organization	Cell Wall	Pigmentation	Ecology/ Importance	Representative Genera
Excavata	Euglenophyta (euglenids)	Mainly unicellular, motile by flagella	None, pellicle instead	Chlorophyll, carotenoids, xanthophyll	Some are close relatives of Mastigophora	*Euglena*
SAR (Alveolate)	Pyrrophyta (dinoflagellates)	Unicellular, dual flagella	Cellulose or atypical wall	Chlorophyll, carotenoids	Cause of "red tide"	*Ceratium*
SAR (Stramenopile)	Diatoms	Unicellular	Silicon dioxide	Chlorophyll, fucoxanthin	Diatomaceous earth, major component of plankton	*Nitzchia*
SAR (Stramenopile)	Phaeophyta (brown algae—kelps)	Multicellular, vascular system, holdfasts	Cellulose	Chlorophyll, carotenoids, fucoxanthin	Source of an emulsifier, alginate	*Macrocystis*
Archaeplastida	Rhodophyta (red seaweeds)	Multicellular	Cellulose	Chlorophyll, carotenoids, xanthophyll, phycobilin	Source of agar and carrageenan, a food additive	*Gelidium*
Archaeplastida	Chlorophyta (green algae)	Varies from unicellular, colonial, filamentous, to multicellular	Cellulose	Chlorophyll, carotenoids, xanthophyll	Precursor of higher plants	Chlamydomonas

HAB (figure 5.23*d*). Harmful algae bloom has replaced the older term *red tide* as, depending on the species involved, the bloom is not always red. When intertidal animals feed, their bodies accumulate toxins given off by the algae that can persist for several months. Paralytic shellfish poisoning is caused by eating toxin-containing clams or other invertebrates. It is marked by severe neurological symptoms and can be fatal. Ciguatera is a serious intoxication caused by algal toxins that have accumulated in fish such as bass and mackerel. Cooking does not destroy the toxin, and there is no antidote.

Several episodes of a severe infection caused by *Pfiesteria piscicida,* a toxic algal form, have been reported over the past several years in the United States. The disease was first reported in fish and was later transmitted to humans. Both fish and humans develop neurological symptoms and bloody skin lesions. The cause of the epidemic has been traced to nutrient-rich agricultural runoff water that promoted the sudden "bloom" of *Pfiesteria.* These microbes first attacked and killed millions of fish and later people whose occupations exposed them to fish and contaminated water.

 CLINIC CASE

Read the Signs Seven friends, travelling as part of a group to the Pacific Northwest, didn't want to waste a minute of their vacation, and during an evening walk on the beach near their hotel, decided to harvest mussels for a late-night snack. An hour later, the mussels, having been shucked, spiced, and boiled, were the main ingredient in mussel soup that they ate between midnight and 2:00 a.m.

Within an hour or two, they began to experience symptoms most often associated with simple food poisoning (nausea, vomiting, and diarrhea). Soon, the symptoms took a decided turn toward the unusual, with a tingling sensation in the lips and tongue, difficulty speaking and breathing, partial paralysis, and a floating sensation. When a woman in their group fell to floor and could not get up, they called the paramedics, who transported the woman and recommended that the entire group be examined at the hospital.

Upon arrival, the woman was intubated, placed on a ventilator, and transferred to the intensive care unit (ICU) as paralysis of her respiratory muscles made it difficult to breathe. Health care providers working near the coast readily recognized the signs and symptoms of paralytic shellfish poisoning, and quickly identified the mussel

soup as the source of the toxin. They pointed out that the saxitoxin produced by species of algae in the genus *Alexandrium*—which was concentrated in the meat of the mussels—is 1,000 times as toxic as cyanide and impervious to boiling, so even after cooking, the toxin was still fully active. After examination, three members of the group were admitted to the ICU, while the remaining three were monitored in the emergency room. There is no antidote for paralytic shellfish poisoning; all that can be done is to provide supportive care, principally artificial ventilation. All seven were discharged within 24 hours, after their symptoms had subsided.

A check of the records the following day revealed that the beach where the group had gathered their mussels had been closed by the Washington State Shellfish Program due to increased saxitoxin levels in shellfish, but because the impromptu mussel collecting had taken place at night, it was too dark to see the warning signs that had been posted.

What environmental conditions contribute to formation of a harmful algae bloom like that seen in this case?

5.7 Survey of Protists: Protozoa

 Learn

29. Summarize the main characteristics of protozoan form, nutrition, and locomotion.

30. Describe the general life cycle and mode of reproduction in protozoans.

31. Explain how protozoans are identified and classified.

32. Outline a classification scheme for protozoans, and provide examples of important members of each group.

33. Explain some biological properties of parasites, and list some common protozoan pathogens.

Beginning once again with the caveat that the term *protozoa* is no longer considered an official taxonomic level, we will nevertheless use it as an informal grouping of eukaryotes that are decidedly more "animal-like" than "plant-like." The protozoa are a polyphyletic collection of organisms, meaning that they do not share a single evolutionary history. In fact, they exist in three of the five eukaryotic supergroups, reflective of their great diversity. Although most members of this group are harmless, free-living inhabitants of water and soil, a few species are parasites collectively responsible for hundreds of millions of infections of humans each year.

Protozoan Form and Function

Most protozoan cells are single cells containing the major eukaryotic organelles except chloroplasts. Their organelles can be highly specialized for feeding, reproduction, and locomotion. The cytoplasm is usually divided into a clear outer layer called the **ectoplasm** and a granular inner region called the **endoplasm.** Ectoplasm is involved in locomotion, feeding, and protection. Endoplasm houses the nucleus, mitochondria, and food and contractile vacuoles. Some ciliates and flagellates[5] even have organelles that work somewhat like a primitive nervous system to coordinate movement. Because protozoa lack a cell wall, they have a certain amount of flexibility. Their outer boundary is a cell membrane that regulates the movement of food, wastes, and secretions. Cell shape can remain constant (as in most ciliates) or can change constantly (as in amoebas). Certain amoebas (foraminiferans) encase themselves in hard shells made of calcium carbonate. The size of most protozoan cells falls within the range of 3 to 300 μm. Some notable exceptions are giant amoebas and ciliates that are large enough (3–4 mm in length) to be seen swimming in pond water.

Nutritional and Habitat Range

Most protozoa are heterotrophic and require their food in a complex organic form. Free-living species graze on live cells of bacteria and algae, and even scavenge dead plant or animal debris. Some species have special feeding structures such as oral grooves, which carry food particles into a passageway or gullet that packages the captured food into vacuoles for digestion. Some protozoa absorb food directly through the cell membrane. Parasitic species live on the fluids of their host, such as plasma and digestive juices, or they can actively feed on tissues.

Although protozoa have adapted to a wide range of habitats, their main limiting factor is the availability of moisture. Their predominant habitats are fresh and marine water, soil, plants, and animals. Even extremes in temperature and pH are not a barrier to their existence; hardy species are found in hot springs, ice, and habitats with low or high pH.

Styles of Locomotion

Except for one group (the Apicomplexa), protozoa are motile by means of **pseudopods** ("false foot"), **flagella,** or **cilia.** A few species have both pseudopods (also called pseudopodia) and flagella. Some unusual protozoa move by a gliding or twisting movement that does not appear to involve any of these locomotor structures. Pseudopods are blunt and branched, or long and pointed, depending on the particular species. The flowing action of the pseudopods results in amoeboid motion, and pseudopods also serve as feeding structures in many amoebas.

The structure and behavior of flagella and cilia were discussed in section 5.1. Flagella vary in number from one to several, and in certain species they are attached along the length of the cell by an extension of the cytoplasmic membrane called the *undulating membrane.* In most ciliates, the cilia are distributed over the surface of the cell in characteristic patterns. Because of the tremendous variety in ciliary arrangements and functions, ciliates are among the most diverse cells in the biological world. In certain protozoa, cilia line the oral groove and function in feeding; in others, they fuse together to form stiff props that serve as primitive rows of walking legs.

Life Cycles and Reproduction

Most protozoa are recognized by a motile feeding stage called the **trophozoite**[*] that requires ample food and moisture to remain active. A large number of species are also capable of entering into a dormant, resting stage called a **cyst** when conditions in the environment become unfavorable for growth and feeding. During *encystment,* the trophozoite cell rounds up into a sphere, and its ectoplasm secretes a tough, thick cuticle around the cell membrane **(figure 5.24).** Because cysts are more resistant than ordinary cells to heat, drying, and chemicals, they can survive adverse periods. They can be dispersed by air currents and may even be an important factor in the spread of diseases such as amebic dysentery. If provided with moisture and nutrients, a cyst breaks open and releases the active trophozoite.

The life cycles of protozoans vary from simple to complex. Several protozoan groups exist only in the trophozoite state. Many alternate between a trophozoite and a cyst stage, depending on the

5. The terms *ciliate* and *flagellate* are common names of protozoan groups that move by means of cilia and flagella.

* *trophozoite* (trof'-oh-zoh'-yte) Gr. *trophonikos,* to nourish, and *zoon,* animal.

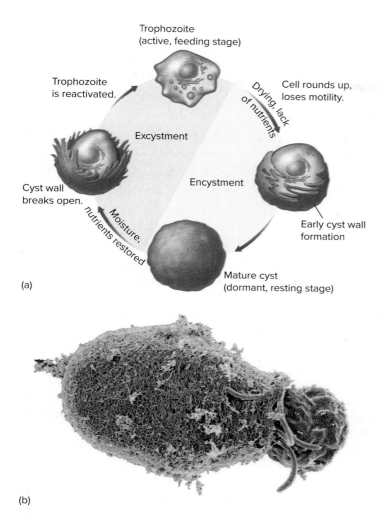

Figure 5.24 **Protozoan cysts. (a)** All protozoa exist in an active, trophozoite form, but some are able to produce a protective cyst (encystment) when environmental conditions become poor. When conditions improve, the trophozoite exits the cysts in a process called excystment. **(b)** *Giardia* sp. undergoing excystment (note the purple flagellated trophozoite exiting from the cyst). In *Giardia*, the cyst is the infective form as it is able to withstand chlorinated water and stomach acid, undergoing excystation in the intestines.
(b): *Source:* Dr. Stan Erlandsen/CDC

 CLINICAL CONNECTIONS

The Parasitic Way of Life

Protozoa are traditionally studied along with the helminths in the science of parasitology. Although a parasite is usually defined as an organism that obtains food and other requirements at the expense of a host, the term *parasite* is also used to denote protozoan and helminth pathogens. The range of host–parasite relationships can be very broad. At one extreme are the so-called "good" parasites, which occupy their host with little harm. An example is *Trichomonas tenax,* a flagellate found in the mouth that may infect and damage the gingiva in people with poor oral hygiene. At the other extreme are parasites (*Plasmodium, Trypanosoma*) that multiply in host tissues such as the blood or brain, causing severe damage and disease. Between these two extremes are parasites of varying pathogenicity, depending on their particular adaptations.

Most human parasites go through three general stages:

- The microbe is transmitted to the human host from a source such as soil, water, food, other humans, or animals.
- The microbe invades and multiplies in the host, producing more parasites that can infect other suitable hosts.
- The microbe leaves the host in large numbers by a specific means and must enter a new host to survive.

There are numerous variations on this theme. For instance, the microbe can invade more than one host species (alternate hosts) and undergo several changes as it cycles through these hosts, such as sexual reproduction or encystment. Some microbes are spread from human to human by means of **vectors,*** defined as animals such as insects that carry diseases. Others can be spread through bodily fluids and feces.

What correlation can be made between the geographic location of a parasite and its vector?

* *vector* (vek′-tur) L. *vectur,* one who carries.

conditions of the habitat. The life cycle of a parasitic protozoan dictates its mode of transmission to other hosts. For example, the flagellate *Trichomonas vaginalis* causes a common sexually transmitted infection. Because it does not form cysts, it is more delicate and must be transmitted by intimate contact between sexual partners. In contrast, intestinal pathogens such as *Entamoeba histolytica* and *Giardia lamblia* form cysts that are readily transmitted in contaminated water and foods.

All protozoa reproduce by relatively simple, asexual methods, usually mitotic cell division. Several parasitic species, including the agents of malaria and toxoplasmosis, reproduce asexually inside a host cell by multiple fission. Sexual reproduction also occurs during the life cycle of most protozoa. Ciliates participate in **conjugation,** a form of genetic exchange in which members of two different mating types fuse temporarily and exchange nuclei. This process of sexual recombination yields new and different genetic combinations that can be advantageous in evolution.

Protozoan Identification and Cultivation

The unique appearance of most protozoa makes it possible for a knowledgeable person to identify them to the level of genus and often species by microscopic morphology alone. Characteristics to consider in identification include the shape and size of the cell; the type, number, and distribution of locomotor structures; the presence of special organelles or cysts; and the number of nuclei. Medical specimens taken from blood, sputum, cerebrospinal fluid, feces, or the vagina are smeared directly onto a slide and observed with or without special stains. Occasionally protozoa are cultivated on artificial media or in laboratory animals for further identification or study.

TABLE 5.8	Major Pathogenic Protozoan Infections and Primary Sources			
Supergroup	**Further Classification**	**Organism**	**Disease**	**Reservoir /Source**
SAR	Alveolates	*Balantidium coli*	Balantidiosis	Zoonotic in pigs
		Plasmodium spp.	Malaria	Human/vector-borne (mosquito)
		Toxoplasma gondii	Toxoplasmosis	Zoonotic
		Cryptosporidium spp.	Cryptosporidiosis	Free-living/water and food
		Cyclospora cayetanensis	Cyclosporiasis	Water/fresh produce
Excavata	Diplomonads	*Giardia intestinalis*	Giardiasis	Zoonotic/water and food
	Parabasilids	*Trichomonas vaginalis*	Trichomoniasis	Humans
	Kinetoplastids	*Trypanosoma cruzi*	Chagas disease	Zoonotic/vector-borne (reduviid bug)
		Trypanosoma brucei	Sleeping sickness	Zoonotic/vector-borne (tsetse fly)
		Leishmania spp.	Leishmaniasis	Zoonotic/vector-borne (sandfly)
Amoebozoans	Amoeboids	*Entamoeba histolytica*	Amoebiasis	Human/water and food
		Naegleria fowleri	Primary amebic meningoencephalitis	Free-living in warm water

Important Protozoan Pathogens

Although protozoan infections are quite common, they are, in fact, caused by a small number of species distributed among three supergroups: SAR, Excavata, and Amoebozoa (**table 5.8**). The following section briefly examines the most medically relevant of these organisms.

Quick Search

Look for "What Are Malaria Protozoa?" on YouTube to learn about the most dominant parasitic protozoan.

Supergroup SAR

Within the SAR, and specifically within the subgroup alveolata, lie two groups of medically important protozoa, the **apicomplexans** and the **ciliates.** The apicomplexans all share a unique structure called an apical complex that is used for penetrating host cells. Nearly all members of the group are parasitic and have complex life cycles that include multiple hosts. A prime example is *Plasmodium,* the causative agent of malaria, a disease that kills upwards of 400,000 people each year. Five species of *Plasmodium*—all carried by infected *Anopheles* mosquitoes—cause malaria in humans, and diagnosis, as well as determination of the infectious species, can be accomplished by examining red blood cells for the presence of the parasite.

Ciliates are named for the numerous cilia they use for motility and, in some cases, to direct food toward a specialized feeding structure (**figure 5.25a**). They are unique in possessing two types of nuclei: **micronuclei** and **macronuclei.** Genes in the macronucleus control what are colloquially known as "housekeeping" functions, such as feeding and waste removal, whereas the micronuclei are exchanged between ciliates in a process called **conjugation** (**figure 5.25b**), resulting in genetic variability. The vast majority of ciliates are free-living and harmless, and they generally exhibit the most complex structures and behaviors of all protists. The only human parasite is *Balantidium coli,* the causative agent of balantidiasis, which can cause bloody and mucus-filled diarrhea, although most infections are thought to be asymptomatic.

Supergroup Excavata

Most members of this supergroup are asymmetrical and have a feeding groove that appears to be excavated into one side of the organism. Two of the groups within the excavata—the **diplomonads** and the **parabasalids**—possess highly reduced (i.e. highly simplified and poorly functioning) mitochondria and generate most of their energy anaerobically.

Diplomonads are exemplified by *Giardia intestinalis* (also known as *G. lamblia* or *G. duodenalis*), the cause of over 15,000 infections per year in the United States. When *Giardia* cysts are ingested, through water contaminated with feces from infected people or animals, or as a result of poor hygiene, the cysts travel through the stomach to the small intestine, where excystation produces two **trophozoites** (**figure 5.26**) per cyst. Infections may be asymptomatic, but most are marked by severe diarrhea lasting as long as 6 weeks. Infected persons periodically release large numbers of cysts into their feces, spreading the organism. Infection can be diagnosed by observing the stool for cysts or through sensitive serological assays.

Parabasalids, like diplomonads, also have reduced mitochondria. A common example is *Trichomonas vaginalis,* the cause of trichomoniasis in humans, a disease marked by inflammation of the genitourinary tract. An important difference between these two parasites is that *T. vaginalis* does not form cysts, leaving the more delicate trophozoite as the infective form. Because the trophozoite is far less hardy than a cyst, *T. vaginalis* must be passed directly from person to person, causing trichomoniasis to be classified as a sexually transmitted disease.

Euglenozoans are the third group of concern within the excavata. This group is characterized by a unique crystalline structure within their flagella, and is further subdivided into the **euglenids** and the **kinetoplastids.**

Most euglenids are **mixotrophs,** meaning they may act photosynthetically or heterotrophically. *Euglena* possesses a red eyespot at one end of the cell that detects light, along with one or two long

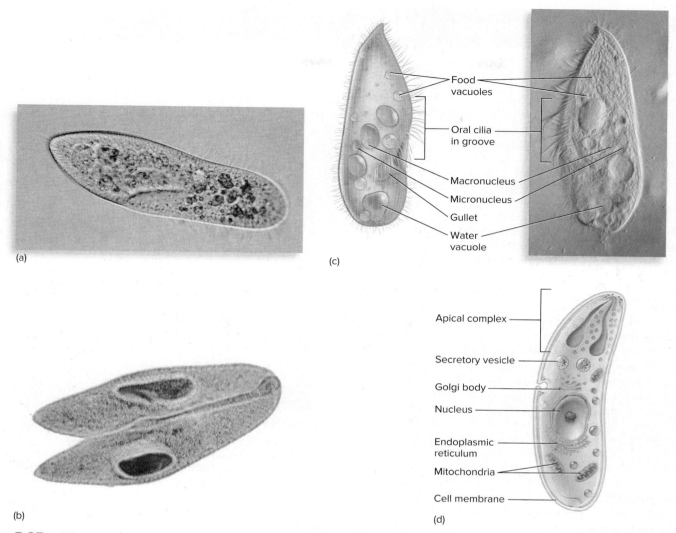

Figure 5.25 **Ciliates. (a)** *Paramecium caudatum,* named for the fact that one end of the cell is pointed, displays cilia along its periphery. The depression seen in the middle of the cell is the oral groove, where cilia help to direct food to the gullet, where it can be ingested (500×). **(b)** Paramecia conjugating, during which time the exchange of genetic material takes place. **(c)** Ciliate structure. Image and artist's interpretation of the ciliate *Blepharisma,* a common inhabitant of pond water. Note the pattern of ciliary movement evident on the left side of the cell and the details of its internal structure. **(d)** Apicomplexan trophozoite structure. Apicomplexans have many of the usual protozoan organelles but also contain an unusual body, the apical complex, involved in feeding. Unlike other protozoa, they lack specialized motility organelles.
(a): Nancy Nehring/Getty Images; (b): Richard Gross/McGraw-Hill Education; (c): BioMedia/Science Source

flagella for motion. Together, the eyespot and the flagella allow the organism to move to areas with the best light intensity for photosynthesis. When light is absent, *Euglena* behaves as a heterotroph, absorbing organic nutrients from the environment or preying on smaller organisms.

The kinetoplastids—named for the kinetoplast, a mass of DNA within their single mitochondrion—include free-living heterotrophs as well as parasites. The most medically important species are in the genera *Trypanosoma* and are spread by the bite of bloodsucking insects. *Trypanosoma brucei* causes sleeping sickness, a potentially fatal neurological disease spread by the bite of the tsetse fly. Because the fly is found only in Africa, the disease is geographically restricted.

Trypanosoma cruzi, the cause of Chagas disease, is endemic to South and Central America, where it infects several million people a

year. The trypanosome of Chagas disease relies on the close relationship of a mammal and an insect that feeds on its blood. The mammalian hosts are numerous, including dogs, cats, opossums, and armadillos. The vector is the *reduviid bug,* an insect that is sometimes called the "kissing bug" because of its habit of biting its host at the corner of the mouth. Transmission occurs from bug to mammal and from mammal to bug, but usually not from mammal to mammal, except across the placenta during pregnancy. The general phases of this cycle are presented in **figure 5.27.** The trypanosome trophozoite multiplies in the intestinal tract of the reduviid bug and is harbored in the feces. The bug seeks a host and bites the mucous membranes, usually of the eye, nose, or lips, releasing the trypanosome in feces near the bite. Ironically, the victims themselves inadvertently contribute to the entry of the microbe by scratching the bite wound. Once in the body, the trypanosomes become established and

5.1 MAKING CONNECTIONS

Who's on Your Money?

Check your wallet. George Washington is on the $1, Alexander Hamilton on the $10, if you're lucky enough to have a $100, Benjamin Franklin. Good choices all. Statesmen, presidents, inventors. The question you should be asking yourself at this point in your study of microbiology is, of course, "Why are there no microbiologists on my money?" Well, for that you'd have to take a look at the Brazillian 10,000 Cruzado note, which sports a likeness of none other than Carlos Chagas on the front.

Chagas was a physician and microbiologist in the early 1900s in Brazil, where he spent most of his time combating outbreaks of malaria. On one of these assignments in the riverside city of Lassance, he studied the behavior of the large bloodsucking reduviid bug. Chagas discovered that the bug carried in its intestines a flagellated protozoan that he named *Trypanosoma cruzi*, after his mentor Oswaldo Cruz. He went on to show that the parasite could be spread through the bite of a bug and that those bitten displayed a specific collection of signs and symptoms, especially swelling of the heart muscle. His work was recognized as one of the great achievements in parasitology, and he was twice nominated for the Nobel Prize in Physiology or Medicine.

Even more interesting than Chagas' face on the right side of the bill, though, is the life cycle of *Trypanosoma cruzi* on the left side. The reduviiad bug is shown defecating into an open wound (caused by its own bite), releasing the parasite into the blood supply where it can encyst within the muscle of the heart. A second break in the skin shows the parasite reentering a reduviid bug, infecting a new vector and completing the life cycle. More information than you'd expect to find on your money. But there's more. Look at the back of your bills. The White House, the U.S. Treasury, and the U.S. Capitol, important places where vital work took place. What's on the backside of the 10,000 Cruzado? Carlos Chagas' laboratory, of course.

One hundred years after the discovery of *Trypanosoma cruzi*, 8 million people in Mexico, Central America, and South America are infected with the parasite and 10,000 people a year will die of the disease.
Barry Chess

What techniques could be employed to prevent the spread of Chagas disease?

multiply in muscle and white blood cells. Periodically these parasitized cells rupture, releasing large numbers of new trophozoites into the blood. Eventually the trypanosomes can spread to many systems, including the lymphoid organs, heart, liver, and brain. Manifestations of the disease range from mild to very severe and include fever, inflammation, and heart and brain damage. In many cases, the disease has an extended course and can cause death.

Supergroup Amoebozoans

Several species of amoebas **(figure 5.28)** cause disease in humans, but the most common disease is amoebiasis, or amebic **dysentery,** * caused by *Entamoeba histolytica*. This microbe is widely distributed, from northern zones to the tropics, and nearly always associated with humans. It lives part of its life as a trophozoite and part as a cyst. Because the cyst can survive in water and soil for several weeks, it is the more important stage for transmission. The most

Figure 5.26 *Giardia sp.* Trophozoites covering the intestinal lining of a gerbil. Each cyst ingested produces two trophozoites.
Source: Dr. Stan Erlandsen/CDC

* *dysentery* (dis'-en-ter"-ee) Any inflammation of the intestine accompanied by bloody stools. It can be caused by a number of factors, both microbial and nonmicrobial.

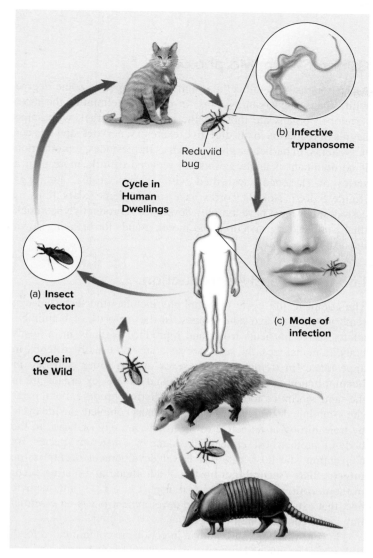

Figure 5.27 Cycle of transmission in Chagas disease. Reduviid bugs (inset a) serve as a biological vector for the trypanosome (inset b), and are transmitted among domestic and wild mammalian hosts by means of a bite from the kissing bug (inset c). (inset c): N. F. Photography/Shutterstock

Figure 5.28 *Amoeba proteus.* The green inclusions are photosynthetic organisms that have been engulfed and will soon be digested. micro_photo/Getty Images

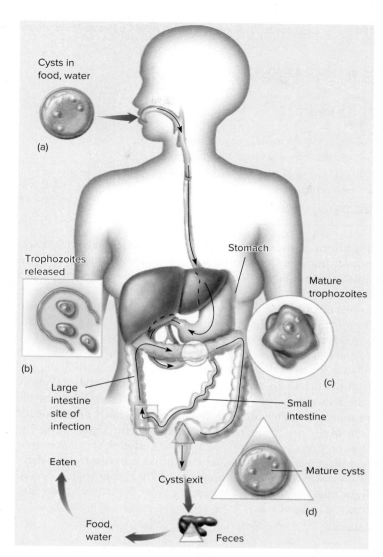

Figure 5.29 Stages in the infection and transmission of amebic dysentery. Arrows show the route of infection; insets show the appearance of *Entamoeba histolytica*. **(a)** Cysts are eaten. **(b)** Trophozoites (amoebas) emerge from cysts. **(c)** Trophozoites invade the large intestinal wall. **(d)** Mature cysts are released in the feces and may be spread through contaminated food and water.

common route of infection is the ingestion of food or water contaminated with human feces.

Figure 5.29 shows the major features of the amebic dysentery cycle, starting with the ingestion of cysts. The heavy-walled cyst passes through the stomach unharmed. Once inside the small intestine, the cyst germinates into a large multinucleate amoeba that subsequently divides to form small amoebas (the trophozoite stage). These trophozoites migrate to the large intestine and begin to feed and grow. From this site, they can penetrate the lining of the intestine and invade the liver, lungs, and skin. Common symptoms include gastrointestinal disturbances such as nausea, vomiting, and diarrhea, leading to weight loss and dehydration. The cycle is completed in the infected human when trophozoites in the feces begin to form cysts, which then pass out of the body with fecal matter. Knowledge of the amoebic cycle and role of cysts has been helpful in controlling the disease. Important preventive measures include sewage treatment, curtailing the use of human feces as fertilizer, and adequate sanitation of food and water.

5.8 The Parasitic Helminths

Learn

34. Describe the major groups of helminths and their basic morphology and classification.

35. Explain the elements of helminth biology, life cycles, and reproduction.

36. Discuss the importance of the helminth parasites.

Tapeworms, flukes, and roundworms are collectively called *helminths,* from the Greek word meaning "worm." Adult animals are usually large enough to be seen with the naked eye, and they range from the longest tapeworms, measuring up to about 25 m in length, to roundworms less than 1 mm in length. Traditionally they have been included among microorganisms because of their infective abilities and because the microscope is needed to identify their tiny egg and larval stages.

On the basis of morphological form, the two major groups of parasitic helminths are the **flatworms** (Phylum Platyhelminthes), with a very thin, often segmented body plan **(figure 5.30)**, and the **roundworms** (Phylum Aschelminthes, also called **nematodes**),* with an elongate, cylindrical, unsegmented body **(figure 5.31)**. The flatworm group is subdivided into the **cestodes,*** or tapeworms, named for their long, ribbonlike arrangement, and the **trematodes,*** also known as flukes, characterized by flat, ovoid bodies. Not all flatworms and roundworms are parasites by nature; many live freely in soil and water.

* *nematode* (neem'-ah-tohd) Gr. *nemato,* thread, and *eidos,* form.
* *cestode* (sess'-tohd) L. *cestus,* a belt, and *ode,* like.
* *trematode* (treem'-a-tohd) Gr. *trema,* hole. Named for the appearance of having tiny holes.

General Worm Morphology

All helminths are multicellular animals equipped to some degree with organs and organ systems. In parasitic helminths, the most developed organs are those of the reproductive tract, with some degree of reduction in the digestive, excretory, nervous, and muscular systems. In particular groups, such as the cestodes, reproduction is so dominant that the worms are reduced to little more than a series of flattened sacs filled with ovaries, testes, and eggs (figure 5.30*a*). Not all worms have such extreme adaptations as cestodes, but most have a highly developed reproductive potential, thick cuticles for protection, and mouth glands for breaking down the host's tissue.

Life Cycles and Reproduction

The complete life cycle of helminths includes the fertilized egg (embryo), larval, and adult stages. In the majority of helminths, adults derive nutrients from, and reproduce sexually in, a host's body. In nematodes, the sexes are separate and usually different in appearance; in trematodes, the sexes can be either separate or **hermaphroditic,** meaning that male and female sex organs are in the same worm; cestodes are generally hermaphroditic. For a parasite's continued survival as a species, it must complete the life cycle by transmitting an infective form, usually an egg or larva, to the body of another host, either of the same or a different species. By convention, the host in which larval development occurs is the **intermediate (secondary) host,** and adulthood and mating occur in the **definitive (final) host.** A transport host is an intermediate host that experiences no parasitic development but is an essential link in the completion of the cycle.

In general, sources for human infection are contaminated food, soil, water, or infected animals, and routes of infection are by oral intake or penetration of unbroken skin. Humans are the definitive

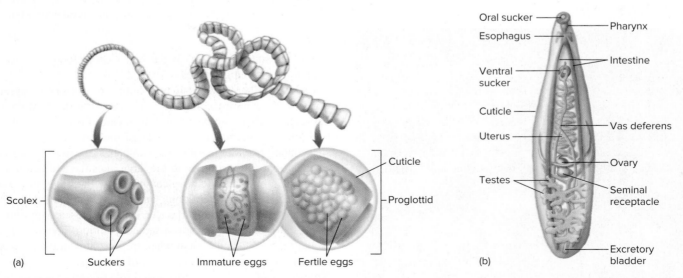

Figure 5.30 **Parasitic flatworms. (a)** A cestode (beef tapeworm), showing the scolex; long, tapelike body; and magnified views of immature and mature proglottids (body segments). **(b)** The structure of a trematode (liver fluke). Note the suckers that attach to host tissue and the dominance of reproductive and digestive organs.

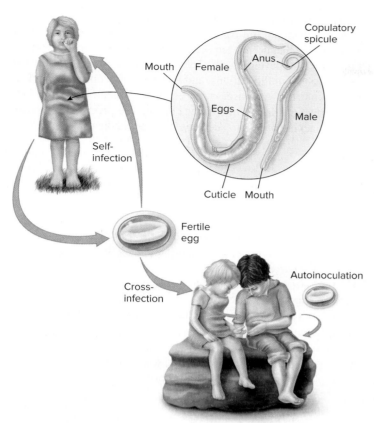

Figure 5.31 **The life cycle of the pinworm, a roundworm.** Eggs are the infective stage and are transmitted by unclean hands. Children frequently reinfect themselves and also pass the parasite on to others.

 CLINIC CASE

Don't Put that in Your Mouth. You Don't Know Where It's Been! For a health care provider, a cranky 19-month-old toddler can be a giant mystery dressed in a Dora the Explorer T-shirt. Teething? Gas? Allergies? The one thing we do know is that we don't get to choose our patients.

Doctors began with a catalog of signs and symptoms. The patient had been, according to mom and dad, perfectly healthy until about a week ago, when he became irritable, suffered tremors in his arms and legs, and lost interest in interacting with others. At the time of his appointment, he was unable to sit or stand without help. A magnetic resonance imaging (MRI) scan showed lesions throughout the brain, while a blood test and spinal tap revealed increased numbers of eosinophils, a type of white blood cell that is elevated during a helminth infection.

With prodding from doctors—who are quite aware of how children acquire worm infections—the parents reported that their child often played outside in a sand box and could possibly have ingested small amounts of dirt, or even animal feces. An O and P exam, where the patient's feces is checked for the presence of eggs (Ova) or adult worms (Parasites), showed that the child was infected with *Baylisascaris procyonis,* a roundworm parasite of the North American raccoon. Of the few cases seen in humans, over half occur in children younger than 2 years of age, who become infected through the consumption of raccoon feces or dirt contaminated with feces.

The patient was treated with albendazole, an antiparasitic medication, for 1 month, by which time he showed a reduction in tremors and his mental status had greatly improved.

An environmental assessment of the child's backyard yielded raccoon feces near the base of a tree where the patient played. The patient's feces exhibited eggs consistent with those of *B. procyonis.* A fecal sample was also taken from the family's healthy dog, but no eggs or worms were found. The parents were advised to fence off the tree until the area could be properly decontaminated, and to consult with a veterinarian about implementing regular deworming for their dog, as canines can be a definitive host for *B. procyonis* and can shed eggs in their feces.

Aside from the health of the dog, why would deworming be especially important in this case?

hosts for many of the parasites, and in about half the diseases, they are also the sole biological reservoir. In other cases, animals or insect vectors serve as reservoirs or are required to complete worm development. In the majority of helminth infections, the worms must leave their host to complete the entire life cycle.

Fertilized eggs are usually released to the environment and are provided with a protective shell and extra food to aid their development into larvae. Even so, most eggs and larvae are vulnerable to heat, cold, drying, and predators, and are destroyed or unable to reach a new host. To counteract this formidable mortality rate, certain worms have adapted a reproductive capacity that borders on the incredible: A single female *Ascaris*[6] can lay 200,000 eggs a day, and a large female can contain over 25 million eggs at varying stages of development! If only a tiny number of these eggs makes it to another host, the parasite will have been successful in completing its life cycle.

A Helminth Cycle: The Pinworm

To illustrate a helminth cycle in humans, we use the example of a roundworm, *Enterobius vermicularis,* the pinworm or seatworm.

This worm causes a very common infestation of the large intestine (figure 5.31). Worms range from 2 to 12 mm long and have a tapered, curved cylinder shape. The condition they cause, enterobiasis, is usually a simple, uncomplicated infection that does not spread beyond the intestine.

A cycle starts when a person swallows microscopic eggs picked up from another infected person by direct contact or by touching contaminated surfaces. The eggs hatch in the intestine and then release larvae that mature into adult worms within about 1 month. Male and female worms mate, and the female migrates out to the anus to deposit eggs, which cause intense itchiness that is relieved

6. *Ascaris* is a genus of parasitic intestinal roundworms.

by scratching. Herein lies a significant means of dispersal: Scratching contaminates the fingers, which, in turn, transfers eggs to bedclothes and other inanimate objects. This person becomes a host and a source of eggs, and can spread them to others in addition to reinfesting himself, a cycle known as the oral-fecal route of transmission. Enterobiasis occurs most often among families and in other close living situations. Its distribution is worldwide among all socioeconomic groups, but it occurs more frequently in children, presumably through their less careful attention to hygiene.

Helminth Classification and Identification

The helminths are classified according to their shape; their size; the degree of development of various organs; the presence of hooks, suckers, or other special structures; the mode of reproduction; the kinds of hosts; and the appearance of eggs and larvae. They are identified in the laboratory by microscopic detection of the adult worm or its larvae and eggs, which often have distinctive shapes or external and internal structures. Occasionally, they are cultured in order to verify all of the life stages.

Distribution and Importance of Parasitic Worms

About 50 species of helminths parasitize humans. They are distributed in all areas of the world that support human life. Some worms are restricted to a given geographic region, and many have a higher incidence in tropical areas. This knowledge must be tempered with

the realization that jet-age travel, along with human migration, is gradually changing the patterns of worm infections, especially of those species that do not require alternate hosts or special climatic conditions for development. The yearly estimate of worldwide cases numbers in the billions, and these are not confined to developing countries. A conservative estimate places 50 million helminth infections in North America alone. The primary targets are children lacking access to adequate diet and medical care.

Practice SECTIONS 5.6–5.8

22. What is a working definition of a "protist"?
23. Describe the principal characteristics of algae that separate them from protozoa.
24. How are algae important? Give examples of algae with medical importance.
25. Explain the general characteristics of the protozoan life cycle.
26. Identify the supergroups that contain protozoans and name the important pathogens in each group.
27. Discuss the adaptations of parasitic worms to their lifestyles, and explain why these adaptations are necessary or advantageous to the worms' survival.
28. Outline the basic steps in an infection cycle of a pathogenic protozoan and a helminth.

CASE STUDY Part 2

Treatment for *Amanita* mushroom poisoning focuses on supportive care, including aggressive fluid and electrolyte replacement to lessen the possibility of kidney damage. The patients were also administered two treatments intravenously that are unproven but show anecdotal evidence of efficacy. The first, octreotide, prevents emptying of the gallbladder in the hope that this may reduce the recirculation of amatoxins in the bile back to the liver. The second, silibinin, is an extract from milk thistle, which inhibits the uptake of amatoxins by the liver.

Both parents responded to treatment and were discharged from the hospital in less than a week. The daughter developed irreversible hepatic failure and underwent a liver transplant 6 days after ingesting the mushrooms.

Postoperative complications unfortunately led to cerebral edema and permanent neurological impairment.

Initial misdiagnosis is common with *Amanita* poisoning as, after the initial gastroenteritis and dehydration, symptoms subside 24–36 hours after ingestion, only to return in the form of sudden-onset hepatic and multiorgan failure. This is exactly what happened to the sister of the woman who prepared the meal, and she fared worse among the adults. She underwent a liver transplant 4 days after entering the hospital.

The family friend, who, not coincidentally, ate only a few small pieces of mushroom, fared the best. She responded well to IV hydration, octreotide, and silibinin, saw her liver function improve, and was discharged 6 days later.

■ How might toxin production be of benefit to the mushroom?

Chapter Summary with Key Terms

5.1 The History of Eukaryotes

5.2 Form and Function of the Eukaryotic Cell: External Structures
A. The exterior configuration of eukaryotic cells is complex and displays numerous structures not found in prokaryotic cells. Biologists have accumulated much evidence that eukaryotic cells evolved through **endosymbiosis** between early prokaryotic cells.
B. Major external structural features include appendages (**cilia, flagella**), **glycocalyx,** cell wall, and cytoplasmic (or cell) membrane.

5.3 Form and Function of the Eukaryotic Cell: Internal Structures
A. The internal structure of eukaryotic cells is compartmentalized into individual organelles.
B. Major **organelles** and internal structural features include **nucleus, nucleolus, endoplasmic reticulum, Golgi complex, mitochondria, chloroplasts, ribosomes, cytoskeleton (microtubules),** intermediate filaments, and actin filaments.

5.4 Eukaryotic-Prokaryotic Comparisons and Taxonomy of Eukaryotes
A. Comparisons between eukaryotic cells and prokaryotic cells show major differences in structure, size, metabolism, motility, and body form.
B. Taxonomic groups of the Domain Eukarya are based on genetic and molecular characteristics, along with body plan, cell structure, nutrition, and metabolism.

5.5 The Kingdom Fungi
Common names of the macroscopic fungi are mushrooms, puffballs, and gill fungi. Microscopic fungi are known as **yeasts** and **molds.**
A. *Overall Morphology:* At the cellular (microscopic) level, fungi are typical eukaryotic cells, with thick cell walls. Yeasts are single cells that form buds and **pseudohyphae. Hyphae** are long, tubular filaments that can be septate or nonseptate and grow in a network called a **mycelium;** hyphae are characteristic of the filamentous fungi called molds.
B. *Nutritional Mode/Distribution:* All are **heterotrophic.** The majority are harmless **saprobes** living off organic substrates such as dead animal and plant tissues. A few are **parasites,** living on the tissues of other organisms, but not obligated to do so. Distribution is extremely widespread in many habitats.
C. *Reproduction:* Primarily through **spores** formed on special reproductive hyphae. In asexual reproduction, spores are formed through budding, partitioning of a hypha, or in special sporogenous structures; examples are **conidia** and **sporangiospores.** In sexual reproduction, spores are formed following fusion of male and female strains and the formation of a sexual structure; sexual spores are one basis for classification.
D. *Major Groups:* The four main phyla among the terrestrial fungi, given with sexual spore type, are **Zygomycota (zygospores), Ascomycota (ascospores), Basidiomycota (basidiospores),** and **Chytridiomycota** (motile zoospores).
E. *Importance:* Fungi are essential decomposers of plant and animal detritis in the environment. Economically beneficial as sources of antibiotics; used in making foods and in genetic studies. Adverse impacts include decomposition of fruits and vegetables, and human infections, or **mycoses;** some produce substances that are toxic if eaten or inhaled.

5.6 Survey of Protists: Algae
General group that traditionally includes single-celled and colonial eukaryotic microbes that lack organization into tissues.
A. *Overall Morphology:* Are unicellular, colonial, filamentous or larger forms such as seaweeds.
B. *Nutritional Mode/Distribution:* Photosynthetic; freshwater and marine water habitats; main component of **plankton.**
C. *Importance:* Provide the basis of the food web in most aquatic habitats and are major producers of oxygen. Certain algae produce neurotoxins that are harmful to humans and animals.

5.7 Survey of Protists: Protozoa
Include large single-celled organisms; a few are pathogens.
A. *Overall Morphology:* Most are unicellular; lack a cell wall. The cytoplasm is divided into ectoplasm and endoplasm. Active, feeding stage is the **trophozoite;** many convert to a resistant, dormant stage called a **cyst.** All but one group has some form of organelle for **motility.**
B. *Nutritional Mode/Distribution:* All are heterotrophic. Most are free-living in a moist habitat (water, soil); feed by engulfing other microorganisms and organic matter.
C. *Reproduction:* Asexual by binary fission and **mitosis,** budding; sexual by fusion of free-swimming gametes, conjugation.
D. *Major Groups:* Protozoa are classified within three different supergroups—SAR, Excavates, and Amoebozoans—based on similarities in their DNA sequence. Protozoans can often be identified microscopically based solely on their unique morphology.
E. *Importance:* Ecologically important in food webs and decomposing organic matter. Medical significance: hundreds of millions of people are afflicted with one of the many protozoan infections (malaria, trypanosomiasis, amoebiasis). Can be spread from host to host by insect **vectors.**

5.8 The Parasitic Helminths
Includes three categories: roundworms, tapeworms, and flukes.
A. *Overall Morphology:* Animal cells; multicellular; individual organs specialized for reproduction, digestion, movement, protection, though some of these are reduced.
B. *Reproductive Mode:* Includes embryo, larval, and adult stages. Majority reproduce sexually. Sexes may be **hermaphroditic.**
C. *Epidemiology:* Developing countries in the tropics are hardest hit by helminth infections; transmitted via ingestion, vectors, and direct contact with infectious stages. They afflict billions of humans.

 Assess Your Knowledge

Level I. These questions require a working knowledge of the concepts in the chapter and the ability to recall and understand the information you have studied.

Developing a Concept Inventory

Select the correct answer from the answers provided. For questions with blanks, choose the combination of answers that most accurately completes the statement.

1. Both flagella and cilia are found primarily in
 a. algae
 b. protozoa
 c. fungi
 d. both b and c

2. Features of the nuclear envelope include
 a. ribosomes
 b. a double membrane structure
 c. pores that allow communication with the cytoplasm
 d. b and c
 e. all of these

3. The cell wall is usually found in which eukaryotes?
 a. fungi
 b. algae
 c. protozoa
 d. a and b

4. What is embedded in rough endoplasmic reticulum?
 a. ribosomes
 b. Golgi apparatus
 c. chromatin
 d. vesicles

5. Yeasts are _____ fungi, and molds are _____ fungi.
 a. macroscopic, microscopic
 b. unicellular, filamentous
 c. motile, nonmotile
 d. water, terrestrial

6. In general, fungi derive nutrients through
 a. photosynthesis
 b. engulfing bacteria
 c. digesting organic substrates
 d. parasitism

7. A hypha divided into compartments by cross walls is called
 a. nonseptate
 b. imperfect
 c. septate
 d. perfect

8. Algae generally contain some type of
 a. spore
 b. chlorophyll
 c. locomotor organelle
 d. toxin

9. Which algal group is most closely related to plants?
 a. diatoms
 b. Chlorophyta
 c. Euglenophyta
 d. dinoflagellates

10. Which characteristic is not typical of protozoan cells?
 a. locomotor organelle
 b. cyst
 c. spore
 d. trophozoite

11. The protozoan trophozoite is the
 a. active feeding stage
 b. inactive dormant stage
 c. infective stage
 d. spore-forming stage

12. Humans are infected with *Plasmodium* through the bite of a
 a. fly
 b. kissing bug
 c. mosquito
 d. worm

13. Parasitic helminths reproduce with
 a. spores
 b. eggs and sperm
 c. mitosis
 d. cysts
 e. all of these

14. Mitochondria likely originated from
 a. archaea
 b. invaginations of the cell membrane
 c. rickettsias
 d. cyanobacteria

15. Human fungal infections involve and affect what areas of the human body?
 a. skin
 b. mucous membranes
 c. lungs
 d. all of these

16. Most helminth infections
 a. are localized to one site in the body
 b. spread through major systems of the body
 c. develop within the spleen
 d. develop within the liver

17. **Matching.** Select the description that best fits the word in the left column.

 _____ diatom
 _____ *Rhizopus*
 _____ *Histoplasma*
 _____ *Cryptococcus*
 _____ euglenid
 _____ dinoflagellate
 _____ *Trichomonas*
 _____ *Entamoeba*
 _____ *Plasmodium*
 _____ *Enterobius*

 a. the cause of malaria
 b. single-celled alga with silica in its cell wall
 c. fungal cause of Ohio Valley fever
 d. the cause of amebic dysentery
 e. genus of black bread mold
 f. helminth worm involved in pinworm infection
 g. motile flagellated alga possessing a pellicle
 h. a yeast that infects the lungs
 i. protozoan genus that causes an STD
 j. alga that causes harmful algal blooms

Case Study Analysis

1. The fungus seen in this case reproduced by means of
 a. zygospores
 b. ascospores
 c. basidiospores
 d. chytridiospores

2. Mushrooms are often seen sprouting from lawns because if there is enough sunlight for grass to grow, there is generally enough sunlight for mushrooms to photosynthesize.
 a. true
 b. false

3. Mushrooms are sometimes seen sprouting from grass in a circular pattern known as a fairy ring. Why do you think mushrooms show this pattern of growth?

NajaShots/Getty Images

On the Test

These questions will help to prepare you to successfully answer similar questions you'll see on the TEAS (Test of Essential Academic Skills) and NCLEX (National Council Licensure Examination).

1. Which structure or molecule is NOT found in the cell nucleus?
 a. chromatin
 b. DNA
 c. Golgi apparatus
 d. nucleolus

2. Fungi are similar to plants in that both
 a. contain chloroplasts
 b. perform photosynthesis
 c. use carbon dioxide as an energy source
 d. have a cell wall

Writing Challenge

For each question, compose a one- or two-paragraph answer that includes the factual information needed to completely address the question. Practice questions can also be used for writing-challenge exercises.

1. Describe the anatomy and functions of each of the major eukaryotic organelles.
2. Trace the synthesis of cell products, their processing, and their packaging through the organelle network.
3. a. What is the reproductive potential of molds in terms of spore production?
 b. How do mold spores differ from bacterial endospores?
4. a. Fill in the following summary table for defining, comparing, and contrasting eukaryotic cells.
 b. Briefly describe the manner of nutrition and body plan (unicellular, colonial, filamentous, or multicellular) for each group.
 c. Explain some ways that helminths differ from the protozoa and algae in structure and behavior.

Organelle/ Structure	Briefly Describe Functions in Cell	Commonly Present In (Check)		
		Fungi	Algae	Protozoa
Flagella				
Cilia				
Glycocalyx				
Cell wall				
Cell membrane				
Nucleus				
Mitochondria				
Chloroplasts				
Endoplasmic reticulum				
Ribosomes				
Cytoskeleton				
Lysosomes				
Microvilli				
Centrioles				

Concept Mapping

On Connect you can find an Introduction to Concept Mapping that provides guidance for working with concept maps, along with concept-mapping activities for this chapter.

 ## Application, Analysis, Evaluation, and Synthesis

Level II. These problems go beyond just restating facts and require higher levels of understanding and an ability to interpret, problem solve, transfer knowledge to new situations, create models, and predict outcomes.

Critical Thinking

Critical thinking is the ability to reason and solve problems using facts and concepts. These questions can be approached from a number of angles and, in most cases, they do not have a single correct answer.

1. Explain the ways that mitochondria resemble rickettsias and chloroplasts resemble cyanobacteria.

2. Give the common name of a eukaryotic microbe that is unicellular, walled, nonphotosynthetic, nonmotile, and bud-forming.

3. How are the eukaryotic ribosomes and cell membranes different from those of prokaryotes?

4. What general type of multicellular parasite is composed primarily of thin sacs of reproductive organs?

5. a. Name two parasites that are transmitted in the cyst form.
 b. How must a non–cyst-forming pathogenic protozoan be transmitted? Why?

6. Explain the factors that could cause opportunistic mycoses to be a growing medical problem.

7. a. How are bacterial endospores and cysts of protozoa alike?
 b. How do they differ?

8. For what reasons would a eukaryotic cell evolve an endoplasmic reticulum and a Golgi apparatus?

9. Can you think of a simple test to determine if a child is suffering from pinworms? Hint: Clear adhesive tape is involved.

Visual Assessment

1. What term is used to describe a single species exhibiting both cell types shown below, and which types of organisms would most likely have this trait?

2. Why are the air bladders (the small bulbs) seen in this kelp necessary?

Joebelanger/123RF

CHAPTER

6

An Introduction to Viruses, Viroids, and Prions

In This Chapter...

(The Sphinx and The Pyramid of Khafre, Giza): Flickr/Getty Images; (Influenza virus): Source: Cynthia Goldsmith/CDC; (bacterial cell): Lee D. Simon/Science Source; (Microbiologist): Source: Greg Knobloch/CDC

CASE STUDY Part 1 I'm Not Ready for Him to Die

When your wife is the chief of the Division of **Global Public Health,** you often spend your vacation in unusual places; such was the circumstance behind Tom Patterson's Thanksgiving celebration in Egypt. Patterson, a professor at the UC San Diego (UCSD) School of Medicine, and his wife, Stephanie Strathdee, were enjoying their Middle Eastern Thanksgiving when Patterson became ill, displaying abdominal pain, **fever,** nausea, vomiting, and a rapid heartbeat. Treatment in Egypt for **pancreatitis** proved ineffective and his condition grew steadily worse. He was moved by air ambulance to Frankfurt, Germany, where doctors discovered that Patterson was **infected** with *Acinetobacter baumannii,* an opportunistic **bacterium** responsible for many infections in wounded combat veterans returning from Iraq and Afghanistan. One of the most disturbing aspects of *A. baumannii* infections is the high frequency of **antibiotic resistance** they display.

The infection was initially controlled with a combination of meropenem, tigecycline, and colistin, a combination of exceptionally strong **antibiotics.** His condition improved enough that he was transferred to the intensive care unit at Jacobs Medical Center, a hospital affiliated with UCSD. Shortly after his arrival, doctors were distressed to find that his infection had become **resistant** to all antibiotics. His abdomen became swollen with the infection and his **white blood cell count** (an indicator of infection) soared. His condition quickly deteriorated, and he fell into a **coma** that would last for nearly 2 months. Strathdee recalled colleagues wondering if she was prepared for her husband to die. She wasn't.

Like most microbiologists, Strathdee had heard of **phage therapy,** a practice where a **virus** (bacteriophage or, simply, phage) is injected into the body to attack bacterial cells directly. An historical anecdote usually placed in the same category as bloodletting and homeopathic treatment, phage therapy seemed **theoretically** possible but had shown little

success in practice. Yet, Strathdee had heard from a friend of a friend who had traveled to Tblisi, Georgia (where medical treatments are far less regulated than in the United States), to undergo phage therapy for a chronic condition and was supposedly cured. In her desperation, she turned to a colleague at UCSD, Dr. Chip Schooley, for help in designing a phage treatment for her husband.

All viruses have a **host range**, a specific, often very narrow, collection of cells that they can infect. So, the first task was to find a phage that would be effective against the *A. baumannii* bacterium that was at the heart of Patterson's infection. Three research teams had strains of phage that were active against *A. baumannii,* and a research team at nearby San Diego State University purified the samples for clinical use. Emergency approval also had to be granted from the U.S. Food and Drug Administration to proceed with the unusual treatment.

Patterson received the phage treatment through a catheter into his **abdominal cavity,** as well as **intravenously** to attack bacteria in his bloodstream. With such a radical, untried treatment, doctors had few ideas as to how to proceed most effectively. "As a treating doctor, it was a challenge," said Schooley. "Usually you know what the **dosage** should be, how often to treat... but when you're doing it for the first time, you don't have anything to compare it to."

■ *Why was no one concerned that the patient in this case would be sickened by the viruses used as part of phage therapy?*

To continue the Case Study, go to Case Study Part 2 at the end of the chapter.

(drug-resistant Acinetobacter): Source: Melissa Brower/CDC

6.1 Overview of Viruses

 Learn

1. Indicate how viruses were discovered and characterized.
2. Describe the unique characteristics of viruses.
3. Discuss the origin and importance of viruses.

Early Searches for the Tiniest Microbes

The discovery of the light microscope made it possible to see first-hand the agents of many bacterial, fungal, and protozoan diseases. But the techniques for observing and cultivating these relatively large microorganisms were useless for viruses. For many years the cause of viral infections such as smallpox and polio was unknown, even though it was clear that the diseases were transmitted from person to person. The French bacteriologist Louis Pasteur was certainly on the right track when he postulated that rabies was caused by a "living thing" smaller than bacteria, and in 1884 he was able to develop the first vaccine for rabies.

The first substantial revelations about the unique characteristics of viruses occurred in the 1890s. First, Dmitri Ivanovski and Martinus Beijerinck showed that a disease in tobacco was caused by a virus (tobacco mosaic virus). In fact, it was Beijerinck who first proposed the term **virus** (L., "poison") to denote this particular group of infectious agents. This discovery was followed by Friedrich Loeffler and Paul Frosch's isolation of the virus that causes foot-and-mouth disease in cattle. These early researchers found that when infectious fluids from host organisms were passed through porcelain filters designed to trap bacteria, the filtrate remained infectious even though they could not see the infectious agent with a microscope.

Over the succeeding decades, virology grew into a multifaceted discipline that promised to provide much information on disease, genetics, and even life itself.

The Position of Viruses in the Biological Spectrum

Viruses are a unique group of biological entities known to infect every type of cell, including bacteria, fungi, protists, plants, and animals. Although the emphasis in this chapter is on animal viruses, much credit for our knowledge must be given to experiments with bacterial and plant viruses. The exceptional and curious nature of viruses prompts numerous questions, including:

1. How did viruses originate?
2. Are they organisms; that is, are they alive?
3. What are their distinctive biological characteristics?
4. How can particles so small, simple, and seemingly insignificant be capable of causing disease and death?
5. What is the connection between viruses and cancer?

In this chapter, we address these ideas and many others.

There is no universal agreement on how and when viruses originated. But there is little disagreement that they have been in existence for billions of years, probably ever since the early history of cells. One theory explains that viruses arose from loose strands of genetic material released by cells. These then developed a protective coating and a capacity to reenter a cell and use its machinery to reproduce. An alternative explanation for their origins suggests that viruses were once cells that have regressed to a highly parasitic existence inside other cells. Both of these viewpoints have some supportive evidence, and it is entirely possible that viruses have originated in more than one way.

In terms of numbers, viruses are considered the most abundant microbes on earth. To quote microbiologist Carl Zimmer, we live on "a planet of viruses." Based on a decade of research on the viral populations in the ocean, "virus hunters" now have evidence that there are hundreds of thousands of distinct virus types that have never been described. Many of them are parasites of bacteria, which are also abundant in most ecosystems. By one estimate, viruses outnumber bacteria by a factor of 10. Because viruses tend to interact with the genetic material of their host cells and can carry genes from one host cell to another (chapter 9), they have played an important part in the evolution of Bacteria, Archaea, and Eukarya.

Viruses are different from their host cells in size, structure, behavior, and physiology. They are a type of **obligate intracellular parasite** that cannot multiply unless it invades a specific host cell and instructs its genetic and metabolic machinery to make and release quantities of new viruses. Because of this characteristic, viruses are capable of causing serious damage and disease. Other unique properties of viruses are summarized in **table 6.1.**

The unusual structure and behavior of viruses have led to debates about their connection to the rest of the microbial world. The most common viewpoint holds that viruses are unable to exist independently from the host cell, so they are not living things but

TABLE 6.1	Properties of Viruses

- Obligate intracellular parasites of bacteria, protists, fungi, plants, and animals
- Ultramicroscopic size, ranging from 20 nm up to 450 nm (diameter)
- Not cellular in nature; structure is very compact and economical
- Do not independently fulfill the characteristics of life
- Inactive macromolecules outside the host cell and active only inside host cells
- Basic structure consists of protein shell (capsid) surrounding nucleic acid core
- Nucleic acid of the viral genome is either DNA or RNA but not both
- Nucleic acid can be double-stranded DNA, single-stranded DNA, single-stranded RNA, or double-stranded RNA
- Molecules on virus surface impart high specificity for attachment to host cell
- Multiply by taking control of host cell's genetic material and regulating the synthesis and assembly of new viruses
- Lack enzymes for most metabolic processes
- Lack machinery for synthesizing proteins

are more akin to large, infectious molecules. In any event, viruses are agents of disease and must be dealt with through control, therapy, and prevention, whether we regard them as living or not. In keeping with their special position in the biological spectrum, it is best to describe viruses as *infectious particles* (rather than organisms) and as either *active* or *inactive* (rather than alive or dead).

 Practice SECTION 6.1

1. Describe 10 *unique* characteristics of viruses (can include structure, behavior, multiplication).

2. After consulting table 6.1, what additional facts can you state about viruses, especially as compared with cells?

3. Explain what it means to be an obligate intracellular parasite.

4. What are some other ways to describe the sort of parasitism exhibited by viruses?

6.2 The General Structure of Viruses

 Learn

4. Describe the general structure and size range of viruses.

5. Distinguish among types of capsids and nucleocapsids.

6. Describe envelopes and spikes, and discuss their origins.

7. Explain the functions of capsids, nucleocapsids, envelopes, and spikes.

8. Summarize the different viral groups based on their basic structure.

Size Range

As a group, viruses are the smallest infectious agents (with some unusual exceptions to be discussed in section 6.8). Their size places them in the realm of the *ultramicroscopic*. This term means that most of them are so minute (<0.2 μm) that an electron microscope is necessary to detect them or to examine their fine structure. They are dwarfed by their host cells: More than 2,000 bacterial viruses could fit into an average bacterial cell, and more than 50 million polioviruses could be accommodated by an average human cell. Animal viruses range in size from the small parvoviruses[1] (around 20 nm in diameter) to megaviruses and pithoviruses that are as large as small bacteria (up to 1,500 nm in width) **(figure 6.1)**. Some cylindrical viruses are relatively long (800 nm in length) but so narrow in diameter (15 nm) that they still cannot be seen without the high magnification and resolution of an electron microscope. Figure 6.1 compares the sizes of several viruses with prokaryotic and eukaryotic cells and molecules.

Super-sized viruses, ranging from 400 μm to 1,500 μm across, are a recent phenomenon to scientists, so large that they were mistakenly viewed as small bacteria and ignored by virus hunters. Mimiviruses, pandorviruses, megaviruses **(figure 6.2),** and pithoviruses are 20 to 50 times larger than an average virus and even larger than small bacteria such as rickettsias. All three viruses were first discovered as parasites inside the cells of amoebas living in aquatic habitats. They have a typical viral cycle, multiplying in the host cytoplasm, and lack cellular structure and ribosomes, metabolic enzymes, and fission-style division. They also have many proteins that are unrelated to other viral groups, raising questions about where these unusual viruses fit on the "tree of life," if anywhere at all.

Viral Components: Capsids, Nucleic Acids, and Envelopes

It is important to realize that viruses bear no real resemblance to cells and that they lack any of the synthetic machinery found in even the simplest cells **(figure 6.3)**. The general plan of virus organization is very simple and compact. Viruses contain only those parts needed to invade and control a host cell: an external coating and a core containing one or more nucleic acid strands of either DNA or RNA. This pattern can be represented with a flowchart:

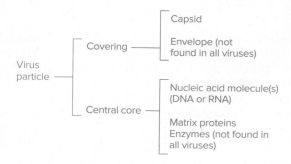

All viruses have a protein **capsid,*** or shell, that surrounds the nucleic acid in the central core. Together, the capsid and the nucleic acid are referred to as the **nucleocapsid.** Viruses that consist of only a nucleocapsid are considered **naked viruses (figure 6.4a)**. Of the 20 families of animal viruses, 13 are **enveloped**—that is, they possess an additional covering external to the capsid called an envelope, which is a modified section of the host's cell membrane **(figure 6.4b)**. As we shall see later, the enveloped viruses also differ from the naked viruses in the possible ways that they enter and leave a host cell.

The Viral Capsid: The Protective Outer Shell

When a virus particle is magnified several hundred thousand times, the capsid appears as the most prominent geometric feature (figure 6.4). In general, the capsid of any virus is constructed from a number of identical protein subunits called **capsomers.*** The capsomers can spontaneously self-assemble into the finished capsid. The shape and arrangement of the capsomers result in the production of one of two different types of capsids: helical or icosahedral.

1. DNA viruses that cause respiratory infections in humans.

* *capsid* (kap′-sid) L. *capsa,* box.
* *capsomer* (kap′-soh-meer) L. *capsa,* box, and *mer,* part.

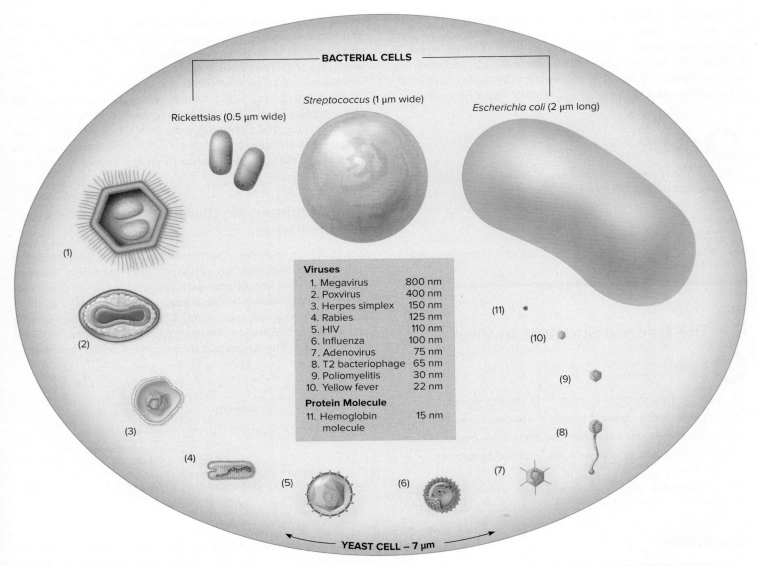

Figure 6.1 **Size comparison of viruses with a yeast cell colored blue (eukaryotic) and various bacteria (prokaryotic).** Viruses range from largest (1) to smallest (10). A molecule of a large protein (11) is included to indicate relative size of macromolecules.

The simpler **helical capsids** have rod-shaped capsomers that bind together to form a series of hollow discs resembling a bracelet. During the formation of the nucleocapsid, these discs link together and form a continuous helix into which the nucleic acid strand is coiled. In electron micrographs, the appearance of a helical capsid varies with the type of virus. The nucleocapsids of naked helical viruses are very rigid and tightly wound into a cylinder-shaped package **(figure 6.5).** Enveloped helical nucleocapsids are more flexible and tend to be arranged as a looser helix within the envelope **(figure 6.6).** This type of capsid is found in several enveloped human viruses, including those of influenza, measles, and rabies.

Several major virus families have capsids arranged in an **icosahedron***—a three-dimensional, symmetrical polygon, with 20 sides and 12 evenly spaced corners. The arrangements of the capsomers vary from one virus to another. The capsid of some viruses contains a single type of capsomer, whereas others may contain several types of capsomers **(figure 6.7).** Although the capsids of all icosahedral viruses have this sort of symmetry, they can vary in the number of capsomers; for example, a poliovirus has 32 capsomers and an adenovirus has 242. During assembly of the virus, the nucleic acid is packed into the center of this icosahedron, forming a nucleocapsid. Another factor that alters the appearance of icosahedral viruses is whether or not they have an outer envelope. Inspect **figure 6.8** to compare a rotavirus and its naked nucleocapsid with herpes simplex (cold sores) and its enveloped nucleocapsid.

The Viral Envelope

When enveloped viruses (mostly animal) are released from the host cell, they take with them a bit of the host's membrane system in the form of an envelope. Some viruses bud off the cell membrane; others

* *icosahedron* (eye″-koh-suh-hee′-drun) Gr. *eikosi,* twenty, and *hedra,* side. A type of polygon.

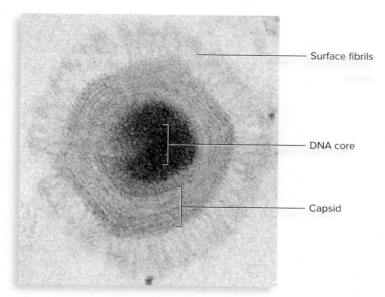

Figure 6.2 **A monster virus—the megavirus.** A TEM of one virus particle reveals its unique geometric shape, dark DNA core, and fine surface fibrils (4,500×). These viruses would be readily visible with an ordinary light microscope.
Courtesy of C. Abergel/IGS-IMM, CNRS-AMU

(a) **Naked Nucleocapsid Virus**

(b) **Enveloped Virus**

Figure 6.4 **Generalized structure of viruses. (a)** The simplest virus is a naked nucleocapsid consisting of a geometric capsid assembled around one or more nucleic acid strands. **(b)** An enveloped virus is composed of a nucleocapsid surrounded by a flexible envelope. The envelope usually has special receptor spikes inserted into its membrane.

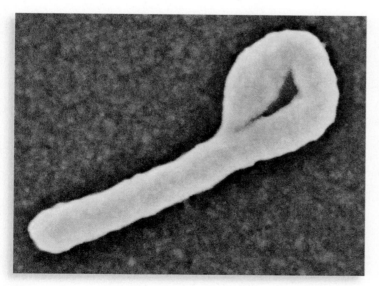

Figure 6.3 **Viruses bear little resemblance to cells.** Transmission electron micrograph of a single Ebola virus particle reveals a structure that has little in common with the eukaryotic cell the virus infects (100,000×).
Source: National Institute of Allergy and Infectious Diseases (NIAID)/CDC

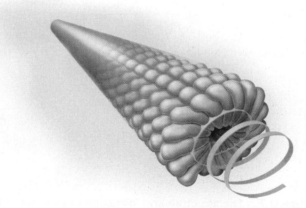

Figure 6.5 **Assembly of helical nucleocapsids.** Capsomers (blue-green) are assembled into a hollow tube while the nucleic acid (yellow) is wound within the lengthening capsid.

leave via the nuclear envelope or the endoplasmic reticulum. Although the envelope is derived from the host, it is different because some or all of the regular membrane proteins are replaced with special viral proteins during the virus assembly process (see process figure 6.11). Some proteins form a binding layer between the envelope and capsid of the virus, and glycoproteins (proteins bound to a carbohydrate) remain exposed on the outside of the envelope. These

protruding molecules, called **spikes** or peplomers, are essential for the attachment of viruses to the next host cell. Because the envelope is more supple than the capsid, enveloped viruses are pleomorphic and range from spherical to filamentous in shape.

Figure 6.6 Helical nucleocapsids (a) Schematic view and **(b)** a colorized micrograph featuring a positive stain of the influenza virus (300,000×), an enveloped helical virus. This virus has a well-developed envelope with prominent spikes.
(b): *Source:* Cynthia Goldsmith/CDC

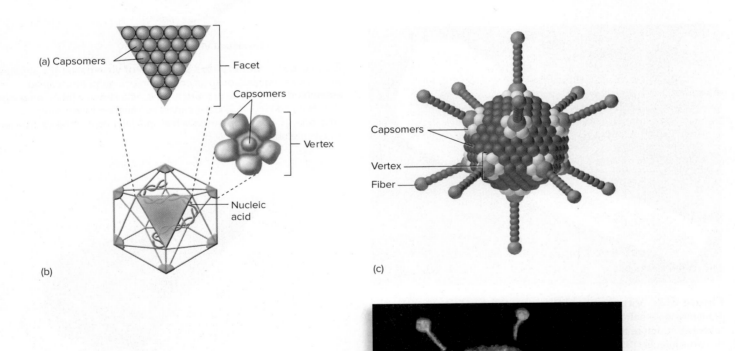

Figure 6.7 The structure and formation of an icosahedral virus (adenovirus is the model). (a) A facet or "face" of the capsid is composed of 21 identical capsomers arranged in a triangular shape. A vertex or "point" consists of five capsomers arranged with a single penton in the center. Other viruses can vary in the number, types, and arrangement of capsomers. **(b)** An assembled virus shows how the facets and vertices come together to form a shell around the nucleic acid. **(c)** A three-dimensional model (640,000×) of this virus shows fibers attached to the pentons. **(d)** A negative stain of this virus highlights its texture and fibers that have fallen off.
(d): Dr. Linda Stannard, UCT/Science Source

(a)

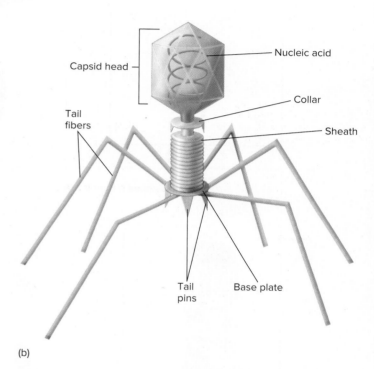

(b)

Figure 6.8 Two types of icosahedral viruses, highly magnified. (a) Transmission electron micrograph of rotavirus, revealing its capsomers that look like spokes on a wheel. (b) A computer-generated illustration of rotavirus reveals the three-dimensional nature of the capsomers. (c) Herpes simplex virus, a type of enveloped icosahedral virus (300,000×).

(a): *Source:* Dr. Erskine Palmer & Byron Skinner/CDC; (b): *Source:* Alissa Eckert, MS/CDC; (c): Eye of Science/Science Source

Functions of the Viral Capsid/Envelope

The outermost covering of a virus is indispensable to viral function because it protects the nucleic acid from the effects of various enzymes and chemicals when the virus is outside the host cell. We see this in the capsids of enteric (intestinal) viruses such as polio and hepatitis A, which are resistant to the acid- and protein-digesting enzymes of the gastrointestinal tract. Capsids and envelopes are also responsible for helping to introduce the viral DNA or RNA into a suitable host cell, first by binding to the cell surface and then by assisting in penetration of the viral nucleic acid (discussed in later sections). In addition, parts of viral capsids and envelopes stimulate the immune system to produce antibodies that can neutralize viruses and protect the host's cells against future infections (see chapter 15).

Complex Viruses: Atypical Viruses

Two special groups of viruses, termed **complex** viruses **(figure 6.9)**, are more intricate in structure than the helical, icosahedral, naked, or enveloped viruses just described. The **poxviruses** (including the agent of smallpox) are very large DNA viruses that lack a typical

(c)

Figure 6.9 Detailed structure of complex viruses. (a) Section through the vaccinia virus, a poxvirus, shows its internal components. (b) Diagram of a T4 bacteriophage of *E. coli* (280,000×). (c) Transmission electron micrograph of a bacteriophage which infects cyanobacteria (90,000×).

(c): ©Bin Ni, Chisholm Lab, MIT

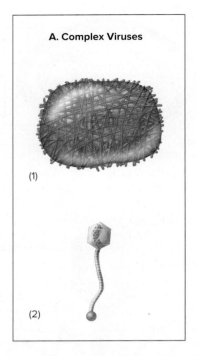

A. Complex Viruses

(1)

(2)

B. Enveloped Viruses

Helical

Icosahedral

(3)

(5)

(4)

(6)

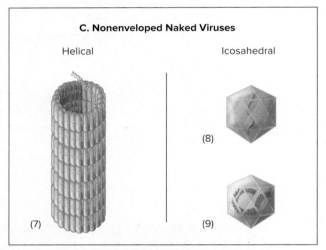

C. Nonenveloped Naked Viruses

Helical

Icosahedral

(7)

(8)

(9)

A. Complex viruses:
 (1) poxvirus, a large DNA virus
 (2) flexible-tailed bacteriophage

B. Enveloped viruses:
 With a helical nucleocapsid:
 (3) mumps virus
 (4) rhabdovirus
 With an icosahedral nucleocapsid:
 (5) herpesvirus
 (6) HIV (AIDS)

C. Naked viruses:
 Helical capsid:
 (7) plum poxvirus
 Icosahedral capsid:
 (8) poliovirus
 (9) papillomavirus

Figure 6.10 Basic types of viral morphology.

capsid and are covered by a dense layer of lipoproteins and coarse fibrils on their outer surface. Some members of another group of very complex viruses, the **bacteriophages,** * have a polyhedral capsid head as well as a helical tail and fibers for attachment to the host cell. Their mode of multiplication is covered in section 6.5. **Figure 6.10** summarizes the primary morphological types found among the viruses.

Nucleic Acids: At the Core of a Virus

The sum total of the genetic information carried by an organism is known as its **genome.** So far, one biological constant is that the genome of all organisms is carried by and expressed through

nucleic acids (DNA, RNA). Even viruses are no exception to this rule, but there is a significant difference. Unlike cells, which contain both DNA and RNA, **viruses contain either DNA or RNA, _but not both,_ as the primary genetic material.** Because viruses must pack into a tiny space all of the genes necessary to instruct the host cell to make new viruses, the number of viral genes is usually quite small compared with that of a cell. It varies from nine genes in human immunodeficiency virus (HIV) to as many as 2,500 genes in pandoraviruses. By comparison, the bacterium *Escherichia coli* has approximately 4,000 genes, and a human cell has around 20,000 genes. Having a larger genome allows cells to carry out the complex metabolic activity necessary for independent life. Viruses typically possess only the genes needed to invade host cells and redirect their synthetic machinery to make new viruses.

In chapter 2, you learned that DNA usually exists as a double-stranded molecule and that RNA is single-stranded. Although most

* *bacteriophage* (bak-teer′-ee-oh-fayj″) From *bacteria,* and Gr. *phagein,* to eat. These viruses parasitize bacteria.

viruses follow this same pattern, viruses exhibit variety in how their RNA or DNA is configured. DNA viruses can have single-stranded (ss) or double-stranded (ds) DNA; the dsDNA can be arranged linearly or in circles. RNA viruses can be double-stranded but are more often single-stranded. Notable examples are the parvoviruses, which contain single-stranded DNA, and reoviruses (a cause of respiratory and intestinal tract infections), which contain double-stranded RNA. You will learn in chapter 9 that all proteins are made by "translating" the nucleic acid code on a single strand of RNA into an amino acid sequence. Single-stranded RNA genomes that are ready for immediate translation into proteins are called *positive-strand* RNA. RNA genomes that have to be converted into the proper form for translation are called *negative-strand* RNA.

RNA genomes may also be *segmented,* meaning that the individual genes exist in separate RNA molecules, similar to the way that the human (DNA) genome is spread across 23 separate chromosomes. The influenza virus (an orthomyxovirus) is an example of this form. Another RNA virus with some unusual features is a *retrovirus,* one of the few virus types that converts its nucleic acid from RNA to DNA inside its host cell.

Whatever the virus type, these tiny strands of genetic material carry the blueprint for viral structure and functions. In a very real sense, viruses are genetic parasites because they cannot multiply until their nucleic acid has reached their haven inside the host cell. At a minimum, they must carry genes for synthesizing the viral capsid and genetic material, for regulating the actions of the host, and for packaging the mature virus.

Other Substances in the Virus Particle

In addition to the protein of the capsid, the proteins and lipids of envelopes, and the nucleic acid of the core, viruses can contain enzymes for specific operations within their host cell. They may come with preformed enzymes that are required for viral **replication.*** Examples include **polymerases*** that synthesize DNA and RNA and replicase enzymes that copy RNA. The human immunodeficiency virus (HIV) comes equipped with *reverse transcriptase* for synthesizing DNA from RNA. However, viruses completely lack the genes for synthesis of metabolic enzymes. As we shall see, this deficiency has little consequence, because viruses have adapted to assume total control over the cell's metabolic resources. Some viruses can actually carry away substances from their host cell. For instance, arenaviruses pack along host ribosomes, and retroviruses "borrow" the host's tRNA molecules.

6.3 How Viruses Are Classified and Named

 Learn

9. Explain the classification scheme used for viruses.

10. Indicate the characteristics used in identifying and naming viruses.

Although viruses are not classified as members of the domains discussed in chapter 1, they are diverse enough to require their own

classification scheme to aid in their study and identification. In an informal and general way, we have already begun classifying viruses—as animal, plant, or bacterial viruses; enveloped or naked viruses; DNA or RNA viruses; and helical or icosahedral viruses. These introductory categories are certainly useful in organization and description, but the study of specific viruses requires a more standardized method of nomenclature. For many years, the animal viruses were classified mainly on the basis of their hosts and the kind of diseases they caused. Newer systems for naming viruses also take into account the actual nature of the virus particles themselves, with only partial emphasis on host and disease. The main criteria presently used to group viruses are structure, chemical composition, and similarities in genetic makeup, which indicate evolutionary relatedness.

The International Committee on the Taxonomy of Viruses lists 10 orders, 134 families, and several hundred genera of viruses. Nomenclature of viruses follows these conventions: Virus families are italicized and given the suffix *-viridae,* and virus genera are likewise italicized and end in *-virus.*

Historically, some virologists had created an informal *species* naming system that mirrors the species names in higher organisms, using genus and species epithets such as *Measles morbillivirus.* The species category has created a lot of controversy within the virology community. Many scientists argue that nonorganisms such as viruses are too changeable and that fine distinctions used for deciding on species classifications will quickly disappear. All the same, virologists have largely accepted the concept of viral species, defining them as distinct virus types that share a collection of properties such as host range, pathogenicity, and genetic makeup. The influenza viruses are an example of how variations in the receptors can give rise to different strains or subtypes, even though they are basically the same viruses in other characteristics.

Because the use of standardized species names are not as widely used, the genus or common English vernacular names (such as poliovirus and rabies virus) predominate in discussions of specific viruses in this text. **Table 6.2** illustrates a system of classification for important viruses and the diseases they cause. To-scale examples of each virus family are included.

Characteristics used for placement in a particular family include type of capsid, nucleic acid strand number, presence and type of envelope, overall viral size, and area of the host cell in which the virus multiplies. Some virus families are named for their microscopic appearance (shape and size). Examples include **rhabdoviruses,*** which have a bullet-shaped envelope, and **togaviruses,*** which have a cloaklike envelope. Anatomical or geographic areas have also been used in naming. For instance, **adenoviruses*** were first discovered in adenoids (one type of tonsil), and **hantaviruses** were originally isolated in the Korean Province of Hantaan. Viruses can also be named for their effects on the host. **Lentiviruses*** tend to cause slow, chronic infections. Acronyms made from blending several characteristics include **picornaviruses,*** which are tiny RNA viruses, and **hepadnaviruses** (for hepatitis and DNA).

* *replication* (rep-lih-kay´-shun) L. *replicare,* to reply. To make an exact duplicate.
* *polymerase* (pol-im´-ur-ace) An enzyme that synthesizes a large molecule from smaller subunits.

* *rhabdovirus* (rab″-doh-vy´-rus) Gr. *rhabdo,* little rod.
* *togavirus* (toh″-guh-vy´-rus) L. *toga,* covering or robe.
* *adenovirus* (ad″-uh-noh-vy´-rus) G. *aden,* gland.
* *lentivirus* (len″-tee-vy´-rus) Gr. *lente,* slow. HIV, the AIDS virus, belongs in this group.
* *picornavirus* (py-kor″-nah-vy´-rus) Sp. *pico,* small, plus RNA.

TABLE 6.2 Important Human Virus Families, Genera, Common Names, and Types of Diseases

Nucleic Acid Type	Family	Genus of Virus	Common Name of Genus Members	Name of Disease
DNA Viruses				
Poxviridae Chordopoxvirinae *Herpesviridae*	*Poxviridae*	*Orthopoxvirus*	Variola and vaccinia	Smallpox, cowpox
	Herpesviridae	*Simplexvirus*	Herpes simplex 1 virus (HSV-1)	Fever blister, cold sores
			Herpes simplex 2 virus (HSV-2)	Genital herpes
		Varicellovirus	Varicella zoster virus (VZV)	Chickenpox, shingles
		Cytomegalovirus	Human cytomegalovirus (CMV)	CMV infections
Adenoviridae	*Adenoviridae*	*Mastadenovirus*	Human adenoviruses	Adenovirus infection
Papillomaviridae *Polyomaviridae*	*Papillomaviridae*	*Papillomavirus*	Human papillomavirus (HPV)	Several types of warts
	Polyomaviridae	*Polyomavirus*	JC virus (JCV)	Progressive multifocal leukoencephalopathy
Hepadnaviridae *Parvoviridae* Parvovirinae	*Hepadnaviridae*	*Hepadnavirus*	Hepatitis B virus (HBV or Dane particle)	Serum hepatitis
	Parvoviridae	*Erythrovirus*	Parvovirus B19	Erythema infectiosum
RNA Viruses				
Picornaviridae	*Picornaviridae*	*Enterovirus*	Poliovirus	Poliomyelitis
			Coxsackievirus	Hand-foot-mouth disease
		Hepatovirus	Hepatitis A virus (HAV)	Short-term hepatitis
		Rhinovirus	Human rhinovirus	Common cold, bronchitis
Caliciviridae	*Caliciviridae*	*Calicivirus*	Norwalk virus	Viral diarrhea, Norwalk virus syndrome
Togaviridae	*Togaviridae*	*Alphavirus*	Eastern equine encephalitis virus	Eastern equine encephalitis (EEE)
			Western equine encephalitis virus	Western equine encephalitis (WEE)
			Yellow fever virus	Yellow fever
			St. Louis encephalitis virus	St. Louis encephalitis
		Rubivirus	Rubella virus	Rubella (German measles)
Flaviviridae	*Flaviviridae*	*Flavivirus*	Dengue fever virus	Dengue fever
			West Nile fever virus	West Nile fever
			Zika virus	Zika fever
Bunyaviridae *Filoviridae*	*Bunyaviridae*	*Bunyavirus*	Bunyamwera viruses	California encephalitis
		Hantavirus	Sin Nombre virus	Respiratory syndrome
		Phlebovirus	Rift Valley fever virus	Rift Valley fever
		Nairovirus	Crimean–Congo hemorrhagic fever (CCHF) virus	Crimean-Congo hemorrhagic fever
Reoviridae	*Filoviridae*	*Filovirus*	Ebola, Marburg virus	Ebola fever
	Reoviridae	*Coltivirus*	Colorado tick fever virus	Colorado tick fever
		Rotavirus	Human rotavirus	Rotavirus gastroenteritis
Orthomyxoviridae *Paramyxoviridae*	*Orthomyxoviridae*	*Influenzavirus*	Influenza virus, type A (Asian, Hong Kong, and swine influenza viruses)	Influenza or "flu"
	Paramyxoviridae	*Paramyxovirus*	Parainfluenza virus	Parainfluenza
			Mumps virus	Mumps
		Morbillivirus	Measles virus	Measles (red)
		Pneumovirus	Respiratory syncytial virus (RSV)	Common cold syndrome

(Continued)

| TABLE 6.2 | Important Human Virus Families, Genera, Common Names, and Types of Diseases *(Continued)* |

Nucleic Acid Type		Family	Genus of Virus	Common Name of Genus Members	Name of Disease
Rhabdoviridae		*Rhabdoviridae*	*Lyssavirus*	Rabies virus	Rabies (hydrophobia)
		Retroviridae	*Oncornavirus*	Human T-cell leukemia virus (HTLV)	T-cell leukemia
	Retroviridae		*Lentivirus*	HIV (human immunodeficiency viruses 1 and 2)	Acquired immunodeficiency syndrome (AIDS)
Arenaviridae		*Arenaviridae*	*Arenavirus*	Lassa virus	Lassa fever
	Coronaviridae	*Coronaviridae*	*Coronavirus*	Infectious bronchitis virus (IBV)	Bronchitis
100 nm				Enteric corona virus	Coronavirus enteritis
				SARS virus	Severe acute respiratory syndrome
				MERS virus	Middle East respiratory syndrome

Practice SECTIONS 6.2–6.3

5. Characterize viruses according to size range. What does it mean to say that they are ultramicroscopic?

6. Describe the general structure of viruses.

7. What is the capsid, and what is its function? How are the two types of capsids constructed?

8. What is a nucleocapsid? Give examples of viruses with the two capsid types.

9. What is an enveloped virus, and how does the envelope arise? What are spikes, how are they formed, and what is their function?

10. What are bacteriophages, and what is unique about their structure?

11. How are the poxviruses different from other animal viruses?

12. Explain the characteristics used in viral classification and the nature of viral families.

13. How are generic and common names used?

6.4 Modes of Viral Multiplication

Learn

11. Describe the virus–host relationship.

12. Relate the stages in the multiplication cycle of animal viruses, and summarize what is happening in each stage.

13. Describe three ways in which animal viruses enter into a host cell.

14. Define *replication* as it relates to viruses.

15. Explain two ways in which animal viruses are released by a host cell.

16. Describe cytopathic effects of viruses and the possible results of persistent viral infections and viral integration.

Viruses are closely associated with their hosts. In addition to providing the viral habitat, the host cell is absolutely necessary for viral multiplication, which is synonymous with infection. The way in which viruses invade a host cell is an extraordinary biological phenomenon. Viruses have been aptly described as minute parasites that seize control of the synthetic and genetic machinery of cells. The nature of this cycle profoundly affects pathogenicity, transmission, the responses of the immune defenses, and human measures to control viral infections. From these perspectives, we cannot overemphasize the importance of a working knowledge of the relationship between viruses and their host cells.

Multiplication Cycles in Animal Viruses

The general phases in the life cycle of animal viruses are **adsorption,*** **penetration, synthesis, assembly,** and **release** from the host cell. Viruses vary in the exact mechanisms of these processes, but we will use a simple animal virus to illustrate the major events **(process figure 6.11).** Other examples are given in chapter 9.

Adsorption and Host Range

Invasion begins when the virus encounters a susceptible host cell and adsorbs specifically to receptor sites on the cell membrane. The membrane receptors that viruses attach to are usually glycoproteins the cell requires for its normal function. For example, the rabies virus affixes to receptors found on mammalian nerve cells, and the human immunodeficiency virus (HIV) attaches to the CD4 protein on certain white blood cells. The mode of attachment varies between the two general types of viruses. In enveloped forms such as influenza virus and HIV, glycoprotein spikes bind to the cell membrane receptors. Viruses with naked nucleocapsids (adenovirus, for example) use surface receptors on their capsids that adhere to cell membrane receptors **(figure 6.12).**

Because a virus can invade its host cell only through making an exact fit with a specific host molecule, the range of hosts it can infect in a natural setting is limited. This limitation, known as the **host range,**

* *adsorption* (ad-sorp′-shun) L. *ad*, to, and *sorbere*, to suck. The attachment of one thing onto the surface of another.

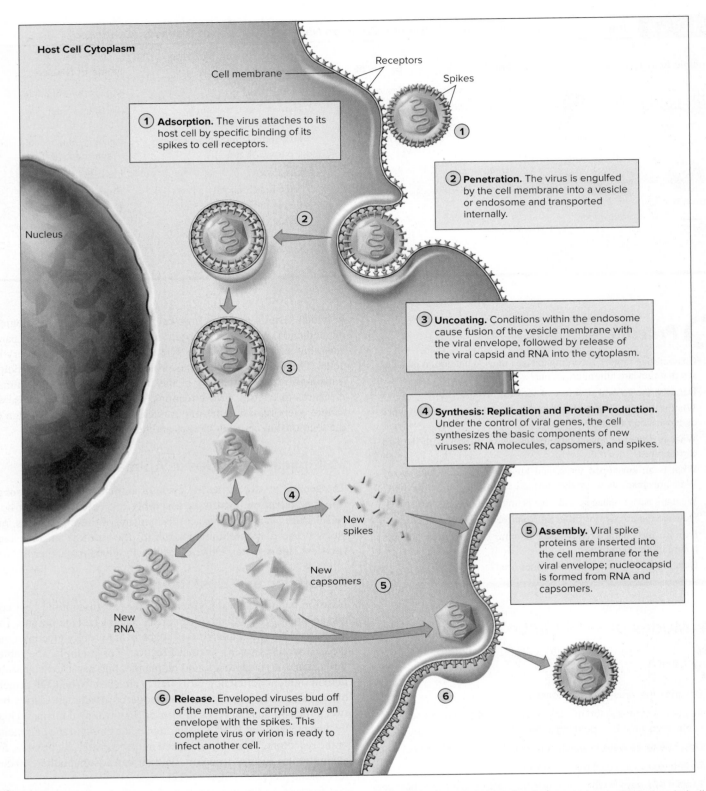

Host Cell Cytoplasm

Cell membrane

Receptors

Spikes

(1) **Adsorption.** The virus attaches to its host cell by specific binding of its spikes to cell receptors.

(2) **Penetration.** The virus is engulfed by the cell membrane into a vesicle or endosome and transported internally.

Nucleus

(3) **Uncoating.** Conditions within the endosome cause fusion of the vesicle membrane with the viral envelope, followed by release of the viral capsid and RNA into the cytoplasm.

(4) **Synthesis: Replication and Protein Production.** Under the control of viral genes, the cell synthesizes the basic components of new viruses: RNA molecules, capsomers, and spikes.

New spikes

New capsomers

(5) **Assembly.** Viral spike proteins are inserted into the cell membrane for the viral envelope; nucleocapsid is formed from RNA and capsomers.

New RNA

(6) **Release.** Enveloped viruses bud off of the membrane, carrying away an envelope with the spikes. This complete virus or virion is ready to infect another cell.

Process Figure 6.11 General features in the multiplication cycle of an enveloped animal virus. Using an RNA virus (rubella virus), the major events are outlined, although other viruses will vary in exact details of the cycle.

(a)

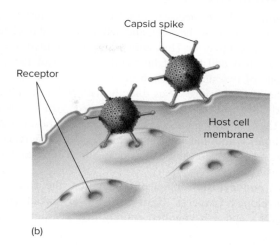

(b)

Figure 6.12 The mode by which animal viruses adsorb to the host cell membrane. (a) An enveloped coronavirus with prominent spikes. The configuration of the spike has a complementary fit for cell receptors. The process in which the virus lands on the cell and plugs into receptors is termed *docking*. **(b)** An adenovirus has a naked capsid that adheres to its host cell by nestling surface molecules on its capsid into the receptors on the host cell's membrane.

can vary from one virus to another. For example, hepatitis B infects only liver cells of humans; the poliovirus infects primarily intestinal and nerve cells of primates (humans, apes, and monkeys); and the rabies virus infects nerve cells of most mammals. Cells that lack compatible virus receptors are resistant to adsorption and invasion by that virus. This explains why, for example, human liver cells are not infected by the canine hepatitis virus

Quick Search

Look up "Flu Attack! How a Virus Invades Your Body" on the Internet.

and dog liver cells cannot host the human hepatitis A virus. It also explains why viruses usually have tissue specificities called **tropisms*** for certain cells in the body. The hepatitis B virus targets the liver, and the mumps virus targets salivary glands. Many viruses can be manipulated in the laboratory to infect cells that they do not infect naturally, thus making it possible to cultivate them.

* *tropism* (troh´-pizm) Gr. *trope*, a turn. Having a special affinity for an object or substance.

 CLINIC CASE

Beware of (Prairie) Dog A small bite from a family pet, especially in a family who already owns 39 cats, dogs, horses, goats, and donkeys, was nothing to get excited about. In this case, the bite came from a new addition to the family, a prairie dog, one of a pair that had been recently purchased. He had clearly been ill the last few days, exhibiting discharge from the nose and eyes, along with a rash. Unfortunately, a day or two later, the prairie dog died, and the mother disposed of its body.

At about the same time, the recipient of the bite, a three-year-old girl, began to develop a high fever, was sweating, and had lesions on her hands; her condition quickly worsened, and she was hospitalized. A biopsy of her lesions showed numerous cytoplasmic inclusions, indicating viral infection. Seeking a connection, the physician treating the young girl sent a technician to retrieve the body of the dead prairie dog and ordered a necropsy. Back home, both mom and dad began displaying similar symptoms and the remaining prairie dog became ill.

The necropsy of the dead pet revealed that he had been infected with monkeypox, a less dangerous relative of the often-lethal smallpox virus. An examination of the lesions on mom, dad, and daughter revealed that all three were similarly infected.

The source of the monkeypox was the next puzzle. The rainforest of central Africa, where monkeypox is endemic, is about as far away as one could get from Wisconsin. An investigation tracked the prairie dogs to an importer in Texas who kept the prairie dogs in a warehouse along with Gambian pouched rats, rope squirrels, tree squirrels, and African brush-tailed porcupines. The African rodents, along with the prairie dogs (and humans) all fell within the host range of the monkeypox virus. The three patients in Wisconsin were part of an outbreak that infected 71 people in five states. Fortunately, no deaths were attributed to the outbreak, likely because of the level of medical care received by those infected.

The biggest worry in a case like this, according to epidemiologists, is that a sick animal could be released into the wild, spreading the non-native virus to a wild animal population. The virus could then become endemic to the United States, much like West Nile virus has over the past several years. To lessen the possibility of this occurrence, shortly after this incident the Centers for Disease Control banned the importation of African rodents, along with the interstate transport of prairie dogs.

Mom and dad were never bitten by the sick prairie dog but still became ill. What does this tell you about how monkeypox is spread?

Penetration/Uncoating of Animal Viruses

For an animal virus to successfully infect a cell, it must penetrate the cell membrane of the host cell and deliver the viral nucleic acid into the host cell's interior. How animal viruses do this varies with the type of virus and type of host cell, but most of them enter through one of two means, fusion or endocytosis. In the case of **fusion,** the viral envelope fuses directly with the host cell membrane, so it can occur only in enveloped viruses (**process figure 6.13a**). Following attachment of the virus to host cell receptors, the lipids within the adjacent membranes become rearranged so that the nucleocapsid can be translocated into the cytoplasm for the synthesis phase.

In the **endocytosis** version of penetration, the virus can be either enveloped (**process figure 6.13b**) or naked (**process figure 6.13c**), and it is engulfed entirely into a vesicle called an endosome after its initial attachment. Once inside the cell, the virus is **uncoated.** This means that the vesicle membrane becomes altered so that the viral nucleocapsid or nucleic acid can be released into the cytoplasm. In some viruses the vesicle membrane fuses with the virus, and in other cases the vesicle membrane develops openings for the virus to leave. There are numerous variations in the details of this process.

Synthesis: Replication and Protein Production

The synthetic and replicative phases of animal viruses are highly regulated and extremely complex at the molecular level. Free viral nucleic acid exerts control over the host's metabolism and synthetic machinery. How this control proceeds will vary, depending on whether the virus is a DNA or an RNA virus. In general, the DNA viruses (except poxviruses) enter the host cell's nucleus and are

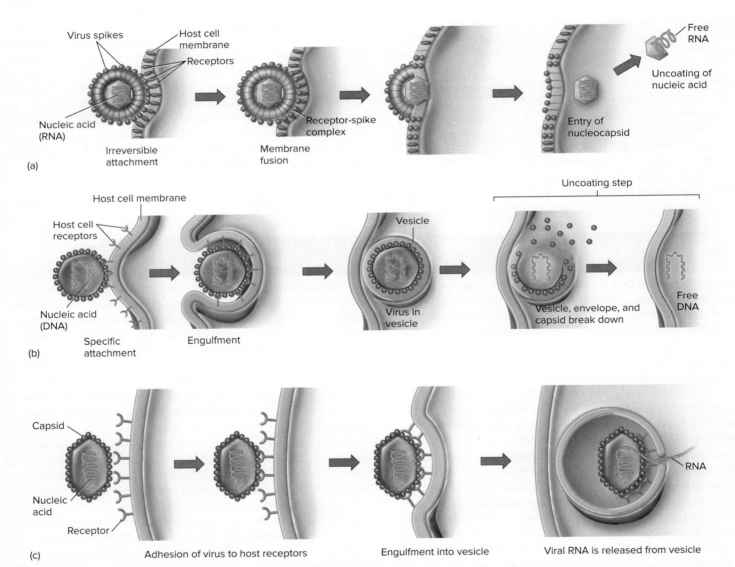

Process Figure 6.13 **Modes of virus penetration.** Pictured in **(a)** is the process of fusion between the envelope of the virus and the host cell membrane, with release of the nucleocapsid into the cytoplasm. This is the mechanism for mumps and HIV viruses. Both **(b)** and **(c)** are examples of entry by endocytosis or engulfment, followed by uncoating. **(b)** In an enveloped virus such as herpesvirus, the entire virus is taken into a vesicle with subsequent release of the DNA. **(c)** A naked virus such as poliovirus is first taken into a vesicle and then releases its nucleic acid through a pore or rupture in the membrane.

(b)

Figure 6.14 **Maturation and release of enveloped viruses.**
(a) As parainfluenza virus is budded off the membrane, it simultaneously picks up an envelope and spikes. **(b)** Ebola viruses leave their host cell by budding off its surface.
(b): *Source: NIH/NIAID*

replicated and assembled there. RNA viruses are replicated and assembled in the cytoplasm, with some exceptions.

The details of animal virus replication are discussed in chapter 9. Here we provide a brief overview of the process, using an RNA virus as a model. Almost immediately upon entry, the viral nucleic acid alters the genetic expression of the host and instructs it to synthesize the building blocks for new viruses. For example, it was recently shown that HIV depends on the expression of 250 human genes to complete its multiplication cycle. First, the RNA of the virus becomes a message for synthesizing viral proteins (translation). Most viruses with positive-strand RNA molecules already contain the correct message for translation into proteins. Viruses with negative-strand RNA molecules must first be converted into a positive-strand message. Some viruses come equipped with the necessary enzymes for synthesis of viral components; others utilize those of the host. During the final phase, the host's

replication and synthesis machinery produces new RNA, proteins for the capsid, spikes, and viral enzymes.

Assembly of Animal Viruses: Host Cell as Factory

Toward the end of the cycle—during the assembly stage—mature virus particles are constructed from the growing pool of parts. In most instances, the capsid is first laid down as an empty shell that will serve as a receptacle for the nucleic acid strand. Electron micrographs taken during this time show cells with masses of viruses, often enclosed in packets (see figure 6.15*a*). One important event leading to the release of enveloped viruses is the insertion of viral spikes into the host's cell membrane so they can be picked up as the virus buds off with its envelope, as discussed.

Release of Mature Viruses

To complete the cycle, assembled viruses leave their host in one of two ways. Nonenveloped and complex viruses that reach maturation in the cell nucleus or cytoplasm are released through cell **lysis** or rupturing. Enveloped viruses are liberated by **budding** or **exocytosis**[2] from the membranes of the cytoplasm, nucleus, endoplasmic reticulum, or vesicles. During this process the nucleocapsid binds to the membrane, which curves completely around it and forms a small pouch. Pinching off the pouch releases the virus with its envelope (**figure 6.14**). Budding of enveloped viruses causes them to be shed gradually, without the sudden destruction of the cell. Regardless of how the virus leaves, most active viral infections are ultimately lethal to the cell because of accumulated damage. Lethal damages include a permanent shutdown of metabolism and genetic expression, destruction of cell membrane and organelles, toxicity of virus components, and release of lysosomes.

The length of a multiplication cycle, from adsorption to lysis, varies to some extent, but it is usually measured in hours. A simple virus such as poliovirus takes about 8 hours; parvovirus takes 16 to 18 hours; and more complex viruses, such as herpesviruses, require 72 hours or more.

2. For enveloped viruses, these terms are interchangeable. They mean the release of a virus from an animal cell by enclosing it in a portion of membrane derived from the cell.

A fully formed, extracellular virus particle that is virulent and able to establish infection in a host is called a **virion.*** The number of virions released by infected cells is variable, controlled by factors such as the size of the virus and the health of the host cell. About 3,000 to 4,000 virions are released from a single cell infected with poxviruses, whereas a poliovirus-infected cell can release over 100,000 virions. If even a small number of these virions happens to meet other susceptible cells and infect them, the potential for viral proliferation is immense.

Visible Damage to the Host Cell

The short- and long-term effects of viral infections on animal cells are well documented. **Cytopathic*** effects (CPEs) are defined as virus-induced damage to the cell that alters its microscopic appearance. Individual cells can become disoriented, undergo gross changes in shape or size, or develop intracellular changes (**figure 6.15***a*). It is common to note **inclusion bodies,** or compacted masses of viruses or damaged cell organelles, in the nucleus and cytoplasm (**figure 6.15***b*). Examination of cells and tissues for cytopathic effects has been a traditional tool for diagnosing viral infections that is usually supplemented with more specific serological and molecular methods (see chapter 17). **Table 6.3** summarizes some prominent cytopathic effects associated with specific viruses. One very common CPE is the fusion of multiple host cells into a **syncytium,** a single large cell containing multiple nuclei. These syncytia are a result of some viruses' ability to fuse together the membranes of several host cells. One virus (respiratory syncytial virus) is even named for this effect.

Persistent Viral Infection and Viral Integration

As a general rule, a viral infection kills its host cell, but some cells escape destruction by harboring the virus in some form. These so-called **persistent infections** can last from a few weeks to years, even for the life of the host. As an example, the hepatitis B virus produces

* *virion* (vir'-ee-on) Gr. *iso,* poison.
* *cytopathic* (sy"-toh-path'-ik) Gr. *cyto,* cell, and *pathos,* disease.

TABLE 6.3	Cytopathic Changes in Selected Virus-Infected Animal Cells
Virus	**Response in Animal Cell**
Smallpox virus	Cells round up; inclusions appear in cytoplasm
Herpesvirus	Cells fuse to form multinucleated syncytia; nuclear inclusions (see figure 6.15)
Adenovirus	Clumping of cells; nuclear inclusions
Poliovirus	Cell lysis; no inclusions
Reovirus	Cell enlargement; vacuoles and inclusions in cytoplasm
Influenza virus	Cells round up; no inclusions
Rabies virus	No change in cell shape; cytoplasmic inclusions (Negri bodies)
Measles virus	Syncytia form (multinucleate giant cells; see figure 6.15)

a chronic progressive infection of the liver that may lead to cirrhosis and cancer. Many viruses remain in a **latent state,** meaning that they remain inactive or nonproductive over long periods. Examples of this are herpes simplex viruses (cold sores and genital herpes) and herpes zoster virus (chickenpox and shingles). Both viruses go into latency in nerve cells and later emerge under the influence of various stimuli to cause recurrent symptoms. Some animal viruses integrate their DNA into the DNA of the host cell, sometimes leading to cancer. Such viruses are termed **oncogenic,** and their effect on the cell is called **transformation.** Transformed cells generally have an increased rate of growth, alterations in chromosomes, changes in the cell's surface molecules, and the capacity to divide for an indefinite period. Examples include DNA viruses like papillomavirus, which is associated with cervical cancer, and herpesviruses like Epstein-Barr virus, which is a cofactor in Burkitt's lymphoma, a cancer affecting one type of white blood cell.

Cancer is not the only outcome of viral integration. For millions of years, humans—or the forbears of the species—have endured viral

(a)

(b)

Figure 6.15 **Cytopathic changes in cells and cell cultures infected by viruses. (a)** A multinucleate giant cell (center) infected with the measles virus. **(b)** Multiple small, dark inclusions are clearly visible within the nuclei of cultured cells infected with the varicella-zoster virus (500×). (a, a inset and b): *Source:* CDC

infection, and we harbor evidence of ancient viral infection in our DNA. As much as 8% of the DNA in the human genome (the total of all the DNA in a human being) is viral in nature, an astonishing amount when you consider that less than 2% of human DNA codes for proteins. Much of this DNA is in the form of endogenous retroviruses, which have converted their RNA to DNA, inserted the DNA into a site in one of our 46 chromosomes, and then become dormant. If this occurred in cells that gave rise to egg or sperm cells, the virus could be transmitted virtually unchanged for hundreds of generations.

Virologists do not agree on the extent to which ancient viruses interact with modern humans, but the evidence is compelling that we owe certain aspects of our biology to ancient viral infection. One type of endogenous retrovirus has been shown to be intimately involved in forming the human placenta, leading microbiologists to conclude that some viruses are an essential factor in evolution and development. Other retroviruses may be involved in diseases such as prostate cancer and chronic fatigue syndrome, while strong evidence links certain viruses to human obesity. Several studies with animals revealed that chickens and mice infected with a human adenovirus called Ad-36 had larger fat deposits and were heavier than uninfected animals.

Practice SECTION 6.4

14. Write a narrative that describes the stages in the multiplication of an enveloped animal virus.

15. Describe some ways animal viruses penetrate the host cell. What is uncoating?

16. Summarize the two major ways in which animal viruses leave their host cells.

17. What is meant by the term *virion?*

18. Describe several cytopathic effects of viruses. What causes the changed appearance of the host cell, and how might it be used to diagnose viral infections?

19. Explain what it means for a virus to become persistent or latent and how these events are important.

20. Briefly describe the effects of an oncogenic virus.

6.5 The Multiplication Cycle in Bacteriophages

 Learn

17. Describe the stages in the multiplication cycle of bacteriophages.

18. Explain what is meant by *lysogeny, prophage, lysogenic induction,* and *lysogenic conversion.*

19. Compare the major stages in multiplication of animal viruses and bacteriophages.

For the sake of comparison, we now turn to multiplication in bacterial viruses—the **bacteriophages.** When Frederick Twort and Felix d'Herelle discovered these viruses in 1915, they first thought that the bacterial host cells were being eaten by some unseen parasite, which they called a bacteriophage.

So far as is known, all bacteria are parasitized by various specific viruses. Most bacteriophages (often shortened to *phage*) contain double-stranded DNA, though single-stranded DNA and RNA types exist as well. Bacteriophages are of great interest to medical microbiologists because they can make the bacteria they infect more virulent for humans.

Probably the most widely studied bacteriophages are those of the intestinal bacterium *Escherichia coli*—especially the T-even **phages** and the lambda phages. They are complex in structure, with an icosahedral capsid head containing DNA, a central tube (surrounded by a sheath), collar, base plate, tail pins, and fibers (see figure 6.9*b*).

Bacteriophages go through stages similar to those of the animal viruses described earlier **(process figure 6.16).** First, they adsorb to host bacteria using specific receptors on the bacterial surface. Although the entire phage cannot enter the host cell, the nucleic acid is injected through a rigid tube the phage inserts through the bacterial membrane and wall **(figure 6.17).** The empty capsid remains attached to the cell surface. Entry of the nucleic acid stops host cell DNA replication and protein synthesis, and it soon prepares the cell machinery for viral replication and synthesis of viral proteins. As the host cell produces new phage parts, the parts spontaneously assemble into bacteriophages.

An average-size *Escherichia coli* cell can contain up to 200 new phage units at the end of this period. Eventually, the host cell becomes so packed with viruses that it undergoes **lysis** and splits open, thereby releasing the mature virions **(figure 6.18).** This process is hastened by viral enzymes produced late in the infection cycle that weaken the cell envelope. Upon release, the virulent phages can spread to other susceptible bacterial cells and begin a new cycle of infection.

Lysogeny: The Silent Virus Infection

The lethal effects of a virulent phage on the host cell present a dramatic view of virus–host interaction. However, not all bacteriophages go immediately into a lytic cycle. Depending upon the conditions in the bacterial host, some special DNA viruses, called **temperate*** **phages,** undergo adsorption and penetration into the bacterial host but are not replicated or released immediately. Instead, the viral DNA enters an inactive **prophage*** state, during which it is usually inserted into the bacterial chromosome. This viral DNA will be retained by the bacterial cell and copied during its normal cell division so that the cell's progeny will also have the phage DNA. This condition, in which the host chromosome carries bacteriophage DNA, is termed **lysogeny.*** Because viral particles are not produced, the bacterial cells carrying temperate phages do not lyse and they appear entirely normal. Later, in a process called **induction,** the prophage in a lysogenic cell will be activated and progress directly into viral replication and the lytic cycle. The lysogenic phase is depicted in the green section of process figure 6.16. Lysogeny is a less deadly form of infection than the full lytic cycle and is thought to be an advancement that allows the virus to spread without killing the host.

* *temperate* (tem′-pur-ut) A reduction in intensity.
* *prophage* (pro′-fayj) L. *pro,* before, plus phage.
* *lysogeny* (ly-soj′-uhn-ee) The potential ability to produce phage.

Process Figure 6.16 Events in the multiplication cycle of lambda bacteriophages. The lytic cycle (1–7) involves full completion of viral infection through lysis and release of virions. Occasionally the virus enters a reversible state of lysogeny (left) and its DNA is incorporated into the host's genetic material.

Because of the close association between the genetic material of the virus and host, phages occasionally serve as transporters of bacterial genes from one bacterium to another and consequently can play a profound role in bacterial genetics. This phenomenon, called transduction, is one way that genes for toxin production and drug resistance are transferred between bacteria (see chapters 9 and 12).

Phages have profound effects on the infectiousness and virulence of pathogenic bacteria. Viral genomes often encode toxins,

enzymes, and other factors that can alter the course and outcome of infections. When a bacterium acquires genes from its temperate phage, it is called **lysogenic conversion** (see process figure 6.16). The phenomenon was first discovered in the 1950s in *Corynebacterium diphtheriae,* the pathogen that causes diphtheria. The diphtheria toxin responsible for the severe nature of the disease is a bacteriophage product. *C. diphtheriae* cells without the phage are less pathogenic. Other bacteria that are made virulent by their

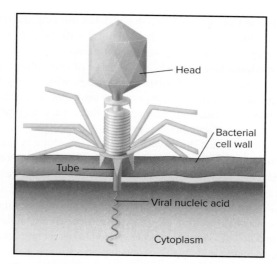

Figure 6.17 Penetration of a bacterial cell by a bacteriophage.
After adsorption, the phage plate becomes embedded in the cell wall, and the sheath contracts, pushing the tube through the cell wall and membrane and releasing the nucleic acid into the interior of the cell.

Figure 6.18 A weakened bacterial cell, crowded with viruses.
The cell has ruptured and released numerous virions that can then attack nearby susceptible host cells. Note the empty heads of "spent" phages lined up around the ruptured wall.
Lee D. Simon/Science Source

prophages are *Vibrio cholerae,* the agent of cholera, and *Clostridium botulinum,* the cause of botulism.

The cycles of bacterial and animal viruses illustrate different patterns of viral multiplication, which are summarized in **table 6.4.**

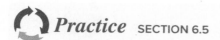 *Practice* SECTION 6.5

21. In simple terms, what does the viral nucleic acid do once it gets into the cell?

22. What processes are involved in bacteriophage assembly?

23. What is a prophage or temperate phage? What is lysogeny?

24. Compare and contrast the main phases in the lytic multiplication cycle in bacteriophages and animal viruses.

25. Why is penetration so different between the two groups?

TABLE 6.4	Comparison of Bacteriophage and Animal Viral Multiplication	
	Bacteriophage	**Animal Virus**
Adsorption	Precise attachment of special tail fibers to cell wall	Attachment of capsid or envelope to cell surface receptors
Penetration	Injection of nucleic acid through cell wall; no uncoating of nucleic acid	Whole virus is engulfed and uncoated, or virus surface fuses with cell membrane; nucleic acid is released
Synthesis and Assembly	Occurs in cytoplasm (no nucleus present)	Occurs in cytoplasm and nucleus
	Cessation of host synthesis	Cessation of host synthesis
	Viral DNA or RNA replicated	Viral DNA or RNA replicated
	Viral components synthesized	Viral components synthesized
Viral Persistence	Lysogeny	Latency, chronic infection, cancer
Release from Host Cell	Cell lyses after being weakened by viral enzymes	Some cells lyse; enveloped viruses bud off host cell membrane.
Cell Destruction	Sudden by lysis	Sudden (lysis) or slow (budding)

6.6 Techniques in Cultivating and Identifying Animal Viruses

 Learn

20. Describe the general purposes of cultivating viruses.

21. Compare the methods and uses of cell culture, bird embryos, and live animals in growing viruses.

Since culturing viruses requires a living host, early investigators had trouble propagating adequate quantities of the specific viruses they wished to study. Virtually all of the initial attempts at cultivation had to be performed in an organism that was the usual host for the virus. But this method had its limitations. How could researchers have ever traced the stages of viral multiplication if they had been restricted to the natural host, especially in the case of human viruses? Fortunately, systems of cultivation with broader applications were developed, including **in vitro*** cell (or tissue) culture methods and **in vivo*** inoculation of laboratory-bred animals and embryonic bird tissues. Such use of substitute

* *in vitro* (in vee′-troh) L. *vitros,* glass. Experiments performed in test tubes or other artificial environments.
* *in vivo* (in vee′-voh) L. *vivos,* life. Experiments performed in a living body.

host systems permits greater control, uniformity, and wide-scale harvesting of viruses.

The primary purposes of viral cultivation are (1) to isolate and identify viruses in clinical specimens; (2) to prepare viruses for vaccines; and (3) to do detailed research on viral structure, multiplication cycles, genetics, and effects on host cells.

Using Cell (Tissue) Culture Techniques

The most important early discovery that led to easier cultivation of viruses in the laboratory was the development of a simple and effective way to grow populations of isolated animal cells in culture. These types of in vitro cultivation systems are termed **cell culture** or tissue culture. This method makes it possible to propagate most viruses. Much of the virologist's work involves developing and maintaining these cultures. Animal cell cultures are grown in sterile chambers with special media that contain the correct nutrients required by animal cells to survive. The cultured cells grow in the form of a *monolayer,* a single, confluent sheet of cells that supports viral multiplication and permits close inspection of the culture for signs of infection **(figure 6.19).**

Cultures of animal cells usually exist in the primary or continuous form. *Primary cell cultures* are prepared by placing freshly isolated animal tissue in a growth medium. Embryonic, fetal, adult, and even cancerous tissues have served as sources of primary cultures. A primary culture retains several characteristics of the original tissue from which it was derived, but this original line generally has a limited existence. Eventually it will die out or mutate into a line of cells that can grow by continuous subculture in fresh nutrient medium. One very clear advantage of cell culture is that a specific cell line can be available for viruses with a very narrow host range. Strictly human viruses can be propagated in one of several primary or continuous human cell lines, such as embryonic kidney cells, fibroblasts, bone marrow, or heart cells.

One way to detect the growth of a virus in culture is to observe degeneration and lysis of infected cells in a monolayer of a cell culture **(figure 6.19a).** The areas where virus-infected cells have been destroyed show up as clear, well-defined patches in the cell sheet called **plaques* (figure 6.19c).** Plaques are essentially the macroscopic manifestation of cytopathic effects (CPEs), discussed in section 6.4. This same technique is used to detect and count bacteriophages, because they also produce plaques when grown in soft agar cultures of their host cells. A plaque develops when the viruses released by an infected host cell radiate out to adjacent host cells. As new cells become infected, they die and release more viruses, and so on. As this process continues, the infection spreads gradually and symmetrically from the original point of infection, causing the macroscopic appearance of round, clear spaces that correspond to areas of lysed cells.

* *plaque* (plak) Fr. *placke,* patch or spot.

(a)

(b)

100 μm

(c)

100 μm

Figure 6.19 Microscopic views of normal and infected cell cultures. (a) Cell culture plate infected with herpes simplex virus. Clear, round spaces are regions of infection (plaques) where the host cells have been destroyed by viruses. **(b)** Close-up of a normal, uninfected region of cultured cells. **(c)** Close-up of plaques, which consist of open spaces where cells have been disrupted by viral infection.
(a): Courtesy of Marylou Gibson, Ph.D., VIRAPUR; (b and c): *Source:* CDC

Using Bird Embryos

An embryo is an early developmental stage of animals marked by rapid differentiation of cells. Birds undergo their embryonic period within the closed protective case of an egg, which makes an incubating bird egg a nearly perfect system for viral propagation. It

(a)

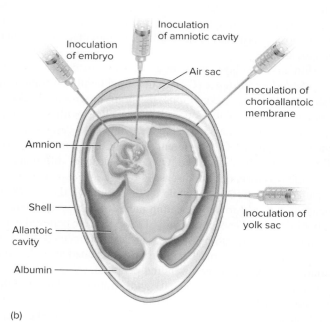

Inoculation of embryo

Inoculation of amniotic cavity

Air sac

Inoculation of chorioallantoic membrane

Amnion

Shell

Inoculation of yolk sac

Allantoic cavity

Albumin

(b)

Figure 6.20 **Cultivating animal viruses in a developing bird embryo. (a)** A technician inoculates fertilized chicken eggs with influenza virus. **(b)** The shell is perforated using sterile techniques, and a virus preparation is injected into a site selected to grow the viruses. Targets include the allantoic cavity, a sac for embryonic waste removal; the amniotic cavity that cushions and protects the embryo; the chorioallantoic membrane, for embryonic gas exchange; the yolk sac, for the nourishment of the embryo; and the embryo itself.
(a): *Source:* Greg Knobloch/CDC

is an intact and self-supporting unit, complete with its own sterile environment and nourishment. Furthermore, it furnishes several embryonic tissues that readily support viral multiplication. Every year, hundreds of millions of chicken embryos are inoculated to prepare influenza vaccines.

Chicken, duck, and turkey eggs are the most common choices for inoculation. The egg must be injected through the shell, necessitating rigorous sterile techniques to prevent contamination by bacteria and fungi from the air and the outer surface of the shell. The exact tissue inoculated is guided by the type of virus being cultivated and the goals of the experiment **(figure 6.20).**

Viruses multiplying in embryos may or may not cause effects visible to the naked eye. The signs of viral growth include death of the embryo, defects in embryonic development, and localized areas of damage in the membranes, resulting in discrete, opaque spots called pocks (a variant of *pox*). Embryonic fluids and tissues can be prepared for direct examination with an electron microscope. Certain viruses can also be detected by their ability to agglutinate red blood cells (form big clumps) or by their reaction with an antibody of known specificity that will affix to its corresponding virus, if it is present.

Using Live Animal Inoculation

Specially bred strains of white mice, rats, hamsters, guinea pigs, and rabbits are the usual choices for animal cultivation of viruses. Invertebrates or nonhuman primates are occasionally used as well. Because viruses can exhibit host specificity, certain animals can propagate a given virus more readily than others. Depending on the particular experiment, tests can be performed on adult, juvenile, or newborn animals. The animal is exposed to the virus by injection of a viral preparation or specimen into the brain, blood, muscle, body cavity, skin, or footpads.

A very unusual method of cultivating viruses that also became a source of controversy happened when scientists at the State University of New York were able to artificially create a virus that is virtually identical to natural poliovirus in a test tube without live cells. They used DNA nucleotides to synthesize the viral genome according to the published poliovirus sequence. They then added an enzyme that would transcribe the DNA sequence into the RNA genome characteristic of poliovirus. They ended up with viruses that mimicked the structure, infectivity, and replication cycle of the poliovirus.

6.7 Viral Infection, Detection, and Treatment

 Learn

22. Discuss the medical impact and importance of viruses.

23. Explain how animal viral infections are treated and detected.

The number of viral infections worldwide is nearly impossible to measure accurately. Certainly viruses are the most common cause of acute infections that do not result in hospitalization, especially when

one considers widespread diseases such as colds, measles, chicken-pox, influenza, herpes, and warts. If one also takes into account prominent viral infections found only in certain regions of the world (dengue fever, Rift Valley fever, and yellow fever), the total could easily exceed several billion cases each year. Although most viral infections do not result in death, some, such as rabies, HIV, and Ebola, have very high mortality rates, and others (polio, hepatitis) can lead to long-term debility. Continuing research is focused on the connection of viruses to chronic afflictions of unknown cause, such as type 1 diabetes, multiple sclerosis, and various cancers.

Because some viral diseases can be life threatening, it is essential to have a correct diagnosis as soon as possible. Obtaining the overall clinical picture of the disease (specific signs) is often the first step in diagnosis. This may be followed by identification of the virus in clinical specimens by means of rapid tests that detect the virus or signs of cytopathic changes in cells or tissues (see figure 6.15). Immunofluorescence techniques or direct examination with an electron microscope are often used for this. Samples can also be screened for the presence of indicator molecules (antigens) from the virus itself. A standard procedure for many viruses is the polymerase chain reaction (PCR), which can detect and amplify minute amounts of viral nucleic acid in a sample. In certain infections, definitive diagnosis requires cultivation of the virus using cell culture, embryos, or animals, but this method can be time-consuming and slow to give results. Screening tests can detect specific antibodies that indicate signs of virus infection in a patient's blood. This is the main test for HIV infection (see figure 17.16). Additional details of viral diagnosis are provided in chapter 17.

The nature of viruses has at times been a major impediment to effective therapy. Because viruses are not bacteria, antibiotics aimed at bacterial infections do not work for viruses. Although more antiviral drugs are being developed, most of them block virus replication by targeting the function of host cells. This can cause severe side effects. Antiviral drugs are designed to target one of the steps in the viral life cycle you learned about earlier in this chapter. Azidothymidine (AZT), a drug used to treat HIV, targets the nucleic acid synthesis stage. A different class of HIV drugs, the protease inhibitors, disrupts the final assembly phase of the viral life cycle. Another compound that shows some potential for treating and preventing viral infections is a naturally occurring human cell product called *interferon* (see chapters 12 and 14). Vaccines that stimulate immunity are an extremely valuable tool but are available for only a limited number of viral diseases (see chapter 15).

↻ *Practice* SECTIONS 6.6–6.7

26. Describe the three main techniques for cultivating viruses.
27. What are the advantages of using cell culture, and what are the disadvantages?
28. What are cell lines and monolayers, and how are plaques formed?
29. What are the primary problems in treating viral infections with drugs?

6.8 Prions and Other Nonviral Infectious Particles

 Learn

24. Describe the properties of nonviral infectious particles.
25. Discuss the importance of prions and viroids and the diseases they cause.

Prions are a group of noncellular infectious agents that are not viruses and really belong in a category all by themselves. The term *prion* is derived from the words **pr**oteinaceous **in**fectious particle to suggest its primary structure: a naked protein molecule. They are the only biologically active agent that lacks any sort of nucleic acid (DNA or RNA) and were unknown until the early 1980s.

The diseases associated with prions are known as **transmissible spongiform encephalopathies (TSEs).** This description recognizes that the diseases are spread from host to host by direct contact, contaminated food, or other means. It also refers to the effects of the agent on nervous tissue, which develops a spongelike appearance due to loss of nerve and glial cells (see figure 25.23*b*). Another pathological effect observed in these diseases is the buildup of tiny protein fibrils in the brain tissue **(process figures 6.21*a* and 6.21*b*).** Several forms of prion diseases are known in mammals, including scrapie in sheep; bovine spongiform encephalopathy (mad cow disease) in cattle; and wasting disease in elk, deer, and mink. These diseases have a long latent period (usually several years) before the first symptoms of brain degeneration appear. The animals lose coordination, have difficulty moving, and eventually collapse and die.

Humans are host to similar chronic diseases, including *Creutzfeldt-Jakob disease (CJD),* kuru, fatal familial insomnia, and others. In all of these conditions, the brain progressively deteriorates and the patient loses coordination, along with sensory and cognitive abilities. There is no treatment, and most cases so far have been fatal. In the 1990s, a different form of CJD—known as variant CJD or **vCJD**—was identified. One of the primary differences between the two forms of the disease is that the median age of death for patients with CJD is 68, while for those with vCJD, it is 28. The disease was traced to people eating meat from cows infected with the bovine form of encephalopathy. The cows were believed to have become infected by eating the nervous tissue of infected sheep. The sheep tissue, known as offal, was ground and added to cattle feed as a source of protein. Several hundred people developed the disease (nearly all in Western Europe and Saudi Arabia), and most of them have since died. This was the first indicator that prions of animals could cause infections in humans. It sparked a crisis in the beef industry and strict controls on imported beef. Although only three cases of human disease have occurred in the United States, infected cattle have been reported.

Researchers discovered that normal prion proteins (abbreviated **PrP**C) are commonly found on the membrane of cells. When the infectious form of the prion (abbreviated **PrP**Sc, with the Sc referring to scrapies) encounters a normal PrPC protein, it can induce spontaneous abnormal folding in the normal protein,

(a)

(b)

Prion protein fibers

② Upon contact with normal proteins, the prions are able to shift the configuration of the normal proteins, converting them to prions.

① Prion proteins

① Prion proteins infect a nerve cell.

③ When this process creates large numbers of prions, they bind tightly together and form elongate chains.

Normal proteins

④ As the chains build up, they form fibers within the cell, which interfere with the cell's function and destroy it.

 Process Figure 6.21 The appearance and mechanism of prion-based diseases. (a) A magnified view of nerve cells infected with prion protein. Red areas indicate places in the cytoplasm where the prion fibers have deposited. **(b)** A diagram of a nerve cell to outline the stages in the conversion of normal prions (PrPC) into diseased prions (PrPSc) and the formation of prion fibers.
(a): *Source:* National Institute of Allergy and Infectious Diseases

converting it to PrPSc. Ultimately, the buildup of these converted proteins damages and kills the cell (process figure 6.21*b*). Another serious issue with prions is their extreme resistance. They are not destroyed by disinfectants, radiation, or the usual sterilization techniques. Even treatments with extreme high temperatures and concentrated chemicals are not always reliable methods to eliminate them. Additional information on prion diseases can be found in chapter 25.

✚ CLINIC CASE

More Than Just the Blues The patient, a man in his forties, first presented to a hospital in Texas at the urging of his family, several months after he began to show symptoms of depression and anxiety. Initially mild, his symptoms soon progressed to include delusions, hallucinations, isolation, secrecy, aggression, and poor judgment. Five months after his initial presentation, he began to experience intermittent numbness and paralysis of his left arm and face. An MRI (magnetic resonance imaging) scan showed changes to his brain tissue, but his illness remained a mystery.

With no diagnosis in sight, physicians followed a multi-pronged approach, simultaneously investigating infectious and autoimmune encephalitides (swelling of tissues lining the brain and spinal cord), cancer, heavy metal intoxication, vitamin deficiency, and rheumatologic and endocrine disorders. Despite treatment of the patient's symptoms, his condition continued to worsen; he was hospitalized five times over a two-month period during the thirteenth and fourteenth month of illness.

Cerebrospinal fluid (CSF) was examined for the presence of viruses and bacteria, and a sample was sent to the National Prion Disease Pathology Surveillance Center for examination. Based on protein levels in the CSF, along with MRI results and worsening physical and behavioral symptoms, the patient was diagnosed with probable vCJD (variant Creutzfeldt-Jakob disease). Shortly thereafter, with the goals of care restricted to comfort measures only, the patient died, 18 months after his initial diagnosis. A brain autopsy revealed large spongiform changes throughout the patient's brain consistent with vCJD and immunostaining that detected the presence of prions in the tissue.

What information from a patient history would be helpful in the diagnosis of this case?

Other fascinating viruslike agents in human disease are defective forms called satellite viruses that depend on other viruses for replication. Two remarkable examples are the adeno-associated virus (AAV), which can replicate only in cells infected with adenovirus, and the delta agent, a naked strand of RNA that is expressed only in the presence of the hepatitis B virus and can worsen the severity of liver damage.

Plants are also parasitized by viruslike agents called **viroids** that differ from ordinary viruses by being very small (about one-tenth the size of an average virus) and being composed of only naked strands of RNA, lacking a capsid or any other type of coating. The existence of these unusual agents is one bit of supportive evidence that viruses may have evolved from naked bits of nucleic acid. Viroids are significant pathogens in several economically important plants, including tomatoes, potatoes, cucumbers, citrus trees, and chrysanthemums.

 Practice SECTION 6.8

30. What is the principal effect of the prion agent of Creutzfeldt-Jakob disease?

31. Explain how prions and viroids are different from viruses.

 CASE STUDY **Part 2**

Three days after receiving the phage therapy, Tom Patterson awakened from his coma. Soon thereafter, he was weaned from the respirator that had been breathing for him and the drugs that had kept his blood pressure high enough to maintain circulation.

The next few months were not easy, and Patterson's condition remained precarious. He suffered several episodes of sepsis, a life-threatening condition caused by overwhelming infection, and lost over 100 pounds. Disturbingly, although not unexpectedly, the bacterium eventually developed resistance to the phages, what Schooley would characterize as "the recurring Darwinian dance" of evolution. The treating physicians responded by continually experimenting with new phage strains—including some that had been isolated from sewage—and antibiotics. In early May, Patterson's antibiotics were discontinued, and he was discharged home on August 12, 2016.

Despite the trials of a massive bacterial infection, coma, 9-month hospital stay, and intense physical rehabilitation, Patterson described the experience as miraculous: "The phage therapy has really been a miracle for me, and for what it might mean that millions of people who may be cured from multidrug-resistant infections in the future. It's been sort of a privilege."

Schooley said Patterson was lucky. From his wife, to colleagues, and even his work environment, he was surrounded by people who were experts in the field and researchers willing to try unusual treatments in the hope of saving a tremendously ill person.

Since this first trial, UC San Diego has successfully treated four additional patients using phage therapy (a fifth patient died, as the bacterial infection had progressed too far prior to phage therapy beginning). The school has also launched the Center for Innovative Phage Applications and Therapeutics (IPATH), the first organization of its kind to study the use of phage in the treatment of bacterial infections. Strathdee and Schooley, along with a third professor from UCSD are co-directors of the institute. Initial research will focus on patients with multidrug-resistant chronic infections associated with cystic fibrosis, organ transplantation, and implantable hardware, such as pacemakers or joint replacements.

Patterson, now back at work, is grateful for the second chance phage therapy gave him: "I am still weaker than I was before, but I feel I have a new life entirely, and it's wonderful to have that gift."

■ While few examples of phage therapy in humans exist, several products have been approved that use phage to control bacteria on butchered meat and raw vegetables. Speculate how these products work and provide some advantages they may offer compared to other means of controlling bacteria.

Chapter Summary with Key Terms

6.1 Overview of Viruses
 A. Viruses, being much smaller than bacteria, fungi, and protozoa, had to be indirectly studied until the 20th century, when they were finally seen with an electron microscope.
 B. Most scientists feel that viruses are not living organisms, as they clearly do not fulfill all of the requirements of life. They are obligate intracellular and genetic parasites.

6.2 The General Structure of Viruses
 A. Viruses are infectious particles and not cells; lack organelles and locomotion of any kind; are large, complex molecules; and can be crystalline in form. A virus particle is composed of a **nucleic acid** core (DNA or RNA, not both) surrounded by a geometric protein shell, or **capsid;** the combination is called a **nucleocapsid;** a capsid is **helical** or **icosahedral** in configuration; many are covered by a membranous **envelope** containing viral protein **spikes.** Complex viruses have additional external and internal structures.
 B. *Shapes/Sizes:* Icosahedral, helical, spherical, and cylindrical shaped. Nearly all viruses are tiny (20 to 450 nm) in

comparison to cells, although a few exceptional viruses approach the size of a small bacterial cell.

 C. *Nutritional and Other Requirements:* Lack enzymes for processing food or generating energy; are tied entirely to the host cell for all needs (obligate intracellular parasites).

 D. Viruses are known to parasitize all types of cells, including bacteria, protists, fungi, animals, and plants. Each viral type is limited in its host range to a single species or group, mostly due to specificity of adsorption of virus to specific host receptors.

6.3 How Viruses Are Classified and Named

 A. The two major types of viruses are **DNA** and **RNA viruses**. These are further subdivided into families, depending on shape and size of capsid, presence or absence of an envelope, whether double- or single-stranded nucleic acid, antigenic similarities, and host cell.

 B. Viruses are classified into orders, families, and genera. These groupings are based on virus structure, chemical composition, and genetic makeup.

6.4 Modes of Viral Multiplication

 A. *Multiplication Cycle: Animal Cells*

 B. The life cycle steps of an animal virus are **adsorption, penetration, synthesis** and **assembly,** and **release** from the host cell. A fully infective virus particle is a **virion.**

 C. Some animal viruses cause chronic and **persistent infections.**

 D. Viruses that alter host genetic material may cause *oncogenic* effects.

6.5 The Multiplication Cycle in Bacteriophages

 A. **Bacteriophages** are viruses that attack bacteria. They penetrate by injecting their nucleic acid and are released as virulent phages upon **lysis** of the cell.

 B. Some viruses go into a **latent**, or **lysogenic,** phase in which they integrate into the DNA of the host cell and later may be active and produce a lytic infection.

6.6 Techniques in Cultivating and Identifying Animal Viruses

 A. The need for an intracellular habitat makes it necessary to grow viruses in living cells, either in **cell culture** (cultures of live, isolated host cells), in bird embryos, or in the intact host animal.

 B. *Identification:* Viruses are identified by means of **cytopathic effects** (CPE) in host cells, direct examination of viruses or their components in samples, genetic analysis to detect virus nucleic acid, and growing viruses in culture.

6.7 Viral Infection, Detection, and Treatment

 A. *Medical:* Viruses attach to specific target hosts or cells. They cause a variety of infectious diseases, ranging from mild respiratory illnesses (common cold) to destructive and potentially fatal conditions (rabies, AIDS). Some viruses can cause birth defects and cancer in humans and other animals.

 B. *Research:* Viruses have become an invaluable tool for studying basic genetic principles. Current research is focused on the connection of viruses to afflictions of unknown causes, such as type I diabetes and multiple sclerosis.

 C. Viral infections are detected by direct examination of specimens, genetic tests, testing patients' blood, and characteristic symptoms. Some viral infections can be treated with drugs that block viral replication.

6.8 Prions and Other Nonviral Infectious Particles

 A. Spongiform encephalopathies are chronic, persistent neurological diseases caused by **prions.**

 B. Prions are infectious agents composed of a protein that can alter the structure of nerve cells.

 C. Examples of neurological diseases include "mad cow disease" and Creutzfeldt-Jakob disease.

 D. Other noncellular infectious agents include satellite viruses and **viroids.**

 ## Assess Your Knowledge

Level I. These questions require a working knowledge of the concepts in the chapter and the ability to recall and understand the information you have studied.

Developing a Concept Inventory

Select the correct answer from the answers provided. For questions with blanks, choose the combination of answers that most accurately completes the statement.

1. A virus is a tiny, infectious
 a. cell
 b. living thing
 c. particle
 d. nucleic acid

2. Viruses are known to infect
 a. plants
 b. bacteria
 c. fungi
 d. all organisms

3. The capsid is composed of protein subunits called
 a. spikes
 b. protomers
 c. virions
 d. capsomers

4. The envelope of an animal virus is derived from the _____ of its host cell.
 a. cell wall
 b. membrane
 c. glycocalyx
 d. receptors

5. The nucleic acid of a virus is
 a. DNA only
 b. RNA only
 c. both DNA and RNA
 d. either DNA or RNA

6. The general steps in a viral multiplication cycle are
 a. adsorption, penetration, synthesis, assembly, and release
 b. endocytosis, replication, assembly, and budding
 c. adsorption, duplication, assembly, and lysis
 d. endocytosis, penetration, replication, maturation, and exocytosis

7. A prophage is a/an _____ stage in the cycle of _____.
 a. latent, bacterial viruses c. early, poxviruses
 b. infective, RNA viruses d. late, enveloped viruses

8. The nucleic acid of animal viruses enters the host cell through
 a. injection c. endocytosis
 b. fusion d. b and c

9. In general, RNA viruses multiply in the cell _____, and DNA viruses multiply in the cell _____.
 a. nucleus, cytoplasm c. vesicles, ribosomes
 b. cytoplasm, nucleus d. endoplasmic reticulum, nucleolus

10. Enveloped viruses carry surface receptors called
 a. buds c. fibers
 b. spikes d. sheaths

11. Viruses that persist in the cell and cause recurrent disease are considered
 a. oncogenic c. latent
 b. cytopathic d. resistant

12. Viruses cannot be cultivated in
 a. cell culture c. live mammals
 b. bird embryos d. blood agar

13. Clear patches in cell cultures that indicate sites of virus infection are called
 a. plaques c. colonies
 b. pocks d. prions

14. Which of these is *not* a general pattern of virus morphology?
 a. enveloped, helical c. enveloped, icosahedral
 b. naked, icosahedral d. complex, helical

15. Which of these is true of prions?
 a. They are small RNA viruses.
 b. They replicate in the nucleus.
 c. They lack protein.
 d. They cause death of brain cells.

Case Study Analysis

1. Phages infect
 a. bacterial cells
 b. viruses
 c. human cells
 d. any type of cell

2. What most likely happened after the patient was cured of his illness by phage therapy?
 a. He was prescribed antiviral medication to inactivate the phage.
 b. Nothing; the phage disappeared from his body when there were no longer any potential host cells.
 c. The phage infected the patient's cells.
 d. He was prescribed antibiotics to prevent further phage replication.

3. Explain the importance of selecting the proper virus for phage therapy.

On the Test

These questions will help to prepare you to successfully answer similar questions you'll see on the TEAS (Test of Essential Academic Skills) and NCLEX (National Council Licensure Examination).

1. Which of the following is a component of a virus?
 a. cell wall
 b. ribosome
 c. capsid
 d. nucleus

2. Which is the earliest step in the replication cycle of hepatitis B virus?
 a. release
 b. assembly
 c. adsorption
 d. penetration

Writing Challenge

For each question, compose a one- or two-paragraph answer that includes the factual information needed to completely address the question. Practice questions can also be used for writing-challenge exercises.

1. a. What characteristics of viruses could be used to describe them as life forms?
 b. What makes them more similar to lifeless molecules?

2. HIV attacks only specific types of human cells, such as certain white blood cells and nerve cells. Can you explain why a virus can enter some types of human cells but not others?

3. a. Since viruses lack metabolic enzymes, how can they synthesize necessary components?
 b. Name some enzymes that viruses may have for invading and completing their cycles.

4. a. What dictates the host range of animal viruses?
 b. How is the influenza virus different in its host range from most other viruses?

Concept Mapping

On Connect you can find an Introduction to Concept Mapping that provides guidance for working with concept maps, along with concept-mapping activities for this chapter.

 ## Application, Analysis, Evaluation, and Synthesis

Level II. These problems go beyond just restating facts and require higher levels of understanding and an ability to interpret, problem solve, transfer knowledge to new situations, create models, and predict outcomes.

Critical Thinking

Critical thinking is the ability to reason and solve problems using facts and concepts. These questions can be approached from a number of angles and, in most cases, they do not have a single correct answer.

1. Comment on the possible origin of viruses. Is it not curious that the human cell welcomes a virus in and hospitably removes its coat as if it were an old acquaintance?

2. a. If viruses that normally form envelopes were prevented from budding, would they still be infectious? Why or why not?
 b. If only the RNA of an influenza virus were injected into a cell by itself, could it cause a lytic infection?

3. The end result of most viral infections is death of the host cell.
 a. If this is the case, how can we account for such differences in the damage that viruses do? (Compare the effects of the cold virus with those of the rabies virus.)
 b. Describe the adaptations of viruses that do not immediately kill the host cell and explain what their functions may be.

4. a. Given that DNA viruses can be carried in the DNA of the host cell's chromosomes, comment on what this phenomenon means in terms of inheritance in the offspring.

 b. Discuss the connection between viruses and cancers, giving possible mechanisms for viruses that cause cancer.

5. a. If you were involved in developing an antiviral drug, what would be some important considerations? (Can a drug "kill" a virus?)
 b. How could multiplication be blocked?

6. Is there such a thing as a "good virus"? Explain why or why not. Consider both bacteriophages and viruses of eukaryotic organisms.

7. Discuss some advantages and disadvantages of bacteriophage therapy in treating bacterial infections.

8. a. Consult table 6.2, right-hand column, to determine which viral diseases you have had and which ones you have been vaccinated against.
 b. Which viruses would more likely be possible oncoviruses? Why?

9. Of the following, list those that are viral infections: cholera, rabies, plague, cold sores, whooping cough, tetanus, genital warts, gonorrhea, mumps, Rocky Mountain spotted fever, syphilis, rubella, rat bite fever.

Visual Assessment

1. Explain what is happening in this photograph, and why the egg is necessary.

Source: Greg Knobloch/CDC

2. Identify the indicated parts of **figure 6.4b.** Which structure was formally part of a host cell?

Microbial Nutrition, Ecology, and Growth

(Vibrio vulnificus bacteria): Source: Janice Haney Carr/CDC; (SEM of E. coli): Source: Eric Erbe/Chris Pooley, USDA-ARS; (Microscopic red snow): Image courtesy of Nozomu Takeuchi; (Root nodules): Source: Scott Bauer/USDA

A 31-year-old Texas man was examined by doctors at Parkland Memorial Hospital in Dallas after complaining of severe pain in both legs and feet, along with **fever,** chills, and **redness** surrounding a recent tattoo on his left calf. Based on the severity of his symptoms, he was admitted to the hospital, where, over the next few hours, the area surrounding the tattoo became increasingly **swollen** and **discolored.** The patient's breathing soon became **rapid and shallow,** while his heartrate increased to compensate for his inefficient respiration. His blood pressure dropped dramatically and remained low despite the administration of intravenous fluids. His **kidneys** began to fail. The patient's collection of signs and symptoms indicated **septic shock,** an often fatal complication of bacterial infection. He was placed on a ventilator and given antibiotics to fight the infection.

Upon admission to the hospital, the patient related that he had gotten the tattoo just over a week ago and had gone swimming in the ocean 5 days later, while it was still healing. He started to feel ill the following morning. He had previously been diagnosed with **chronic liver disease,** due to excessive alcohol consumption.

The combination of the recent tattoo, the ocean visit, and the patient's liver disease pointed towards infection with *Vibrio vulnificus,* a small, gram-negative bacterium occasionally referred to as a comma bacterium because of its curved appearance. People are often more familiar with *Vibrio cholera,* the agent of diarrhea, but in the United States, *V. vulnificus* is far more prevalent. Infection occurs either via consumption of undercooked shellfish or through contact with open wounds. Most cases of **vibriosis** are mild and include watery diarrhea accompanied by abdominal cramping, nausea, vomiting, fever, and chills. Persons who are **immunosuppressed,** or who have underlying conditions, including cancer, diabetes, HIV, or liver disease, are at risk for more severe infection.

The patient initially showed progress and was removed from the ventilator after 18 days. Unfortunately, he soon deteriorated and, despite the best efforts of doctors, died 2 months after his initial admission to the hospital. In this case, the patient's recent tattoo served as a near-perfect **portal of entry** for the bacterium. Tattoo aftercare instructions routinely include warnings against bathing or swimming until the tattoo has completely healed. Furthermore, the patient's chronic liver disease put him at risk for serious infection, an unfortunate confluence of events.

- Given the facts of this case, what environmental factor is probably necessary for Vibrio to grow adequately?

- Even though millions of people swim in the ocean with open wounds, relatively few contract serious infections. Why do you think this is?

To continue the Case Study, go to Case Study Part 2 at the end of the chapter.

(infected tattoos): Dr. Nicholas Hendren

7.1 Microbial Nutrition

Learn

1. Describe the major environmental factors to which microbes must adapt for survival.

2. Define *nutrition* and *nutrients* and their subcategories based on need and quantity.

3. Differentiate between organic and inorganic nutrients.

4. Discuss the origins, types, and functions of bioelements and nutrients.

There are millions of habitats on earth, of both natural and human origin. In these settings, microorganisms are exposed to a tremendous variety of conditions that affect their survival. Environmental factors with the greatest impact on microorganisms are nutrient and energy sources, temperature, gas content, water, salt, pH, radiation, and other organisms. Microbes survive in their habitats through the process of gradual adjustment of anatomy and physiology, a process called **adaptation.*** It is this adaptability that allows microbes to inhabit all parts of the biosphere. The process is also a major force behind the evolution of species, in that those species with greater adaptability will survive and pass on favorable characteristics to their offspring.

Microbial **nutrition** is a complex activity through which microbes acquire chemical compounds from the environment in order to sustain life. These compounds, called **nutrients,** are absorbed, assimilated, and subsequently used for cellular metabolism, growth, energy, and many other functions. With respect to their nutrition, microbes are not really so different from humans and other macroorganisms. Although bacteria living deep in a swamp on a diet of inorganic sulfur, or protozoa digesting wood in a termite's intestine, may seem to show radical adaptations, even these organisms require a constant influx of certain specific substances from their habitat.

In general, all living things have an absolute need for the **bioelements,** traditionally listed as carbon, hydrogen, oxygen, phosphorus, potassium, nitrogen, sulfur, calcium, iron, sodium, chlorine, magnesium, and a few other other elements.[1] Beyond these basic requirements, microbes show significant differences in the source, chemical form, and amount of the elements they use. Any substance, whether an element or compound, that an organism must get from a source outside its cells is called an **essential nutrient.** Once absorbed, these nutrients are processed and transformed into the chemicals of the cell.

Two categories of essential nutrients are **macronutrients** and **micronutrients.** Macronutrients are required in relatively large quantities and play principal roles in cell structure and metabolism. Examples of macronutrients are compounds such as sugars and amino acids that contain carbon, hydrogen, and oxygen. Micronutrients, or **trace elements,** such as manganese, zinc, and nickel, are present in much smaller amounts and are involved in enzyme function and maintenance of protein structure. What constitutes a micronutrient can vary from one microbe to another and often must be determined in the laboratory. This determination is made by deliberately omitting the substance in question from a growth medium to see if the microbe can grow in its absence.

Another way to categorize nutrients is according to their carbon content. Most **organic** nutrients are molecules that contain a basic framework of carbon and hydrogen. Natural organic molecules are nearly always the products of living things. They range from the simplest organic molecule, methane (CH_4), to large polymers (carbohydrates, lipids, proteins, and nucleic acids).

In contrast, an **inorganic** nutrient is composed of an element or elements lacking some combination of both carbon and hydrogen. The natural reservoirs of many inorganic compounds are mineral deposits in the soil, bodies of water, and the atmosphere. Examples include metals and their salts (magnesium sulfate, ferric nitrate, sodium phosphate), gases (oxygen, carbon dioxide), and water.

Chemical Analysis of Cell Contents

To gain insight into a cell's nutritional makeup, it can be useful to analyze its chemical composition. The following is a brief summary of what one would find in an *Escherichia coli* cell (**figure 7.1**), a fair representative of any cell on earth:

- Water is the greatest component, making up 70% of the cell
- Proteins make up about 15%

Figure 7.1 **Microbial nutrition.** The best way to understand the nutritional needs of a cell like *Escherichia coli* is to analyze the contents of a culture of those cells (SEM 7000×).
Source: Eric Erbe/Chris Pooley, USDA-ARS

* *adaptation* L. *adaptare,* to fit. Changes in structure and function that improve an organism's survival in a given environment.

1. See critical thinking question 1. b for a useful mnemonic device to recall the essential elements.

- Nucleic acids constitute 7% (DNA 1%, RNA 6%)
- Carbohydrates are roughly 3%
- Lipids make up 2%

Those doing the math realize that this adds up to 97%. The remaining 3% consists of countless micronutrients and minerals, from calcium to zinc. It should also be noted that all of the molecules listed above are composed of only six elements—sulfur, phosphorous, oxygen, nitrogen, carbon, and hydrogen—often remembered by the acronym SPONCH. Although a typical cell like *E. coli* contains about 5,000 different compounds, nothing happens without SPONCH.

Forms, Sources, and Functions of Essential Nutrients

The elements that comprise nutrients ultimately exist in an environmental inorganic reservoir of some type, such as carbon in atmospheric carbon dioxide. These reservoirs not only serve as a source of these elements but can be replenished by the activities of organisms. Thus, elements cycle in a pattern from an inorganic form in an environmental reservoir to an organic form in organisms. Organisms may, in turn, serve as a continuing source of that element for other organisms. Eventually the element is recycled to the inorganic form, usually by the actions of microorganisms. All in all, a tremendous variety of microorganisms are involved in processing the elements. From a broader perspective, the overall cycle of life on this planet depends upon the combined action of several interacting nutritional schemes, each performing a necessary step. In fact, as we shall see in a later chapter, the framework of microbial nutrition underlies the nutrient cycles of all life on earth.

The source of nutrients is extremely varied: Microbes such as photosynthetic bacteria obtain their nutrients entirely in inorganic form from the environment. Others require a combination of organic and inorganic nutrients. For example, parasites that invade and live on the human body derive all essential nutrients from host tissues, tissue fluids, secretions, and wastes.

Refer to **table 7.1** to see an overview of the major bioelements, compounds, their sources, and their importance to microorganisms.

Carbon-Based Nutritional Types

The element carbon is so key to the structure and metabolism of all life forms that the source of carbon defines two basic nutritional groups:

- A **heterotroph*** is an organism that must obtain its carbon in an organic form. Because most organic carbon originates from organisms, heterotrophs are nutritionally dependent on other

life forms. Among the common organic molecules that can satisfy this requirement are proteins, carbohydrates, lipids, and nucleic acids. In most cases, these nutrients provide several other elements as well. Some organic nutrients (such as **monosaccharides** and amino acids) already exist in a form that is simple enough for absorption, but many larger molecules must be digested by the cell before absorption. Not all heterotrophs can use the same organic carbon sources. Some are restricted to a few substrates, whereas others (certain *Pseudomonas* bacteria, for example) are so versatile that they can metabolize hundreds of different substrates.

- An **autotroph*** is an organism that uses inorganic CO_2 as its carbon source. Because autotrophs have the special capacity to convert CO_2 into organic compounds, they are not nutritionally dependent on other living things. We later enlarge on the topic of nutritional types based on carbon and energy sources.

Growth Factors: Essential Organic Nutrients

Many **fastidious** bacteria are not as versatile as *E. coli* and lack the genetic and metabolic mechanisms to synthesize every organic compound they need for survival. An essential nutrient such as an amino acid, nitrogenous base, or vitamin that cannot be synthesized by an organism and must be provided as a nutrient is considered a **growth factor.** For example, all cells require 20 different amino acids for proper assembly of proteins, but many cells cannot synthesize all of them. Those that must be obtained from food are called essential amino acids. A notable example of the need for growth factors occurs in *Haemophilus influenzae,* a bacterium that causes meningitis and respiratory infections in humans. It can grow only when hemin (factor X), NAD^+ (factor V), thiamine and pantothenic acid (vitamins), uracil, and cysteine are provided by another organism or a growth medium.

Practice SECTION 7.1

1. Summarize the main environmental factors that microbes encounter and their basic characteristics.
2. Differentiate between micronutrients, macronutrients, and essential nutrients.
3. List the general functions of the essential bioelements in the cell.
4. Define *growth factors* and *metallic ions* with examples, and explain their functions in cells.

* *heterotroph* (het′-uhr-oh-trohf) Gr. *hetero,* other, and *troph,* to feed.

* *autotroph* (aw′-toh-trohf) Gr. *auto,* self, and *troph,* to feed.

TABLE 7.1	Sources and Biological Functions of Essential Elements and Nutrients	
Element/Nutrient Forms Found in Nature	Sources/Reservoirs of Compounds	Significance to Cells
Carbon: CO_2 (carbon dioxide) gas, CO_3^{2-} (carbonate), Organic compounds	Air (0.036%*), Sediments/soils, Living things	CO_2 is produced by respiration and used in photosynthesis; CO_3^{2-} is found in cell walls and skeletons; organic compounds are essential to the structure and function of all organisms and viruses.
Nitrogen: N_2 gas, NO_3^- (nitrate), NO_2^- (nitrite), NH_3 (ammonium), Organic nitrogen (proteins, nucleic acids)	Air (79%*), Soil and water, Soil and water, Soil and water, Organisms	Nitrogen gas is available only to certain microbes that fix it into other inorganic nitrogen compounds—nitrates, nitrites, and ammonium—the primary sources of nitrogen for algae, plants, and the majority of bacteria; animals and protozoa require organic nitrogen; all organisms use NH_3 to synthesize amino acids and nucleic acids.
Oxygen: O_2 gas, Oxides, H_2O	Air (20%*), a major product of photosynthesis, Soil	Oxygen gas is necessary for the metabolism of nutrients by aerobes. Oxygen is a significant element in organic compounds and inorganic compounds (see water, sulfates, phosphates, nitrates, carbon dioxide in this table).
Hydrogen: H_2 gas, H_2O, H_2S (hydrogen sulfide), CH_4 (methane), Organic compounds	Water, swamps, mud, Volcanoes, vents, Swamps, Organisms	Water is the most abundant compound in cells and a solvent for metabolic reactions; H_2, H_2S, and CH_4 gases are produced and used by bacteria and archaea; H^+ ions are the basis for transfers of cellular energy and help maintain the pH of cells.
Phosphorus: PO_4^{3-} (phosphate)	Rocks, mineral deposits, Soil	Phosphate, a key component of DNA and RNA, is critical to the genetic makeup of cells and viruses; also found in ATP and NAD, where it takes part in numerous metabolic reactions; its presence in phospholipids provides stability to cell membranes.
Sulfur: S, SO_4^{2-} (sulfate), SH (sulfhydryl)	Mineral deposits, volcanic sediments, Soil	Elemental sulfur (S) is oxidized by some bacteria as an energy source; sulfur is found in vitamin B_1; sulfhydryl groups are part of certain amino acids, where they form disulfide bonds that shape and stabilize proteins.
Potassium: K^+	Mineral deposits, ocean water, soil	Plays a role in protein synthesis and membrane transport
Sodium: Na^+	Same as potassium	Major participant in membrane actions; maintains osmotic pressure in cells
Calcium: Ca^+	Oceanic sediments, rocks, and soil	A component of protozoan shells (as $CaCO_3$); stabilizes cell walls; adds resistance to bacterial endospores
Magnesium: Mg^{2+}	Geologic sediments, rocks, and soil	A central atom in the chlorophyll molecule; required for function of membranes, ribosomes, and some enzymes
Chloride: Cl^-	Ocean water, salt lakes	May function in membrane transport; required by obligate halophiles to regulate osmotic pressure
Zinc: Zn^{2+}	Rocks, soil	An enzyme cofactor; regulates eukaryotic genetics
Iron: Fe^{2+}	Rocks, soil	Essential element for the structure of respiratory proteins (cytochromes)
Micronutrients: copper, cobalt, nickel, molybdenum, manganese, iodine	Geologic sediments, soil	Required in tiny amounts to serve as cofactors in specialized enzyme systems of some microbes but not all

*As a portion of the earth's atmosphere.

7.2 Classification of Nutritional Types

 Learn

5. Describe the main categories of nutritional types among organisms.

6. Distinguish different types of autotrophs and their energy sources.

7. Distinguish different types of heterotrophs and their energy sources.

The earth's limitless habitats and microbial adaptations are matched by an elaborate menu of microbial nutritional schemes. Fortunately, most organisms show consistent trends and can be described by a few general categories (table 7.2) and a few selected terms (7.1 Making Connections).

The main determinants of a microbe's nutritional type are its sources of carbon and energy. We saw earlier that microbes can be defined according to their carbon sources as autotrophs or heterotrophs. Another system classifies them according to their energy

TABLE 7.2	Nutritional Categories of Microbes by Energy and Carbon Source				
Category	**Photoautotroph**	**Chemoautotroph**	**Chemoheterotroph (saprobe)**	**Chemoheterotroph (symbiotic microbe)**	**Photoheterotroph**
	Buccaneer/123RF *Cladophora*, a green alage	*Source:* NPS photo by Canter Thermophilic bacteria growing in a hot spring	Mark Dierker/Bear Dancer Studios *Auricularia auricula-judae*, an edible fungi growing on a rotting tree	Kateryna Kon/Shutterstock *Trichomonas vaginalis*	Johnny Madsen/Alamy Stock Photo Purple sulfur bacteria
Examples	Photosynthetic organisms: Algae, plants cyanobacteria	Some Bacteria and archaea: Methanogens and deep-sea vent bacteria	Fungi, bacteria, some protists	Parasites, commensals, mutualistic microbes	Purple and green photosynthetic bacteria
Carbon Source	CO_2	CO_2	Organic carbon	Organic carbon	Organic carbon
Energy Source	Sunlight	Simple inorganic chemicals	Metabolize the organic matter of dead organisms	Obtain organic matter from living organisms	Sunlight or organic matter

source as **phototrophs** or **chemotrophs.** Microbes that photosynthesize (acquire energy from light) are phototrophs, and those that gain energy from chemical compounds are chemotrophs. The terms for carbon and energy source are often merged into a single word for convenience (as in table 7.2). The categories described here are meant to cover only the major nutritional groups and do not include unusual exceptions.

Autotrophs and Their Energy Sources

Autotrophs derive energy from one of two possible nonliving sources: sunlight and chemical reactions involving simple chemicals.

Photoautotrophs and Photosynthesis

Photoautotrophs are photosynthetic; that is, they capture the energy of light rays and transform it into chemical energy that can be used in cell metabolism. In general, photosynthesis relies on special pigments to collect the light and uses the energy to convert CO_2 into simple organic compounds. There are two major variations in the mechanisms of photosynthesis.

Oxygenic (oxygen-producing) photosynthesis can be summed up by the equation:

$$CO_2 + H_2O \xrightarrow[\text{by chlorophyll}]{\text{Sunlight absorbed}} (CH_2O)_n + O_2$$

in which $(CH_2O)_n$ is shorthand for a carbohydrate. This type of photosynthesis occurs in plants, algae, and cyanobacteria and uses chlorophyll as the primary pigment. Carbohydrates formed by the

reaction can be used by the cell to synthesize other cell components. This topic is covered in greater depth in chapter 8. Because these organisms are the primary producers in most ecosystems, they constitute the basis of food chains by providing nutrition for heterotrophs. This type of photosynthesis is also responsible for maintaining the level of oxygen gas in the atmosphere that is so vital to many organisms.

The other form of photosynthesis is termed **anoxygenic** (no oxygen produced). It may be summarized by the equation:

$$CO_2 + H_2S \xrightarrow[\text{by bacteriochlorophyll}]{\text{Sunlight absorbed}} (CH_2O)_n + S^0 + H_2O$$

Note that this type of photosynthesis is different in several respects: (1) It uses a unique pigment, bacteriochlorophyll; (2) its hydrogen source is hydrogen sulfide gas; (3) it gives off elemental sulfur as one product; and (4) the reactions all occur in the absence of oxygen. Common groups of photosynthetic bacteria are the purple and green sulfur bacteria that live in various aquatic habitats, often in mixtures with other photosynthetic microbes (see figure 4.32).

Chemoautotrophy—A Radical Existence

Compared to common, familiar organisms, **chemoautotrophs** have adapted to the most stringent nutritional strategy on earth. All chemoautotrophs are bacteria or archaea that survive totally on inorganic substances such as minerals and gases. They require neither light nor organic nutrients in any form, and they derive energy in diverse and sometimes surprising ways. In very simple terms, they remove electrons from inorganic substrates such as hydrogen gas,

7.1 MAKING CONNECTIONS

A Guide to Terminology

Much of the vocabulary for describing microbial adaptations is based on some common root words. These are combined in various ways that assist in discussing the types of nutritional or ecological adaptations, as shown in the list below.

Modifier terms are also used to specify the nature of an organism's adaptations. **Obligate** or **strict** means being confined to a narrow niche or habitat, such as an obligate thermophile that requires high temperatures to grow. By contrast, **facultative*** means not being so restricted but adapting to a wider range of environmental conditions. A facultative halophile can grow with or without high salt concentrations. **Tolerance** is another term that can be used to describe the capacity to survive a range of conditions.

Using this guide, define *obligate halophile, facultative psychrophile,* **and** *aerotolerant anaerobe.*

* *facultative* (fak′-uhl-tay-tiv) Gr. *facult,* capability or skill, and *tatos,* most.

Root	Meaning	Example of Use
troph-	Food, nourishment	Trophozoite—the feeding stage of protozoa
-phile	To love	Extremophile—an organism that has adapted to ("loves") extreme environments
-obe	To live	Microbe—to "live small"
hetero-	Other	Heterotroph—an organism that requires nutrients from other organisms
auto-	Self	Autotroph—an organism that "feeds by itself"
photo-	Light	Phototroph—an organism that uses light as an energy source
chemo-	Chemical	Chemotroph—an organism that uses chemicals rather than light for energy
sapro-	Rotten	Saprobe—an organism that lives on dead organic matter
halo-	Salt	Halophile—an organism that can grow in high-salt environments
thermo-	Heat	Thermophile—an organism that grows at high temperatures
psychro-	Cold	Psychrophile—an organism that grows at cold temperatures
aero-	Air (O_2)	Aerobe—an organism that uses oxygen in metabolism

hydrogen sulfide, sulfur, or iron and combine them with other inorganic substances such as carbon dioxide, oxygen, and hydrogen. These reactions release simple organic molecules and a modest amount of energy to drive the synthetic processes of the cell. **Figure 7.2***a* provides an example of an unusual bacterium that inhabits hot springs in New Zealand. Chemoautotrophs play an important part in recycling inorganic nutrients and elements. For an example of chemoautotrophy and its importance to deep-sea communities, see 7.1 Making Connections.

The Methanogen World

Methanogens* are a unique type of chemoautotroph widely distributed in the earth's habitats. All known methanogens are archaea, and many of them are found in extreme habitats, ranging from hot springs and vents to the deepest, coldest parts of the ocean **(figure 7.2***b***).** Others are common in soil, swamps, and even the intestines of humans and other animals.

* *methanogen* (meth-an″oh-jen′) From *methane,* a colorless, odorless gas, and *gennan,* to produce.

Methanogens' metabolism is adapted to producing methane gas (CH_4 or "swamp gas") by reducing carbon dioxide, using hydrogen gas under anaerobic conditions, summarized as:

$$4 H_2 + CO_2 \rightarrow CH_4 + 2 H_2O$$

Researchers sampling deep underneath the seafloor have uncovered massive deposits of methanogens. The immensity of this community has led one group of scientists to estimate that it comprises nearly one-third of all life on the planet! Evidence points to its extreme age: It has been embedded in the earth's crust for billions of years. Placed under tremendous pressures, the methane it releases becomes frozen into crystals. Some of it serves as a nutrient source for other extreme archaea, and some of it escapes into the ocean. From this position, it may be a significant factor in the development of the earth's climate and atmosphere. Some microbial ecologists suggest that rises in sea temperature could increase the melting of these methane deposits. Because methane is an important "greenhouse gas," this process could contribute considerably to ongoing global climate change.

(a) (b)

Figure 7.2 **Examples of chemotrophy. (a)** *Venenivibrio,* an extremophilic bacterium that lives in acidic hot springs and derives energy by combining hydrogen gas with oxygen to form water and hydrogen peroxide. **(b)** *Methanocaldococcus jannaschii* is an archaeon and methanogen that inhabits hot vents in the seafloor. It also metabolizes hydrogen gas but its product is methane gas (180,000×).
(a): Dr. Adrian Hetzer; (b): Electron Microscope Lab, UC Berkeley

Heterotrophs and Their Energy Sources

The majority of heterotrophic microorganisms are **chemoorganotrophs** that derive both carbon and energy from organic compounds. Processing these organic molecules by respiration or fermentation releases energy in the form of ATP. We will explore these topics in greater depth in chapter 8. An example of chemoheterotrophy is *aerobic respiration,* the principal energy-yielding pathway in animals, most protozoa and fungi, and aerobic bacteria. It can be simply represented by the equation:

$$\text{Glucose } [C_6H_{12}O_6] + 6O_2 \rightarrow 6CO_2 + 6H_2O + \text{Energy (ATP)}$$

Note that this reaction is complementary to photosynthesis. Here, glucose and oxygen are reactants and carbon dioxide is given off. Indeed, the earth's balance of both energy and metabolic gases greatly depends on this relationship. Chemoheterotrophic microbes are all similar in requiring an organic carbon source, but they differ in how they obtain it. This category includes a wide variety of organisms that feed on other organisms: animals, protozoa, fungi, and many types of bacteria. Examples of varied nutritional patterns include grazers, scavengers, and predators, but the dominant chemoheterotrophic microorganisms fit the description of saprobes or symbionts. **Saprobes**[2] are free-living microbes that feed primarily on organic detritis released by dead organisms, and **symbionts*** derive their organic nutrients from the bodies of living organisms. These categories are not absolute, in that some saprobes can adapt to living organisms, and some symbionts can obtain nutrients from a nonliving source. Because many of these nutritional patterns are also ecological in nature, they will be given fuller coverage in section 7.5. In this section, we introduce saprobes and parasites as they relate to nutrition.

Saprobic Microorganisms

The primary niche of saprobes is as decomposers of plant litter, animal matter, and dead microbes. If not for the work of decomposers, the earth would gradually fill up with organic material and the nutrients it contains would not be recycled. Most saprobes, notably bacteria and fungi, have a rigid cell wall and cannot engulf large particles of food. To compensate, they release enzymes to the extracellular environment and digest the food particles into smaller molecules that can be transported into the cell **(figure 7.3).**

Many saprobes exist strictly on dead organic matter in environmental reservoirs such as soil and water, and are unable to adapt to the body of a live host. This group includes free-living protozoa, most fungi, and a variety of bacteria. Apparently there are fewer of these microbes than was once thought, and many supposedly nonpathogenic saprobes can adapt to and invade a susceptible host. When a saprobe does infect a host, it is considered a *facultative parasite.* Because such an infection usually occurs when the host is compromised, the microbe is said to be an **opportunistic pathogen.** A notable example is *Pseudomonas aeruginosa*—its natural habitat is soil and water, yet it is a frequent cause of infections in hospital patients and compromised individuals, especially burn patients and those suffering from cystic fibrosis.

Parasitic Microorganisms

Most human infections are caused by heterotrophic microorganisms, but those having the greatest adverse impact on human health are **parasites.** By definition, a parasite is a microbe that invades the body of a host, uses it as a habitat and source of nutrients, and, in the process, harms the host to some degree. Such parasitic microbes that grow inside sterile tissues and cause damage, and even death, are also termed **pathogens.** Parasites range from viruses to helminth worms, and they can live on the body (ectoparasites), in the organs

2. Synonyms are *saprotroph* and *saprophyte.* We prefer to use the terms *saprobe* and *saprotroph* because they are more consistent with other terminology.

* *symbiont* (sim-bee'-ont) An organism that lives in association with another organism, from the term *symbiosis* (sim″-bye-oh′-sis) Gr, *syn,* together, and *bios,* to live. Literally, living together.

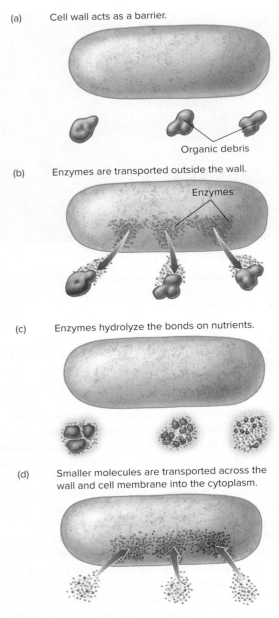

(a) Cell wall acts as a barrier.

Organic debris

(b) Enzymes are transported outside the wall.

Enzymes

(c) Enzymes hydrolyze the bonds on nutrients.

(d) Smaller molecules are transported across the wall and cell membrane into the cytoplasm.

Figure 7.3 **Extracellular digestion in a saprobe with a cell wall (bacterium or fungus). (a)** A walled cell is inflexible and cannot engulf large pieces of organic debris. **(b)** In response to a usable food substrate, the cell synthesizes enzymes that are transported across the wall into the extracellular environment. **(c)** The enzymes hydrolyze the bonds in the debris molecules. **(d)** Digestion produces molecules small enough to be transported into the cytoplasm.

and tissues (endoparasites), or even within cells (intracellular parasites, the most extreme type). The more successful parasites generally have no fatal effects and may eventually evolve to a less harmful relationship with their host (see section 7.5).

Obligate parasites (for example, the leprosy bacillus and the syphilis spirochete) are so dependent on their hosts that they are unable to grow outside of the host. Less strict parasites, such as the gonococcus and pneumococcus, can be cultured artificially if provided with the correct nutrients and environmental conditions in the laboratory.

5. Compare autotrophs and heterotrophs with respect to the form of carbon-based nutrients they require.
6. Describe the nutritional strategy of two types of chemoautotrophs described in this section.
7. Contrast chemoautotrophs and chemoheterotrophs as to carbon and energy sources and other unique strategies they may have.
8. What are the main differences between saprobes, symbionts, and parasites?

7.3 Transport: Movement of Substances across the Cell Membrane

Learn

8. Describe the basic factors in diffusion and passive transport systems.
9. Define *osmosis* and describe varying osmotic conditions.
10. Analyze adaptations microbes make in response to osmosis.
11. Describe the features of active transport and differentiate among its mechanisms.

A microorganism's habitat provides necessary substances—some abundant, others scarce—that must still be taken into the cell for nutrition. The reverse is also true: cells must transport waste materials out of the cell (and into the environment). Whatever the direction, transport occurs across the **cell membrane,** the structure specialized for this role. This is true even in organisms with cell walls (bacteria, algae, and fungi), because the cell wall is usually only a partial, nonselective barrier. In this section, we discuss some important physical forces in cell transport.

Diffusion and Molecular Motion

All atoms and molecules, regardless of being in a solid, liquid, or gas, are in continuous movement. As the temperature increases, the molecular movement becomes faster due to an increase in kinetic energy. In any solution, including cytoplasm, these moving molecules cannot travel very far without having collisions with other molecules, and they will bounce off each other like millions of colliding pool balls every second **(figure 7.4).** As a result of each collision, the directions of the colliding molecules are altered and the direction of any one molecule is unpredictable and considered random. An example would be a situation in which molecules of a substance are more concentrated in one area than in another. Just by random thermal movement, the molecules will become dispersed away from an area of higher concentration to an area of lower concentration. Over time this will evenly distribute the molecules in the solution. This net movement of molecules down their concentration gradient by random thermal motion is known as **diffusion.** It can be demonstrated by a variety of simple observations. A drop of perfume released into one part of a room is soon smelled in another part, or a dye spreads through a beaker of water without stirring (figure 7.4).

Figure 7.4 **Diffusion of molecules in aqueous solutions.** A brown dye crystal diffuses down a concentration gradient, from high concentration, near the crystal, to low concentration (farther away). As diffusion continues (left to right), the dye eventually is spread evenly throughout the aqueous phase, and a gradient ceases to exist. The system is now said to be at equilibrium.
McGraw-Hill Education

Diffusion is a driving force in cell activities, but its effects are greatly controlled by membranes. Two special cases are osmosis and facilitated diffusion. Both processes are considered a type of **passive transport.** This means that the cell does not expend extra energy for them to function. The inherent energy of the molecules moving down a gradient does the work of transport.

The Diffusion of Water: Osmosis

Diffusion of water through a selectively permeable membrane, a process called **osmosis,*** is a physical phenomenon that is easily demonstrated in the laboratory with nonliving materials. Simple experiments provide a model of how cells deal with various solute concentrations in aqueous solutions **(figure 7.5).** In an osmotic system, the membrane is *selectively,* or *differentially, permeable,* having passageways that allow free diffusion of water but can block certain dissolved molecules. When this type of membrane is placed between solutions of differing concentrations where the solute (protein, for example) cannot pass across, then under the laws of diffusion, water will diffuse at a faster rate from the side that has more water to the side that has less water. As long as the concentrations of the solutions differ, one side will experience a net loss of water and the other a net gain of water until equilibrium is reached and the rate of diffusion is equalized.

Osmosis in living systems is similar to the model shown in figure 7.5. Living membranes generally block the entrance and exit of larger molecules and permit free diffusion of water. Because most cells contain and are surrounded by some sort of aqueous solution, osmosis can have far-reaching effects on cellular activities and survival. Depending on the water content of a cell as compared with its environment, a cell can gain or lose water, or it may remain unaffected. Terms that we use for describing these conditions are *isotonic, hypotonic,* and *hypertonic*[3] **(figure 7.6).**

Under **isotonic*** conditions, the environment is equal in solute concentration to the cell's internal environment; and because diffusion of water proceeds at the same rate in both directions, there is no net change in cell volume. Isotonic solutions are generally the most stable environments for cells, because they are already in an osmotic steady state with the cell. Parasites living in host tissues are most likely to be living in isotonic habitats.

Under **hypotonic*** conditions, the solute concentration of the external environment is lower than that of the cell's internal environment. Pure water provides the most hypotonic environment for cells because it has no solute. Because the net direction of osmosis is from the hypotonic solution into the cell, cells without walls swell and can burst when exposed to this condition.

Slight hypotonicity is tolerated quite well by most bacteria because of their rigid cell walls. The light flow of water into the cell keeps the cell membrane fully extended and the cytoplasm full. This is the optimum condition for the many processes occurring in and on the membrane.

A cell in a **hypertonic*** environment is exposed to a solution with higher solute concentration than its cytoplasm. Because hypertonicity will force water to diffuse out of a cell, it is said to create high *osmotic pressure* or potential. In cells with a wall, water loss causes shrinkage of the protoplast away from the wall, a condition called **plasmolysis.*** Although the whole cell does not collapse, this event can still damage and even kill many kinds of cells. The effect on cells lacking a wall is to shrink down and usually to collapse (figure 7.6). The growth-limiting effect of hypertonic solutions on microbes is the principle behind using concentrated salt and sugar solutions as preservatives for food, such as in salted hams and fish. Such solutions effectively remove moisture from the food, which inhibits the growth of microbial contaminants.

Adaptations to Osmotic Variations in the Environment

Let us now see how specific microbes have adapted osmotically to their environments. In general, isotonic conditions place little stress

* *osmosis* (oz-moh′-sis) Gr. *osmos,* impulsion, and *osis,* a process.

3. It will help you to recall these osmotic conditions if you remember that the prefixes *iso-, hypo-,* and *hyper-* refer to the environment *outside* of the cell.

* *isotonic* (eye-soh-tahn′-ik) Gr. *iso,* same, and *tonos,* tension.

* *hypotonic* (hy-poh-tahn′-ik) Gr. *hypo,* under, and *tonos,* tension.
* *hypertonic* (hy-pur-tahn′-ik) Gr. *hyper,* above, and *tonos,* tension.
* *plasmolysis* (plaz′-moh-ly′-sis) L. *plasmo,* mold, and G. *lusis,* loosening.

Solute

Water

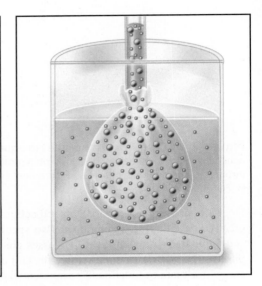

(a) Inset shows a close-up of the osmotic process. The gradient goes from the outer container (higher concentration of H_2O) to the sac (lower concentration of H_2O). Some water will diffuse the opposite direction but the net gradient favors osmosis into the sac.

(b) As the H_2O diffuses into the sac, the volume increases and forces the excess solution into the tube, which will rise continually.

(c) Even as the solution becomes diluted, there will still be osmosis into the sac. Equilibrium will not occur because the solutions can never become equal. (Why?)

Figure 7.5 **Model system to demonstrate osmosis.** Here we have a solution enclosed in a membranous sac and attached to a hollow tube. The membrane is permeable to water (solvent) but not to solute. The sac is immersed in a container of pure water and observed over time.

on cells, so survival depends on counteracting the adverse effects of hypertonic and hypotonic environments.

An alga and an amoeba living in fresh pond water are examples of cells that live in constantly hypotonic conditions. The rate of water diffusing across the cell membrane into the cytoplasm is rapid and constant, and the cells would die without a way to adapt. As with bacteria, the majority of algae have a cell wall that protects them from bursting even as the cytoplasmic membrane becomes **turgid*** from pressure. The amoeba has no cell wall to protect it, so it must expend energy to deal with the influx of water. This is accomplished with a water, or contractile, vacuole that siphons excess water out of the cell like a tiny pump.

A microbe living in a high-salt environment (hypertonic) has the opposite problem and must either restrict its loss of water to the environment or increase the salinity of its internal environment. Halobacteria living in the Great Salt Lake and the Dead Sea must absorb salt to make their cells isotonic with the environment; thus, they have a physiological need for a high-salt concentration in their habitats (see halophiles in section 7.4).

The Movement of Solutes across Membranes

Simple diffusion works well for movement of small nonpolar molecules such as oxygen or lipid soluble molecules that readily pass

through membranes. But many substances that cells require are polar and ionic chemicals with greatly reduced permeability. Simple diffusion alone would be unable to transport these substances. One way that cells have adapted to this limitation involves a process called **facilitated diffusion (figure 7.7).** This passive transport mechanism utilizes a carrier protein in the membrane that will bind a specific substance. This binding changes the conformation of the carrier proteins in a way that facilitates movement of the substance across the membrane. Once the substance is transported, the carrier protein resumes its original shape and is ready to transport again. These carrier proteins exhibit **specificity,** which means that they bind and transport only a single type of molecule. For example, a carrier protein that transports sodium will not bind glucose. A second characteristic exhibited by facilitated diffusion is **saturation.** The rate of transport of a substance is limited by the number of binding sites on the transport proteins. As the substance's concentration increases, so does the rate of transport until the concentration of the transported substance causes all of the transporters' binding sites to be occupied. Then the rate of transport reaches a steady state and cannot move faster despite further increases in the substance's concentration.

Other examples of passive protein carriers found in a wide variety of cells are *aquaporins*, also known as water channels. These openings in the membrane facilitate passive transport of water molecules following an existing osmotic gradient. They appear to be involved in regulating volume and osmotic pressure.

* *turgid* (ter'-jid) A condition of being swollen or congested.

**Cells with
cell walls**

Isotonic Solution

Cell wall

Cell membrane

Hypotonic Solution

Hypertonic Solution

Cell
membrane

Water concentration is equal inside and outside the cell, thus rates of diffusion are equal in both directions.

Net diffusion of water is into the cell; this swells the protoplast and pushes it tightly against the wall; wall usually prevents cell from bursting.

Water diffuses out of the cell and shrinks the cell membrane away from the cell wall; process is known as plasmolysis.

**Cells lacking
walls**

Cell membrane

Early

Late
(osmolysis)

Early

Late

Rates of diffusion are equal in both directions.

Diffusion of water into the cell causes it to swell, and may burst it if no mechanism exists to remove the water.

Water diffusing out of the cell causes it to shrink and become distorted.

 Direction of net water movement.

Figure 7.6 **Cell responses to solutions of differing osmotic content.**

Active Transport: Bringing in Molecules against a Gradient

Free-living microbes exist under relatively nutrient-starved conditions and cannot rely completely on slow and rather inefficient passive transport mechanisms. To ensure a constant supply of nutrients and other required substances, microbes must capture those that are in low concentrations and actively transport them into the cell. Cells must likewise transport substances in the reverse direction to the external environment. Some microbes have such efficient active transport systems that an essential nutrient can be found in

Facilitated diffusion

Extracellular

High

Concentration

Intracellular

Figure 7.7 **Facilitated diffusion.** Facilitated diffusion involves the attachment of a molecule to a specific protein carrier. Bonding of the molecule causes a conformational change in the protein that facilitates the molecule's passage across the membrane (left view). The membrane protein releases the molecule into the cell interior (right view). The cell does not have to expend energy for transport.

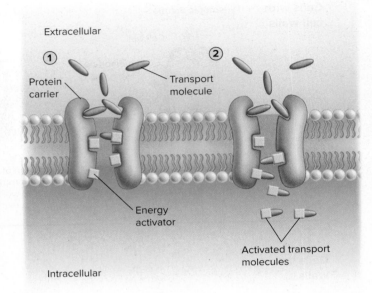

(a) **Carrier-mediated active transport.** (1) Membrane-bound transporter proteins (permeases) interact with nearby solute-binding proteins that carry essential solutes (sodium, iron, sugars). (2) Once a binding protein attaches to a specific site, an ATP is activated and generates energy to pump the solute into the cell's interior through a special channel in the permease.

(b) **In-group translocation,** (1) a specific molecule is actively captured, but on its passage through the membrane protein carrier (2) it is chemically altered or activated for use in the cell. By coupling transport with synthesis, the cell conserves energy.

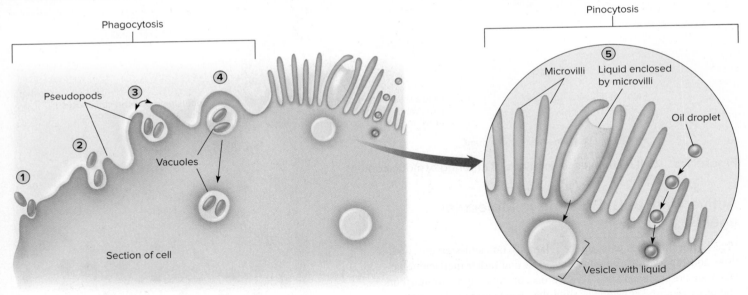

(c) **Endocytosis.** With phagocytosis, solid particles are engulfed by flexible cell extensions or pseudopods (1-4) (1,000×). (5) With pinocytosis, fluids and/or dissolved substances are enclosed in vesicles by very fine protrusions called microvilli (3,000×). Oil droplets fuse with the membrane and are released directly into the cell.

Figure 7.8 **Active transport.** In active transport mechanisms, energy is expended (ATP) to transport the molecule across the cell membrane.

intracellular concentrations that are hundreds of times greater than in the environment surrounding the cell.

Features inherent in **active transport** systems are:

1. the transport of nutrients against the diffusion gradient or in the same direction as the natural gradient but at a rate faster than by diffusion alone,

2. the presence of specific membrane proteins (permeases and pumps; **figure 7.8a**), and

3. the expenditure of additional cellular energy in the form of ATP-driven uptake. Examples of substances transported actively are monosaccharides, amino acids, organic acids, phosphates, and metal ions.

TABLE 7.3	Summary of Transport Processes in Cells			
General Process	**Nature of Transport**	**Examples**	**Description**	**Qualities**
Passive	Energy expenditure by the cell is not required. Substances exist in a gradient and move from areas of higher concentration toward areas of lower concentration in the gradient.	(1) Diffusion and osmosis	A fundamental property of atoms and molecules that exist in a state of random motion	Nonspecific movement Movement of small uncharged molecules across membranes
		(2) Facilitated diffusion	Molecule binds to a carrier protein in membrane and is carried across to other side	Molecule specific; transports both ways Transports sugars, amino acids, water
Active	Energy expenditure is required. Molecules need not exist in a gradient. Rate of transport is increased. Transport may occur against a concentration gradient.	(3) Carrier-mediated active transport	Atoms or molecules are pumped into or out of the cell by specialized receptors; driven by ATP or other high-energy molecules.	Transports simple sugars, amino acids, inorganic ions (Na^+, K^+)
		(4) Group translocation	Molecule is moved across membrane and simultaneously converted to a metabolically useful substance	Alternate system for transporting nutrients (sugars, amino acids)
		(5) Bulk transport	Mass transport of large particles, cells, and liquids by engulfment and vesicle formation	Process is endocytosis; examples are phagocytosis and pinocytosis

Carrier-mediated active transport involves specific membrane proteins that bind both ATP and the molecules to be transported. Release of energy from ATP drives the movement of the molecule through the protein carrier. This can occur in either direction. Some bacteria transport certain sugars, amino acids, vitamins, and phosphate into the cell by this mechanism. Other bacteria can actively pump drugs out of the cell, thereby providing them resistance to the drugs. Another type of active transport pump can rapidly carry ions such as K^+, Na^+, and H^+ across the membrane. It is this type of transport protein, defective in cystic fibrosis patients, that is responsible for its basic pathology.

Another type of active transport, **group translocation,** couples the transport of a nutrient with its conversion to a substance that is immediately useful inside the cell (**figure 7.8b**). This method is used by certain bacteria to transport sugars (glucose, fructose) while simultaneously adding phosphate molecules that activate them in preparation for a metabolic cycle.

Endocytosis: Eating and Drinking by Cells

Some cells can transport large molecules, particles, liquids, or even other cells across their cell membranes. Because the cell usually expends energy to carry out this movement, it is also a form of active transport. The substances transported do not pass physically through the membrane but are carried into the cell by **endocytosis.** First, the cell encloses the substance in its membrane, simultaneously forming a vacuole and engulfing it (**figure 7.8c**). Amoebas and certain white blood cells ingest whole cells or large solid matter by a type of endocytosis called **phagocytosis.** Liquids, such as oils or molecules in solution, enter the cell through **pinocytosis.** The mechanisms for transport of molecules into cells are summarized in **table 7.3.**

Practice SECTION 7.3

9. Compare and contrast passive and active forms of transport, using examples of what is being transported and the requirements for each.

10. How are phagocytosis and pinocytosis similar? How are they different?

11. Explain the differences between facilitated diffusion and group translocation.

12. Compare the effects of isotonic, hypotonic, and hypertonic solutions on an amoeba and on a bacterial cell. If a cell lives in a hypotonic environment, what will occur if it is placed in a hypertonic one? Answer for the opposite case as well.

7.4 Environmental Factors that Influence Microbes

Learn

12. Differentiate between habitat and niche.

13. Describe the range of temperatures a microbe can function within.

14. Explain the adaptive temperature groups, with examples of microbes that exist in them.

15. List the major gases and describe microbial requirements for these gases.

16. Outline the adaptations of microbial groups to variations in pH.

17. Identify microbial adaptations to osmotic pressure.

Going to Extremes

Any extreme habitat—whether hot, cold, salty, acidic, alkaline, high-pressure, arid, oxygen-free, or toxic—is likely to harbor microorganisms with special adaptations to these conditions. Most such inhabitants are archaea and bacteria, but certain fungi, protozoans, algae, and even viruses are also capable of living in severe habitats. Microbiologists have termed such remarkable organisms **extremophiles.** Discoveries of new types of extremophiles flourishing in forbidding environments are reported rather frequently. For microbiologists these findings are often astounding but not unexpected, because they confirm our perception that the earth has been "incubating" microbes for billions of years and there are still multitudes of hidden life forms to uncover.

Extreme Temperatures

Some of the most extreme habitats are hot springs, geysers, volcanoes, and ocean vents, all of which support flourishing microbial populations. Temperatures in these regions range from 50°C (122°F) to well above the boiling point of water, with some ocean vents approaching 350°C (662°F). Many heat-adapted microbes are ancient archaea whose genetics and metabolism are extremely modified for this mode of existence. A unique ecosystem based on hydrogen sulfide–oxidizing bacteria exists in the hydrothermal vents lying along deep oceanic ridges. Other denizens of hot volcanic waters are unusual invertebrates such as the Pompeii worm, which frequents rocky hideouts around sea vents measuring 80°C (176°F) **(photo a).** Their survival is greatly dependent on symbiotic bacteria that form an insulated coat on the worm's surface.

A large part of the earth exists at cold temperatures. Microbes settle and grow throughout the Arctic and Antarctic and in the deepest parts of the ocean in near-freezing temperatures. Several species of algae and fungi thrive on the surfaces of snow and glacier ice (see figure 7.10). More surprising still is that some bacteria and algae flourish in the sea ice of Antarctica. Although the ice appears to be completely solid, it is honeycombed by various-size pores and tunnels filled with a solution that is

−20°C (−4°F). These frigid microhabitats are home to a microcosm of planktonic bacteria, algae, and predators that feed on them.

Life in Very Salty Places

The growth of most microbial cells is inhibited by high amounts of salt; for this reason, salt is a common food preservative. But there are many salt lovers, including rich communities of bacteria and algae living in oceans, salt lakes, and inland seas, some of which are saturated with salt (30%). Microbiologists recently discovered salt pockets that supported archaea living in water 100 times more concentrated than seawater.

"Conan the Bacterium"

A tiny gram-positive coccus, *Deinococcus radiodurans* **(photo b),** has been called "Conan the bacterium" because of its capacity to survive extreme dryness and very high levels of radiation. This bacterium is widespread in many habitats, but its resistance to radiation sets it apart from every other known organism. The DNA and proteins of most organisms are very sensitive to gamma rays and other high-energy radiation, which is why radiation is so damaging to cells. But we now know its secret. *Deinococcus* carries around several copies of its genome, making it easily replaceable, and it contains radiation-resistant enzymes that help it rapidly repair DNA damage. This microbe is being studied for its potential in bioremediation of radioactive waste and as a model organism for Mars studies.

Brave "Old" World

When samples of ancient Antarctic ice (several million years old) were brought into the lab, they yielded living bacteria. Some of the oldest isolates were unusual, very slow-growing forms, but others were similar to modern bacteria.

Another bizarre, ancient ultraextremophile was discovered 3 kilometers down in an African gold mine. The bacterium *Desulforudis* is the

Microbes are exposed to a wide variety of environmental factors that affect growth and survival. Microbial ecology focuses on ways in which microorganisms deal with or adapt to such factors as heat, cold, gases, acid, radiation, osmotic and hydrostatic pressures, and even other microbes. Adaptation involves a complex adjustment in biochemistry or genetics that enables long-term survival and growth. The term biologists use to describe the totality of adaptations organisms make to their habitats is **niche.*** For most microbes, environmental factors fundamentally affect the function of metabolic enzymes. Thus, survival is largely a matter of whether the enzyme systems of microorganisms can continue to function even in a changing environment. Looking at **7.2 Making Connections** will introduce you to the broad range of conditions that support microbial life.

Adaptations to Temperature

Microbial cells cannot control their temperature and therefore assume the ambient temperature of their natural habitats. So, to survive, they must adapt to whatever temperature variations are encountered in their habitat. The range of temperatures for microbial growth can be expressed as three **cardinal temperatures.** The **minimum temperature** is the lowest temperature that permits a microbe's continued growth and metabolism; below this temperature, its activities are inhibited. The **maximum temperature** is the highest temperature at which growth and metabolism can proceed. If the temperature rises slightly above maximum, growth will stop. If it continues to rise beyond that point, the enzymes and nucleic acids will eventually become permanently inactivated—a condition known as **denaturation**—and the cell will die. This is why heat works so well as an agent in microbial control. The **optimum temperature** covers a small range, intermediate between the minimum and maximum, which promotes the fastest rate of growth and metabolism. Only rarely is the optimum a single point.

* *niche* (nitch) Fr. *nichier,* to nest.

only occupant of this totally dark, anaerobic, hot, alkaline habitat, and it derives its energy from the radioactive decay of uranium. This is the first organism on earth known to have established its own ecosystem and to sustain itself without the contributions of other organisms.

Numerous species have carved a niche for themselves in the deepest layers of mud, swamps, and oceans, where oxygen gas and sunlight cannot penetrate. The predominant living things in the deepest part of the oceans (10,000 m or below) are pressure- and cold-loving microorganisms. Even parched zones in sand dunes and deserts harbor a hardy brand of microbes; and thriving bacterial populations can be found in petroleum,

coal, and mineral deposits containing copper, zinc, gold, and uranium. Microbes that can adapt and survive under such lethal conditions are called toxophiles.

As a rule, a microbe that has adapted to an extreme habitat will not survive in a moderate one. And except for rare cases, none of the organisms living in these extremes is a pathogen, because the human body would be a rather hostile habitat for them.

Explain how extremophiles can survive such severe and adverse conditions.

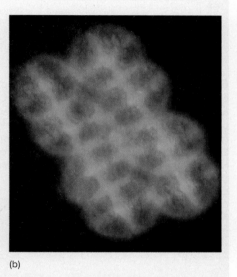

(a) (b)

(a) The hottest animal on earth is this Pompeii worm, wearing a coat of symbiotic bacteria (fine filaments) to protect against the heat. **(b)** A fluorescent micrograph of *Deinococcus radiodurans,* showing its packet arrangement, cell walls (red), and chromosomes (green).
(a): Image contributed by M. Cottrell and C. Cary, College of Marine Studies, University of Delaware; (b): Dea Slade

Depending on their natural habitats, some microbes have a narrow cardinal range, others a broad one. Some strict parasites will not grow if the temperature varies more than a few degrees below or above the host's body temperature. For instance, rhinoviruses (one cause of the common cold) multiply successfully only in tissues that are slightly below normal body temperature (33°C to 35°C or 91°F to 95°F). Other microbes are not so limited. Strains of *Staphylococcus aureus* grow within the range of 6°C to 46°C (43°F to 114°F), and the intestinal bacterium *Enterococcus faecalis* grows within the range of 0°C to 44°C (32°F to 112°F).

Another way to express temperature adaptation is to describe whether an organism grows optimally in a cold, moderate, or hot temperature range. The terms used for these ecological groups are *psychrophile, mesophile,* and *thermophile* (**figure 7.9**).

A **psychrophile*** is a microorganism (bacterium, archaea, fungus, or alga) with an optimum temperature below 15°C

(59°F) but generally can grow at 0°C (32°F). It is obligate with respect to cold and generally cannot grow above 20°C (68°F). Laboratory work with true psychrophiles can be a real challenge. Inoculations have to be done in a cold room because ordinary room temperature can be lethal to these organisms. Unlike most laboratory cultures, storage in the refrigerator incubates rather than inhibits them. As one might predict, true psychrophiles are not capable of surviving in the human body and do not cause infections. Instead, they populate some of the coldest places on earth, including snowfields (**figure 7.10**), polar ice, permafrost, and the deep ocean. Recently bacteria were isolated from an undersea lake in Antarctica that were living at −15°C (5°F). True psychrophiles must be distinguished from *psychrotrophs* or *facultative psychrophiles* that grow slowly in cold but have an optimum temperature above 20°C (68°F). Psychrotrophs such as *Staphylococcus aureus* and *Listeria monocytogenes* are a concern because they can grow in refrigerated food and cause food-borne illness.

* *psychrophile* (sy′-kroh-fyl) Gr. *psychros,* cold, and *philos,* to love.

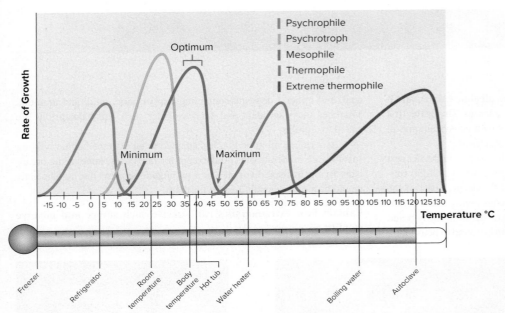

Figure 7.9 **Ecological groups by temperature of adaptation.** Psychrophiles can grow at or near 0°C and have an optimum below 15°C. As a group, mesophiles can grow between 10°C and 50°C, but their optima usually fall between 20°C and 40°C. One type of mesophile, termed a *psychrotroph,* is capable of growth at temperatures below 20°C. Generally speaking, thermophiles require temperatures above 45°C and grow optimally between this temperature and 80°C. Extreme thermophiles (hyperthermophiles) are bacteria and archaea with optima above 80°C. Note that the extremes of the ranges can overlap to some extent.

(a) (b)

Figure 7.10 **Red snow. (a)** The surface of an Alaskan glacier provides a perfect habitat for psychrophilic photosynthetic organisms such as *Chlamydomonas nivalis.* **(b)** Microscopic views of this snow alga, which is classified as a "green" alga although a red pigment dominates at this stage of its life cycle (600×).
(a and b): Image courtesy of Nozomu Takeuchi

The majority of medically significant microorganisms are **mesophiles,*** organisms that grow at intermediate temperatures. Although an individual species can grow between the extremes of 10°C and 50°C (50°F and 122°F), the optimum growth temperatures

(optima) of most mesophiles fall into the range of 20°C to 40°C (68°F to 104°F). Organisms in this group inhabit animals and plants, as well as soil and water in temperate, subtropical, and tropical regions. Most human pathogens have optima somewhere between 30°C and 40°C (human body temperature is 37°C or 98°F). *Thermoduric* microbes, which can survive short exposure to high temperatures but are normally mesophiles, are common contaminants of heated or pasteurized foods (see chapter 11). Examples include heat-resistant cysts such as *Giardia* or sporeformers such as *Bacillus* and *Clostridium.*

A **thermophile*** is a microbe that grows optimally at temperatures greater than 45°C (113°F). Such heat-loving microbes live in soil and water associated with volcanic activity, in compost piles, and in habitats directly exposed to the sun. Thermophiles generally range in growth temperatures from 45°C to 80°C (113°F to 176°F). Most eukaryotic forms cannot survive above 60°C (140°F), but a few bacteria and archaea, called **hyperthermophiles,** are adapted to life in extreme temperatures. They can grow at between 80°C and 121°C (250°F), currently thought to be the highest temperature limit endured by enzymes and cell structures. Strict thermophiles are so heat tolerant that researchers can use a heat-sterilizing device to isolate them from non-thermophiles in culture.

Currently biotechnology companies are intensely interested in thermal microorganisms. One of the most profitable discoveries so far was a strict thermophile *Thermus aquaticus,* which produces an enzyme that can make copies of DNA even at high temperatures. This enzyme—Taq polymerase—is now an essential component of the polymerase chain reaction or PCR, a process used in many areas of medicine, forensics, and biotechnology (see chapter 10).

Gas Requirements

The atmospheric gases that most influence microbial growth are oxygen (O_2) and carbon dioxide (CO_2). Oxygen comprises about 20% of the atmosphere and CO_2 about 0.04%. Oxygen gas has a great impact on microbial adaptation. It is an important respiratory gas, and it is also a powerful oxidizing agent that exists in many toxic forms. In general, microbes fall into one of three categories: those that use oxygen and can detoxify it; those that can neither use oxygen nor detoxify it; and those that do not use oxygen but can detoxify it.

How Microbes Process Oxygen

As oxygen gas enters into cellular reactions, it can be transformed into several toxic products. Singlet oxygen (1O_2) is an extremely reactive molecule produced by both living and nonliving processes.

* *mesophiles* (mez'-oh-fylz) Gr. *mesos,* middle.

* *thermophile* (thur'-moh-fyl) Gr. *therme,* heat.

CLINIC CASE

But It's Always Been Safe A patient sought care in the emergency department of his local hospital in Nevada. He said he had been suffering from diarrhea, abdominal cramping, nausea, vomiting, fever, and chills for the past 48 hours. When asked about his meals over the past few days he volunteered that he had just returned from a cruise on Prince William Sound (off the coast of Alaska) and had eaten, like many cruise passengers, everything in sight, 24 hours a day.

Testing of the patient's stool revealed the presence of *Vibrio parahaemolyticus,* a pathogenic bacterium known to cause gastroenteritis. Further investigation by health officials from the state of Alaska revealed that a total of 54 people had recently tested positive for the presence of *V. parahaemolyticus,* all within 2 days of consuming raw oysters collected from Alaskan waters.

As it requires a minimum temperature of at least 16.5°C to grow, *V. parahaemolyticus* is considered a mesophile, and Alaskan waters have historically been too cold for the bacterium to thrive. Because of this, people have routinely eaten raw oysters from the area without concern for their safety. But climate change has warmed the waters of Prince William Sound, allowing *V. parahaemolyticus* to spread from its usual habitat to an area more than 900 kilometers (600 miles) miles farther north, contaminating oysters and causing illness. This incident led to the closure of several oyster farms in Alaska, and testing for *V. parahaemolyticus* is now routine throughout the state. Many oyster farmers have also developed a new practice: When sea temperatures approach 15°C, baskets of oysters are lowered to the colder waters 100 feet below the surface to rid them of bacteria.

Keeping food cold would seem to promote the growth of psychrophilic bacteria. Why are we generally less concerned about this than we are about mesophilic bacteria?

Notably, it is one of the substances produced by phagocytes to kill invading bacteria (see chapter 14). The buildup of singlet oxygen and the oxidation of membrane lipids and other molecules can damage and destroy a cell. The highly reactive superoxide ion (O_2^-), peroxide (H_2O_2), and hydroxyl radicals (OH) are other destructive metabolic by-products of oxygen. To survive these toxic oxygen products, many microorganisms have developed enzymes capable of scavenging and neutralizing these chemicals. The complete conversion of superoxide ion into less harmful oxygen gas involves a two-step process and at least two enzymes:

Step 1. $2O_2^- + 2H^+ \xrightarrow{\text{Superoxide dismutase}} H_2O_2 \text{ (hydrogen peroxide)} + O_2$

Step 2. $2H_2O_2 \xrightarrow{\text{Catalase}} 2H_2O + O_2$

In this series of reactions essential for aerobic organisms, the superoxide ion is first converted to hydrogen peroxide and normal oxygen by the action of an enzyme called superoxide dismutase. Because hydrogen peroxide is also toxic to cells (it is used as a disinfectant and antiseptic), it must be degraded by an enzyme—either catalase or peroxidase—into water and oxygen. If a microbe

is not capable of dealing with toxic oxygen by these or similar mechanisms, it will be restricted to habitats free of oxygen.

With respect to oxygen requirements, several general categories are recognized. An **aerobe*** (aerobic organism) can use gaseous oxygen in its metabolism and possesses the enzymes needed to process toxic oxygen products. An organism that cannot grow without oxygen is an **obligate aerobe.** Most fungi and protozoa, as well as many bacteria (genera *Micrococcus* and *Bacillus*), have strict requirements for oxygen in their metabolism.

A **facultative anaerobe** is an aerobe that does not require oxygen for its metabolism and is capable of growth in its absence. This type of organism metabolizes by aerobic respiration when oxygen is present, but in its absence, it adopts an anaerobic mode of metabolism such as fermentation. Facultative anaerobes usually possess catalase and superoxide dismutase. A number of bacterial pathogens fall into this group. This includes gram-negative intestinal bacteria and staphylococci. A **microaerophile*** does not grow at normal atmospheric concentrations of oxygen but requires a small amount of it (1%–15%) in metabolism. Most organisms in this category live in a habitat such as soil, water, or the human body that provides small amounts of oxygen but is not directly exposed to the atmosphere.

A true **anaerobe** (anaerobic microorganism) lacks the metabolic enzyme systems for using oxygen gas in respiration. Because **strict,** or **obligate, anaerobes** also lack the enzymes for processing toxic oxygen, they cannot tolerate any free oxygen in the immediate environment and will die if exposed to it. Strict anaerobes live in highly reduced habitats, such as deep muds, lakes, oceans, and soil.

Determining the oxygen requirements of a microbe from a biochemical standpoint can be a very time-consuming process. An initial clarification comes from cultures made with reducing media that contain an oxygen-removing chemical such as thioglycollate. The location of growth in a tube of fluid thioglycollate medium is a fair indicator of an organism's adaptation to oxygen use **(figure 7.11)**. Growing strictly anaerobic bacteria usually requires special media, methods of incubation, and handling chambers that exclude oxygen. **Figure 7.12** shows special systems for handling and growing anaerobes.

Even though human cells use oxygen, and oxygen is found in the blood and tissues, some body sites present anaerobic pockets or microhabitats where colonization or infection can occur. Dental caries are partly due to the complex actions of aerobic and anaerobic bacteria in plaque. Most gingival infections consist of similar mixtures of oral bacteria that have invaded damaged gum tissues. Another common site for anaerobic infections is the large intestine, a relatively oxygen-free habitat that harbors a rich assortment of strictly anaerobic bacteria. Anaerobic infections can occur following abdominal surgery and traumatic injuries (gas gangrene and tetanus).

Aerotolerant anaerobes do not utilize oxygen gas but can survive and grow in its presence. These anaerobes are not harmed by oxygen, and some of them possess alternative mechanisms for breaking down peroxide and superoxide. For instance, lactobacilli, which are common residents of the intestine, inactivate these compounds with manganese ions.

* *aerobe* (air'-ohb) Although the prefix means air, it is used in the sense of oxygen.
* *microaerophile* (myk"-roh-air'-oh-fyl)

(a)

Figure 7.11 **Use of thioglycollate broth to demonstrate oxygen requirements.** Thioglycollate is a reducing medium that can establish a gradation in oxygen content. Oxygen concentration is highest at the top of the tube and absent in the deeper regions. When a series of tubes is inoculated with bacteria that differ in O_2 requirements, the relative position of growth provides some indication of their adaptations to oxygen use. Tube 1 (far left): aerobic (*Pseudomonas aeruginosa*); Tube 2: facultative (*Staphylococcus aureus*); Tube 3: facultative (*Escherichia coli*); Tube 4: obligate anaerobe (*Clostridium butyricum*).
Terese M. Barta, Ph.D.

Although microbes require some carbon dioxide in their metabolism, **capnophiles** grow best at higher CO_2 concentrations (3%–10%) than are normally present in the atmosphere (0.033%). This becomes important in the initial isolation of some pathogens from clinical specimens, notably *Neisseria* (gonorrhea, meningitis), *Brucella* (undulant fever), and *Streptococcus pneumoniae*. Incubation is carried out in a CO_2 incubator that provides the correct range of CO_2. Keep in mind that CO_2 is an essential nutrient for autotrophs, which use it to synthesize organic compounds.

Effects of pH

Microbial growth and survival are also influenced by the pH of the habitat. The pH was defined in chapter 2 as the degree of acidity or alkalinity of a solution. It is expressed by the pH scale, a series of numbers ranging from 0 to 14, pH 7 being neither acidic nor alkaline. As the pH value decreases toward 0, the acidity increases, and as the pH increases toward 14, the alkalinity increases. The majority of organisms live or grow in habitats between pH 6 and pH 8 because stronger acids and bases can be highly damaging to enzymes and other cellular substances.

Although most microorganisms living in soil, freshwater, or the bodies of plants and animals are **neutrophiles,** living within the range of pH 5.5 to 8, some can manage exposure to pH extremes. Highly acidic or alkaline habitats, such as acidic bogs and streams or alkaline soils and ponds, can provide numerous habitats for specialized microbial communities. Obligate **acidophiles** include *Euglena mutabilis*, an

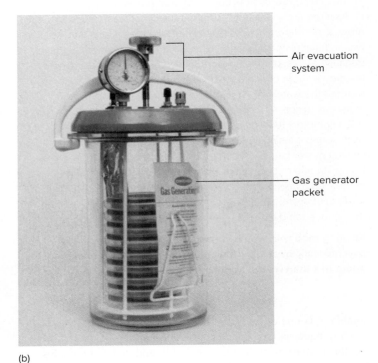

— Air evacuation system

— Gas generator packet

(b)

Figure 7.12 **Culturing techniques for anaerobes.** **(a)** An anaerobic environmental chamber is equipped with ports for handling strict anaerobes without exposing them to air. It also has provisions for incubation and inspection in a completely O_2-free system. **(b)** An anaerobic jar, equipped to evacuate air and be refilled with oxygen-free gases such as nitrogen or carbon dioxide.
(a): *Source:* Keith Weller, USDA/ARS; (b): *Source:* Dr. Gilda Jones/CDC

alga that grows in acid pools between 0 and 1.0 pH, and *Thermoplasma,* an archaea that lives in hot coal piles at a pH of 1 to 2 and will lyse if exposed to pH 7. A few species of algae, archaea, and bacteria can survive at a pH near that of concentrated hydrochloric acid near a pH of 0. Not only do they require such a low pH for growth, but a few species of bacteria actually help maintain the low pH by releasing strong acid. Because many molds and yeasts tolerate moderate acidity, they are the most common spoilage agents of acid-pickled foods.

Alkalinophiles live in hot pools and soils that contain high levels of basic minerals. Probably the upward limit of tolerance is shown by proteobacteria in California's Mono Lake that have adapted to pH 12. Bacteria that decompose urine create alkaline conditions, because ammonium (NH_4^+) can be produced when urea (a component of urine) is digested. Metabolism of urea is one way that *Proteus* spp. can neutralize the acidity of the urine to colonize and infect the urinary system.

Osmotic Pressure

Although most microbes exist under hypotonic or isotonic conditions, a few, called **osmophiles,** live in habitats with a high solute concentration. Common types of osmophiles that survive and grow in high concentrations of salt are referred to as **halophiles.***

Obligate halophiles such as *Halobacterium* and *Halococcus* inhabit salt lakes, ponds, and other hypersaline habitats. They grow optimally in solutions of 25% NaCl but require at least 9% NaCl (combined with other salts) for growth. These archaea have significant modifications in their cell walls and membranes, and will lyse in hypotonic habitats. Perhaps the most extreme saline habitat exists in a shallow pond in frigid Antarctica. The salt concentration of Don Juan Pond tests at 33% $CaCl_2$. For a time researchers thought this site would be a good model for duplicating the lifeless conditions on Mars, until they discovered an active biofilm community of cyanobacteria and diatoms residing there!

Some microbes adapt to wide concentrations in solutes. These are considered **osmotolerant** and are sometimes referred to as **facultative halophiles.** Such organisms are remarkably resistant to salt, even though they do not normally reside in high-salt environments. For example, *Staphylococcus aureus* can grow on NaCl media ranging from 0.1% up to 20%. Although it is common to use high concentrations of salt and sugar to preserve food (jellies, syrups, and brines), many bacteria and fungi thrive under these conditions and are common spoilage agents. One particularly hardy sugar-loving or *saccharophilic* yeast withstands the high sugar concentration of honey and candy.

Miscellaneous Environmental Factors

Descent into the ocean depths subjects organisms to increasing hydrostatic pressure. Deep-sea microbes called **barophiles** exist under pressures many times that of the atmosphere. Marine biologists sampling deep-sea trenches 7 miles below the surface isolated unusual eukaryotes called foraminifera that were being exposed to pressures 1,100 times greater than what would occur at the sea's surface. These microbes are so strictly adapted to high pressures that they will rupture when exposed to normal atmospheric pressure at sea level.

Because of the high water content of cytoplasm, all cells require water from their environment to sustain growth and metabolism. Water is the solvent for cell chemicals, and it is needed for enzyme function and digestion of macromolecules. A certain amount of water on the external surface of the cell is required for the diffusion of nutrients and wastes. Even in apparently dry habitats, such as sand or dry soil, the particles retain a thin layer of water usable by microorganisms. Only dormant, dehydrated cell stages (for example, spores and cysts) tolerate extreme drying because of the inactivity of their enzymes.

* *halophile* (hay'-loh-fyl)

 Practice SECTION 7.4

13. Why are most pathogens mesophilic?
14. What are the ecological roles of psychrophiles and thermophiles?
15. Explain what it means to be an obligate intracellular parasite. Name three groups of obligate intracellular parasites.
16. Where in the body are anaerobic habitats apt to be found?
17. Where do superoxide ions and hydrogen peroxide originate? What are their toxic effects?

7.5 Ecological Associations among Microorganisms

 Learn

18. Outline the types of associations among microorganisms and describe their basic differences.
19. Explain what occurs in symbiosis and in coevolution.
20. Differentiate among mutual, commensal, and parasitic associations, providing examples.
21. Explain syntrophy and amensalism, using examples.
22. Describe interactions between humans and their microbiota.

To this point, we have discussed how microbes have evolved to deal with the *abiotic* (nonliving) environment, oxygen concentration, temperature, pH, and the like. But microorganisms must also deal with one another, the so-called *biotic* environment. And though the number of organisms, microscopic and otherwise, is tremendous, there are only five types of relationships that typically exist.

Symbioses,[4]* are defined as close associations between organisms that are advantageous to at least one of the members (each member is known as a symbiont). A few facts about symbiotic relationships include:

- Can be obligatory or nonobligatory
- Can involve animals, plants, and other microbes
- Can include complex multipartner interactions

Endosymbionts live within their partner, whereas exosymbionts are associated with the outside surfaces of their partner. **Figure 7.13** provides an overview of the major categories of symbiosis with examples. Symbiotic relationships differ based on who receives benefits from the relationship.

Mutualism is a relationship in which all members share in the benefits produced by the partnership. Many mutualistic associations have developed over hundreds of millions, and even billions,

4. Although it is sometimes misused as a synonym for mutualism, be aware that the term *symbiosis* does not refer only to mutually beneficial associations, as parasitism is also a form of symbiosis.

**symbiosis, symbioses* (sim-bye-oh'-sis, sym-bye-oh'-seez) Gr. *sym,* together, and *bios,* to live

Figure 7.13 **Part 1—Symbiosis: A shared existence.** These relationships vary in the degree of interaction and its outcome.

(a1): *Source:* Scott Bauer/USDA; (a2): Louisa Howard - Dartmouth Electron Microscope Facility; (b1): jeridu/Getty Images; (b2): Science History Images/Alamy Stock Photo; (c): Courtesy of Dr. Ralf Wagner; (d): *Source:* Nick Hill/USDA; (e): Kathy Park Talaro; (f1): *Source:* Image courtesy of Dr. CSBR Prasad, Vindhya Clinic and Diagnostic Lab, India/CDC-DPDx; (f2): *Source:* Janice Carr/CDC; (g): *Source:* Cynthia Goldsmith/CDC; (h1): *Source:* James Gathany/CDC; (h2): *Source:* Blaine A. Mathison/CDC-DPDX

Obligate Mutualism Organisms are so intimately associated that they require each other to survive. Root nodules **(a1)** have nitrogen-fixing endosymbiotic bacteria that supply the plant with usable nitrogen and provide a nurturing habitat for the bacteria **(a2 inset)**. Termites **(b1)** rely on endosymbiotic *Trichonympha* **(b2)** for survival.

(a1) Root nodules on a legume; **(a2)** *Bradyhizobium* bacteria inside a nodule (3,000×).

(b1) Termites would not be able to digest wood if not for a variety of endosymbiotic protists **(b2)**, like Trichonympha (6,500×).

Nonobligate Mutualism Organisms interact at the cellular level for mutual benefit, but they can be separated and live apart. The protozoan in **(c)** engulfs the algae but absorbs the nutrients they release and shelters them. **(d)** The plant supplies nutrients to the fungus and the fungus protects the plants against drying and insects.

(c) The ciliophoran *Euplotes* (800×) harbors unicellular green algae.

(d) Fungal hyphae (blue filaments—500×) growing in close contact with the cells of a grass leaf.

Commensalism The members have an unequal relationship. One partner is favored by the association and the other is not harmed or helped. **(e)** Tiny colonies of *Haemophilus* absorb required growth factors given off by *Staphylococcus*. **(f1 and f2)** Human commensals associated with the epidermis survive off of flakes and excretions, generally with neutral effects.

(e) Satellite *Haemophilus* colonies clustered around *Staphylococcus* (white line of growth).

(f1) *Demodex* mite lives in or around human hair follicles (100×) and **(f2)** *Micrococcus luteus* bacteria live on the skin surface (2,000×).

Parasitism A microbe invades the sterile regions of a host and occupies its tissues and cells, causing some degree of damage. **(g)** All viruses are parasites that invade cells and take over their function. **(h)** Malaria shows multilevel parasitism. Mosquitoes **(h1)** are blood-sucking ectoparasites of humans that carry their own parasites **(h2)** that can also infect humans.

(g) Sin Nombre hantavirus, a human pathogen carried in the waste of mice (5,000×).

(h1) The malaria vector, a female *Anopheles* mosquito; **(h2)** malaria parasites (*Plasmodium,* 1,000×) from blood.

Figure 7.13 Part 2—Additional microbial adaptations.

(j): MedicalRF.com; (k): Paul Bertner/Getty Images; (l1): *Source:* Jorg Barke, Ryan F Seipke, Sabine Grüschow, Darren Heavens, Nizar Drou, Mervyn J Bibb, Rebecca JM Goss, Douglas W Yu, and Matthew I Hutchings; (l2): Microfield Scientific Ltd/Science Source

Syntrophy Microbes sharing a habitat feed off substances released by other organisms, **(i)** *Azotobacter* releases NH_4 that feeds *Cellulomonas*, and *Cellulomonas* degrades cellulose that feeds *Azotobacter*. **(j)** A dust mite lives in human settings and feeds off dead skin flakes.

(i) Cycle of cross-feeding in two soil bacteria.

(j) *Dermatophagoides* mite (100×).

Amensalism One member of an association produces a substance that harms or kills another. **(k)** Ants have complex symbiotic relationships that involve mutualism and amensalism with fungi and bacteria. **(l1 and l2)** In the amensal phase of their ecology, the ants cultivate actinomycetes to protect their habitat from microbial pests.

Zone with no growth where antibiotic inhibits undesirable fungus

Actinomycete colony that produces antibiotic

(k) Leaf-cutting ants gathering food for a fungus garden that is their source of food.

(l1) Antibiosis by an actinomycete against a pathogenic fungus; **(l2)** micrograph of actinomycete (800×).

of years of shared evolution, a process termed **coevolution.** Coevolving symbionts remain in very close contact and must evolve together to sustain themselves. A change in one partner exerts a selective pressure on the other partner to adapt to these changes, and vice versa. A classic example of mutualism occurs between termites and a protozoan endosymbiont, *Trichonympha*. While termites eat wood, it is the *Trichonympha* living within the termite's gut that digests the cellulose in the wood fibers **(figure 7.13*b*)**. Both organisms receive benefits from the relationship (the relationship is actually far more complex, as many species of protozoans live in the termite's gut and help to digest cellulose, but that is a minor point in our discussion).

The nondependent forms of mutualism are sometimes referred to as **cooperation,** to emphasize the fact that the organisms gain mutual benefit from their association but can survive independently outside of the partnership. Many of these cooperative relationships are coevolving to greater dependency. One example is the protozoan *Euplotes,* which harbors endosymbiotic algae in its cells **(figure 7.13*c*)**. Although both members can survive apart from this mutualistic interaction, they appear to receive significant survival benefits from being together. Other examples include fungi that grow within plant tissues and protect the plant from drought and insects while being harbored and fed **(figure 7.13*d*)**.

When only a single member of a symbiotic partnership benefits, while the other is neither benefited or harmed, the relationship is described as **commensalism.*** The members of the association are called **commensals.** One form of commensalism observed in cultured microbes is termed the *satellite phenomenon,* in which one species releases various growth factors that are required by a nearby species to grow. The feeder microbe grows around its partner as tiny colonies, while the passive partner is neither harmed nor helped **(figure 7.13*e*)**. Many of the microbes that occupy a niche on the human body are considered commensals. They make a living by feeding off dead skin and secretions, but do not usually cause harm **(figure 7.13*f*1, 2)**.

The last type of symbiotic interrelationship is **parasitism,** in which one member benefits at the expense of the other. There are various degrees of parasitism. The most extreme form is **obligate intracellular parasitism,** which means the microbe spends all or most of its life cycle inside the host cell, from which it derives essential nutrients and other types of support. Prime examples are viruses that are incapable of surviving without a host **(figure 7.13*g*)**. Other examples include intracellular bacteria like *Rickettsia* and

* *commensalism* (kuh-men′-sul-izm) L. *com,* together, and *mensa,* table.

Chlamydia, which poach energy from their (bacterial) hosts, and protozoans like *Plasmodium* (the cause of malaria) that parasitizes red blood cells (**figure 7.13h1, 2**). The kinds of harm that parasites do to their hosts varies from superficial damage (ringworm on the skin from a fungal infection) to significant damage (peptic ulcers) to rapid death (rabies virus). It's also interesting to note that the most successful parasites are often the ones that have evolved to cause the least damage to their host, sometimes even evolving to a commensal or mutualistic existence. After all, a dead host is no host at all.

The final two types of relationships don't require a particularly close association between microbes. One of these, **syntrophy,*** or **crossfeeding,** is communal feeding between organisms sharing a habitat. In essence, products given off by one organism are usable by another (**figure 7.13i**). The organisms involved do not require this relationship for survival, but they generally benefit from it. Many syntrophic associations occur in aquatic habitats and soils within biofilms and are related to nutrient and bioelement recycling. A simple example involves a pair of free-living soil bacteria that share their metabolic products cyclically (**figure 7.13j**). *Cellulomonas* uses its enzymes to digest plant cellulose into glucose, but it cannot fix nitrogen. *Azotobacter* fixes nitrogen gas from the air and releases ammonium, but it does not digest cellulose. The glucose is a source of carbon for *Azotobacter,* and the ammonium supplies *Cellulomonas* with usable nitrogen. Even more complex interactions occur in the cycling of elements such as sulfur, phosphorus, and nitrogen.

Lastly, **amensalism*** describes an action of one microbe that causes harm to another microbe. It usually involves antagonism or competition and occurs in a community where microbes are sharing space and nutrient sources. Some microbes effectively compete by using up a vital nutrient to grow faster and dominate the habitat. Other microbes may release specific inhibitory chemicals (**antibiotics**) into the surrounding environment that inhibit or kill microbes. Many fungi and bacteria are adapted to this survival strategy. An intriguing example can be found in the complex symbiosis of certain ants that actively cultivate specialized gardens of fungi as a source of food. To protect the fungi from other microbes, the ants also cultivate species of filamentous bacteria called actinomycetes that produce antibiotics. The ants spread the actinomycetes through their gardens to protect the fungi from invasion by parasites. **Figures 7.13k** and *l* feature some aspects of this relationship.

Biofilms—A Microbial Conversation

Among the most common and prolific associations of microbes are **biofilms,** first described chapter 4. Biofilms result when organisms attach to a substrate by some form of extracellular matrix that binds them together in complex organized layers. Biofilms are so prevalent that they dominate the structure of most natural environments

* *syntrophy* (sin'-trof-ee) Gr, *sym,* together, and *troph,* to feed.
* *amensalism* (ae-men'-sul-izm) Gr, *a,* not, and L. *mensa,* table.

CLINICAL CONNECTIONS

Our Microbial Passengers

Microbial interrelationships obviously affect humans in many ways, but those having the most impact are microbes that naturally live on or in the body and parasites that attack the body. The normal residents, called **microbiota,** are so abundant that, cell for cell, they outnumber us by a 3-to-1 margin. From this standpoint, one could argue that we are more microbial than human. Obviously, a community of microbes this large is bound to have enormous effects on our physiology, immunity, and genetics.

Resident microbes come from nearly all groups and include viruses, archaea, bacteria, fungi, and protozoa that have adapted to specialized niches throughout our surfaces. Certainly some are commensals that make a living on the body without harm or benefit, but a greater number are probably mutualistic, providing some form of nutrition or protection. For example, lactobacilli growing in the vagina maintain an acidic pH that can protect the female reproductive tract from infections (see photo), and other species are involved in digestive processes and the function of the intestine. The mutualist *Bacteroides thetaiotaomicron* processes complex food molecules and even regulates the expression of the human genome. The stabilizing effects of bacteria on the intestinal environment are the basis behind probiotic supplements and foods. Results of hundreds of new studies are rapidly accumulating information on the complex interrelationships we have with our microbiota.

Most of the time our 100 trillion microbial passengers do more good than harm, but if certain types are displaced from their niche or are allowed to enter the sterile tissues, they become opportunistic pathogens and can cause infections. Microbes living in biofilms can create mixed infections, meaning that several microbes acting together invade the tissues and cause damage. This is the pattern in dental caries, periodontal disease, and gas gangrene.

Stained vaginal smear reveals a large pink epithelial cell harboring gram-positive rods of Lactobacillus, an important member of the normal microbiota that helps protect against infection.
Source: Dr. Mike Miller/CDC

Explain the role of broad-spectrum antibiotics in disrupting the microbial symbionts of humans and the possible problems this can cause.

on earth, and microbes within the biofilm participate in such an intimate association that they begin to resemble a single "superorganism," influencing such microbial activities as adaptation to a particular habitat, content of soil and water, nutrient cycling, and even the course of infections.

It is generally accepted that the individual cells in the bodies of multicellular organisms such as animals and plants have the capacity to produce, receive, and react to chemical signals such as hormones made by other cells. Microbes show a well-developed capacity to communicate and cooperate in the formation and function of biofilms. This is especially true of bacteria, although fungi and other microorganisms can participate in these activities.

One idea to explain the development and behavior of biofilms is termed **quorum sensing.** This process occurs in several stages, including self-monitoring of cell density, secretion of chemical signals, and genetic activation (**process figure 7.14**). Early in biofilm formation, free-floating or swimming microbes—often described as **planktonic**—are attracted to a surface and come to rest or settle down. Settling stimulates the cells to secrete a slimy or adhesive matrix, usually made of polysaccharide, that binds them to the substrate. Once attached, cells begin to release **inducer* molecules** that accumulate as the cell population grows. By this means, they can monitor the size of their own population. In time, a critical number of cells, termed a **quorum,*** accumulates and this ensures that there will be sufficient quantities of inducer molecules. These inducer molecules enter biofilm cells and stimulate specific genes on their chromosomes to begin expression.

> ### Quick Search
> Watch "How Biofilms Form" and "Quorum Sensing" on YouTube.

The nature of this expression varies, but generally it allows the biofilm to react as a unit. For example, by coordinating the expression of genes that code for specific proteins, the biofilm can simultaneously produce large quantities of a digestive enzyme or toxin. This regulation of expression accounts for several observations made about microbial activities. For instance, it explains how saprobic microbes in soil and water rapidly break down complex substrates and how some pathogens release their toxins into the tissues simultaneously.

The effect of quorum sensing has also given greater insight into how pathogens invade their hosts and produce large quantities of substances that damage host defenses. It has been well studied in a number of pathogenic bacteria. Infections by *Pseudomonas aeruginosa* give rise to tenacious lung biofilms in cystic fibrosis patients and some types of pneumonia. *Staphylococcus aureus* commonly forms biofilms on inanimate medical devices and in wounds. *Streptococcus* species are the initial colonists that create dental plaque on tooth surfaces.

Although the best-studied biofilms involve just a single type of microorganism, most biofilms observed in nature are polymicrobial. In fact, many symbiotic and cooperative relationships are

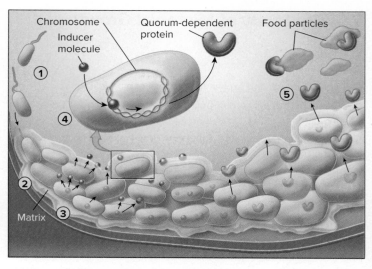

① Free-swimming cells lose their motility and settle down onto a surface or substrate.

② Cells synthesize an adhesive matrix that holds them tightly to the substrate.

③ When biofilm grows to a certain density (quorum), the cells release inducer molecules that can coordinate a response.

④ Enlargement of one cell to show genetic induction. Inducer molecule stimulates expression of a particular gene and synthesis of a protein product, such as an enzyme.

⑤ Cells secrete their enzymes in unison to digest food particles.

Process Figure 7.14 Stages in biofilm formation, quorum sensing, induction and expression.

based on complex communication patterns among coexisting organisms. As each organism in the biofilm carries out its specific niche, signaling among the members sustains the overall partnership. Biofilms are known to be a rich ground for genetic transfers among neighboring cells. As our knowledge of biofilm patterns grows, it will likely lead to greater understanding of their involvement in infections and their contributions to disinfectant and drug resistance.

Practice SECTION 7.5

18. Explain the process of coevolution and how it influences the development of microorganisms.

19. Define *symbiosis* and differentiate among mutualism, commensalism, syntrophy, parasitism, and amensalism, using examples.

20. Outline quorum sensing by using a concept map to organize the stages.

21. Relate several advantages to communication within a biofilm.

* *inducer* (in-doos'-ur) L. *inducere,* to lead. Something that brings about or causes an effect.

* *quorum* (kwor'-uhm) L. *qui,* who. Indicates the minimum number of group members necessary to conduct business.

7.6 The Study of Microbial Growth

 Learn

23. Define *growth* and explain the process of binary fission.
24. Describe the process of population growth and how it is measured.
25. Explain the stages in the population growth curve and its practical importance.
26. Relate the techniques and tools used to detect and count cells in culture.

When microbes are provided with nutrients and the required environmental factors, they become metabolically active and grow. Growth takes place on two levels. On one level, a cell synthesizes new cell components and increases its size; on the other level, the number of cells in the population increases. This capacity for multiplication, increasing the size of the population by cell division, has tremendous importance in microbial control, infectious disease, and biotechnology. In the following sections, we focus primarily on the characteristics of bacterial growth that are generally representative of single-celled microorganisms.

The Basis of Population Growth: Binary Fission and the Bacterial Cell Cycle

The division of a bacterial cell occurs mainly through **binary,** or **transverse, fission.**[5] The term *binary* means that one cell becomes two, and *transverse* refers to the division plane forming across the width of the cell. During the bacterial cell division cycle, the parent cell enlarges, duplicates its chromosome, and forms a central transverse septum that divides the cell into two daughter cells. This process is repeated at intervals by each new daughter cell in turn; and with each successive round of division, the population increases. The stages in this continuous process are shown in greater detail in **process figure 7.15** and **figure 7.16.**

The Rate of Population Growth

The time required for a complete fission cycle—from parent cell to two new daughter cells—is called the **generation,** or **doubling, time.** The term *generation* has a meaning similar to that for humans. It is the period between an individual's birth and the time of producing offspring. In bacteria, each new fission cycle or generation increases the population

5. Research with bacteria that are not culturable indicates that not all cells divide this way. Some bud and others divide by multiple fission.

1 **A parent cell at the beginning of the cell cycle**
What cannot be seen is the synthesis and activity gearing up for cell division.

2 **Chromosome replication and cell enlargement**
The parent cell duplicates the chromosome and synthesizes new structures that enlarge the cell in preparation for the daughter cells.

3 **Chromosome division and septation**
The chromosomes affix to the cytoskeleton and are separated into the forming cells. The cell lays down a septum that begins to wall off the new cells. Other components (ribosomes) are equally distributed to the developing cells.

4 **Completion of cell compartments**
The septum is synthesized completely through the center, and the cell membrane patches itself so that there are two separate cell chambers.

5 **End of cell division cycle**
Daughter cells are now independent units. Some species will separate completely, as shown here, while others will remain attached, forming chains or pairs, for example.

 Cell wall 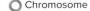 Cell membrane ◯ Chromosome 1 ◯ Chromosome 2 Cytoskeleton • Ribosomes

⚙ **Process Figure 7.15** **Stages in the bacterial cell cycle and binary fission of a rod-shaped bacterium.**

Number of cells	1	2	4	8	16	32
Number of generations		1	2	3	4	5
Exponential value		2^1 (2×1)	2^2 (2×2)	2^3 (2×2×2)	2^4 (2×2×2×2)	2^5 (2×2×2×2×2)

(a)

Figure 7.16 **The mathematics of population growth. (a)** Starting with a single cell, if each product of reproduction goes on to divide by binary fission, the population doubles with each new cell division or generation. This process can be represented by logarithms (2 raised to an exponent) or by simple numbers. **(b)** Plotting the logarithm of the cells produces a straight line indicative of exponential growth, whereas plotting the cell numbers arithmetically gives a curved slope. *Note that the left scale is logarithmic and the right scale is arithmetic.

by a factor of 2, or doubles it. Thus, the initial parent stage consists of 1 cell, the first generation consists of 2 cells, the second 4, the third 8, then 16, 32, 64, and so on. As long as the environment remains favorable, this doubling effect can continue at a constant rate. With the passing of each generation, the population will double, over and over again.

The length of the generation time is a measure of the growth rate of an organism. Compared with the growth rates of most other living things, bacteria are notoriously rapid. The average generation time is 30 to 60 minutes under optimum conditions. The shortest generation times average 5 to 10 minutes, and longest generation times require days. For example, *Mycobacterium leprae,* the cause of Hansen's disease, has a generation time of 10 to 30 days—as long as in some animals. Most pathogens have relatively short doubling times. Cultures of *Salmonella enteritidis* and *Staphylococcus aureus,* bacteria that cause food-borne illness, double in 20 to 30 minutes, which explains why leaving food at room temperature even for a short period has caused many a person to be suddenly stricken with an attack of food-borne disease. In a few hours, a population of these bacteria can easily grow from a small number of cells to several million.

Figure 7.16 illustrates growth: (1) The cell population size can be represented by the number 2 with an exponent (2^1, 2^2, 2^3, 2^4); (2) the exponent increases by one in each generation; and (3) the number of the exponent also gives the number of the generation. This growth pattern is termed **exponential.** Because these populations often contain very large numbers of cells, it is useful to express them by means of exponents or logarithms (see "Exponents," Online Appendix 3). The data from a growing bacterial population are graphed by plotting the number of cells as a function of time. The cell number can be represented logarithmically or arithmetically. Plotting the logarithm number over time provides a straight line indicative of exponential growth. Plotting the data arithmetically gives a constantly curved slope. In general, logarithmic graphs are preferred because an accurate cell number is easier to read, especially during early growth phases.

Predicting the number of cells that will arise during a long growth period (yielding millions of cells) is based on a relatively simple concept. One could use the method of addition 2 + 2 = 4;

4 + 4 = 8; 8 + 8 = 16; 16 + 16 = 32, and so on, or a method of multiplication (for example, $2^5 = 2 \times 2 \times 2 \times 2 \times 2$), but it is easy to see that for 20 or 30 generations, this calculation could be very tedious. An easier way to calculate the size of a population over time is to use an equation such as:

$$N_f = (N_i)2^n$$

In this equation, N_f is the total number of cells in the population at some point in the growth phase, N_i is the starting number, the exponent n denotes the generation number, and 2^n represents the number of cells in that generation. If we know any two of the values, the other values can be calculated. Let us use the example of *Staphylococcus aureus* to calculate how many cells (N_f) will be present in an egg salad sandwich after it sits in a warm car for 4 hours. We will assume that N_i is 10 (number of cells deposited in the sandwich while it was being prepared). To derive n, we need to divide 4 hours (240 minutes) by the generation time (we will use 20 minutes). This calculation comes out to 12, so 2^n is equal to 2^{12}. Using a calculator we find that 2^{12} is 4,096.

Final number (N_f) = 10 × 4,096
= 40,960 bacterial cells in the sandwich

This same equation, with modifications, is used to determine the generation time, a more complex calculation that requires knowing the number of cells at the beginning and end of a growth period. Such data are obtained through actual testing by a method discussed in the following section.

Determinants of Population Growth

In reality, a population of bacteria does not double endlessly, because in most systems numerous factors prevent the cells from continuously dividing at their maximum rate. Quantitative laboratory studies indicate that a population typically displays a predictable pattern, or **growth curve,** over time. The method traditionally used to observe the population growth pattern is a viable count technique, in which

the live cells in a culture are sampled, grown, and counted during a growth period, as described in the next section.

The Viable Plate Count: Batch Culture Method

A growing population is established by inoculating a flask containing a known quantity of sterile liquid medium with a few cells of a pure culture. The flask is incubated at that bacterium's optimum temperature and timed. The population size at any point in the growth cycle is quantified by removing a tiny measured sample of the culture from the growth chamber and plating it out on a solid medium to develop isolated colonies. This procedure is repeated at evenly spaced intervals (i.e., every hour for 24 hours) **(figure 7.17).**

Evaluating the samples involves a common and important principle in microbiology: One colony on a plate represents one cell or colony-forming unit (CFU) from the original sample. Because the CFU of some bacteria is actually composed of several cells (consider the clustered arrangement of *Staphylococcus,* for instance), using a colony count can underestimate the exact population size to an extent. This is not a serious problem, because in such bacteria the CFU is the smallest unit of colony formation and dispersal. Multiplication of the number of colonies in a single sample by the container's volume gives a fair estimate of the total population size (number of cells) at any given point. The growth curve is determined by graphing the number for each sample in sequence for the whole incubation period (see figure 7.18).

Because of the scarcity of cells in the early stages of growth, some samples can give a zero reading even if there are viable cells in the culture. The sampling itself can remove enough viable cells to alter the tabulations, but because the purpose is to compare relative trends in growth, these factors do not significantly change the overall pattern.

Stages in the Normal Growth Curve

The system of batch culturing just described is *closed,* meaning that nutrients and space are finite and there is no mechanism for the removal of waste products. Data from an entire growth period of 3 to 4 days typically produce a curve with a series of phases termed the lag phase, the exponential growth (log) phase, the stationary phase, and the death phase **(figure 7.18).**

The **lag phase** is an early "flat" period on the graph when the population is growing at less than the exponential rate. Growth lags primarily because cells in the newly inoculated culture must adapt to their new environment. Chief among these adaptations is the synthesis of new enzymes required to metabolize nutrients in the culture media.

The length of the lag period varies from one population to another, depending on the condition of the microbes and medium.

The cells reach the maximum rate of cell division during the **exponential growth (logarithmic or log) phase,** a period during which the curve increases geometrically. This phase will continue as long as cells have adequate nutrients and the environment is favorable. During this phase, cells reach their maximum rate of growth.

At the **stationary growth phase,** the population reaches a size limit in which some cells divide more slowly or stop dividing entirely and may even have died. The curve levels off because the number of

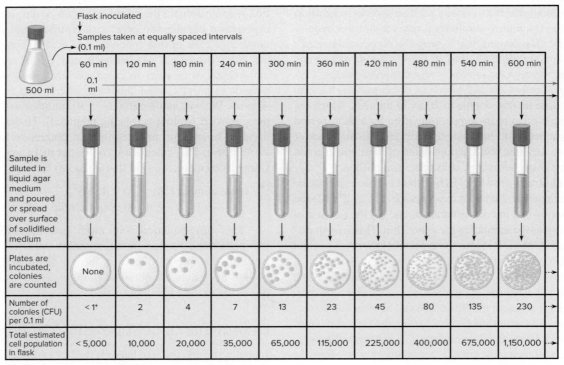

*The culture is probably in lag period with no new cells added.

Figure 7.17 **The general steps in a viable plate count. 1.** Place a few cells into a sterile liquid medium. **2.** Incubate this culture over a period of several hours. **3.** Sample the broth at regular intervals during incubation. **4.** Plate each sample onto solid media. **5.** Count the number of colonies present after incubation.

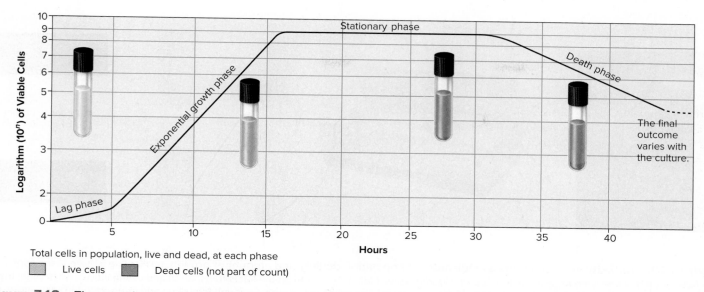

Total cells in population, live and dead, at each phase
- ▢ Live cells
- ▢ Dead cells (not part of count)

Figure 7.18 **The growth curve in a bacterial culture.** On this graph, the number of viable cells expressed as a logarithm (log) is plotted against time. See text for discussion of the various phases. Note that with a generation time of 30 minutes, the population has risen from 10 (10^1) cells to 1,000,000,000 (10^9) cells in only 16 hours. Even though they are not counted, dead cells are indicated to show stages in the cycle where death affects the appearance of the curve.

new cells produced equals the number that have died. The number of viable cells has reached maximum and remains relatively constant during this period. The decline in the growth rate is caused by several factors. A common reason is the depletion of nutrients and oxygen. Another is that the increased cell density often causes an accumulation of organic acids and other toxic biochemicals.

As the limiting factors intensify, the population begins to show a decline, seen as a downward slope on the curve. This stage has been called the **death phase,** but what is actually happening is more complex. Some cells go into dormancy and remain viable but do not grow. Some cells enter a starvation mode that helps them resist the lack of nutrients and other factors. Depending upon the species, some microbes could remain in these states for long periods. It is also apparent that many cells go through a programmed cell death and lyse during this phase, which accounts for the overall reduction in population size. Under these conditions, it is possible for persistent members of the culture to survive by using the nutrients released by the dead cells.

Practical Importance of the Growth Curve The tendency for populations to exhibit phases of rapid growth, slow growth, and death has important implications in microbial control, infection, food microbiology, and culture technology. Antimicrobial agents such as heat and disinfectants rapidly accelerate the death phase in all populations, but microbes in the exponential growth phase are more vulnerable to these agents than are those that have entered the stationary phase. In general, actively growing cells are more vulnerable to conditions that disrupt cell metabolism and binary fission.

Growth patterns in microorganisms can account for the stages of infection (see chapter 13). A person shedding bacteria in the early and middle stages of an infection is more likely to spread it to others than is a person in the late stages. The course of an infection is also influenced by the relatively faster rate of multiplication of the microbe, which can overwhelm the slower growth rate of the host's own cellular defenses.

Understanding the stages of cell growth is crucial for work with cultures. Sometimes a culture that has reached the stationary phase is incubated under the mistaken impression that enough nutrients are present for the culture to continue to multiply. In most cases it is unwise to incubate a culture beyond the stationary phase, because doing so will reduce the number of active cells and the culture could die out completely. It is also preferable to do stains (an exception is the spore stain) and motility tests on young cultures, because the cells will show their natural size and correct reaction, and motile cells will have functioning flagella.

For certain research or industrial applications, closed-batch culturing with its four phases is inefficient. The alternative is an automatic growth chamber called the **chemostat,** or continuous culture system. This device can admit a steady stream of new nutrients and siphon off used media and old bacterial cells, thereby stabilizing the growth rate and cell number. The chemostat is very similar to industrial fermentors used to produce vitamins and antibiotics. It has the advantage of maintaining the culture in a biochemically active state and preventing it from entering the death phase.

Other Methods of Analyzing Population Growth

Microbiologists have developed several alternative ways of analyzing bacterial growth qualitatively and quantitatively. One of the simplest methods for estimating the size of a population is through turbidometry. This technique relies on the simple observation that a tube of clear nutrient solution becomes cloudy, or **turbid,** as microbes grow in it. In general, a greater turbidity indicates a higher microbial count. Differences in turbidity can be measured by means of sensitive instruments such as a spectrophotometer, which measures the ability of cells to scatter light as it passes through a liquid culture, a phenomenon called absorbance. The higher the absorbance measurement, the more growth or cell mass there is in the culture, and vice versa **(figure 7.19*b*).**

(a) (b) (1) Absorbance of light by culture (2)

Figure 7.19 **Turbidity measurements as indicators of population density and amount of growth. (a)** Holding a broth to the light is a practical method of checking for gross differences in cloudiness (turbidity). The broth on the left is transparent, indicating little or no growth; the broth on the right is cloudy and opaque, indicating heavy growth. **(b)** The eye is not sensitive enough to pick up fine degrees in turbidity; more sensitive measurements can be made with a spectrophotometer. A culture placed into the machine is exposed to a beam of light. A detector picks up the amount of light transmitted through the tube and registers this on a screen as absorbance. In **(b1)**, very little light is being scattered and the absorbance reads low, indicating few cells are present. In **(b2)**, more light is scattered, and the absorbance reads higher, indicating significant numbers of cells and growth.
(a): Kathy Park Talaro

Quantifying and Analyzing Cultures

Turbidity readings are useful for evaluating relative amounts of growth, but if a more quantitative evaluation is required, the viable colony count or some other enumeration (counting) procedure is necessary. The **direct,** or **total, cell count** involves counting the number of cells in a sample microscopically **(figure 7.20)**. This technique, very similar to that used in blood cell counts, employs a special microscope slide (cytometer) calibrated to accept a tiny sample that is spread over a premeasured grid. The cell count from a cytometer can be used to estimate the total number of cells in a larger sample (for instance, of milk or water). One inherent inaccuracy in this method as well as in spectrophotometry is that no distinction can be made between dead and live cells, both of which are included in the count. Additional procedures that can assay the microbial content of water are the most probable number (MPN) and membrane filtration techniques discussed later in the book.

Counting can be automated by sensitive devices such as the *Coulter counter,* which electronically scans a culture as it passes through a narrow tube. As each cell flows by, it is detected and registered on an electronic sensor. A **flow cytometer** is a device

that works on a similar principle. It is widely used for counting, sorting, sizing, and identifying cells in suspension **(figure 7.21a)**. For most applications, the cells to be analyzed have to be stained with different fluorescent dyes. They are streamed one at a time through a flow chamber and illuminated by a laser that causes each one to fluoresce in a specific color. As each color signal is detected, it is compiled in graph form **(figure 7.21b)**. Final separation is accomplished by magnets that pull the cells into collection chambers according to their charge. Some of the more common applications include blood cell counts and blood cell separation and identification, analysis of cancer cells, and differentiation of gram-negative and gram-positive bacteria. Even live and dead cells can be differentiated with this method.

Although flow cytometry can be used to count bacteria in natural samples without the need for culturing them, it still requires fluorescent labeling of the cells, which is not always possible. In this event, there are newer DNA-based techniques (for instance, real-time PCR) that can detect and differentiate microbes that have not been isolated, cultured, or identified.

![Practice icon] *Practice* SECTION 7.6

22. What is microbial growth? Explain the stages in the bacterial cell cycle and binary fission.

23. Why is growth called exponential? What causes the pattern of the growth curve?

24. Contrast two different methods of detecting and counting microbial populations, and discuss their advantages and disadvantages.

25. Explain the relationship between colony counts and colony-forming units. Why can one use the number of colonies as an index of population size?

Figure 7.20 **Direct microscopic count of bacteria.** A small sample is placed on the grid under a cover glass. Individual cells, both living and dead, are counted. This number can be used to calculate the total number of cells in a sample.

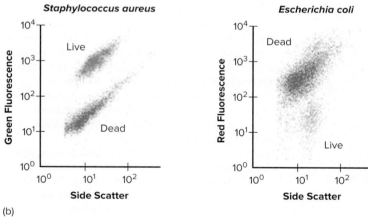

(b)

Figure 7.21 Design and functions of a flow cytometer. (a) The main body of the device is a sheath and flow chamber, which holds fluid and cells. As the labeled cells pass through it, they are lasered and detected by the color they emit. The cells are then diverted into collection chambers. **(b)** A graphic readout analyzes the pattern of cells detected. The result here reveals live and dead bacterial cells stained with red and green fluorescent colors. Each dot on the graph represents one bacterial cell.

CASE STUDY Part 2

Bacteria, like other organisms, are acutely sensitive to the concentration of salt in their environment. In saline surroundings, there is a net movement of water from a bacterial cell to its surroundings, causing the cell to plasmolyze. With little water available for biochemical reactions, the cell becomes metabolically inactive and usually dies. While bacteria are commonly restricted to either marine or freshwater habitats, *V. vulnificus* has evolved to thrive in brackish waters, which are part marine water and part freshwater. These waters typically occur where rivers empty into the sea, diluting ocean water near the coastline. The combination of low salinity and warm temperatures, especially during the spring and summer months, have made *Vibrio vulnificus* infection a common occurrence in the southern United States, where it is responsible for 80,000 illnesses and 100 deaths annually.

The effects of osmotic pressure and the restrictions they place on the growth of bacteria more often work to keep us safe. Salt or sugar is commonly used to slow the growth of microbes in foods like corned beef (the large rocks of salt used to cure the beef were known as corns) as well as bacon, salt pork, sugar-cured ham, fruit preserves, jams, and jellies.

In fact, salt and sugar inhibit microbial growth in multiple ways, with osmosis being only the most obvious. When water is drawn out of the cell, the result is a reduction in what is sometimes called the water activity (a_w) of food, a measure of unbound, free water molecules needed for the survival and growth of microbes. A water activity of 0.91 is low enough to prevent most bacterial growth (most fresh food has an a_w of 0.99); however, yeasts and molds may grow if the a_w rises above 0.60, a value seen in marshmallow, honey, and powdered milk.

In other cases, sugar is converted to compounds with antimicrobial activity, providing an indirect form of preservation. This is seen when yeasts convert sugars to ethanol in wine or when lactic acid bacteria ferment sugars to organic acids in sauerkraut. Finally, salts and sugars may weaken the molecular structure of DNA and interfere with the activity of enzymes.

Because nature abhors a vacuum, there also exist some microbes that grow only in extraordinarily salty or sugary conditions. Members of the bacterial genera *Halococcus* or *Halobacterium* require at least 13% salt to grow and are capable of causing the spoilage of the saltiest food, while *Zygosaccharomyces* is a sugar-loving yeast that grows well in concentrated fruit juices.

■ Most bacterial cells live in hypotonic environments, where water tends to move into the cell. What cellular structure protects the cell in such an environment?

■ Why must we refrigerate foods like orange juice while honey, corn syrup, and soy sauce are generally safe to store at room temperature?

Chapter Summary with Key Terms

7.1 Microbial Nutrition

Environmental factors that have the greatest impact on microbes are nutrients, temperature, pH, amount of available water, atmospheric gases, light, pressure, and other organisms. **Nutrition** consists of taking in chemical substances (nutrients) and assimilating and extracting energy from them.

A. Substances required for survival are **essential nutrients**—usually containing the elements (S, P, O, N, C, H, Na, Cl, K, Ca, Fe, Mg). Essential nutrients are considered **macronutrients** (required in larger amounts) or **micronutrients** (trace elements required in smaller amounts—Zn, Mn, Cu). Nutrients are classed as either **inorganic** or **organic.**

B. A **growth factor** is an organic nutrient (amino acid and vitamin) that cannot be synthesized and must be provided.

7.2 Classification of Nutritional Types

A. An **autotroph** depends on carbon dioxide for its carbon needs. An autotroph that derives energy from light is a **photoautotroph;** one that extracts energy from inorganic substances is a **chemoautotroph. Methanogens** are chemoautotrophs that produce methane.

B. A **heterotroph or chemoorganotroph** acquires carbon from organic molecules originating from the bodies of dead or living organisms. A **saprobe** is a decomposer that feeds primarily upon dead organic matter, and a **parasite** feeds from a live host and usually causes harm. Parasites that cause damage or death are called **pathogens.**

7.3 Transport: Movement of Substances across the Cell Membrane

A. A microbial cell must take in nutrients from its surroundings by transporting them across the cell membrane.

B. Passive transport involves the natural movement of substances down a concentration gradient and requires no additional energy **(diffusion).** A form of passive transport that can move specific substances is **facilitated diffusion.**

C. **Osmosis** is diffusion of water through a selectively permeable membrane.

D. Osmotic changes that affect cells are **hypotonic** solutions, which contain less solute than the cell, and **hypertonic** solutions, which contain more solute than the cell. **Isotonic** solutions have the same solute concentration as the inside of the cell. A **halophile** thrives in hypertonic surroundings, and an **obligate halophile** requires a salt concentration of at least 15% but grows optimally in 25%.

E. In **active transport**, substances are taken into the cell by a process that consumes energy. In **group translocation**, molecules are altered during transport.

F. **Phagocytosis** and **pinocytosis** are forms of active transport in which bulk quantities of solid and fluid material are taken into the cell.

7.4 Environmental Factors that Influence Microbes

Every organism adapts to a particular habitat and niche.

A. *Temperature:* An organism exhibits **optimum, minimum,** and **maximum temperatures.** Organisms that cannot grow above 20°C but thrive below 15°C and continue to grow even at 0°C are known as **psychrophiles. Mesophiles** grow from 10°C to 50°C, having temperature optima from 20°C to 40°C. The growth range of **thermophiles** is 45°C to 80°C. Extreme thermophiles may grow to temperatures of 250°C.

B. *Oxygen Requirements:* The ecological need for free oxygen (O_2) is based on whether a cell can handle toxic by-products such as superoxide and peroxide.

1. **Aerobes** grow in normal atmospheric oxygen and have enzymes to handle toxic oxygen by-products. An aerobic organism capable of living without oxygen if necessary is a **facultative anaerobe.** An aerobe that requires a small amount of oxygen but does not grow under anaerobic conditions is a **microaerophile.**

2. **Strict (obligate) anaerobes** do not use free oxygen and cannot produce enzymes to dismantle reactive oxides. They are actually damaged or killed by oxygen. An aerotolerant anaerobe cannot use oxygen for respiration, yet is not injured by it.

C. *Effects of pH:* Acidity and alkalinity affect the activity and integrity of enzymes and the structural components of a cell. Optimum pH for most microbes ranges from 6 to 8. **Acidophiles** prefer a pH below 7, **alkalinophiles** prefer a pH above 7, and **neutrophils** grow best around pH 7.

D. *Other Environmental Factors:* Radiation and barometric pressure affect microbial growth. A **barophile** is adapted to life under high pressure (bottom dwellers in the ocean, for example).

7.5 Ecological Associations among Microorganisms

A. *Microbial Interactions:* Microbes coexist in varied relationships in nature.

1. Types of **symbiosis** are **mutualism,** a reciprocal, obligatory, and beneficial relationship between two organisms, and **commensalism,** an organism receiving benefits from another without harming the other organism in the relationship. **Parasitism** occurs between a host and an infectious agent; the host is harmed in the interaction.

2. **Syntrophism** is a beneficial but not obligatory coexistence in which organisms cross-feed. **Amensalism** entails competition, inhibition, and injury directed against an opposing organism. A common example is antibiotic production.

3. **Quorum sensing** is an interaction among members of a biofilm that results in a coordinated reaction, such as secretion of **inducer molecules** and enzymes. By behaving as a unit, the biofilm remains stable and organized. It can occupy and exploit a wide variety of habitats.

7.6 The Study of Microbial Growth

A. During the bacterial cell cycle, the parent cell splits to form a pair of daughter cells by means of **binary,** or **transverse, fission.**

B. It involves replication of the chromosome and the equal division of other cell components.

C. The duration of each division is called the **generation,** or **doubling, time.** A population theoretically doubles with each generation, so the growth rate is **exponential,** and each cycle increases in geometric progression.

D. A **growth curve** is a graphic representation of a closed population over time, using an estimate of live cells called a viable count. The initial flat period of the curve is called the **lag phase,** followed by the **exponential growth phase,** in

which viable cells increase in logarithmic progression. Adverse environmental conditions create a plateau, or **stationary growth phase.** In the **death phase,** nutrient depletion and waste buildup cause increased cell death.

E. Cell numbers can be counted by a viable plate count, microscope counting chamber, Coulter counter, or **flow cytometer.** Cell growth can also be determined by turbidometry and a total cell count.

 ## Assess Your Knowledge

Level I. These questions require a working knowledge of the concepts in the chapter and the ability to recall and understand the information you have studied.

Developing a Concept Inventory

Select the correct answer from the answers provided. For questions with blanks, choose the combination of answers that most accurately completes the statement.

1. An organic nutrient essential to an organism's metabolism that cannot be synthesized itself is termed a/an
 a. trace element
 b. micronutrient
 c. growth factor
 d. mineral

2. The source of the necessary elements of life is
 a. an inorganic environmental reservoir
 b. the sun
 c. rocks
 d. the air

3. An organism that can synthesize all its required organic components from CO_2 using energy from the sun is a
 a. photoautotroph c. chemoautotroph
 b. photoheterotroph d. chemoheterotroph

4. An obligate halophile requires high
 a. pH c. salt
 b. temperature d. pressure

5. Chemoautotrophs can survive on _____ alone.
 a. minerals c. minerals and CO_2
 b. CO_2 d. methane

6. Which of the following substances are required by *all* organisms?
 a. organic nutrients c. growth factors
 b. inorganic nutrients d. oxygen gas

7. A pathogen would most accurately be described as a
 a. parasite c. saprobe
 b. commensal d. symbiont

8. Which of the following is true of passive transport?
 a. requires a gradient c. includes endocytosis
 b. uses the cell wall d. only moves water

9. A cell exposed to a hypertonic environment will _____ by osmosis.
 a. gain water c. neither gain nor lose water
 b. lose water d. burst

10. Active transport of a substance across a membrane requires
 a. a gradient c. water
 b. the expenditure of ATP d. diffusion

11. Psychrophiles would be expected to grow
 a. in hot springs c. at refrigeration temperatures
 b. on the human body d. at low pH

12. Which of the following is *not* involved in quorum sensing?
 a. accumulation of inducer molecules
 b. a certain level of biofilm density
 c. self-monitoring
 d. release of genetic material

13. Superoxide ion is toxic to strict anaerobes because they lack
 a. catalase c. dismutase
 b. peroxidase d. oxidase

14. The time required for a cell to undergo binary fission is called the
 a. exponential growth rate c. generation time
 b. growth curve d. lag period

15. In a viable plate count, each _____ represents a _____ from the sample population.
 a. cell, colony c. hour, generation
 b. colony, cell d. cell, generation

16. The stage in population growth with the highest rate of cell division is the
 a. stationary phase c. exponential phase
 b. lag phase d. enlargement phase

Case Study Analysis

1. Cells of *Vibrio vulnificus* are common near the coastline, but are rare farther out to sea. Why?
 a. Cells at sea lyse as freshwater enters the cells.
 b. Cells at sea plasmolyze as freshwater enters the cells.
 c. Cells at sea plasmolyze as salt leaves the cell.
 d. Cells at sea plasmolyze as water leaves the cell.

2. Many protists collect water that enters the cell via osmosis in membrane-bound organelles called water vacuoles. When a vacuole reaches a certain size, the protist moves the vacuole to the edge of the cell and uses active transport to expel the water out of the cell. If a protist moves from briny water to freshwater, what would happen to the water vacuoles?

 a. They would form at the same rate regardless of the salt concentration.

 b. They would form more slowly.

 c. They would form more rapidly.

 d. They would disappear entirely, as salt would leave the cell through osmosis.

3. Dehydrated foods like instant soup, hot chocolate, or ramen may generally be stored at room temperature, but once they have been rehydrated, must be refrigerated. Why is this?

On the Test

These questions will help to prepare you to successfully answer similar questions you'll see on the TEAS (Test of Essential Academic Skills) and NCLEX (National Council Licensure Examination).

1. What type of energy is converted to chemical energy in photosynthesis?

 a. heat

 b. light

 c. chemical

 d. organic

2. Diffusion and osmosis are examples of

 a. active transport

 b. passive transport

 c. extracellular transport

 d. intracellular transport

Writing Challenge

For each question (except 7), compose a one- or two-paragraph answer that includes the factual information needed to completely address the question. Practice questions can also be used for writing-challenge exercises.

1. Look at the following diagrams and predict in which direction osmosis will take place. Use arrows to show the net direction of osmosis. Is one of these microbes a halophile? Which one?

6. Explain what is happening to the population at points A, B, C, and D in the following diagram.

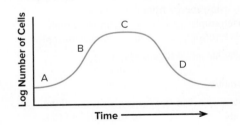

7. Fill in the following table:

2. Describe the basic metabolism of methanogens.

3. Discuss extreme environments and types of extremophiles that live there.

4. Differentiate between mutualism and syntrophy with examples.

5. a. What biochemical events in quorum sensing ensure that a biofilm can function as a unit?

 b. Explain how biofilm self-monitoring would favor infections.

Source of Carbon	Usual Source of Energy	Example
Photoautotroph		
Photoheterotroph		
Chemoautotroph		
Chemoheterotroph		
Saprobe		
Parasite		

Concept Mapping

On Connect you can find an Introduction to Concept Mapping that provides guidance for working with concept maps, along with concept-mapping activities for this chapter.

 ## Application, Analysis, Evaluation, and Synthesis

Level II. These problems go beyond just restating facts and require higher levels of understanding and an ability to interpret, problem solve, transfer knowledge to new situations, create models, and predict outcomes.

Critical Thinking

Critical thinking is the ability to reason and solve problems using facts and concepts. These questions can be approached from a number of angles and, in most cases, they do not have a single correct answer.

1. a. Is there a microbe that could grow on a medium that contains only the following compounds dissolved in water: $CaCO_3$, $MgNO_3$, $FeCl_2$, $ZnSO_4$, and glucose? Defend your answer.

 b. A useful mnemonic device for keeping track of major elements required by most organisms is: **C HOPKINS Ca Fe, Na Cl Mg**ood. Read aloud, it becomes "See Hopkin's Cafe, NaCl (salt) M good!" What does each letter stand for?

2. Describe how one might determine the nutrient requirements of a microbe from Mars. If, after exhausting various nutrient schemes, it still does not grow, what other factors might one take into account?

3. Patients with ketoacidosis associated with diabetes are especially susceptible to fungal infections. Propose why this might be the case.

4. a. Explain how osmotic pressure and pH are used in preserving foods.
 b. What effects do they have on microbes?

5. Provide some suggestions for treating anaerobic infections by manipulating the gas content of the environment.

6. Could anaerobes and aerobes coexist in the same habitat? Why or why not?

7. a. If an egg salad sandwich sitting in a warm car for 4 hours develops 40,960 bacterial cells, how many more cells would result with just one more hour of incubation? Use the same criteria that were stated in the sample problem under the heading "Rate of Population Growth" in section 7.6.

 b. How many would result after 10 additional hours of incubation?

 c. What do your answers tell you about using clean techniques in food preparation and storage (other than aesthetic considerations)?

8. The noted microbial ecologist Martin W. Beijerinck has stated: "Everything is everywhere, the environment selects." Use this concept to explain what ultimately determines whether a microorganism can live in a certain habitat.

9. Describe the similarities and differences between a mutualistic endosymbiont and a parasitic endosymbiont.

Visual Assessment

1. Place appropriate points on the axes and draw and label separate graphs that fit a psychrotroph and an obligate thermophile.

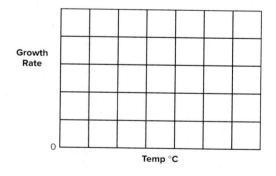

2. Enter points on the axes and graph the probable results for an acidophile, a neutrophile, and an alkalinophile.

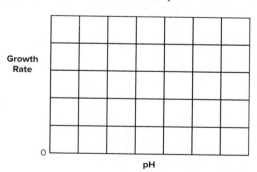

An Introduction to Microbial Metabolism:

The Chemical Crossroads of Life

In This Chapter...

CASE STUDY Part 1 — Driving Under the Influence of Yeast

In late 2014, police in Hamburg, New York, a small city a few miles south of Buffalo, received a 911 call reporting a car weaving dangerously in traffic lanes. The police officer responding to the scene pulled the car over and noted that not only was the car was weaving, but a great deal smoke and the smell of burning rubber was coming from a deflated front passenger-side tire, of which the driver seemed to be unaware. The officer reported that the driver of the car, a 35-year-old schoolteacher, had **alcohol** on her breath, slurred speech, and glassy, bloodshot eyes. Although she was able to recite the alphabet, she had difficulty completing other field **sobriety** tests, including standing on one foot and turning heel to toe, the proverbial "walking a straight line." She said she had had three drinks earlier in the day while visiting her parents in Buffalo and was aware of the flat tire, but felt she was close enough that she could safely make it home before dealing with it. The woman later maintained that although she felt a little woozy, she was confident of her ability to drive safely. The officer administered a breathalyzer test, which measured the driver's **BAC (blood alcohol content)** at 0.33%, more than four times the legal limit of 0.08%. At 0.33%, most people would be in a drunken stupor, and the threat of **coma and death via respiratory failure** would be a distinct possibility. The woman was arrested for driving while **intoxicated** and, because of her exceedingly high BAC, transported to a nearby hospital. A blood test administered later in the evening at Erie County Medical Center measured 0.30%, confirming the findings of the field breathalyzer test.

In court, what appeared at first to be a straightforward drunk-driving case took an abrupt turn when the woman's attorney announced that his client had not ingested the alcohol in her bloodstream, but rather created it herself. He declared that his client suffered from **gut fermentation syndrome** (sometimes also known as auto-brewery syndrome). A rare condition, with perhaps as few as 100 diagnosed sufferers, gut fermentation syndrome occurs when **yeast** in the small intestine **ferment** dietary carbohydrates to produce alcohol. The alcohol enters the bloodstream, resulting in **intoxication,** just as if the person had consumed a great many drinks.

On December 9, 2014, Hamburg town Judge Walter Rooth dismissed the charges against the defendant.

- *Would gut fermentation syndrome best be described as anabolic or catabolic?*

- *Besides the alcoholic pathway, what other pathway exists for the fermentation of carbohydrates?*

To continue the Case Study, go to Case Study Part 2 at the end of the chapter.

(Yeast cells): Brand X/Getty Images

8.1 An Introduction to Metabolism and Enzymes

 Learn

1. Define *metabolism* and differentiate its two types.
2. Describe the basic functions of enzymes in cells.
3. Outline the prominent characteristics of enzymes.
4. Explain how enzymes lower the energy required for a reaction to occur.
5. Discuss enzyme structure and interactions between enzymes and substrates.
6. Describe the types of enzyme functions and methods of naming them.
7. Summarize the key features of enzyme regulation.

Metabolism, from the Greek term *metaballein,* meaning change, pertains to all chemical workings of cells. It is a shorthand term for encapsulating almost any activity or behavior of an organism, from the general to the specific, including growth, synthesis, transport, digestion, energy release and consumption, and movement. Although metabolism entails thousands of different reactions, most of them can be placed into one of two general categories. In the case of **catabolism,** larger molecules are degraded or broken down into smaller molecules, usually with the release of energy. In the case of **anabolism,** also called biosynthesis, larger molecules are built from smaller ones, which results in the formation of cell structures. It is usually driven by energy derived from catabolism. Even though they have somewhat opposite effects, these two forms of metabolism are tightly linked and highly complementary. As we will see, the

result of them working together is that all metabolism is coordinated for the cell to carry out essential life functions **(figure 8.1).** The major metabolic functions in cells and the sections of the chapter that cover them are listed here:

1. Enzymes serve as catalysts for both catabolic and anabolic activities. Because of their importance in all areas of microbiology, the remainder of section 8.1 is devoted to characteristics of enzymes.
2. Cells acquire energy from an external source (outside the cell) such as nutrients or the sun. Discussion of this idea began in chapter 7 and continues in sections 8.2 and 8.6.
3. Cells extract the energy and transfer it to a high-energy molecule, adenosine triphosphate (ATP), a universal compound for managing energy. This is accomplished by several different types of catabolic pathways, covered in sections 8.3 and 8.4.
4. Cells use ATP to power anabolic processes. Simple building blocks are bonded into larger molecules and cell structures, thereby creating greater complexity through the input of this energy. Anabolic pathways are covered in section 8.5.

We suggest you review relevant sections in chapter 2 covering organic molecules and biochemistry.

Enzymes: Catalyzing the Chemical Reactions of Life

A microbial cell could be viewed as a microscopic factory, complete with basic building materials, a source of energy, and a genetic "blueprint" for running its extensive network of metabolic reactions. But the chemical reactions of life would never proceed without a special class of proteins called **enzymes.** Enzymes are a remarkable example of **catalysts,** chemicals that increase the rate of

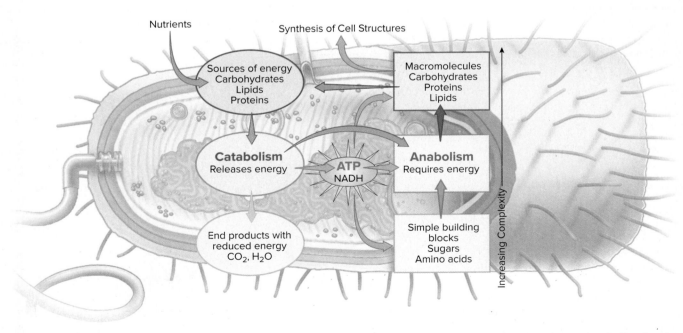

Figure 8.1 Simplified model of metabolism. Chemical reactions that occur in cells fall into two major categories. Catabolism involves the breakdown of complex organic molecules to extract energy and form simpler end products. Anabolism uses the energy to synthesize necessary macromolecules and cell structures from simple precursors, increasing chemical complexity. The two systems interact in a continuous cycle that maintains the metabolic balance inside cells.

8.1 MAKING CONNECTIONS

Enzymes as Biochemical Levers

An analogy will allow us to envision the relationship of enzymes to the energy of activation. A large boulder sitting precariously on a cliff's edge contains a great deal of potential energy, but it will not fall to the ground and release this energy unless something disturbs it. It might eventually be disturbed spontaneously as the cliff erodes below it, but that could take a very long time. Maneuvering it with a crowbar (to overcome the resistance of the boulder's weight) will cause it to tumble down freely by its own momentum. If we relate this analogy to chemicals, the reactants are the boulder on the cliff, the activation energy is the energy needed to move the boulder, the enzyme is the crowbar, and the product is the boulder at the bottom of the cliff. Like the crowbar, an enzyme permits a reaction to occur rapidly by getting it over the energy "hump." Although this analogy concretely illustrates the concept of the energy of activation, it is imperfect in that the enzyme, unlike the person with the crowbar, does not actually add any energy to the system.

This phenomenon can be represented by plotting the energy of the reaction against the direction of the reaction. The curve of reaction is shown in the accompanying graph. Reactants must overcome the energy of activation (E_{act}) for the reaction to proceed. When a catalyst is present, it lowers the E_{act}. It does this by providing the reactants with an alternative pathway, requiring less energy, by which they can progress to the final state. Note that the products reach the same final energy state with or without an enzyme.

What is the actual physical process performed by the enzyme that speeds up a reaction?

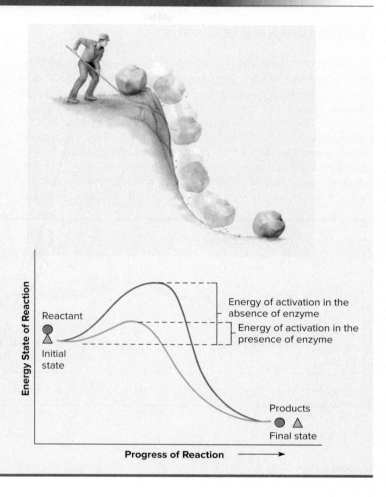

a chemical reaction without becoming part of the products or being consumed in the reaction. Do not make the mistake of thinking that an enzyme creates a reaction. Because of the free energy inherent in molecules, a reaction could occur spontaneously at some point even without an enzyme but at a very slow rate. A study of the enzyme urease shows that it increases the rate of the breakdown of urea by a factor of 100 trillion as compared to an uncatalyzed reaction. Because most uncatalyzed metabolic reactions do not occur fast enough to sustain cell processes, enzymes are indispensable to life. Other major qualities of enzymes are summarized in **table 8.1.**

How Do Enzymes Work?

We have said that an enzyme speeds up the rate of a metabolic reaction, but just how does it do this? During a chemical reaction, reactants are converted to products by bond formation or breakage. A certain amount of energy is required to initiate every such reaction, which limits its rate. This resistance to a reaction, which must be overcome for a reaction to proceed, is measurable and is called the **energy of activation** or activation energy (**8.1 Making Connections**). In the laboratory, overcoming this initial resistance can be achieved by

- increasing thermal energy (heating) to increase molecular velocity,

TABLE 8.1	Checklist of Enzyme Characteristics

- Composed mostly of protein; may require nonprotein cofactors
- Act as organic catalysts to speed up the rate of cellular reactions
- Lower the activation energy required for a chemical reaction to proceed (see 8.1 Making Connections)
- Enable metabolic reactions to proceed at a speed compatible with life
- Have unique characteristics such as shape, specificity, and function
- Provide an active site for target molecules called substrates
- Are much larger in size than their substrates
- Associate closely with substrates but do not become integrated into the reaction products
- Are not used up or permanently changed by the reaction
- Can be recycled and function in extremely low concentrations
- Are greatly affected by temperature and pH
- Can be regulated by feedback and genetic mechanisms

- increasing the concentration of reactants to increase the rate of molecular collisions, or
- adding a catalyst.

8.2 MAKING CONNECTIONS

A Different Kind of Catalyst

The molecular reactions of cells are still an active and rich source of discovery, and new findings come along on a regular basis that break older "rules" and adjust our understanding. Originally, proteins were considered the only biological molecules that act as catalysts. Then biologists found a novel type of RNA they termed **ribozymes.** Ribozymes appear to be rather common, with around 500 having been identified in all types of cells and some viruses. They display some of the properties of protein catalysts, such as having a specific active site and interacting with a substrate. But these molecules are remarkable because their substrates are other molecules of RNA. Ribozymes are thought to be remnants of the earliest molecules on earth that could have served as both catalysts and genetic material. In natural systems, ribozymes are involved in self-splicing or cutting of RNA molecules during processing of the genetic code, and even ribosomes function as ribozymes during protein synthesis (see chapter 9). Further research has shown that ribozymes can be designed to handle other kinds of activities, such as inhibiting gene expression. Several companies have developed and are testing ribozyme-based therapies for treating cancer and HIV infection.

Propose some effects that ribozymes have on microorganisms that would make them suitable for therapy.

A ribozyme (here a "hairpin loop" type) can clip RNA and remove sections of it.

In most living systems, the first two alternatives are not feasible, because elevating the temperature is potentially harmful, and higher concentrations of reactants are often not practical. This leaves only the action of catalysts, and enzymes fill this need efficiently and potently.

At the molecular level, an enzyme promotes a reaction by serving as a physical site upon which the reactant molecules, called **substrates,** can be positioned for various interactions. The enzyme is much larger in size than its substrate, and it presents a uniquely shaped pocket that fits only that particular substrate. Although an enzyme binds to the substrate and participates directly in changes to the substrate, it does not become a part of the products, it is not used up by the reaction, and it can function over and over again. Enzyme speed, defined as the number of substrate molecules converted per enzyme per second, is well documented. Speeds range from several million for catalase to a thousand for lactate dehydrogenase. A key to understanding the roles of enzymes in metabolism is their structure.

> **Quick Search**
> Go online to find the video "Functions of Enzymes—How Do Enzymes Work?" and observe a quick animation of enzyme reactions.

Connections). Enzymes can be classified as simple or conjugated. Simple enzymes consist of protein alone, whereas conjugated enzymes **(figure 8.2)** contain protein and nonprotein molecules. A conjugated enzyme, sometimes referred to as a **holoenzyme,** is a combination of a protein, now called the **apoenzyme,** and one or more **cofactors (table 8.2).** Cofactors are either organic molecules, called **coenzymes,** or inorganic elements (metal ions) that many enzymes require to become functional. In some enzymes, the cofactor is loosely associated

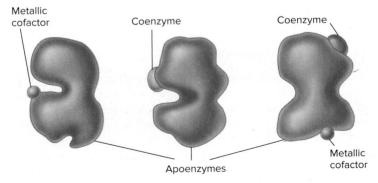

Enzyme Structure

Enzymes are composed largely of protein molecules, although certain types of RNA can function as nonenzyme catalysts **(8.2 Making**

Figure 8.2 Conjugated enzyme structure. All examples have an apoenzyme (polypeptide or protein) component and one or more cofactors.

TABLE 8.2	Selected Enzymes, Catalytic Actions, and Cofactors*	
Enzyme	**Action**	**Cofactor Required**
Catalase	Breaks down hydrogen peroxide	Iron (Fe)
Oxidase	Adds electrons to oxygen	Iron, copper (Cu)
Hexokinase	Transfers phosphate to glucose	Magnesium (Mg)
Arginase	Acts on the amino acid arginine	Manganese
Nitrate reductase	Reduces nitrate to nitrite	Molybdenum (Mo)
DNA polymerase	Synthesis of DNA	Zinc (Zn) and Mg
Botulinum toxin	Hydrolyzes protein needed for vesicle transport	Zinc
Pyruvate dehydrogenase	Converts pyruvic acid to acetyl CoA and CO_2	Thiamine and magnesium
Succinate dehydrogenase	Oxidizes succinate to fumarate in the Krebs cycle	FAD (contains riboflavin)

* The first seven are metals and the last two are coenzymes containing vitamins.

with the apoenzyme by noncovalent bonds; in others, it is linked by covalent bonds.

Apoenzymes: Specificity and the Active Site

Apoenzymes range in size from small polypeptides with about 100 amino acids and a molecular weight of 12,000 to large polypeptide conglomerates with thousands of amino acids and a molecular weight of over 1 million. Like all proteins, an apoenzyme exhibits levels of molecular complexity called the primary, secondary, tertiary, and, in larger enzymes, quaternary organization **(figure 8.3).** As we saw in chapter 2, the first three levels of structure arise when a single polypeptide chain undergoes an automatic folding process and achieves stability by forming disulfide and other types of bonds. Folding causes the surface of the apoenzyme to acquire three-dimensional features that create the enzyme's specificity for substrates. The actual pocket where the substrate binds is called the **active site,** or **catalytic site,** and there can be from one to several such sites (figure 8.3). Because each type of enzyme has a different primary structure (type and sequence of amino acids), this gives rise to variations in folding and unique active sites.

Enzyme-Substrate Interactions

For a reaction to take place, a temporary **enzyme–substrate** union must occur at the active site. There are several explanations for the way this happens **(figure 8.4).** The specificity is often described as a "lock-and-key" fit in which the substrate is inserted into the active site's pocket. This is a useful analogy, but an enzyme is not a rigid lock mechanism. It is likely that the enzyme actually helps the substrate move into the active site through slight changes in its shape. This is called an *induced fit* (figure 8.4*d*). The bonds formed between the substrate and enzyme are weak and, of necessity, easily reversible. Once the enzyme–substrate complex has formed, appropriate reactions occur on the substrate, often with the aid of a cofactor, and a product is formed and released. The enzyme can then attach to another substrate molecule and repeat this action.

Cofactors: Supporting the Work of Enzymes

In chapter 7, you learned that microorganisms require specific metal ions called trace elements and certain organic growth factors. In many cases,

(a) As the polypeptide forms intrachain bonds and folds, it assumes a three-dimensional (tertiary) state that displays an active site (AS).

(b) Because each unique polypeptide folds differently, each apoenzyme will have a differently shaped active site.

(c) More complex enzymes have a quaternary structure consisting of more than one polypeptide. New active sites may be formed by the junction of polypeptides.

Levels of Structure

Primary Secondary Tertiary Quaternary

AS

Figure 8.3 **How the active site and specificity of the apoenzyme arise.** Review figure 2.24 for details of this process.

Figure 8.4 Enzyme–substrate reactions. (a) When the enzyme and substrate come together, the substrate (S) will have a correct fit and position with respect to the enzyme (E). **(b)** When the ES complex is formed, it enters a transition state. During this temporary but tight interlocking union, the enzyme participates directly in breaking or making bonds. **(c)** Once the reaction is complete, the enzyme releases the products. **(d)** The induced-fit model proposes that the enzyme recognizes its substrate and adapts slightly to it so that the final binding is even more precise.

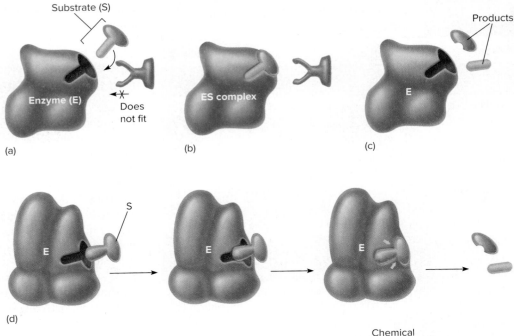

the need for these substances arises from their roles as **cofactors** (table 8.2). The **metallic cofactors,** including iron, copper, magnesium, manganese, zinc, cobalt, selenium, and many others, participate in precise functions between the enzyme and its substrate. In general, metals activate enzymes, help bring the active site and substrate close together, and participate directly in chemical reactions with the enzyme–substrate complex.

Coenzymes are organic cofactors that work in conjunction with the apoenzyme to perform a necessary alteration of a substrate. The general function of a coenzyme is to remove a chemical group from one substrate molecule and add it to another substrate, thereby serving as a temporary carrier of this group **(figure 8.5).** The specific activities of coenzymes are many and varied. In section 8.3, we shall see that coenzymes carry and transfer hydrogen atoms, electrons, carbon dioxide, and amino groups. Some of the most common components of coenzymes are **vitamins,** which explains why vitamins are important to nutrition and may be required as growth factors for living things. Vitamin deficiencies prevent the complete holoenzyme from forming, which compromises both the chemical reaction and the structure or function that is dependent upon that reaction.

Classification of Enzyme Functions

Enzymes are classified and named according to characteristics such as site of action, type of action, and substrate **(8.3 Making Connections).**

Location and Regularity of Enzyme Action

Enzymes perform their tasks either inside or outside of the cell in which they were produced. After initial synthesis in the cell, **exoenzymes** are transported extracellularly, where they break

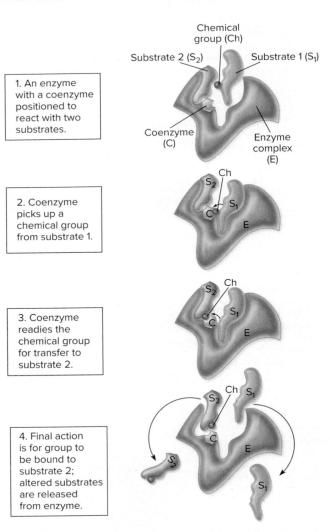

1. An enzyme with a coenzyme positioned to react with two substrates.

2. Coenzyme picks up a chemical group from substrate 1.

3. Coenzyme readies the chemical group for transfer to substrate 2.

4. Final action is for group to be bound to substrate 2; altered substrates are released from enzyme.

Figure 8.5 The carrier functions of coenzymes. Many enzymes use coenzymes to transfer chemical groups from one substrate to another.

8.3 MAKING CONNECTIONS

The Enzyme Name Game

Most metabolic reactions require a unique enzyme, and researchers have discovered and named over 5,000 of them. Given the complex chemistry of the cell and the extraordinary diversity of living things, many more enzymes probably remain to be discovered. A standardized system of nomenclature and classification was developed to prevent discrepancies.

In general, an enzyme name is composed of two parts: a prefix or stem word derived from a certain characteristic—usually the substrate acted upon or the type of reaction catalyzed, or both—followed by the ending *-ase*.

The system classifies the enzyme in one of these six classes, on the basis of its general biochemical action:

1. *Oxidoreductases* transfer electrons from one substrate to another, and *dehydrogenases* transfer a hydrogen from one compound to another.
2. *Transferases* transfer functional groups from one substrate to another.
3. *Hydrolases* cleave bonds on molecules with the addition of water.
4. *Lyases* add groups to or remove groups from double-bonded substrates.
5. *Isomerases* change a substrate into its isomeric form. An **isomer** is a compound that has the same molecular formula as another compound but differs in arrangement of the atoms.

6. *Synthases* are enzymes that catalyze the formation of large molecules; for example, fatty acid synthase makes one component of triglycerides.

Each enzyme is also assigned a technical name that indicates the specific reaction it catalyses. These names are useful for biochemists but are often too lengthy for routine use. More often a common name is derived from some notable feature such as the substrate or enzyme action. For example, *hydrogen peroxide oxidoreductase* is more commonly known as *catalase*. With this simpler system, an enzyme that digests a carbohydrate substrate is a *carbohydrase;* a specific carbohydrase, *amylase,* acts on starch (amylose is a major component of starch). An enzyme that hydrolyzes peptide bonds of a protein is a *proteinase, protease,* or *peptidase,* depending on the size of the protein substrate. Some fats and other lipids are digested by *lipases.* DNA is hydrolyzed by *deoxyribonuclease,* generally shortened to *DNase,* and a *polymerase* synthesizes DNA or RNA. Other examples of enzymes are presented in **table 8.A.** (See also table 8.2.)

Give the common names for enzymes that digest collagen, that make ATP, and that clot blood.

TABLE 8.A	A Sampling of Enzymes, Their Substrates, and Their Reactions			
Common Name	**Systematic Name**	**Enzyme Class**	**Substrate**	**Action**
Lactase	β,D galactosidase	Hydrolase	Lactose	Breaks lactose down into glucose and galactose
Penicillinase	Beta-lactamase	Hydrolase	Penicillin	Hydrolyzes beta-lactam ring
DNA polymerase	DNA nucleotidyl-transferase	Synthase	DNA nucleosides	Synthesizes a strand of DNA using the complementary strand as a model
Lactate dehydrogenase	Same as common name	Oxidoreductase	Pyruvic acid	Catalyzes the conversion of pyruvic acid to lactic acid
Oxidase	Cytochrome oxidase	Oxidoreductase	Molecular oxygen	Catalyzes the reduction (addition of electrons and hydrogen ions) to O_2

down large food molecules or harmful chemicals (see discussion of hydrolysis reactions under the next heading). Examples of exoenzymes are cellulase, amylase, and penicillinase. By contrast, **endoenzymes** are retained intracellularly and function there **(figure 8.6).** Most enzymes of the metabolic pathways are of this variety.

In terms of their presence in the cell, enzymes are not all produced in equal amounts or at equal rates. Some, called **constitutive enzymes (figure 8.7a),** are continually present in relatively constant amounts, regardless of the amount of substrate. The enzymes involved in utilizing glucose, for example, are very important in metabolism and thus are constitutive. Other enzymes are **regulated enzymes (figure 8.7b),** the production of which is either turned on (induced) or turned off (repressed) in response to changes in concentration of the substrate or product. The level of inducible and repressible enzymes is controlled by variations in expression of the genes for these proteins, as discussed in chapter 9.

Figure 8.6 **Types of enzymes, as described by their location of action. (a)** Exoenzymes are transported outside the cell to become active. **(b)** Endoenzymes remain in the cell and function there.

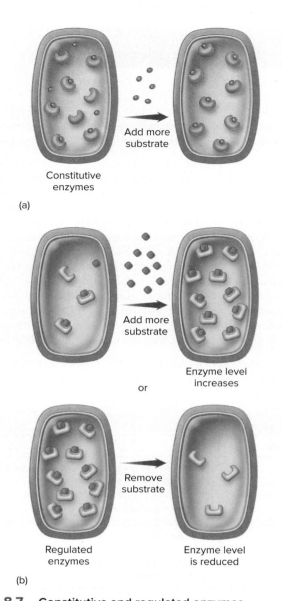

Constitutive
enzymes

(a)

Add more
substrate

Add more
substrate

or

Enzyme level
increases

Remove
substrate

Regulated
enzymes

Enzyme level
is reduced

(b)

Figure 8.7 **Constitutive and regulated enzymes**
(a) Constitutive enzymes are present in constant amounts in a cell.
The addition of more substrate does not increase the numbers of
these enzymes. **(b)** The concentration of some regulated enzymes
in a cell increases or decreases in response to substrate levels.

Synthesis and Hydrolysis Reactions A growing cell is in a
constant state of synthesis. All such anabolic reactions require en-
zymes (synthases) to form covalent bonds between smaller sub-
strate molecules. Also known as **condensation** (dehydration)
reactions, synthesis reactions release one water molecule for each
bond made **(figure 8.8a).** Catabolic reactions are also highly active
in a growing cell and require their own, different set of enzymes.
For example, large substrates must be broken down or digested by
enzymes into smaller molecules so they can be used. Because the
breaking of bonds usually requires the input of water, digestion is
also termed a **hydrolysis* reaction (figure 8.8b).**

* *hydrolysis* (hy-drol'-uh-sis) Gr. *hydro,* water, and *lysis,* setting free.

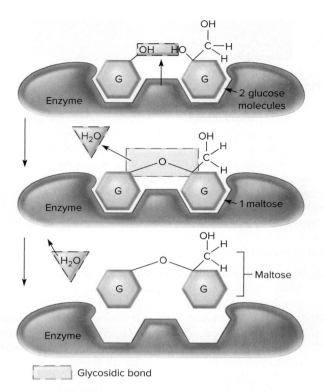

Glycosidic bond

(a) Condensation Reaction. Forming a glycosidic bond
between two glucose molecules to generate maltose requires
the removal of a water molecule.

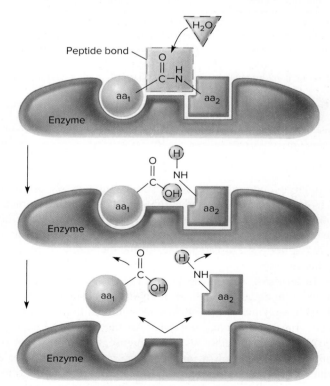

(b) Hydrolysis Reaction. Breaking a peptide bond between two
amino acids requires a water molecule that adds OH to one
amino acid and H to the other.

Figure 8.8 **Examples of enzyme-catalyzed synthesis and
hydrolysis reactions.**

8.4 MAKING CONNECTIONS

The Role of Microbial Enzymes in Disease

Many pathogens secrete unique exoenzymes that help them avoid host defenses or promote their multiplication in tissues. Because these enzymes contribute to pathogenicity, they are referred to as virulence factors, or toxins in some cases (look ahead to chapter 13). *Streptococcus pyogenes* (a cause of throat and skin infections) produces a streptokinase involved in the digestion of blood clots and can assist the pathogen in invading wounds. Another exoenzyme from this bacterium is called streptolysin.[1] In mammalian hosts, streptolysin damages blood cells and tissues. It is also responsible for lysing red blood cells used in blood agar media, which can be used to identify some bacteria growing in culture (see figure 3.17).

 Pseudomonas aeruginosa, a respiratory and skin pathogen, produces elastase and collagenase, which digest elastin and collagen, two proteins found in connective tissue. These increase the severity of certain lung and burn infections. Members of the genus *Clostridium* secrete toxins with significant pathological effects. Many of these toxins—for example, botulinum and tetanus toxins—have an enzymatic component that causes the symptoms of the diseases. Both of them prevent cell vesicles containing neurotransmitters from releasing their contents and thus block nerve transmission to muscles. The botulism toxin causes loss of muscle tone (flaccid paralysis); the tetanus toxin causes sustained muscle tone (rigid paralysis). *Clostridium perfringens,* an agent of gas gangrene, synthesizes lecithinase C, a lipase that profoundly damages cell membranes and accounts for the tissue death associated with this disease. Other medically important enzymes of microbes do not target tissues. Some, such as the beta-lactamases, act on portions of some penicillin and cephalosporin antibiotics and inactivate them. This makes the bacteria drug-resistant and protected from the effects of the drugs.

Even though viruses lack most features of metabolism, a few of them can express genes for enzymes. How would you describe the actions of the following viral enzymes: neuraminidase, reverse transcriptase, and integrase?

1. Even though most enzyme names end in *-ase* (see 8.3 Making Connections), not all do.

The Sensitivity of Enzymes to Environmental Conditions

The activity of an enzyme is highly influenced by the cell's environment. In general, enzymes operate only under the natural temperature, pH, and osmotic pressure of an organism's habitat. When enzymes are subjected to departures from these normal conditions, they tend to be chemically unstable, or **labile.** Low temperatures inhibit catalysis, and high temperatures can denature the apoenzyme. **Denaturation** is a process by which the bonds that collectively maintain the native shape of the apoenzyme are disrupted. This loss causes extreme distortion of the enzyme's shape and prevents the substrate from attaching to the active site. Such nonfunctional enzymes block metabolic reactions and can lead to cell death. Low or high pH and certain chemicals (heavy metals, alcohol) are also denaturing agents.

Regulation of Enzymatic Activity and Metabolic Pathways

Metabolic pathways proceed in a stepwise, highly regulated manner that maximizes the use of available nutrients and energy. The cell responds to environmental conditions by adopting those metabolic reactions that most favor its growth and survival. Because enzymes are critical to these reactions, the regulation of metabolism is largely the regulation of enzymes by an elaborate system of checks and balances. Let us take a look at some general features of metabolic pathways.

Patterns of Metabolic Pathways

Metabolic reactions rarely consist of a single action or step. More often, they occur in a multistep series or pathway, with each step catalyzed by an enzyme. An individual reaction is shown in various ways, depending on the pathway pattern **(figure 8.9).** The product

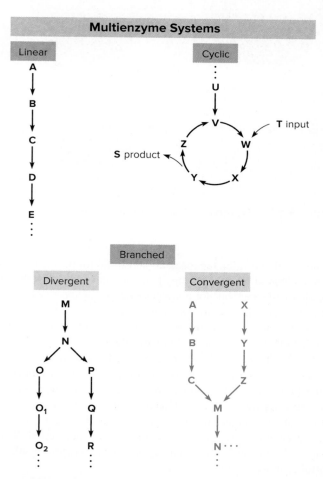

Figure 8.9 Patterns of metabolic pathways. In general, metabolic pathways consist of a linked series of individual chemical reactions that produce intermediary metabolites and lead to a final product. These pathways occur in several patterns, including linear, cyclic, and branched. Anabolic pathways involved in biosynthesis result in a more complex molecule, each step adding on a functional group, whereas catabolic pathways involve the dismantling of molecules and can generate energy. Virtually every reaction in a series involves a specific enzyme.

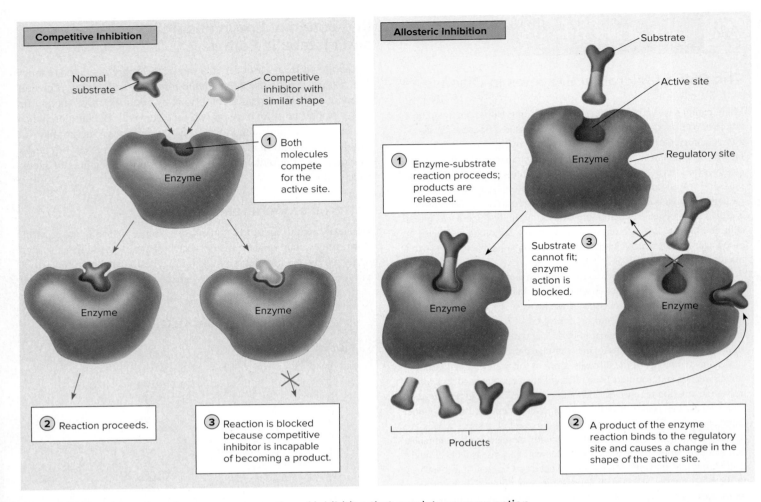

Competitive Inhibition

Normal substrate

Competitive inhibitor with similar shape

Enzyme

① Both molecules compete for the active site.

Enzyme

Enzyme

② Reaction proceeds.

③ Reaction is blocked because competitive inhibitor is incapable of becoming a product.

Allosteric Inhibition

Substrate

Active site

Enzyme

Regulatory site

① Enzyme-substrate reaction proceeds; products are released.

Substrate ③ cannot fit; enzyme action is blocked.

Enzyme

Enzyme

Products

② A product of the enzyme reaction binds to the regulatory site and causes a change in the shape of the active site.

Figure 8.10 Examples of two common modes of inhibition that regulate enzyme action.

of one reaction is often the reactant (substrate) for the next, forming a linear chain of reactions. Many pathways have branches that provide alternative methods for nutrient processing. Others take a cyclic form, in which the starting molecule is regenerated to initiate another turn of the cycle. Pathways generally do not stand alone; they are interconnected and merge at many sites.

Every pathway has one or more enzyme pacemakers that set the rate of a pathway's progression. Regulation of pacemaker enzymes proceeds on two fundamental levels. Either the enzyme itself is directly inhibited or activated, or the amount of the enzyme in the system is altered (decreased or increased). When factors affect the enzyme directly, the system can be finely controlled or "tuned." When regulation is at the genetic level (enzyme synthesis), control is slower and less sensitive.

Direct Controls on the Action of Enzymes

The bacterial cell has many ways of directly influencing the activity of its enzymes. It can inhibit enzyme activity by supplying a molecule that resembles the enzyme's normal substrate. The "mimic" can then occupy the enzyme's active site, preventing the actual substrate from binding there. Because the mimic cannot actually be acted on by the enzyme and a product is not released, the enzyme is

effectively shut down. This is one example of **competitive inhibition,** because the mimic is competing with the substrate for the binding site **(figure 8.10).** In chapter 12 you will see that some antibiotics work on the same strategy of competing with enzymatic active sites to shut down metabolic processes.

Another form of competitive inhibition can occur with special types of enzymes that have two binding sites: the active site and another area called the **regulatory** or **allosteric* site** (figure 8.10). The action of these enzymes is controlled by the binding of molecules other than the substrate in the regulatory site. Often the regulatory molecule is the product of the enzymatic reaction itself. This provides a **negative feedback** mechanism that can slow down enzymatic activity once a certain concentration of product is produced.

Noncompetitive inhibition is a third mechanism that does not involve an inhibitor molecule competing with substrate for the active site or disable the active site. This type of inhibitor binds to the entire enzyme-substrate complex and prevents the enzyme from completing its action on the substrate.

** allosteric* (al-oh-stair′-ik) Gr. *allos,* other, and *steros,* solid. Literally, "another space."

CLINIC CASE

Methanol Poisoning, I'll Drink to That! The patient was a 35-year-old man with chronic alcoholism. He presented to the local hospital in Dhaka, Bangladesh, complaining of vomiting, abdominal pain, breathlessness, and blurry vision. He displayed a deep, slow respiratory rate common in people suffering metabolic acidosis, a decrease in the pH of the blood. An ophthalmic examination revealed severe damage to the patient's optic nerve. For the past few days he had been drinking locally brewed alcohol—what would be known as moonshine in the United States. Doctors diagnosed the patient with methanol poisoning which, if not aggressively treated, leads to blindness and death.

During the fermentation process, microorganisms convert sugar to ethanol, along with an insignificant amount of methanol (an industrial alcohol) as a by-product. However, done incorrectly, fermentation can lead to high concentrations of methanol in the finished liquor. While methanol is not toxic by itself, it is rapidly converted to formaldehyde by the enzyme alcohol dehydrogenase, and the formaldehyde is later broken down to toxic formic acid.

The key to treating methanol poisoning is to prevent the breakdown of methanol and, historically, this has been accomplished by getting the patient drunk. Providing an IV of pure ethanol competitively inhibits the alcohol dehydrogenase enzyme by making ethanol more available than methanol. In this way, the active site of the enzyme is almost always filled with ethanol molecules and methanol is never converted to formaldehyde, allowing it to be removed from the body via dialysis over several days.

The doctors unfortunately did not have access to IV ethanol, so instead purchased whiskey from a local store and treated the patient with 10 ml of whiskey orally every hour for 2 days, followed by 10 ml every other hour for 3 additional days. For the entire treatment, the patient's blood alcohol concentration (BAC) remained above 0.1%, higher than the 0.08% BAC which constitutes driving under the influence in all 50 states. Although the patient survived, he never regained his vision.

If the patient, when he had first become ill, had stopped drinking with the hope of feeling better, what probably would have happened?

Controls on Enzyme Synthesis

Controlling enzymes by controlling their synthesis is another effective mechanism. Because enzymes do not last indefinitely, they eventually degrade and must be replaced. This cycle works into the scheme of the cell, where replacement of enzymes can be regulated according to cell demand. The mechanisms of this system are genetic in nature; that is, they require regulation of DNA and protein synthesis, a topic we cover in more depth in chapter 9.

Enzyme repression is a means to stop further synthesis of an enzyme somewhere along its pathway. As the level of the end product from a given enzymatic reaction has built to excess, the genetic apparatus responsible for replacing these enzymes is automatically suppressed **(process figure 8.11).** The response time is longer than for feedback inhibition, but its effects are more enduring.

A response that resembles the inverse of enzyme repression is **enzyme induction.** In this process, enzymes appear (are induced) only when suitable substrates are present; that is, the synthesis of enzyme is induced by its substrate. This response enables the organism to adapt to a variety of nutrients, and it also prevents a microbe

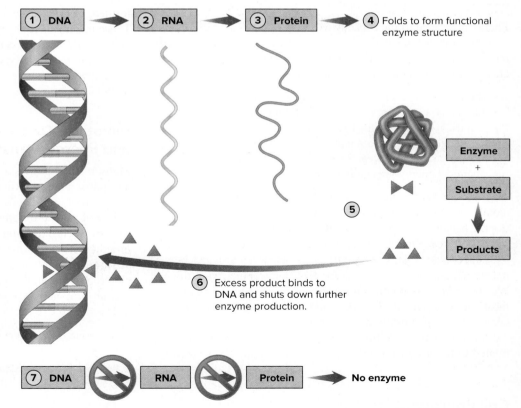

⚙ **Process Figure 8.11 One type of genetic control of enzyme synthesis: enzyme repression. (1–5)** Genetic controls are active and the enzyme is synthesized continuously until enough product has been made. **(6)–(7)** Excess product reacts with a site on DNA that regulates the enzyme's synthesis, thereby inhibiting further enzyme production.

from wasting energy by making enzymes for which substrates are lacking.

Practice SECTION 8.1

1. Differentiate between catabolism and anabolism using examples.
2. Describe 10 important biochemical properties of enzymes.
3. Describe the chemistry of enzymes, and explain how the apoenzyme forms.
4. Show diagrammatically the interaction of holoenzyme and its substrate and general products that can be formed from a reaction.
5. Differentiate among the chemical composition and functions of various cofactors. Provide examples of each type.
6. Summarize the direct and indirect controls that regulate enzymes.

8.2 The Pursuit and Utilization of Energy

 Learn

8. Relate the diverse sources of energy and the cellular management of energy.

9. Describe biological oxidation-reduction and energy transfer.

10. Discuss the structure, basic formation, and roles of ATP in cells.

Energy is defined as the capacity to do work or to cause change. In order to carry out the work of an array of metabolic processes, cells require constant input and expenditure of some form of usable energy. Energy commonly exists in these forms:

- thermal (heat) energy from molecular motion,
- radiant (wave) energy from visible light or other rays,
- electrical energy from a flow of electrons,
- mechanical energy from a physical change in position,
- atomic energy from reactions in the nucleus of an atom, and
- chemical energy present in the bonds of molecules.

Cells are far too fragile to rely in any constant way on thermal or atomic energy for cell transactions. Except for certain chemoautotrophic bacteria, the ultimate source of energy is the sun, but only phototrophs can tap this source directly. This capacity of photosynthesis to convert solar energy into chemical energy provides both a nutritional and an energy basis for all heterotrophic living things. We cover this essential form of metabolism in section 8.6. For the most part, only chemical energy and reactions can fuel cellular energetics of nonphotosynthetic organisms.

In this section, we further explore the role of energy as it is related to the use of nutrients, redox carriers, and the generation of ATP.

Cell Energetics

Cells manage energy in the form of chemical reactions that change molecules. This often involves activities such as the making or breaking of bonds and the transfer of electrons. Not all cellular reactions have the same relation to energy. Some release energy and others require it to proceed. For example, a reaction with this equation:

$$X + Y \xrightarrow{\text{Enzyme}} Z + \text{Energy}$$

releases energy as it goes forward. This type of reaction is termed **exergonic.*** Energy of this type is considered free: it is available for doing cellular work. Energy transactions such as the following:

$$\text{Energy} + A + B \xrightarrow{\text{Enzyme}} C$$

are called **endergonic*** because they are driven forward with the addition of energy.

Summaries of metabolism might make it seem that cells "create" energy from nutrients, but they do not. What they actually do is extract chemical energy already present in nutrient fuels and apply that energy toward useful work in the cell, much like a gasoline engine releases energy as it burns fuel. The engine does not actually produce energy, but it converts the potential energy of the fuel to the free energy that drives a machine.

The basis for cell energetics lies in the chemical bonds, electron transfers, and special pathways along with their enzymes. During exergonic reactions, electrons are pulled out of atoms, thereby releasing their inherent energy. These electrons are picked up by special carriers and transferred through a series of reactions until they reach a **final electron acceptor.** As we will see in section 8.3, the production of ATP is intimately tied to this process. As ATP is formed, it is used to support endergonic reactions such as synthesis. These reactions are balanced and cyclic, so that ATP is constantly being made, used, regenerated, and so on. The actual process of electron transfer is a type of redox reaction that was first described in chapter 2. Let us revisit this topic and see how it is involved in metabolism.

Biological Oxidation and Reduction: Electron and Energy Transfer

Many chemical substances readily donate or receive electrons and participate in oxidation (the loss of electrons) or reduction (the gain of electrons). The compound that loses the electrons is **oxidized,** and the compound that receives the electrons is **reduced.** Such oxidation-reduction or **redox reactions** are common in cells and indispensable to energy transactions (look back at figure 2.9). Redox reactions always occur in pairs, with an electron donor and an electron acceptor, which constitute a *conjugate pair,* or *redox pair.* The reaction can be represented as follows:

Electron donor + Electron acceptor ⟷ Electron donor + Electron acceptor

 •e⁻ •e⁻

Reduced Oxidized Oxidized Reduced

* *exergonic* (ex-er-gon′-ik) Gr. *exo,* without, and *ergon,* work. In general, catabolic reactions are exergonic.

* *endergonic* (en-der-gon′-ik) Gr. *endo,* within, and *ergon,* work. Anabolic reactions tend to be endergonic.

Redox reactions in cells involve not only electrons but also the hydrogen atoms which donate them. Recall that a hydrogen atom consists of a single proton and a single electron. When a hydrogen atom gives up its single electron to a positively charged molecule, this leaves a hydrogen ion or proton (H^+). For simplicity's sake, our discussions will emphasize the process of electron transfer. But be aware that many pathways need hydrogen ions (protons) generated by oxidation-reduction to carry out essential functions in the metabolic pathways.

One example of a typical redox reaction is seen in this overall equation associated with aerobic respiration:

$$\overbrace{C_6H_{12}O_6}^{\text{Oxidation}} + 6O_2 \rightarrow 6CO_2 + 6H_2O + \text{Energy}$$
$$\underbrace{\text{Glucose}}_{\text{Reduction}}$$

Note that the electron donor is hydrogen and the electron acceptor is oxygen. The electrons are transported and energy is released through a stepwise series of reactions, covered in section 8.3.

For energy to be biologically useful, it must ultimately be captured through **phosphorylation,** a process that adds an inorganic phosphate P_i to adenosine diphosphate, converting it to ATP:

$$ADP + P_i + \text{Energy} \leftrightarrows ATP$$

The handling and transportation of electrons and protons, from electron donor to electron acceptor, is carried out by molecules called, simply enough, electron carriers. These carriers readily accept electrons from one substrate and donate them to another substrate. The most common of these molecules is the coenzyme **nicotinamide adenine dinucleotide (NAD^+) (figure 8.12).** Other related carriers are FAD (flavin adenine dinucleotide), coenzyme A, and the compounds of the respiratory chain, all discussed in section 8.3. NAD^+ reduces 2 hydrogen atoms and carries 2 electrons away from this reaction, represented as NADH. The electrons are carried in the nicotinamide ring, where they can be accessed during subsequent electron transfers. Electrons will eventually be received by a final electron acceptor, which in aerobic metabolism is molecular oxygen. An important function of this carrier system is that every transfer of electrons from NADH to another carrier molecule automatically replenishes NAD^+ for use in the numerous redox reactions in cells.

Adenosine Triphosphate: Metabolic Money

ATP has been described as metabolic currency because it can be earned, spent, and exchanged. You can gain some appreciation for the enormous need for ATP if you consider that even one tiny cell of *Escherichia coli* consumes around 2.5 million ATP molecules per second for synthesis alone! As a temporary energy repository, ATP provides a connection between energy-yielding catabolism and all other cellular activities that require energy. Some clues to its energy-storing properties lie in its unique molecular structure.

The Molecular Structure of ATP ATP is a three-part molecule consisting of a nitrogen base (adenine) linked to a 5-carbon sugar (ribose), with a chain of three phosphate groups bonded to the

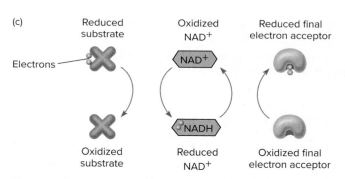

Figure 8.12 Structure of NAD^+ and its carrier function. (a) The coenzyme NAD^+ contains the vitamin nicotinamide (niacin) bound to two ribose phosphates and an adenine. **(b)** The site of reduction is at the nicotinamide ring portion (box), which carries 2 electrons, one at the ring nitrogen and the other on a hydrogen bound to a ring carbon. **(c)** An important function of this carrier system is that every transfer of electrons from NADH to another carrier molecule automatically replenishes NAD^+ for use in another redox reaction.

ribose **(figure 8.13).** The type, arrangement, and especially the proximity of atoms in ATP combine to form a compatible but unstable high-energy molecule. The high energy of ATP originates in the orientation of the phosphate groups, which are relatively bulky and carry negative charges. The proximity of these repelling electrostatic charges imposes a strain that is most acute on the bonds between the last two phosphate groups. When the strain on the phosphate bonds is released by removal of the terminal phosphates, free energy is released.

Figure 8.13 **A model of adenosine triphosphate (ATP).** A structural view of ATP and its related components ADP and AMP. Note that the last two phosphate bonds release energy when they are cleaved.

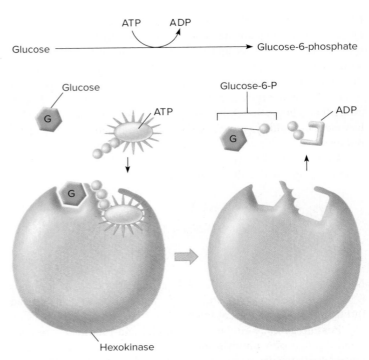

Figure 8.14 **The phosphorylation of glucose by ATP.** The first step in catabolizing glucose is the addition of a phosphate from ATP by an enzyme called hexokinase. This use of high-energy phosphate as an activator is a recurring feature of many metabolic pathways.

Breaking the bonds between the second and third phosphates of ATP yields adenosine diphosphate (ADP), which can then be converted to adenosine monophosphate (AMP). It is worthwhile noting how economically a cell manages its pool of adenosine nucleotides. AMP derivatives help form the backbone of RNA and are also a major component of certain coenzymes (NAD^+, FAD, and coenzyme A).

The Metabolic Roles of ATP ATP is at the center of a cell's energy cycle, regardless of whether it is a chemoheterotroph using respiration, a photosynthetic organism, or a chemoautotroph. Expenditure of ATP powers nearly all processes that are part of cellular work. This energy cycle can be depicted as shown here:

Respiration
Fermentation
Photosynthesis
Chemoautotrophy

ADP + P$_i$

ATP

Chemical work
Transport work
Mechanical work

In many instances, the energy released from the high-energy bond in ATP activates individual subunits before they are enzymatically bonded during synthesis. ATP is also used to prepare a molecule for catabolism such as the phosphorylation of a 6-carbon sugar during the early stages of glycolysis **(figure 8.14).**

Because ATP needs to be constantly replenished, reactions are constantly continuing in the reverse order. The ADPs generated during phosphorylation will repeat the cycle by reacting immediately with inorganic phosphate and a high-energy source that can regenerate ATP. The energy for these high-energy phosphate bonds comes from catabolic pathways where substrates or electron carriers are harvesting energy.

Most ATPs in aerobic organisms are formed during **oxidative phosphorylation,** a series of reactions involving electron transport and an enzyme (ATP synthase) that can trap energy and store it in ATP. Some ATP molecules are formed through **substrate-level phosphorylation,** a process that all cells carry out, regardless of their metabolic type. In this mode of phosphorylation, ATP is formed by transfer of a phosphate group from a high-energy compound (substrate) directly to ADP **(figure 8.15;** see also process figure 8.17, step 6).

Photosynthetic organisms have a system involving **photophosphorylation,** in which the ATP is formed by means of a light-driven electron transport mechanism that we discuss in more detail in section 8.6.

Phosphorylated substrate

+ ADP

Enzyme

Substrate

+ ATP

Figure 8.15 **ATP formation by substrate-level phosphorylation.** The substrate has been bound to a phosphate, creating a bond with high potential energy. Transfer of the high-energy phosphate to ADP gives rise to ATP and returns the substrate to its original form.

 Practice SECTION 8.2

7. Explain how oxidation of a substrate proceeds without oxygen.

8. Refer to the blue redox equation for glucose. Which substance is reduced? Which is oxidized? Which is the oxidizing agent? Which is the reducing agent?

9. In the following redox pairs, which compound is reduced and which is oxidized?
 a. NAD^+ and $NADH$
 b. $FADH_2$ and FAD
 c. NO_3^- and NO_2^-

10. a. Describe the roles played by ATP and NAD^+ in metabolism.
 b. What particular features of their structure lend them to these functions?

11. Name the major ways that substrate-level phosphorylation is different from oxidative phosphorylation.

12. What is meant by the concept of the "final electron acceptor"?

8.3 Pathways of Bioenergetics

Learn

11. Relate the main points of bioenergetics and energy strategies in microorganisms.

12. Describe the main catabolic pathways and their locations in aerobic respiration.

13. Define *glycolysis* and explain its input and output, its basic steps, and how it is linked to the Krebs cycle and oxidative phosphorylation.

14. Explain the basic steps in the Krebs cycle, its input and output, and how it is linked to oxidative phosphorylation.

15. Describe the components of the respiratory chain and their functions.

16. Explain the chemiosmotic mechanism of ATP formation, its relationship to electron transport, and the final step in electron transfer.

17. Summarize the results of aerobic respiration.

18. Define and describe some reactions of anaerobic respiration.

One of the scientific community's greatest achievements was deciphering the biochemical pathways of cells. Initial work with bacteria and yeasts, followed by studies with animal and plant cells, clearly demonstrated metabolic similarities and strongly supported the presence of metabolic patterns that are universal. **Bioenergetics** is a study of the mechanisms of cellular energy release, including catabolic and anabolic routes. Although these pathways are interconnected and interdependent, anabolic pathways are not simply reversals of catabolic ones. At first glance it may seem more economical to use identical pathways, but having different enzymes and divided pathways allows anabolism and catabolism to proceed simultaneously without interference.

In the following sections, we focus our discussion on the most common catabolic pathways that illustrate general principles of other pathways as well.

Catabolism: An Overview of Nutrient Breakdown and Energy Release

For most chemoheterotrophs, the primary catabolism of fuels (such as glucose) that release energy proceeds through a series of three coupled pathways:

1. **glycolysis,**[*] also called the Embden-Meyerhof-Parnas (EMP) pathway[2];
2. the **Krebs cycle,** also known as the citric acid or tricarboxylic acid cycle TCA[2]; and
3. the **respiratory chain** (electron transport and oxidative phosphorylation).

Each segment of the pathway is responsible for a specific set of actions on various products of glucose. The major interconnections of these pathways in aerobic respiration are represented in **figure 8.16,** and their reactions are summarized in **table 8.3.** In the following sections, we consider each of these pathways in greater detail.

Energy Strategies in Microorganisms

In chapter 7, we gained insight into the metabolic diversity of microbes. There are numerous strategies used by microbes to derive energy and synthesize cell components. Because microbial metabolism is so varied, we have chosen to cover elements of the most common types of metabolism, based on the three basic catabolic pathways. In previous discussions, microorganisms were categorized according to their requirement for oxygen gas, and this requirement is related directly to their mechanisms of energy release. As we shall see, **aerobic respiration** is a series of reactions (glycolysis, Krebs cycle, and the respiratory chain) that converts glucose to CO_2, produces H_2O, and generates energy (figure 8.16*a*). It relies on molecular oxygen (O_2) as the final acceptor for electrons and hydrogens, and releases a relatively large amount of ATP. Aerobic respiration is characteristic of fungi, protozoa, animals, plants, and many bacteria, and it will be the system we emphasize here.

Some facultative and aerotolerant anaerobes may use only glycolysis or similar pathways to ferment glucose. In this case, oxygen is not required, organic compounds are the final electron acceptors, and a relatively small amount of ATP is synthesized (figure 8.16*c* and section 8.4).

Some anaerobic microorganisms metabolize by means of **anaerobic respiration.** This system may involve the same three pathways as aerobic respiration, but it does not use molecular oxygen as the final electron acceptor (figure 8.16*b*). Instead, it uses other oxidized ions such as NO_3^-, SO_4^{2-}, or CO_2 for the final electron acceptor. Aspects of anaerobic respiration and fermentation are covered later in this section and the next one.

[*] *glycolysis* (gly-kol′-ih-sis) Gr. *glykys,* sweet, and *lysis,* to split.

2. The EMP pathway is named for the biochemists who first outlined its steps. Krebs is in honor of Sir Hans Krebs who, with F. A. Lipmann, delineated this pathway, an achievement for which they won the Nobel Prize in Physiology or Medicine in 1953. TCA refers to the involvement of several organic acids containing three carboxylic acid groups, citric acid being the first tricarboxylic acid formed.

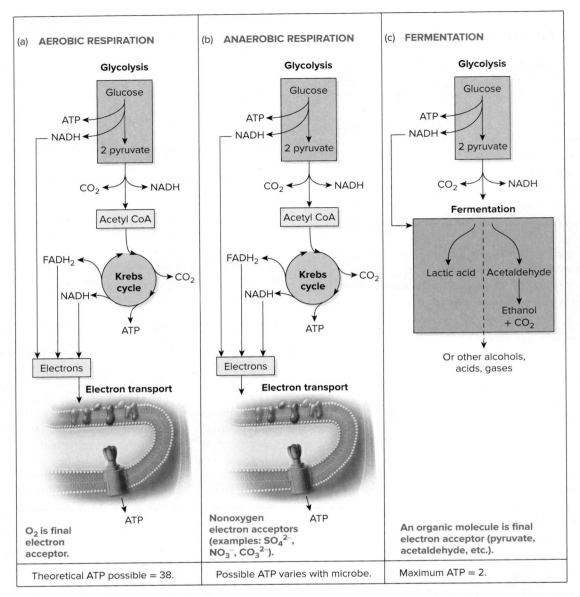

Figure 8.16 Side-by-side comparison of the stages, reactions, and major products of pathways for aerobic respiration, anaerobic respiration, and fermentation. Note that all begin with glycolysis but vary in use of other pathways, electron acceptors, and ATP yield.

TABLE 8.3	Metabolic Strategies Among Heterotrophic Microorganisms Growing on Glucose			
Scheme	Pathways Involved	Final Electron Acceptor	Products	Primary Pathway Found In
Aerobic respiration	Glycolysis, Krebs cycle, electron transport	O_2	ATP, CO_2, H_2O	Aerobes; facultative anaerobes
Anaerobic metabolism Fermentative	Glycolysis	Organic molecules	ATP, CO_2, ethanol, lactic acid*	Facultative, aerotolerant, strict anaerobes
Respiration	Glycolysis, Krebs cycle, electron transport	Various inorganic ions (NO_3^-, SO_4^{2-}, CO_3^{3-})	Highly varied, but can include CO_2, ATP, organic acids, H_2S, CH_4, N_2	Anaerobes; some facultatives and aerotolerants

* The products of microbial fermentations are extremely varied and include organic acids, alcohols, and gases.

Aerobic Respiration

Aerobic respiration is a series of enzyme-catalyzed reactions in which electrons are transferred from fuel molecules such as glucose to oxygen as a final electron acceptor. This pathway is the principal energy-yielding scheme for aerobic heterotrophs, and it provides both ATP and metabolic intermediates for many other pathways in the cell, including those of protein, lipid, and carbohydrate synthesis (see figure 8.25).

Aerobic respiration in microorganisms can be summarized by this equation:

Glucose $(C_6H_{12}O_6) + 6O_2 + 38\ ADP + 38P_i \rightarrow 6CO_2 + 6H_2O + 38\ ATP$

The seeming simplicity of the equation for aerobic respiration conceals the complexity of the process. Fortunately we do not have to present all of the details to address some important concepts concerning its reactants and products, as follows:

1. the steps in the oxidation of glucose,
2. the involvement of coenzyme carriers and the final electron acceptor,
3. where and how ATP originates,
4. where carbon dioxide originates, and
5. where oxygen is required.

Glucose: The Starting Compound

Carbohydrates such as **glucose** are good fuels because these compounds are readily oxidized; that is, they are superior electron donors. The electrons they donate can be used in energy transfers. The end products of the oxidation of such organic compounds are energy-rich ATP and energy-poor carbon dioxide and water. Polysaccharides (starch, glycogen) and disaccharides (maltose, sucrose) are stored sources of glucose also available for the respiratory pathways. Although we use glucose as the main starting compound, other hexoses (fructose, galactose) and fatty acid subunits can enter the pathways of aerobic respiration as well, as we will see in section 8.5.

Glycolysis: The Starting Lineup

The process called **glycolysis (EMP)** is a pathway that converts glucose through several steps into **pyruvic acid.** Depending on the organism and the conditions, it may be only the first phase of respiration, or it may serve as the primary metabolic pathway for fermentative microbes. Glycolysis provides a way to synthesize a small amount of ATP, to release another potential source of energy—NADH, and to generate pyruvic acid, an essential intermediary metabolite. None of these reactions involve the direct input of oxygen.

Steps in the Glycolytic Pathway Glycolysis proceeds along nine linear steps. The first portion of glycolysis involves activation of glucose, which is followed by oxidation reactions of the glucose fragments, the synthesis of ATP, and the formation of pyruvic acid. Although each step of metabolism is catalyzed by a specific enzyme, we will mention only certain key ones. The following outline lists the principal steps of glycolysis. To see an overview of glycolysis, go to **process figure 8.17.** Detailed illustrations appear in Appendix A.

1. First, glucose is phosphorylated at the number six carbon by an **ATP** to produce glucose-6-phosphate (see figure 8.14). This is a way of "priming" the system and preventing the glucose from being transported out of the cell.
2. Glucose-6-phosphate is converted to its isomer, fructose-6-phosphate.
3. Another **ATP** is spent in phosphorylating the first carbon of fructose-6-phosphate, which yields a molecule with two phosphates called fructose-1,6-diphosphate.

Up to this point, no energy has been released, no oxidation-reduction has occurred, and, in fact, 2 ATPs have been used and the molecules remain in the 6-carbon state.

4. Fructose-1,6-diphosphate is split into two 3-carbon fragments: glyceraldehyde-3-phosphate (G3P) and dihydroxyacetone phosphate (DHAP).
5. Glyceraldehyde-3-phosphate (G3P) and dihydroxyacetone phosphate (DHAP) are isomers, and DHAP is converted to G3P, which is the more reactive form for the following reactions.

The effect of the splitting of fructose diphosphate is to double every subsequent reaction, because where there was once a single molecule, there are now two to be fed into the remainder of glycolysis and other pathways.

6. Each molecule of glyceraldehyde-3-phosphate becomes involved in the single oxidation-reduction reaction of glycolysis. This sets the scene for ATP synthesis. The **NAD$^+$** coenzyme complex picks up hydrogens from G3P, forming **NADH.** This step is accompanied by the addition of an inorganic phosphate (PO_4^{3-}) to form an unstable bond on the third carbon of the G3P substrate. The product of these reactions is diphosphoglyceric acid (DPGA).
7. One of the high-energy phosphates of diphosphoglyceric acid is donated to ADP via **substrate-level phosphorylation,** resulting in a molecule of **ATP.** The other product of this reaction is 3-phosphoglyceric acid (3-PGA).
8. During this phase, the 3-phosphoglyceric acid is converted to 2-phosphoglyceric acid (2-PGA) through the shift of a phosphate from the third to the second carbon.
9. The removal of a water molecule from 2-phosphoglyceric acid converts it to phosphoenolpyruvic acid (PEPA). The result gives rise to a high-energy phosphate bond.
10. In the final reaction of glycolysis, phosphoenolpyruvic acid gives up its high-energy phosphate to form a second ATP, again via **substrate-level phosphorylation.** This reaction also produces **pyruvic acid** (pyruvate), a compound with many roles in metabolism.

The reactions of glycolysis thus give rise to two pyruvic acids per glucose. The two substrate-level phosphorylations produce a total of 4 ATPs. However, 2 ATPs were expended for steps 1 and 3, so the net number of ATPs available to the cell from these reactions is 2.

In aerobic organisms, the two NADHs formed during step 5 are shuttled to the electron transport system, where the final electron acceptor will be oxygen, and additional ATPs will be generated. In organisms that ferment glucose, the NADH will be oxidized back to NAD$^+$, and the electron acceptor will be an organic compound (see figure 8.23).

Process Figure 8.17 **Summary of the steps in glycolysis.** **(1)** Glucose is phosphorylated to form glucose-6-phosphate. **(2)** Glucose-6-phosphate is converted to fructose-6-phosphate. **(3)** Fructose-6-phosphate is phosphorylated to produce fructose-1,6-bisphosphate. **(4)** Fructose 1,6-bisphosphate is split into two 3-carbon molecules, glyceraldehyde-3-phosphate (G3P), and dihydroxyacetone phosphate (DHAP). **(5)** DHAP is converted to G3P, resulting in the production of two molecules of G3P from each molecule of glucose (because of this, each of the reactions past this point occur twice for each molecule of glucose). **(6)** G3P is converted to 1,3-bisphosphoglyceric acid, yielding one NADH (two per glucose molecule). **(7)** 1,3-bisphosphoglyceric acid is converted to 3-phosphoglyceric acid, yielding one ATP (two per glucose molecule). **(8)** 3-phosphoglyceric acid is converted to 2-phosphoglyceric acid. **(9)** 2-phosphoglyceric acid is converted to phosphoenolpyruvic acid (PEP), producing a high energy phosphate bond, along with a molecule of water (two per glucose molecule). **(10)** A high-energy phosphate is transferred from PEP to ADP to produce ATP (two ATP per glucose molecule) and a molecule of pyruvic acid. A more detailed version of glycolysis can be found in **Appendix A.**

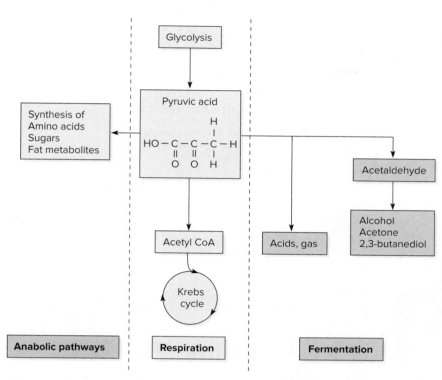

Figure 8.18 **The fates of pyruvic acid (pyruvate).** This metabolite is an important hub in the processing of nutrients by microbes. It may be fermented anaerobically to several end products or oxidized completely to CO_2 and H_2O through the Krebs cycle and the electron transport system. It can also serve as a source of raw material for synthesizing amino acids and carbohydrates (see figure 18.25).

Pyruvic Acid—A Central Metabolite

Pyruvic acid occupies an important position in several pathways, and different organisms handle it in different ways **(figure 8.18).** In strictly aerobic organisms and some anaerobes, pyruvic acid is channeled into the Krebs cycle for processing and energy release. Facultative anaerobes can adopt a fermentative metabolism, in which pyruvic acid is further reduced into acids or other products.

The Preparation of Pyruvic Acid for the Krebs Cycle

The oxidation of glucose by glycolysis yields a comparatively small amount of energy. Pyruvic acid is still energy-rich, containing a number of extractable electrons to power ATP synthesis, and this will be achieved through the work of the second and third phases of respiration, during which pyruvic acid is converted to CO_2 and H_2O. In the following section, we examine the second phase—the Krebs cycle—which takes place in the mitochondrial matrix in eukaryotes and in the cytoplasm of bacteria.

To connect the glycolysis pathway to the Krebs cycle, the pyruvic acid is first converted to the starting compound for that cycle (**process figure 8.19,** tan oval at top). This step

Artist's concept of pyruvate dehydrogenase
Source: Sriram Subramaniam/ National Cancer Institute (NCI)

brings in an enzyme complex and coenzyme A to participate in the oxidation of pyruvic acid, the reduction of NAD^+ to NADH, and the decarboxylation of pyruvic acid to a 2-carbon acetyl group accompanied by release of carbon dioxide. The acetyl group remains attached to coenzyme A, forming **acetyl coenzyme A** (acetyl CoA) that feeds into the Krebs cycle. Pyruvate dehydrogenase, the enzyme complex that makes this reaction possible, is huge. In *E. coli*, it contains four vitamins and has a molecular weight of 6 million—larger than a ribosome!

The NADH produced in the formation of acetyl CoA will be shuttled into electron transport and used to generate ATP via oxidative phosphorylation in the third phase of aerobic respiration.

Keep in mind that all reactions during these subsequent phases happen twice for each glucose because of the two pyruvates that are released during glycolysis.

The Krebs Cycle—A Carbon and Energy Wheel

As you learned earlier, a cyclic pathway is one in which the starting compound is regenerated at the end of the cycle so it will be ready to go around again. The Krebs cycle has eight steps, beginning with citrate formation and ending with oxaloacetate (figure 8.19). The 2-carbon acetyl groups from coenzyme A combine with a 4-carbon oxaloacetate molecule to form citrate, a 6-carbon molecule. Although this seems a cumbersome way to dismantle such a small molecule, it is necessary in biological systems for extracting the remaining energy from the acetyl fragment.

As we take a single spin around the Krebs cycle, it will be helpful to keep track of

1. the numbers of carbons (#C) of each substrate and product,
2. reactions where CO_2 is generated,
3. reductions of the electron carriers NAD^+ and FAD, and
4. the site of ATP synthesis.

Be aware that the terms and structures used for organic acids can be shown as either the acid form (oxaloacetic acid) or its salt (oxaloacetate). We present the salt form in this text for the most part.

The eight reactions in the Krebs cycle are:

1. Oxaloacetate (4C) reacts with the acetyl group (2C) on acetyl CoA, forming citrate (6C) and releasing coenzyme, making it immediately available for another acetyl group.
2. Citrate is converted to its isomer, isocitrate (6C), to prepare this substrate for the decarboxylation and redox reaction of the next step.
3. Isocitrate is acted upon by an enzyme complex including NAD^+ or NADP (depending on the organism) in a reaction that generates NADH or NADPH, splits off a carbon dioxide, and leaves α-ketoglutarate (5C).
4. Alpha-ketoglutarate serves as a substrate for the final decarboxylation reaction and yet another redox reaction, involving coenzyme A and yielding NADH. The product is the high-energy compound succinyl CoA (4C).

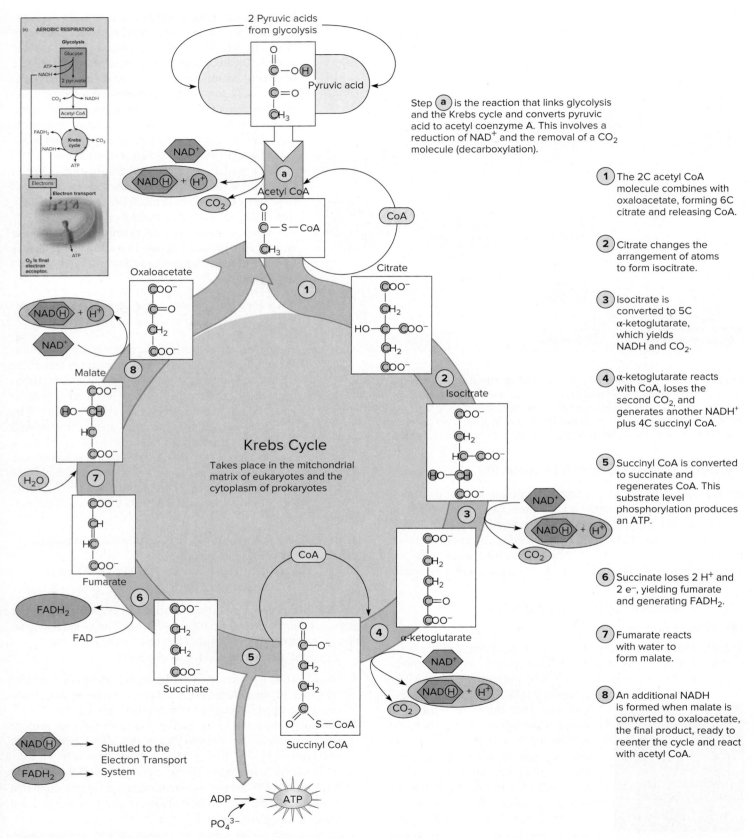

Step (a) is the reaction that links glycolysis and the Krebs cycle and converts pyruvic acid to acetyl coenzyme A. This involves a reduction of NAD^+ and the removal of a CO_2 molecule (decarboxylation).

(1) The 2C acetyl CoA molecule combines with oxaloacetate, forming 6C citrate and releasing CoA.

(2) Citrate changes the arrangement of atoms to form isocitrate.

(3) Isocitrate is converted to 5C α-ketoglutarate, which yields NADH and CO_2.

(4) α-ketoglutarate reacts with CoA, loses the second CO_2, and generates another $NADH^+$ plus 4C succinyl CoA.

(5) Succinyl CoA is converted to succinate and regenerates CoA. This substrate level phosphorylation produces an ATP.

(6) Succinate loses 2 H^+ and 2 e^-, yielding fumarate and generating $FADH_2$.

(7) Fumarate reacts with water to form malate.

(8) An additional NADH is formed when malate is converted to oxaloacetate, the final product, ready to reenter the cycle and react with acetyl CoA.

Krebs Cycle

Takes place in the mitchondrial matrix of eukaryotes and the cytoplasm of prokaryotes

Process Figure 8.19 **The reactions of a single turn of the Krebs cycle.** Each glucose will produce two turns of this pathway. The top portion (a) depicts the conversion of pyruvic acid to acetyl coenzyme A, a necessary reaction that sets up the first step of Krebs. Note that this is an enlarged, more detailed view of the central portion of figure 8.16a.

At this point, the cycle has completed the formation of 3 CO_2 molecules that balance out each original 3-carbon pyruvic acid released by glycolysis. The remaining steps serve not only to regenerate the oxaloacetate to start the cycle again but also to extract more energy from the intermediate compounds leading to oxaloacetate.

5. Succinyl CoA is the source of the one substrate level phosphorylation in the Krebs cycle. In most bacteria, it proceeds with the formation of ATP, although eukaryotes produce guanosine triphosphate (GTP), an equivalent source of energy. The other product at this step is succinate (4C).
6. Succinate undergoes a redox reaction, but in this case, the electron and H^+ acceptor is flavin adenine dinucleotide (FAD). The enzyme that catalyzes this reaction, succinyl dehydrogenase, is found in the bacterial cell membrane and mitochondrial crista of eukaryotic cells. The $FADH_2$ generated directly enters the electron transport system but at a different carrier site than NADH. Fumarate (4C) is the product of this reaction.
7. The addition of H_2O to fumarate results in malate (4C). This is one of the few reactions in respiration that directly incorporates a water molecule.
8. Malate is dehydrogenated (with formation of a final NADH), and oxaloacetate is formed. This step brings the cycle back to its original starting position, where the oxaloacetate molecule is available to react with acetyl coenzyme A.

An important feature of this pathway is that acetyl groups from the breakdown of certain fats can enter the pathway at step one and be used as an energy source (discussed in section 8.5).

The full Krebs cycle is not present in all cells, and it may not function under all metabolic conditions. But even in cells with alternate metabolic schemes, it is essential for generating small organic molecules that microbes require for synthesis.

The Respiratory Chain: Electron Transport and Oxidative Phosphorylation

We now come to the energy chain, which is the final "processing mill" for electrons and protons. Overall, the electron transport system (ETS) consists of a chain of special carriers that receive electrons from reduced carriers (NADH, $FADH_2$) generated by glycolysis and the Krebs cycle. The ETS shuttles the electrons through a series of redox transfers **(figure 8.20)**. The flow of electrons down this chain is highly energetic and ultimately drives the synthesis of ATP. The step that finalizes the transport process is the acceptance of electrons and hydrogen ions by oxygen, with the production of water.

> **Quick Search**
> Observe this process in action at "Cellular Respiration: The Electron Transport Chain" on YouTube.

Some variability exists from one organism to another, but the principal compounds that carry out these complex reactions are NADH dehydrogenase, iron-sulfide complexes (FeS), coenzyme Q (**ubiquinone**),* and several **cytochromes**.* The cytochromes

* *ubiquinone* (yoo-bik′-wih-nohn) L. *ubique*, everywhere. A type of chemical, similar to vitamin K, that is very common in cells.
* *cytochrome* (sy′-toh-krohm) Gr. *cyto*, cell, and *kroma*, color. Cytochromes are pigmented, iron-containing molecules similar to hemoglobin.

contain a tightly bound metal atom at their center that is actively involved in accepting electrons and donating them to the next carrier in the series. The highly compartmentalized structure of the respiratory chain is an important factor in its function. Note in figure 8.20 that the electron transport carriers and enzymes are associated in complexes in the inner mitochondrial membranes in eukaryotes. The cell membrane is the equivalent structure for housing them in bacteria **(figure 8.21)**.

The Carriers of Electron Transport: The Energy Cascade in the Mitochondria

The principal questions about the electron transport system are these: How are the electrons passed from one carrier to another in the series? How is this progression coupled to ATP synthesis? Where and how is oxygen utilized? Although the biochemical details of this process are somewhat complicated, the basic reactions consist of a number of redox reactions now familiar to us. In general, the carrier compounds and their associated enzymes are arranged in linear sequence and are reduced and oxidized while shuttling the electrons along to their final acceptor **(figure 8.20, part 2)**.

The electron carrier complexes and associated molecules present in aerobic organisms are as follows:

1. **Complex I** consists of a huge multienzyme cluster termed *NADH dehydrogenase* (reductase), which receives the NADH from glycolysis and the Krebs cycle.
2. **Complex II** is made up of a series of iron-sulfur (FeS) proteins that receive electrons from $FADH_2$ produced in the sixth step of the Krebs cycle.
3. **Coenzyme Q,** or **ubiquinone,** is a mobile carrier not embedded in the membrane that can pick up electrons from both complexes I and II and donate them to complex III.
4. **Complex III** is composed of cytochromes b and c_1, which deliver electrons to cytochrome c.
5. **Cytochrome c** is another mobile carrier that shuttles electrons between complexes III and IV.
6. **Complex IV** catalyzes the reaction between electrons, H^+, and oxygen, yielding H_2O and completing the electron transfer process.

In addition to the roles outlined here, complexes I, III, and IV have the function of pumping protons from the matrix into the intermembrane space to establish a charge gradient (discussed under the next heading). With each redox exchange, the energy level of the reactants is lessened. This free energy is captured and processed by **ATP synthase** complexes stationed in the cristae in close association with the ETS carriers. Each NADH that enters electron transport can potentially give rise to a maximum of 3 ATPs. Because $FADH_2$ from the Krebs cycle enters the cycle after complex I, its reactions result in a maximum yield of about 2 ATPs. This coupling of ATP synthesis to electron transport is termed **oxidative phosphorylation.**

> **Quick Search**
> Explore this concept at such sites as "Gradients: ATP Synthase" on YouTube.

The Formation of ATP and Chemiosmosis What biochemical processes are involved in coupling electron transport to the

Cutaway view of a mitochondrion

- Outer membrane
- Inner membrane
- Matrix
- Intermembrane space
- Cristae
- ATP synthases

① The mitochondrion is the site of electron transport and oxidative phosphorylation in eukaryotic cells. Its double membrane feature creates two separate compartments: the intermembrane space (brown) between the outer and inner membranes and the matrix (yellow) entirely enclosed by the inner membrane folded into cristae (blue). The electron transport proteins and the ATP synthases are stationed throughout the cristae. From here, the pathways have access to both matrix and intermembrane compartments.

Cell membrane, Nucleus, Ribosomes, Mitochondria, Cilium

② Close-up of the ETS. NAD dehydrogenase accepts electrons from NADH and transfers them to CoQ. Electrons removed from $FADH_2$ by the FeS complex are also transferred to CoQ. These electrons are passed through the remaining carriers: the cytochrome b/c_1 complex, cytochrome c, and cytochrome a/a_3. At cytochrome a/a_3, 2 electrons combine with 2 protons (H^+) and an oxygen atom to form H_2O. Electron transport is coupled with the pumping of protons across the crista membrane into the intermembrane space by three of the carrier complexes. This process forms the basis of chemiosmosis.

② Close-up shows relative positions of cristae, compartments, ETS, and ATP synthase.

I		NADH dehydrogenase (N)
II		FeS proteins (F)
		Coenzyme Q
III		Cytochrome b Cytochrome c_1
		Cytochrome c
IV		Cytochrome a Cytochrome a_3

(a)

(b)

Crista membrane

From glycolysis and Krebs → NAD(H) → NAD

FAD(H_2) ← From Krebs → FAD

$2 H^+$ $2 e^-$ $\frac{1}{2} O_2$

H O H

ADP + P_i → ATP

F_1

Matrix

ATP synthase F_0

Intermembrane space

Outer membrane

■ + Charged ■ − Charged

③ (a) Proton transport by the ETS into the intermembrane space (IMS) sets up a chemical and charge gradient between the IMS and the matrix called the proton motive force. **(b)** ATP synthase. The gradient creates an electrical potential for capturing the free energy of electron movement to drive ATP synthesis. As protons (H^+) diffuse from the intermembrane space through the F_0 portion of the ATP synthase into the matrix, the F_1 portion rotates, pulls in ADP and P_i, and releases ATP. This is an exergonic reaction that requires 3 protons for each ATP.

Figure 8.20 Electron transport, oxidative phosphorylation, the proton motive force, chemiosmosis, and ATP synthesis in the mitochondrion.

Figure 8.21 **Chemiosmosis in bacteria.** Enlarged view of bacterial cell envelope to show the relationship of electron transport and ATP synthesis. Bacteria have the ETS carriers and ATP synthase stationed in the cell membrane. As the ETS shuttles electrons delivered by NADH and FADH$_2$, some of the ETS carriers also transport protons into the periplasmic space between the membrane and the cell wall, which sets up a gradient similar to mitochondria. Bacteria will vary in the exact nature of the carriers in the ETS.

production of ATP? According to a widely accepted concept called **chemiosmosis,** during electron transport, some of the carriers actively transport protons across the cristae membrane and into the intermembrane compartment of the mitochondrion. This process sets up a concentration gradient of hydrogen ions called the **proton motive force (PMF)**. The PMF consists of a difference in charge between the intermembrane compartment (+) and the matrix compartment (−) **(figure 8.20, part 3).**

Separating the charge has an effect similar to a battery, which can temporarily store potential energy. This charge will be maintained by the impermeability of the cristae membranes to protons (H$^+$). The only sites where protons can diffuse into the matrix compartment is at the ATP synthase complexes, which sets the stage for ATP synthesis.

ATP synthase is one of the most remarkable enzymes in the molecular world. Its structure includes two motors, an ion pump, and an enzyme that can capture energy and store it as ATP. These synthases are located throughout the membranes of the cristae in high numbers (one estimate is around 10,000 per mitochondrion). Each ATP synthase complex consists of two large units, F$_0$ and F$_1$ (figure 8.20, part 3). The F$_0$ portion is embedded in the membrane and can rotate like a motor to pull in protons. As protons flow through the F$_0$ portion by diffusion, the F$_1$ compartments pull in ADP and P$_i$. Rotation induces a change in the three-dimensional structure of ATP synthase. This adjustment creates a high-energy bond between ADP and P$_i$. The ATP that forms is released into the matrix, where it will serve as a constant supply for cellular reactions (figure 8.20, part 3). The enzyme is then rotated back to the start position for the next round of ATP synthesis.

An important issue is just how the ATP is delivered out of the mitochondrion and into the cytoplasm for use in cell synthesis and other activities. The mitochondrial membranes are impregnated with a number of specialized active transporters called ATP-ADP translocases that constantly transport ATP out of, and ADP into, the mitochondrion.

Bacterial ATP synthesis occurs by means of this same overall process. However, bacteria have the ETS stationed in the cell membrane, and the direction of the proton movement is from the cytoplasm to the periplasmic space between the membrane and cell wall. Bacteria may also show variations in the number and types of electron carriers **(figure 8.21)**. As we will see, these differences will affect the amount of ATP produced. In both cell types, the chemiosmotic theory has been supported by tests showing that oxidative phosphorylation is blocked if the mitochondrial or bacterial cell membranes are disrupted.

The Terminal Step of Electron Transport

The terminal step, during which oxygen accepts the electrons, is catalyzed by cytochrome a/a_3, also called cytochrome oxidase. This large enzyme complex is specifically adapted to receive electrons from cytochrome c, pick up hydrogen ions from solution, and react with oxygen to form a molecule of water (figure 8.20, part 3). This reaction, though in actuality more complex, is summarized as follows:

$$2H^+ + 2e^- + \tfrac{1}{2}O_2 \rightarrow H_2O$$

Most eukaryotic aerobes have a fully functioning cytochrome system, but bacteria exhibit wide-ranging variations in this part of the system. Some species lack one or more of the redox steps; others have several alternative electron transport schemes. Because many bacteria lack cytochrome oxidase, this variation can be used to differentiate among certain genera of bacteria. An oxidase detection test can be used to help identify members of the genera *Neisseria* and *Pseudomonas* and some species of *Bacillus*. Another variation in the cytochrome system is evident in certain bacteria (*Klebsiella, Enterobacter*) that can grow even in the presence of cyanide because they lack cytochrome oxidase. Cyanide will cause rapid death in humans and other eukaryotes because it blocks cytochrome oxidase, thereby completely terminating aerobic respiration, but it is harmless to these bacteria.

A potential side reaction of the respiratory chain in aerobic organisms is the incomplete reduction of oxygen to superoxide ion (O_2^-) and hydrogen peroxide (H_2O_2). As mentioned in chapter 7, these toxic oxygen products can be very damaging to cells. Aerobes have neutralizing enzymes to deal with these products, including *superoxide dismutase* and *catalase*. One exception is the genus *Streptococcus,* which can grow well in oxygen yet lacks both cytochromes and catalase. The tolerance of these organisms to oxygen can be explained by the neutralizing effects of a special peroxidase. The lack of cytochromes, catalase, and peroxidases in strict anaerobes as a rule limits their ability to process free oxygen and contributes to its toxic effects on them.

Summary of Aerobic Respiration

Reviewing the summary equation for respiration, we are now in a position to estimate the theoretical total of ATP molecules arising from a single glucose molecule through a combination of substrate-level phosphorylation and oxidation of NADH and $FADH_2$:

- There are 3 substrate-level reactions that give rise directly to ATP—2 in glycolysis and 1 in the Krebs cycle. Because these are happening **twice** for each event, they provide **6 ATPs** overall.
- There are **5 NADHs**—1 from glycolysis, 1 from pyruvic acid oxidation, and 3 from the Krebs cycle. Each NADH could potentially power the synthesis of 3 ATPs, yielding $5 \times 3 = 15$ ATPs. Again, this happens **twice for each glucose** and could potentially generate **30 ATPs.**
- There is a single reaction in the Krebs cycle that yields $FADH_2$, which can power synthesis of 2 ATPs, and multiplied by 2 provides **4 ATPs.**
- The theoretical total for ATP synthesis could be $6 + 30 + 4 = 40$; however, because the first and second reactions of glycolysis use up 2 ATPs, the **final net number** is **38 ATPs.**

We emphasize that these totals are theoretical because the yields for NADH and $FADH_2$ are lower when the actual conditions in cells are taken into account. It is likely that oxidation of each $NADH^+$ provides closer to 2.5 ATPs and oxidation of $FADH_2$, about 1.75 ATPs. This will decrease the practical total to around **32 ATPs.** Another reason this total will be reduced for eukaryotic cells is that they must use active transport (and ATP) to carry the NADH from glycolysis into the mitochondrial cristae, bringing the total down to **30 ATPs** per glucose. Most prokaryotic cells probably produce even less ATP because they lack one or more of the carriers in the electron transport system or do not generate as much NADH. **Figure 8.22** charts the course of these calculations as they occur in the three phases of aerobic respiration.

No summary would be complete without considering three other key participants:

- Six carbon dioxide molecules are generated by reactions just prior to and during the Krebs cycle. These represent all of the carbons and oxygens from the original glucose molecule.
- Six oxygen molecules are consumed during the final transfer of electrons and hydrogens to cytochrome oxidase a_3.
- Six water molecules are produced in electron transport and 2 in glycolysis, but because 2 are used in the Krebs cycle, this leaves a net number of 6.

Pathways and Products **Net Output Summary****

Glycolysis — Glucose 6C	2 ATPs
Pyruvic acid 3C	2 NADHs
	2 Pyruvic acids
Transition step — Acetyl CoA 2C	2 NADHs
	2 CO₂s
Krebs cycle — 2 Turns	4 CO₂s
	6 NADHs
	2 ATPs
	2 FADH₂s
Electron transport and oxidative phosphorylation	34 ATPs
	6 H₂Os

*These compounds are processed by the electron transport system.

**This net figure accounts for total ATPs minus the 2 used in glycolysis and the doubling of the products after the split into 2 3C compounds in glycolysis.

Figure 8.22 **Summary of aerobic metabolism products and ATP yields.** Compare this figure with the original equation: Glucose ($C_6H_{12}O_6$) + $6O_2$ + 38 ADP + 38P_i → $6CO_2$ + $6H_2O$ + 38 ATP.

Anaerobic Respiration

Some bacteria have evolved an anaerobic respiratory system that functions like the aerobic cytochrome system, except that it utilizes oxygen-containing ions rather than free oxygen as the final electron acceptor. Of these, the nitrate (NO_3^-) and nitrite (NO_2^-) reduction systems are best known. The reaction in species such as *E. coli* is represented as follows:

$$\text{Nitrate reductase}$$
$$NO_3^- + NADH + H^+ \xrightarrow{\quad\downarrow\quad} NO_2^- + H_2O + NAD^+$$

The enzyme nitrate reductase catalyzes the removal of oxygen from nitrate, leaving nitrite and water as products. This reaction is the basis for a physiological test used in identifying certain bacteria.

Some species of *Pseudomonas* and *Bacillus* possess enzymes that can further reduce nitrite to nitric oxide (NO), nitrous oxide (N_2O), and even nitrogen gas (N_2). This process, called **denitrification,** is a very important step in recycling nitrogen in

the biosphere. Other oxygen-containing nutrients reduced anaerobically by various bacteria are carbonates and sulfates.

Most obligate anaerobes use the NADH they generate during glycolysis and the Krebs cycle to reduce some compound other than O_2 but still follow the oxidative phosphorylation pathway. Methanogens (described in chapter 7) reduce CO_2 or CO_3^- (carbonate) to CH_4 (methane gas), and certain sulfate bacteria reduce SO_4^{2-} to S (sulfide) or hydrogen sulfide gas (H_2S). Some use metals or organic compounds as the final electron acceptor. These microbes live in subterranean habitats such as swamps and deep oceanic vents that are devoid of O_2 gas.

 Practice SECTION 8.3

13. Describe the basic energy strategies of microbes and the catabolic pathways they use.

14. Compare and contrast the location of glycolysis, Krebs cycle, and electron transport in prokaryotic and eukaryotic cells.

15. Outline the basic steps in glycolysis, indicating where ATP is used and where it is given off.

16. Where does NADH originate, and what is its fate in an aerobe?

17. What is the fate of NADH in a fermentative organism?

18. Summarize the chemiosmotic theory of ATP formation.

19. How many ATPs could *theoretically* be formed from a glucose molecule carried through aerobic respiration, and how many are *probably* formed?

20. Why does the total of ATPs generated differ between bacteria and many eukaryotes?

21. Name the sources of oxygen in bacteria that use anaerobic respiration.

22. What are the final electron acceptors in aerobic, anaerobic, and fermentative metabolism?

23. Describe the reaction between electrons, H^+, and oxygen at the final step of electron transport.

8.4 The Importance of Fermentation

 Learn

19. Explain what is meant by the term *fermentation* and how fermentation is used by natural biological systems and biotechnology.

20. Describe some of the processes of fermentation and the products that result.

Of all the results of pyruvate metabolism, probably the most varied is fermentation. Technically speaking, **fermentation*** is a process that involves (1) the incomplete oxidation of glucose or other carbohydrates in the absence of oxygen; (2) the oxidation of NADH to

* *fermentation* (fur-men-tay'-shun) L. *fervere,* to boil, or *fermentatum,* leaven or yeast.

NAD^+, which is essential to the continuation of the glycolytic pathway; (3) the use of organic compounds as the terminal electron acceptors; and (4) the release of a small amount of ATP.

Over time, the term *fermentation* has acquired several looser meanings. Originally Pasteur called the microbial action of yeast during wine production *ferments,* and to this day, biochemists use the term in reference to the production of ethyl alcohol by yeasts acting on glucose and other carbohydrates. Fermentation is traditionally what bacteriologists call the formation of acid, gas, and other products by the action of various bacteria on pyruvic acid. Industrial processes that produce chemicals on a massive scale through the actions of microbes are also called fermentations. Each of these usages is acceptable for one application or another.

It may seem that fermentation yielding only meager amounts of energy (2 ATPs maximum per glucose) would slow down growth. And yet the process is a common metabolic strategy among bacteria. What actually happens is that many bacteria can grow as fast as they would in the presence of oxygen. This rapid growth is made possible by an increase in the rate of glycolysis. From another standpoint, fermentation permits survival and growth in the absence of molecular oxygen and allows colonization of anaerobic environments. It also enables microorganisms with a versatile metabolism to adapt to variations in the availability of oxygen. For such facultative microbes, fermentation provides a means to function even when oxygen levels are too low for aerobic respiration or the usual electron acceptor is unavailable. An additional advantage of fermentation is that it generates a number of intermediates that can be used in **anabolic** pathways and shared within a population of microbes.

Bacteria that digest cellulose in the rumens of cattle and other ruminants are largely fermentative. After initially hydrolyzing cellulose to glucose, they ferment the glucose to organic acids, which are then absorbed as the bovine's principal energy source. Even human muscle cells can undergo a form of fermentation that permits short periods of activity after the oxygen supply in the muscle has been exhausted. Muscle cells convert pyruvic acid into lactic acid, which allows anaerobic production of ATP to proceed for a time. But this cannot go on indefinitely, and after a few minutes, the accumulated lactic acid causes muscle fatigue.

Products of Fermentation in Microorganisms

Alcoholic beverages (wine, beer, whiskey) are perhaps the most prominent among fermentation products; others are solvents (acetone, butanol), organic acids (lactic, acetic), dairy products, and many other foods. Derivatives of proteins, nucleic acids, and other organic compounds are fermented to produce vitamins, antibiotics, and even hormones such as hydrocortisone.

Fermentation products can be grouped into two general categories: alcoholic fermentation products and acidic fermentation products **(figure 8.23)**. **Alcoholic fermentation** occurs in yeast or bacterial species that have metabolic pathways for converting pyruvic acid to ethanol. This process involves a decarboxylation of pyruvic acid to acetaldehyde, followed by a reduction of the acetaldehyde to ethanol. In oxidizing the NADH formed during glycolysis, NAD^+ is regenerated, thereby feeding back to and maintaining the glycolytic pathway. These processes are crucial in

Figure 8.23 **The fermentation systems that produce acid and alcohol.** In both cases, the final electron acceptor is an organic compound. In yeasts, pyruvic acid is decarboxylated to acetaldehyde and CO_2, and the NADH given off in the glycolytic pathway reduces acetaldehyde to ethyl alcohol. In homolactic fermentative bacteria, pyruvic acid is reduced by NADH to lactic acid. Both systems regenerate NAD^+ to feed back into glycolysis or other cycles (pink dotted lines).

for the bubbles in champagne and beer and the rising of bread dough.

Alcohols other than ethanol can be produced during bacterial fermentation pathways. Certain clostridia produce butanol and isopropanol through a complex series of reactions. Although this process was once an important source of alcohols for industrial use, it has been largely replaced by a nonmicrobial petroleum process.

The pathways of **acidic fermentation** are extremely varied. Lactic acid bacteria ferment pyruvate in the same way that humans do—by reducing it to lactic acid. If the product of this fermentation is mainly lactic acid, as in certain species of *Streptococcus* and *Lactobacillus*, it is termed *homolactic*. The souring of milk is due largely to the production of this acid by bacteria. When glucose is fermented to a mixture of lactic acid, acetic acid, and carbon dioxide, as is the case with *Leuconostoc* and other species of *Lactobacillus*, the process is termed *heterolactic fermentation*.

Many members of the family Enterobacteriaceae (*Escherichia*, *Shigella*, and *Salmonella*) possess enzyme systems for converting pyruvic acid to several acids simultaneously **(figure 8.24)**. **Mixed acid fermentation** produces a combination of acetic, lactic, succinic, and formic acids, and it lowers the pH of a medium to about 4.0. *Propionibacterium* produces primarily propionic acid, which gives the characteristic flavor to Swiss cheese; gas (CO_2) from the same fermentation reaction produces the holes. Some members also further decompose formic acid completely to carbon dioxide and hydrogen gases. Because enteric bacteria commonly occupy the intestine, this fermentative activity accounts for the accumulation of some types of gas—primarily CO_2 and H_2—in the intestine. Some bacteria reduce the organic acids and produce the neutral end product 2,3-butanediol. Several of these end products are the basis of biochemical tests described in chapter 17.

We have provided only a brief survey of fermentation products, but it is worth noting that microbes can be harnessed to synthesize a variety of other substances by varying the raw materials provided to them. In fact, so broad is the meaning of the word *fermentation* that the large-scale industrial syntheses by microorganisms are not technically fermentations and often utilize entirely different mechanisms from those described here. They even occur aerobically, particularly in antibiotic, hormone, vitamin, and amino acid production, but they still produce a valuable commercial product.

the production of beer and wine, though the actual techniques for arriving at the desired amount of ethanol and the prevention of unwanted side reactions are important tricks of the brewer's trade **(8.5 Making Connections)**. Note that the products of alcoholic fermentation include both ethanol *and* CO_2, a gas that accounts

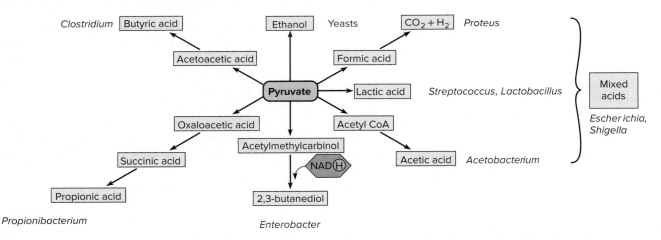

Figure 8.24 Miscellaneous products of pyruvate fermentation and some of the bacteria involved in their production.

8.5 MAKING CONNECTIONS

Pasteur and the Wine-to-Vinegar Mystery

The microbiology of alcoholic fermentation was greatly clarified by Louis Pasteur after French winemakers hired him to uncover the causes of periodic spoilage in wines. Especially troublesome was the conversion of wine to vinegar and the resultant sour flavor. Up to that time, wine formation had been considered strictly a chemical process. After extensively studying beer making and wine grapes, Pasteur concluded that wine, both fine and not so fine, was the result of microbial action on the juices of the grape and that wine "disease" was caused by contaminating organisms that produced undesirable products such as acid. Although he did not know it at the time, the bacterial contaminants responsible for the acidity of the spoiled wines were likely to be *Acetobacter* or *Gluconobacter* introduced by the grapes, air, or wine-making apparatus. These common gram-negative genera further oxidized ethanol to acetic acid and are presently used in production of some types of vinegar. The following formula shows how this is accomplished:

Ingram Publishing/Alamy Stock Photo

$$H-\underset{\underset{H}{|}}{\overset{\overset{H}{|}}{C}}-\underset{\underset{H}{|}}{\overset{\overset{H}{|}}{C}}-OH \xrightarrow{O_2} H-\underset{\underset{H}{|}}{\overset{\overset{H}{|}}{C}}-\overset{\overset{O}{\parallel}}{C} + 2H_2O$$

Ethanol $\qquad$ Acetic acid

Pasteur's far-reaching solution to the problem is still with us today—mild heating, or *pasteurization*, of the grape juice to destroy the contaminants,

followed by inoculation of the juice with a pure yeast culture. The topic of pasteurization is explored further in chapter 11.

An analysis of wine shows that it contains, in addition to water and ethyl alcohol, thousands of other chemical compounds (see "Wine Chemistry" on Wikipedia). What does this tell you about the metabolism of yeasts during alcoholic fermentation?

Practice SECTION 8.4

24. What adaptive advantages does a fermentative metabolism confer on a microbe?
25. Describe three patterns of fermentation typical of microbes.

8.5 Biosynthesis and the Crossing Pathways of Metabolism

Learn

21. Explain how cells perform anabolic functions and what is involved in amphibolism.
22. Identify major pathways where molecules can be redirected or converted into useful cell products.
23. Briefly describe several mechanisms in biosynthesis of macromolecules.

Our discussion now turns from catabolism and energy extraction to anabolic functions and biosynthesis. In this section, we will explore this area, also called intermediary metabolism, that includes

amphibolic pathways, the synthesis of simple molecules, and the synthesis of macromolecules.

The Frugality of the Cell—Waste Not, Want Not

It must be obvious by now that cells have mechanisms for careful management of carbon compounds. Rather than being dead ends, most catabolic pathways contain strategic molecular intermediates (metabolites) that can be diverted into anabolic pathways. In this way, a given molecule can serve multiple purposes, and the maximum benefit can be derived from all nutrients and metabolites of the cell pool. The property of a system to integrate catabolic and anabolic pathways to improve cell efficiency is termed **amphibolism.***

At this point in the chapter, you can appreciate a more complex view of metabolism than that presented at the beginning in figure 8.1. **Figure 8.25** demonstrates the amphibolic nature of intermediary metabolism. The pathways of glucose catabolism are an especially rich "metabolic marketplace." The principal sites of amphibolic interaction occur during glycolysis (glyceraldehyde-3-phosphate and pyruvic acid) and the Krebs cycle (acetyl coenzyme A and various organic acids).

* *amphibolism* (ăm-fee-bol'-izm) Gr. *amphi,* two-sided, and *bole,* a throw.

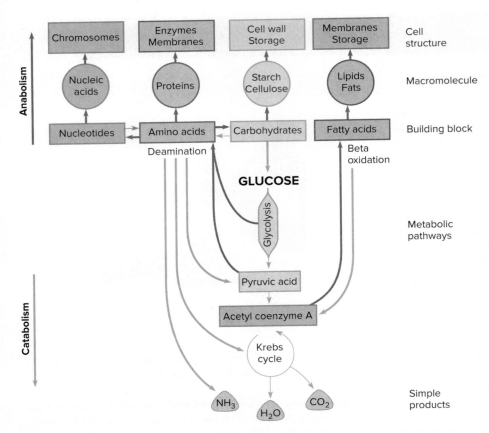

Figure 8.25 An amphibolic view of metabolism. Intermediate compounds such as pyruvic acid and acetyl coenzyme A serve multiple functions. With comparatively small modifications, these compounds can be converted into other compounds and enter a different pathway. Note that catabolism of glucose (center) furnishes numerous intermediates for anabolic pathways that synthesize amino acids, fats, nucleic acids, and carbohydrates. These building blocks can serve in further synthesis of larger molecules to construct a wide array of cell components.

enter the Krebs cycle via acetyl coenzyme A. This aerobic process, called **beta oxidation,** releases significant energy. Oxidation of a 6-carbon fatty acid with glycerol potentially yields 50 ATPs, compared with 38 for a 6-carbon sugar.

Two carbohydrate metabolites from the Krebs cycle are oxaloacetic acid and α-ketoglutaric acid—essential intermediates in the synthesis of certain amino acids. This occurs through **amination,** the addition of an amino group to a carbon skeleton **(figure 8.26a).** A certain core group of amino acids can then be used to synthesize others. Amino acids and carbohydrates can be interchanged through **transamination** as well **(figure 8.26b).**

Pathways that synthesize the nitrogen bases (purines, pyrimidines), which are components of DNA and RNA, originate in amino acids and so can be dependent on intermediates from the Krebs cycle as well. Because the coenzymes NAD^+, NADP, FAD, and others contain purines and pyrimidines similar to the nucleic acids, their synthetic pathways are also dependent on amino acids. During times of carbohydrate deprivation, organisms can likewise convert amino acids to intermediates of the Krebs cycle by **deamination** (removal of an amino group) and thereby derive energy from proteins. Deamination results in the formation of nitrogen waste products such as ammonium ions or urea **(figure 8.26c).**

Amphibolic Sources of Cellular Building Blocks

Glyceraldehyde-3-phosphate can be diverted away from glycolysis and converted into precursors for amino acid, carbohydrate, and triglyceride (fat) synthesis. (A precursor molecule is one that gives rise to a different compound.) Earlier, we noted the numerous directions that pyruvic acid catabolism can take. In terms of synthesis, pyruvate also plays a pivotal role in providing intermediates for amino acids. In the event of an inadequate glucose supply, pyruvate serves as the starting point in glucose synthesis from various metabolic intermediates, a process called **gluconeogenesis.***

The acetyl group that starts the Krebs cycle is another extremely versatile metabolite that can be fed into a number of synthetic pathways. This 2-carbon fragment can be converted as a single unit into one of several amino acids, or a number of these fragments can be condensed into hydrocarbon chains that are important building blocks for fatty acid and lipid synthesis. Note that the reverse is also true: Fats can be degraded to acetyl and thereby

Formation of Macromolecules

Monosaccharides, amino acids, fatty acids, nitrogen bases, and vitamins—the building blocks that make up the various macromolecules and organelles of the cell—come from two possible sources. They can enter the cell from the outside as nutrients, or they can be synthesized through various cellular pathways. The degree to which an organism can synthesize its own building blocks (simple molecules) is determined by its genetic makeup, a factor that varies tremendously from group to group. In chapter 7, you learned that autotrophs require only CO_2 as a carbon source, a few minerals to synthesize all cell substances, and no organic nutrients. Even some heterotrophic organisms (*E. coli,* yeasts) are so metabolically complete that they can synthesize all cellular substances from minerals and one organic carbon source such as glucose. Compare this with a strict parasite lacking or having lost significant synthetic capabilities and having to obtain most essential nutrient molecules from its host.

Whatever their source, once these building blocks are added to the metabolic pool, they are available for synthesis of polymers by the cell. The details of synthesis vary among the types of macromolecules, but all of them involve the formation of bonds by specialized enzymes and the expenditure of ATP.

* *gluconeogenesis* (gloo″-koh-nee″-oh-gen′-uh-sis) Literally, the formation of "new" glucose.

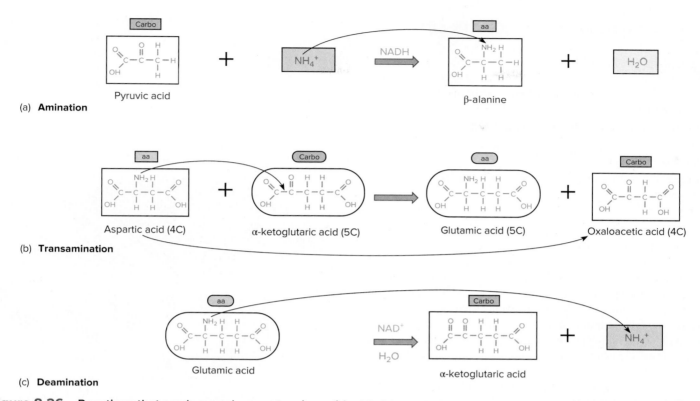

(a) **Amination**

(b) **Transamination**

(c) **Deamination**

Figure 8.26 Reactions that produce and convert amino acids. All of the reactions require energy as ATP or NADH and specialized enzymes. **(a)** Through amination (the addition of an ammonium molecule [amino group]), a carbohydrate can be converted to an amino acid. **(b)** Through transamination (transfer of an amino group from an amino acid to a carbohydrate), metabolic intermediates can be converted to amino acids that are in low supply. **(c)** Through deamination (removal of an amino group), an amino acid can be converted to a useful intermediate of carbohydrate catabolism. This is how proteins are used to derive energy. Ammonium is one waste product of deamination. Note that carbohydrate structures are in brown and amino acids are in blue.

Carbohydrate Biosynthesis

The role of glucose in bioenergetics is so crucial that its biosynthesis is ensured by several alternative pathways. Certain structures in the cell depend on an adequate supply of glucose as well. It is the major component of the cellulose cell walls of some eukaryotes and of certain storage granules (starch, glycogen). One of the intermediaries in glycolysis, glucose-6-P, is used to form glycogen. Monosaccharides other than glucose are important in the synthesis of bacterial cell walls. Peptidoglycan contains a linked polymer of muramic acid and glucosamine. Fructose-6-P from glycolysis is used to form these two sugars. Carbohydrates (deoxyribose, ribose) are also essential building blocks in nucleic acids. Polysaccharides are the predominant components of cell surface structures such as capsules and the glycocalyx, and they are commonly found in slime layers (dextran is an example). Remember that most polymerization reactions occur via loss of a water molecule (see figure 2.17) and the input of energy.

Assembly of the Cell

The component parts of a bacterial cell are being synthesized on a continuous basis, and catabolism is also taking place, as long as nutrients are present and the cell is in a nondormant state. When anabolism produces sufficient macromolecules, and when DNA replication produces duplicate copies of the cell's genetic material, the cell undergoes binary fission. The two new cells will need twice as many ribosomes, twice as many enzymes, and so on. The cell has created these during the initial anabolic phases we have described. Before cell division, the membrane(s) and the cell wall will have increased in size to create a cell that is almost twice as big as a "newborn" cell. Once synthesized, the phospholipid bilayer components of the membranes assemble themselves spontaneously, but proteins and other components must be added to the membranes. Growth of the cell wall, accomplished by the addition and coupling of sugars and peptides, requires energy input. The catabolic processes provide constant energy for these complex building reactions.

 Practice SECTION 8.5

26. What is meant by amphibolism, and what are its most important functions?

27. Identify major ways that amino acids are processed.

28. Which macromolecules are synthesized by specialized anabolic pathways?

8.6 Photosynthesis: The Earth's Lifeline

 Learn

24. Outline the general reactions of photosynthesis and the importance it holds for the energetics of life.

25. Describe the pigment systems and how they function.

26. Describe the main events in the light-dependent reactions and the products that result.

27. Describe the main events in the light-independent reactions and the products that result.

As mentioned earlier, the ultimate source of most of the chemical energy in cells is the sun. Because this source is *directly* available only to the cells of photosynthesizers, most organisms on earth are either directly or indirectly dependent on photosynthesis, except for a few chemoautotrophs that derive their energy and nutrients solely from inorganic substrates. The other major products of photosynthesis are organic carbon compounds, which are produced from carbon dioxide through a process called **carbon fixation.** On land, green plants are the primary photosynthesizers; and in aquatic ecosystems, where 80% to 90% of all photosynthesis occurs, this role is filled by algae, cyanobacteria, and green sulfur, purple sulfur, and purple nonsulfur bacteria.

The summary equation for the main reactants and products of photosynthesis in aerobic organisms is

$$6CO_2 + 6H_2O \xrightarrow{\text{Light and pigment}} \underset{\text{Glucose}}{C_6H_{12}O_6} + 6O_2 \uparrow$$

The anatomy of photosynthetic cells is adapted to trapping sunlight, and their physiology effectively uses this solar energy to produce high-energy glucose from low-energy CO_2 and water. Photosynthetic organisms achieve this remarkable feat through a series of reactions involving light, pigment, CO_2, and water, which is used as a source for electrons.

Photosynthesis proceeds in two phases: the **light-dependent reactions,** which proceed only in the presence of light waves, and the **light-independent reactions,** which can operate without direct exposure to light, but are still reliant on the energy molecules made in the light-dependent reactions (**figure 8.27**).

Solar energy is delivered in discrete energy packets called **photons** (also called quanta) that travel as waves. The wavelengths of light operating in photosynthesis occur in the visible spectrum between 400 nanometers (violet) and 700 nanometers (red) and above. As this light strikes photosynthetic pigments, some wavelengths are absorbed, some pass through, and some are reflected. The activity that has the greatest impact on photosynthesis is the absorbance of light by photosynthetic pigments. These include the **chlorophylls,** which are green; **carotenoids,** which are yellow, orange, or red; and **phycobilins,** which are red or blue-green.[3] By far the most important of these

pigments are the chlorophylls, which contain a *photocenter* that consists of a magnesium atom held in the center of a complex ringed molecule called a *porphyrin* (**process figure 8.28, part 3**). As we will see, the chlorophyll molecule harvests the energy of photons and converts it to electron (chemical) energy. Accessory photosynthetic pigments such as carotenes trap light energy and shuttle it to chlorophyll, thereby functioning like antennae. These light-dependent reactions are responsible for **photophosphorylation,** the channeling of energy extracted from light to make high-energy bonds of ATP. This sets the scene for the light-independent reactions, which use both ATP and NADPH for synthesis. During this phase, carbon atoms from CO_2 are fixed to the carbon backbones of organic molecules.

The detailed biochemistry of photosynthesis is beyond the scope of this text, but we will provide an overview of the general process as it occurs in green plants, algae, and cyanobacteria. It is worth noting that many of the basic activities are biochemically similar to certain pathways of aerobic metabolism.

Figure 8.27 Overview of photosynthesis. The general reactions of photosynthesis are into two phases called light-dependent reactions and light-independent reactions. The light-dependent reactions involve two major events: (1) the trapping of light with a photosensitive pigment, such as chlorophyll, and converting the light energy into chemical energy in the form of ATP and NADPH; and (2) the splitting of water molecules with the release of oxygen gas. The light-independent reactions utilize ATP and NADPH produced during the light-dependent reactions to fix CO_2 into organic compounds such as glucose.

3. The color of the pigment corresponds to the wavelength of light it reflects.

Process Figure 8.28 **The location and participants in the light-dependent reactions of a chloroplast.** **(1)** A cell of the algae, *Chlamydomonas*, with a cutaway view of a single chloroplast to show the internal structure of stroma and grana. **(2)** A granum consists of a stack of hollow membrane-bound discs called thylakoids, which house **(3)** the chlorophyll molecules, arranged in arrays (antennae) for capturing light. **(4)** The chlorophylls exist in separate systems called PS II and PS I, embedded in the thylakoid membrane. Other players in the process are an electron transport chain, an oxygen-evolving complex, a final electron acceptor ($NADP^+$), and ATP synthase. The text covers the main mechanisms of this process.

Light-Dependent Reactions

The systems that carry the photosynthetic pigments are also the sites for the light-dependent reactions. They occur in the **thylakoid** membranes of compartments called **grana** (singular, granum) in chloroplasts **(process figure 8.28, part 1)** and in thylakoid layers of the cell membranes of cyanobacteria. These systems exist as two separate complexes called **photosystem I (PS700)** and **photosystem II (PS680)**[4] **(process figure 8.28, part 4).**

4. The numbers refer to the wavelength of light to which each system is most sensitive.

Both systems contain chlorophyll, but their chlorophylls are sensitive to different wavelengths: PS I absorbs longer wavelengths (above 680 nm) and PS II absorbs shorter wavelengths (680 nm and below), which efficiently covers the range of light to which phototrophs are exposed. Both photosystems are stationed in **antennae**—clusters of about 300 molecules of chlorophyll located in the thylakoid membranes. Antennae absorb light and convey it to **reaction centers,** where the light-dependent reactions take place (process figure 8.28, part 4).

The chloroplast is composed of separate compartments similar to mitochondria. One compartment—the **stroma**—is the region surrounding the grana and thylakoids, and the other one is the space inside the thylakoids called the **lumen** (process figure 8.28, part 4).

Overview of the Light-Dependent Reactions and Photophosphorylation

The thylakoids are specially situated to bring together all components of the light-dependent reactions. Most of these components are embedded in the thylakoid membranes and are accessible from both the lumen and the stroma. They include chlorophyll molecules and their photosystems (PS II and PS I)[5]; an oxygen-evolving complex; electron transport systems—consisting of a mobile electron carrier plastoquinone (PQ); cytochrome b_f complex; plastocyanin (PC), a second mobile electron carrier; ferredoxin (Fd) with nicotinamide adenine dinucleotide phosphate ($NADP^+$) reductase (FNR); and ATP synthase. Several of the systems and their actions are very similar to those we previously examined in mitochondria.

The light-dependent pathway proceeds as follows:

PS II Reactions
1. When light strikes the magnesium in PS II, an electron becomes excited (is raised to a higher energy level) and is released by PS II to the first electron transport system.
2. An oxygen-evolving complex associated with PS II splits two water molecules into 4 electrons, 4 protons (H^+), and oxygen. Because it occurs in the presence of light, this step is termed **photolysis,** and it results in **the first major product** of the light-dependent reactions—the **O_2 gas** required by all aerobic organisms, including even most photosynthesizers. In addition, the electrons released by photolysis return the PS II complex to a ground state so it is again ready to respond to light. Another important effect of photolysis is the release of protons into the lumen, which contributes to the chemiosmotic proton gradient so essential to ATP synthesis.

Electron Transport
1. An electron given off by PS II is picked up by the first compound of the electron transport chain—PQ—which moves it to

the cytochrome b_f complex. From here, it is transported to plastocyanin and to the PS I complex.
2. An event coupled to electron transport is the delivery of protons (H^+) from the stroma side to the lumen side by the actions of the cytochrome b_f complex, which helps maintain the electrochemical gradient between the stroma and lumen.

PS I Reactions
1. When PS I is excited by light, it also releases an electron that will be transported through a different series of carriers. In addition, it picks up the electrons from PS II delivered by plastocyanin.
2. These electrons are shuttled to the final electron acceptors—ferredoxin and the FNR complex. The function of the FNR is to transfer 2 electrons (and 2 protons) to $NADP^+$, converting it to **NADPH.** This is the **second major product** of the light-dependent reactions, one which provides reducing power for the light-independent reactions.

ATP Synthase and Photophosphorylation ATP synthase complexes are distributed throughout the thylakoid membranes. They have the same structure as those of mitochondria and they, too, capture the free energy inherent in the proton motive force to synthesize ATP. As protons flow through the F_0 portion of the synthase from the lumen to the stroma, the F_1 component pulls in ADP and P_i, releasing ATP, the **third major product** of the light reactions. You may notice that the energy-associated molecules (NADPH and ATP) are released in the stroma, which situates them for immediate use in the light-independent reactions covered in the next section.

Light-Independent Reactions

The anabolic reactions of photosynthesis occur in the stroma of a chloroplast or the cytoplasm of cyanobacteria. These reactions use energy produced by the light phase to synthesize glucose by means of the Calvin cycle **(figure 8.29).**

The cycle begins at the point where CO_2 is combined with a 5-carbon acceptor molecule with two terminal phosphates called ribulose-1,5-bisphosphate **(RuBP).** This first critical step in **carbon fixation** generates a 6-carbon intermediate compound that immediately splits into two 3-carbon molecules of 3-phosphoglyceric acid (PGA). The subsequent steps use ATP and NADPH generated by the photosystems to form high-energy intermediates. First, 2 ATPs are expended to add a second phosphate to 3-PGA, producing two molecules of 1,3-bisphosphoglyceric acid (BPG). This is followed by NADPH contributing its electrons to BPG with the removal of one high-energy phosphate. These events give rise to two glyceraldehyde-3-phosphate (G3P). This molecule and its isomer dihydroxyacetone phosphate (DHAP) are key compounds in hexose synthesis leading to fructose and glucose. Some of the G3P is conveyed to the remainder of the cycle, where it participates in the regeneration of RuBP. This involves numerous steps not depicted in figure 8.29.

5. These numbers signify the order in which they were discovered, not the order of reactivity.

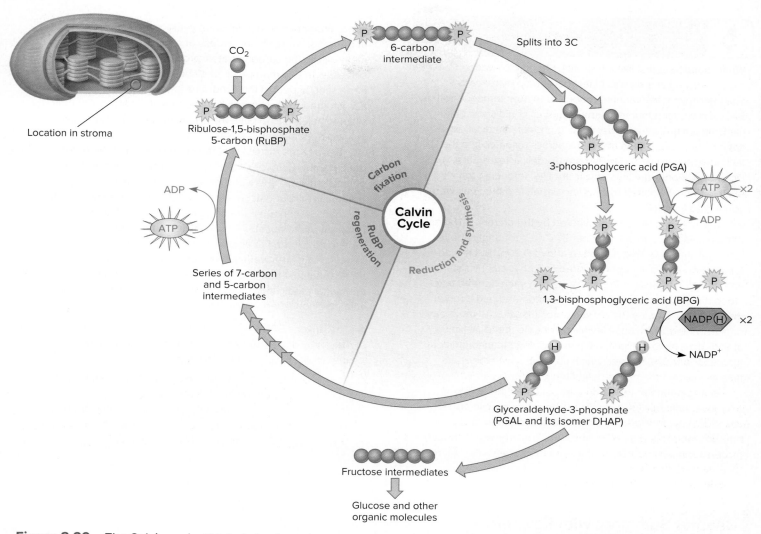

Figure 8.29 The Calvin cycle. This includes the main events of photosynthesis during which carbon is fixed into organic form using the energy (ATP and NADPH) released by the light reactions. The end product, glucose, can be stored as complex carbohydrates, or it can be used in various amphibolic pathways to produce other carbohydrate intermediates or amino acids. Some PGAL is used in the regeneration of RuBP, which uses additional ATP made during the light-dependent reactions.

You may notice that this pathway is very similar to glycolysis, except that it runs in reverse (see process figure 8.17).

Other Mechanisms of Photosynthesis

The **oxygenic,** or oxygen-releasing, photosynthesis described in the previous section occurs in plants, algae, and cyanobacteria and is the dominant type on the earth. Other photosynthesizers such as green and purple sulfur bacteria possess bacteriochlorophyll, which is more versatile in capturing light. They have only a cyclic photosystem I, which routes the electrons from the photocenter to the electron carriers and back to the photosystem again. This pathway generates a relatively small amount of ATP, and it may not produce NADPH. As photolithotrophs, these bacteria use H_2, H_2S, or elemental sulfur rather than H_2O as a source of electrons and reducing power. As a consequence, they are **anoxygenic** (non–oxygen-producing), and many are strict anaerobes.

Practice SECTION 8.6

29. Indicate whether each of the following is produced during the light-independent or light-dependent reactions of photosynthesis: O_2, ATP, NADPH, and glucose.

30. During which reactions are water and CO_2 consumed, and what is the outcome?

31. What are the functions of chlorophyll and the photosystems?

32. What are the fates of the ATP and NADH in the Calvin cycle?

33. Compare oxygenic with anoxygenic photosynthesis.

CASE STUDY **Part 2**

What sounded at first like a last-ditch attempt to evade a drunk-driving charge was in fact backed up by research. The attorney for the woman, curious as to how someone with a BAC of more than four times the legal limit could show only mild impairment, began investigating possible medical explanations for her condition and came across research into the little known syndrome by Dr. Barbara Cordell, a Texas nurse, and Dr. Anup Kanodia, an Ohio physician. The defendant traveled to Ohio to be examined by Dr. Kanodia, while other tests were conducted in Buffalo.

Breathalyzer tests, administered by the driver on 18 separate occasions, showed that her BAC was routinely above the legal limit of 0.08%, and often above 0.20%. But the defense attorney wasn't done. "I hired two physician assistants and a person trained in Breathalyzers to watch her and take blood alcohol levels over a 12-hour period and had it run at the same lab used by the prosecution," he said. "Without any drinks, her blood [alcohol] level was double the legal limit at 9:15 a.m., triple the limit at 6 p.m. and more than four times the legal limit at 8:30 p.m., which correlates with the same time of day that the police pulled her over."

Gut fermentation syndrome depends on the ability of microbes, primarily yeasts, to decarboxylate pyruvic acid to acetaldehyde, followed by reduction of acetaldehyde to ethanol, the same process that occurs in a brewery. Although most evidence is anecdotal, the syndrome seems to require a larger-than-normal population of yeast in the small intestine, and is made worse by an excess of carbohydrates. Glycolysis metabolizes the carbohydrates, producing pyruvic acid, which serves as the starting point for alcoholic fermentation. One interesting aspect of the syndrome is that sufferers become accustomed to functioning with high levels of alcohol in their system, helping to explain the relatively mild symptoms seen in the defendant in this case.

Despite the dismissal of the charges against the defendant, Hamburg Police Chief Gregory Wickett defended his officers, saying, "She was highly intoxicated, as shown by the Breathalyzer. Our officers did the right thing in getting her off the road. . . . Whether she has a medical issue that caused it is not for me to decide." Court officials have said that the prosecutors intend to appeal and hope to have charges reinstated against the woman, but so far this hasn't happened. In the meantime, the woman has been treated with a dose of antifungal medication, and is restricted to a yeast-free diet with no alcohol and very low levels of carbohydrates.

■ The driver's BAC in this case seems to rise throughout the day. Why do you think this is, considering that yeast metabolism is consistent throughout the day?

■ There have been anecdotal incidents where people with uncontrolled diabetes have tested positive for alcohol in their urine, especially when the urine sample has been allowed to sit at room temperature for several hours prior to being tested. Explain how this could occur.

Chapter Summary with Key Terms

8.1 An Introduction to Metabolism and Enzymes

A. *Metabolism*

1. **Metabolism** is the sum of biochemical activities in cells; it involves chemical changes to reactants and the release of products using well-established pathways.

2. Metabolism is a complementary process consisting of **anabolism,** synthetic reactions that convert small molecules into large molecules, and **catabolism,** in which large molecules are degraded. Together, they generate thousands of intermediate molecular states, called metabolites, which are regulated at many levels.

B. *Enzymes: Metabolic Catalysts*

1. Metabolism is made possible by organic **catalysts,** or **enzymes,** that speed up reactions by lowering the **energy of activation.** Enzymes are not consumed and can be reused. Each enzyme acts specifically upon its matching molecule or **substrate.**

2. *Enzyme Structure:* A conjugated enzyme consists of a protein component called the **apoenzyme** and one or more activators called **cofactors.**

3. *Enzyme Specificity:* Substrate attachment occurs in the special pocket called the **active,** or **catalytic, site.** In order to fit, a substrate must conform to the active site of the enzyme. This three-dimensional state is determined by the shape of the apoenzyme, making enzymes **substrate-specific.**

4. *Cofactors:* Metallic cofactors impart greater reactivity to the enzyme-substrate complex. **Coenzymes** such as **NAD⁺** (nicotinamide adenine dinucleotide) are transfer agents that pass functional groups from one substrate to another. Coenzymes usually contain **vitamins.**

5. *Enzyme Classification:* Enzyme names often consist of a prefix derived from the type of reaction or the substrate and the ending *-ase.*

6. *Microbial Enzymes and Disease:* Many pathogens secrete enzymes or toxins, which are referred to as virulence factors, that enable them to avoid host defenses.

7. *Types of Enzyme Function:* The release of water that comes with formation of new covalent bonds is a **condensation** reaction. **Hydrolysis** reactions involve addition of water to break bonds. Functional groups may be added, removed, or traded in many reactions. Coupled **redox reactions** transfer electrons and protons (H⁺) from one substrate to another.

8. *Enzyme Sensitivity:* Enzymes are **labile** (unstable) and function only within narrow operating ranges of temperature, osmotic pressure, and pH; extreme conditions can cause **denaturation.** Enzymes are frequently the targets for physical and chemical agents used in control.

C. *Regulation of Enzymatic Activity*
Regulatory controls can act on enzymes directly or on the process that gives rise to the enzymes.
1. A substance that resembles the normal substrate and can occupy the same active site is said to exert **competitive inhibition.**
2. **Allosteric inhibition** occurs when a substance binds to a regulatory site and prevents substrate binding.
3. **Noncompetitive inhibition** occurs when the regulator molecule binds the enzyme-substrate complex and keeps a product from being formed.
4. The mechanisms of **enzyme repression** and **enzyme induction** exert control at the genetic level by controlling the synthesis of key enzymes.

8.2 The Pursuit and Utilization of Energy
A. *Cell Energetics*
Energy is the capacity of a system to perform work. It is consumed in **endergonic reactions** and is released in **exergonic reactions.**
B. *A Closer Look at Biological Oxidation and Reduction*
1. Extracting energy requires a series of electron carriers arrayed in a downhill redox chain between electron donors and electron acceptors.
2. NAD^+ is the primary carrier of electrons from one pathway to another.
3. In **substrate-level** and **oxidative phosphorylation,** energy is transferred to high-energy compounds such as ATP.

8.3 Pathways of Bioenergetics
A. *Pathways in Aerobic Respiration*
These use oxygen as a final electron acceptor and glucose as the electron and energy source. The three pathways involved are glycolysis, the Krebs cycle, and electron transport.
1. **Glycolysis** is a pathway that degrades glucose to **pyruvic acid** without requiring oxygen.
2. Pyruvic acid is an important key molecule in several catabolic and anabolic pathways.
B. *Fate of Pyruvic Acid in Krebs Cycle and Electron Transport*
1. Pyruvic acid is completely metabolized via the **Krebs cycle** and its associated electron transport chain.
2. **Acetyl coenzyme A** is the initial product of pyruvic acid processing that undergoes further oxidation and decarboxylation in the Krebs cycle and generates ATP, CO_2, and H_2O.
3. The respiratory chain carries electrons that support final energy extraction.
4. The **chemiosmotic** theory and **proton motive force** are conceptual models that explain the origin and maintenance of electropotential gradients across a membrane that leads to ATP synthesis by **ATP synthase.**

5. The final electron acceptor in aerobic respiration is oxygen. In **anaerobic respiration,** compounds such as sulfate, nitrate, or nitrite serve this function. Bacteria serve as important agents in the nitrogen cycle **(denitrification).**

8.4 The Importance of Fermentation
A. **Fermentation** is based on the glycolysis pathway in which both the electron donor and final electron acceptors are organic compounds. It is an essential source of NAD^+ required for electron transport.
B. Fermentation enables anaerobic and facultative microbes to survive in environments devoid of oxygen. Production of alcohol, vinegar, and certain industrial solvents relies upon fermentation.

8.5 Biosynthesis and the Crossing Pathways of Metabolism
A. *Amphibolism*
The ability of a cell or system to integrate catabolic and anabolic pathways to improve efficiency is called **amphibolism.**
B. *Anabolism: Formation of Macromolecules*
Macromolecules, such as proteins, carbohydrates, and nucleic acids, are made of building blocks from two possible sources: from outside the cell (preformed) or via synthesis in one of the anabolic pathways.
C. *Versatility of Glycolysis and Krebs Cycle*
Glycolysis and the Krebs cycle are central pathways that link catabolic and anabolic pathways, allowing cells to break down different classes of molecules in order to synthesize compounds required by the cell.
1. Metabolites of these pathways double as building blocks and sources of energy. Intermediates such as pyruvic acid are convertible into amino acids through **amination.** Amino acids can be **deaminated** and used as a source of glucose and other carbohydrates **(gluconeogenesis).**
2. Two-carbon acetyl molecules from pyruvate **decarboxylation** can be used in fatty acid synthesis.

8.6 Photosynthesis: The Earth's Lifeline
Photosynthesis takes place in two stages—**light-dependent** and **light-independent reactions.**
A. During the light-dependent reactions, **photons** of solar energy are absorbed by **chlorophyll** and other pigments in **thylakoid** membranes of **chloroplast grana** in eukaryotes and the cell membrane in cyanobacteria. Light energy is captured by two photosystems (**PS II** and **PS I**), and water is split by **photolysis.** This releases oxygen gas. The light energy harvested by photosystems becomes the chemical energy of electrons; electron transport energy is stored in NADPH and ATP; ATP is formed through **photophosphorylation** and chemiosmosis. Light energy is used to synthesize ATP and NADPH.
B. The **Calvin cycle** (light-independent) occurs in the **stroma** of chloroplasts and uses ATP to **fix** carbon dioxide to a carrier molecule, ribulose-1,5-bisphosphate, and convert it to glucose in a multistep process.
C. The type of photosynthesis commonly found in plants, algae, and cyanobacteria is called **oxygenic** because it liberates molecular oxygen as a by-product of the light-dependent reactions. **Anoxygenic** photosynthesis occurs in photolithotrophs, which do not produce oxygen.

Assess Your Knowledge

Level I. These questions require a working knowledge of the concepts in the chapter and the ability to recall and understand the information you have studied.

Developing a Concept Inventory

Select the correct answer from the answers provided. For questions with blanks, choose the combination of answers that most accurately completes the statement.

1. _____ is another term for biosynthesis.
 a. Catabolism c. Metabolism
 b. Anabolism d. Catalyst

2. Catabolism is a form of metabolism in which _____ molecules are transformed into _____ molecules.
 a. larger, smaller c. amino acid, protein
 b. smaller, larger d. glucose, starch

3. An enzyme _____ the activation energy required for a chemical reaction.
 a. increases c. lowers
 b. converts d. catalyzes

4. An enzyme
 a. becomes part of the final products
 b. is nonspecific for substrate
 c. is consumed by the reaction
 d. is heat and pH labile

5. Catalysis occurs at the _____ site of an enzyme.
 a. cofactor c. redox
 b. allosteric d. active

6. Many coenzymes contain
 a. metals c. proteins
 b. vitamins d. substrates

7. To digest cellulose in its environment, a fungus produces a/an
 a. endoenzyme c. catalase
 b. exoenzyme d. polymerase

8. Energy in biological systems is primarily
 a. electrical c. radiant
 b. chemical d. mechanical

9. Energy is carried from catabolic to anabolic reactions in the form of _____.
 a. ADP c. coenzymes
 b. high-energy ATP bonds d. inorganic phosphate

10. Exergonic reactions
 a. release potential energy c. form bonds
 b. consume energy d. occur only outside the cell

11. A reduced compound is
 a. NAD^+ c. NADH
 b. FAD d. ADP

12. Most oxidation reactions in microbial bioenergetics involve the
 a. removal of electrons c. addition of oxygen
 b. addition of electrons d. removal of oxygen

13. A product or products of glycolysis is/are
 a. ATP c. CO_2
 b. pyruvic acid d. both a and b

14. Fermentation of a glucose molecule has the potential to produce a net number of _____ ATPs.
 a. 4 b. 2 c. 38 d. 32

15. Complete oxidation of glucose in aerobic respiration by a eukaryote could potentially yield a net maximum output of _____ ATPs.
 a. 40 b. 30 c. 38 d. 2

16. The compound that enters the Krebs cycle is
 a. citric acid c. pyruvic acid
 b. oxaloacetic acid d. acetyl coenzyme A

17. The $FADH_2$ formed during the Krebs cycle enters the electron transport system at which site?
 a. NADH dehydrogenase c. complex IV
 b. complex II d. ATP synthase

18. The proton motive force is the result of
 a. ATP synthase transporting protons during ATP synthesis
 b. an electron gradient between the matrix and the intermembrane space of a mitochondrion
 c. a proton gradient between the matrix and intermembrane space of a mitochondrion
 d. a buildup of negatively charged ions

19. Photosynthetic organisms convert the energy of _____ into chemical energy.
 a. electrons c. photons
 b. protons d. hydrogen atoms

20. The Calvin cycle operates during which part of photosynthesis?
 a. only the light-dependent phase
 b. only in the dark
 c. the light-independent phase
 d. only during photosystem I

21. The oxygen produced by photosynthesis comes from
 a. CO_2 c. H_2O
 b. NO_3 d. glucose

22. **Multiple Matching.** Match the process a, b, or c with the metabolic events in the list.
 a. glycolysis
 b. Krebs cycle
 c. electron transport/oxidative phosphorylation
 _____ H^+ and e^- are delivered to O_2 as the final acceptor.
 _____ Pyruvic acid is formed.
 _____ ATP is formed.
 _____ H_2O is produced.
 _____ CO_2 is formed.
 _____ Fructose diphosphate is split into two 3-carbon fragments.
 _____ NADH is oxidized.
 _____ ATP synthase is active.

Case Study Analysis

1. Small intestinal bacterial overgrowth (known by its acronym, SIBO) is a condition similar to gut fermentation syndrome. SIBO occurs when an overabundance of bacteria, rather than yeast, in the small intestine ferment carbohydrates. What product would be produced in the gut of someone suffering from SIBO?
 a. phospholipids
 b. sugars
 c. acid
 d. proteins

2. Diagnosis of SIBO is sometimes accomplished by testing expelled breath gases for the products of bacterial fermentation (much like a Breathalyzer detects alcohol). What gas would be produced in excess in someone suffering from SIBO?
 a. oxygen
 b. hydrogen
 c. nitrogen
 d. chlorine

3. Both gut fermentation syndrome and SIBO are caused by the actions of microorganisms in the body, yet neither is considered a communicable disease. Why not?

On the Test

These questions will help to prepare you to successfully answer similar questions you'll see on the TEAS (Test of Essential Academic Skills) and NCLEX (National Council Licensure Examination).

1. Photosynthesis converts _____ energy to chemical energy.
 a. light
 b. nuclear
 c. electrical
 d. heat

2. Enzymes facilitate chemical reactions by
 a. lowering the energy level of the reactants
 b. increasing the energy level of the products
 c. lowering the activation energy of the reaction
 d. increasing the energy level of the reactants

Writing Challenge

For each question, compose a one- or two-paragraph answer that includes the factual information needed to completely address the question. Practice questions can also be used for writing-challenge exercises.

1. Discuss the relationship of
 a. anabolism to catabolism
 b. ATP to ADP
 c. glycolysis to fermentation
 d. electron transport to oxidative phosphorylation

2. Give the general name of the enzyme that
 a. converts citrate to isocitrate
 b. reduces pyruvic acid to lactic acid
 c. reduces nitrate to nitrite

3. Explain what is unique about the actions of ATP synthase.

4. Compare the general equation for aerobic metabolism (section 8.3) with the summary of aerobic metabolism (figure 8.22), verify the final totals of reactants and products, and indicate where they occur in the pathways.

5. Describe four requirements required for fermentation to take place.

6. Is fermentation catabolic or anabolic? Explain your choice.

7. Name three electron carriers and the vitamins that are essential to their function. Explain what actions the electron carriers and their associated vitamins have in metabolic reactions.

8. Explain the similarities and differences between anaerobic respiration and fermentation.

Concept Mapping

On Connect you can find an Introduction to Concept Mapping that provides guidance for working with concept maps, along with concept-mapping activities for this chapter.

Application, Analysis, Evaluation, and Synthesis

Level II. These problems go beyond just restating facts and require higher levels of understanding and an ability to interpret, problem solve, transfer knowledge to new situations, create models, and predict outcomes.

Critical Thinking

Critical thinking is the ability to reason and solve problems using facts and concepts. These questions can be approached from a number of angles and, in most cases, they do not have a single correct answer.

1. Use the following graph to diagram the energetics of a chemical reaction, with and without an enzyme. Be sure to position reactants and products at appropriate points and to indicate the stages in the reaction and the energy levels.

2. Explain what is meant by the "biochemical circle of life" that exists between phototrophs and heterotrophs.

3. Explain how it is possible for certain microbes to survive and grow in the presence of cyanide, which would kill many other organisms.

4. Suggest the advantages of having metabolic pathways staged in specific membrane or organelle locations rather than being free in the cytoplasm.

5. Two steps in glycolysis are catalyzed by allosteric enzymes. These are: (1) step 2, catabolized by phosphoglucoisomerase, and (2) step 10, catabolized by pyruvate kinase. Suggest what metabolic products might regulate these enzymes. How might one place these regulators in process figure 8.17?

6. Beer production requires an early period of rapid aerobic metabolism of glucose by yeast. Given that anaerobic conditions are necessary to produce alcohol, can you explain why this step is necessary?

7. What would be the expected pHs of the matrix and intermembrane space of the mitochondrion? What about the stroma and thylakoid lumen of the chloroplast? Explain your answers.

8. At which site in the mitochondrion and chloroplast do the ATP molecules collect after being made by ATP synthases, and what is the advantage of this?

9. Explain the relationship between enzyme sensitivity and the adaptations microbes make to their environments.

10. Why wouldn't antibiotics work as therapy for botulism?

Visual Assessment

1. From **chapter 7, figure 7.11** (reproduced below), describe the likely metabolic strategies of the microbes growing in tubes 1 through 4. Specify the pathways, final electron acceptor, and end products.

Terese M. Barta, Ph.D.

2. Look at the two figure parts (a) and (b) from **figure 8.8** (reproduced below), and explain what processes are depicted and what the results of the reactions will be.

(a)

(b)

An Introduction to Microbial Genetics

In This Chapter...

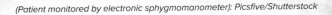

(Patient monitored by electronic sphygmomanometer): Picsfive/Shutterstock

Vancomycin-Resistant *Staphylococcus aureus*— Delaware, 2015

In April 2014, a **chronic infection** on the toe of a 67-year-old woman was noted during an examination. The woman was being treated in a Delaware hospital for diabetes mellitus, along with end-stage renal disease that required **hemodialysis.** Evaluation of the wound in August and October revealed the presence of **methicillin-resistant** *Staphylococcus aureus* **(MRSA),** a strain of the bacterium resistant to all the drugs commonly used to treat staphylococcal infections. This species of bacteria had been successfully treated with **penicillin** since the introduction of the drug in the 1940s. Over the next three decades, resistance to the drug developed and became widespread, first to penicillin in the 1950s and later to semisynthetic penicillin derivatives (oxacillin, methicillin, nafcillin, dicloxacillin) in the 1970s. By the 1990s, strains of MRSA were commonplace, and these infections could only be treated successfully with **vancomycin,** often referred to as the antibiotic of last resort for MRSA infections. In 2002, the first infections due to *Staphylococcus aureus* strains resistant to vancomycin (VRSA) were seen; 12 more cases were identified over the next 10 years.

In January 2015, MRSA, along with **vancomycin-resistant enterococci (VRE),** were isolated from the woman's wound. VRE is resistant to vancomycin by virtue of the **vanA** operon, an 11-kilobase stretch of DNA located within a **transposon.** All known instances of VRSA have arisen when an MRSA strain acquired the *vanA* operon through genetic transfer, so the presence of both bacteria in the same person was an ominous sign. In February 2015, VRSA was isolated from the toe wound and sent to the **Centers for Disease Control** for further analysis, where it was confirmed to have acquired the *vanA* operon; the CDC designated the isolate VRSA 14, as it was the fourteenth documented case of such an infection. All VRSA infections seen since 2010 have occurred in Delaware (with 8 of the 10 cases prior to that occurring in Michigan), likely due to a higher prevalence of MRSA to act as precursor organisms.

- *Aside from the bacterial chromosome, where else may DNA be found in a prokaryotic cell?*

- *In what ways is genetic material transferred from one bacterial cell to another?*

To continue the Case Study, go to Case Study Part 2 at the end of the chapter.

(Methicillin-resistant Staphylococcus aureus Bacteria): Source: Janice Carr/CDC

9.1 Introduction to Genetics and Genes: Unlocking the Secrets of Heredity

 Learn

1. Define *heredity, genetics, genome, gene, phenotype,* and *genotype.*

2. Compare the basic nature of genetic material in eukaryotes, prokaryotes, and viruses.

3. Explain how DNA is organized and packaged.

4. Describe the chemical structure of DNA and its significance.

5. List the nitrogen bases and explain their bonding patterns.

6. Describe the process of DNA replication as it occurs in prokaryotic cells.

Genetics is the science that studies the inheritance of biological characteristics by life forms. This subject, also known as heredity, is a wide-ranging science that examines:

- the transmission of biological properties (traits) from parent to offspring,
- the expression and variation of those traits,
- the structure and function of the genetic material, and
- how this material changes or evolves.

The study of genetics takes place on several levels **(figure 9.1).** Organismal genetics looks at the transmission and expression of genetic factors in the whole organism or cell; chromosomal genetics examines the characteristics and actions of chromosomes; and molecular genetics deals with the biochemistry of gene function. All of these levels provide insight into microbial structure, physiology, evolution, and pathogenicity. It should also be noted that the study of microbial genetics will emphasize universal themes in the genetics of all organisms, and it will increase appreciation for the astounding advances in genetic engineering covered in chapter 10.

The Nature of the Genetic Material

Deoxyribonucleic acid or **DNA** serves as the foundation for most genetic studies. In order to appreciate and understand a broad range of genetic principles, it will be essential to develop a working knowledge of DNA's characteristics. With this in mind, we will use the first section of this chapter to lay some groundwork on DNA organization, structure, and duplication. This will be followed by coverage of related concepts such as RNA and protein synthesis, genetic control, mutations, and genetic recombination in the remaining five sections.

The Levels of Structure and Function of the Genome

The **genome** is the sum total of genetic material (DNA) carried within a cell. Although most of the genome exists in the form of chromosomes, genetic material can appear in nonchromosomal sites as well **(figure 9.2).** For example, bacteria and some fungi contain tiny extra pieces of DNA **(plasmids),** and the mitochondria and chloroplasts of eukaryotes are equipped with their own functional chromosomes. Genomes of cells are composed exclusively of DNA, but viruses contain either DNA or RNA as the principal genetic material. Although the specific genome of an individual organism is unique, the general pattern of nucleic acid structure and function is similar among all organisms and viruses.

In general, a **chromosome** is a discrete cellular structure composed of a neatly packaged DNA molecule. The chromosomes of eukaryotes and bacterial cells differ in several respects. The structure of eukaryotic chromosomes consists of a DNA molecule tightly wound around histone proteins, whereas a bacterial chromosome is condensed and secured into a packet by means of a different type of protein. Eukaryotic chromosomes are located in the nucleus; they vary in number from a few to hundreds; they can occur in pairs (diploid) or singles (haploid); and they are linear in format. In contrast, most bacteria have a single, circular chromosome, although some have multiple chromosomes and a few have linear chromosomes.

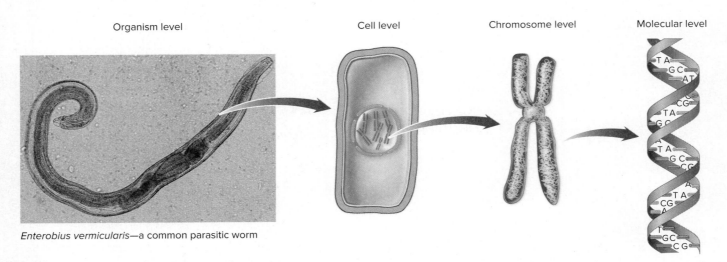

Organism level Cell level Chromosome level Molecular level

Enterobius vermicularis—a common parasitic worm

Figure 9.1 Levels of genetic study. Genetic processes can be observed at the levels of organism, cell, chromosome, and DNA sequence (molecular level). Although levels shown here are for a eukaryotic organism, they would follow a similar pattern in prokaryotes.
Source: Image contributed by the Centre for Tropical Medicine and Imported Infectious Diseases, Bergen, Norway./CDC-DPDX

All chromosomes contain a series of basic informational "packets" called genes. A **gene** can be defined from more than one perspective. In classical genetics, the term refers to the fundamental unit of heredity responsible for a given trait in an organism. In the molecular and biochemical sense, it is a portion of the chromosome that provides information for a given cell function. More specifically still, it is a specific segment of DNA that contains the necessary information to make a molecule of **protein** or **RNA.** This last definition of a gene is emphasized in this chapter.

All of the genes in an organism constitute its distinctive genetic makeup, or **genotype.*** The expression of the genotype creates traits (certain structures or functions) referred to as the **phenotype.*** For example a person inherits a combination of genes (genotype) that gives a certain eye color or height (phenotype), a bacterium inherits genes that direct the formation of a flagellum or the ability to metabolize a certain substrate, and a virus has genes that dictate its capsid structure. All organisms contain more genes in their genotypes than are being seen as a phenotype at any given time. In other words, the phenotype can change depending on which genes are "turned on" or expressed.

The Size and Packaging of Genomes

Genomes vary greatly in size. Viruses have anywhere from a few to over a thousand genes; the bacterium *Escherichia coli* has a single chromosome containing 4,288 genes, and a human cell packs about five times that many into 46 chromosomes. The chromosome of *E. coli* would measure about 1 mm if unwound and stretched out linearly, and yet this fits within a cell that measures just over 1 μm across, making the stretched-out DNA 1,000 times longer than the cell **(figure 9.3).** Still, the bacterial chromosome takes up only about one-third to one-half of the cell's volume. Likewise, if the sum of all DNA contained in the 46 human chromosomes were unraveled and laid end to end, it would measure about 6 feet. How can such elongated genomes fit into the minuscule volume of a cell and, in the case of eukaryotes, into an even smaller compartment, the nucleus? The answer lies in the complex coiling of the DNA chain.

* *genotype* (jee′-noh-typ) Gr. *gennan,* to produce, and *typos,* type.
* *phenotype* (fee′-noh-typ) Gr. *phainein,* to show. The physical manifestation of gene expression.

Cells

Eukaryotic (composite)

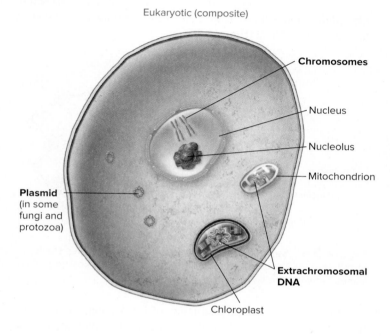

Chromosomes

Nucleus

Nucleolus

Mitochondrion

Plasmid (in some fungi and protozoa)

Extrachromosomal DNA

Chloroplast

Prokaryotic

Chromosome

Plasmids

Viruses

DNA

RNA

Figure 9.2 The general location and forms of the genome in two cell types and selected viruses (not to scale).

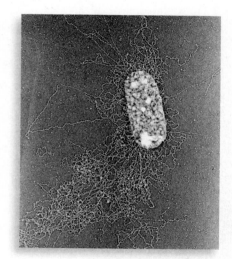

Figure 9.3 A disrupted *Escherichia coli* cell. The cell has ejected its unraveled chromosome, which now appears as thin strings radiating around the outer surface (10,000×). These strings are the uncoiled DNA strand.
Dr. Jack Griffith

The Packaging of DNA

Packing the mass of DNA into the cell involves compacting the DNA molecule by means of supercoils or superhelices. In the simpler system of prokaryotes, the circular chromosome is packaged by the action of a special enzyme called a **topoisomerase** (specifically, DNA **gyrase**). This enzyme coils the chromosome into a tight bundle by introducing a reversible series of twists into the DNA molecule.

> **Quick Search**
>
> To see an animation of the how a bacterial chromosome is packaged, google "Cell Structure—Bacterial Chromosome Compaction."

The system in eukaryotes is more complex, with three or more levels of coiling. First, the DNA molecule of a chromosome, which is linear, is wound twice around the histone proteins, creating a chain of **nucleosomes.** The nucleosomes fold in a spiral formation upon one another. An even greater supercoiling occurs when this spiral arrangement further twists on its radius into a giant spiral with loops radiating from the outside. This extreme degree of compactness is what makes the eukaryotic chromosome visible during mitosis (**figures 9.4** and 5.6).

The condensation of DNA and protein into chromatin was once thought to function mainly as a way to fit such a long molecule into a cell. However, it is now evident that the coiling of DNA also serves to make certain segments of the genetic program either more or less available. This action provides a major control on the expression of many traits, especially in eukaryotes. Having an additional regulatory function creates an alternative mechanism to guide when and how genes are accessed. The realization that the phenotype of a cell is due to more than just the order of nucleotides in the DNA (genotype) has led to a rethinking of some of the most basic concepts of genetics (see 9.2 Making Connections).

Figure 9.4 **Eukaryotic DNA interacts with a variety of proteins and small molecules.** This relationship modulates the expression of many genes while at the same time allowing for the ordered condensation of DNA into a compact supermolecule.

The Structure of DNA: A Double Helix with Its Own Language

To analyze the structure of DNA at the molecular level, imagine being able to magnify a small piece of a gene about 5 million times. What you would see is one of the great marvels of life. The pieces of this molecular puzzle were finally worked out by James Watson and Francis Crick in 1953 (**9.1 Making Connections**). They determined that DNA is a giant molecule with two strands bound together into a double helix. The structure of DNA is universal, except in some viruses that contain single-stranded DNA.

The basic unit of DNA structure is a **nucleotide,** composed of **phosphate, deoxyribose sugar,** and a **nitrogen base,** as shown in this simplified model (**figure 9.5**):

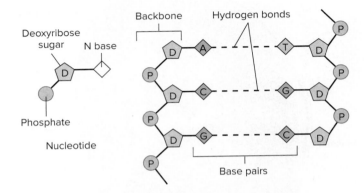

Figure 9.5 **Simplified structure of DNA.** Nucleotides stack together to form two opposing strands held together by hydrogen bonds between the base pairs.

Figure 9.6 lays out the structure of DNA going from general (*a,b,c*) to specific (*d*). To make the vertical sugar-phosphate backbones of the molecule, each deoxyribose sugar bonds covalently in a repeating pattern with two phosphates. One of the bonds is to the number 5′ (read "five prime") carbon on deoxyribose, and the other is to the 3′ (three prime) carbon. This pattern will format the direction of the strands, which run opposite to each other, as shown in figure 9.6*d* and discussed next.

The nitrogen bases—**purines** and **pyrimidines**—attach by covalent bonds at the 1′ position of the sugar (figure 9.6*c, d*). When these nitrogen bases span the center of the molecule and bind with their complementary bases from the opposite strand, they form a double-stranded helix. The **paired bases** are held together by hydrogen bonds, which can be readily disrupted, allowing the molecule to be "unzipped" into two strands. This feature is of great importance in gaining access to the information encoded in the nitrogen base sequence. Pairing of purines and pyrimidines is not random; it is dictated by the structure of the bases and how they align to form hydrogen bonds. Thus, in DNA, the purine **adenine (A)** pairs with the pyrimidine **thymine (T),** and the purine **guanine (G)** pairs with the pyrimidine **cytosine (C).** Note that adenine forms two hydrogen bonds with thymine, and cytosine forms three hydrogen bonds with guanine. This difference will influence a number of DNA functions. Evidence also indicates that the bases are attracted to each other in this pattern because each base has a three-dimensional shape that conforms exactly to its mate. Although the

base-pairing partners generally do not vary, the sequence of base pairs along the DNA molecule can assume any order, resulting in an infinite number of possible nucleotide sequences. One significant finding that has emerged from sequencing chromosomal DNA is how extremely long it can be for a single molecule. An average bacterial chromosome consists of 5 million to 6 million nucleotides; the 46 chromosomes (diploid) of humans total about 6.4 billion nucleotides.

Other important considerations of DNA structure concern the nature of the double helix itself. As indicated previously, one side of the helix runs in the opposite direction of the other, in what is called an *antiparallel arrangement*. Using the order of the bond between the carbon on deoxyribose and the phosphates, we see that one helix runs from the 5′ to 3′ direction and the other runs from the 3′ to 5′ direction (figure 9.6*d*). This characteristic is a significant factor in DNA synthesis, transcription, and translation. Although the DNA is constructed somewhat like a twisted ladder, it is not symmetrical. The curvature of the helix and the stepwise stacking of the nitrogen bases produce two different-size surface features, the major and minor grooves (**figure 9.7**).

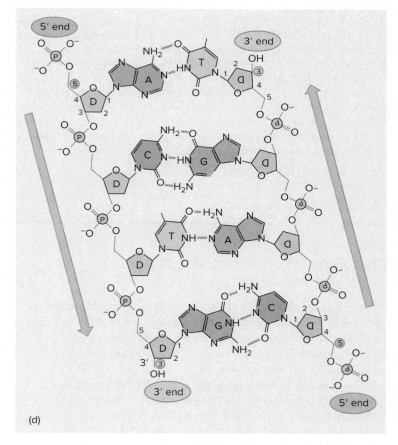

Figure 9.6 **Levels of DNA structure. (a)** A space-filling model of DNA shows its basic configuration as a double helix of sugar-phosphate backbones holding the nitrogen bases between them. **(b)** The twisted ladder model depicts how the complementary nitrogen bases (bars) pair with each other across the center of the molecule. **(c)** A schematic lays out the basic chemical makeup and bonding pattern of the molecule. **(d)** A more detailed view of the base pairs, hydrogen bonds, and the antiparallel arrangement of the two helices. Note that in one strand, the deoxyribose-phosphate runs in the 5′ to 3′ direction and the other side is oriented from 3′ to 5′.

9.1 MAKING CONNECTIONS

Deciphering the Structure of DNA

The search for the primary molecules of heredity was a serious focus throughout the first half of the twentieth century. At first many biologists thought that protein was the genetic material. An important milestone occurred in 1944 when Oswald Avery, Colin MacLeod, and Maclyn McCarty purified DNA and demonstrated at last that it was indeed the blueprint for life. This was followed by an avalanche of research, which continues today.

"We Have Discovered the Secret of Life!"*

One area of extreme interest concerned the molecular structure of DNA. In 1951, American biologist James Watson and English physicist Francis Crick collaborated on solving the DNA puzzle. Although they did little of the original research, they were intrigued by several findings from other scientists. It had been determined by Erwin Chargaff that any model of DNA structure would have to contain deoxyribose, phosphate, purines, and pyrimidines arranged in a way that would provide variation and a simple way of copying itself. Watson and Crick spent long hours constructing models with cardboard cutouts and kept alert for any and every bit of information that might give them an edge.

Two English biophysicists, Maurice Wilkins and Rosalind Franklin,* had been painstakingly collecting data on X-ray crystallographs of

Dr. James Watson (left) and Dr. Francis Crick (right) stand next to their model that finally explained the structure of DNA in 1953.
A. Barrington Brown/Science Source

DNA for several years. With this technique, molecules of DNA bombarded by X-rays produce a photographic image that can predict the three-dimensional structure of the molecule. After Dr. Wilkins allowed them to view their data, Watson and Crick noticed an unmistakable pattern: The molecule appeared to be a double helix. In a short time, the pieces of the puzzle fell into place and a final model was assembled—a model that explained all of the qualities of DNA, including how it is copied. Although Watson and Crick were hailed for the clarity of their solution, it must be emphasized that their success was built on the considerable efforts of a number of English and American scientists. This historic discovery spawned ingenious research in all areas of molecular genetics that is still ongoing.

> **Quick Search**
> Find out more of the story by searching for "The Secret of Life: Discovery of DNA Structure."

Since the discovery of the double helix in 1953, an extensive body of biochemical, microscopic, and crystallographic analysis has left little doubt that the model first proposed by Watson and Crick is correct. Scanning tunneling microscopes produce three-dimensional images of DNA that verify the helical shape and twists of DNA represented by models.

How did Watson and Crick's model of DNA accurately fit the requirements needed to predict its structure?

* Comment by Watson and Crick after publication of their monumental discovery.
* Unfortunately, Dr. Franklin died before she could be properly recognized by receiving a Nobel Prize. Without her contributions, Watson and Crick could not have deciphered the puzzle as quickly as they did.

DNA Replication: Preserving the Code and Passing It On

For its long-term survival, a species must reproduce. In bacteria, this involves division of the cell by means of binary fission or budding, but it also involves the accurate duplication and separation of the genetic material into each daughter cell to ensure that each offspring receives a functional genome.

The sequence of bases along the length of DNA constitutes its "language." For this language to be preserved for hundreds of generations, the codes it contains will need to be duplicated with high fidelity. This process of duplication is called **DNA replication.** In the following example, we will show replication in bacteria, but with some exceptions it generally applies to the process as it occurs in eukaryotes and some viruses. Recall from chapter 7 that early in binary fission, the metabolic machinery of a bacterium is programmed to initiate the duplication of the chromosome. Despite its

complexity, DNA replication can be very rapid: This must be completed in a single generation time (around 20 minutes in *E. coli*).

The Overall Replication Process

What features allow the DNA molecule to be exactly duplicated, and how is its integrity retained? DNA replication requires a careful orchestration of the actions of 30 different enzymes (see the partial list in **table 9.1**), which separate the strands of the existing DNA molecule, copy its template, and produce two complete daughter molecules.

A simplified version of replication is shown in **figure 9.7** and includes the following:

1. uncoiling the parent DNA molecule, beginning at a predetermined point of origin;
2. separating the two strands and exposing the nucleotide sequence of each strand (which is normally hidden in the center of the helix) to serve as templates; and

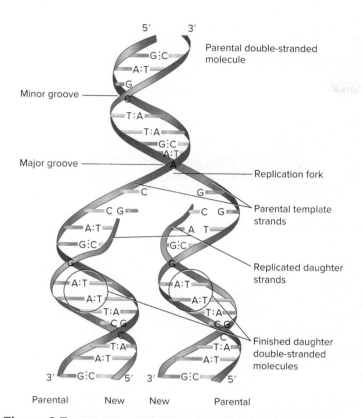

5′ 3′
G:C
A:T
G
C — Minor groove
T:A
T:A
G:C
A:T
A — Major groove

Parental double-stranded molecule

Replication fork

Parental template strands

Replicated daughter strands

Finished daughter double-stranded molecules

3′ G:C 5′ 3′ G:C 5′

Parental New New Parental

Figure 9.7 **Simplified steps to show the semiconservative replication of DNA.** The two strands of the parental double helix are unwound and separated. Each single strand will serve as a template (blue) to synthesize a new strand of DNA (red), starting at the replication fork. As synthesis proceeds, the correct nucleotides are added according to the pattern of the template. An A on the template will pair with a T on the new molecule, and a C will pair with a G. The finished daughter DNA molecules contain one strand of the newly synthesized DNA and the original template (parental) strand. This keeps the code intact because the same linear arrangement of the bases is maintained during this process. This process is covered in greater detail in process figure 9.8.

3. synthesizing two new strands by using each single strand as a template for the synthesis of a new, complementary strand.

A critical requirement of DNA replication is that each completed daughter molecule be identical to the parent in composition, but neither one is completely new. The strand that serves as a template is an original parental DNA strand and is retained in the daughter molecule. The preservation of the parent molecule in this way, termed **semiconservative replication,** helps explain the reliability and accuracy of replication.

Events in Replication

All chromosomes have a specific **origin of replication** that serves as the place where replication will be initiated. It is recognized by a short sequence rich in adenine and thymine that, you will recall, are held together by only two hydrogen bonds rather than three. Because the origin of replication is AT-rich, less energy is required to separate the two strands than would be required if the origin were rich in guanine and cytosine.

TABLE 9.1	Some Enzymes Involved in DNA Replication and Their Functions
Enzyme	**Function**
Helicase	Unzipping the DNA helix
Primase	Synthesizing an RNA primer
DNA polymerase III	Adding bases to the new DNA chain, proofreading the chain for mistakes
DNA polymerase I	Removing RNA primers, replacing gaps between Okazaki fragments with correct nucleotides, repairing mismatched bases
Ligase	Final binding of nicks in DNA during synthesis and repair
Gyrase	Supercoiling

The process of synthesizing a new daughter strand of DNA using the parental strand as a template is carried out by a giant enzyme complex that brings in the primary replication enzyme—**DNA polymerase III**—along with numerous accessory enzymes. The DNA polymerase III is responsible for duplicating DNA codes, but it has some major conditions that will affect the overall process **(process figure 9.8):**

- DNA polymerase can only add nucleotides to an existing nucleotide. It is unable to begin the process on its own. The enzyme primase will synthesize a short stretch of nucleotides, allowing DNA polymerase to begin its work.
- Nucleotides may only be added to a growing DNA chain in the 5′ to 3′ direction.

Prior to the start of replication, enzymes called helicases (unzipping enzymes) bind to the DNA at the origin. These enzymes untwist the helix and break the hydrogen bonds holding the two strands together, resulting in two separate strands, each of which will be used as a template for the synthesis of a new strand **(process figure 9.8b, step 1).**

Replication begins when RNA **primers** are synthesized by a primase at the origin of replication **(process figure 9.8a).** DNA polymerase III will use this short strand of RNA as a starting point for adding nucleotides. In the circular DNA molecule of bacteria, there are two **replication forks,** each containing its own set of replication enzymes. Each fork requires two active DNA polymerases along with several other proteins and enzymes whose main functions are to stabilize the polymerase and provide a means of removing and replacing nucleotides. The enzyme complex encircles the DNA near the replication fork and synthesizes new DNA as guided by the parental strand. As synthesis proceeds, the forks are continually opened up to expose the template for replication.

Because DNA polymerase III can only synthesize new DNA in the 5′ to 3′ direction, just one strand, called the **leading strand,** will be synthesized continuously **(process figure 9.8b, step 2).** After addition of an RNA primer, a DNA polymerase complex enters and moves along the template strand in the 3′ to 5′ direction toward the replication fork, adding nucleotides in the 5′ to 3′ direction on the new strand.

The other template strand runs the opposite direction, which prevents the DNA polymerase from synthesizing a continuous,

4. Before synthesis of the lagging strand can start, a primase adds an RNA primer to direct the DNA polymerase III. Synthesis produces unlinked segments of RNA primer and new DNA called Okazaki fragments.

5. DNA polymerase I removes the RNA primers and fills in the correct complementary DNA nucleotides at the open sites.

6. Unjoined ends of the nucleotides (a nick) must be connected by a ligase.

3. The template for the lagging strand runs 5' to 3' (opposite to the leading strand), so to make the new strand in the 5' to 3' orientation, synthesis must proceed backward, away from the replication fork.

Okazaki fragment

Nick

LAGGING STRAND SYNTHESIS

1. The chromosome to be replicated is unwound by a helicase, forming a replication fork with two template strands.

2. The template for the leading strand (blue) is oriented 3' to 5'. This allows the DNA polymerase III to add nucleotides in the 5' to 3' direction toward the replication fork, so it can be synthesized as a continuous strand. Note that direction of synthesis refers to the order of the new strand (red).

(b)

LEADING STRAND SYNTHESIS

Replication forks

Origin of a replication

Key:

Template strand		Primase	
New strand		DNA polymerase III	
RNA primer		DNA polymerase I	
Helicase		Ligase	

(a)

Process Figure 9.8 **The assembly line of DNA replication in a circular bacterial chromosome. (a)** A bacterial chromosome showing the overall pattern of replication. There are two replication forks where new DNA is being synthesized. **(b)** An enlarged view of the left replication fork to show the details of replication.

unbroken strand of new DNA. This strand, termed the **lagging strand,** will be synthesized in a series of shorter fragments that will later be connected into a continuous strand (**process figure 9.8b, steps 3** and **4**). It still requires primers, and each new fragment will require its own separate primer. The DNA polymerase adds nucleotides to the new strand in the 5' to 3' direction, producing short fragments of DNA (100 to 1,000 bases long) called **Okazaki fragments** on the lagging strand. The lagging strand will be completed when the enzyme, **DNA polymerase I,** removes the RNA primers from the Okazaki fragments and fills in the missing segments with the correct complementary DNA nucleotides (**process figure 9.8b, step 5**). The replacement strand is not completely bonded to the finished part of the new strand, so an enzyme, **ligase,** makes these final phosphate-sugar connections (**process figure 9.8b, step 6**).

The addition of nucleotides proceeds at an astonishing pace, estimated in some bacteria to be 750 bases per second at each fork!

As replication proceeds, one newly synthesized strand loops down (**figure 9.9a**). When the forks have gone full circle, a termination site shuts replication down. The two circular daughter molecules remain connected briefly but are nicked and separated by a helicase (**figure 9.9b**).

The double-stranded nature of DNA and the rules of base pairing (adenine to thymine and guanine to cytosine) ensure that the correct order of the DNA bases will be retained during cell division. When the two strands are separated, each one provides a template (pattern or model) for the replication (exact copying) of a new molecule (figure 9.7). Because the sequence of one strand provides the correct pattern for its complementary strand, the code can be duplicated with accuracy.

Like any language, DNA is occasionally "misspelled" when an incorrect base is added to the growing chain. Studies have shown that such mistakes are made once in approximately 10^8 to 10^9 bases,

(a)

Nick

Daughter cell Daughter cell

(b)

Figure 9.9 Completion of chromosome replication in bacteria. (a) As replication proceeds, one strand loops down. **(b)** Final separation is achieved when an enzyme cuts and releases the two completed molecules. Each daughter cell receives one completed chromosome during binary fission.

but most of these are corrected. If not corrected, they are considered mutations that can lead to major cell dysfunction. Because continued cellular function is dependent on accurate replication, cells have evolved their own proofreading ability. Both DNA polymerase III and DNA polymerase I have the ability to recognize and replace incorrect nucleotides in newly synthesized DNA.

> **Quick Search**
>
> Search online for "DNA Interactive" and explore the process of replication—copying the code.

 Practice SECTION 9.1

1. Compare the genetic material of eukaryotes, bacteria, and viruses in terms of general structure, size, and mode of replication.
2. Characterize the organization of genetic material, going from the genome down to the gene.
3. Briefly describe how DNA is packaged to fit inside a cell.

4. What are the fundamental building blocks of DNA, and how are they bonded together?
5. Describe what is meant by the antiparallel arrangement of DNA.
6. Explain the synthesis of the leading and lagging strands during DNA replication, and identify the enzymes required for producing a finished product.
7. Name several characteristics of DNA structure that enable it to be replicated with such great accuracy generation after generation.

9.2 Applications of the DNA Code: Transcription and Translation

Learn

7. Present an overview of the main aspects of the flow of genetic information in cells.

8. Explain the relationship between the structure of DNA and the structure of proteins.

9. Describe the different types of RNA and their basic functions in genetic expression.

10. Relate the major events of transcription.

11. Describe the genetic code, codons, and anticodons, and how they relate to one another.

12. Recount the participants and steps in translation (protein synthesis).

13. Distinguish major points of difference between prokaryotic and eukaryotic transcription and translation.

We have explored how the genetic language of the DNA molecule is conserved through replication. Next we consider exactly how this language is expressed. Given that the sequence of bases in DNA is a genetic code, just what is the nature of this code, and how is it utilized? Although the genome is full of critical information, the DNA molecule itself cannot perform cell processes directly. Instead, its information is conveyed to RNA molecules, which carry out the instructions it contains. The concept that genetic information flows from DNA to RNA to protein has long been a central theme of molecular biology **(figure 9.10).** It states that the master code of DNA is first used to synthesize RNA via a process called **transcription,** and the information contained in the RNA is then used to produce proteins in a process known as **translation.** The principal exceptions to this pattern are found in RNA viruses, which convert RNA to other RNA, and in retroviruses, which can convert RNA to DNA.

As with many established concepts in biology, the science of molecular genetics continues to add significant discoveries to our understanding. In addition to the RNA used to produce proteins, a wide variety of specialized RNAs act by regulating gene function (figure 9.10). We will introduce some of the expanded functions for RNA in 9.3 Making Connections, but we will start with its direct participation in protein synthesis.

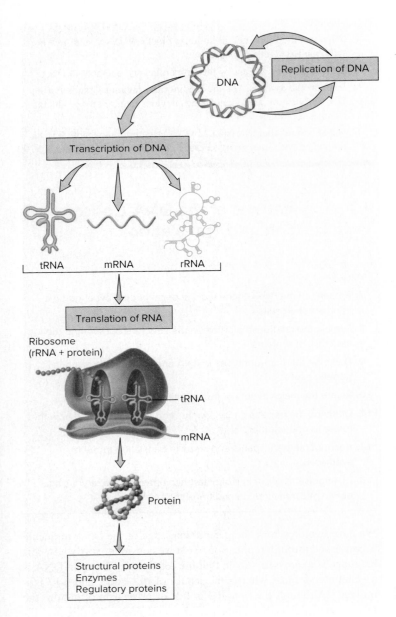

Figure 9.10 Summary of the flow of genetic information in cells. DNA serves as a stable, permanent, storehouse of genetic information. Replication copies DNA to be distributed to daughter cells. Transcription of DNA uses the information in a short stretch of DNA to synthesize a molecule of RNA, several types of which exist in the cell. Translation occurs when ribosomes use the information in RNA to synthesize a protein, which is then used to carry out functions within the cell.

The Gene-Protein Connection

The Triplet Code and Its Relationship to Proteins

Several questions invariably arise concerning the relationship between genes and cell function. For instance, how does gene structure lead to the expression of traits in the individual, and what features of gene expression cause one organism to be so distinctly

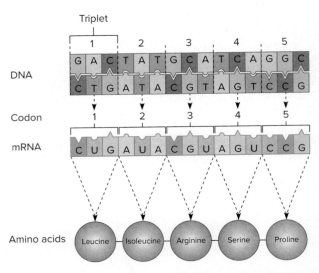

Figure 9.11 Simplified view of the DNA–protein relationship. The DNA molecule is a continuous chain of base pairs, but the sequence must be interpreted in groups of three base pairs (a triplet or codon). The exact rules for transcription and translation are discussed later in this section.

different from another? For answers, we must turn to the correlation between gene and protein structure. We know that each structural gene is an ordered sequence of nucleotides that codes for a protein. Because each protein is different, each gene must also differ somehow in its composition. In fact, the language of DNA exists in the order of groups of three consecutive bases designated as **triplets** or **codons,** on one DNA strand **(figure 9.11).** In short, one gene differs from another in the order and number of its triplets. An equally important part of this concept is that each triplet represents a code for a particular amino acid. When the triplet code is transcribed and translated, it dictates the type and order of amino acids in a polypeptide (protein) chain.

To summarize the key points that connect DNA and protein function:

1. DNA is a blueprint that indicates which kinds of proteins to make and how to make them. This blueprint exists in the order of triplets along the DNA strands.
2. The order of triplets directs a protein's primary structure—the order and type of amino acids in the chain—which determines its characteristic shape and function.
3. Proteins contribute significantly to the phenotype by functioning as enzymes and structural molecules.

The Major Participants in Transcription and Translation

Transcription, the formation of RNA using DNA as a template, and translation, the synthesis of proteins using RNA as a template, are highly complex. A number of components participate: most prominently, messenger RNA, transfer RNA, ribosomes, several types of enzymes, and a storehouse of raw materials. After first examining each of these components, we shall see how they come together in the assembly line of the cell.

RNAs: Tools in the Cell's Assembly Line

Ribonucleic acid (RNA) is an encoded molecule like DNA, but its general structure is different in several ways:

1. It is a **single-stranded** molecule that can assume secondary and tertiary levels of complexity due to bonds within the molecule, leading to specialized forms of RNA (mRNA, tRNA, and rRNA—**figure 9.12**).
2. RNA contains **uracil,** instead of thymine, as the complementary base-pairing mate for adenine. This does not change the inherent DNA code in any way because the uracil still follows the pairing rules.
3. Although RNA, like DNA, is structured with a backbone of alternating sugar and phosphate molecules, the sugar in RNA is **ribose** rather than deoxyribose (see figure 2.25).

The many functional types of RNA range from small regulatory pieces to large structural ones. All types of RNA are formed through transcription of a DNA gene, but only mRNA is further translated into protein. See **table 9.2** for a comparison of types of RNA and their functions. Additional forms of RNA are introduced in section 9.3.

(a) **Messenger RNA (mRNA)**
A short piece of messenger RNA (mRNA) illustrates the general structure of RNA: single-strandedness; repeating phosphate-ribose sugar backbone attached to single nitrogen bases; use of uracil instead of thymine.

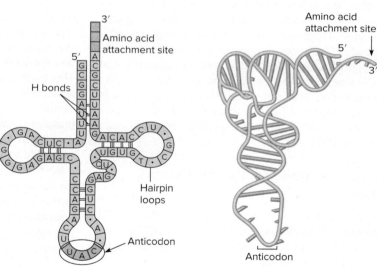

(b) **Transfer RNA (tRNA)**
Left: The tRNA strand loops back on itself to form intrachain hydrogen bonds. The result is a cloverleaf structure, shown here in simplified form. At its bottom is an anticodon that specifies the attachment of a particular amino acid at the 3′ end. Right: A three-dimensional view of tRNA structure.

Figure 9.12 Characteristics of messenger and transfer RNA.

TABLE 9.2	Types of Ribonucleic Acid		
RNA Type	**Contains Codes For**	**Function In Cell**	**Translated**
Messenger (mRNA)	Sequence of amino acids in protein	Carries the DNA master code to the ribosome	Yes
Transfer (tRNA)	Specifying a given amino acid	Carries amino acids to ribosome during translation	No
Ribosomal (rRNA)	Several large structural rRNA molecules	Forms the major part of a ribosome and participates in protein synthesis	No
Primer	An RNA that can begin DNA replication	Primes DNA	No
Micro (miRNA), antisense, riboswitch, and small interfering RNA (siRNA)	Regulatory RNAs	Regulation of gene expression	No
Splicosomes (snRNA) and ribozymes	Catalytic RNAs	Remove introns from eukaryotic RNA, catalyze reactions	No

Messenger RNA: Carrying DNA's Message

Messenger RNA (mRNA) is a transcribed version of a structural gene or genes in DNA. It is synthesized by a process similar to synthesis of the leading strand during DNA replication, and the complementary base-pairing rules ensure that the code will be faithfully copied in the mRNA transcript. The message of this transcribed strand is later read as a series of triplets called **codons (figure 9.12a),** and the length of the mRNA molecule varies from about 100 nucleotides to several thousand. The details of transcription and the function of mRNA in translation are covered later in this section.

Transfer RNA: The Key to Translation

Transfer RNAs (tRNAs) are also complementary copies of specific regions of DNA; however, they differ from mRNA. Transfer RNAs typically range from 75 to 95 nucleotides in length, and they contain sequences of bases that form hydrogen bonds with complementary sections in the same tRNA strand. At these points, the molecule bends back upon itself into several *hairpin loops,* giving the molecule a secondary *cloverleaf* structure that folds even further into a complex, three-dimensional helix **(figure 9.12b).** This compact molecule acts as a translator that converts RNA language into protein language. The bottom loop of the cloverleaf exposes a triplet, the **anticodon,** that both designates the specificity of the tRNA and complements mRNA's codons. At the opposite end of the molecule is a binding site for the amino acid that is specific for that tRNA's anticodon. For each of the 20 amino acids, there is at least one specialized type of tRNA to carry it. Binding of an amino acid to its specific tRNA requires a specific enzyme that can correctly match each tRNA with its amino acid.

The Ribosome: A Mobile Molecular Factory for Translation

The prokaryotic (70S) ribosome is a particle composed of tightly packaged **ribosomal RNA (rRNA)** and protein. The rRNA component of the ribosome is an extensive polynucleotide molecule. It forms complex three-dimensional figures that contribute to the structure and function of ribosomes. The interactions of proteins and rRNA create the two subunits of the ribosome that engage in final translation of the genetic code (see figure 9.14). A metabolically active bacterial cell can accommodate up to 20,000 of these tiny factories—all actively engaged in reading the genetic program, taking in raw materials, and producing proteins at an impressive rate.

Transcription: The First Stage of Gene Expression

Like so many other genetic events, transcription is a marvel of efficiency. It is highly organized and guided by special codes on DNA itself. To describe it in more detail, we use the formation of mRNA in bacteria as a model. It is important to keep in mind that all types of RNA are synthesized by a similar process. The other RNAs have important functions; they just do not provide the code for the amino acids in a protein as mRNA does.

During transcription, an RNA molecule is synthesized using the codes on DNA as a guide or template. A large enzyme complex, **RNA polymerase,** is responsible for this process. This polymerase is more multipurpose than DNA polymerase, because the RNA enzyme works alone and does not require a helicase. It can bind to DNA and unwind it, as well as synthesize RNA **(process figure 9.13).**

Transcription proceeds in three stages: *initiation, elongation,* and *termination.* Initiation requires the RNA polymerase to recognize a region on a gene called the **promoter region (process figure 9.13, step 1).** This region consists of two sets of DNA sequences located just before the *initiation site.* The first sequence is about 35 nucleotides from the initiation site, and the second is about 10 nucleotides from it. The primary function of the promoter is to provide a position for initial binding of the RNA polymerase. A special protein molecule, the *sigma factor,* guides the RNA polymerase to the correct position on the promotor. These promoter sequences are not highly varied, and they tend to be rich in adenine and thymine base pairs, which have one less hydrogen bond than guanine-cytosine pairs, which facilitates the separation of the DNA strands.

Prior to the first synthesis step of transcription, the RNA polymerase begins to separate the two strands of the DNA helix and forms an open "bubble" for transcription **(process figure 9.13, steps 2** and **3).** This bubble serves as the space where the nucleotides of mRNA will actually be assembled. Only one strand of DNA—the **template strand**—is transcribed. This strand will have a reading frame oriented in the $3'$ to $5'$ direction recognized by the RNA polymerase, similar to replication. The mRNA made by transcription of the template strand is a message for the correct sequence of amino acids that will be linked together during translation (protein synthesis). The other strand—the **nontemplate strand**—is sometimes called the coding strand because its sequence is the same order as the mRNA (although it will have thymine instead of uracil). In some cases, this strand may serve a genetic function, but it is not transcribed. Which strand acts as the template varies from one gene to another. One important triplet appearing early in a DNA template is **TAC.** This will be transcribed into **AUG** on the mRNA, which we can see in figure 9.15 and process figure 9.17 is the start codon, as it signals the location on the mRNA where translation starts. Note that the promotor sequences are not transcribed as part of the final mRNA molecule.

As elongation proceeds, the polymerase moves the transcription bubble forward, exposing subsequent sections of DNA. It simultaneously brings in nucleotides that are complementary to the DNA template and continues to assemble the mRNA strand. As with replication, this growing mRNA strand runs in the $5'$ to $3'$ direction. DNA that has already been transcribed rewinds back into its double helix structure **(process figure 9.17, step 4).** The part of the mRNA strand that is already assembled remains attached to the enzyme complex but is kept out of the way of the processing machinery.

At termination, the polymerase recognizes a site on DNA near the end of the gene that signals the separation and release of the completed mRNA, which will next enter the ribosome for translation.

Quick Search

Get an animated view of this dynamic process by searching online for "Stages of Transcription— McGraw-Hill."

① Each gene contains a specific promoter region and a leader sequence for guiding the beginning of transcription. Next is the region of the gene that codes for a polypeptide and ends with a series of terminal sequences that stop translation.

② **Initiation.** Guided by the sigma factor, the RNA polymerase binds to the DNA at the promoter region. DNA is unwound at the promoter by RNA polymerase. Only one strand of DNA, called the template strand, supplies the codes to be transcribed by RNA polymerase. This strand runs in the 3′ to 5′ direction.

③ **Elongation.** The RNA polymerase moves along the DNA strand, adding complementary nucleotides as dictated by the DNA template. The mRNA strand is synthesized in the 5′ to 3′ direction.

④ **Termination.** The polymerase continues transcribing until it reaches a termination site, and the mRNA transcript is released to be translated. Note that the section of the transcribed DNA is rewound into its original configuration.

⚙ **Process Figure 9.13** The major events in transcription.

As we will see in section 9.3, this mRNA delivers its message in co-dons that are the master code for protein synthesis. The length of the final mRNA molecule depends upon the polypeptide or protein that it encodes. In bacteria, the smallest mRNA might consist of 100 nu-cleotides, an average one, 1,000 nucleotides, and the largest, 4,600.*

Translation: The Second Stage of Gene Expression

In translation, all of the elements needed to synthesize a protein, from the mRNA to the tRNAs with amino acids, are brought to-gether on the ribosomes **(figure 9.14).** The process occurs in five stages: initiation, elongation, termination, and protein folding and processing.

*What would be the corresponding numbers of amino acids in the final proteins for these three mRNAs?

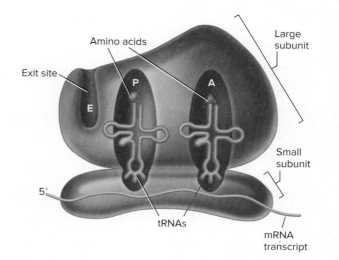

Figure 9.14 The "players" in translation. A ribosome serves as the stage for protein synthesis. Assembly of the small and large subunits results in specific sites for placement of the mRNA (small subunit) and two tRNAs with their amino acids (P and A sites).

Initiation of Translation

In prokaryotic cells, the mRNA molecule leaves the DNA transcription site and is transported directly to ribosomes. Ribosomal subunits are specifically assembled in a way that forms sites to hold the mRNA and tRNAs. The ribosome thus recognizes these molecules and stabilizes reactions between them. The small subunit binds to the 5′ end of the mRNA and provides molecules to initiate translation. The large subunit holds the tRNAs and is actively involved in peptide bond formation by means of a specialized ribozyme, which is an RNA-based catalyst (see 8.2 Making Connections). The small subunit of the ribosome binds at a specific site on the mRNA and places the start codon (AUG) in correct alignment with the P site.

With the mRNA message in place on the assembled ribosome, the next step in translation involves entrance of tRNAs with their amino acids. The pool of cytoplasm around the region contains a complete array of tRNAs, previously charged by having the correct amino acid attached. The step in which the complementary tRNA meets with the mRNA code is guided by the two sites on the large subunit of the ribosome called the P site (left) and the A site (right).[1] Think of these sites as recessed spaces tucked within the two subunits of the ribosome, with each site accommodating a tRNA. The ribosome also has an exit or E site where used tRNAs are released.

The Master Genetic Code: The Message in Messenger RNA

By convention, the master genetic code is represented by the mRNA codons and the amino acids they specify **(figure 9.15).** Except in a very few cases (the genes of mitochondria and chloroplasts, for example), this code is universal, whether for prokaryotes, eukaryotes, or viruses. It is worth noting that once the mRNA codon is known, the original DNA sequence, the complementary tRNA code, and the types of amino acids in the protein are automatically known **(figure 9.16).** However, one cannot predict (backward) from protein structure what the exact mRNA codons are because of a factor called **redundancy** or **degeneracy,** meaning that a particular amino acid can be coded for by more than one codon.

In figure 9.15 the mRNA codons and their corresponding amino acid specificities are given. Because there are 64 different triplet codes[2] and only 20 different amino acids, some amino acids are represented by several codons. For example, leucine and serine can each be represented by any of six different triplets, but tryptophan and methionine are represented by a single codon. In such codons as leucine, only the first two nucleotides are required to encode the correct amino acid, and the third nucleotide does not change its sense. This property, called *wobble,* is thought to permit some level of variation or mutation without changing the message.

1. P stands for peptidyl site; A stands for aminoacyl site; E stands for exit site.

2. This number 64 comes from 4^3 (the 4 different nucleotides in all possible combinations of 3).

		Second Base Position			
	U	**C**	**A**	**G**	
U	UUU UUC } Phenylalanine UUA UUG } Leucine	UCU UCC UCA UCG } Serine	UAU UAC } Tyrosine UAA UAG } STOP**	UGU UGC } Cysteine UGA STOP** UGG Tryptophan	U C A G
C	CUU CUC CUA CUG } Leucine	CCU CCC CCA CCG } Proline	CAU CAC } Histidine CAA CAG } Glutamine	CGU CGC CGA CGG } Arginine	U C A G
A	AUU AUC } Isoleucine AUA AUG* START Methionine	ACU ACC ACA ACG } Threonine	AAU AAC } Asparagine AAA AAG } Lysine	AGU AGC } Serine AGA AGG } Arginine	U C A G
G	GUU GUC GUA GUG } Valine	GCU GCC GCA GCG } Alanine	GAU GAC } Aspartic acid GAA GAG } Glutamic acid	GGU GGC GGA GGG } Glycine	U C A G

First Base Position (left) / *Third Base Position* (right)

* This codon initiates translation.
**For these codons, which give the orders to stop translation, there are no corresponding tRNAs with amino acids.

Figure 9.15 **The genetic code: Codons of mRNA that specify a given amino acid.** The master code for translation is provided by mRNA codons.

DNA triplets

Nontemplate strand

A T G C T G A C T A C G
T A C G A C T G A T G C
 Template strand

mRNA codons A U G C U G A C U A C G

tRNA anticodons UAC GAC UGA UGC

Protein (amino acids specified) fMethionine Leucine Threonine Threonine

Same amino acid; has a different codon and anticodon

Figure 9.16 Interpreting the DNA code. If the DNA sequence is known, the mRNA codon can be surmised. If a codon is known, the anticodon and, finally, the amino acid sequence can be determined. The reverse is not possible (determining the exact codon or anticodon from amino acid sequence) due to the redundancy of the code.

The Beginning of Protein Synthesis

When the correct tRNA enters the P site, hydrogen bonds will form between the codon (mRNA) and anticodon (tRNA). These bonds will stabilize the tRNA, and it will remain in place. If an incorrect tRNA enters, no bonding occurs between the codon and anticodon and the tRNA will float out of the ribosome. It happens that the amino acid corresponding to the **start codon (AUG)** is *formyl methionine* (fMet), though in many cases it may not remain a part of the completed protein.

Continuation and Completion of Protein Synthesis: Elongation and Termination

Beginning with the start codon, the mRNA is read by the ribosome one codon (three nucleotides) at a time. The ribosome is mobile and moves along the mRNA. When two tRNAs, each carrying a single amino acid, are present in the ribosome (one in the A site and one in the P site), joining of the amino acids is carried out by a *ribozyme* (a catalytic RNA molecule) that is part of the large subunit of the ribosome. It forms a peptide bond between the amino acids on the adjacent tRNAs, and the polypeptide grows in length. Several steps of this process are outlined here:

- Initiation begins when a start codon (AUG) is encountered.
- Elongation starts with the filling of the A site by a second tRNA (**process figure 9.17, step 1**). The identity of this tRNA and its amino acid is dictated by the second mRNA codon.
- A peptide bond forms between the amino acids attached to the two adjacent tRNAs in the ribosome. The fMet is transferred

from the first tRNA to amino acid 2, resulting in two coupled amino acids called a dipeptide (**process figure 9.17, step 2**).

- For the next step to proceed, some room must be made on the ribosome, and the next codon in sequence must be brought into position for reading. This process is accomplished by *translocation,* the enzyme-directed shifting of the ribosome to the next position on the mRNA strand, which causes the empty tRNA (tRNA 1) to be discharged from the ribosome (**process figure 9.17, step 3**) at the E site.
- This simultaneously shifts the tRNA holding the dipeptide into the P position. Site A is temporarily left empty. The tRNA that has been released is now free to drift away and become recharged with an amino acid for later additions to this or another protein.
- The stage is now set for the insertion of tRNA 3 at site A as directed by the third mRNA codon (**process figure 9.17, step 4**). Another peptide bond is formed (creating a tripeptide), the empty tRNA is released, and the ribosome translocates to the next codon (**process figure 9.17, step 5**).
- This action releases tRNA 2, shifts mRNA to the next position, moves tRNA 3 to position P, and opens position A for tRNA 4 (**step 6**). From this point on, peptide elongation proceeds repetitively by this same series of actions out to the end of the mRNA (**steps 7** and **8**).

The termination of protein synthesis is not simply a matter of reaching the last codon on mRNA. It is brought about by the presence of at least one special codon occurring just after the codon for the last amino acid. Termination codons—UAA, UAG, and UGA—are codons for which there is no corresponding tRNA. Termed **stop codons,** they carry a necessary message: *Stop here.* When this codon is reached, a special enzyme breaks the bond between the final tRNA and the finished polypeptide chain, releasing it from the ribosome.

> **Quick Search**
> See this in animation by searching online for "VCAC: Molecular Processes: Translation: The Movie."

Before newly made proteins can carry out their structural or enzymatic roles, they often require finishing touches. Even before the peptide chain is released from the ribosome, it begins folding upon itself to achieve its biologically active conformation. Other alterations, called *posttranslational modifications,* may be necessary. Some proteins must have the starting amino acid (formyl methionine) clipped off; proteins destined to become complex enzymes have **cofactors** added; and some join with other completed proteins to form **quaternary** levels of structure.

The operation of transcription and translation is machinelike in its precision. Protein synthesis in bacteria is both efficient and rapid. At 37°C, 12 to 17 amino acids per second are added to a growing peptide chain. An average protein consisting of about 400 amino acids requires less than half a minute for complete synthesis. Further efficiency is gained when the translation of mRNA starts while transcription is still occurring (**figure 9.18**). A single mRNA is long enough to be fed through more than one ribosome simultaneously. This permits the synthesis of hundreds of protein molecules from the same mRNA transcript arrayed along a chain of ribosomes. This **polyribosomal complex** is indeed an assembly

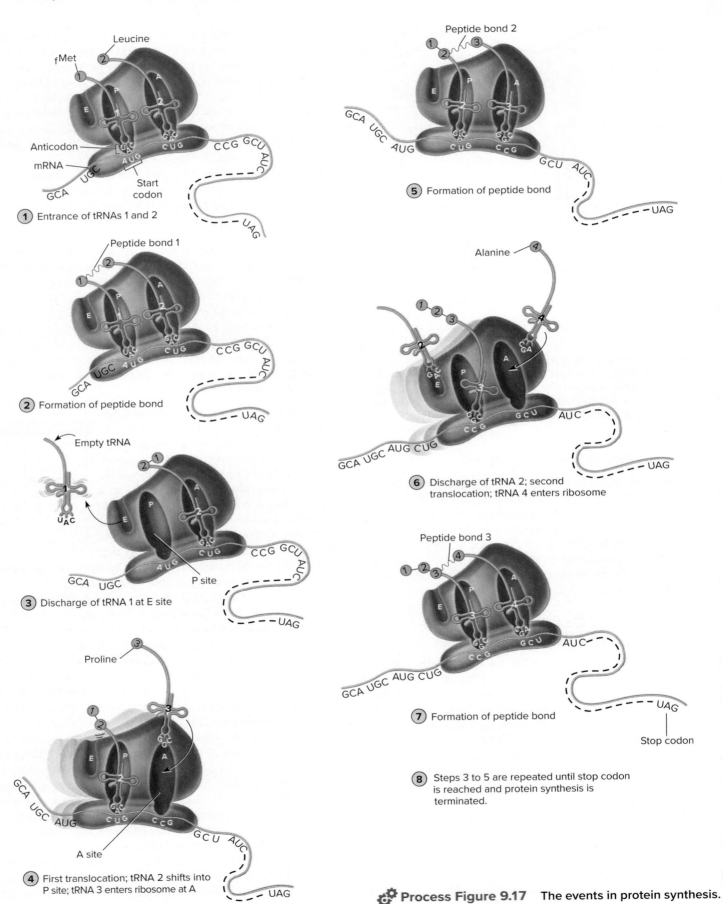

① Entrance of tRNAs 1 and 2

② Formation of peptide bond

③ Discharge of tRNA 1 at E site

④ First translocation; tRNA 2 shifts into P site; tRNA 3 enters ribosome at A

⑤ Formation of peptide bond

⑥ Discharge of tRNA 2; second translocation; tRNA 4 enters ribosome

⑦ Formation of peptide bond

⑧ Steps 3 to 5 are repeated until stop codon is reached and protein synthesis is terminated.

Process Figure 9.17 The events in protein synthesis.

(a)

(b)

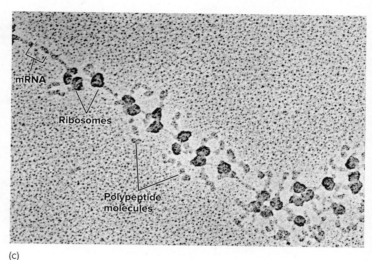

(c)

Figure 9.18 **Speeding up the protein assembly line in bacteria.** **(a)** The mRNA transcript encounters ribosomal parts immediately as it leaves the DNA. **(b)** The ribosomal factories assemble along the mRNA in a chain, each ribosome reading the message and translating it into protein. Many products will thus be well along the synthetic pathway before transcription has even terminated. **(c)** Photomicrograph of a polyribosomal complex in action. Note that the protein "tails" vary in length depending on the stage of translation (30,000×).
(c) Steven McKnight and Oscar L Miller, Department of Biology, University of Virginia

line for mass production of proteins. Protein synthesis consumes an enormous amount of energy. Approximately 1,200 ATPs or ATP equivalents are consumed for synthesis of an average-size protein.

Eukaryotic Transcription and Translation: Similar yet Different

Eukaryotes share many aspects of protein synthesis with prokaryotes. They show similarities in the operation of the ribosomes, the functions of start and stop codons, and the mass production of proteins by means of polyribosomes. But they do differ in significant ways. The start codon in eukaryotes is also AUG, but it codes for an alternative form of methionine. Another difference is that eukaryotic mRNAs code for just one protein, unlike bacterial mRNAs, which often contain information from several genes in series. See 9.2 Making Connections to discover other exceptional aspects of eukaryotic genetics.

Prokaryotic and eukaryotic cells also differ in location and structure of genes. The presence of DNA in the nucleus of eukaryotic cells means that eukaryotic transcription and translation cannot be simultaneous as it is in prokaryotes. The mRNA transcript must pass through pores in the nuclear membrane and be carried to the ribosomes in the cytoplasm or on the endoplasmic reticulum for translation.

So far we have introduced a simplified definition of a gene that fits well for the majority of prokaryotes. The pattern of their genes

is colinear, meaning that their message can be directly read into proteins without any additional processing.[3] Eukaryotic genes differ significantly in this characteristic because they are not colinear. Located within their genes are one to several intragenic regions, called **introns,** that do not code for protein.[4] These introns are interspersed between coding regions, called **exons,** that will be translated into protein **(figure 9.19).** To illustrate this we can use words as examples. A short section of colinear prokaryotic gene might read: SAM SAW HIS NEW CAR GET HIT; a eukaryotic gene that codes for the same portion would read SAM SAW SVXF FPL HIS NEW CAR QZWVP GET HIT. The recognizable words are the exons, while the other letters represent the introns.

This discontinuous genetic structure, also called a split gene, requires further processing before translation. Transcription of the entire gene with both exons and introns occurs first, producing a pre-mRNA. Next, an RNA-protein complex called a *spliceosome* recognizes the exon-intron junctions and enzymatically cuts through them in a process called RNA splicing. The action of this splicer enzyme loops the introns into lariat-shaped pieces, excises them, and joins the exons end to end. By this means, a strand of mRNA with no intron material is produced. This completed mRNA strand can then proceed to the cytoplasm to be translated.

Several different types of introns have been discovered, some of which do code for cell substances. For example, certain introns

3. With colinearity, an mRNA transcript can be translated directly into the correct sequence of amino acids.

4. Introns have also been found in some prokaryotes (cyanobacteria), archaea, and even viruses.

DNA template

Exon Intron

Primary mRNA transcript

Occurs in nucleus

Transcript processed by special enzymes

Lariat forming Spliceosomes

Lariat excised

Spliceosomes released

Exons spliced together

Occurs in cytoplasm

mRNA transcript can now be translated

Figure 9.19 **The split gene of eukaryotes.** Eukaryotic genes have an additional complication in their transcription/translation. Their coding sequences, or exons (E), are interrupted at intervals by segments called introns (I) that are not part of that protein's code. Introns are transcribed but not translated, which necessitates their removal by RNA splicing enzymes before translation.

12. What are the template and nontemplate strands of DNA?
13. Why is only one strand transcribed, and is the same strand of DNA always transcribed?
14. Distinguish between a codon and an anticodon.
15. Briefly describe the events in translation.
16. What are the functions of start and stop codons? Give examples.
17. Summarize how bacterial and eukaryotic cells differ in gene structure, transcription, and translation.
18. Discuss the roles of exons and introns.

9.3 Genetic Regulation of Protein Synthesis and Metabolism

 Learn

14. Explain the functions of operons in bacterial genetic control.
15. Describe the main features of the lactose operon and inducible operons.
16. Describe the main features of repressible operons.
17. Summarize some aspects of genetic control by RNA.

have been found to code for an enzyme called reverse transcriptase, which can convert RNA into DNA. Other introns are translated into endonucleases, enzymes that can snip DNA and allow insertions and deletions into the DNA sequence. Some introns have an innate catalytic function and can splice themselves out of an RNA transcript. A great deal of non-protein-coding DNA is proving to be vital for cell function. Human DNA has an average of eight introns per gene, which represents a significant percentage of the DNA found in chromosomes. One role alternative splicing plays is in providing greater flexibility in creating alternative versions of genes. It is likely that future research will discover additional roles of introns in regulating gene expression.

 Practice SECTION 9.2

8. How is the language of a gene expressed?
9. If a bacterial protein is 300 amino acids long, how many nucleotide pairs long is the gene sequence that codes for it?
10. Construct a table that compares the structure and functions of DNA and RNA.
11. Where does transcription begin?

In chapter 8, we surveyed the metabolic reactions in cells and the enzymes involved in those reactions. There we learned that some enzymes are regulated and that one form of regulation occurs at the genetic level. This control mechanism ensures that genes are active only when their products are required. In this way, enzymes will be produced as they are needed and the waste of energy and materials in dead-end synthesis is prevented. A major form of gene regulation in prokaryotes is through systems called **operons.** An operon is a section of DNA that contains one or more structural genes along with a corresponding operator gene that controls transcription. Such an arrangement permits genes for a particular metabolic pathway to be induced or repressed in unison by the same regulatory element.

Operons are described as either inducible or repressible. The category of an operon is determined by how it is affected by the environment within the cell. Many catabolic operons are **inducible,** meaning that the operon is turned on (induced) by the substrate of the enzyme for which the structural genes code. In this way, the enzymes needed to metabolize a nutrient (lactose, for example) are produced only when that nutrient is present. **Repressible operons** often contain genes coding for anabolic enzymes, such as those used to synthesize amino acids. In the case of these operons, several genes in series are turned off (repressed) by the product synthesized by the enzyme.

① **Operon Off: No Lactose**
In the absence of lactose, a repressor protein (the product of a regulatory gene located elsewhere) attaches to the operator of the operon. This effectively blocks transcription of structural genes downstream (to its right). Suppression of transcription (and translation) prevents the unnecessary synthesis of enzymes for processing lactose.

② **Operon On: Lactose Present**
Upon entering the cell, the substrate (lactose) becomes a genetic inducer by attaching to the repressor, which is rendered inactive and falls away. The operator is no longer closed off and its DNA becomes accessible to the RNA polymerase. The RNA polymerase transcribes the structural genes, and the mRNA is translated into enzymes that can act on the lactose substrate.

Process Figure 9.20 The lactose operon in bacteria: How inducible genes are controlled by substrate.

The Lactose Operon: A Model for Inducible Gene Regulation in Bacteria

The best understood cell system for explaining control through genetic induction is the **lactose (*lac*) operon.** The system, first described in 1961 by François Jacob and Jacques Monod, accounts for the regulation of lactose metabolism in *Escherichia coli.* Many other operons with similar modes of action have since been identified, and together they furnish convincing evidence that a cell's metabolic actions can have great impact on gene expression.

The lactose operon has three important features (**process figure 9.20**):

1. the **regulator,** a gene that codes for a protein capable of repressing the operon (a **repressor**);
2. the *control locus,* composed of two areas, the promoter recognized by RNA polymerase (see figure 9.13) and the **operator,** a sequence that acts as an on/off switch for transcription; and
3. the *structural locus,* made up of three genes, each coding for a different enzyme needed to catabolize lactose. One of the enzymes, β-galactosidase, hydrolyzes the lactose into its monosaccharides; another, permease, brings lactose across the cell membrane.

The promoter, operator, and structural components lie adjacent to one another, but the regulator can be at a distant site.

In inducible systems such as the *lac* operon, the operon is normally in an *off* mode and does not initiate enzyme synthesis when the appropriate substrate is absent (**process figure 9.20, step 1**). How is the operon maintained in this mode? The key is in the repressor

protein that is encoded by the regulatory gene. This relatively large molecule is **allosteric,** meaning that its activity can be altered, depending on which active site and substrate are in play. A substrate binding to one site can distort a different site and prevent it from accepting its substrate (see figure 8.10, right). In the absence of lactose, the repressor protein interacts with the operator and causes the operator to distort into a temporary loop configuration. This loop blocks access of the RNA polymerase to the DNA of the operator and prevents transcription. Think of the repressor as a lock on the operator, and if the operator is locked, the structural genes cannot be transcribed. Importantly, the regulator gene is located in a separate site from the operator region and is not affected by this block on the operon.

If lactose is added to the cell's environment, it triggers several events that turn the operon *on.* First, the binding of lactose to the repressor protein creates a shape change in the repressor that dislodges it from the operator segment (**process figure 9.20, step 2**). This opens up the operator to allow RNA polymerase to bind to it

and begin transcription. The structural genes are transcribed in a single unbroken transcript coding for all three enzymes. During translation, however, each protein is synthesized separately. Because lactose is ultimately responsible for stimulating the chain of events leading to protein synthesis, it is considered an **inducer.**

As lactose is depleted, further enzyme synthesis is not necessary, so the order of events reverses. At this point, there is no longer sufficient lactose to inhibit the repressor; hence, the repressor regains its active shape for attachment to the operator. The operator is locked, and transcription of the structural genes and enzyme synthesis related to lactose are arrested.

A fine but important point about the *lac* operon is that it functions only in the absence of glucose or if the cell's energy needs are not being met by the available glucose. Glucose is the preferred carbon source because it can be used immediately in growth and does not require induction of an operon. When a supply of glucose is present, a second regulatory system ensures that the *lac* operon is inactive, regardless of lactose levels in the environment.

A Repressible Operon

Bacterial systems for synthesis of amino acids, purines and pyrimidines, and other processes work on a principle that is the reverse of the *lac* operon—that of repression. Similar factors such as repressor proteins, operators, and a series of structural genes are part of a repressible operon, but with some important differences. Unlike the *lac* operon, this operon is normally in the *on* mode and will be turned *off* only when the product of the pathway is no longer required. Excess product plays a role as a **corepressor** that slows the transcription of the operon.

A metabolically active cell that is consuming large amounts of the amino acid arginine (arg) will serve to illustrate the operation of a repressible operon. Under these conditions, the *arg* operon is set to *on,* and arginine is being actively synthesized through the action of the operon's enzymatic products **(process figure 9.21, step 1).** In such an active cell, the arginine will be used immediately, and the repressor will remain inactive (unable to bind the operator) because there is too little free arginine to activate it. As the cell's metabolism begins to

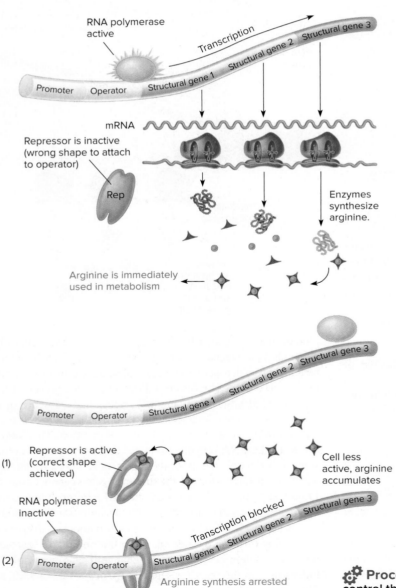

(1) Operon On: Arginine Being Used by Cell
A repressible operon remains on when its nutrient products (here, arginine) are in great demand by the cell. The repressor has the wrong shape to bind to the DNA operator without a corepressor, so that RNA polymerase is free to actively transcribe the genes and translation actively proceeds.

(2) Operon Off: Arginine Building Up
The operon is repressed when (1) arginine builds up and, serving as a corepressor, activates the repressor. (2) The activated repressor complex affixes to the operator and blocks the RNA polymerase and further transcription of genes for arginine synthesis.

Process Figure 9.21 Repressible operon: Genetic control through excess product.

9.2 MAKING CONNECTIONS

Is It Really an RNA World?

Evidence about the roles of RNAs in gene expression is accumulating rapidly. We have learned how the introns of eukaryotic mRNAs are removed by the catalytic RNA of the spliceosome complex, and the peptide bonds of proteins are catalyzed by ribosomal RNA. Based on our current understanding, it is clear that various forms of RNA dominate genetic control of transcription and translation. This type of RNA, called noncoding RNA (ncRNA) because it does not code for protein, regulates how the coded molecules are expressed.

Recently described ncRNAs in bacteria are **riboswitches**—short leader segments of mRNA that are transcribed but not expressed in a finished protein. Acting as a switch means that they can be turned on or off, depending on their folding pattern, which means they can both start or stop a step in gene expression. Some riboswitches work at the level of transcription and others alter translation, but the outcome of both is to affect protein synthesis. Riboswitches have a unique ability to sense and bind a specific molecule (ligand) such as an amino acid, vitamin, or cofactor that changes their folding pattern and action.

Riboswitches in gram-negative bacteria regulate translation at the ribosome. When the riboswitch is on, the leader sequence of mRNA forms a loop with itself that opens up the binding sequence and makes it available for the ribosome and protein synthesis. The riboswitch is turned off when a ligand binds to it and repositions the binding sequence. This makes the mRNA binding position on the ribosome inaccessible, thereby blocking translation (see figure). Like the *lac* operon, this mechanism will be reversed in the absence of the ligand, and translation can proceed. This riboswitch regulates synthesis of some vitamins.

Eukaryotes have their own versions of controls on transcription and translation. We are just beginning to understand the functions of small RNAs containing around 20 to 25 nucleotides that are found in animal and plant cells. Small RNAs have been termed *gene silencers* because they shut down final products of gene expression. Examples are micro-RNAs and si (short interfering) RNAs, both of which control the fate of mRNA following transcription. Both types of small RNAs attach to mRNA and keep it from being translated. In some cases, they suppress mRNA functions, and in others, they actually control the synthesis of enzymes that can destroy the mRNA. SiRNA is also known to signal the destruction of foreign RNA from viruses.

Another form of eukaryotic regulation acts at the level of the chromosomes, by means of reorganization and modification of the chromatin—a type of epigenetic effect. By fine-tuning the tightness and looseness of the chromatin structure, certain small RNAs can control which genes are accessible for function (see figure 9.4). Other small RNAs are involved in methylation of DNA, which also modulates gene availability.

Knowledge of these novel types of RNA molecules has answered some questions that came out of genome sequencing studies. Most of the DNA in organisms was found *not* to code for functional proteins. This DNA was once considered "junk," but its percentage in humans was 85%! Obviously, in bacteria as well as in humans, it is far from junk. In fact, this DNA has been preserved in the same form for many millions of years of evolution, suggesting it has a very important function. We now know that much of it codes for these important RNA regulatory molecules.

In what ways could knowledge of these regulatory RNAs inspire new types of drug therapies?

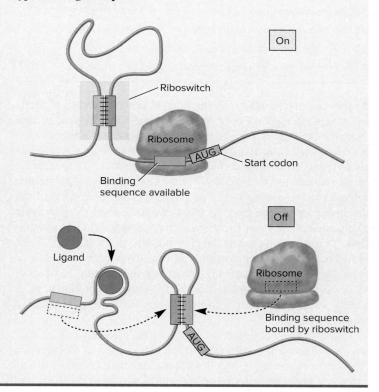

slow down, however, the synthesized arginine is no longer used up and accumulates. The free arginine is then available to act as a corepressor by attaching to the repressor. This reaction changes the shape of the repressor, making it capable of binding to the operator and stopping transcription. Arginine will cease to be synthesized until the cell once again requires it in metabolism (**process figure 9.21, step 2**).

Additional Methods of Gene Expression

Analogous gene control mechanisms in eukaryotic cells are not as well understood, but it is known that gene function can be altered by intrinsic regulatory segments similar to operons. Some molecules, called transcription factors, insert on the grooves of the DNA molecule and enhance transcription of specific genes. These transcription factors can regulate gene expression in response to environmental stimuli such as nutrients, toxin levels, or even temperature. Eukaryotic genes are also regulated during growth and development, leading to the hundreds of different tissue types found in higher multicellular organisms. Considerable interest has been generated in the functions of regulatory RNAs that exert control on several levels in both prokaryotic and eukaryotic cells (**9.2 Making Connections**).

Practice SECTION 9.3

19. What is an operon? Describe the functions of regulators, promoters, and operators.

20. Compare and contrast the *lac* operon and repressible operon systems.

21. For both process figures 9.20 and 9.21, draw a simple stepwise diagram indicating the events that would reverse the operon's action.

22. At which levels of DNA regulation do small RNAs function?

9.4 Mutations: Changes in the Genetic Code

Learn

18. Define *mutation* and explain how mutant forms are identified.

19. Summarize the causes and types of mutations and their effects.

20. Describe some mutation repair mechanisms.

21. Compare beneficial and detrimental effects of mutations.

As precise and predictable as the rules of genetic expression seem, permanent changes do occur in the genetic code. Indeed, genetic change is the driving force of evolution through its addition of variation to populations of organisms. Changes may become evident in altered gene expression, such as in the appearance or disappearance of anatomical or physiological traits. For example, a pigmented bacterium can lose its ability to form pigment, or a strain of the malarial parasite can develop resistance to a drug. A phenotypic change that is due to an alteration in the genotype is called a **mutation.** On a strictly molecular level, a mutation is an alteration in the nitrogen base sequence of DNA. It can involve the loss of base pairs, the addition of base pairs, or a rearrangement in the order of base pairs. Do not confuse this with genetic recombination, in which microbes transfer whole segments of genetic information between themselves.

A microorganism that exhibits a natural, nonmutated characteristic is known as a **wild type** or wild strain. If a microorganism develops a mutation, it is called a **mutant strain.** Mutant strains can show variance in morphology, nutritional characteristics, genetic mechanisms, resistance to chemicals, temperature preference, and nearly any type of enzymatic function. Mutant strains are very useful for tracking genetic events, unraveling genetic organization, and pinpointing genetic markers.

The simplest way to detect mutant bacteria is to inoculate solid media containing differential or selective agents such as metabolic substrates or antibiotics. Growing a pure culture on a plate of media and observing the appearance of colonies can reveal strains of a species that express genetic variations. For instance, in cultures of wild-type *E. coli* grown on differential MacConkey agar, most of the isolated colonies will indicate a positive result for lactose fermentation, but invariably there will be a small number of colonies that are negative and have lost the genes for using lactose. This colony can be readily pulled out for further study. Antibiotics are frequently added to media as selective agents for separating out strains of bacteria that are drug resistant. Figure 10.12 shows how this method works for detecting recombinant cells used in genetic engineering.

Causes of Mutations

A mutation is described as spontaneous or induced, depending upon its origin. A **spontaneous mutation** is a change in the DNA arising from errors in replication that occur without a known cause. The frequency of spontaneous mutations can range from 1 mutation every 10,000 bases to 1 per 10,000,000,000, oftentimes related to the complexity of the DNA at that point. Areas of the DNA that are repetitive or show a great deal of secondary structure such as loops or hairpins **(figure 9.22)** tend to have higher mutation rates.

Induced mutations result from exposure to known **mutagens,** which are physical or chemical agents that damage DNA and interfere with its functioning **(table 9.3).** The carefully controlled use of mutagens has proved a useful way to induce mutant strains of microorganisms for study.

Chemical mutagenic agents act in a variety of ways to change the DNA. Agents such as acridine dyes insert completely across the DNA helices between adjacent bases. This results in distortion of

Figure 9.22 Secondary structure in DNA can lead to increased mutation rates. (a) Stretches of DNA that are repetitive may lead to mutations as the DNA polymerase skips a nucleotide or reads the same nucleotide twice. (b) Sequences that allow complementary base pairing within the DNA strand may cause secondary structures (loops, bends, or hairpins) to form in the DNA, which also increases the mutation rate.

TABLE 9.3	Selected Mutagenic Agents and Their Effects
Agent	**Effect**
Chemical	
Nitrous acid, bisulfite	Remove an amino group from some nitrogen bases
Ethidium bromide	Inserts between the paired bases
Acridine dyes	Cause frameshifts due to insertion between base pairs
Nitrogen base analogs	Compete with natural bases for sites on replicating DNA
Radiation	
Ionizing (gamma rays, X-rays)	Form free radicals that cause single or double breaks in DNA
Ultraviolet	Causes cross-links between adjacent pyrimidines

the helix and can cause frameshift mutations. Analogs[5] of the nitrogen bases (5-bromodeoxyuridine and 2-aminopurine, for example) are chemical mimics of natural bases that are incorporated into DNA during replication. The addition of these abnormal bases leads to mistakes in base-pairing. Many chemical mutagens are also carcinogens, or cancer-causing agents (see the discussion of the Ames test later in this section).

Physical agents that alter DNA are primarily types of radiation. High-energy gamma rays and X-rays introduce major physical changes into DNA, which can accumulate breaks that may not be repairable. Ultraviolet (UV) radiation induces abnormal bonds between adjacent pyrimidines so that normal replication of that region is blocked. Exposure to large doses of radiation can be fatal, which is why radiation is so effective in microbial control; it can also be carcinogenic in animals. The use of radiation to control microorganisms is described further in chapter 11.

Categories of Mutations

Mutations range from large mutations, in which long genetic sequences are gained or lost, to small ones that affect only a few bases on a gene. These latter mutations, which involve addition, deletion, or substitution of no more than a few bases, are called **point mutations.**

To understand how a change in DNA influences the cell, remember that the DNA code appears in a particular order of triplets (three bases) that is transcribed into mRNA codons, each of which specifies an amino acid. A permanent alteration in the DNA that is copied faithfully into mRNA and translated can change the structure of the protein. A change in a protein can likewise change the morphology and physiology of a cell. Most mutations have a harmful effect on the cell, leading to cell dysfunction or death. Neutral mutations produce neither adverse nor helpful changes. A small number of mutations are beneficial in that they provide the cell with a useful change in structure or physiology.

Any change in the code that leads to placement of a different amino acid is called a **missense mutation.** A missense mutation can do one of the following:

* create a faulty, nonfunctional (or less functional) protein,
* produce a protein that functions in a different manner, or
* cause no significant alteration in protein function.

 CLINIC CASE

If Only We Could Give You a Mutation The patient, Timothy Ray Brown, presented to doctors in Berlin with overwhelming fatigue. Used to 20 miles a day on his bicycle back and forth to work, he was suddenly unable to make the 1-mile ride to a restaurant near his office. Diagnosed with the human immunodeficiency virus (HIV) 10 years earlier, Brown had been keeping the virus in check with a combination of AZT and protease inhibitors. He was in good health and had a life expectancy about the same as someone uninfected by the virus. Doctors in Berlin diagnosed Brown with anemia (unrelated to his HIV) and provided blood transfusions to increase the number of circulating erythrocytes. An oncologist performed a bone marrow biopsy, and less than a week after his initial symptoms, Brown was diagnosed with acute myeloid leukemia (AML), a cancer of the bone marrow.

After several failed rounds of chemotherapy, doctors brought up the idea of a bone marrow transplant, a treatment for leukemia in which the bone marrow, both cancerous and healthy, is destroyed and new, healthy bone marrow is transplanted into the body. Brown's doctor wanted to go one step further though, and proposed a treatment that would, perhaps, cure Brown of his HIV at the same time.

To enter cells of the immune system, the human immunodeficiency virus must first bind to a cell surface receptor protein known as CCR-5. Approximately 1% of the population has a mutation in both copies of their CCR-5 gene (called CCR-5 delta 32, or CCR-5 Δ32) that creates a stop codon. HIV cannot use these mutant proteins to enter the cell and is therefore unable to replicate. If a bone marrow donor with the CCR-5 Δ32 mutation could be found, perhaps Brown's AML and HIV could be cured simultaneously.

As luck would have it, Brown is of northern European descent and the CCR-5 Δ32 mutation is most commonly found in that group as well. An appropriate donor was found that possessed the mutation and Brown underwent transplant on February 6, 2007, the same day he stopped taking his anti-HIV medication. A second transplant, from the same donor, was required in 2008, but in more than 10 years, Brown has shown no signs of his HIV progressing, leaving him the first person cured of HIV infection.

Δ32 refers to a 32-base-pair deletion in the CCR-5 gene. Besides a deletion mutation and nonsense mutation, what other type of mutation was created in the gene?

5. An analog is a chemical structured very similarly to another chemical except for minor differences in functional groups.

A **nonsense mutation,** on the other hand, changes a normal codon into a stop codon that does not code for an amino acid and stops the production of the protein wherever it occurs. A nonsense mutation almost always results in a nonfunctional protein. A **silent mutation** alters a base but does not change the amino acid and thus has no effect. For example, because of the redundancy of the code, ACU, ACC, ACG, and ACA all code for threonine, so a mutation that changes only the last base will not alter the sense of the message in any way. A **back-mutation** occurs when a gene that has undergone mutation reverses (mutates back) to its original base composition. An **inversion** occurs when two nucleotides have switched their order, which will nearly always change the amino acid, as we see by inverting GUC (valine) to GCU (threonine).

Mutations also occur when one or more bases are inserted into or deleted from a newly synthesized DNA strand (see **table 9.4, IIB**). This type of mutation, known as a **frameshift,** is so named because the reading frame of mRNA will shift to the left or right, depending on the type of change. Frameshift mutations nearly always result in a nonfunctional protein because the codon structure will become reset from that point on, will code for a different sequence of amino acids from the original DNA, and is likely to introduce stop codons. Also note that insertion or deletion of bases in multiples of three (3, 6, 9, etc.) does not disturb the reading frame downstream from the mutation site. It can still disrupt the structure of the protein, depending on the change in the amino acid sequence. The effects of these types of mutations is modelled in **table 9.4.**

Repair of Mutations

Earlier, we indicated that DNA has a proofreading mechanism to repair mistakes in replication that might otherwise become permanent. Because mutations are potentially life-threatening, the cell has additional systems for finding and repairing DNA that has been damaged by various mutagenic agents and processes. Most ordinary DNA damage is resolved by enzymatic systems specialized for finding and fixing such defects.

DNA that has been damaged by ultraviolet radiation can be restored by photoactivation or light repair. This repair mechanism requires visible light and a light-sensitive enzyme, DNA photolyase, which can attach to sites of abnormal pyrimidine bonding and restore the original DNA structure. Ultraviolet repair mechanisms are successful only for a relatively small number of UV mutations. Mutations can be excised by a series of enzymes that remove the incorrect bases and add the correct ones. This process is known as *excision repair*. First, enzymes break the bonds between the bases and the sugar-phosphate strand at the site of the error. A different enzyme subsequently removes the defective bases one at a time, leaving a gap that will be filled in by DNA polymerase I and ligase. A repair system can also locate mismatched bases that were missed during proofreading: for example, C mistakenly paired with A, or G with T. The base must be replaced soon after the mismatch is made, or it will not be recognized by the repair enzymes.

> **Quick Search**
>
> See this process animated by going to the video "DNA Nucleotide Excision Repair" on YouTube.

TABLE 9.4	Classification of Major Types of Mutations

	Example
I. Wild-type (nonmutated) sequence	THE BIG BAD CAT ATE THE FAT RED BUG

The wild-type sequence of a gene is the DNA sequence found in most organisms and is generally considered the "normal" sequence.

II. Categories of mutations based on type of DNA alteration

A. Substitution mutations

1. Missense	THE BIG MAD CAT ATE THE FAT RED BUG

A missense mutation causes a different amino acid to be incorporated into a protein. Effects range from unnoticeable to severe, based on how the new amino acid alters protein function.

2. Nonsense	THE BIG BAD XXX (stop)

A nonsense mutation converts a codon to a stop codon, resulting in premature termination of protein synthesis. Effects of this type of mutation are almost always severe.

B. Inversion mutations	THE BIG ABD CAT ATE THE FAT RED BUG
	THE BIB GAD CAT ATE THE FAT RED BUG

Inversions arise when adjacent letters exchange places, which alters 1 or 2 bases, depending on the location of the inversion. This does not change the reading frame, but can result in significant changes in amino acids and protein function.

C. Frameshift Mutations

1. Insertion	THE BIG BAB DCA TAT ETH EFA TRE DBU G
2. Deletion	THE BIG *ADC ATA TET HEF ATR EDB UG

Insertion (addition of letter) and deletion (removal of letter) mutations cause a change in the reading frame of the mRNA, resulting in a protein in which every amino acid after the mutation can be affected. Because of this, frameshift mutations almost always result in a nonfunctional protein.

The Ames Test

New agricultural, industrial, and medicinal chemicals are constantly being added to the environment, and exposure to them is widespread. The discovery that many such compounds are mutagenic and that up to 83% of these mutagens are linked to cancer is significant. Although animal testing has been a standard method of detecting chemicals with carcinogenic potential, a more rapid screening system called the **Ames test**[6] is also commonly used. In this inventive test, the experimental subjects are bacteria whose gene expression and mutation rate can be readily observed and monitored. The premise is that any chemical capable of mutating bacterial DNA can similarly mutate mammalian (and thus human)

6. Named for its creator, Bruce Ames.

DNA and is therefore potentially hazardous. Many potential carcinogens (benzanthracene and aflatoxin, for example) are mutagenic agents only after being acted on by mammalian liver enzymes, so an extract of these enzymes is added to the test medium.

One indicator organism in the Ames test is a mutant strain of *Salmonella enterica*[7] that has lost the ability to synthesize the amino acid histidine, a defect highly susceptible to back-mutation because the strain also lacks DNA repair mechanisms. Mutations that cause reversion to the wild strain, which is capable of synthesizing histidine, occur spontaneously at a low rate. A test agent is considered a mutagen if it enhances the rate of back-mutation beyond levels that would occur spontaneously. **Figure 9.23** compares a standard version of the test with a multiwell method that streamlines result taking. The Ames test has proved invaluable for screening an assortment of environmental and dietary chemicals for mutagenicity and carcinogenicity without resorting to animal studies.

Positive and Negative Effects of Mutations

Many mutations are not repaired. How the cell copes with them depends on the nature of the mutation and the strategies available to that organism. Mutations are passed on to the offspring of organisms during reproduction and to new viruses during replication. They become a long-term part of the gene pool. Most mutations are harmful to organisms, but some can provide adaptive advantages.

If a mutation leading to a nonfunctional protein occurs in a gene for which there is only a single copy, as in haploid organisms, the cell will probably die. This happens when certain mutant strains of *E. coli* acquire mutations in the genes needed to repair damage by UV radiation. Mutations of the human genome affecting the action of a single protein (mostly enzymes) are responsible for more than 3,500 diseases.

Although most spontaneous mutations are not beneficial, a small number contribute to the success of the individual and the population by creating variant strains with alternative ways of expressing a trait. Microbes are not "aware" of this advantage and do not direct these changes; they simply respond to the environment they encounter. In the long-range view, mutations and the variations they produce are the raw materials for change in the population and, thus, for evolution.

Mutations that create variants occur frequently enough that any population contains mutant strains for a number of characteristics, but as long as the environment is stable, these mutants will never comprise more than a tiny percentage of the population. When the environment changes, however, it can become hostile for the survival of certain individuals, and only those microbes bearing protective mutations will be equipped to survive in the new environment.

Such observations can be explained by the important biological principles of natural selection and survival of the fittest. This theory states that environmental pressure selects for organisms that have greater adaptability due to beneficial mutations. They are more likely to survive, reproduce, and pass the changed genes on to succeeding generations. In time, these survivors become the

dominant members of the population as long as the mutation continues to favor their survival. One of the clearest models for natural selection in action is acquired drug resistance in bacteria (discussed in chapter 12).

As we will see in section 9.5, bacteria have additional mechanisms for changing their genetic makeup by sharing genes with other bacteria through recombination.

(c) The degree of mutagenicity of the chemical agent can be calculated by comparing the number of colonies growing on the control plate with the number on the test plate. Chemicals that induce an increased incidence of back-mutation (right side) are considered carcinogens.

(d) Ames fluctuation tests using multiple wells; a blue well indicates no back-mutation occurring; yellow indicates back-mutations.

Counting the number of (+) yellow wells provides the number of back-mutations; the result on the right indicates a strong mutagen.

Figure 9.23 **The Ames test. (a, b, c)** In this traditional plate method, a strain of *Salmonella enterica* that cannot synthesize histidine [his(−)] is the test species. If the chemical causes an increase in mutation rate to histidine-producing cells as compared to a control, the chemical is considered mutagenic. **(d)** The newer well fluctuation test is based on the same basic scheme; however, it has greater sensitivity and is easier to evaluate.
(d): Courtesy of Xenometrix AG

7. *S. enterica* inhabits the intestine of poultry and causes food poisoning in humans. It is used extensively in genetic studies of bacteria.

Practice SECTION 9.4

23. Explain what is meant by the terms *mutation* and *mutant*.
24. Describe the primary causes, types, and outcomes of mutations. Give an example of a mutation that is beneficial and one that is lethal or harmful.
25. Explain the purposes behind replica plating and the Ames test.

9.5 DNA Recombination Events

Learn

22. Explain recombination in bacteria and what it involves.
23. Describe the main features of conjugation and its outcomes.
24. Discuss what is required for bacterial transformation and its outcomes.
25. Identify the basic processes involved in transduction and the end results.
26. Discuss transposons and their importance to microorganisms.

Genetic recombination through sexual reproduction is an important means of genetic variation in eukaryotes. Although bacteria have no exact equivalent to sexual reproduction, they exhibit a primitive means for sharing or recombining parts of their genomes. An event in which one bacterium donates DNA to another bacterium is a type of genetic transfer termed **recombination,** the end result of which is a new strain different from both the donor and the original recipient strain. In general, any organism that has acquired genes that originated in another organism is called a **recombinant.**

Recombination in bacteria depends largely on their extreme versatility in acquiring and expressing the genetic material of other bacteria and even other organisms. This capacity for genetic sharing has tremendous effects on the diversity and evolution of bacteria. Unlike spontaneous mutations, recombinations are generally beneficial. They can provide additional genes for resistance to

drugs and metabolic poisons, new nutritional and metabolic schemes, increased virulence, and adaptations to changing environmental conditions.

Transmission of Genetic Material in Bacteria

DNA transfer between bacterial cells typically involves small pieces of DNA in the form of **plasmids** or chromosomal fragments. Plasmids are small, circular pieces of DNA that contain their own origin of replication and therefore can replicate independently of the bacterial chromosome. Plasmids are found in many bacteria (as well as some fungi) and typically contain a few dozen genes. Although plasmids are not necessary for bacterial survival, they often carry adaptive genes, such as those for drug resistance.

Chromosomal fragments that have escaped from a lysed bacterial cell are also commonly involved in the transfer of genetic information between cells. An important difference between plasmids and fragments is that, while a plasmid can be stably replicated and inherited, chromosomal fragments must integrate themselves into the bacterial chromosome in order to be replicated and eventually passed to progeny cells. The rate of natural genetic recombination varies a great deal among bacteria, but its frequency can be increased in the laboratory, where the ability to transfer genes between organisms has become an important tool of research and technology.

Depending upon the mode of transmission, the means of genetic recombination in bacteria is called conjugation, transformation, or transduction. **Conjugation** requires the attachment of two cells and the formation of a bridge that can transport DNA. **Transformation** entails the transfer of free DNA and requires no special vehicle. **Transduction** is DNA transfer mediated through the action of bacterial viruses **(table 9.5).**

Conjugation: Genetic Transmission through Direct Contact

Conjugation is a mode of genetic recombination in which a plasmid or fragment of DNA is transferred from a donor cell to a recipient cell via a direct connection. Both gram-negative and gram-positive bacteria can conjugate, but only gram-negative cells operate with a

TABLE 9.5	Types of Genetic Recombination in Bacteria		
Mode	Factors Involved	Direct or Indirect*	Examples of Genes Transferred
Conjugation	Donor cell with pilus Fertility plasmid in donor Both donor and recipient alive Bridge forms between cells to transfer DNA.	Direct	Drug resistance; resistance to metals; toxin production; enzymes; adherence molecules; degradation of toxic substances; uptake of iron
Transformation	Free donor DNA (fragment or plasmid) Live, competent recipient cell, donor usually dead	Indirect	Polysaccharide capsule; metabolic enzymes; drug resistance; unlimited with cloning techniques
Transduction	Donor is lysed bacterial cell. Defective bacteriophage is carrier of donor DNA. Live recipient cell of same species as donor	Indirect	Exotoxins; enzymes for sugar fermentation; drug resistance

*Direct means the donor and recipient are in contact during exchange; indirect means they are not.

specialized plasmid called a **fertility,** or **F, factor.** This plasmid directs the synthesis of a unique **pilus,** also called a sex pilus,[8] that functions in most conjugation transfers. The recipient cell is usually a related bacterium with a recognition site on its surface for interacting with the pilus (**process figure 9.24, step 1**).

A cell's role in conjugation is denoted by F⁺ for the cell that has the F plasmid and by F⁻ for the cell that lacks it. Contact is made when a pilus grows out from the F⁺ cell, attaches to the surface of the F⁻ cell, contracts, and draws the two cells together (process figure 9.24, step 1). At the site where the pilus attaches the two

cells, a mating or conjugative bridge is formed that serves as a transfer system for the plasmid. The latest reliable information indicates that the pilus becomes part of a complex secretory system that opens a gateway between the cell walls and membranes of the two cells and serves as a passageway for the plasmid.

There are hundreds of conjugative plasmids with some variations in their properties. One of the best understood plasmids is the F factor in *E. coli,* which exhibits these patterns of transfer:

1. Because bacteria tend to conserve plasmids, the donor cell first makes a copy of the F factor, which is simultaneously transferred across the bridge (**process figure 9.24, step 2**). This way, it retains the original plasmid, remains F⁺, and can continue to conjugate with other bacteria. The F⁻ cell has been changed into an F⁺ cell capable of producing a pilus and

8. This term refers to its function in the mating of bacteria, but it has nothing to do with sexual reproduction, which is absent in bacteria.

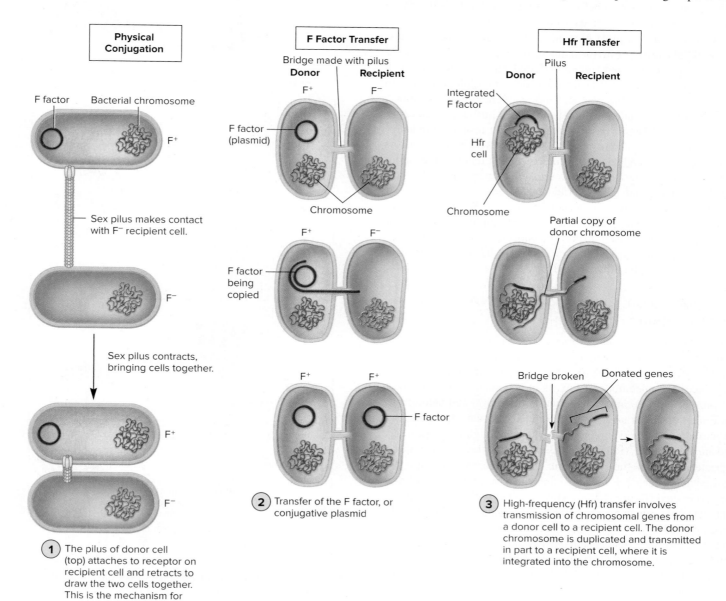

Process Figure 9.24 Conjugation: Genetic transmission through direct contact between two cells.

conjugating with other cells. No additional donor genes are transferred during this transfer.

2. In high-frequency recombination (Hfr) donors, the fertility factor has been integrated into the F$^+$ donor chromosome.

The term *high-frequency recombination* denotes that a cell with an integrated F factor transmits its chromosomal genes at a higher frequency than other cells. This is because the F factor can direct a more comprehensive transfer of part of the donor chromosome to a recipient cell. This transfer occurs through replication of the donor chromosome along with the F factor. One strand of DNA is retained by the donor, and the other strand is transported across to the recipient cell (**process figure 9.24, step 3**). The F factor may not be transferred during this process. The transfer of an entire chromosome takes about 100 minutes, but the pilus bridge between cells is ordinarily broken before this time, and rarely is the entire genome of the donor cell transferred.

Conjugation has great biomedical importance. Special **resistance (R) plasmids,** or **factors,** that bear genes for resisting antibiotics and other drugs are commonly shared among bacteria through conjugation. Transfer of R factors can confer multiple resistance to antibiotics such as tetracycline, chloramphenicol, sulfonamides, and penicillin. This phenomenon is discussed further in chapter 12. Other types of R factors carry genetic codes for resistance to heavy metals (nickel and mercury) or for synthesizing virulence factors (toxins, enzymes, and adhesion molecules) that increase the pathogenicity of the bacterial strain. Conjugation studies have also provided a means to map the bacterial chromosome.

A few gram-positive bacteria (*Bacillus* and *Streptococcus,* for example) are known to recombine through conjugation. Because they lack pili, they must transport the plasmids via specialized proteins activated during adhesion of the two cells. The mechanisms involved are yet to be fully worked out.

Transformation: Capturing Free DNA from Solution

One of the cornerstone discoveries in microbial genetics was made in the late 1920s by the English physician and bacteriologist Frederick Griffith working with *Streptococcus pneumoniae* and laboratory mice. The pneumococcus exists in two major strains based on the presence of the capsule, colonial morphology, and pathogenicity. Encapsulated strains bear a smooth (S) colonial appearance and are virulent; strains lacking a capsule have a rough (R) appearance and are nonvirulent. (Recall from chapter 4 that the capsule protects a bacterium from the phagocytic host defenses.) Griffith first showed that when mice were injected with a live, virulent (S) strain, they soon died (**figure 9.25a**). Mice injected with a live, nonvirulent (R) strain remained alive and healthy (**figure 9.25b**). Next he tried a variation on this theme. He heat-killed an S strain and injected it into mice, which remained healthy (**figure 9.25c**). Then came the ultimate test: Griffith injected both dead S cells and live R cells into mice, with the result that the mice died from pneumococcal blood infection (**figure 9.25d**). If killed bacterial cells do not come back to life and the nonvirulent live strain was harmless, why did the mice die? Although he did not know it at the time, Griffith had demonstrated that dead S cells, while passing through the body

(a)

(b)

(c)

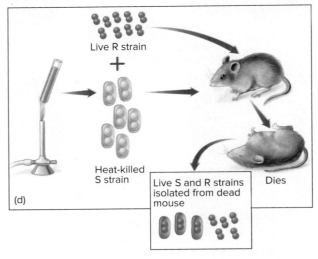

(d)

Figure 9.25 **Griffith's classic experiment in transformation.** In essence, this experiment proved that DNA released from a killed cell can be acquired by a live cell. The cell receiving this new DNA is genetically transformed—in this case, from a nonvirulent strain to a virulent one.

of the mouse, broke open and released some of their DNA (by chance, a segment containing the genes for making a capsule). A few of the live R cells subsequently picked up this loose DNA and were transformed by it into virulent, capsule-forming strains.

Later studies supported the concept that a chromosome released by a lysed cell breaks into fragments small enough to be accepted by a recipient cell and that DNA, even from a dead cell, retains its genetic code. This nonspecific acceptance by a bacterial cell of small fragments of soluble DNA from the surrounding environment is termed **transformation (figure 9.26).** Transformation is facilitated by special DNA-binding proteins on the cell wall that capture DNA from the surrounding medium. Cells that are capable of accepting genetic material through this means are termed **competent.** The new DNA is passed through a DNA uptake system in the cell wall and membrane. Within the cytoplasm, the donated strand is inserted into the chromosome of the recipient cell, now said to be *transformed*. Natural transformation is found in several

groups of gram-positive and gram-negative bacterial species. In addition to genes coding for the capsule, bacteria exchange genes for antibiotic resistance and bacteriocin synthesis in this way.

Because transformation requires no special appendages, and the donor and recipient cells do not have to be in direct contact, the process is useful for applications in recombinant DNA technology. With this technique, foreign genes from a completely unrelated organism are inserted into a plasmid, which is then introduced into a competent bacterial cell through transformation. These recombinations can be carried out in a test tube, and human genes can be experimented upon and even expressed outside the human body by placing them in a microbial cell. Transformation is often used in the production of genetically engineered organisms such as yeasts, plants, and animals, and has been proposed as a future technique for curing genetic diseases in humans. These topics are covered in more detail in chapter 10.

Transduction: Viruses as Vectors

Bacteriophages (bacterial viruses) have been previously described as destructive bacterial parasites. Viruses can also serve as genetic vectors (an entity that can bring foreign DNA into a cell). The process by which a bacteriophage serves as the carrier of DNA from a donor cell to a recipient cell is **transduction.** Although it occurs naturally in a broad spectrum of bacteria, the participating bacteria in a single transduction event must be the same species because of the specificity of viruses for host cells.

There are two versions of transduction. In *generalized transduction* **(process figure 9.27),** random fragments of disintegrating host DNA are taken up by the phage during assembly. Virtually any gene from the bacterium can be transmitted through this means. In *specialized transduction* **(process figure 9.28),** a highly specific part of the host genome is regularly incorporated into the virus. This specificity is explained by the prior existence of a temperate prophage inserted in a fixed site on the bacterial chromosome. When activated, the prophage DNA separates from the bacterial chromosome, carrying a small segment of host genes with it. During a lytic cycle, these specific viral-host gene combinations are incorporated into the viral particles and carried to another bacterial cell. Instances of transduction include the transfer of drug resistance seen in *Staphylococcus* spp. and the transmission of gene regulators in gram-negative rods such as *Escherichia* and *Salmonella*.

Transposons: "The Case of the Jumping Genes" One type of genetic transferral of great interest involves transposable elements, or **transposons.** Transposons have the distinction of shifting from one part of the genome to another and so are termed "jumping genes." When the idea of their existence in corn plants was first postulated by the geneticist Barbara McClintock, it was greeted with wide skepticism, because it had long been believed that the location of a given gene was set and that genes did not or could not move around. Now it is evident that jumping genes are widespread among prokaryotic and eukaryotic cells and viruses. Results from analysis of human DNA indicates that they make up nearly 45% of the human genome.

Transposons contain DNA sequences coding for two enzymes— a transposase and a resolvase—that allow the transposon to excise

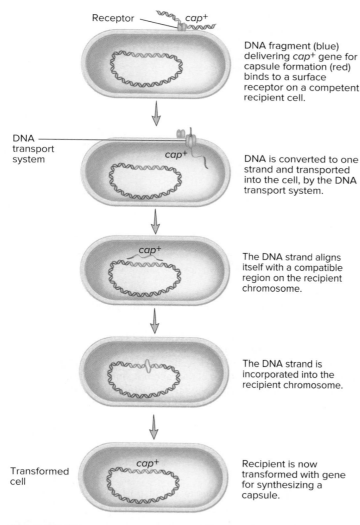

Figure 9.26 Steps in bacterial transformation as seen in *S. pneumoniae.* This shows how genes coding for capsule formation are brought into the cell and inserted into the chromosome. *Cap+* indicates genes for forming a capsule.

Receptor — *cap+*

DNA fragment (blue) delivering *cap+* gene for capsule formation (red) binds to a surface receptor on a competent recipient cell.

DNA transport system — *cap+*

DNA is converted to one strand and transported into the cell, by the DNA transport system.

cap+

The DNA strand aligns itself with a compatible region on the recipient chromosome.

The DNA strand is incorporated into the recipient chromosome.

Transformed cell — *cap+*

Recipient is now transformed with gene for synthesizing a capsule.

Process Figure 9.27 **Generalized transduction: Genetic transfer by means of a virus carrier.** **(1)** A phage infects cell A (the donor cell) by normal means. **(2)** During replication and assembly, a phage particle incorporates a segment of bacterial DNA by mistake. **(3)** Cell A then lyses and releases the mature phages, including the genetically altered one. **(4)** The altered phage adsorbs to and penetrates another host cell (cell B), injecting the DNA from cell A rather than viral nucleic acid. **(5)** Cell B receives this donated DNA, which recombines with its own DNA. Because the virus is defective (biologically inactive as a virus), it is unable to complete a lytic cycle. The transduced cell survives and can use this new genetic material.

Recombination results in two possible outcomes.

Process Figure 9.28 **Specialized transduction: Transfer of specific genetic material by means of a virus carrier.** **(1)** Specialized transduction begins with a cell that contains a prophage (red). **(2)** When the virus enters a lytic cycle, it excises itself from its host cell, carrying along some host DNA. **(3)** Replication and assembly results in production of a **chimeric** virus containing viral and bacterial DNA. **(4)** Release of the recombinant virus and infection of a new host result in transfer of bacterial DNA between cells. **(5)** Recombination can occur between the new host chromosome and the virus DNA, resulting in either bacterial DNA or a combination of viral and bacterial DNA being incorporated into the bacterial chromosome.

itself from one area of the genome and integrate itself somewhere else, akin to cutting and pasting a sentence in a word-processing document. Movement may be from one chromosomal site to another, from a chromosome to a plasmid, or from a plasmid to a chromosome **(figure 9.29).** Because transposons can occur in plasmids, they can also be transmitted from one cell to another in bacteria and a few eukaryotes. Some transposons replicate themselves before jumping to the next location, and others simply move without replicating first.

Flanking the coding region of the transposon DNA are sequences called inverted repeats, which mark the point at which the

Figure 9.29 **Transposons: Shifting segments of the genome.** **(1)** A transposon exists as a small piece of DNA integrated into the host cell chromosome (red). **(2)** The transposon may excise itself and move from one location to another in the genome, maintaining itself as a single copy per cell. **(3)** It may also replicate prior to moving, leading to an increase in the copy number and a greater effect on the genome of the host. **(4)** Finally, the transposon may jump to a plasmid, which can then be transferred to another bacterial cell.

transposon is removed or reinserted into the genome. The smallest transposons consist of only these two genetic sequences and are often referred to as *insertion elements.* A type of transposon called *retrotransposon* can transcribe DNA into RNA and then back into DNA for insertion in a new location. Another example is the *integron,* which can carry large blocks of genetic material that are especially prominent in transmitting drug resistance.

The overall effect of transposons—to scramble the genetic language—can be beneficial or adverse, depending upon such variables as where insertion occurs in a chromosome, what kinds of genes are relocated, and the type of cell involved. In bacteria, transposons are known to be involved in

- changes in traits such as colony morphology, pigmentation, and antigenic characteristics;
- replacement of damaged DNA; and
- the transfer of drug resistance in bacteria.

 Practice SECTION 9.5

26. Compare conjugation, transformation, and transduction on the basis of general method, donor, and recipient.
27. Explain the differences between general and specialized transduction, using drawings.
28. By means of a flowchart, show the possible jumps that a transposon can make. Show the involvement of viruses in its movement.

9.6 The Genetics of Animal Viruses

 Learn

27. Explain the major elements of viral genetics.
28. Compare aspects of the genetics of DNA and RNA viruses, using examples.

Viruses essentially consist of one or more pieces of DNA or RNA enclosed in a protective coating. They are genetic parasites that require access to their host cell's genetic and metabolic machinery to be replicated, transcribed, and translated, and they also have the potential for genetically changing the cells. Because they contain mainly those genes needed for the production of new viruses, the genomes of viruses tend to be very small and compact.

Viruses show extensive variety in genetic patterns. In many viruses, the nucleic acid is linear in form; in others, it is circular. The genome of most viruses exists in a single molecule, though in a few, it is segmented into several smaller molecules. Most viruses contain normal double-stranded (ds) DNA or single-stranded (ss) RNA, but other patterns exist. There are ssDNA viruses, dsRNA viruses, and retroviruses, which work backward by making dsDNA from ssRNA. In some instances, viral genes overlap one another, and in a few DNA viruses, both strands contain a translatable message.

With few exceptions, replication of the DNA molecule of DNA animal viruses occurs in the nucleus, where the cell's DNA replication machinery lies. The genome of most RNA viruses is replicated in the cytoplasm. In all viruses, viral mRNA is translated into viral proteins on host cell ribosomes using host tRNA.

Replication Strategies in Animal Viruses

Replication, Transcription, and Translation of dsDNA Viruses

Replication of dsDNA viruses is divided into phases (**process figure 9.30**). During the early phase, viral DNA enters the nucleus, where several genes are transcribed into a messenger RNA. Next, the mRNA transcript then moves into the cytoplasm to be translated into viral proteins (enzymes) needed to replicate the viral DNA. This replication usually occurs in the nucleus with the host cell's own DNA polymerase, though some viruses (herpes, for example) have their own. During the late phase, other viral genes are transcribed and translated into proteins required to form the capsid and other structures. The new viral genomes and capsids are assembled, and the mature viruses are released by budding or cell disintegration.

Double-stranded DNA viruses can interact directly with the DNA of their host cell. In some viruses, the viral DNA becomes silently *integrated* into the host's genome by insertion at a particular site on the host genome. Persistence of viral DNA may also lead to the transformation of the host cell into a cancer cell. Several DNA viruses, including hepatitis B (HBV), the herpesviruses, and papillomaviruses (warts), are known to be initiators of cancers and are thus termed **oncogenic.** The mechanisms of oncogenic transformation involve viral genes that regulate cellular genomes and control the cell division cycle.

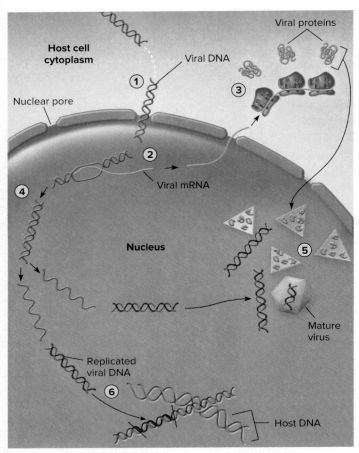

Process Figure 9.30 **General stages in the multiplication of double-stranded DNA viruses.** The virus penetrates the host cell and releases DNA, which (1) enters the nucleus and (2) is transcribed by host cell enzymes into mRNA. (3) Viral mRNA leaves the nucleus and is translated into structural proteins; these proteins are transported into the nucleus. (4) Viral DNA is replicated repeatedly in the nucleus. (5) Viral DNA and proteins are assembled into a mature virus in the nucleus. (6) Because it is double-stranded, some viral DNA can insert itself into host DNA (latency). Some exceptions to this pattern occur in the poxviruses.

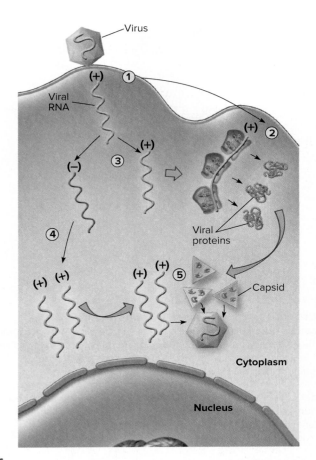

Process Figure 9.31 Replication of positive-strand, single-stranded RNA viruses. In general, these viruses do not enter the nucleus. (1) Penetration of viral RNA. (2) Because it is positive in message and single-stranded, the RNA can be directly translated on host cell ribosomes into various necessary viral proteins. (3) A negative genome is synthesized against the positive template to produce large numbers of positive genomes for final assembly. (4) The negative template is then used to synthesize a series of positive replicates. (5) RNA strands and proteins assemble into mature viruses released when the cell lyses.

Replication, Transcription, and Translation of RNA Viruses

RNA viruses exhibit several differences from DNA viruses. Their genomes are smaller, they enter the host cell already in an RNA form, and the virus cycle occurs entirely in the cytoplasm for most viruses. RNA viruses can have one of the following genetic messages:

1. a positive-strand (+) genome that comes ready to be translated into proteins,
2. a negative-strand (−) genome that must be converted to a positive-strand before translation, and
3. a positive-strand (+) genome that can be converted to DNA or a dsRNA genome.

Positive-Strand Single-Stranded RNA Viruses

The ssRNA of positive-strand viruses such as polio come ready to be translated, so it is immediately translated into a large protein and cleaved into individual functional units. One of these is an RNA polymerase that initiates the replication of the viral strand. Replication of a positive-message strand happens in two steps (process figure 9.31). First, a negative strand is synthesized using the positive strand as a template by the usual base-pairing mechanism. The resultant negative strand becomes a master template that formats the formation of new positive daughter strands. Further translation of the viral genome produces large numbers of structural proteins for final assembly and maturation of the virus.

RNA Viruses with Reverse Transcriptase: Retroviruses

A most unusual class of viruses can reverse the order of the flow of genetic information. Thus far in our discussion, all genetic entities have shown the patterns DNA → DNA, DNA → RNA, or RNA → RNA. Retroviruses, including HIV, the cause of AIDS, and HTLV I, a cause of one type of human leukemia, synthesize DNA using

their RNA genome as a template. They accomplish this by means of a **reverse transcriptase** that comes packaged with each virus particle. This enzyme synthesizes a single-stranded DNA against the viral RNA template and then directs the formation of a complementary strand of this ssDNA, resulting in a double strand of viral DNA. The dsDNA strand enters the nucleus, where it can be transcribed by the usual mechanisms into new viral ssRNA and used to assemble new viral particles. When the DNA of some retroviruses becomes inserted into the host's DNA as a provirus, cells may be transformed and produce tumors. Insertion allows HIV to remain latent in an infected cell for several years.

 Practice SECTION 9.6

29. Explain why some viruses must enter the nucleus to replicate whereas others do not.
30. Explain the difference between positive-strand and negative-strand viral genomes.
31. Outline the basic steps in the replication cycles of a dsDNA virus and an RNA virus.

 CASE STUDY **Part 2**

Aside from the judicious use of antibiotics, there is little that can be done to prevent the occasional selection of vancomycin-resistant organisms, so efforts are focused on preventing these organisms from infecting others and spreading rapidly through the population. Persons considered to be at increased risk for VRSA acquisition in this case were health care providers at the wound and dialysis clinics, along with dialysis patients sharing the same dialysis shift as the VRSA patient. Investigators obtained groin and nasal swabs from 3 of 6 wound clinic health care workers, all 13 dialysis clinic workers, and the 3 health care providers who evaluated the wound at an outpatient clinic. Twelve of 13 patients who shared a dialysis shift with the VRSA patient consented to nasal swabs. No MRSA, VRSA, or VRE were cultured from the health care workers or dialysis patients, indicating that close contacts did not share precursor organisms or VRSA with the patient. To prevent potential spread of VRSA, Delaware public health authorities notified all facilities where the patient routinely sought health care, allowing health care workers in these facilities to immediately institute contact precautions in the event the patient presented for care. These precautions include isolating the patient, using personal protective equipment like gloves and gown, limiting movement of the patient within the health care facility, using disposable equipment when possible, and ensuring that the room of an infected patient is subject to a more frequent cleaning schedule.

While a bacterium carrying a gene for drug resistance may be thought of as having an advantage over other cells, this is not entirely true. The advantage—the ability to withstand a certain antibiotic—only exists when the antibiotic is present in the environment. If the antibiotic is absent, there is no advantage, while carrying excess DNA and transcribing and translating genes carries a biological cost (this is the same reason you don't carry an umbrella when there is no rain in the forecast). It is thought that expression of the genes in the *vanA* operon may hinder the growth of the bacteria by up to 38%, indicating a substantial biological burden, but the operon has evolved an ingenious way of avoiding this cost. *VanA* is inducible (like the lactose operon discussed in this chapter) and neither transcribes nor translates its genes in the absence of vancomycin, limiting the cost of carrying the genes. When vancomycin suddenly appears in the environment, the resistance mechanism is activated, creating an immediate advantage. The minimal biological burden imposed on *Staphylococcus aureus* by the *vanA* operon in the absence of vancomycin enhances the spread of clinical isolates like the one seen in this case, and likely means VRSA will be with us for some time.

■ What strategies could be employed to prevent the spread of VRSA if a health care worker is found to be infected with the bacterium?

■ Why are patients with chronic conditions (diabetes, kidney failure, cancer) at greater risk of developing infections with drug-resistant organisms like VRSA?

Chapter Summary with Key Terms

9.1 Introduction to Genetics and Genes: Unlocking the Secrets of Heredity
A. Genetics is the study of heredity and can be studied at the level of the organism, genome, chromosome, gene, and DNA. Genes provide the information needed to construct proteins, which have structural or catalytic functions in the cell.

B. DNA is a long molecule in the form of a double helix. Each strand of the helix consists of a string of nucleotides.
1. A **nucleotide** consists of a phosphate, **deoxyribose sugar,** and **nitrogen base.** The bases form **hydrogen bonds** with their counterparts on the other strand.
2. **Adenine** base-pairs with **thymine** while **guanine** base-pairs with **cytosine.**

3. The order of the nucleotides specifies which amino acids will be used to construct proteins during the process of translation.

C. **Replication** of DNA–making copies of the genetic program.
 1. Requires unwinding the double helix and exposing the nucleotides to serve as templates for synthesis of 2 identical molecules by **DNA polymerase.**
 2. Is **semiconservative** and proceeds in the 5′ to 3′ direction of the newly synthesized DNA.

9.2 Applications of the DNA Code: Transcription and Translation

A. DNA is used to produce RNA **(transcription)** and RNA is then used to produce protein **(translation).**

B. **RNA:** Unlike DNA, RNA is single-stranded, contains **uracil** instead of thymine and **ribose** instead of deoxyribose.
 1. Major forms of RNA found in the cell include **mRNA, tRNA,** and **rRNA.**
 2. The genetic information contained in DNA is copied to produce an RNA molecule. **Codons** in the mRNA pair with **anticodons** on the tRNA to specify which amino acids to assemble on the **ribosome** during translation.

C. *Transcription and Translation:*
 1. Transcription occurs when **RNA polymerase** copies the template strand of a segment of DNA. RNA is always made in the 5′ to 3′ direction.
 2. Translation occurs when the mRNA is used to direct the synthesis of proteins on the ribosome.
 3. Codons in the mRNA pair with anticodons on the tRNA to assemble a string of amino acids. This occurs until a stop codon is reached.

D. *Eukaryotic Gene Expression:* Eukaryotic genes are composed of **exons** (expressed sequences) and **introns** (intragenic regions). The introns must be removed and the exons spliced together to create the final mRNA.

9.3 Genetic Regulation of Protein Synthesis and Metabolism

Protein synthesis is regulated through gene induction or repression, as controlled by an **operon.** Operons consist of several structural genes controlled by a common regulatory element.

A. **Inducible operons** such as the lactose operon are normally off but can be turned on by a lactose inducer.

B. **Repressible operons** are usually on but can be turned off when their end product is no longer needed.

C. Newly described types of RNA can serve in gene regulation.
 1. Micro and small interfering RNAs can block the action of other RNAs and shut down gene expression in eukaryotes.
 2. **Riboswitches** can also control RNA functions related to transcription and translation in bacteria.

9.4 Mutations: Changes in the Genetic Code

A. Changes in the genetic code occur primarily through **mutation** and recombination.

B. Inheritable changes in the genome of a microorganism are known as mutations. They usually entail an alteration in the nucleotide composition of the genetic material. Mutations may be **spontaneous** or **induced.**

C. Mutations may be detected by observing the growth of bacteria on selective and differential media.

D. Point mutations entail a change in one or a few bases and are categorized as **missense, nonsense, silent** mutations, and **back-mutations,** based on the effect of the change in nucleotide(s).

E. **Frame-shift mutations** that disrupt the reading frame of the ribosome are caused by **deletions** and **insertions** of nucleotides.

F. The **Ames test** measures the mutagenicity of chemicals by their ability to induce mutations in bacteria.

9.5 DNA Recombination Events

A. **Recombination** involves the acquisition of new genetic material from an outside source.

B. Intermicrobial transfer and genetic recombination permit gene sharing between bacteria. Major types of recombination include **conjugation, transformation,** and **transduction.**

C. **Transposons** are DNA sequences that regularly move to different places within the genome of a cell, generating mutations and variations in chromosome structure.

9.6 The Genetics of Animal Viruses

A. Viruses contain various forms of DNA and RNA that are transcribed and translated by the genetic machinery of their host cells to form functioning viral particles.
 1. Genomes of viruses are found in double-stranded (ds) DNA and single-stranded (ss) RNA forms. A few contain unusual ssDNA and dsRNA not found in cells.
 2. DNA viruses tend to replicate in the nucleus while RNA viruses replicate in the cytoplasm. **Retroviruses** synthesize dsDNA using ssRNA as a template.

 Assess Your Knowledge

Level I. These questions require a working knowledge of the concepts in the chapter and the ability to recall and understand the information you have studied.

Developing a Concept Inventory

Select the correct answer from the answers provided. For questions with blanks, choose the combination of answers that most accurately completes the statement.

1. What is the smallest unit of heredity (genotype)?
 a. chromosome c. codon
 b. gene d. intron

2. A nucleotide contains which of the following?
 a. 5-carbon sugar d. b and c only
 b. nitrogen base e. all of these
 c. phosphate

3. The nitrogen bases in DNA are bonded to the
 a. phosphate c. ribose
 b. deoxyribose d. hydrogen

4. DNA replication is considered semiconservative because the
 _____ strand will remain as half of the _____ molecule.
 a. antisense, DNA
 b. template, final DNA
 c. sense, mRNA
 d. codon, anticodon

5. In DNA, adenine is the complementary base for _____ , and
 cytosine is the complement for _____.
 a. guanine, thymine c. thymine, guanine
 b. uracil, guanine d. thymine, uracil

6. The base pairs are held together primarily by
 a. covalent bonds c. hydrogen bonds
 b. ionic bonds d. gyrases

7. Why must the lagging strand of DNA be replicated in short pieces?
 a. because of limited space
 b. otherwise, the helix will become distorted
 c. the DNA polymerase can synthesize in only one direction
 d. to make proofreading of code easier

8. Messenger RNA is formed by _____ of a gene on the DNA
 template strand.
 a. transcription c. translation
 b. replication d. transformation

9. Transfer RNA is the molecule that
 a. contributes to the structure of ribosomes
 b. adapts the genetic code to protein structure
 c. transfers the DNA code to mRNA
 d. provides the master code for amino acids

10. As a general rule, the first codon on a the DNA template strand that
 signals the start for a protein is
 a. TAC c. ATG
 b. AUG d. UAC

11. What components are involved in transcription?
 a. sigma factor d. only b and c
 b. RNA polymerase e. all of these
 c. promotor

12. The *lac* operon is usually in the _____ position and is activated
 by a/an _____ molecule.
 a. on, repressor c. on, inducer
 b. off, inducer d. off, repressor

13. For mutations to have an effect on populations of microbes, they
 must be
 a. inheritable d. a and b
 b. permanent e. all of these
 c. beneficial

14. Which of the following characteristics is *not* true of a plasmid?
 a. It is a circular piece of DNA.
 b. It is required for normal cell function.
 c. It is found in bacteria.
 d. It can be transferred from cell to cell.

15. Which genetic material could be transmitted naturally by all three
 methods of intermicrobial transfer?
 a. an *E. coli* chromosome d. a and c
 b. F factor e. all of these
 c. drug resistance genes

16. Which of these features is found in eukaryotes but not bacteria?
 a. polygene mRNAs c. stop codon
 b. introns d. AUG codon

17. Which of the following is present in prokaryotes but not
 eukaryotes?
 a. exons
 b. polyribosomes
 c. spliceosomes
 d. simultaneous transcription and translation

18. **Multiple Matching.** Fill in the blanks with all the letters of the
 words below that apply.
 _____ site of protein synthesis
 _____ carries the codon
 _____ carries the anticodon
 _____ a process synonymous with mRNA synthesis
 _____ bacteriophages participate in this transfer
 _____ duplication of the DNA molecule
 _____ process in which transcribed DNA code is deciphered
 into a polypeptide
 _____ involves plasmids
 a. replication b. tRNA
 c. conjugation d. ribosome
 e. transduction f. mRNA
 g. transcription h. transformation
 i. translation j. none of these

Case Study Analysis

1. The enzymes responsible for the movement of the *vanA* transposon in this case are
 a. transposase and polymerase
 b. replicase and resolvase
 c. transposase and resolvase
 d. transposase and replicase

2. With regard to the *vanA* operon, vancomycin acts as a(n)
 a. promoter
 b. repressor
 c. inducer
 d. operator

3. Given the fact that vancomycin does not **cause** bacterial mutations, why do we worry that over-prescription of vancomycin will lead to more cases of vancomycin resistance?

On the Test

These questions will help to prepare you to successfully answer similar questions you'll see on the TEAS (Test of Essential Academic Skills) and NCLEX (National Council Licensure Examination).

1. Which base will pair with uracil in RNA?
 a. adenine
 b. guanine
 c. thymine
 d. cytosine

2. What cell structure is responsible for protein synthesis?
 a. Golgi body
 b. lysosome
 c. DNA
 d. ribosome

Writing Challenge

For each question, compose a one- or two-paragraph answer that includes the factual information needed to completely address the question. Practice questions can also be used for writing-challenge exercises.

1. Explain what is meant by the following diagram:

2. On paper, replicate the following segment of DNA:

 5′ A T C G G C T A C G T T C A C 3′
 3′ T A G C C G A T G C A A G T G 5′

 a. Show the direction of replication of the new strands and explain what causes lagging and leading strands to show different patterns of replication.
 b. Explain how this is semiconservative replication. Are the new strands identical to the original segment of DNA?

3. The following sequence represents triplets on DNA:

 TAC CAG ATA CAC TCC CCT GCG ACT

 a. Give the mRNA codons and tRNA anticodons that correspond with this sequence, and then give the sequence of amino acids in the polypeptide.
 b. Provide a different mRNA strand that can be used to synthesize this same protein.

4. Describe the actions of all of the enzymes involved in replication of a DNA molecule.

5. Compare and contrast the actions of DNA polymerase and RNA polymerase.

6. Examine the following series of words and identify what kind of a mutation occurred in each, starting with the first word in non-mutated form: BEAST FEAST BREAST BEST BEATS

Concept Mapping

On Connect you can find an Introduction to Concept Mapping that provides guidance for working with concept maps, along with concept-mapping activities for this chapter.

Application, Analysis, Evaluation, and Synthesis

Level II. These problems go beyond just restating facts and require higher levels of understanding and an ability to interpret, problem solve, transfer knowledge to new situations, create models, and predict outcomes.

Critical Thinking

Critical thinking is the ability to reason and solve problems using facts and concepts. These questions can be approached from a number of angles and, in most cases, they do not have a single correct answer.

1. Knowing that retroviruses operate on the principle of reversing the direction of transcription from RNA to DNA, propose a drug that might possibly interfere with their replication.

2. Using the piece of DNA in writing-challenge question 3, show a deletion, an insertion, a substitution, and nonsense mutations. Which ones are frameshift mutations? Are any of your mutations nonsense? Are any missense? (Use the universal code to determine this.)

3. Why will a mistake in the RNA code alone not become a mutation?

4. The enzymes required to carry out transcription and translation are produced through these same processes. Speculate which may have come first in evolution—proteins or nucleic acids—and explain your choice.

5. Why can one not reliably predict the sequence of nucleotides on mRNA or DNA by observing the amino acid sequence of proteins?

6. Activation, transcription, and translation of the *lac* operon will release which exact nutrients?

7. Explain the mechanisms by which RNA can control transcription, translation, and gene expression.

8. Explain how epigenetics is related to the expression: phenotype = genotype + environment.

9. Use the concepts of chapters, letters, a whole library, words, and books to make an analogy that fits the levels of genetic structure and function.

Visual Assessment

1. From process figure 9.17, step 3. Label each part of the illustration.

2. Examine process figure 8.11, and explain which type of operon is functioning here. How would another operon differ from this?

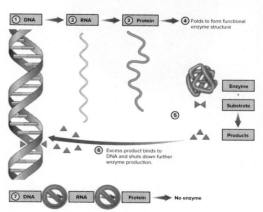

Genetic Engineering:
A Revolution in Molecular Biology

In This Chapter...

(Zika virus): AuntSpray/Shutterstock; (Oocyte injection): Source Zephyr/Science Source; (Embryonic mouse): Source: National Institute of Mental Health

CASE STUDY **Part 1**

When Is a Mosquito Not a Mosquito? When It's a Pesticide.

A t 1 minute after birth, the health of a newborn is summarized using an **APGAR** score, which provides a measurement of the baby's **A**ppearance, **P**ulse rate, **G**rimace (response to unpleasant stimuli), **A**ctivity, and **R**espiration. For Maria Rios, however, the number she was most interested in was the size of her daughter Aryanna's head.

Aryanna was born at Providence St. Peter Hospital in Olympia, Washington, where a few days earlier her 20-year-old mother had been told by doctors that she was infected with **Zika virus**. Aryanna was born with **microcephaly**, a birth defect related to Zika virus infection, and blood tests confirmed that Aryanna, too, was infected with the virus. Additional exams revealed **calcium deposits** in the baby's brain, and scarring in the center of her retina, further symptoms of disease. While most people infected with Zika show few, if any, symptoms, women infected while pregnant may give birth to children with severe neurological birth defects.

Zika is transmitted through the bite of an infected *Aedes aegypti* mosquito, and Maria was likely infected while living with her parents in Colima, Mexico, the previous summer. The explosion of Zika cases over the past few years—over half a million infections worldwide and 3,720 confirmed cases of **neurological symptoms** in newborns—has elevated Zika virus, and the mosquitoes that carry it, from obscurity to a worldwide health emergency. Brazilians are quite familiar with the *Aedes aegypti* mosquito that, aside from Zika, has been responsible for massive outbreaks of **dengue fever** and **chikungunya disease** for more than a century.

Having seen firsthand the shortcomings of pesticides like **DDT** (dichlorodiphenyltrichloroethane), which pose serious risks to humans and the environment, government officials in Brazil looked for new ways to **eradicate** the mosquito. It turns out that the best way to get rid of disease-spreading mosquitoes is to release an enormous horde of killer mosquitoes.

The city of Piraciciba, Brazil, turned to a biotechnology firm called Oxitec to supply it with killer mosquitoes. The insects, bred in a factory about an hour outside the city, had been engineered to carry what is known as a **limiting gene**. When the adult mosquitoes were released—millions at a time, all male—they interbred with the wild mosquitoes and passed on the limiting gene. Soon thereafter, the offspring died, eventually reducing the population of wild mosquitoes in the area by 82%.

- *What is a genetically modified organism?*
- *How does the function of the Oxitec mosquitoes differ from most other genetically modified animals?*

To continue the Case Study, go to Case Study Part 2 at the end of the chapter.

(Mosquito): Akil Rolle-Rowan/Shutterstock

10.1 Basic Elements and Applications of Genetic Engineering

Learn

1. Define *genetic engineering,* and describe some of its subcategories and aims.

2. Explain the properties of DNA that lend to its manipulation in the laboratory.

3. Summarize the major methods of analyzing DNA and their results.

4. Describe the technology behind identifying, synthesizing, sequencing, and amplifying DNA.

Just as an understanding of the structure and function of the atom led to the advent of laptops, cell phones, and Instagram, an understanding of the workings of DNA is leading to an era where DNA fingerprints are commonplace, human proteins are created in animals, and genetic diseases may one day be cured. Such are the promises of genetic engineering.

The primary goals of this science are to isolate, identify, and manipulate DNA in various ways. A major part of its work falls into the category of **genetic engineering** or **bioengineering,** defined as the direct, deliberate modification of an organism's genome. It also belongs to the larger scheme of **synthetic biology** and **biotechnology,** whose major aims are the design of biological systems that can synthesize new forms of molecules, cells, organs, and even organisms.

Source: Office of Biological and Environmental Research of the U.S. Department of Energy Office of Science. http://genomicscience.energy.gov

Information on genetic engineering and its biotechnological applications is growing at such an expanding rate that some new discovery or product is disclosed almost daily. To keep this subject somewhat manageable, we present essential concepts and applications, organized under the following six topics:

- Basic techniques in manipulating and analyzing DNA
- Recombinant DNA technology
- Biochemical products of recombinant DNA technology
- Genetically modified organisms
- Genetic treatments
- Genome analysis

Tools and Techniques of DNA Technology

In chapter 9, we examined the ways in which microorganisms duplicate, change, and express their genomes. All of the intrinsic properties of DNA that we touched on hold true whether the DNA is in a bacterium or a test tube. For example, the enzyme helicase is able to unwind the two strands of the double helix just as easily inside or outside a bacterial cell. But in the laboratory we can take advantage of our knowledge of DNA chemistry to make helicase unnecessary. It turns out that when DNA is heated to just below

(a) **DNA heating and cooling.** DNA responds to heat by denaturing—losing its hydrogen bonding and thereby separating into its two strands. When cooled, the two strands rejoin at complementary regions. The two strands need not be from the same organisms as long as they have matching sites.

Endonuclease	*Eco*RI	*Hind*III	*Hae*III
Cutting pattern	G A A T T C C T T A A G	A A G C T T T T C G A A	G G C C C C G G

(b) **Examples of endonucleases, palindromes, and cutting patterns.** The first two are staggered cuts, and the third is a blunt cut.

Figure 10.1 **Some properties of DNA that are an integral part of DNA manipulation.** The method in **(a)** can be used to separate the DNA strands lengthwise and make them single-stranded. The method in **(b)** uses enzymes called endonucleases to make cuts across both DNA strands at specific sites called palindromes.

boiling (90°C to 95°C), the two strands separate, revealing the information contained in their bases. With the nucleotides exposed, DNA can be easily identified, replicated, or transcribed. If heat-denatured DNA is then slowly cooled, complementary nucleotides will hydrogen-bond with one another, and the strands will renature or regain their familiar double-stranded form **(figure 10.1a)**. As we shall see, this process is a necessary feature of the polymerase chain reaction and nucleic acid probes described later in this section.

Enzymes for Dicing, Splicing, and Reversing Nucleic Acids

DNA can also be clipped crosswise at selected positions by means of **restriction endonucleases** (or restriction enzymes) that are a natural product of bacterial cells. They recognize foreign DNA and are capable of breaking the phosphodiester bonds between adjacent nucleotides on both strands of DNA, leading to a break in the DNA strand. In the bacterial cell, these enzymes protect against the incompatible DNA from bacteriophages. In the biotechnologist's lab, the enzymes can be used to cleave DNA at desired sites and are a must for the techniques of recombinant DNA technology.

3-D view of restriction endonuclease cutting DNA (orange strands).
Courtesy Konrad F- Koehler, Ph.D

Restriction endonuclease makes staggered cut at palindrome.

(1)

Site of cut

C T A G
G A T C

T A G
C

C
G A T

★ Sticky ends

(2)

DNA Organism 1

CGA
T

T
AGC

T
AGC

CGA
T

TCGA
AGCT

TCGA
AGCT

DNA Organism 2

Action of restriction endonucleases. (1) A restriction endonuclease recognizes and cleaves DNA at the site of a specific palindromic sequence. Cleavage usually produces staggered tails called sticky ends that accept complementary tails for gene splicing. This palindrome is cut by *Aci* I. (2) The sticky ends can be used to join DNA from different organisms by cutting it with the same restriction enzyme, ensuring that both fragments have two complementary ends. This palindrome is cut by *Taq* I.

Figure 10.2 Examples of cutting patterns by restriction endonucleases and how they are used in gene splicing.

So far, about 3,000 restriction endonucleases have been discovered in bacteria. Each restriction endonuclease has a sequence of 4 to 10 base pairs referred to as its **recognition site or sequence**, and every time the enzyme encounters that sequence, it will cut both strands of DNA. Interestingly, recognition sites tend to be **palindromic**[1] **(figure 10.1b)**, meaning that the sequence of bases on one strand (in the 5' to 3' direction) is the same as the sequence of bases on the complementary strand (again, in the 5' to 3' direction).

Endonucleases are named by combining the first letter of the bacterial genus, the first two letters of the species, and the endonuclease number. Thus, *Eco*RI is the first endonuclease found in *Escherichia coli*'s R strain, and *Hin*dIII is the third endonuclease discovered in *Haemophilus influenzae* Type d (figure 10.1b).

Endonucleases are used in the laboratory to cut DNA into smaller pieces for further study as well as to remove and insert it during recombinant DNA techniques, described in section 10.2. Usually the enzymes make staggered symmetrical cuts that leave short, single-stranded tails called "sticky ends." Such adhesive tails will base-pair with complementary tails on other DNA fragments or plasmids. This effect makes it possible to splice genes into specific sites **(figure 10.2).** A few endonucleases such as

1. This term originated from words or phrases with letters that read the same backward or forward, as in "Radar," "Madam, I'm Adam," and "A man, a plan, a canal, Panama."

*Hae*III make straight, blunt cuts on DNA and do not form sticky ends.

The separated segments of DNA produced by restriction endonucleases are termed **restriction fragments.** Because DNA sequences vary, even among members of the same species, differences in the cutting pattern of specific restriction endonucleases give rise to restriction fragments of differing lengths, known as restriction fragment length polymorphisms (RFLPs). RFLPs allow the direct comparison of the DNA cutting patterns of two different organisms with the same endonuclease, which is one step in preparing genes from different organisms to be spliced together (see process figure 10.11).

Another enzyme, called a **ligase,** is necessary to seal the sticky ends together by rejoining the phosphate-sugar bonds cut by endonucleases. Its main application is in final splicing of genes into plasmids and chromosomes.

An enzyme called **reverse transcriptase** is best known for its role in the replication of HIV and other retroviruses. It also provides geneticists with a valuable tool for converting RNA into DNA. Copies called **complementary DNA,** or **cDNA,** can be made from RNA. The technique provides a valuable means of synthesizing eukaryotic genes from processed mRNA transcripts **(figure 10.3).** The bacteria often used to transcribe and translate eukaryotic genes in genetic engineering lack the cellular machinery to splice out introns (intragenic sequences) found in

Quick Search
Find the video "Cloning in a Plasmid Vector" on the Internet to see the process.

(a) Exon Intron Exon Intron Exon

Eukaryotic DNA

Transcription of eukaryotic DNA generates precursor mRNA.

Precursor mRNA with exons and introns

Splicing removes the introns from the precursor mRNA, generating the final mRNA for translation.

Finished mRNA transcript

(b)

mRNA extracted from cells

mRNA

Reverse transcriptase synthesizes DNA from mRNA.

Single strand of cDNA

DNA polymerase completes the cDNA, free from introns.

Double-stranded cDNA

Figure 10.3 **Synthesizing cDNA from eukaryotic mRNA.** Bacterial cloning hosts cannot process intact eukaryotic genes. To provide a gene that will be transcribable and translatable by a bacterium, **(a)** first modified mRNA, lacking introns, is isolated from the source eukaryotic cell. **(b)** This strand is converted in a test tube to a single-stranded DNA by reverse transcriptase and double-stranded DNA by a polymerase. This copy of DNA (cDNA) can be transcribed and translated by bacteria.

Figure 10.4 Electrophoresis setup. Electrophoresis uses an electrical current to separate DNA molecules of different sizes. The samples are loaded into small wells in an agarose gel submerged in a buffer solution. The gel contains tiny pores that allow the passage of molecules according to their size. DNA, which is negatively charged, is attracted to the positively charged end of the gel, with smaller fragments moving more rapidly. The result is that larger DNA fragments remain close to the wells at the positively charged end of the gel (red wire) while smaller fragments appear nearer the negatively charged end (black wire). Barry Chess

unprocessed eukaryotic mRNA. So the advantage with synthesized cDNA genes is that they already have the introns removed and consist only of exons and can be readily transcribed and translated by bacteria. cDNA also provides a powerful tool for converting RNA for sequencing, analyzing ribosomes, and identifying RNA viruses.

Analysis of DNA

One way to produce a readable pattern of DNA fragments is through **electrophoresis (figure 10.4).** In this technique, samples are placed in compartments (wells) in an agar gel or similar soft medium and subjected to an electrical current. The phosphate groups in DNA give the entire molecule an overall negative charge, which causes the DNA to move toward the positive pole in the gel. The rate of movement is based primarily on the size of the fragments. The larger fragments are pulled into the gel more slowly and remain nearer the wells, whereas the smaller fragments migrate faster and are positioned farther from the wells. The gel can then be stained to reveal the position of the bands of DNA within the gel. **(figure 10.5).** Electrophoresis patterns can be quite distinctive and are very useful in displaying DNA fragments and comparing the degree of genetic similarities among samples in a Southern blot or DNA profile (see Visual Assessment #1).

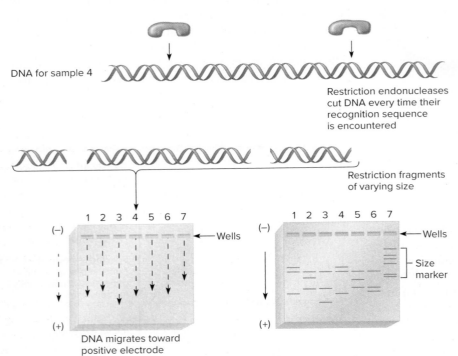

DNA for sample 4

Restriction endonucleases cut DNA every time their recognition sequence is encountered

Restriction fragments of varying size

(−) 1 2 3 4 5 6 7 Wells

(−) 1 2 3 4 5 6 7 Wells
Size marker

(+)

(+)

DNA migrates toward positive electrode of the gel

(a)

(b)

1 2 3 4 5 6 DNA marker

Sample wells

23130
9416
6557
4361 Number of base pairs per band

2322
2027

Figure 10.5 Separating DNA restriction fragments with electrophoresis. (a) A restriction endonuclease is used to cut a DNA sample (using sample 4 in this example). The restriction endonuclease cuts the DNA every time it encounters a recognition site. In this case, the DNA is cut twice, producing three fragments. The DNA fragments are then loaded into a well at one end of the gel and electrophoresed; small DNA samples move more quickly through the gel and end up closer to the positive electrode. **(b)** A stained gel reveals the position of the DNA fragments. The size of each fragment (each band) can be determined by comparing the distance traveled to the distance traveled by a set of DNA fragments of known size called a marker (lane 7), measured in number of base pairs. Different DNA sequences will produce different sets of DNA fragments. Identical fragments in lanes 1 and 4 are evidence that these samples came from the same individual. Barry Chess

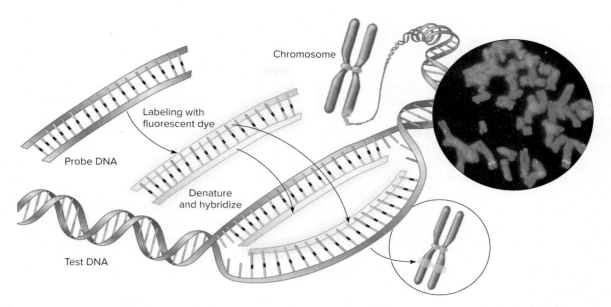

Figure 10.6 **Fluorescent in situ hybridization (FISH) technique.** This is a microscopic technique using fluorescently labeled probes to react with intact cells and chromosomes. The probe is mixed with test cells or chromosomes to hybridize any matching DNA sequences and observed with a UV microscope for fluorescence indicative of a particular location and type of gene. The inset displays chromosomes that have DNA from a papillomavirus integrated into chromosomes (yellow dots).

Jaana Tammur, Hiljar Sibul, Ene Ustav, Mart Ustav, Andres Metspalu. A bovine papillomavirus-1 based vector restores the function of the low—density lipoprotein receptor In the receptor-deficient CHO-IdIA7 cell line. *BMC Molecular Biology* 2002, 3:5.

Nucleic Acid Hybridization and Probes

Two different nucleic acids can **hybridize** by uniting at their complementary sites. All different combinations are possible: Single-stranded DNA can unite with other single-stranded DNA or RNA, and RNA can hybridize with other RNA. This knowledge has led to the development of short, single strands of 6 to 25 nucleotides called *oligonucleotides* to be used as **gene probes.** These probes consist of a segment of DNA or RNA of known sequence that can base-pair with a stretch of DNA that has a complementary sequence, if one exists in a test sample. Hybridization probes have practical value because they can detect specific nucleotide sequences in unknown samples. So that areas of hybridization can be visualized, the probes carry reporter molecules, such as fluorescent dyes, which can be visualized with ultraviolet radiation (see figure 10.6), or radioactive labels, which are revealed by placing photographic film in contact with the test reaction.

When probes hybridize with an unknown sample of DNA or RNA, they confirm the presence of that RNA or DNA sequence in a sample. In a method called the **Southern blot,**[2] DNA fragments are first separated by electrophoresis and then denatured and transferred to a special filter. A DNA probe is then incubated with the sample, and wherever this probe encounters the segment for which it is complementary, it will attach and form a hybrid, showing up as one or more bands. This method is a sensitive and specific way to find specific gene sequences. Much of the information obtained through Southern blotting can be achieved in more detail from another hybridization procedure called a microarray, discussed in section 10.4.

Southern blots and similar hybridization techniques can be used to identify specific nucleotide sequences found only in one particular organism, facilitating identification. Commercially available diagnostic kits are now on the market for identifying intestinal pathogens such as *E. coli, Salmonella, Campylobacter, Shigella, Clostridium difficile,* rotaviruses, and adenoviruses. Other bacterial probes exist for *Mycobacterium, Neisseria, Staphylococcus, Mycoplasma, Bordetella,* and *Chlamydia;* probes are available for herpes simplex and zoster, papilloma, hepatitis A and B, and HIV viruses. DNA probes have also been developed for human genetic markers and some types of cancer.

With another method, called *fluorescent in situ hybridization* (FISH), probes are applied to intact cells *in situ,* meaning that the DNA is left intact in the cell and probed in place rather than being extracted. The preparation is then observed microscopically for signs of genetic marker sequences on genes that have hybridized with the probe. FISH is a very effective way to locate genes on chromosomes **(figure 10.6).** *In situ* techniques can also be used to identify unknown bacteria living in natural habitats without having to culture them, and they can be used to detect RNA in cells and tissues.

DNA Sizing, Sequencing, and Synthesizing

The relative sizes of nucleic acids are usually denoted by the number of base pairs (bp) or nucleotides they contain. For example, the palindromic sequences recognized by endonucleases are usually 4 to 10 bp in length; an average gene in *E. coli* is approximately 1,300 bp, or 1.3 kilobases (kb); and its entire genome is approximately 4,700,000 bp, 4,700 kb, or 4.7 megabases (mb). The DNA of the human mitochondrion contains 16 kb, and the Epstein-Barr virus (a cause of infectious mononucleosis) has 172 kb. Humans have approximately 6.4 billion base pairs (bbp)

2. Named for its developer, E. M. Southern. The "northern" blot is a similar method used to analyze RNA, whereas the "western" blot detects proteins. There is a reason scientists became scientists and not comedians.

arrayed along 46 chromosomes. The Human Genome Project, finished in 2001, produced a map containing every base in the entire human genome.

DNA Sequencing: Determining the Exact Genetic Code

One of the most powerful kinds of genetic knowledge attainable for organisms is to decipher the order and types of base pairs in their genes and genome. This process, called **DNA sequencing,** can be used on all types of DNA, including genomic, cDNA, chromosomal, plasmid, and mitochondrial DNA. Many sequencing techniques are based on Frederick Sanger's original idea, using the synthesis and analysis of a complementary strand of DNA **(figure 10.7).** Even though mostly automated techniques are used today, we will illustrate the basic principles behind this process using the Sanger type of sequencing as a model.

Because most DNA being sequenced is usually very long, it is made more manageable by cutting it into a number of shorter fragments, which are then separated. The test strands, typically several hundred nucleotides long, are denatured to expose single strands that will serve as templates to synthesize complementary strands. The concepts behind the sequencing procedure involve the same enzymes and raw materials as would be present for regular DNA synthesis as performed in a cell. A DNA primer is bound to the template, then a DNA polymerase adds the complementary nucleotides using the template strand as a guide.

Besides the DNA molecule to be sequenced, DNA polymerase III, and short DNA primers (recall from chapter 9 that DNA polymerase III requires a primer before it can begin DNA synthesis), the reaction tube also contains all of the normal nucleotides (A, T, C, G) and a small amount of dideoxynucleotides (ddNT) that have two special features: (1) They are color-labeled with four different fluorescent dyes that can report their identity, and (2) they are missing the hydroxyl group (OH⁻) bound to the 3′ carbon of deoxyribose that is required for the chemical bonding of a nucleotide to the growing DNA strand. The addition of a ddNT at any location terminates the further elongation of the strand. As the synthesis proceeds, most strands will elongate

(1) Original DNA to be sequenced.

(2) DNA is denatured to produce single template strand.

(3) Strand is labeled with specific primer molecule.

(4) A reaction tube contains DNA polymerase, primed single strands, all four regular nucleotides, and a small amount of the four fluorescently labeled dideoxy (dd) nucleotides that provide a visible tracer of the locations of terminal bases added by the polymerase.

Incubate

(5) During replication each new strand is terminated (↓) at the point of addition of a dd nucleotide.

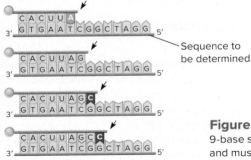

Sequence to be determined

(6) Left: A schematic view illustrating how finished fragments will end with a labeled dideoxynucleotide. Electrophoresis separates the labeled fragments and displays them in order by size. The color of the label gives the type of base in its exact sequence. Note that this sequence is not the final product – it is the complement of the template strand of interest.

(7) Automated display of a short segment of human DNA. The computer substitutes black for G for ease in reading.

Figure 10.7 **Some basic techniques in DNA sequencing.** (1–7) The sequencing of a 9-base strand using the Sanger method. The sequence in #6 is read from the bottom to the top and must be converted to its complement to get the true nucleotide order of TCGGCTAGG.

normally, except for a small percentage of fragments that will have a ddNT nucleotide incorporated and be terminated there. Late in the process, all possible positions in the sequence will have a terminal ddNT nucleotide. The reaction tube will thus have a series of strands reflecting the correct sequence that can be traced by its color from the first nucleotide to the last.

During analysis, the reaction products are subjected to electrophoresis in fine capillaries that separate strands differing by only a single nucleotide in length. This arrays the fragments in order of size, and only the fragments carrying the labeled nucleotides will be readable (figure 10.7). Automatic sequencing machines scan the electrophoresis pattern and record the DNA sequence by detecting the color of each band with a sensing device. In this way, the DNA sequence of the synthesized strand is analyzed and that of the template strand can easily be inferred. Most sequencers have computers that read the sequence and display it as a graphic figure. This method of sequencing is remarkably accurate, with only about one mistake in every 1,000 bases. All of these steps have been automated to obtain the speed necessary to sequence the entire genomes of humans and other organisms.

Whole genome sequencing projects have increased as the efficiency and speed of new sequencing technologies has improved. As of 2020, whole genome sequence maps of thousands of viruses, prokaryotes, and eukaryotes have been published. The eukaryotic genomes include chimpanzee, rat, mouse, a nematode worm, yeast, honeybee, cats, dogs, horses, cows, rice, and corn. One of the remarkable discoveries in this huge enterprise has been how similar the genomes of relatively unrelated organisms can be. Humans share around 99% of their genome with chimpanzees, 80% with mice, about 50% with corn, and even 30% with the roundworm *Caenorhabditis elegans.*

Although sequencing provides the ultimate genetic map, it does not immediately inform us about gene function. For that we need additional information about gene expression. Because the data consist of both biological and mathematical content, whole new disciplines have grown up around managing them. The fields of **genomics** and **bioinformatics** focus on analyzing, comparing, and classifying DNA; determining protein sequences; and ultimately understanding the functions of specific genes and proteins. Like other all-encompassing fields, genomics and bioinformatics can be subdivided into more manageable subspecialties:

- **Transcriptomics:** analysis of all RNA molecules in a cell. This includes mRNA, tRNA, rRNA, and the regulatory RNAs. It is an intermediate link between the activity of genes and the protein products of translation.
- **Proteomics:** the study of an organism's complement of proteins (its "proteome") and functions mediated by the proteins.
- **Metagenomics:** the study of all the genomes in a particular ecological niche, as opposed to individual genomes from single species.
- **Metabolomics:** the study of the complete complement of small chemicals present in a cell at any given time; provides a snapshot of the physiological state of the cell and the end products of its metabolism.

One of the fastest growing of these subspecialties is metagenomics, a field designed to survey the scope of organisms that live in various habitats. In the past it was difficult to study complex communities where millions of organisms coexist, and it has not been possible to isolate and culture most of them. Metagenomics provides microbiologists a window through which to view the diversity of such habitats and makes it possible to pull out the microbial genomes, study them, and begin to understand their interactions. This technique has been used for several years in the large-scale genetic sampling of the oceans. Other research efforts on dozens of habitats, including the human body, are yielding massive amounts of new genetic data.

Polymerase Chain Reaction: A Molecular Copy Machine for DNA

Some of the techniques used to analyze DNA and RNA are limited by the small amounts of nucleic acid available. This problem was largely solved by the invention of a simple, versatile way to amplify DNA called the **polymerase chain reaction (PCR).** This technique rapidly increases the amount of DNA in a sample without the need for making cultures or carrying out complex purification techniques. It is so sensitive that it holds the potential to detect cancer from a single cell or to diagnose an infection from a single gene copy. It is comparable to being able to pluck a single DNA "needle" out of a "haystack" of other needles and make unlimited copies of the DNA. PCR makes it possible to replicate a target DNA from a few copies to billions of copies in a few hours. It can amplify DNA fragments that consist of a few base pairs to whole genomes containing several million base pairs.

To understand the idea behind PCR, it will be instructive to review figures 9.7 and 9.8, which model DNA synthesis as it occurs naturally in cells. The PCR method uses essentially the same events, with the opening of the double strand, using the exposed strands as templates, the addition of primers, and the actions of a DNA polymerase.

Initiating the reaction requires a few specialized ingredients (**process figure 10.8**). The **primers** are synthetic oligonucleotides (short DNA strands) of a known sequence of 15 to 30 bases that serve as landmarks to indicate where DNA amplification will begin. These take the place of RNA primers that would normally be provided by the cell. Depending upon the purposes and what is known about the DNA being replicated, the primers can be random, attaching to any sequence they may fit, or they may be highly specific and chosen to amplify a known gene. To keep the DNA strands separated, processing must be carried out at a relatively high temperature. This necessitates the use of heat-resistant DNA polymerases isolated from thermophilic bacteria. Examples of these unique enzymes are Taq polymerase obtained from *Thermus aquaticus* and Vent polymerase from *Thermococcus litoralis.* Enzymes isolated from these thermophilic organisms remain active at the elevated temperatures used in PCR. Another useful component of PCR is a machine called a thermal cycler that automatically initiates the cyclic temperature changes.

(a) In cycle 1, the DNA to be amplified is denatured, primed, and replicated by a polymerase that can function at high temperatures. The two resulting strands then serve as templates for a second cycle of denaturation, priming, and synthesis.

Cycle 1

DNA Sample

Segment of DNA to be amplified

Heat to 94°C

Denaturation

Strands separate.

↓ 50°C–65°C

Priming

Oligonucleotide primers attach at ends of strands to promote replication of amplicons.

Amplicons Primer Primer

↓ 72°C

Extension

Heat-stable DNA polymerase synthesizes complementary strand.

Polymerase

Cycle 1

Cycle 2

Denaturation

Completed copies New strand

New strand Original strands

Heat to 94°C

Priming

50°C–65°C

Extension

72°C

4 copies

Cycle 2

Cycles 3, 4, . . . repeat same steps, with the copies of DNA

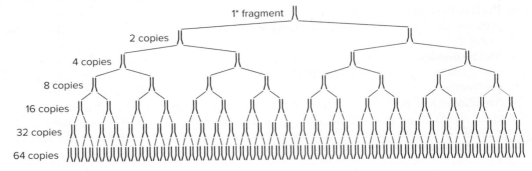

(b) A view of the process after 6 cycles, with 64 copies of amplified DNA. Continuing this process for 20 to 40 cycles can produce millions of identical DNA molecules.

1* fragment

2 copies

4 copies

8 copies

16 copies

32 copies

64 copies

Process Figure 10.8 Diagram of the polymerase chain reaction. (a) Details of the process over two cycles. **(b)** Yield after the cycle continues past the second cycle.

The PCR technique operates by repetitive cycling of three basic steps: denaturation, priming, and extension:

1. **Denaturation.** The first step involves heating target DNA to 94°C to separate it into two strands. Each strand will become a template DNA, or *amplicon.*
2. **Priming.** As the reaction is cooled to between 50°C and 65°C (depending on the exact sequence of the primers), the oligonucleotide primers base-pair with specific sites on the amplicons.
3. **Extension.** In the third phase, which proceeds at 72°C, the DNA polymerase is activated and begins to synthesize DNA from a pool of available nucleotides. Beginning at the free end of the primers on both strands, the polymerases move along the strands, which serve as templates for the synthesis of two complete double strands of DNA.

It is through cyclic repetition of these steps that DNA becomes amplified. When the DNAs formed in the first cycle are denatured, they become amplicons to be primed and extended in the second cycle. Each subsequent cycle converts the new DNAs to amplicons and doubles the number of copies. The number of cycles required to produce a million molecules is 20, but the process is usually carried out to 30 or 40 cycles. One significant advantage of this technique has been its natural adaptability to automation. A thermal cycler can perform 20 cycles on nearly 100 samples in 2 or 3 hours.

DNA amplified by PCR can be analyzed by any of the techniques discussed earlier. PCR can also be adapted to analyze RNA by initially converting an RNA sample to DNA with reverse transcriptase. This cDNA can then be amplified by PCR in the usual manner. It is by such means that ribosomal RNA and messenger RNA are readied for sequencing and RNA viruses are sequenced and identified. The PCR technique has found prominence as a powerful workhorse of molecular biology, medicine, and biotechnology. It often plays an essential role in gene mapping, the study of genetic defects and cancer, forensics, taxonomy, and evolutionary studies.

For all of its advantages, PCR techniques can encounter problems. One concern is the introduction and amplification of nontarget DNA from the surrounding environment, such as a skin cell from the technician carrying out the PCR rather than material from the sample DNA that was supposed to be amplified. Such contamination can be minimized by using equipment and rooms dedicated for DNA analysis and maintained with the utmost degree of cleanliness. Problems with contaminants can also be reduced by using gene-specific primers and treating samples with enzymes that can degrade the contaminating DNA before it is amplified.

Practice SECTION 10.1

1. Define *genetic engineering* and *biotechnology*, and summarize the important purposes of these fields. Review the use of the terms *genome, chromosome, gene, DNA,* and *RNA* from chapter 9.
2. Describe the processes involved in denaturing and renaturing of DNA, and explain what is useful about this procedure.
3. Define *restriction endonuclease* and explain what it does.
4. Define *palindrome* and draw three different palindromic sequences.
5. Explain how electrophoresis works and the general way that DNA is sized.
6. How would you make a copy of DNA from an mRNA transcript, what is this molecule called, and how would it be used?
7. Briefly summarize the steps involved in DNA sequencing and describe its applications.
8. Outline the steps in the PCR technique and describe the effects of temperature change.
9. What are the functions of primer and Taq polymerase?

10.2 Recombinant DNA Technology: How to Imitate Nature

Learn

5. Explain what is involved in recombinant DNA technology.
6. Characterize the events in cloning, using an example.
7. List and discuss some protein products of recombinant DNA and their applications.

The primary intent of **recombinant DNA technology** is to deliberately remove genetic material from one organism and combine it with that of a different organism. Its origins can be traced to 1970, when microbiologists first began to duplicate the clever tricks bacteria do naturally with bits of extra DNA such as plasmids, transposons, and proviruses. The discovery that bacteria can readily accept, replicate, and express foreign DNA made them powerful agents for studying the genes of other organisms in isolation. The practical applications of this work were soon realized by biotechnologists. Bacteria could be genetically engineered to mass-produce substances such as hormones, enzymes, and vaccines that have been difficult to synthesize by the usual industrial methods.

Figure 10.9 provides an overview of the recombinant DNA procedure. An important objective of this technique is to form genetic **clones.** This type of cloning involves the removal of a selected gene from an animal, plant, or microorganism (the genetic donor) followed by its propagation in a different host organism. Cloning requires that the desired donor gene first be selected, excised by restriction endonucleases, and isolated. The gene is next inserted into a **vector** (usually a plasmid or a virus) that will insert the DNA into a **cloning host.** The cloning host is usually a bacterium or a yeast that can replicate the gene and transcribe and translate it into the protein product for which it codes. Next we examine the elements of gene isolation, vectors, and cloning hosts and show how they participate in a complete recombinant DNA procedure.

Technical Aspects of Recombinant DNA and Gene Cloning

The first hurdles in cloning a target gene are to locate its exact site on the genetic donor's chromosome and to isolate it. Some of the

Nucleus

Human, other mammal, microorganism, or plant cell

DNA of interest is isolated or produced from mRNA (cDNA).

DNA is inserted into vector

Microbial cloning host is transformed when it picks up vector with foreign DNA.

Multiplication of cloning host to amplify gene

Transformed cell processes foreign DNA into protein

Growth of transformed cell supplies DNA for study and engineering of other organisms.

Gene therapy

Protein Production
Pharmaceuticals
Hormones
• insulin
• human growth hormone
Vaccines
• hepatitis B
Industrial chemicals

Altered Organisms with Economically Useful Traits
Transgenic plants
• pest resistance
• herbicide resistance
• improved nutritional value
Transgenic animals

Multiple Applications in Genome Research, Testing, and Therapy
Gene function
Nucleotide sequencing
Identification
Gene libraries
Gene therapy

Figure 10.9 **Overview of methods and applications of genetic engineering.** Practical applications of genetic engineering include the development of pharmaceuticals, genetically modified organisms, and identification techniques. See process figure 10.11 for details of these steps used in recombinant DNA.
Source: Linda Bartlett/National Cancer Institute

first isolated genes came from viruses, which have extremely small and manageable genomes, and later genes were isolated from bacteria and yeasts. One of the greatest benefits of the Human Genome Project is that the exact sequence and location of each gene in the human genome is known, greatly simplifying its initial

isolation. Beyond this first step, there are common strategies for obtaining isolated genes, including:

1. Synthesizing a cDNA from a mRNA transcript.
2. Isolating a gene from a larger segment of DNA using PCR.
3. Synthesizing a gene using purely chemical means. Laboratory equipment exists that can synthesize a strand of DNA containing any combination of nucleotides, even sequences that don't exist in nature.

Although the initial phases of gene isolation and cloning can be labor-intensive, a fortunate outcome is that, once isolated, genes can be maintained in a cloning host and vector just like a microbial pure culture. Genomic libraries, which contain fragments of DNA representing all the genes in a particular species, have been created for thousands of organisms and viruses.

Characteristics of Cloning Vectors

A good recombinant vector has two indispensable qualities: It must be capable of carrying a significant piece of the donor DNA, and it must be readily accepted by the cloning host. Plasmids are excellent vectors because they are small, well characterized, and easy to manipulate, and they can be transferred into appropriate host cells through transformation. Bacteriophages also serve well because they have the natural ability to inject DNA into bacterial hosts through transduction. A modified phage vector, the *Charon*[3] phage, has had sections of its genome deleted so it can carry a fairly large segment of foreign DNA.

Today, thousands of unique cloning vectors are available commercially. Although every vector has characteristics that make it ideal for a specific project, all vectors can be thought of as having three important attributes **(figure 10.10):**

1. An origin of replication (ORI) is needed somewhere on the vector so that it will be replicated by the DNA polymerase of the cloning host.
2. The vector must accept DNA of the desired size. Early plasmids were limited to an insert size of less than 10 kb of DNA, far too small for most eukaryotic genes, with their sizable introns. Newer vectors called cosmids can hold 45 kb, whereas complex *bacterial artificial chromosomes* (BACs) and *yeast artificial chromosomes* (YACs) can hold as much as 300 kb and 1,000 kb, respectively.
3. Vectors typically contain a gene that confers drug resistance to their cloning host. In this way, cells can be inoculated into drug-containing media, and only those cells that harbor a plasmid will be selected for growth.

Characteristics of Cloning Hosts

The best cloning hosts possess several key characteristics **(table 10.1).** The traditional cloning host—and the one still used in basic experiments—is *Escherichia coli*. Because this bacterium was the original recombinant host, the protocols using it are well

3. Named for the mythical boatman in Hades who carried souls across the River Styx.

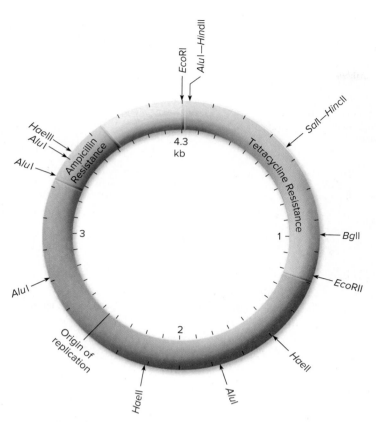

Figure 10.10 **Partial map of the pBR322 plasmid.** Arrows delineate sites cleaved by various restriction endonucleases. Numbers indicate the size of regions in kilobases (kb). Other important components are genes for ampicillin and tetracycline resistance and the origin of replication. Most plasmids in use today are derivatives of pBR322.

TABLE 10.1	Desirable Features in a Microbial Cloning Host
Rapid turnover, fast growth rate	
Can be grown in large quantities using ordinary culture methods	
Nonpathogenic	
Genome that is well delineated (mapped)	
Capable of accepting plasmid or bacteriophage vectors	
Maintains foreign genes through multiple generations	
Will secrete a high yield of proteins from expressed foreign genes	

visiae, which would be able to process and modify eukaryotic genes and products.

Certain techniques may also employ animal cell culture, and even live animals and plants, to serve as cloning hosts. Although a number of recombinant proteins are produced by transformed bacterial hosts, many of the enzymes, hormones, and antibodies used in drug therapy are currently being manufactured with mammalian cell cultures as the cloning and expression hosts. One of the primary advantages to this alternative procedure is that these cell cultures can modify the proteins (adding carbohydrates, for example) so that they are biologically more active. Some forms of reproductive hormones, human growth hormone, and interferon are products of cell culture. In our coverage, we present the recombinant process as it is performed in bacteria and yeasts.

Construction of a Recombinant, Insertion into a Cloning Host, and Genetic Expression

This section emphasizes the main steps in recombinant DNA technology needed to produce a protein. A drug called alpha-2a interferon (Roferon-A) will serve as an example, but it should be remembered that the steps are essentially the same regardless of the protein being produced. This form of interferon is used to treat cancers such as hairy-cell leukemia and hepatitis C. The human alpha interferon gene is a DNA molecule of approximately 500 bp that codes for a polypeptide of 166 amino acids. It was originally isolated and identified from human blood cells and prepared from processed mRNA transcripts that are free of introns.

The first step in cloning the interferon gene or any desired gene is to prepare it for splicing into an *E. coli* plasmid **(process figure 10.11).** This can be accomplished by digesting both the gene and the plasmid with the same restriction enzyme, resulting in complementary sticky ends on both the vector and insert DNA. In the presence of the endonuclease, the plasmid's circular molecule is nicked open, and its sticky ends are exposed. When the gene and plasmid are placed together, their free ends base-pair, and a ligase makes the final covalent seals. The resultant gene and plasmid combination is called a **recombinant.**

Following this procedure, the recombinant is introduced by transformation into the cloning host, a special laboratory strain of *E. coli* that lacks any extra plasmids that could complicate the expression of the gene. Because the recombinant plasmid enters only some of the cloning host cells, it is necessary to locate these recombinant clones. Cultures are plated out on medium containing an antibiotic such as ampicillin or tetracycline, and only those clones that carry the plasmid with resistance to this antibiotic can form colonies **(figure 10.12).** These recombinant colonies are selected from the plates and cultured. As the cells multiply, the plasmid is replicated along with the cell's

Quick Search
See this played out in "Steps in Cloning a Gene," a video from McGraw-Hill on YouTube.

established, relatively easy, and reliable. Hundreds of specialized cloning vectors have been developed for it. The main disadvantages with this species are that the splicing of mRNA and the modification of proteins that would normally occur in the eukaryotic endoplasmic reticulum and Golgi apparatus are unavailable in this prokaryotic cloning host. One alternative host for certain industrial processes and research is the eukaryotic yeast *Saccharomyces cere-*

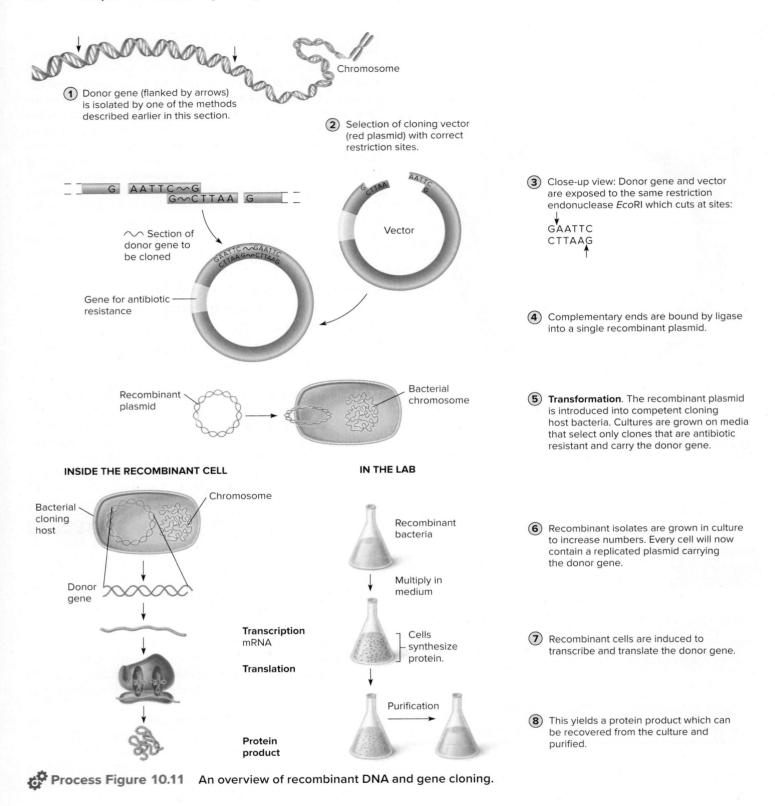

① Donor gene (flanked by arrows) is isolated by one of the methods described earlier in this section.

Chromosome

② Selection of cloning vector (red plasmid) with correct restriction sites.

G AATTC∿G
G∿CTTAA G

∿ Section of donor gene to be cloned

Vector

③ Close-up view: Donor gene and vector are exposed to the same restriction endonuclease *Eco*RI which cuts at sites:

GAATTC
CTTAAG

Gene for antibiotic resistance

④ Complementary ends are bound by ligase into a single recombinant plasmid.

Recombinant plasmid

Bacterial chromosome

⑤ **Transformation**. The recombinant plasmid is introduced into competent cloning host bacteria. Cultures are grown on media that select only clones that are antibiotic resistant and carry the donor gene.

INSIDE THE RECOMBINANT CELL

Chromosome

Bacterial cloning host

Donor gene

Transcription
mRNA

Translation

Protein product

IN THE LAB

Recombinant bacteria

Multiply in medium

Cells synthesize protein.

Purification

⑥ Recombinant isolates are grown in culture to increase numbers. Every cell will now contain a replicated plasmid carrying the donor gene.

⑦ Recombinant cells are induced to transcribe and translate the donor gene.

⑧ This yields a protein product which can be recovered from the culture and purified.

Process Figure 10.11 An overview of recombinant DNA and gene cloning.

chromosome. In a few hours of growth, there can be billions of cells, each containing the target donor gene. Once the gene has been successfully cloned and tested, this step does not have to be repeated; the recombinant strain can be maintained in culture indefinitely.

The bacteria's ability to express the eukaryotic gene is ensured because the plasmid has been modified with the necessary transcription and translation recognition sequences. As the *E. coli* culture grows, it transcribes and translates the donor gene, synthesizes the peptide, and secretes it into the growth medium.

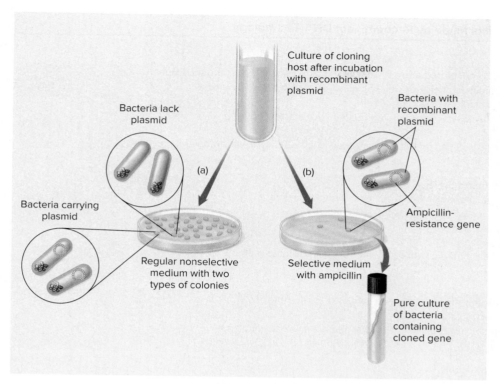

Figure 10.12 **One method for screening clones of bacteria that have been transformed with the donor gene. (a)** Plating the culture on nonselective medium will not separate the transformed cells from normal cells, which lack the plasmid. **(b)** Plating on selective medium containing ampicillin will permit only cells containing the plasmid to multiply. Colonies growing on this medium that carry the cloned gene can be used to make a culture for gene libraries, industrial production, and other processes. (Plasmids are shown disproportionate to size of cell.)

Final processing to excise a terminal amino acid from the peptide yields the protein product in a relatively pure form. The scale of this procedure can range from test tube size to gigantic industrial tanks that can manufacture thousands of gallons of product. The basic process we have presented here can be harnessed to mass-produce a variety of immune treatments such as interferon, hormones, enzymes, vaccines, and agricultural products (see table 10.2).

Protein Products of Recombinant DNA Technology

Recombinant DNA technology is used by pharmaceutical companies to manufacture medications that are difficult to procure by other means. Diseases such as diabetes and dwarfism, caused by the lack of an essential hormone, are treated by replacing the missing hormone. Insulin of animal origin was once the only form available to treat diabetes, even though such animal products can cause allergic reactions in sensitive individuals. In contrast, pituitary dwarfism cannot be treated with animal growth hormones, so originally the only source of human growth hormone (HGH) was the pituitaries of cadavers. At one time, not enough HGH was available to treat the thousands of children in need.

Another serious problem with using natural human products is the potential for infection. For example, infectious agents such

as the prion responsible for Creutzfeldt-Jakob disease, described in chapter 6, can be transmitted in this manner. Similarly, clotting factor VIII, a protein needed for blood to clot properly, is missing in persons suffering from hemophilia A. In the early 1980s a large percentage of the patients receiving plasma-derived factor VIII contracted HIV infections as a result of being exposed to the virus through the donated plasma.

Recombinant technology changed the outcome of these and many other conditions by enabling large-scale manufacture of hormones and enzymes derived from human genes. Recombinant human insulin was the first rDNA hormone to be marketed for diabetics, followed by recombinant HGH for children with dwarfism and Turner syndrome. HGH is also used to prevent the wasting syndrome that occurs in AIDS and cancer patients. In all of these applications, recombinant DNA technology has led to both a safer product and one that can be manufactured in mass quantities. Other protein-based hormones, enzymes, and vaccines produced through recombinant DNA are summarized in **table 10.2.**

Nucleic acid products also have a number of medical applications. A new development in vaccine formulation involves using microbial DNA as a stimulus for the immune system. So far, animal tests using DNA vaccines for HIV and influenza indicate that this may be a breakthrough in vaccine design. Recombinant DNA could also be used to produce DNA-based drugs for some types of gene therapy, discussed in section 10.3.

Practice SECTION 10.2

10. What characteristics of plasmids and bacteriophages make them good cloning vectors?

11. Name several types of vectors, and list the types of genes they need to function.

12. Describe the basic principles behind recombinant DNA technology.

13. Summarize the characteristics of bacteria and yeasts that make them good cloning hosts.

14. Outline the main steps in cloning a gene, including how this gene is used.

15. What is one way to determine whether a bacterial culture has received a recombinant plasmid?

16. Characterize several products that have resulted from recombinant DNA technology.

TABLE 10.2	Examples of Protein Products Made by Recombinant DNA Technology

Immune Treatments

Interferons—peptides used to treat some types of cancer, multiple sclerosis, and viral infections such as hepatitis and genital warts
Interleukins—types of cytokines that regulate the immune function of white blood cells; used in cancer treatment
Orthoclone—an immune suppressant in transplant patients
Macrophage-colony-stimulating factor—used to stimulate bone marrow activity after bone marrow grafts
Tumor necrosis factor (TNF)—used to treat cancer
Granulocyte-colony-stimulating factor (Neupogen)—developed for treating cancer patients suffering from low neutrophil counts

Hormones

Insulin—a small protein that is used to treat some forms of diabetes
Erythropoietin (EPO)—a peptide that stimulates bone marrow used to treat some forms of anemia
Tissue plasminogen activator (tPA)—can dissolve potentially dangerous blood clots
Hemoglobin A—form of artificial blood to be used in place of real blood for transfusions
Factor VIII—needed as replacement blood-clotting factor in type A hemophilia
Human growth hormone (HGH)—stimulates growth in children with dwarfism; prevents wasting syndrome

Enzymes

rH DNase (pulmozyme)—a treatment that can break down the thick lung secretions of cystic fibrosis
Antitrypsin—replacement therapy to benefit emphysema patients
PEG-SOD—a form of superoxide dismutase that minimizes damage to brain tissue after severe trauma
Lipases—added to laundry detergents

Vaccines

Vaccines for hepatitis A and B, *Haemophilus influenzae*, meningitis, influenza, rotavirus, and human papillomavirus
Experimental malaria and HIV vaccines based on recombinant surface antigens

Miscellaneous

Bovine growth hormone or bovine somatotropin (BST)—given to cows to increase milk production
Apolipoprotein—used to deter the development of fatty deposits in the arteries and to prevent strokes and heart attacks
Spider silk—a light, tough fabric for parachutes and bulletproof vests

10.3 Genetically Modified Organisms and Other Applications

 Learn

8. Define what is meant by the term *transgenic* or *genetically modified organisms.*

9. Describe the uses of genetically modified bacteria and viruses.

10. Discuss genetic modifications in plants and animals, explaining how they are carried out and giving examples of applications.

11. Explain how DNA technology can be used to treat genetic diseases.

Recombinant organisms produced through the introduction of foreign genes are called **genetically modified organisms (GMOs),** or **transgenic organisms.** Although foreign genes have been inserted into a variety of life forms, including microbes, plants, and animals, the techniques used to create them owe their existence to the early work that took place in bacterial systems.

Recombinant Microbes: Modified Bacteria and Viruses

One of the first practical applications of recombinant DNA was the creation of a genetically altered strain of the bacterium *Pseudomo-*

nas syringae. The wild strain ordinarily contains an ice formation gene that promotes ice or frost formation on moist plant surfaces. Genetic alteration of the frost gene using recombinant plasmids created a different strain that could prevent ice crystals from forming. A commercial product called Frostban was developed but never marketed due to the controversy arising from its release into the environment. In another trial, a strain of *Pseudomonas fluorescens* was engineered with the gene from a bacterium (*Bacillus thuringiensis*) that codes for an insecticide (*Bt* toxin). These recombinant bacteria are released to colonize plant roots and help destroy invading insects. All releases of recombinant microbes must be approved by the U.S. Environmental Protection Agency and are closely monitored.

Although primarily known for its ability to cause colds, the adenovirus has been bioengineered to attack and destroy cancer cells. These *oncolytic adenoviruses* have been altered so that their host range consists exclusively of cells that produce cancer-specific proteins. By simply infecting a cancerous cell and replicating, the engineered virus will eventually lyse and kill the cell. Although this procedure is not yet approved for use in humans, this novel use of viral vectors speaks to the potential of genetically engineered viruses. This technology is currently used to engineer viruses to deliver genes into animals and humans (see figure 10.16).

In 2010, a milestone was reached when Craig Venter's laboratory team created an entirely new bacterial species by inserting

10.1 MAKING CONNECTIONS

A Moment to Think

"When we seed millions of acres of land with these plants, what happens to foraging birds, to insects, to microbes, to other animals, when they come in contact with and digest plants that are producing materials ranging from plastics to vaccines to pharmaceutical products?"

Jeremy Rifkin, Foundation on Economic Trends

"If you put a label on genetically modified food, you might as well put a skull and crossbones on it."

Norman Brasick, of Monsanto.

There is no denying that many aspects of synthetic biology are highly controversial and emotionally charged, but few would deny that this technology is here to stay. As evidenced by the graph, as of 2015, 85% to 95% of major crops are now composed of genetically modified plants. Most of these plants have been altered to either make their own insecticide or resist herbicides that kill weeds. The edible crops are already winding up in the foods we eat. With regard to animals, so far only one GMO has received approval for human consumption—the AquAdvantage salmon—a farmed Atlantic salmon that has been engineered with genes from other fish. Time will tell what kind of acceptance these fish will have in the consumer market.

One aspect working against the widespread acceptance of GMOs is the fact that it is not possible to prove that a food is safe, only that there has never been any evidence that it is unsafe. This allows those with an unsubstantiated bias against genetically modified organisms to make statements along the lines of "We don't know what the future will hold...," or "It could turn out that...," or perhaps worst of all "You never

know" According to Robert Goldberg, a plant molecular biologist at UCLA, these fears still exist despite "hundreds of millions of genetic experiments involving every type of organism on earth, and people eating billions of meals without a problem."

The benefits of GMOs are easily seen. Corn engineered to resist the western corn rootworm produces higher yields and has fewer fungal toxins than nonmodified varieties, while golden rice, a crop engineered many years ago to supply vitamin A, prevents millions of cases of blindness each year. Currently, scientists are working to engineer tomatoes with high levels of antioxidant-rich pigments from blueberries and, for those who don't like tomatoes, pineapples containing the tomato-based antioxidant lycopene. These examples are especially important because rather than the benefits of GMOs being targeted toward the farmers (higher yields, less pesticide use), the consumer is finally starting to see an advantage from genetically modified organisms.

Ethical choices can be properly made only from a standpoint of intellectual awareness; and in this era of advertising, polling, and focus groups, people with a stake in genetic technology know that the most effective way to drum up support (both for or against) is *not* by carefully educating the public as to the uses and limits of our newfound powers but, rather, by publicizing exaggerated claims or frightening scenarios. Enlightenment is often a casualty of these advertising campaigns, and you as a student, voter, and potential consumer of bioengineered products need to realize that the truth lies somewhere between nightmare scenarios and the blissful utopia often portrayed by some proponents of biotechnology.

Throughout this chapter, a common theme has been that biotechnology, genetically modified organisms, and gene-based therapies are simply new ways of achieving long-held goals. This is, of course, a vast understatement. Society has never before had the ability to do even a fraction of the things we can do today, and at some point we must decide where we as individuals and as a society draw the line. The answer will differ for each person, based on his or her unique experiences and personal philosophy, but should certainly include a factual knowledge of the probable benefits and possible risks. We live in serious times, and these are choices requiring serious thought.

Can you think of any adverse effects that might arise from eating GMO corn or fish? After all, every type of non-GMO food we eat already contains large amounts of foreign DNA from the food organism.

Adoption of Genetically Engineered Crops in the United States, 1996–2018

Graph tracking the percentage of crops in the United States grown from genetically engineered seeds. *Bt* is short for *Bacillus thuringiensis,* a bacterium that produces a natural insecticide, and HT indicates herbicide resistance.

Source: https://www.ers.usda.gov/data-products/adoption-of-genetically-engineered-crops-in-the-us/recent-trends-in-ge-adoption.aspx

a completely synthesized genome of artificial origin into *Mycoplasma genitalium*. The new species, named *Mycoplasma laboratorium,* contains the smallest functional genome of any bacterium, with 382 genes of around 1.1 million base pairs. So far the scale of this experiment is small—a single-celled organism—but its implications are large. The growing power of genetic engineering

and synthetic biology has fostered a deeper examination of the **bioethics**[4] involved in modifying the genetics of organisms (**10.1 Making Connections**).

4. A field that relates biological issues to human conduct and moral judgment.

Bacterium with selected gene

Chromosome

Isolated gene for herbicide resistance

Chromosome

Ti plasmid

T-DNA

Agrobacterium cell

(a) The large plasmid (Ti) of this bacterium can be used as a cloning vector for foreign genes that code for herbicide or disease resistance.

Gene spliced into Ti plasmid

Recombinant *Agrobacterium*

(b) The recombinant plasmids are taken up by the *Agrobacterium* cells, which multiply and copy the foreign gene.

Agrobacterium with Ti plasmid vector

Plant cell

(c) Genetically engineered *Agrobacterium* is inoculated into a culture of target plant cells and infects the cells.

Process in plant

(d) Bacterium fuses with the plant cell wall and the Ti plasmid enters. The T-DNA carries the herbicide gene into the plant nucleus. Mature plants can be grown from single cells, and these transgenic plants will express the new gene.

(e) Because the gene will be part of the plant's genome, it will be transmitted to offspring in seeds.

Figure 10.13 **Bioengineering of plants. (a).** Most techniques employ a natural tumor-producing bacterium called *Agrobacterium tumefaciens* **(b–e).** The example here shows the insertion of a gene to create a herbicide-resistant plant

Recombination in Multicellular Organisms

Although the terms *genetically modified, genetically engineered,* and *transgenic organism* apply to any life form whose genome has been deliberately altered, it is often used in reference to plants and animals that possess genes that were not acquired through traditional breeding. The basic techniques covered in this chapter have given scientists a limited ability to custom-build an organism that expresses a certain trait, in a sense accelerating the pace of evolution. Because of the universal nature of the genetic code, however, scientists can take nature one step further and combine genes from more than a single species, creating plants or animals that would never have existed otherwise. Examples of genetically modified

organisms include plants with added nutritional value, animals that excrete clot-dissolving proteins in their milk, and humans who have gained the ability to produce an enzyme crucial to the immune response.

Transgenic Plants

Engineering plants to produce new traits often revolves around *Agrobacterium tumefaciens,* a plant pathogen particularly adept at transferring small amounts of DNA to plant cells. These bacteria live in soil and can invade injured plant tissues. Inside the wounded tissue, the bacteria adhere to plant cells and introduce a large plasmid termed **Ti** (tumor-inducing). This plasmid inserts into the genome of the infected plant cell and transforms it **(figure 10.13).** Over time this causes development of a tumor called *crown gall disease,* a mass of undifferentiated tissue on the stem.

The primary factor that induces this transformation is a discrete region of the Ti plasmid called T-DNA. This series of genes is integrated into a plant cell's chromosome, where it directs the synthesis of nutrients to feed the bacteria and hormones to stimulate plant growth. Even after the bacteria in a tumor are dead, the plasmid genes remain in the cell nucleus and the tumor continues to grow.

This plasmid is an effective vector for inserting foreign genes into plant genomes. The procedure involves removing the Ti plasmid, inserting a specially selected gene such as herbicide resistance into it, and returning the plasmid to *Agrobacterium.* Infection of the plant by the recombinant bacteria automatically transfers the plasmid with the foreign gene into the plant cells. Transformed cells can be grown into mature plants that express the donor gene and transmit it to their offspring. The insertion of genes with a Ti plasmid works primarily to engineer important plants such as potatoes, tomatoes, cotton, and grapes.

For plants that cannot be transformed with *Agrobacterium,* seed embryos have been successfully implanted with additional genes using gene guns—small shotguns that shoot the genes into plant embryos with tiny gold bullets.

Although more than 1,200 genetically modified plants have been approved for field testing, only 11 are currently available, including apples that don't easily brown, potatoes that don't bruise, and rice engineered to contain genes that supply a precursor to vitamin A. However, the most common genes engineered into plants provide resistance to insects and tolerance to herbicides. The principal concern about plants with these last two traits is the potential for genetic recombination with nearby wild plants, leading to the creation of "superweeds" that are resistant to herbicides and disease. This has already happened in parts of Canada, where canola plants have transferred their genes to wild mustard. Because this could alter the ecology of natural

TABLE 10.3	Examples of Genetically Modified Plants	
Plant	**Trait(s)**	**Results**
Cherry tomatoes	High levels of anthocyanin, an antioxidant	Tomatoes were engineered with pigment gene from snapdragons, producing five times the purple pigment anthocyanin and greatly increasing the nutrition value (**figure *a***).
Wheat	Resistance to head blight	Genes added to break down the cell wall of the fungus *Fusarium* protect wheat plants from being attacked (**figure *b***).
Wheat	Improved nutrition	Engineered with genes to increase zinc and iron levels in the plant.
Golden rice	Improved nutrition	Genes added to produce beta-carotene, a precursor to vitamin A; aim is to prevent deficiencies in developing countries that lead to blindness.
Soybeans, corn, cotton	Herbicide resistance	Plants were engineered to withstand chemical herbicides.
Peanuts	Insect resistance	Genes for a biopesticide called Bt were added to kill insects that feed on the plants (**figure *c***).
Banana	Vaccine production	Vaccines for hepatitis B in development
Plum	Viral resistance	Genes for resistance to plum poxvirus prevent infection and destruction of plant

(a) This purple tomato contains high levels of a pigment that has numerous health benefits.

(b) Researcher holds a genetically engineered wheat plant being tested for its resistance to a fungal infection.

(c) Peanut plant (left) genetically modified to produce its own insecticide is unharmed by larvae; unmodified plant (right) shows damage from insect larvae.

(photos): (a): Andrew Davis and Sue Bunnewell/John Innes Centre; (b): *Source:* Jack Dykinga, USDA/ARS; (c): *Source:* Herb Pilcher, USDA/ARS

environments, the U.S. Department of Agriculture is increasing the regulation of all releases of transgenic plants. See **table 10.3** for examples of plants that have been engineered.

Transgenic Animals: Engineering Embryos

Animals such as mice, pigs, sheep, cattle, fish, and poultry are prominent candidates for genetic engineering. Thousands of animal strains now exist for the purposes of agriculture, industry, and research into genetic diseases.

The most effective way to insert genes into animals is to use a virus to transfect the fertilized egg or early embryo (germ-line engineering). Foreign genes can also be delivered into a fertilized egg by pulsing the egg with high voltage or by injection (**figure 10.14**). The success rate does not have to be high, because once created, a transgenic animal will pass the genes on to its offspring.

The dominant animals in the genetic engineer's laboratory are transgenic forms of mice. In one pioneering experiment, fertilized mouse embryos were injected with a gene from a jellyfish that produces a green fluorescent protein. The cells of these mice fluoresce in ultraviolet radiation. One serious use has been to study the developmental stages in mice. This strategy has led to the design of animal models to study human genetic diseases and to use these natural systems to test new genetic therapies before they are used in humans. Animals such as sheep or goats can also be engineered to become "factories" capable of manufacturing proteins and excreting them in their milk or semen, a process often referred to (when done to produce medically useful proteins) as "pharming."

Embryonic mouse displaying green fluorescent protein
Source: National Institute of Mental Health

Figure 10.14 Microinjection of DNA into a fertilized egg.
After being removed from the female, the egg is held with a pipette while a small needle is used to inject the transgene. Several injected embryos will be placed within the oviduct of a female mouse. After birth, a small piece of the tail of each new mouse is snipped off and examined to ensure the presence of the gene of interest.
Zephyr/Science Source

One benefit of transgenic animals is that they will automatically transcribe and translate eukaryotic genes and accurately carry out posttranslational modification of the protein. By ensuring that the protein product is produced in the milk or semen of animals, recovery and purification are made that much simpler. For example, alpha-1 antitrypsin (AAT), produced in sheep, is used to treat an inherited form of emphysema. A single animal produces AAT at concentrations of 35 grams per liter of milk. A few hundred sheep could easily meet the needs of the 20,000 people a year who suffer from this debilitating disease. Dolly the sheep was the first animal ever to be cloned precisely because she produced this protein. See **table 10.4** to examine some other examples and applications of transgenic animals.

TABLE 10.4	Selected Applications for Transgenic Animals
Animal/Product	**Application**
Production of Pharmaceuticals	
Pig/Factors VIII and IX	Treatment of human blood-clotting disorders.
Sheep/Alpha antitrypsin	Replacement protein to prevent emphysema.
Rabbit/Human interleukin-2	Stimulates the production of T cells to fight cancer.
Cow/Lactoferrin	Iron-binding protein inhibits bacterial and viral infections.
Cow/Human albumin	Used in surgery to maintain blood volume.
Goat/Tissue plasminogen activating factor	Dissolves blood clots and reduces heart damage.
Goat/Antithrombin	*Atryn* was the first drug from a genetically engineered animal approved by the FDA; used to prevent blood clots.
Research/Industry/Environment	
Anopheles mosquito malaria resistance	Mosquito embryos have new genes inserted to make them resistant to infection by *Plasmodium*, the malaria parasite. Modified mosquitoes would no longer carry and spread the parasite.
Goat/Silk fibers	Female animals secrete silk protein in their milk. Silk has many uses for constructing strong, lightweight material.
Pig/Pork meat	*Enviropig* has enzymes in its saliva to process excess phosphate in its feed, reducing pollution.
Mice, cats, pigs, monkeys/research animals, tropical fish	Engineered with the green fluorescent protein from jellyfish that causes their cells to glow green in UV light. Animals are used to trace development in embryos and the stages of certain diseases.
Cats and dogs/Hypoallergenic	Genes that code for allergens from animal's saliva and sebaceous glands have been silenced.
Salmon/Farmed fish	Atlantic salmon engineered with the growth hormone gene from a different species of salmon to increase growth rate.
Cow/Human breast milk	Produces milk with the same composition as human breast milk.

Genetically engineered Atlantic salmon grow two times faster than regular salmon.

A mother mouse genetically modified to have mosaic-pattern fur, and her two transgenic pups with solid-pattern fur.

(photos): (salmon): Troutlodge, Inc/USDA/Science Source; (mice): *Source:* National Institute of Mental Health

Figure 10.15 **CRISPR/Cas-9.** By synthesizing a CRISPR guide RNA to hybridize to a specific sequence of DNA, the Cas-9 endonuclease (purple) can be used to cut the genome at any location. A new DNA sequence can then be inserted into the cut region.

An inventive newer technology known as **CRISPR**—an acronym of clustered regularly interspaced short palindromic repeats—is rapidly becoming the chosen method for manipulating DNA. CRISPR and a related protein, CAS-9 (CRISPR-associated protein 9), were discovered in bacterial cells where they work together to excise viral DNA from the genome of the cell.

The CRISPR DNA, along with adjacent viral DNA sequences, are transcribed to produce a CRISPR RNA. Hybridization between the CRISPR RNA and complementary sequences in the viral DNA create a "guide" for the Cas-9 enzyme. The Cas-9 enzyme is a restriction endonuclease and will cut any DNA to which it is guided, which in nature is the location in the genome where viral DNA has chosen to integrate. The CRISPR/Cas-9 system acts like a prokaryotic immune system, allowing bacterial cells to excise integrated viral DNA. And, like the immune system, a memory is created as the CRISPR RNA remains in the cell, ready to respond to any future attack by the same virus.

Where CRISPR/Cas-9 has been most useful (at least to humans) has been in the laboratory. By synthesizing a specific sequence of nucleotides, a guide RNA can be made that will hybridize to any location in the genome (**figure 10.15**). In this way, CRISPR/Cas-9 can be used to edit DNA with a specificity never before possible. CRISPR/Cas-9 has already been used to study the effect of a gene by creating "knockout" strains of bacteria and mice, allowing scientists to see how organisms missing that specific gene function. Potential uses also include introducing genes into mosquitoes, making them sterile, thereby limiting their ability to spread diseases like malaria and Zika virus (see this chapter's Case Study). Further in the future, scientists may be able to use CRISPR/Cas-9 to genetically engineer pigs to produce human organs for transplant or insert a CCR-5 mutation into white blood cells to prevent HIV infection (see chapter 9's Clinic Case).

Medical Applications of DNA Technology

One offshoot of studies with transgenic animals has been the advancement of medical treatments for human diseases that involve manipulating genetics, rather than administering drugs. The applications that show the most promise are gene therapy, which aims to replace a nonfunctional gene with its normal counterpart, and regulatory RNAs, which manage DNA expression of abnormal genes.

Gene Therapy

We have known for decades that for certain diseases, the disease phenotype is due to a missing or non-functioning protein. Often referred to as "loss of function" diseases, examples include cystic fibrosis, hemophilia, sickle-cell anemia, some forms of dwarfism, and muscular dystrophy. A few of these diseases can be treated by administering the correct protein—recall the use of recombinant growth hormone to treat pituitary dwarfism. But in the majority of cases, a replacement protein is not yet available. About 30 years ago, medical geneticists began to explore the possibility of restoring function by means of **gene therapy,** by inserting the normal functioning gene into the cells of afflicted patients.

The goal of gene therapy would be to permanently cure the physiological dysfunction by repairing the genetic defect. There are two strategies for this therapy. In ex vivo therapy, the normal gene is cloned in vectors such as adenoviruses or retroviruses that have been modified to carry a corrective gene into cells of the patient. Tissues removed from the patient are incubated with these genetically modified viruses to transfect them with the normal gene. The transfected cells are then reintroduced into the patient's body by transfusion (**process figure 10.16).** In contrast, the in vivo type of

1. Normal gene is isolated from healthy subject.

2. Gene is cloned.

3. Gene is inserted into virus vector.

4. Bone marrow sample is taken from patient with genetic defect.

5. Stem cells from marrow are transfected with virus (enlarged view).

6. Transfected cells (red dots) are infused into patient.

7. Patient is observed for expression of normal gene.

Marrow stem cell

Process Figure 10.16 Protocol for the ex vivo type of gene therapy in humans.

 CLINIC CASE

Because You've Got to Get Your Protein The patient was born in 2024. Two days after birth, a few drops of blood were taken from the baby's heel and used to screen the newborn for a variety of genetic abnormalities. This type of newborn screening is done in every state to test for a number of conditions, including cystic fibrosis and sickle-cell disease. For this patient, the screening indicated that she suffered from phenylketonuria, an inborn error of metabolism in which the amino acid phenylalanine is not properly metabolized. Left untreated, a buildup of phenylalanine causes severe neurological disease. Management of the disease requires the patient to adhere to a strict, low-protein diet (to reduce the amount of phenylalanine ingested), but compliance is difficult, and the overall lack of protein may lead to failure to thrive.

In 2018, researchers engineered an *E. coli* bacterium that contained two genes needed to import phenylalanine into the bacterium and metabolize it to hippuric acid, which can be excreted harmlessly in the urine. The bacterium is taken orally and reproduces within the large intestine, providing a robust population of phenylalanine-metabolizing bacteria. Ensuring that the bacterium is present in the gut and working as it should be is simple; hippuric acid can be monitored in the urine at home.

By 2020, the genetically engineered bacterium was in clinical trials and not yet available to the public, but for 16,500 people a year, plus the patient in this case who has not yet been born, this genetically engineered probiotic may be a lifesaver. Or, as the headline of one article put it, referring to the common abbreviation for phenylalanine, "Treating Phenylketonuria Now Phe-sible with Engineered Bacteria?"

The test for phenylketonuria is given a day or two after birth, after the newborn has had several opportunities to nurse or bottle feed. Why do you think this is?

therapy skips the intermediate step of incubating excised patient tissue. Instead, the naked DNA or a virus vector is directly introduced into the patient's tissues.

Clinical testing using various types of gene therapy is performed on human volunteers with a diagnosed genetic disorder. Over 2,000 of these trials have been or are being implemented in the United States and other countries. Most trials target cancer, single-gene defects, and infections. The most dramatic example of this type of treatment was seen in the very first gene therapy trial conducted in 1990. In this case, two girls suffering from adenosine deaminase (ADA) deficiency, a fatal immunologic disorder caused by a missing enzyme, received infusions of their own hematopoietic stem cells that had been transformed with a healthy copy of the adenosine deaminase gene.

As with most medical experimentation, some of the earlier gene therapy trials experienced setbacks. A serious problem arose with the use of the viral vectors. Even though they were supposed to be "harmless," five children infused with a recombinant mouse retrovirus developed leukemia when the vector DNA integrated at a cancer-inducing site on a chromosome. After this event, researchers worked to develop modified adeno-associated viral vectors to greatly reduce the chances of this happening.

Over the past several years, medical geneticists reported major successes in curing 20 children born with the devastating genetic disease termed X-1-linked SCID (severe combined deficiency disease). These children lacked a functioning immune system from birth, which researchers restored by inserting copies of the functioning gene into their stem cells using a safer recombinant virus. Two giant strides in gene therapy have been made in the last few years. In 2018, the FDA approved Luxturna, a gene therapy for a progressive form of blindness called Leber congenital amaurosis. The treatment uses a genetically engineered virus to deliver a healthy gene, designated RPE65, directly to the retina after doctors inject the virus into the eyeball itself. The protein product of the gene is an enzyme that nourishes the cells of the retina; many of the children in the clinical trial reported immediate and dramatic improvement in their vision. In 2019, Zolgensma was approved to cure spinal muscular atrophy (SMA), a group of debilitating neuromuscular disorders that is a leading genetic cause of death in infants. The disorder is caused by lack of a working SMN1 gene, and the treatment uses an adenovirus capsid to deliver a functional SMN1 gene to the nucleus of motor neurons. Zolgensma has the dubious distinction of being the most expensive medication on earth, as a one-time dose costs $2.125 million.

Therapy with Regulatory RNAs

Tens of thousands of genetic disorders have been described. Most are due to nonfunctional or missing genetic material, but a proportion of them result from the expression of abnormal, mutated genes. These conditions, termed "gain of function" diseases, include a number of cancers, some forms of Alzheimer's disease, Huntington's disease, and fragile X syndrome. Since every cell in the body carries these faulty but active genes, merely replacing them is not yet an option.

For these types of diseases, genetic researchers are taking a lesson from the natural strategies used by bacteria and eukaryotic organisms for regulating gene expression (chapter 9). Recall that these organisms use regulatory RNA or RNAi, including small interfering RNAs and microRNAs, to silence gene expression. This knowledge has driven the development of genetic-based drugs that interfere with mRNA processing and protein synthesis. Some of the most promising therapies involve the targeting of RNA virus genomes by small RNAs. They have been used to degrade HIV and respiratory syncytial viruses. They have also been tested as a treatment for macular degeneration and as a therapy to silence cancer genes.

Early clinical trials of RNAi therapeutics have been promising, with most of them dramatically lowering the rate of synthesis of the targeted protein. Because the RNAi agent can be targeted to a specific sequence of DNA, side effects are rare. The biggest obstacles involve how to deliver the RNAi drugs into deep tissues where their targets lie and the fact that these drugs would have to be taken for life.

 Practice SECTION 10.3

17. Describe several uses of genetically modified bacteria and viruses in medicine or industry.

18. Explain the techniques for genetically modifying plants.

19. Why must animals usually be modified in the embryo stage to arrive at successful outcomes?

20. Describe the possible ethical or biological problems associated with eating peanuts from an engineered plant or pork from a transgenic pig.

21. What are some ethical and biological considerations when using transgenic animals to manufacture various human products?

22. Outline the uses of gene therapy and gene editing to control genetic diseases and the possible harm they may cause.

10.4 Genome Analysis: DNA Profiling and Genetic Testing

Learn

12. Discuss the concept of the use of DNA in genome identification.

13. Describe two methods in performing a DNA analysis, its possible applications, and how it can be so precise.

14. Describe several applications of DNA profiling and microarray analysis.

A geneticist's joke begins: "How would you describe a cat?" The answer, "ACATACATACAT . . . ," is becoming more and more a reality. As we mentioned earlier, DNA technology has allowed us to accomplish many age-old goals by new and improved means. By remembering that phenotypes, whether human, bacterial, or even viral, are the result of specific sequences of DNA, we are now at a point where knowledge of DNA can be even more effective than observing phenotypes to differentiate among organisms and people. Additionally, DNA can be used to "see" the phenotype of an organism or person no longer present, as when a criminal is identified by DNA extracted from a strand of hair left behind at the crime scene. Finally, possession of a particular sequence of DNA may indicate an increased risk of a genetic disease. Detection of a specific and unique region of DNA, or **marker,** can identify a person as being at increased risk for cancer or Alzheimer's disease long before symptoms arise. The ability to detect diseases before symptoms arise is especially important for conditions such as cancer, where early treatment can make the difference between life and death. With examples like this in mind, let's look at several ways in which new DNA technology offers extraordinary glimpses into the present, past, and future.

DNA Profiling: A Unique Picture of a Genome

Although all DNA is based on a structure of nucleotides, the exact way these nucleotides are combined is unique for each organism.

Such genetic variations, or polymorphisms, will vary to some extent even among close relatives (except identical twins, whose DNA comes from the same fertilized egg). A major goal of DNA technology is to discover these unique qualities, emphasize their differences, and provide a pattern for comparison and identification. **DNA profiling** (sometimes called DNA fingerprinting or typing) was developed as a **forensic*** technique in the mid-1980s by English geneticist Alex Jeffreys. The first methods of analysis used restriction enzymes to cut DNA located at specific recognition sites and to target genetic polymorphisms called RFLPs, introduced earlier in the chapter. The results were rendered into a series of bands or "barcodes" that could be used to compare several samples alongside each other. It turns out that hidden within genomes are large numbers of other types of DNA variations that can be used in identifying individuals that are even more specific and widespread than RFLP fingerprints.

Several of the methodologies discussed previously in this chapter are essential to creating a DNA profile. This includes PCR amplification for increasing the number of copies of a certain gene, electrophoresis to separate DNA fragments, and hybridization probes or primers that link to specific nucleotide sequences. The primary idea is to distinguish one isolated piece of DNA from another by comparing the genetic variations at a specific location, or **locus***. Note that DNA profiling is not the same as whole genome sequencing but instead focuses on a few selected genetic loci to produce a "snapshot" of a particular polymorphism pattern. Millions of such differences are known to exist throughout the genome. Many of these polymorphisms are located in regions of the DNA that do not code for protein and are considered normal rather than harmful variations.

The most reliable methods of DNA profiling presently available are (1) **short tandem repeats** (STRs), relatively short fragments of nuclear DNA that are covered below in some detail; (2) **mtDNA** or mitotyping to identify the DNA found in mitochondria; and (3) **single nucleotide polymorphisms** (SNPs) that locate variants of a single nucleotide in the population. Important features of STR analysis and mitochondrial profiling will be discussed under the next headings.

STR Profiling

The most routine methods in forensic identification are based on short tandem repeats. These are segments of DNA that consist of a short chain 2 to 8 nucleotides long. These STRs are repeated in series multiple times. Both the number of nucleotides in a sequence and the number of repeats of it vary throughout the genome. An example of this type of sequence in which four bases (GATA) repeat five times would read:

AGCT|*GATA*|*GATA*|*GATA*|*GATA*|*GATA*|GGCC

Studies have identified thousands of these repeated sequences, which provide the background data for producing a profile. Almost

** forensic* (for'-en-sik) The application of science to law, especially as it relates to the investigation of crime.

** locus* (loh'-kuss) The specific site on a DNA molecule where a particular gene or sequence of nucleotides is located.

(a) Samples may be taken from many sources, including tissues, semen, saliva, hair, and blood. Nuclear DNA is isolated and run through a PCR amplifier to produce large numbers of selected DNA fragments. During this process, specific primer/probes with fluorescent dyes are incorporated into the DNA so that they can be readily traced (right).

Sample, suspect #1

Sample from evidence

Sample, suspect #2

(b) Close-up of tagged DNA; the fluorescent primers are specific to known STR sequences that have been associated with human genomes.

(c) Sample of amplified, tagged DNA is loaded into a capillary tube electrophoresis system. As each band migrates through a laser detector, its fluorescent code is scanned, which sends a signal to a computer analyzer that displays the identity of each band.

(d) The pattern reads out as a series of colored peaks. The color and position of the peak indicate a specific STR allele. The height of the peak indicates the amount of DNA in that STR. The red peaks are known standards to verify accuracy of the result. Three profiles are shown here. To have a match, you will see close correlation with regard to location and number of peaks. Can you tell if there is a match? Further analysis will compare the samples and predict the odds that one of the suspects is the source of the evidence.

Figure 10.17 **(a–d) An outline of short tandem repeat (STR) profiling.** This technique is widely used in forensics, geneology, population studies, identification of types of cancer, and genetic diseases.

all of them occur in noncoding regions of the genome, but they are inherited the same way that genes are—as a pair of alleles, one from each parent. The genotype of a given allele can be the same or can be different, just as for eye color or blood type. At the heart of STR analysis is the pattern of nucleotides and number of repeats detected. This form of DNA profiling is mostly conducted by specialized machinery that is computer-driven and computer-analyzed, as outlined in **figure 10.17** and discussed below.

A sample of DNA is isolated from a person or object and tagged with a number of known STR-specific primers to ready them for PCR amplification. These primers not only complement a known sequence of DNA, they also carry fluorescent dyes for later detection. After these sequences are amplified, they are electrophoresed and scanned by a laser that detects the fluorescent pattern of the primers and thus the specific STR alleles. The resultant readout, called an electropherogram, is a series of colored peaks that coincide with the STRs from that sample (figure 10.17d). This pattern undergoes further analysis to indicate possible matches and a mathematical probability of the pattern being anyone other than the in-

dividual from the sample. The database contains a cross reference of the frequencies of the combinations of STRs from real populations for accuracy in comparisons.

Let us examine how this analysis would work: Imagine that a sample of blood found at a crime scene is thought to have come from a suspect and has tested positive for STR markers (alleles) A, B, C, and D. If marker A is normally present in 1 person out of 80, marker B in 1 person out of 60, marker C in 1 person out of 45, and marker D in 1 person out of 70, the probability that a single person would have all four markers is $(1/80 \times 1/60 \times 1/45 \times 1/70)$ or 1 out of 15,120,000. When the suspect's markers match those seen in blood from the crime scene, it is a powerful indicator that the suspect was involved in the crime, especially when supported by traditional evidence, such as the suspect's having been seen near the crime scene. Adding even more STR loci can increase the probability to as high as 1 out of several billion or trillion, solidifying the match to an undeniable degree.

DNA profiling has been widely used to convict or exonerate many thousands of accused defendants in criminal cases. Besides

actual fingerprints, criminals often leave other evidence at the site of a crime—hair, skin, semen, blood, and saliva. In fact, the technology is so reliable that many older cases for which samples are available are being reopened and solved. The FBI has established a national database (the **Combined DNA Index System** or **CODIS**) to support this effort. The CODIS technology analyzes 13 common STRs, with a fourteenth that determines sex. This provides a uniform source for comparisons across law enforcement and forensics. Present laws require that prisoners, felons, and other violent offenders have their CODIS profiles entered into this system to keep tabs on known criminals.

The most frequent uses of DNA profiling are in forensics, identifying missing persons, detecting genetic diseases, determining parentage, analyzing the family trees of humans and animals, tracing the lineage of organisms, and identifying microorganisms. In a stunning application of DNA profiling, forensic scientists were able to positively identify the Unibomber, Ted Kaczynski, by DNA recovered from the back of postage stamps he had licked. This same technology has also been effective in identifying the remains of astronauts from the shuttle *Columbia,* some victims of Hurricane Katrina, nearly 2,000 individuals from the World Trade Center attack, and even to verify that the person killed in the raid on a Pakistani compound in 2011 was indeed Osama Bin Laden. This sort of identification of unknown DNA always requires a sample of the known DNA of the suspected person or close relatives who would share some of the STR alleles.

Mitotyping

Recall that only eukaryotic organisms have mitochondria and that each mitochondrion is self-sustaining and carries its own chromosome. Mitochondrial DNA (mtDNA) consists of about 16,500 base pairs that code for 37 genes. One advantage of mtDNA is that it is highly conserved in evolution and does not change greatly over long periods of time. Even with this small genome, it has a number of unique variations that are sufficiently varied to identify humans, plants, and animals to the

level of species and even individuals. Another advantage of mtDNA is that it does not break down as readily as chromosomal DNA and remains intact even after being exposed to harsh conditions for thousands of years. Also, it is inherited only from the mother's egg, because sperm do not contribute mitochondria during fertilization of an egg. This means that children from the same mother will have the same mtDNA profile. MtDNA was integral to the identification of the Romanovs—the family of the last czar of Russia, who were assassinated and buried in a mass grave in 1919. It has also become a tool of geneology as a way to trace the maternal lineage of families and to clarify cases of maternity.

Because even fossilized or ancient DNA can remain partially intact, ancient DNA is being studied for comparative and evolutionary purposes. Anthropologists have traced the migrations of ancient people by analyzing the mitochondrial DNA found in bone fragments. Evolutionary biologists have been able to recover Neanderthal mtDNA and use it to show that these ancient primates were in a line of evolution separate from the modern human line. Biologists studying canine origins have also been able to show that the wolf is the ancestral species for modern canines.

Several large databanks are currently collecting genomic profiles on mtDNA markers for thousands of species of plants, animals, and fungi. Two of these—Genbank and Barcodes of Life—offer these sites as a way to keep track of biodiversity (the varieties of life on earth) and to provide information for researchers and commercial operations needing to identify specimens of fish, invertebrates, plants, and other organisms that cannot be identified by the usual methods.

Miscellaneous DNA Analysis Single nucleotide polymorphisms, or "SNIPs," are the most specific polymorphisms because they are the most variable, occurring around 10 million times among a person's 3.2 billion base pairs. They appear as single base differences at random sites throughout the chromosomes, both in genes and noncoding DNA. SNPs are a valuable tool in disease diagnosis, population genetics, personalized medicine, and

 CLINIC CASE

It's Not Him, but It's Close The patient's name was Laura Moore. After accepting a ride from what she thought was a kind stranger, she was assaulted and shot six times, barely escaping with her life. Police investigating the crime felt sure that she was a victim of a serial killer dubbed the Grim Sleeper, who was thought to be responsible for the death of several young women in the mid-1980s in Los Angeles.

Ballistic evidence, along with analysis of DNA from the various crime scenes, convinced police they were looking for a single killer, but they were unable to identify a suspect. A DNA profile from the crime scene was compared to profiles in CODIS, the FBI's Combined DNA Index System, but no match was found. The killer remained free.

In 2010, with the search relegated to the cold case files, investigators looked at DNA samples in CODIS that did not match DNA

from the crime scenes, but were similar. A single person, Christopher Franklin, was found whose DNA shared a number of similarities with the DNA at the crime scenes, but he was too young to have committed the crimes. Police then looked to his father, Lonnie Franklin, Jr., but did not have his DNA for comparison. An undercover police officer followed Lonnie Franklin to a pizza parlor and, posing as a busboy, collected his napkin, drinking glass, and a piece of uneaten pizza crust.

Franklin's DNA profile matched that found at the crime scenes and, in 2016, Franklin was convicted of 10 counts of murder.

It is likely that the napkin, glass, and pizza crust provided police investigators very little DNA with which to work. What could they have done to increase the size of their sample?

biomedical research. More and more, infectious disease laboratories are employing DNA test procedures based on SNPs to identify bacteria. Other forms of DNA typing are rapidly becoming the method of choice to identify pathogens, including *Neisseria gonorrhoeae*, *Chlamydia*, the syphilis spirochete, *Staphylococcus* MRSA, *Mycobacterium tuberculosis*, and a number of viruses. It is also an essential tool for determining genetic similarities between microbes involved in disease outbreaks.

Determining Gene Activity with Microarrays

Having a DNA profile or a sequence of a genome is really only half the battle. With very few exceptions, all cells in a multicellular organism contain the same DNA, so knowing the sequence of that DNA, while certainly helpful, is of very little use when comparing two cells or tissues from the same organism. Recall that genes are expressed in response to both internal needs and external stimuli and that although the DNA content of a cell remains constant, the mRNA (and hence protein) content at any given time provides scientists with a profile of genes currently being expressed in the cell. What truly distinguishes a liver cell from a kidney cell or a healthy cell from a diseased cell is their manner of gene expression.

Twin advances in biology and electronics have allowed biologists to view the expression of genes in any given cell using a technique called DNA *microarray analysis.* Prior to the advent of this technology, scientists were able to track the expression of at most only a few genes at a time. Given the complex interrelationship that exists between genes in a typical cell, tracking two or three genes would be of very little practical use. Microarrays are able to track the expression of thousands of genes at once and are able to do so in a single efficient experiment. Microarrays consist of a "chip" (made of glass, silicon, or nylon) that carries bound sequences from tens of thousands of different known genes. A solution containing fluorescently labeled cDNA, representing all of the mRNA molecules active in a cell at a given time, is applied to the chip. The labeled cDNA is allowed to hybridize with any complementary DNA bound to the chip. Bound cDNA is then detected by exciting the fluorescent tag on the cDNA with a laser and recording the fluorescence with a detector linked to a computer. The computer is programmed to interpret this data by highlighting what mRNAs are present in the cell under a variety of conditions. Look at **figure 10.18** for an example of results comparing a normal cell with a cancer cell.

Microarrays permit the development of extraordinarily sensitive diagnostic tests that search for a specific pattern of gene

Figure 10.18 **Gene expression analysis using microarrays.** Microarrays display large numbers of genes being expressed at the same time in the same cell. Small slides or chips are coated with fluorescently labeled genes and exposed to unknown cDNAs. A laser excites the bound cDNAs, while a detector records those spots that fluoresce. The color of each spot reveals whether the DNA on the microarray is present in the normal cell, the cancer cell, both cells, or neither.
Source: Darryl Leja, NHGRI

expression. As an example, being able to identify a patient's cancer as one of many subtypes (rather than just, for instance, breast cancer) will allow selection of a cancer drug that appears to be most effective. Again, we see how genetic technology can greatly assist in medical decisions.

 Practice SECTION 10.4

23. Describe what a DNA profile is and how STRs and other polymorphic fragments can be used to display the unique qualities of DNA.

24. Discuss briefly how DNA profiling is being used routinely by medicine, the law, the military, and studies of human biology and history.

25. Explain the origins of mtDNA and its importance in identification.

26. Explain the difference between a DNA profile and a microarray.

 CASE STUDY | **Part 2**

The limiting gene carried by each male mosquito codes for a protein known as tTAV (tetracycline-repressible transactivator variant). The tTAV protein binds to transcriptional machinery within the cell—proteins and DNA sequences responsible for binding and stabilizing the RNA polymerase—and prevents the transcription of genes necessary for maturation. Without expression of these genes, the mosquito does not develop and dies before it can pass on the virus. Making this strategy even more powerful, tTAV enhances its own production. Through a mechanism called a positive feedback loop, the tTAV protein binds to regulatory regions of the limiting gene, increasing transcription of the gene and causing more of the tTAV protein to be produced. This loop means that the longer a mosquito survives, the more of the limiting protein it will produce, ensuring its own eventual demise. The tTAV protein is non-toxic and will not harm any animal that eats a genetically modified mosquito, another advantage over traditional insecticides.

One question that should come to mind is that if the mosquitoes are engineered to carry a gene that kills them, how are they ever raised in the first place? The answer is that the *t* of the tTAV gene stands for *tetracycline repressible*. The antibiotic tetracycline binds to the tTAV protein and disables it, preventing transcription of the tTAV gene, interrupting the positive feedback loop, and allowing the mosquito to survive, until tetracycline is removed from the environment.

Like a bacterial colony containing millions of cells, the mosquitoes in the production facility were all descendants of an individual organism. Using a technique called microinjection, a single *Aedes agypti* egg was injected with the limiting gene, which was permanently incorporated into the mosquito's genome. The mosquito carrying the gene was mated many times to create thousands of offspring to use as breeding stock, all held in cages at the production facility that smells of the damp fish food used to feed the genetically engineered insects. Each cage contains 12,000 females and 4,000 males, and will yield nearly 3 million eggs, which are collected and induced to hatch simultaneously. Eight days later, relying on the fact that females are much larger than males, the sexes are separated and most of the females killed (a small number are kept for breeding purposes); only males are released because they do not bite and are thus incapable of spreading the virus.

The size of mosquito populations is determined by counting insects caught in thousands of traps spread across the area being studied. The number of trapped mosquitoes is then used to estimate the total number of mosquitoes in the environment. To determine whether trapped mosquitoes are the offspring of released self-limited mosquitoes or fertile wild ones, Oxitec mosquitoes were engineered to carry a second gene that produces a fluorescent protein, allowing rapid identification of trapped mosquitoes as engineered or wild-type. Being able to follow fluctuating mosquito populations allows scientists to accurately target resources and evaluate the success of the program.

■ What is the importance of causing the mosquito eggs to hatch simultaneously?

■ If the genetically engineered mosquitoes did not produce a fluorescent protein, would there have been any way to identify and track the mosquitoes?

Chapter Summary with Key Terms

10.1 Basic Elements and Applications of Genetic Engineering
 Genetic engineering refers to the manipulation of an organism's genome and is often used in conjunction with biotechnology, the use of an organism's biochemical and metabolic pathways for industrial production of proteins.
 A. *Practical Properties of DNA*
 1. **Restriction endonucleases** are used to cut DNA at specific recognition sites, resulting in small segments of DNA that can be more easily managed in the laboratory.
 2. The enzyme **ligase** is used to covalently join DNA molecules, whereas **reverse transcriptase** is used to obtain a DNA copy of a particular mRNA.
 3. Short strands of DNA called oligonucleotides are used either as probes for specific DNA sequences or as primers for DNA polymerase.
 B. *Nucleic Acid Hybridization and Probes*
 1. The two strands of DNA can be separated (denatured) by heating. These single-stranded nucleic acids will bind, or **hybridize,** to their complementary sequence, allowing them to be used as **probes.**
 a. In the Southern blot method, DNA isolated from an organism is probed to identify specific DNA sequences.
 b. **FISH** (fluorescent in situ hybridization) is a method of hybridizing and identifying intact DNA inside cells.
 C. *Methods Used to Size, Synthesize, and Sequence DNA*
 1. A technique called **DNA sequencing,** originally developed by Frederick Sanger, allows for the determination of the exact sequence of DNA.

a. The ultimate map is a whole genome sequence map, which provides the exact order of all of the nucleotides that make up an entire genome of an organism. This can provide detailed information on the function of genes and can be useful in identification of genetic diseases. Sequencing is also a common method of choice to identify microbes.

2. The **polymerase chain reaction** is a technique used to amplify a specific segment of DNA several million times in just a few hours.

10.2 Recombinant DNA Technology: How to Imitate Nature

A. *Technical Aspects of Recombinant DNA Technology*

1. **Recombinant DNA** methods have as their goal the transfer of DNA from one organism to another. This commonly involves inserting the DNA into a **vector** (usually a plasmid or virus) and transferring the recombinant vector to a **cloning host** (usually a bacterium or yeast) for expression.

 a. Examples of cloning vectors include plasmids, bacteriophages, and cosmids, as well as the larger bacterial and yeast artificial chromosomes (BACs and YACs).

 b. Cloning hosts are fast-growing, nonpathogenic organisms that are genetically well understood. Examples include *E. coli* and *Saccharomyces cerevisiae.*

2. **Recombinant organisms** are created by cutting both the donor DNA and the plasmid DNA with restriction endonucleases and then joining them together with ligase. The vector is then inserted into a cloning host by transformation, and those cells containing the vector are cultured and selected by their resistance to antibiotics.

3. When the appropriate recombinant cell has been identified, it is grown on an industrial scale. The cloning host expresses the gene it contains, and the resulting protein is excreted from the cell where it can be recovered from the media and purified.

B. *Protein Products of Recombinant DNA Technology*

1. In many instances, the final product of recombinant DNA technology is a protein.

2. Medical conditions such as diabetes, dwarfism, and blood-clotting disorders can be treated with recombinant insulin, human growth factor, and clotting factors produced by recombinant DNA technology.

10.3 Genetically Modified Organisms and Other Applications

A. Recombinant organisms, also known as **transgenics** and **genetically modified organisms (GMOs)** include microbes, plants, and animals that have been engineered to express genes inserted from another organism.

1. Transformed bacteria produce a wide variety of drugs, vaccines, and other useful materials.

2. Modified viruses function as genetic vectors and vaccines.

3. Plants are **transfected** using *Agrobacterium,* that can shuttle donor genes into cells.

4. Animals are genetically engineered by having selected genes inserted into an embryo.

5. The CRISPR/Cas-9 system acts to excise integrated viral DNA from the chromosomal DNA of bacterial cells. The system is commonly used to edit DNA in the laboratory, allowing researchers to remove or replace genes quite easily.

B. *Medical Applications of DNA Technology*

1. **Gene therapy** describes a collection of techniques in which defective genes are replaced or have their expression increased or decreased. Therapy is said to be in vivo if cells are altered within the body and ex vivo if the alteration is done on cells taken from the body.

2. Several proposed treatments involve gene silencing with regulatory RNA.

10.4 Genome Analysis: DNA Profiling and Genetic Testing

A. **DNA Profiling**

1. Because the DNA sequence of an organism is unique, it can be analyzed by identifying specific genetic markers or combinations of DNA sequences unique to each individual. These are known as **polymorphisms** ("many forms") because they vary widely within a population.

2. Common polymorphisms include **short tandem repeats (STRs),** which are repeats of the same nucleotide sequence, and **single nucleotide polymorphisms (SNPs),** which are variations of a single nucleotide at a given locus on a chromosome.

3. Technologies exist for targeting these markers for use in forensic identification, disease diagnosis, anthropology, and identifying microorganisms.

4. **Mitochondrial DNA (mtDNA)** also has sequences unique to a given eukaryotic species. It is useful in tracing family history and ancient origins, and in identifying species of animals, plants, and fungi.

B. *Microarray analysis* is a method of determining which genes are actively transcribed in a cell under a variety of conditions, such as health versus disease or growth versus differentiation.

 ## Assess Your Knowledge

Level I. These questions require a working knowledge of the concepts in the chapter and the ability to recall and understand the information you have studied.

Developing a Concept Inventory

Select the correct answer from the answers provided. For questions with blanks, choose the combination of answers that most accurately completes the statement.

1. Which gene is incorporated into plasmids to detect recombinant cells?
 a. restriction endonuclease
 b. virus receptor
 c. a gene for antibiotic resistance
 d. reverse transcriptase

2. Which of the following is *not* essential to carry out the polymerase chain reaction?
 a. primer
 b. DNA polymerase
 c. gel electrophoresis
 d. high temperature

3. Which of the following is *not* a part of the Sanger method to sequence DNA?
 a. dideoxynucleotide
 b. DNA polymerase
 c. electrophoresis
 d. reverse transcriptase

4. The function of ligase is to
 a. rejoin segments of DNA
 b. make longitudinal cuts in DNA
 c. synthesize cDNA
 d. break down ligaments

5. The pathogen of plant roots that is used as a cloning host is
 a. *Pseudomonas*
 b. *Agrobacterium*
 c. *Escherichia coli*
 d. *Saccharomyces cerevisiae*

6. Which of the following sequences, when combined with its complement, would be clipped by a restriction endonuclease?
 a. ATCGATCGTAGCTA
 b. AAGCTTCGAA
 c. GAATTC
 d. ACCATTGGA

7. Which DNA fragment will be closest to the top (negative pole) of an electrophoretic gel?
 a. 450 bp
 b. 3,560 bp
 c. 5 kb
 d. 1,500 bp

8. Which of the following is or are required for cloning a gene?
 a. restriction endonuclease
 b. vector
 c. cloning host
 d. a and b
 e. all of these

9. Which of the following would not require a nucleic acid probe?
 a. locating a gene on a chromosome
 b. developing a Southern blot
 c. identifying a microorganism with FISH
 d. constructing a recombinant plasmid

10. **Matching.** Match the term with its description.
 _____ nucleic acid probe
 _____ nontemplate strand
 _____ template strand
 _____ reverse transcriptase
 _____ Taq polymerase
 _____ RNAi
 _____ primer
 _____ restriction endonuclease
 a. enzyme that transcribes RNA into DNA
 b. complementary strand that blocks mRNA expression
 c. the nontranslated strand of DNA or RNA
 d. enzyme that snips DNA at palindromes
 e. oligonucleotide that initiates the PCR
 f. strand of nucleic acid that is transcribed or translated
 g. thermostable enzyme for synthesizing DNA
 h. oligonucleotide used in hybridization

Case Study Analysis

1. When producing the genetically engineered mosquitoes in this case, what was tetracycline used for?
 a. to prevent infection of the mosquitoes by pathogenic bacteria in the laboratory
 b. to protect farm animals who may be bitten by genetically engineered mosquitoes
 c. to cause production of the tTAV protein
 d. to prevent production of the tTAV protein

2. After each round of production (resulting in millions of genetically engineered mosquitoes), males were released while nearly all females were killed. This was done because
 a. females don't carry the limiting gene
 b. males cannot spread Zika virus
 c. females have a short life span and will die before mating
 d. female mosquitoes are too large to easily release

3. Tetracycline is sometimes added to animal feed to ward off infections in farm animals. How might this practice decrease the effectiveness of the engineered mosquitoes?

On the Test

These questions will help to prepare you to successfully answer similar questions you'll see on the TEAS (Test of Essential Academic Skills) and NCLEX (National Council Licensure Examination).

1. Which enzyme can synthesize a molecule of DNA from a mRNA molecule?
 a. DNA polymerase
 b. ligase
 c. RNA polymerase
 d. reverse transcriptase

2. DNA fragments can be separated using which technique?
 a. gel electrophoresis
 b. microarray identification
 c. polymerase chain reaction
 d. DNA sequencing

Writing Challenge

For each question, compose a one- or two-paragraph answer that includes the factual information needed to completely address the question. Practice questions can also be used for writing-challenge exercises.

1. Why do bacteria make restriction endonucleases?

2. What is it about the endonucleases that prevents bacteria from destroying their own DNA? Using nucleotide letters, show the kind of cut that could be made on a DNA molecule to circularize it into a plasmid.

3. Why would it be an advantage to synthesize eukaryotic genes by using reverse transcriptases to make cDNA?

4. a. Explain what hybridization is and how it is used in the Southern blot.
 b. Explain how gene probes and FISH techniques work.

5. Look at figure 10.7, and determine the correct DNA sequence for the fragment's template strand. (Be careful of orientation.)

6. a. Explain why the PCR is unlikely to amplify contaminating bacterial DNA in a sample of human DNA.
 b. Explain how PCR could be used to pick a gene out of a complex genome and amplify it.

7. The way PCR amplifies DNA is similar to the doubling in a population of growing bacteria—a single DNA strand is used to synthesize 2 DNA strands, which become 4, then 8, then 16, etc. If a complete cycle takes 3 minutes, how many strands of DNA would theoretically be present after 10 minutes? After 1 hour?

8. Explain the kinds of study involved in genomics, proteomics, and bioinformatics.

9. For what reasons would gene therapy be more effective performed on embryos rather than fully developed animals?

10. Explain the basics of DNA STR profiling for identification of unknown DNA.

Concept Mapping

On Connect you can find an Introduction to Concept Mapping that provides guidance for working with concept maps, along with concept-mapping activities for this chapter.

Application, Analysis, Evaluation, and Synthesis

Level II. These problems go beyond just restating facts and require higher levels of understanding and an ability to interpret, problem solve, transfer knowledge to new situations, create models, and predict outcomes.

Critical Thinking

Critical thinking is the ability to reason and solve problems using facts and concepts. These questions can be approached from a number of angles and, in most cases, they do not have a single correct answer.

1. a. Give an example of a benefit of genetic engineering to society and a possible adverse outcome. Discuss.
 b. Give an example of an ecological benefit and a possible adverse side effect. Discuss.

2. a. When gene probes, DNA profiling, and sequencing make it possible to detect genetic diseases in you or one of your children, would you want you or them to be tested?
 b. How would you react to it being used as a screening method for employment or insurance?

c. Most of us would agree to growth hormone therapy for a child with dwarfism, but what would you think about parents who want to give growth hormones to their 8-year-old son so that he will be "better at sports"?

3. Which suspect is the likely perpetrator according to the profile in figure 10.17? Explain your reasoning.

4. Trace the genetic steps in the development of a peanut plant that is resistant to insect larvae (table 10.3). (Hint: You need to use *Agrobacterium*.)

5. You are on a jury to decide whether a person committed a homicide, and you have to weigh evidence from DNA profiling. Two different sets of profiles were done: one that tested 5 markers, and one that tested 10. Both sets match the defendant's profile. Which one is more reliable and why?

6. Can you think of some reasons it would *not* be possible to re-create dinosaurs using the technology we have described in this chapter?

7. What would be some major impediments to genetically modifying human embryos with CRISPR?

8. Could actual fingerprints taken from human fingers be used to perform a DNA profile? Explain.

9. Describe the main differences between genome sequencing and DNA profiling as a means of identifying a person or microbe.

10. Itemize all of the ways that microbes have contributed to the development of genetic engineering and biotechnology.

Visual Assessment

1. Below are two unrelated DNA paternity tests: one indicates the man is the father and the other shows he is not. Can you tell which is which? C/AF = Child/Alleged father in one lane combined.

LADDER
Mother
Child
Alleged Father
C/AF Mix
LADDER

LADDER
Mother
Child
Alleged Father
C/AF Mix
LADDER

Courtesy of Genelex Corporation

2. Figure 9.25d, shows the original transformation experiment as done by Griffith. Explain how this outcome would be accomplished with modern technology, using figure 10.11 as your guide.

Live R strain

+

Heat-killed S strain

Live S and R strains isolated from dead mouse

Dies

CHAPTER

11

Physical and Chemical Agents for Microbial Control

In This Chapter...

(carbapenem-resistant enterobacteriaceae bacteria): Source: Melissa Brower/CDC; (Endoscope): Tadaki crew/Shutterstock; (Medical sterilization): Ganay Mutlu/Getty Images; ("radura" symbol): Kathy Park Talaro; (Surface pasteurization): Source: Paul Pierlott, USDA-ERRC/VGT

I Refuse to Die from Something I Can't Pronounce

Aaron Young could barely stand. The pain that kept the 18-year-old from getting dressed after showering now had him doubled over in agony. His mother called 911, and shortly thereafter Aaron was admitted to the pediatric intensive care unit at UCLA Medical Center. Diagnosed with an **inflamed pancreas,** the next step was to place a small stent in his **biliary duct** by threading a long, flexible **duodenoscope** (or endoscope) through his mouth, esophagus, stomach, and the first part of the small intestine. The procedure—endoscopic retrograde cholangiopancreatography (ERCP)—is performed nearly 700,000 times annually in the United States and provides a means of accessing the pancreas without the inherent complications of surgery.

A few days later, when Aaron should have been preparing to go home, he was instead shivering under the cooling blanket doctors were using to fight his **104°F fever.** He had developed a serious infection from a bacterium known as **carbapenem-resistant Enterobacteriaceae (CRE),** a group of enteric bacteria with high levels of **resistance** to antibiotics. These infections are seen almost exclusively in **compromised patients** whose care depends upon devices like **ventilators, catheters,** or **endoscopes.** Even with aggressive treatment, up to 50% of patients infected with CRE die. Aaron Young was one of the lucky ones, and was discharged on January 6, 83 days after first entering the hospital.

Any new, life-threatening infection at UCLA Medical Center quickly garnered the attention of Dr. Zachary Rubin, the hospital's medical director of **clinical epidemiology** and infection prevention. He immediately focused on the endoscope, realizing that it was the perfect vehicle for transmitting **pathogenic bacteria.** Costing $40,000 apiece, duodenoscopes are complex instruments containing a light, camera, air and water nozzle, and a movable control called an elevator, to which catheters or guide wires can be attached. Cleaning (referred to as **reprocessing**) the scope between patients was done following a specific protocol in which scrub brushes, detergents, **disinfectants,** and sterile water were used to remove biological debris. Dr. Rubin visited the cleaning room, where workers scrubbed the scopes and flushed out their internal channel before placing them in washing machines with powerful disinfectants. His visit served only to confirm that the scopes were being properly reprocessed between patients.

He then began searching UCLAs records for the previous year, finding 34 patients diagnosed with CRE infections, half of whom had become infected during their hospital stay. His next task was to look for commonalities between the patients. Were they hospitalized on the same floor? Did they undergo the same procedure? Were they attended to by the same health care providers? A team of doctors at UCLA scrutinized patient records, expanding their search to include every CRE patient seen at UCLA since 2011.

On January 25, Aaron Young returned to UCLA for a second ERCP procedure, this time to have his stent removed. Shortly after the procedure, his infection returned, and his survival was in doubt.

- *Why did suspicion immediately fall on the endoscope as a source of infection?*
- *What's the difference between sterilization, disinfection, and antisepsis?*

To continue the Case Study, go to Case Study Part 2 at the end of the chapter.

(endoscope): Tadaki crew/Shutterstock

11.1 Controlling Microorganisms

 Learn

1. Summarize the major categories of microbial control and its purposes.

2. Evaluate the relative resistance of different groups of infectious agents.

3. Define and differentiate among the major terms for microbial control, citing examples of each.

4. Characterize the parameters of microbial death, and describe several factors that influence the rate of death.

5. Summarize what factors influence the effectiveness of an antimicrobial agent.

6. Identify the targets of antimicrobial control agents, and explain what effects these agents have.

Much of the time in our daily existence, we take for granted tap water that is drinkable, food that is not spoiled, shelves full of products to eradicate "germs," and drugs to treat infections. Controlling our degree of exposure to potentially harmful microbes is of monumental concern to our lives, and it has been a concern even before we were aware of the germ-disease connection.

Historians have discovered that during the great plague pandemic of the Middle Ages it was commonplace to bury corpses in mass graves, burn the clothing of plague victims, and ignite aromatic woods in the houses of the sick in the belief that fumes would combat the disease. In a desperate search for some sort of protection, survivors wore peculiar garments and anointed their bodies with herbs, strong perfume, and vinegar **(figure 11.1).** These attempts may sound foolish and antiquated, but it now appears that

Figure 11.1 **Illustration of protective clothing used by doctors in the 1700s to avoid exposure to plague victims.** The beaklike portion of the hood contained volatile perfumes to protect against foul odors and possibly inhaling "bad air."
Universal History Archive/UIG/Getty Images

they may have had some benefits. Burning wood releases formaldehyde, which could have acted as a disinfectant; herbs, perfume, and vinegar contain mild antimicrobial substances. Each of these early methods, although somewhat crude, laid the foundations for microbial control methods that are still in use today.

General Considerations in Microbial Control

The methods of microbial control belong to the general category of *decontamination* procedures, in that they destroy or remove contaminants. In microbiology, contaminants are microbes present at a given place and time that are undesirable or unwanted. Most decontamination methods employ either physical agents, such as heat or radiation, or chemical agents, such as disinfectants and antiseptics. This separation is convenient, even though the categories overlap in some cases; for instance, radiation can cause damaging chemicals to form, and chemicals can generate heat. A flowchart **(figure 11.2)** summarizes the major applications and aims in microbial control.

Relative Resistance of Microbial Forms

Processes for controlling microbes generally target microorganisms that are constantly present in the external environment and on the human body and that could cause infection or spoilage. This targeted population is rarely simple or uniform; in fact, it often contains mixtures of microbes with extreme differences in resistance and harmfulness. Contaminants that can have detrimental effects if not adequately controlled include bacterial vegetative cells and endospores, fungal hyphae and spores, yeasts, protozoan trophozoites and cysts, worms, viruses, and prions. This scheme compares the general resistance of these forms to physical and chemical methods of control:

Highest resistance
Prion (proteinaceous infectious particles); bacterial endospores, primarily from bacteria in the genera *Bacillus* and *Clostridium.*

Moderate resistance
Protozoan cysts; some fungal sexual spores (zygospores); some viruses. In general, naked viruses are more resistant than enveloped forms.
Several groups of bacteria lack endospores but have vegetative cells with increased resistance to microbial control agents. These include *Mycobacterium,* whose cell walls have thick, waxy layers that can block the entrance of many disinfectants. The cell walls of *Pseudomonas, Acinetobacter,* and other gram-negative pathogens have an outer membrane that also prevents penetration of some chemical agents. *Staphylococcus* species are among the most heat- and chemical-resistant of all bacteria due to their thick, protective peptidoglycan cell walls.

Least resistance
Most bacterial vegetative cells; fungal spores (other than zygospores) and hyphae; enveloped viruses; yeasts; and protozoan trophozoites.

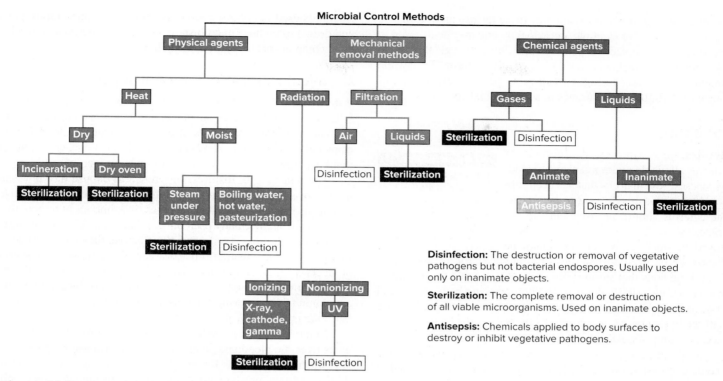

Figure 11.2 An overview of microbial control methods.

Disinfection: The destruction or removal of vegetative pathogens but not bacterial endospores. Usually used only on inanimate objects.

Sterilization: The complete removal or destruction of all viable microorganisms. Used on inanimate objects.

Antisepsis: Chemicals applied to body surfaces to destroy or inhibit vegetative pathogens.

Actual comparative figures on the requirements for destroying various groups of microorganisms are shown in **table 11.1.** Bacterial endospores have traditionally been considered the most resistant microbial entities, being as much as 18 times harder to destroy than vegetative cells. Because endospores show such high resistance to microbial control and have widespread distribution, destroying them is the goal of **sterilization.** Any process that kills endospores will invariably kill all less-resistant microbial forms. Other methods of control (disinfection, antisepsis) target primarily microbes that are less hardy than endospores.

Prions present a problem in the context of decontamination. This chapter defines *sterile* as the absence of all viable microbial life. But prions are not microbes or living, and most of the procedures described here are not sufficient to destroy them. Prion proteins are extraordinarily resistant to heat, chemicals, and radiation. Instruments or other objects contaminated with these unique agents must be incinerated at very high temperatures or decontaminated with a combination of chemicals. The substances that have proved most effective are sodium hydroxide and hypochlorite (bleach) solutions that render them noninfectious after a significant period of exposure. When tissues, fluids, or instruments are suspected of containing prions, consultation with the CDC is recommended to ensure effective sterilization

Endospore of *Bacillus* sp.

SJ Jones, CJ Paredes, B Tracy, N Cheng, R Sillers, RS Senger, ET Papoutsakis, "The transcriptional program underlying the physiology of clostridial sporulation," *Genome Biol.,* 2008. 9:R114

conditions. In terms of routine sterilization procedures, this chapter will treat bacterial endospores as the most resistant form of microbial life targeted by antimicrobial agents. Prions are not environmentally widespread in the way that bacterial endospores and other microbes are.

Terminology and Methods of Microbial Control

Through the years, a growing terminology has emerged for describing and defining measures that control microbes. To complicate

TABLE 11.1	Relative Resistance of Bacterial Endospores and Vegetative Cells to Control Agents		
Method	Endospores*	Vegetative Forms*	Relative Resistance**
Heat (moist)	120°C	80°C	1.5×
Radiation (X-ray) dosage	4,000 grays	1,000 grays	4×
Sterilizing gas (ethylene oxide)	1,200 mg/1	700 mg/1	1.7×
Sporicidal liquid (2% glutaraldehyde)	3 hours	10 min	18×

*Values are based on methods (concentration, exposure time, intensity) that are required to destroy the most resistant pathogens in each group.

**This number is a comparison of the conditions required to kill endospores versus vegetative cells and is an average of the most resistant pathogens in each group.

matters, the everyday use of some of these terms can at times be vague or inexact. For example, occasionally one may be directed to "sterilize" or "disinfect" a patient's skin, even though this usage does not fit the technical definition of either term. To lay the groundwork for the coverage to follow, we present here a series of concepts, definitions, and usages in antimicrobial control.

Sterilization

Sterilization is a process that destroys or removes all viable microorganisms, including viruses. Any material that has been subjected to this process is said to be **sterile.** These terms should be used only in the strictest sense for methods that have been proved to sterilize. An object cannot be slightly sterile or almost sterile—it is either sterile or not sterile.

> **Quick Search**
> Find out more by searching for "What is Sterilization" on YouTube.

Control methods that sterilize are generally reserved for inanimate objects, because sterilizing tissues within a living body would call for such harsh treatment that it would be highly dangerous. As we shall see in chapter 13, many parts of the body—the brain and most internal organs, for example—are naturally free of microbes.

Sterilized products—surgical instruments, syringes, and some commercially packaged foods, just to name a few—are essential to human well-being. Although most sterilization is performed with a physical agent such as heat, a few chemicals called *sterilants* can be classified as sterilizing agents because of their ability to destroy spores.

At times, sterilization is neither practicable nor necessary, and only certain groups of microbes are of concern. Some antimicrobial agents eliminate only the susceptible vegetative states of microorganisms but do not destroy the more resistant endospore and cyst stages. Keep in mind that the destruction of spores is not always a necessity, because most of the infectious diseases of humans and animals are caused by non–spore-forming microbes.

Microbicidal Agents

The root *-cide,* meaning to kill, can be combined with other terms to define an antimicrobial agent aimed at destroying a certain group of microorganisms. For example, a **bactericide** is a chemical that destroys bacteria except for those in the endospore stage. It may or may not be effective on other microbial groups. A **fungicide** is a chemical that can kill fungal spores, hyphae, and yeasts. A **virucide** is any chemical known to inactivate viruses, especially on living tissue. A **sporicidal** agent can destroy bacterial endospores, which makes it also a sterilizing agent.

Agents that Cause Microbistasis

The words *stasis* and *static* mean to stand still. They can be used in combination with various prefixes to denote a condition termed **microbistasis** in which microbes are temporarily prevented from multiplying but are not killed outright. Although killing or permanently inactivating microorganisms is the usual goal of microbial control, microbistasis can have meaningful applications. **Bacteriostatic** agents prevent the growth of bacteria on tissues or on objects in the environment, and *fungistatic* chemicals inhibit fungal growth.

Materials used to control microorganisms in the body (antiseptics and drugs) often have microbistatic effects because many microbicidal compounds are highly toxic to human cells.

Germicides, Disinfection, Antisepsis

A **germicide,*** also called a *microbicide,* is any chemical agent that kills pathogenic microorganisms. A germicide can be used on inanimate (nonliving) materials or on living tissue, but it ordinarily cannot kill resistant microbial cells. Any physical or chemical agent that kills "germs" is said to have germicidal properties.

The related term **disinfection*** refers to the use of a physical process or a chemical agent—a **disinfectant**—to destroy vegetative pathogens but not bacterial endospores. It is important to note that disinfectants are normally used only on inanimate objects because, at the concentrations required to be effective, they can be toxic to living tissue. Disinfection processes can also remove the harmful products of microorganisms (toxins) from materials. Examples of disinfection include applying a diluted solution of bleach to an examination table, exposing drinking water to UV radiation, and pasteurizing milk with heat.

In modern usage, **sepsis** is defined as the growth of microorganisms in the blood and other tissues. The term **asepsis*** refers to any practice that blocks the entry of infectious agents into sterile tissues and thus prevents infection. Aseptic techniques commonly practiced in health care range from sterile methods that exclude all microbes to **antisepsis.*** With antisepsis, chemical agents called **antiseptics** are applied directly to exposed body surfaces (skin and mucous membranes), wounds, and surgical incisions to destroy or inhibit vegetative pathogens. Examples of antisepsis include preparing the skin before surgical incisions with iodine compounds, swabbing a wound with hydrogen peroxide, and ordinary hand washing with a germicidal soap.

Methods that Reduce the Numbers of Microorganisms

Although medical applications quite often require sterility, especially with regard to invasive instruments such as scalpels, clamps, dental hand tools, and the like, in other situations this high level of microbial control is often unwarranted and perhaps even unwanted. In many cases it is more important to focus on reducing the size of a microbial population, or its *microbial load.* **Sanitization*** refers to any cleansing technique that removes debris, soil, microorganisms, and toxins, and in this way reduces the potential for infection and spoilage. Soaps and detergents are the most commonly employed sanitizers. From a practical standpoint, sanitization can have an advantage over sterilization. For example, in a restaurant you could be given a sterile fork with someone else's old food on it and a sterile glass with lipstick on the rim. Given that sanitization is in general far less expensive than sterilization, its cleansing effect has obvious advantages.

* *germicide* (jer′-mih-syd) L. *germen,* germ, and *caedere,* to kill. *Germ* is a common term for a pathogenic microbe.
* *disinfection* (dis″-in-fek′-shun) L. *dis,* apart, and *inficere,* to corrupt.
* *asepsis* (ay-sep′-sis) Gr. *a,* no or none, and *sepsis,* decay.
* *antisepsis anti,* against.
* *sanitization* (san″ih-tih-zay′-shun) L. *sanitas,* health.

TABLE 11.2	Microbial Control Terminology	
Term	**Definition**	**Example**
Decontamination	The destruction, removal, or reduction in number of undesirable microbes	Asepsis, disinfection, sanitization, degermation, sterilization
Sepsis	The growth of microorganisms in the tissues	The presence of infected wounds, blood infection
Asepsis	Techniques that prevent the entry of microorganisms into sterile tissues	Cleansing the skin with iodine prior to surgery, using sterile needles
Antiseptic	Chemicals applied to body surfaces to destroy or inhibit vegetative pathogens	Iodophors, antibacterial soap, chlorhexidine
Disinfection	Destruction of vegetative pathogens on inanimate objects	5% bleach, boiling water
Sanitization	Cleansing technique that removes microorganisms and debris from inanimate surfaces	Dishwashing, laundering clothes
Degermation	Cleansing technique that removes microorganisms and debris from living tissue	Surgical handscrub, alcohol wipes
Sterilization	The removal or destruction of all viable microbes	Autoclaving, ionizing radiation

With living tissues, the reduction in microbial load through mechanical means is referred to as **degermation.** This process usually involves scrubbing the skin or immersing it in chemicals, or both. Microorganisms are removed both mechanically and indirectly by emulsifying the oils that coat the skin and provide a habitat for their growth. Examples of degerming procedures include the surgical handscrub, the application of alcohol wipes, and the cleansing of a wound with germicidal soap and water. **Table 11.2** summarizes several of the important terms involved in microbial control.

What Is Microbial Death?

Signs of life in complex organisms such as animals are self-evident, and death is made clear by loss of nervous function, respiration, or heartbeat. In contrast, death in microscopic organisms that are composed of just one or a few cells is hard to detect, because such organisms often reveal no conspicuous vital signs to begin with. Lethal agents (such as radiation and chemicals) do not necessarily alter the overt appearance of microbial cells. Even the loss of movement in a motile microbe cannot be used to indicate death. This situation has made it necessary to develop special qualifications that define microbial death and answer the questions: How do antimicrobial agents cause death? and Why do they vary in their effects?

The destructive effects of chemical or physical agents occur at the cellular and molecular level. As a cell is exposed to an agent such as intense heat or toxic chemicals, various cell structures break down, and the entire cell can sustain irreversible damage. At present, the most practical way to detect this damage is to determine if a microbial cell can still reproduce when exposed to a suitable environment. If the microbe has sustained metabolic or structural damage to such an extent that it can no longer reproduce, even in an ideal environment, then it is considered dead. In most circumstances, microbial death is defined as **the permanent loss of reproductive capacity, even under optimal growth conditions.**

Factors that Affect Death Rate

The ability to define microbial death has tremendous theoretical and practical importance. It allows medicine and industry to test the conditions required to destroy microorganisms, to pinpoint the ways antimicrobial agents kill cells, and to establish standards of sterilization and disinfection in these fields. Hundreds of testing procedures have been developed for evaluating physical and chemical agents. Some examples can be found in appendix B.

The cells of a culture show marked variation in susceptibility to a given microbicidal agent. Death of the whole population is not instantaneous but begins when a certain threshold of the microbicidal agent (some combination of time and concentration) is met. Death continues in a logarithmic manner as the time of exposure is increased **(figure 11.3).** Because many microbicidal agents target the cell's metabolic processes, active cells (younger, rapidly dividing) tend to die more quickly than those that are less metabolically active (older, dormant). Eventually a point is reached at which survival of any cells is highly unlikely; this point is equivalent to sterilization.

The effectiveness of a particular agent is governed by several factors besides time. These additional factors influence the action of antimicrobial agents:

1. The number of microorganisms **(figure 11.3b).** A higher load of contaminants requires more time to destroy.
2. The nature of the microorganisms in the population **(figure 11.3c).** In most actual circumstances of disinfection and sterilization, the target population is not a single species of microbe but a mixture of bacteria, fungi, spores, and viruses, presenting a broad spectrum of microbial resistance.

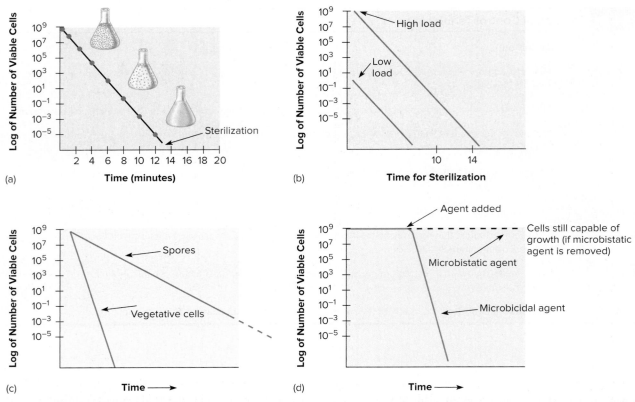

Figure 11.3 **Factors that influence the rate at which microbes are killed by antimicrobial agents.** **(a)** Length of exposure to the agent. During exposure to a chemical or physical agent, all cells of a microbial population, even a pure culture, do not die simultaneously. Over time, the number of viable organisms remaining in the population decreases logarithmically, giving a straight-line relationship on a graph. The point at which the number of survivors is infinitesimally small is considered sterilization. **(b)** Effect of the microbial load. **(c)** Relative resistance of spores versus vegetative forms. **(d)** Action of the agent, whether microbicidal or microbistatic.

3. The temperature and pH of the environment.
4. The concentration (dosage, intensity) of the agent. For example, UV radiation is most effective at 260 nm and most disinfectants are more active at higher concentrations.
5. The mode of action of the agent **(figure 11.3d).** How does it kill or inhibit microorganisms?
6. The presence of solvents, interfering organic matter, and inhibitors. Saliva, blood, and feces can inhibit the actions of disinfectants and even of heat.

Some Practical Concerns in Selecting Antimicrobial Agents

A remarkable variety of substances and objects require sterilization, disinfection, and other forms of decontamination. They range from durable materials made of glass and rubber to highly sensitive liquids such as blood plasma and even human tissues such as bone. Sometimes entire rooms with their contents and large pieces of equipment such as space vehicles and satellites may need to be sterilized. In accordance with an international agreement, all spacecraft landing on extraterrestrial bodies must have a highly reduced microbe load. This policy is to prevent the introduction of earth microbes that could potentially alter those environments or interfere with experiments being conducted by

NASA. Parts of the probes are sterilized with heat, radiation, and certain chemicals (peroxide), and then maintained in very controlled clean rooms that require extreme precautions against contamination by workers **(figure 11.4).**

There are literally hundreds of situations in health care settings alone where prevention of infection must be taken into consideration at all times. The CDC provides guidelines for recommended sterilization and disinfection procedures.

When choosing a procedure, one of the first questions to arise is, What will render materials free of potential pathogens? Consider, for instance, reusable dental instruments that are highly contaminated with saliva, blood, and other fluids and tissues. These are all potential sources of infection, so it is critical that they be sterilized between patients with a method that will kill endospores.

The next concern is selecting the best method of sterilization. Because they are mostly made of metal, dental instruments can be sterilized with heat, although some forms of radiation and chemical treatments could also work. Clinics generally opt for a method such as steam sterilization that is simplest, fastest, and least expensive. This would not work on other types of delicate instruments such as endoscopes, which must be disinfected between patients using heat-free techniques (see the Case Study for this chapter).

On the other hand, certain single-use medical supplies used in hospitals and clinics, such as plastic syringes and catheters, come

Figure 11.4 Employees in a clean room at NASA's Goddard Space Flight Center in Greenbelt, Maryland. Technicians examine the James Webb space telescope mirror, which is due to be launched on March 30, 2021.
Source: Desiree Stover/NASA

Figure 11.5 **Mode of action of surfactants on the cell membrane.** Surfactants inserting in the lipid bilayer disrupt it and create abnormal channels that alter permeability and cause leakage both into and out of the cell.

already sterilized and packaged at the factory. Because they are usually made of heat-sensitive plastics, this is done with penetrating radiation or chemicals. These items are not meant to be reused, but they still must be decontaminated before being discarded to prevent the transmission of disease. Disposal of such medical wastes is regulated by various governmental agencies.

How Antimicrobial Agents Work: Their Modes of Action

An antimicrobial agent's adverse effect on cells is known as its **mode** (or **mechanism**) **of action.** Agents affect one or more cellular targets, inflicting damage progressively until the cell is no longer viable. Antimicrobials have a range of cellular targets, with the agents that are least selective in their targeting tending to be effective against the widest range of microbes (examples include heat and radiation). More selective agents (drugs, for example) tend to target only a single cellular component and are much more restricted in their effect on microbes.

The cellular targets of physical and chemical agents fall into four general categories: (1) cell walls, (2) cell membranes, (3) protein and nucleic acid synthesis, and (4) protein structure and function.

The Effects of Agents on the Cell Wall

The cell wall maintains the structural integrity of bacterial and fungal cells. Several types of chemical agents damage the cell wall by blocking its synthesis, digesting it, or breaking down its surface. A cell deprived of a functioning cell wall becomes fragile and is lysed very easily. Examples of this mode of action include some antimicrobial drugs (penicillins) that interfere with the synthesis of the cell wall in bacteria (described in chapter 12). Detergents and alcohol can also disrupt cell walls, especially in gram-negative bacteria.

How Agents Affect the Cell Membrane

All microorganisms have a cell membrane composed of lipids and proteins, and even some viruses have an outer membranous envelope. As we learned in previous chapters, a cell's membrane provides a two-way system of transport. If this membrane is disrupted, a cell loses its selective permeability and can neither prevent the loss of vital molecules nor bar the entry of damaging chemicals. Loss of those functions usually leads to cell death. Chemicals called **surfactants*** work as microbicidal agents because they lower the surface tension of cell membranes. Surfactants are polar molecules such as detergents with hydrophilic and hydrophobic regions that can physically bind to the lipid layer and penetrate the internal hydrophobic regions of membranes. In effect, this process "opens up" the once-tight interface, leaving leaky spots that allow harmful chemicals to seep into the cell and important ions to seep out **(figure 11.5).** Alcohols exert a related effect by dissolving membrane lipids and stripping membranes away from cells.

Agents that Affect Protein and Nucleic Acid Synthesis

Microbial life depends upon an orderly and continuous supply of proteins to function as enzymes and structural molecules. As we saw in chapter 9, these proteins are synthesized on the ribosomes during translation. Any chemical that blocks this process can affect function and survival. For example, certain drugs bind to the ribosomes of bacteria in a way that stops peptide bonds from forming. In the presence of such a chemical, many bacterial cells are inhibited from forming proteins required in growth and metabolism and are thus inhibited from multiplying. Many of the drugs used to treat

* *surfactant* (sir-fak'-tunt) A word derived from **surf**ace-**act**ing ag**ent.**

infections are chemicals that block protein synthesis in microbes without adversely affecting human cells. This subject is discussed in greater detail in chapter 12.

The nucleic acids are also needed for the continued functioning of microbes. DNA must be regularly replicated and transcribed in growing cells, and any agent that either impedes these processes or changes the genetic code is potentially antimicrobial. Some agents bind irreversibly to DNA, preventing both transcription and translation, whereas others are mutagenic agents. Gamma, ultraviolet, or X radiation causes mutations that result in permanent inactivation of DNA. Chemicals such as formaldehyde and ethylene oxide also interfere with DNA and RNA function.

Agents that Alter Protein Function

A microbial cell contains large quantities of proteins that function properly only if they remain in a normal three-dimensional configuration called the *native state*. The antimicrobial properties of some agents arise from their capacity to disrupt the structure of, or **denature,** proteins. In general, **denaturation** occurs when the bonds that maintain the secondary and tertiary structure of the protein are broken. Breaking these bonds will cause the protein to unfold or create random, irregular loops and coils **(figure 11.6)**. One way to

(a) Native State

Substrate ——

Enzyme

—— Substrate

(b) Complete
Denaturation

Heat
pH Change

Heat
pH Change

Heavy metal

(d) Blocked Active Site

(c) Different
Shape

Active site can
no longer accept
the substrate,
and the enzyme
is inactive.

Figure 11.6 **Modes of action affecting protein function.**
(a) The native (functional) state is maintained by bonds that create active sites to fit the substrate. Some agents denature the protein by breaking all or some secondary and tertiary bonds. Results are **(b)** complete unfolding or **(c)** random bonding and incorrect folding. **(d)** Some agents react with functional groups on the active site and interfere with bonding.

denature proteins is through coagulation by moist heat (think of the irreversible solidification of egg white when cooked). Chemicals such as strong organic solvents (alcohols, acids) also coagulate proteins. A few antimicrobial agents, such as metallic ions, attach to the active site of the protein and prevent it from interacting with its correct substrate. Regardless of the exact mechanism, such losses in normal protein function can promptly stop metabolism and exert broad effects on all types of microbes.

Practice SECTION 11.1

1. Explain the purposes of microbial control and differentiate between physical, mechanical, and chemical methods.
2. Compare sterilization with disinfection and sanitization. Describe the relationship of the concepts of sepsis, asepsis, and antisepsis.
3. Contrast various microbes and rate their variations in resistance to control agents.
4. Explain how the types and numbers of microorganisms can influence the effectiveness of control agents.
5. How is microbial death defined?
6. Explain why a population of microbes does not die instantaneously when exposed to an antimicrobial agent.
7. Distinguish between microbicidal and microbistatic effects on microbes, and tell why it is important to understand the difference.
8. Describe four modes of action of antimicrobial agents, and provide examples of how they work.

11.2 Physical Methods of Control: Heat

Learn

7. List the major types of physical agents used in controlling microbes.
8. Describe the basic effects of temperature on microbes.
9. Define *moist* and *dry heat,* and explain their modes of action and relative effectiveness.
10. Differentiate between thermal death point and thermal death time, and provide examples of their uses.
11. Describe several moist heat methods and their chief applications for sterilization and disinfection.
12. Describe some methods using dry heat and its chief applications.
13. Explain how cold temperatures and desiccation are used in microbial control.

Microorganisms have adapted to a tremendous diversity of habitats on earth, some having severe conditions of temperature, moisture, pressure, and light. For microbes that normally withstand such extreme physical conditions, our usual attempts at control would probably have little effect. Fortunately for us, we are most interested in controlling microbes that flourish in the same environment

in which humans live. The vast majority of these microbes are readily controlled by abrupt changes in their environment. Most prominent among antimicrobial physical agents is heat. Other less widely used agents include radiation and filtration. The following sections examine these and other methods, and explore their practical applications in medicine, commerce, and the home.

Effects of Temperature on Microbial Activities

A sudden departure from a microbe's temperature of adaptation is likely to have a detrimental effect on it. As a rule, temperatures that exceed the maximum growth temperature are microbicidal, whereas temperatures below the minimum growth temperature are microbistatic. This essentially means that, for most microbes, the effects of temperatures below minimum can be reversible, whereas the effects of temperatures above maximum are not reversible and most microbes will be destroyed by them.

The two physical states of heat used in microbial control are moist and dry. **Moist heat** occurs in the form of hot water, boiling water, or steam (vaporized water). In practice, the temperature of moist heat usually ranges from 60°C to 135°C. As we shall see, the temperature of steam can be regulated by adjusting its pressure in a closed container. The expression **dry heat** denotes air with a low moisture content that has been heated by a flame or electric heating coil. In practice, the temperature of dry heat ranges from 160°C to several thousand degrees Celsius.

Mode of Action and Relative Effectiveness of Heat

Moist heat and dry heat differ in their modes of action as well as in their efficiency. Moist heat operates at lower temperatures and shorter exposure times to achieve the same effectiveness as dry heat **(table 11.3).** Although many cellular structures are damaged by moist heat, its most microbicidal effects are the coagulation and denaturation of proteins, which quickly and permanently halt cellular metabolism.

Dry heat with a moderate temperature dehydrates the cell, removing the water necessary for metabolic reactions, and it alters protein structure. However, the lack of water actually increases the stability of some protein conformations, necessitating the use of

higher temperatures when dry heat is employed as a method of microbial control. At very high temperatures, dry heat oxidizes cells, burning them to ashes. This method is the one used in the laboratory when a loop is flamed or in industry when medical waste is incinerated.

Heat Resistance and Thermal Death of Spores and Vegetative Cells

Bacterial endospores exhibit the greatest resistance, and vegetative states of bacteria and fungi are the least resistant to both moist and dry heat. Destruction of spores usually requires temperatures above boiling, although resistance varies widely. The following table compares some times and temperatures required to kill spore-formers using moist versus dry heat:

Moist Heat	Temp/Time	Dry Heat	Temp/Time
Bacillus subtilis	121°C/1 min	*Bacillus subtilis*	121°C/120 min
B. stearothermophilis	121°C/12 min	*B. stearothermophilis*	140°C/5 min
Clostridium botulinum	120°C/10 min	*Clostridium botulinum*	120°C/120 min
C. tetani	105°C/10 min	*C. tetani*	100°C/60 min

In general, reliable killing of the most heat-resistant species of sporeformers requires 121°C for 20 minutes in moist heat.

Vegetative cells also vary in their sensitivity to heat, though not to the same extent as spores. Among bacteria, the death conditions for moist heat range from 50°C for 3 minutes (*Neisseria gonorrhoeae*) to 60°C for 60 minutes (*Staphylococcus aureus*). It is worth noting that vegetative cells of spore-formers are just as susceptible as vegetative cells of non–spore-formers and that pathogens are neither more nor less susceptible than nonpathogens. Other microbes, including fungi, protozoa, and worms, are rather similar in their sensitivity to heat. Viruses can be surprisingly resistant to heat, with a tolerance range extending from 55°C for 2 to 5 minutes (adenoviruses) to 60°C for 600 minutes (hepatitis A virus). For practical purposes, all non–heat-resistant forms of bacteria, yeasts, molds, protozoa, worms, and viruses are destroyed by exposure to 80°C for 20 minutes.

Practical Concerns in the Use of Heat: Thermal Death Measurements

Adequate sterilization requires that both temperature and length of exposure be considered. As a general rule, higher temperatures allow shorter exposure times, and lower temperatures require longer exposure times. A combination of these two variables constitutes the **thermal death time,** or **TDT,** defined as the shortest length of time required to kill all test microbes at a specified temperature. The TDT has been experimentally determined for the microbial species that are common or important contaminants in various heat-treated materials. Another way to compare the susceptibility of microbes to heat is the **thermal death point (TDP),** defined as the lowest temperature required to kill all microbes in a sample in 10 minutes.

Many perishable substances are processed with moist heat. Some of these products are intended to remain on the shelf at room

TABLE 11.3	Comparison of Times and Temperatures to Achieve Sterilization with Moist and Dry Heat	
	Temperature	**Time to Sterilize**
Moist Heat	121°C	15 min
	125°C	10 min
	134°C	3 min
Dry Heat	121°C	600 min
	140°C	180 min
	160°C	120 min
	170°C	60 min

temperature for several months or even years. The chosen heat treatment must render the product free of agents of spoilage or disease. At the same time, the quality of the product and the speed and cost of processing must be considered. For example, in the commercial preparation of canned green beans, one of the cannery's greatest concerns is to prevent growth of the agent of botulism. From several possible TDTs (that is, combinations of time and temperature) for *Clostridium botulinum* spores, the cannery must choose one that kills all spores but does not turn the beans to mush. These many considerations produce an optimal TDT for a given processing method. Commercial canneries heat low-acid foods like green beans at 121°C for 30 minutes, a treatment that renders the foods sterile. Because of such strict controls in canneries, cases of botulism from commercially canned foods are rare.

Common Methods of Moist Heat Control

The four ways moist heat is employed to control microbes are (1) steam under pressure, (2) nonpressurized steam, (3) boiling water, and (4) pasteurization.

Sterilization with Steam under Pressure At sea level, normal atmospheric pressure is 15 pounds per square inch (psi), or 1 atmosphere. At this pressure, water will boil (change from a liquid to a gas) at 100°C, and the resultant steam will not go above 100°C, regardless of the method of heating. But boiling temperature is not hot enough to reliably kill all targeted microbes. The only way to raise the temperature of steam is to expose it to increased pressure. At higher pressures the temperature at which water boils and the temperature of steam both rise. For example, at a pressure of 20 psi (5 psi above normal), the temperature of steam is 109°C. As the temperature is increased to 10 psi above normal, the steam's temperature rises to 115°C, and at 15 psi above normal (a total of 2 atmospheres), it will be 121°C. It is not the pressure by itself that is killing microbes but the increased temperature it produces.

Such pressure-temperature combinations can be achieved only with a special device that can subject pure steam to pressures greater than 1 atmosphere. Health and commercial industries use an **autoclave** for this purpose, and a comparable home appliance is the pressure cooker. Autoclaves have a fundamentally similar plan: an enclosed metal chamber with an airtight door on one end and racks to hold materials **(figure 11.7).** Its construction includes a network of valves, pressure and temperature gauges, and ducts for regulating and measuring pressure and conducting the steam into the chamber. Sterilization is achieved when the steam condenses against the objects in the chamber and gradually raises their temperature.

Experience has shown that the most efficient pressure-temperature combination for achieving sterilization is 15 psi, which yields 121°C. It is possible to use higher pressure to reach higher temperatures (for instance, increasing the pressure to 30 psi raises the temperature to 132°C), but doing so will not significantly reduce the exposure time and can harm the items being sterilized.

The duration of the process is adjusted according to the bulkiness of the items in the load (thick bundles of material or large flasks of liquid) and how full the chamber is. The range of holding times varies from 10 minutes for light loads to 40 minutes for heavy or bulky ones; the average time is 20 minutes.

 CLINIC CASE

The Pressure's On . . . or Not A husband and wife in Indiana presented to the emergency department of their local hospital suffering from difficulty swallowing, blurred vision, drooping eyelids, and difficulty breathing, a collection of signs and symptoms that pointed to botulism. Four days earlier, the Centers for Disease Control had received a similar report from Texas, where two siblings had been similarly diagnosed.

Botulism, an often-fatal form of food intoxication, kills by paralyzing the muscles needed for respiration, slowly suffocating its victims. All four patients required mechanical ventilation to assist with breathing. Botulism occurs when food containing botulism toxin—a protein produced by *Clostridium botulinum* cells—is consumed. Food-borne botulism is linked to improper canning practices that allow endospores of the bacterium to survive, multiply, and produce toxin. Since the 1920s, commercially canned foods have been prepared in a retort, a piece of equipment similar to an autoclave or pressure cooker, where high-pressure steam is used to kill *C. botulinum* endospores. Thanks to the invention of the retort, botulism from commercially canned food is almost unheard of today (although botulism is still an occasional problem in home canning).

A search of the homes in both Indiana and Texas revealed cans of Hot Dog Chili Sauce, with production codes indicating that the cans had been processed in the same set of retorts, 5 hours apart. Tests of the facility's canning equipment revealed problems in 2 of the 100 retorts in the plant, such that either the temperature or pressure was not high enough to destroy endospores. Botulism toxin was found in other products cooked in these retorts and a recall of 39 million canned products, from chili to dog food, was initiated.

A total of eight people, including the mother of the two children in Texas, were affected by the outbreak. Thankfully, all survived.

How are the temperature and pressure inside a retort related to one another?

Nonpressurized Steam Selected substances that cannot withstand the high temperature of the autoclave can be subjected to **intermittent sterilization,** also called **tyndallization.**[1] This technique requires a chamber to hold the materials and a reservoir for boiling water. Items in the chamber are exposed to free-flowing steam for 30 to 60 minutes. This temperature is not sufficient to reliably kill spores, so a single exposure will not suffice. On the assumption that surviving spores will germinate into less resistant vegetative cells, the items are incubated at appropriate temperatures for 23 to 24 hours and then again subjected to steam treatment. This cycle is repeated for 3 days in a row. Because the temperature never gets above 100°C, highly resistant spores that do not germinate could survive even after 3 days of this treatment.

1. Named for the British physicist John Tyndall, who did early experiments with sterilizing procedures.

(a)

(b)

Figure 11.7 Sterilization using steam under pressure.
(a) A small tabletop autoclave for sterilizing surgical instruments.
(b) Cutaway section, showing autoclave components and the
flow of steam through the autoclave.
(a): Ganay Mutlu/Getty Images

Boiling Water: Disinfection A simple boiling water bath or
chamber can quickly decontaminate items in the clinic and home.
Because a single processing at 100°C will not kill all resistant cells,
this method can be relied on only for disinfection and not for steril-
ization. Exposing materials to boiling water for 30 minutes will kill
most non–spore-forming pathogens, including resistant species
such as the tubercle bacillus and staphylococci. Probably the great-
est disadvantage with this method is that the items can be easily
recontaminated when removed from the water.

Pasteurization: Disinfection of Beverages Fresh beverages
such as milk, fruit juices, beer, and wine are easily contaminated
during collection and processing. Because microbes have the po-
tential to spoil these foods or cause illness, heat is frequently used
to reduce the microbial load and destroy pathogens. **Pasteurization**
is a technique of applying heat to consumable liquids to kill poten-
tial agents of infection and spoilage, while at the same time retain-
ing the liquid's flavor and food value.

A widely used pasteurization technique is the **flash method,**
that exposes the liquid to heat exchangers at 71.6°C for 15 seconds.
This first method does not appreciably change flavor and nutrient
content, and it is effective against certain resistant pathogens such
as *Coxiella* and *Mycobacterium.* Although these treatments inacti-
vate most viruses and destroy the vegetative stages of 97% to 99%
of bacteria and fungi, they do not kill endospores or **thermoduric**
microbes (mostly nonpathogenic lactobacilli, micrococci, and
yeasts). Flash-pasteurized milk is not sterile after regular pasteuri-
zation. In fact, it can contain 20,000 microbes per milliliter or more,
which explains why even an unopened carton of milk will eventu-
ally spoil. Many commercial dairies now produce *sterile milk* with
an increased storage life of several months. This ultrapasteurized
milk is processed using ultrahigh temperature (UHT)—134°C for 2
to 5 seconds.

One important aim in pasteurization is to prevent the transmis-
sion of milk-borne diseases from infected cows or milk handlers.
The primary targets of pasteurization are non–spore-forming patho-
gens: *Salmonella* species (a common cause of food infection),
Campylobacter jejuni (acute intestinal infection), *Listeria monocy-
togenes* (listeriosis), *Brucella* species (undulant fever), *Coxiella
burnetii* (Q fever), *Mycobacterium bovis, M. tuberculosis,* and sev-
eral enteric viruses.

Dry Heat: Hot Air and Incineration

Dry heat is not as versatile or as widely used as moist heat, but it
has several important sterilization applications. The temperatures
and times employed in dry heat vary according to the particular
method, but in general they are greater than with moist heat.
Incineration in a flame or electric heating coil is perhaps the
most rigorous of all heat treatments. The flame of a Bunsen burner
reaches 1,870°C at its hottest point, and furnaces/incinerators op-
erate at temperatures of 800°C to 6,500°C. Direct exposure to
such intense heat ignites and reduces microbes and other sub-
stances to ashes and gas.

Incineration of microbial samples on inoculating loops and
needles using a Bunsen burner is a very common practice in the
microbiology laboratory. This method is fast and effective, but it is
also limited to metals and heat-resistant glass materials. Tabletop
infrared incinerators (see table 11.4), an alternative to Bunsen burn-
ers, are safer and prevent splatter of the inoculum.

The hot-air oven provides another means of dry-heat steriliza-
tion. The so-called *dry oven* is usually electric (occasionally gas)
and has coils that radiate heat within an enclosed compartment.
Heated, circulated air transfers its heat to the materials in the oven.
Depending on the type of oven and the material being decontami-
nated, a cycle takes 12 minutes to 4 hours to complete and involves
temperatures of 150°C to 180°C.

TABLE 11.4	Applications Using Heat for Sterilization and Disinfection	
Form of Heat	Equipment Temperature/Time	Medical and Commercial Uses and Limitations
Moist heat: Employs steam, boiling, or hot water; mode of action coagulates proteins		
Steam under pressure	Autoclave, pressure cooker; 121°C, pressure of 15 psi for 10 to 40 minutes, depending on load size; kills endospores.	Sterilization of heat-resistant materials made of glass, cloth, rubber, metal; media; a few plastics; canned food, spices. Decontamination of cultures. Not appropriate for moisture-repellent oil or powder.
Unpressurized steam (tyndallization)	Arnold's Sterilizer—100°C for 30 minutes on 3 days; items are incubated between treatments to allow endospores to germinate.	Limited uses in sterilizing some media and foods that cannot be autoclaved; can be used to disinfect but not sterilize some medical supplies
Pasteurization	Pasteurizer; flash method works at 71.6°C for 15 seconds; ultrahigh temperature (UHT) uses 134°C for a few seconds.	Disinfection of milk and dairy products to destroy milk-borne pathogens; UHT can sterilize for longer shelf life. Fruit juices, beer, and wine may be pasteurized to destroy contaminants and preserve the products.
Boiling water	Water bath or pan heated to 100°C; items are placed in water for 30 minutes to kill vegetative pathogens.	Limited to disinfection and sanitization of heat-resistant household objects such as eating utensils, clothing, sick room supplies, baby supplies, bedding, and water in emergencies; problem with recontamination
Dry heat: Employs dried hot air, flame, or heat coil; works by dehydration or combustion		
Dry oven	Electric or gas chamber heated to 150°C to 180°C for 2 to 4 hours	Materials that can withstand hot temperatures and dehydration; glassware, metals, powders, oils. Poor choice for liquids, rubber, plastics; time-consuming.
Incineration	Bunsen burner flame up to 1,800°C; small infrared incinerators to 800°C	Furnaces, incinerators up to 6,500°C. For sterilizing tips of inoculation instruments; limited to high-temperature metals. Permanent disposal of waste material from laboratories; burning reduces bulky packages and garbage to ashes. For permanent disposal only.

A small flash pasteurizer used by dairies for calves' milk.
Olena Kachmar/123RF

Dry heat incineration. Infrared incinerator with shield to prevent spattering of microbial samples during flaming.
Kathy Park Talaro

Table 11.4 presents an illustrated summary of heating methods for microbial control.

The Effects of Cold and Desiccation

The principal benefit of cold treatment is to slow the growth of cultures and microbes in food and other perishable materials during processing and storage. *It must be emphasized that cold merely retards the activities of most microbes.* Although it is true that some sensitive microbes are killed by cold temperatures, most are not adversely affected by gradual cooling, long-term refrigeration, or deep-freezing. In fact, freezing temperatures, ranging from −70°C to −135°C, provide an environment that can preserve cultures of bacteria, viruses, and fungi for long periods. Recall from chapter 7 that some psychrotrophs grow very slowly even at freezing temperatures and can continue to secrete toxic products. Pathogens

able to survive several months in the refrigerator are *Staphylococcus aureus; Clostridium* species (sporeformers); *Listeria;* and several types of yeasts, molds, and viruses. Outbreaks of *Salmonella* food infection traced backed to refrigerated foods such as ice cream and eggs are testimony to the inability of cold temperatures to reliably kill pathogens.

Most vegetative cells directly exposed to normal room air gradually become dehydrated, or **desiccated.*** Delicate pathogens such as *Streptococcus pneumoniae,* the spirochete of syphilis, and *Neisseria gonorrhoeae* can die after a few hours of air-drying, but many others are not killed and some are even preserved. Staphylococci and streptococci in dried secretions and the tubercle bacillus surrounded by sputum can remain viable in air and dust for lengthy periods. Many viruses (especially nonenveloped) and fungal spores can also withstand long periods of desiccation. Endospores of *Bacillus* and *Clostridium* are viable for millions of years under extremely arid conditions. Desiccation can be a valuable way to preserve foods because it greatly reduces the amount of water available to support microbial growth.

It is interesting to note that a combination of freezing and drying—**lyophilization***—is a common method of preserving microorganisms and other cells in a viable state for many years. Pure cultures are frozen instantaneously and exposed to a vacuum that rapidly removes the water. This method avoids the formation of ice crystals that would damage the cells. Although not all cells survive this process, enough of them do to permit future reconstitution of that culture.

As a general rule, chilling, freezing, and desiccation should not be construed as methods of disinfection or sterilization, because their antimicrobial effects are erratic and uncertain and one cannot be sure that pathogens subjected to them have been killed.

Practice SECTION 11.2

9. What happens to microbes that encounter temperatures below their minimum and above their maximum growth temperatures?

10. Summarize the nature, mode of action, and effectiveness of moist and dry heat on spores and vegetative cells.

11. Explain the concepts of TDT and TDP, using examples.

12. What are the minimum TDTs for vegetative cells and endospores?

13. How can the temperature of steam be raised above 100°C? Which instrument is based on this technique, and how is it used?

14. What are the primary purposes of pasteurization, and what is ultrapasteurization?

15. What are several microbial targets of pasteurization?

16. Explain why desiccation and cold are not reliable methods of disinfection but how they can still be effective in microbial control.

* *desiccate* (des'-ih-kayt) To dry at normal environmental temperatures.
* *lyophilization* (ly-off"-il-ih-za'-shun) Gr. *lyein,* to dissolve, and *philein,* to love.

11.3 Physical Methods of Control: Radiation and Filtration

Learn

14. Define *radiation* and assess the use of irradiation as a method of microbial control.

15. Differentiate between ionizing and nonionizing radiation in their modes of action.

16. Summarize the primary uses of ionizing and nonionizing radiation in sterilization and disinfection.

17. Describe the concept behind sterilization by filtration, including examples of applications.

Radiation as a Microbial Control Agent

Another form of energy that can serve as an antimicrobial agent is radiation. **Radiation** is defined as energy emitted from atomic activities and dispersed at high velocity through matter or space. It is characterized by a range of wavelengths known as the electromagnetic spectrum **(figure 11.8)**. Although radiation exists in many energy states, we will consider only those types suitable for microbial control: gamma rays, X-rays, and ultraviolet radiation.

Modes of Action of Ionizing Versus Nonionizing Radiation

The actual physical effects of radiation on microbes can be understood by visualizing the process of **irradiation,** or bombardment with radiation, at the cellular level **(figure 11.9)**. When a cell is bombarded by certain waves or particles, its molecules absorb some of the available energy, leading to one of two consequences: (1) If the radiation ejects orbital electrons from an atom, it causes ions to form; this type of radiation is termed **ionizing radiation.** One of the most sensitive targets for ionizing radiation is DNA, which will

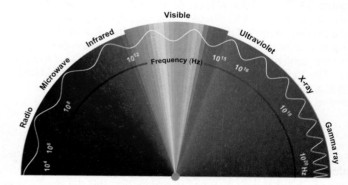

Figure 11.8 **The electromagnetic spectrum.** Waves range from the longest radio waves to the shortest gamma rays. The frequency of the wave (measured in Hertz, Hz) is simply the number of wave cycles that occur in 1 second. Only ionizing radiation (X-rays and gamma rays), ultraviolet and infrared have applications in microbial control.
Fouad A. Saad/Shutterstock

Ionizing Radiation

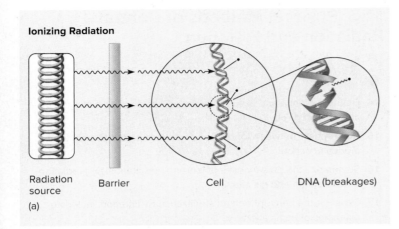

Radiation source Barrier Cell DNA (breakages)

(a)

Nonionizing Radiation

(b)

DNA
(abnormal bonds)
See figure 11.11

UV does not penetrate
No effect on cell

Radiation source Barrier

(c)

Figure 11.9 **Cellular effects of irradiation.** (a) Ionizing radiation can penetrate a solid barrier, bombard a cell, enter it, and dislodge electrons from molecules. Breakage of DNA prevents the growth of organisms that could cause illness or spoilage. (b) Nonionizing radiation enters a cell, strikes molecules, and excites them. The effect on DNA is mutation by formation of abnormal bonds. (c) A solid barrier cannot be readily penetrated by nonionizing radiation.

undergo mutations on a broad scale. Secondary lethal effects appear to be chemical changes in organelles and the production of toxic substances. Gamma rays, X-rays, and high-speed electrons are all ionizing in their effects. (2) **Nonionizing radiation,** best exemplified by UV, excites atoms by raising them to a higher energy state, but it does not ionize them. This atomic excitation, in turn, leads to the formation of abnormal bonds

within molecules such as DNA and is thus a source of mutations (see figure 11.11).

Ionizing Radiation: Gamma Rays and X-Rays

Over the past several years, ionizing radiation has become safer and more economical to use, and its applications have expanded. It is a highly effective alternative for sterilizing materials that are sensitive to heat or chemicals. Because it sterilizes in the absence of heat, irradiation is a type of **cold** (or low-temperature) **sterilization.** Devices that emit ionizing rays include gamma-ray machines containing radioactive cobalt and X-ray machines similar to those used in medical diagnosis. Items are placed in these machines and irradiated for a short time with a carefully chosen dosage. The dosage of radiation is measured in grays. Depending on the application, exposure ranges from 5 to 50 kilograys (kGy; a kilogray is equal to 1,000 grays). Although all ionizing radiations can penetrate liquids and most solid materials, gamma rays are more penetrating and X-rays less so.

Irradiation as a Method of Microbial Control

Foods have been subject to irradiation in limited circumstances for more than 50 years. From flour to pork and ground beef, to fruits and vegetables, radiation is used to kill bacterial pathogens, insects, and worms, and even to inhibit the sprouting of potatoes. As soon as radiation is involved, however, consumers become concerned that ionizing radiation could make food less nutritious, unpalatable, or even unsafe. But irradiated food has been extensively studied, and each of these concerns has been addressed. **Figure 11.10** demonstrates how irradiation of fruit can greatly reduce spoilage and improve shelf life.

> **Quick Search**
>
> Access YouTube to view the video "Irradiation in Food Processing."

Raspberries exposed to radiation, 5 days later Raspberries not treated with radiation, 5 days later

Figure 11.10 **Sterilization with ionizing radiation.** Many foods can be effectively sterilized by utilizing the penetrating power of ionizing radiation. The "radura" symbol (meaning treated with radiation; see the green image on the package on the left) applied to fresh foods signifies that the food has been irradiated and is required to be displayed on all food so treated.

(photos): Kathy Park Talaro

Irradiation may lead to a small decrease in the amount of thiamine (vitamin B$_1$) in food, but this change is small enough to be inconsequential. The irradiation process does produce short-lived free-radical oxidants, which disappear almost immediately (this same type of chemical intermediate is produced through cooking as well). Certain foods do not irradiate well and are not good candidates for this type of treatment. The whites of eggs becomes milky, and alfalfa seeds do not germinate properly. It should be emphasized that food is not made radioactive by the irradiation process, and many studies, in both animals and humans, have concluded that there are no ill effects from eating irradiated food. In fact, NASA relies on irradiated meat for its astronauts.

One of the potential benefits of irradiated foods has to do with infection control. It has been estimated that irradiation of 50% of the meat and poultry in the United States would result in 900,000 fewer cases of infection, 8,500 fewer hospitalizations, and 350 fewer deaths each year. Radiation is currently approved in the United States for the reduction of bacterial pathogens such as *E. coli* and *Salmonella* in beef and chicken, reduction of *Trichinella* worms in pork, and the reduction of pathogens and pests on fruits and vegetables. An additional benefit of irradiation is that microbes responsible for food spoilage are killed along with pathogens, leading to an increased shelf life. In any event, no irradiated food can be sold to consumers without clear labeling that this method has been used (figure 11.10).

Sterilizing medical products with ionizing radiation is a rapidly expanding field. Drugs, vaccines, medical instruments (especially plastics), and other delicate materials can be irradiated without harming them. Its main advantages include speed, high penetrating power (it can sterilize materials through outer packages and wrappings), and the absence of heat. Its main disadvantages are potential dangers from factory exposure to radiation and possible damage to some materials. See table 11.5 for a summary of the applications of ionizing radiation.

Nonionizing Radiation: Ultraviolet Rays

Ultraviolet (UV) radiation ranges in wavelength from approximately 100 nm to 400 nm. It is most lethal from 240 nm to 280 nm (with a peak at 260 nm). In everyday practice, the source of UV rays is the germicidal lamp, which generates radiation at 254 nm. Owing to its lower energy state, UV radiation is not as penetrating as ionizing radiation. Because UV radiation passes readily through air, slightly through liquids, and only poorly through solids, the object to be disinfected must be directly exposed to it for full effect.

As UV radiation passes through a cell, it is initially absorbed by DNA. Specific molecular damage occurs on the pyrimidine bases (thymine and cytosine), which form abnormal linkages with each other called **pyrimidine dimers (figure 11.11).** These bonds occur between adjacent bases on the same DNA strand and interfere with normal DNA replication and transcription. The results are inhibition of growth and cellular death. In addition to altering DNA directly, UV radiation disrupts cells by generating toxic photochemical products called free radicals. These highly reactive molecules interfere with essential cell

Figure 11.11 Formation of pyrimidine dimers by the action of ultraviolet (UV) radiation. This shows what occurs when two adjacent thymine bases on one strand of DNA are induced by UV rays to bond laterally with each other. The result is a thymine dimer shown in greater detail. Dimers can also occur between adjacent cytosines and thymine and cytosine bases. If they are not repaired, dimers can prevent that segment of DNA from being correctly replicated or transcribed. High levels of dimerization are lethal to cells.

processes by binding to DNA, RNA, and proteins. Ultraviolet rays are a powerful tool for destroying fungal cells and spores, bacterial vegetative cells, protozoa, and viruses. Bacterial spores are about 10 times more resistant to radiation than are vegetative cells, but they can be killed by increasing the time of exposure.

Ultraviolet radiation is usually aimed more at disinfection than at sterilization. Germicidal lamps can cut down on the concentration of airborne microbes by as much as 99%. Ultraviolet disinfection of air has proved effective in reducing postoperative infections, preventing the transmission of infections by respiratory droplets, and curtailing the growth of microbes in food-processing plants and slaughterhouses.

Ultraviolet irradiation of liquids requires special equipment to spread the liquid into a thin, flowing film that is exposed directly to a lamp. This method can be used to treat water **(figure 11.12)** and to purify other liquids (milk and fruit juices) as an alternative to heat. The surfaces of solid, nonporous materials such as walls and floors, as well as meat, nuts, tissues for grafting, and drugs, can be successfully disinfected with UV. Several types of small UV disinfection appliances have been marketed for personal items.

One major disadvantage of UV is its poor powers of penetration through solid materials such as glass, metal, cloth, plastic, and even paper. Another drawback to UV is the damaging effect of overexposure on human tissues, including sunburn, retinal damage, cancer, and skin wrinkling. These harmful results occur only if a person is directly exposed to the UV rays, but it necessitates placement of barriers to cut down on this possibility. **Table 11.5** summarizes UV applications.

Figure 11.12 An ultraviolet (UV) treatment system for disinfection of water. Water is directed through channels at a water treatment plant, past racks of UV lamps (green glow). This system has a capacity of several million gallons per day and can be used as an alternative to chlorination. Home systems that fit under the sink are also available.
Dmitry Rogachev/Shutterstock

Filtration—A Physical Removal Process

Filtration is an effective method to remove microbes from air and liquids. In practice, a fluid is strained through a filter with openings large enough for the fluid to pass through but too small for microorganisms to pass through (**figure 11.13a**).

Most modern microbiological filters are thin membranes of cellulose acetate, polycarbonate, and a variety of plastic materials (Teflon, nylon) whose pore size can be carefully controlled and standardized. Ordinary substances such as charcoal, diatomaceous earth, or unglazed porcelain are also used in some applications. Viewed microscopically, most filters are perforated by very precise, uniform pores (**figure 11.13b**). The pore diameters vary from coarse (8 μm) to ultrafine (0.02 μm), permitting selection of the minimum particle size to be trapped. Those with even smaller pore diameters permit true sterilization by removing viruses, and some will even remove large proteins. A sterile liquid filtrate is typically produced by suctioning the liquid through a sterile filter into a presterilized container. These filters are also used to separate mixtures of microorganisms and to enumerate bacteria in water analysis.

Form of Radiation	Equipment/Mode of Action	Medical and Commercial Uses and Limitations
TABLE 11.5	**Applications Using Radiation for Sterilization and Disinfection**	
Ionizing radiation		
Sporicidal and penetrating	Cobalt radiation gives off gamma rays; others are X-rays, cathode rays. Rays fragment DNA and create ionized bases; highly mutagenic.	Cold sterilization of packaged products such as medical supplies and instruments that cannot be heat sterilized Sterilization of foods, including fruits, lettuce and spinach, grains, spices, meats, and packaged meals Sterilization of drugs and vaccines Rapid and penetrating, prevents infection and spoilage
Nonionizing ultraviolet (UV) radiation		
Sporicidal and nonpenetrating	Germicidal lamps or generators set to deliver UV rays from 240 to 280 nm in wavelength; action creates abnormal bonds between adjacent thymines and cytosines and produces deletion mutations on DNA.	Mostly disinfection of air, some liquids, a few solids; reduces airborne pathogens in medical and dental offices, hospital rooms, and operating rooms Commercial use for clean rooms, food processing areas Works on liquids such as water, milk, drugs, vaccines if exposed to UV in thin layers Solid materials such as room surfaces, foods, tissue grafts, drugs, and instruments Lack of penetration through solids limits applications; direct exposure can be dangerous to eyes and skin

Pallets of apples are being irradiated with a cobalt 60 machine that emits gamma rays. *Source:* Pacific Northwest National Laboratory

Tabletop chamber generates ultraviolet rays to disinfect a toothbrush.
DonNichols/iStock/Getty Images

CLINIC CASE

Even Shallow Water Can Be Dangerous Dozens of patients presenting at the same time with diarrhea, abdominal cramps, vomiting, and pain usually trigger thoughts of food poisoning, but doctors in Ontario County, New York, quickly ruled out any common food consumption. They did find that their pediatric patients had all spent time at the Seneca Lakes Sprayground, an interactive water fountain at Seneca Lakes Park, in upstate New York. An O and P (ova and parasite) exam revealed that the children were suffering from cryptosporidiosis, the result of ingesting water contaminated with the protozoan *Cryptosporidium*. Over the next few weeks, more than 700 people were sickened with similar symptoms.

The sprayground itself was an 11,000-square-foot deck with hundreds of individual water jets, spouts, and hoses. After being sprayed into the air, water flowed back into a holding tank below the play area before being recycled through the jets once again. The sprayground was popular because even small children could play

there without the risk of drowning associated with swimming pools. The design of the play area unfortunately allowed animals to access the area at night, and their feces—often containing bacterial or protozoan pathogens—could easily wash into the water-holding tanks supplying the fountains. Testing of the water revealed the presence of *Cryptosporidium,* which is resistant to chlorination and small enough to pass through swimming pool filters. The sprayground was closed until an ultraviolet light could be integrated into the filtration system; although *Cryptosporidium* is resistant to chlorine, it is susceptible to ultraviolet (UV) light. The sprayground reopened the following year, and no additional cases of cryptosporidiosis have been seen.

Chlorine will in fact kill *Cryptosporidium* in high concentrations. Why did the operators of the sprayground not simply increase the concentration of chlorine in the water?

(a)

(b)

Applications of Filtration Sterilization

Sterilization by means of filtration is used to prepare liquids that cannot withstand heat, including serum and other blood products, vaccines, drugs, IV fluids, enzymes, and media. Filtration has been employed as an alternative method for sterilizing milk and beer without altering their flavor. It is also an important step in water purification. Its use extends to filtering out particulate impurities (crystals, fibers) that can cause severe reactions in the body. It has the disadvantage of not removing soluble molecules (toxins) that can cause disease.

Filtration is a very effective means of removing airborne contaminants that are a common source of infection and spoilage. High-efficiency particulate air (HEPA) filters are widely used to provide a flow of sterile air to hospital rooms and sterile rooms.

 Practice SECTION 11.3

17. Define *radiation* and *irradiation.*
18. Differentiate between the modes of action of ionizing radiation and ultraviolet radiation.
19. What are some advantages and disadvantages of ionizing radiation as a method of control?
20. Describe some applications of ionizing and ultraviolet radiation.
21. What are the advantages and disadvantages of using filtration as a method of control?

Figure 11.13 Membrane filtration. (a) Vacuum assembly for achieving filtration of liquids through suction. Inset shows filter as seen in cross section, with tiny passageways (pores) too small for the microbial cells to enter but large enough for liquid to pass through. **(b)** Scanning electron micrograph of *Enterococcus* trapped on the surface of a membrane filter (10,400×). Average cells measure about 0.5 μm to 1 μm in diameter, and average pore size is about 0.3 μm.
(b): *Source:* Janice Haney Carr/CDC

11.4 Chemical Agents in Microbial Control

Learn

18. Define the terms that are used to describe chemical control of microbes.

19. Explain the desirable features of antimicrobial chemicals and what factors influence their effectiveness.

20. Describe the types of halogens, their modes of action, and their clinical and commercial applications.

21. Identify the characteristics of phenolic compounds and alcohols, explain how they act, and evaluate their primary uses.

22. Describe the characteristics of oxidizing agents and aldehydes, and summarize their main applications.

23. Differentiate among the sterilizing gases and aerosols, and describe how they are used.

24. Explain how detergents, soaps, and heavy metals can be employed in clinical, commercial, and household microbial control.

Chemical control of microbes probably emerged as a serious science in the early 1800s, when physicians used chloride of lime and iodine solutions to treat wounds and to wash their hands before surgery. At the present time, approximately 10,000 different antimicrobial chemical agents are manufactured; probably 1,000 of them are used routinely in the health care and home environments. A genuine need exists to avoid infection and spoilage, but the abundance of products available to "kill germs," "disinfect," "antisepticize," "clean and sanitize," "deodorize," "fight plaque," and "purify the air" indicates a preoccupation with eliminating microbes from the environment that, at times, seems excessive.

Antimicrobial chemicals occur in the liquid, gaseous, or even solid state. They serve as **disinfectants, antiseptics, sterilants** (chemicals that sterilize), degermers, or preservatives (chemicals that inhibit the deterioration of substances). In most cases, solid or gaseous antimicrobial chemicals are dissolved in water, alcohol, or a mixture of the two to produce a liquid solution. Solutions containing pure water as the solvent are termed **aqueous,** whereas those dissolved in pure alcohol or water-alcohol mixtures are termed **tinctures.**

Choosing a Microbicidal Chemical

The choice and appropriate use of antimicrobial chemical agents are of constant concern in medicine and dentistry. Although actual clinical practices of chemical decontamination vary widely, some desirable qualities in a germicide have been identified, including:

- rapid action in low concentrations,
- solubility in water or alcohol and long-term stability,
- broad-spectrum microbicidal action without being toxic to human and animal tissues,
- penetration of inanimate surfaces to sustain a cumulative or persistent action,
- resistance to becoming inactivated by organic matter,
- noncorrosive or nonstaining properties,
- sanitizing and deodorizing properties, and
- affordability and ready availability.

As of yet, no chemical can completely fulfill all of those requirements, but chlorhexidine and hydrogen peroxide approach this ideal. At the same time, we should question the rather overinflated claims made about certain commercial agents such as mouthwashes and disinfectant air sprays.

Germicides are evaluated in terms of their effectiveness in destroying microbes in medical and dental settings. The three levels of chemical decontamination procedures are *high, intermediate,* and *low* **(table 11.6).**

- High-level germicides kill endospores and, if properly used, are **sterilants.** Materials that necessitate high-level control are medical devices—for example, catheters, endoscopes, and implants—that are not heat-sterilizable and are intended to enter body tissues during medical procedures.
- Intermediate-level germicides kill fungal (but not bacterial) spores, resistant pathogens such as the tubercle bacillus, and viruses. They are used to disinfect items (respiratory equipment, thermometers) that come into intimate contact with the mucous membranes but are noninvasive.
- Low levels of disinfection eliminate only vegetative bacteria, vegetative fungal cells, and some viruses. They are used to clean materials such as electrodes, straps, and fixtures that touch the skin surfaces but not the mucous membranes.

Factors that Affect the Germicidal Activities of Chemical Agents

Several concepts of microbial control introduced in section 11.1 apply to germicides and other chemical agents. Many of these substances target the same cellular structures and functions previously discussed: cell walls and membranes, proteins, and nucleic acids. The effectiveness of the agents depends on several factors, including (1) the numbers and kinds of microbes that are present, (2) the kinds of materials that are being treated, (3) the time of exposure required, and (4) the strength and mode of action of the agent. Here, we focus on the latter two because of their importance to chemical agents.

Length of Exposure Most compounds require adequate contact time for the chemical to penetrate and to act on the microbes present. The composition of the material being treated can greatly affect this process. Smooth, solid objects are more rapidly disinfected than are those with pores or pockets that can trap soil. An item contaminated with common biological matter such as serum, blood, saliva, pus, fecal material, or urine presents an additional barrier to effective disinfection. Large amounts of this

TABLE 11.6 Qualities of Chemical Agents Used in Health Care

Agent	Target Microbes	Level of Germicidal Activity	Toxicity	Comments
Chlorine	Sporicidal (slowly)	Intermediate	Gas is highly toxic; solution irritates skin	Inactivated by organics; unstable in sunlight
Iodine	Sporicidal (slowly)	Intermediate	Can irritate tissue; toxic if ingested	Iodophors* are milder forms
Phenolics	Some bacteria, viruses, fungi	Low to intermediate	Can be absorbed by skin; can cause CNS damage	Poor solubility; expensive
Chlorhexidine*	Most bacteria, some viruses, fungi	Low to intermediate	Low toxicity	Fast-acting, mild, has residual effects
Alcohols	Most bacteria, viruses, fungi	Intermediate	Toxic if ingested; a mild irritant; dries skin	Flammable, fast-acting
Hydrogen peroxide,* stabilized	Sporicidal	High (sterilant)	Toxic to eyes; toxic if ingested	Improved stability; works well in organic matter
Quaternary ammonium compounds	Some bactericidal, virucidal, fungicidal activity	Low to intermediate	Irritating to mucous membranes; poisonous if taken internally	Weak solutions can support microbial growth; easily inactivated
Soaps	Certain very sensitive species	Very low	Nontoxic; few if any toxic effects	Used for removing soil, oils, debris
Mercurials	Weakly microbistatic	Low	Highly toxic if ingested, inhaled, absorbed	Easily inactivated
Silver nitrate	Bactericidal	Low	Toxic, irritating	Discolors skin
Glutaraldehyde*	Sporicidal	High (sterilant)	Can irritate skin; toxic if absorbed	Not inactivated by organic matter; unstable
Ortho-phthaldehyde*	Sporicidal, with time	Intermediate to high	Mild, no odor	Less toxic than glutaraldehyde; highly stable; stains skin
Ethylene oxide gas*	Sporicidal	High (sterilant)	Very dangerous to eyes, lungs; carcinogenic	Explosive in pure state; good penetration; materials must be aerated
Dyes	Weakly bactericidal, fungicidal	Low	Low toxicity	Stains materials, skin

*These chemicals approach the ideal by having many of the following characteristics: broad spectrum, low toxicity, fast action, penetrating abilities, residual effects, stability, potency in organic matter, and solubility.

organic material can hinder penetration and, in some cases, can form bonds that reduce a chemical's activity. Adequate cleaning of instruments and other reusable materials will ensure that the germicide or sterilant will better accomplish the job for which it was chosen.

Concentration of the Chemical Agent

A chemical's strength or concentration is expressed in various ways, depending upon convention and the method of preparation. The content of many chemical agents can be formulated in more than one way. For dilutions, a small volume of the liquid chemical (solute) is diluted in a larger volume of solvent to achieve a certain ratio. For example, a common laboratory phenolic disinfectant such as Lysol is usually diluted 1:200; that is, one part of chemical (solute) has been added to 199 parts of water (solvent) by volume. Solutions such as chlorine that are effective in very diluted concentrations are expressed in parts per million (ppm). In percentage solutions, the solute is added to solvent by weight or volume to achieve a certain percentage in the solution. Alcohol, for instance, is used in percentages ranging from 50% to 95%. In general, solutions of low dilution or

high percentage have more of the active chemical (are more concentrated) and tend to be more germicidal, but expense and potential toxicity can necessitate using the minimum strength that is effective.

Standardized procedures for testing the effectiveness of germicides are summarized in appendix B.

Categories of Chemical Agents

Several general groups of chemical compounds are widely used for antimicrobial purposes in medicine and commerce (table 11.6). Prominent agents include halogens, phenolic compounds, alcohols, oxidizers, aldehydes, gases, detergents, and heavy metals. These groups are surveyed in the following section from the standpoint of each agent's specific forms and modes of action. Applications and methods of delivery are described in tables.

The Halogen Antimicrobial Chemicals

The **halogens*** are fluorine, bromine, chlorine, and iodine, a group of nonmetallic elements with similar chemical properties. Although they can exist in either the ionic (halide) or nonionic state, most halogens exert their antimicrobial effect primarily in the nonionic state, not the halide state (chloride, iodide, for example). Because fluorine and bromine are difficult and dangerous to handle and no more effective than chlorine and iodine, only the latter two are used routinely in germicidal preparations. These elements are highly effective components of disinfectants and antiseptics because they are microbicidal and not just microbistatic, and they are sporicidal with longer exposure. For these reasons, halogens are the active ingredients in nearly one-third of all antimicrobial chemicals currently marketed.

Chlorine and Its Compounds Chlorine has been used for disinfection and antisepsis for approximately 200 years. The major forms used in microbial control are liquid and gaseous chlorine (Cl_2), hypochlorites (O^-Cl), and chloramines (NH_2Cl). In solution, these compounds combine with water and release hypochlorous acid (HClO):

$$Cl_2 + H_2O \rightarrow HClO + HCl \text{ (hydrochloric acid)}$$
$$Ca(OCl)_2 + 2H_2O \rightarrow Ca(OH)_2 + 2HClO$$

Hypochlorous acid oxidizes the sulfhydryl (S—H) groups on the amino acid cysteine and breaks disulfide (S—S) bridges on numerous enzymes. The resulting denaturation of the enzymes is permanent and suspends metabolic reactions. It also damages the structure of DNA, RNA, and fatty acids. Death of almost all microorganisms usually occurs within 30 minutes, although endospores may require several hours. Chlorine compounds are less effective and relatively unstable if exposed to light, alkaline pH, and excess organic matter.

Iodine and Its Compounds Iodine (I_2) is a pungent blue-black element that forms a brown-colored solution when dissolved in water. It rapidly penetrates the cells of microorganisms, where it disturbs a variety of metabolic functions by interfering with the disulfide bonds of proteins. This mode of action is similar to that seen in chlorine, although iodine is less susceptible to inactivation by organic material. All classes of microorganisms can be killed if proper exposure times and iodine concentrations are used.

See **table 11.7** for information on the main uses and forms of halogens.

Phenol and Its Derivatives

Phenol (carbolic acid) is an acrid, poisonous compound derived from the distillation of coal tar. First adopted by Joseph Lister in 1867 as a surgical germicide, phenol was the dominant antimicrobial chemical until other phenolics with fewer toxic and irritating effects were developed. Solutions of phenol are now used only in certain limited cases, but it remains one standard against which other phenolic disinfectants are rated. The *phenol coefficient* quantitatively compares a chemical's antimicrobic properties to those of phenol. Substances chemically related to phenol are often referred to as phenolics.

Phenolics consist of one or more aromatic carbon rings with added functional groups (**figure 11.14**). Among the more common phenolics are alkylated phenols (cresols), chlorinated phenols, and bisphenols. In high concentrations, phenolics are cellular poisons, rapidly disrupting cell walls and membranes and precipitating proteins; in lower concentrations they inactivate certain critical enzyme systems. The phenolics will destroy vegetative bacteria (including the tuberculosis bacillus), fungi, and many viruses (not hepatitis B), but they are not reliably sporicidal. Their sustained activity in the presence of organic matter and their detergent actions contribute to their usefulness. Unfortunately, the toxicity of many of the phenolics makes them a questionable choice as antiseptics.

Chlorhexidine

The compound chlorhexidine (Hibiclens, Hibitane) is a complex organic base containing chlorine and two phenolic rings. Its mode of action targets cell membranes by lowering surface tension and causing denaturation of proteins. At moderate to high concentrations it is bactericidal for both gram-positive and gram-negative bacteria but inactive against spores. Its effects on viruses and fungi vary. It possesses distinct advantages over many other antiseptics because of its mildness, low toxicity, and rapid action, and it is not absorbed into deeper tissues to any extent. It is the antiseptic cleanser of choice to control *Staphylococcus* MRSA and *Acinetobacter* outbreaks in hospitals.

Applications for phenolic compounds and chlorhexidine are given in **table 11.8**.

* *halogen* (hay'-loh-jen) Gr. *halos*, salt, and *gennan*, to produce.

TABLE 11.7	Applications of Halogen Compounds	
Form of Chlorine	**Primary Applications**	**How Delivered/Concerns**
Chlorine Gas (Cl$_2$)	Large-scale disinfection of drinking water, sewage, and wastewater.	Chlorination to a concentration of 0.6 to 1.0 parts of chlorine per million parts of water destroys most vegetative pathogens.*
Hypochlorites (HClO) Bleach	Used extensively in sanitization and disinfection of food equipment, treatment of swimming pools, spas, drinking water, and fresh foods; for wound antisepsis and routine medical and household disinfection, deodorizing, and stain removal.	Common household bleach is a 5% solution of sodium hypochlorite; dilutions of 1:10–1:1,000 are highly effective germicides.
Chloramines (Dichloramine, Halazone)	An alternative to pure chlorine in treating water supplies; also as sanitizers and disinfectants; for treating wounds and skin surfaces.	Because standard gas chlorination of water is now believed to produce unsafe levels of trihalomethanes, some water districts are required to use chloramine treatment of water supplies.
Form of Iodine	**Primary Applications**	**How Delivered/Concerns**
Iodophors	Most common iodine for skin and mucous membranes; antiseptic prep for surgery and injections; for surgical handscrubs; to disinfect equipment and surfaces; possibly for burns; and may be an alternative preventive for eye infections in newborns.	A complex of iodine and a neutral protein polymer provides slow release and reduced toxicity or irritation of tissues; less prone to staining. Common products are povidone-iodine (PVI; Betadine), which contain 2% to 10% available iodine.
Elemental Iodine: Aqueous or Tinctures	Topical antiseptic prior to surgery; sometimes for burned or injured skin. Medium-level disinfection for plastic instruments, thermometers; tablet form available for disinfection of contaminated water.	Weak solutions of 1% to 3% in water or in alcohol tinctures. Aqueous solutions or tinctures of 5% to 10%; somewhat limited by their toxicity and tendency to stain.

Cantaloupes are disinfected with chlorine treated water to kill *Salmonella* carried on their surfaces.

Patient has been treated with a povidone-iodine solution in preparation for surgery.

*Some cyst-forming protozoans such as *Giardia* and *Cryptosporidium* can survive this level of chlorination. (left): *Source:* Paul Pierlott, USDA-ERRC/VGT; (right): BSIP/Universal Images Group/Getty Images

Alcohols as Antimicrobial Agents

Alcohols are colorless hydrocarbons with one or more —OH functional groups. Of several alcohols available, only ethyl and isopropyl are suitable for microbial control. Methyl alcohol is not particularly microbicidal, and more complex alcohols are either poorly soluble in water or too toxic for routine use. Alcohols are employed alone in aqueous solutions or as solvents for tinctures (with iodine, for example).

Alcohol's mechanism of action depends in part upon its concentration. Concentrations of 50% and higher dissolve membrane lipids, disrupt cell surface tension, and compromise membrane integrity. Alcohol that has entered the protoplasm denatures proteins through coagulation, but only in alcohol-water solutions of 50% to 95%. Alcohol is the exception to the rule that higher concentrations of an antimicrobial chemical have greater microbicidal activity. Because water is needed for proteins to coagulate, alcohol shows a greater microbicidal activity at 70% concentration (that is, 30% water) than at 100% (0% water). Absolute alcohol (100%) dissolves cell membranes and inhibits cell growth but is generally not a protein coagulant.

Phenol
(basic aromatic
ring structure)

o-cresol

p-cresol

Chlorophene
(a chlorinated phenol)

Hexachlorophene
(a bisphenol)

Figure 11.14 **Examples of phenolic structures.** All contain a basic aromatic ring, but they differ in the types of additional side groups, such as Cl and CH_3.

Although useful in intermediate- to low-level germicidal applications, alcohol does not destroy bacterial spores at room temperature. Alcohol can, however, destroy resistant vegetative forms, including tuberculosis bacteria and fungal spores, provided the time of exposure is adequate. Alcohol tends to inactivate enveloped viruses more readily than nonenveloped viruses because of the surfactant effect on the envelope.

Hydrogen Peroxide and Related Germicides

Hydrogen peroxide (H_2O_2) is a colorless, caustic liquid that decomposes in the presence of light, metals, or catalase into water and oxygen gas. Early formulations were unstable and inhibited by organic matter, but manufacturing methods now permit synthesis of H_2O_2 so stable that even dilute solutions retain activity through several years of storage.

The germicidal effects of hydrogen peroxide are due to the direct and indirect actions of oxygen. Oxygen forms hydroxyl free radicals (—OH), which, like the superoxide radical (see chapter 7), are highly toxic and reactive to cells. Although most microbial cells produce catalase to inactivate the metabolic hydrogen peroxide, catalase cannot neutralize the amount of hydrogen peroxide penetrating these cells during disinfection and antisepsis. Hydrogen peroxide is bactericidal, virucidal, fungicidal, and, in higher concentrations, sporicidal. The need for heat-free rapid sterilization of small medical devices has led to the development of chambers that circulate combinations of peroxide and peracetic acid. A vaporized form of hydrogen peroxide is effective as an environmental sterilant used in decontaminating large spaces and objects (see figure 11.4).

Coverage on the applications of alcohols and peroxides is provided in **table 11.9**.

Aldehyde Sterilants and Disinfectants

Organic substances bearing a —CHO functional group (a strong reducing group) on the terminal carbon are called aldehydes. The two aldehydes used most often in microbial control are *glutaraldehyde* and *ortho-phthaldehyde*.

Glutaraldehyde is a yellow liquid with a mild odor. The molecule's two aldehyde groups favor the formation of polymers. The

TABLE 11.8	Applications of Phenolics and Chlorhexidine	
Form of Phenolic	**Primary Applications**	**How Delivered/Concerns**
Creolin	Common household version of phenol; for low or intermediate levels of disinfection in rooms, floors, and veterinary clinics.	1% to 3% emulsions that are combined with soap; can be too toxic for antisepsis; tend to be absorbed by membranes into the blood.
Bisphenols	Widely employed commercially, clinically, and in the home.	Orthophenyl phenol is a major ingredient in fungicides. This same phenolic is also found in some disinfectants used in the hospital and laboratory.
Hexachlorophene	Formerly a widespread additive of cleansing soaps (pHisoHex) for hospital and home use; may be used to control outbreaks of skin infections.	When hexachlorophene was found to be absorbed through the skin and a cause of neurological damage, it was no longer available without a prescription.
Form of Chlorhexidine	**Primary Applications**	**How Delivered/Concerns**
Chlorhexidine (Hibiclens, Hibitane)	Alcoholic or aqueous solutions are now commonly used for hand scrubbing, preparing skin sites for surgical incisions and injections, and patient cleansing. Solutions also serve as an obstetric and neonatal wash, a wound degermer, a mucous membrane irrigant, and a preservative for eye solutions.	Complex base containing chlorine and two phenolic rings; mode of action targets cell membranes and protein structure. At moderate to high concentrations, destroys both gram-positive and gram-negative bacteria but not spores. It may be fungicidal and virucidal. It is milder and less toxic than phenolics and is not absorbed into the skin.

TABLE 11.9	Applications of Alcohols and Peroxides (and Other Oxidizing Agents)	
Form of Alcohol*	**Primary Applications**	**How Delivered/Concerns**
Ethyl Alcohol (Ethanol, Grain Alcohol)	Skin degerming agent and antiseptic; surfactant action removes skin oil, soil, and some microbes sheltered in deeper skin layers; occasionally used to disinfect electrodes and face masks.	Solutions of 70% to 95% are germicidal, inexpensive, nonirritating; limited by its rate of evaporation. Items need to first be cleaned and then soaked in alcohol for 15 to 20 minutes.
Isopropyl Alcohol (Rubbing Alcohol)	Some disinfection of objects, surfaces; limited skin cleansing.	More microbicidal and less expensive than ethanol, but these benefits must be weighed against its toxicity; inhaling its vapors can adversely affect the nervous system.
Form of Oxidizing Agent	**Primary Applications**	**How Delivered/Concerns**
Hydrogen Peroxide (H_2O_2)	Versatile use as an antiseptic, including skin and wound cleansing, bedsore care, and mouthwashing; disinfectant for soft contact lenses, surgical implants, plastics, bedding, and room interiors.	3% hydrogen peroxide—most common form—is useful in treating infections by anaerobic bacteria because of the lethal effects of the oxygen released.
Sterilizing H_2O_2	Vaporized H_2O_2 is a sterilant; hydrogen peroxide plasma sterilizers used for industrial parts or medical items; for isolators, clean rooms, and space vehicles.	Hydrogen peroxide (35%) penetrates into delicate medical instruments, kills the most resistant microbes, and does not corrode small parts; vapors are sporicidal.
Peracetic Acid	Used to sterilize rooms, space shuttle; a chemical sterilant for medical devices.	Oxidizing agent—actions similar to those of hydrogen peroxide.
Ozone (O_3)	A gas used to disinfect air, water, industrial air conditioners, and cooling towers.	Difficult to handle in gaseous form.

A nurse takes advantage of an alcohol gel hand-cleansing station. These are widespread in hospitals and clinics to encourage hand antisepsis.

Disinfection of contact lenses with peroxide-based cleaner. Note the bubbles produced, indicating the release of oxygen gas.

*Both forms of alcohol are in alcohol gels used for universal precautions and hand degerming in hospitals. (left): BELMONTE/BSIP SA/Alamy Stock Photo; (right): Kathy Park Talaro

mechanism of activity involves cross-linking protein molecules on the cell surface. In this process, amino acids are alkylated, meaning that a hydrogen atom on an amino acid is replaced by the glutaraldehyde molecule itself. This irreversibly disrupts the activity of enzymes and other proteins within cells. Glutaraldehyde is rapid and broad-spectrum, and is officially labeled as a sterilant and high-level disinfectant. It is one of the few chemicals that can be used to sterilize delicate reusable medical and dental instruments. It kills spores in 3 hours and fungi and vegetative bacteria (even *Mycobacterium* and *Pseudomonas*) in a few minutes. Viruses, including the most resistant forms, appear to be inactivated after relatively short exposure. A special device known as a chemiclave

(similar to an autoclave) vaporizes the solution under pressure to sterilize delicate instruments without heat. Glutaraldehyde retains its potency even in the presence of organic matter, is noncorrosive, does not damage plastics, and is less toxic or irritating than formaldehyde. Its principal disadvantage is that it is somewhat unstable, especially with increased pH and temperature.

Another aldehyde, ortho-phthalaldehyde (OPA), has been approved by the EPA as a high-level disinfectant. OPA is a pale blue liquid with a barely detectable odor. It has a mechanism of action similar to glutaraldehyde, is stable and nonirritating, and for most uses is much faster acting than glutaraldehyde. It is effective against vegetative bacteria, including *Mycobacterium* and *Pseudomonas*,

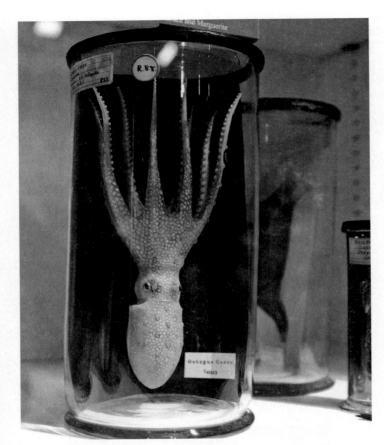

Figure 11.15 **Uses of Formaldehyde.** Its extreme toxicity makes formaldehyde impractical for use on living tissue but formalin (a 37% solution of formaldehyde in water) is commonly used to preserve biological specimens for study.
Jennifer Santolla/Alamy Stock Photo

Figure 11.16 **Sterilization using an ethylene oxide sterilizer.** The machine is equipped with gas canisters containing ethylene oxide (ETO) and carbon dioxide, a chamber to hold items, and mechanisms that evacuate gas and introduce air.

fungi, and viruses. Chief among its disadvantages are an inability to reliably destroy spores and a tendency to stain proteins, including those in human skin.

Formaldehyde is a sharp, irritating gas that readily dissolves in water to form an aqueous solution called **formalin.** Pure formalin is a 37% solution of formaldehyde gas dissolved in water. The chemical is microbicidal through its attachment to nucleic acids and functional groups of amino acids. Formalin is an intermediate- to high-level disinfectant, but its extreme toxicity (it is classified as a carcinogen) and irritating effects on the skin and mucous membranes greatly limit its clinical usefulness (**figure 11.15**).

Gaseous Sterilants and Disinfectants

Processing inanimate substances with chemical vapors, gases, and aerosols provides a versatile alternative to heat or liquid chemicals. Currently the vapors and aerosols having the broadest applications are ethylene oxide (ETO), propylene oxide, and chlorine dioxide.

Ethylene oxide (ETO) and its relative propylene oxide (PO) are colorless gases at room temperature. The structure of ETO is shown below:

$$CH_2 - CH_2$$
$$\diagdown \; O \; \diagup$$

ETO is very explosive in air, a feature that can be eliminated by combining it with a high percentage of carbon dioxide or fluorocarbon. Like the aldehydes, ETO is a very strong alkylating agent, and it reacts vigorously with functional groups of DNA and proteins. Through these actions, it blocks both DNA replication and enzymatic actions. Ethylene oxide is one of a very few gases generally accepted for chemical sterilization because, when employed according to strict procedures, it is a sporicide. A specially designed ETO sterilizer is equipped with a chamber; gas ports; and controls for temperature, pressure, and humidity (**figure 11.16**). Ethylene oxide is rather penetrating but relatively slow-acting, requiring from 90 minutes to 3 hours. Some items absorb ETO residues and must be aerated with sterile air for several hours after exposure to remove as much residual gas as possible. For all of its effectiveness, ETO has some unfortunate features. Its explosiveness makes it dangerous to handle; it can damage the lungs, eyes, and mucous membranes if contacted directly; and it is rated as a carcinogen by the government. Both ETO and propylene oxide are used mainly as disinfectant-sterilants for some foods and plastic items.

Chlorine dioxide is another gas used for sterilization. Despite the name, chlorine dioxide works in a completely different way from the chlorine compounds discussed earlier in the chapter. It is a

TABLE 11.10 Applications of Aldehydes and Sterilant Gases

Form of Aldehyde	Primary Applications	How Delivered/Concerns
Glutaraldehyde	A sterilant for materials usually damaged by heat. Examples include respiratory therapy equipment, hemostats, fiberoptic endoscopes, kidney dialysis equipment, and dental instruments; an alternate vaccine preservative, and sanitizer for poultry carcasses.	Solutions diluted to 2% are relatively mild but require 2 to 4 hours' soaking. Usual commercial products are Cidex, Sporocidin. Instrument sterilization involves precleaning along with autoclaving to inactivate hepatitis B and other blood-borne viruses.
Ortho-phthalaldehyde (OPA)	High-level disinfectant similar in uses and effects to glutaraldehyde.	Faster acting and more stable than glutaraldehyde but less sporicidal.

Form of Gas	Primary Applications	How Delivered/Concerns
Ethylene Oxide (ETO)	An official sterilant for heat-sensitive plastics and delicate instruments in hospitals and industries—prepackaged medical supplies and disposable Petri dishes; used extensively to disinfect foods, spices, dried fruits, and drugs.	Carboxide and cryoxide are commercial products; gas is explosive and must be used with a stabilizer; ETO is rather toxic to humans; penetrating but slow, requiring 1 to 3 hours of exposure inside a special chamber.
Propylene Oxide	Sterilization of foods such as nuts, powders, starches, and spices.	Physical properties and mode of action similar to ETO but safer because it breaks down into a relatively harmless substance.
Chlorine Dioxide	Air and surface sterilant; for treatment of water, food-processing equipment, and medical waste; decontamination of whole rooms and space probes.	Similar in action to ETO but does not require a chamber; thus, effective for large spaces or objects.

Technician treats surgical instruments with glutaraldehyde prior to heat sterilization.
Arno Massee/Science Source

Examples of prepackaged medical supplies sterilized in an ethylene oxide sterilizer.
Courtesy of Printpack, Inc.

strong alkylating agent, which disrupts proteins and is effective against vegetative bacteria, fungi, viruses, and endospores. Chlorine dioxide has mainly been used for the treatment of drinking water, wastewater, food-processing equipment, and medical waste, but it also has numerous applications in decontamination of rooms, buildings, and large spaces or objects.

Betapropiolactone (BPL) is a substance somewhat similar to ETO in applications. It is rapidly microbicidal when used as an aerosol or liquid to disinfect whole rooms and instruments, to sterilize bone and arterial grafts, and to inactivate viruses in vaccines.

A summary of applications for aldehydes and sterilizing gases is presented in **table 11.10.**

Chemicals with Surface Action: Detergents and Soaps

Detergents are polar molecules that act as surfactants. Most anionic detergents have limited microbicidal power. This includes most soaps. Much more effective are positively charged (cationic)

detergents, particularly the **quaternary ammonium compounds** (usually shortened to *quats*). The activity of cationic detergents arises from the attachment of four organic radicals (the origin of the term *quaternary*) to a central, positively charged nitrogen atom. At least one of these radicals is a long-chain hydrocarbon surfactant that disrupts the cell membranes of sensitive microbes (see **table 11.11**). After a few minutes of contact, the cells burst and die.

The effects of detergents are varied. When used at high enough concentrations, quaternary ammonium compounds are effective against some gram-positive bacteria, viruses, fungi, and algae. In low concentrations, they exhibit only microbistatic effects. Drawbacks to the quats include their ineffectiveness against the tuberculosis bacterium, hepatitis virus, *Pseudomonas,* and spores at any concentration. Furthermore, their activity is greatly reduced in the presence of organic matter, and they require alkaline conditions to function. As a result of these limitations, quats are rated only for low to moderate-level disinfection in the clinical setting.

TABLE 11.11	Applications of Detergents and Soaps		
Form of Detergents or Soaps	**Primary Applications**		**How Delivered/Concerns**
Quaternary Ammonium Compounds (Quats) Benzalkonium chloride	Mixed with cleaning agents to disinfect and sanitize floors, equipment surfaces, and restrooms; for sanitizing restaurant utensils, food-processing equipment, and clothing; common preservatives in ophthalmic solutions and cosmetics.		Names include benzalkonium chloride (Zephiran), the active ingredient in Lysol spray, and cetylpyridinium chloride (Ceepryn); in dilutions ranging from 1:100 to 1:1,000; the level of disinfection is too low for disinfecting medical instruments. Quats are active ingredients in many household disinfectant sprays.
Soaps Proper hand washing with soap is one of the most important control methods for health care and personal hygiene. OJO Images/SuperStock	Cleansing agents and sanitizers in industry and the home; preparing instruments for heat sterilization; degerming patients' skin, routine hand washing by medical and dental personnel, surgical and preoperative hand scrubbing.	Alkaline salts of fatty acids; weak germicides with superior sudsing and wetting properties; can remove large amounts of surface soil, grease, and other debris; antimicrobial chemicals added to make germicidal soaps with greater disinfection power.	**Quick Search** Go to CDC TV and watch the video "Put Your Hands Together" about the importance of hand washing.

Soaps are alkaline compounds made by combining the fatty acids in oils with sodium or potassium salts. In usual practice, soaps alone are weak microbicides, and they destroy only highly sensitive forms such as the agents of gonorrhea, meningitis, and syphilis. The common hospital pathogen *Pseudomonas* is so resistant to soap that some species grow abundantly in soap dishes. Soaps function primarily as cleansing agents and sanitizers in industry, the home, and the medical setting. Combining germicides such as chlorhexidine or iodophor with soaps produces highly active antiseptics, degermers, and disinfectants. Vigorously brushing the hands with germicidal soap over a 15-second period can remove dirt, oil, and surface contaminants as well as some superficial resident microbes, but it is unable to remove those deeply entrenched in the skin (see **Clinical Connections, "The Quest for Sterile Skin,"** and **figure 11.17**).

See table 11.11 for coverage on the main uses of detergents and soaps.

Heavy Metal Compounds

Various forms of the metallic elements mercury, silver, gold, copper, arsenic, and zinc have been applied in microbial control over several centuries. These are often referred to as heavy metals because of their relatively high atomic weights. However, from this list, only preparations containing mercury and silver still have any significance as germicides. Although some metals (zinc, iron) are needed in small concentrations as cofactors on enzymes, the higher molecular weight metals (mercury, silver, gold) can be very toxic, even in minute quantities (parts per million). This property of having antimicrobial effects in exceedingly small

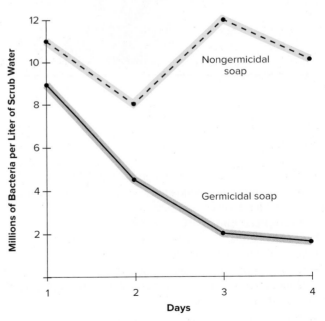

Figure 11.17 Graph showing some effects of hand scrubbing. Comparison of scrubbing over several days with a nongermicidal soap versus a germicidal soap. Germicidal soap has persistent effects on skin over time, reducing and keeping the microbial count low. Soap alone does not cause a sustained reduction in the microbial count; it even raises it. This effect is presumably due to the uncovering of skin layers with higher levels of normal resident microbiota.

CLINICAL CONNECTIONS

The Quest for Sterile Skin

About 140 years ago, before sterile gloves were a routine part of medical procedures, the hands remained bare during surgery. Even then, medical practitioners understood the risk for infections and attempted to "sterilize" the hands of surgeons and their assistants. Several stringent (and probably very painful) techniques involving strong chemical germicides and vigorous scrubbing were practiced. Here are a few examples.

In Schatz's method, the hands and forearms were first cleansed by brisk scrubbing with liquid soap for 3 to 5 minutes, then soaked in a saturated solution of permanganate at a temperature of 110°F until they turned a deep mahogany brown. Next, the limbs were immersed in saturated oxalic acid until the skin became decolorized. Then, as if this were not enough, the hands and arms were rinsed with sterile limewater and washed in warm bichloride of mercury for 1 minute.

Park's method was even more like torture. First, the surfaces of the hands and arms were rubbed completely with a mixture of cornmeal and green soap to remove loose dirt and superficial skin. Next, a paste of water and mustard flour was applied to the skin until it began to sting. This potion was rinsed off in sterile water, and the hands and arms were then soaked in hot bichloride of mercury for a few minutes, during which time the solution was rubbed into the skin.

Another method once earnestly suggested for getting rid of microorganisms was to expose the hands to a hot-air cabinet to "sweat the germs" out of skin glands. Pasteur himself advocated a quick flaming of the hands to maintain asepsis.

The old dream of sterilizing the skin was finally reduced to some basic realities: The microbes entrenched in the epidermis and skin glands cannot be completely eradicated even with the most intense efforts, and the skin cannot be sterilized without also seriously damaging it. Because this is true for both medical personnel and their patients, the chance always exists that infectious agents can be

Heavy growth of microbial colonies on a plate of blood agar prepared by having a classroom of 30 students touch its surface. The result was a mixed population of bacteria and fungi, many of which could be pathogens (clear zones of hemolysis).
Kathy Park Talaro

introduced during invasive medical procedures. Safer surgery had to wait until 1890, when rubber gloves first became available to place a sterile barrier around the hands. Of course, this did not mean that skin cleansing and antiseptic procedures were abandoned or downplayed. A thorough scrubbing of the skin with antiseptic soap is still needed to remove the most dangerous source of infections—the superficial contaminants constantly picked up from whatever we touch.

What would be some of the more serious problems associated with sterilizing or trying to sterilize the skin?

amounts is called an **oligodynamic* action (figure 11.18).** Heavy metal germicides contain either an inorganic or an organic metallic salt, and they come in the form of aqueous solutions, tinctures, ointments, or soaps.

Mercury, silver, and most other metals exert microbicidal effects by binding onto functional groups of proteins and inactivating them, rapidly bringing metabolism to a standstill (see figure 11.6c). This mode of action can destroy many types of microbes, including vegetative bacteria, fungal cells and spores, algae, protozoa, and viruses (but not endospores). A newer use of metals is their incorporation into medical supplies and hospital facilities. Silver is now added to catheters, IV lines, and prosthe-

ses to prevent biofilm formations and infections. Studies have demonstrated that copper has superior killing powers over chrome and aluminum when added to metal parts of lavatory fixtures, doors, and doorknobs. It destroys the most problematic drug-resistant pathogens such as MRSA, as well as *Clostridioides difficile* vegetative cells, influenza virus, and gram-negative opportunists.

The main drawbacks to heavy metals are (1) metals (especially mercury) are very toxic to humans if ingested, inhaled, or absorbed through the skin, even in small quantities, for the same reasons that they are toxic to microbial cells; (2) they commonly cause allergic reactions; (3) large quantities of biological fluids and wastes neutralize their actions; and (4) microbes can develop resistance to metals.

Table 11.12 provides an overview of applications for heavy metals.

* *oligodynamic* (ol″-ih-goh-dy-nam′-ik) Gr. *oligos*, little, and *dynamis*, power.

Figure 11.18 Demonstration of the oligodynamic action of heavy metals. A pour plate inoculated with saliva has small fragments of heavy metals pressed lightly into it. During incubation, clear zones indicating growth inhibition developed around both fragments. The slightly larger zone surrounding the amalgam (used in tooth fillings) probably reflects the combined effect of the silver and mercury it contains.
Kathy Park Talaro

Dyes as Antimicrobial Agents

Dyes are important in staining techniques and as selective and differential agents in media; they are also a primary source of certain drugs used in chemotherapy. Their antimicrobial effects are apparently due to the way they insert into nucleic acids and cause mutations. There is also some evidence they can interfere with cell wall synthesis. Because aniline dyes such as crystal violet and malachite green are most active against gram-positive species of bacteria and some fungi, they are incorporated into solutions and ointments to treat skin infections (ringworm, for example). The yellow acridine dyes, acriflavine and proflavine, are sometimes utilized for antisepsis and wound treatment in medical and veterinary clinics. For the most part, applications for dyes will continue to be limited because dyes stain and have a narrow spectrum of activity.

Acids and Alkalis

Conditions of very low or high pH can destroy or inhibit microbial cells, but they are limited in applications due to their corrosive, caustic, and hazardous nature. Alkaline solutions are good for cleaning and some types of disinfection because they inactivate proteins. Ammonium hydroxide is a major component of detergents and cleansers, and a strong sodium hydroxide solution is one of the few substances that reliably destroys prions. Organic acids are widely used in food preservation because they prevent spore germination and bacterial and fungal growth and because they are generally regarded as safe to eat. Acetic acid (in the form of vinegar) is a pickling agent that inhibits bacterial growth; propionic acid is commonly incorporated into breads and cakes to retard molds; lactic acid is added to sauerkraut and olives to prevent growth of anaerobic bacteria (especially the clostridia); and benzoic and sorbic acids are added to beverages, syrups, and margarine to inhibit yeasts.

For a look at the antimicrobial chemicals found in some common household products, see **table 11.13.**

Practice SECTION 11.4

22. Describe situations that require high-level disinfection and those for which medium- or low-level disinfection is adequate.
23. What is the difference between a tincture and an aqueous solution?
24. Define *sterilant*, and name the principal sporicidal chemical agents.
25. Summarize the chief forms and uses of chlorine compounds.
26. What are the superior characteristics of iodophors over free iodine solutions?
27. What are the modes of action of alcohols and phenolics?
28. Why is hydrogen peroxide solution so effective against anaerobes?
29. Give the uses and disadvantages of the heavy metal chemical agents, glutaraldehyde, and the sterilizing gases.
30. What does it mean to say that a chemical has an oligodynamic action, and which compounds have this effect?

TABLE 11.12	Applications of Heavy Metals	
Form of Metal	Primary Applications	How Delivered/Concerns
Organic Mercury	Thimerosal (Merthiolate) and nitromersol (Metaphen) are weak antiseptics and infection preventives; can be preservatives in cosmetics and ophthalmic solutions.	Tinctures (0.001% to 0.2%) are fairly effective but a poor choice for broken skin because they are toxic and can delay healing. Mercurochrome is now considered one of the poorest of antiseptics.
Silver Sulfadiazine Ointment	Added to dressings, it effectively prevents infection in second- and third-degree burn patients.	A yellow ointment containing silver salts and a sulfa drug.
Silver Nitrate (AgNO$_3$)	Primarily as a topical germicide for mouth ulcers and occasionally root canals.	1% to 2% solutions have been used as antiseptics, but they discolor skin and other tissues.
Metallic Silver	Incorporated into catheters to prevent urinary tract infections in the hospital; added to paint, plastics, and steel as a way to control microbial survival on items such as toilet seats, stethoscopes, and even walls and floors in homes.	
Colloidal Silver	Mild germicidal ointments or rinses for the mouth, nose, eyes, and vagina.	

Product	Specific Chemical Agent	Antimicrobial Category
TABLE 11.13	**Active Ingredients of Various Commercial Antimicrobial Products**	
Lysol and Clorox Sanitizing Wipes	Dimethyl benzyl ammonium chloride	Detergent (quat)
Tilex and Lysol Mildew Remover	Sodium hypochlorites	Halogen
Dial Antibacterial Hand Soap	Benzalkonium chloride	Detergent (quat)
Lysol Disinfecting Spray	Alkyl dimethyl benzyl ammonium/ethanol	Detergent (quat)/alcohol
ReNu Contact Lens Solution	Polyaminopropyl biguanide	Chlorhexidine
Wet Ones Antibacterial Moist Towelettes	Benzethonium chloride	Detergent (quat)
Scope Mouthwash	Ethanol	Alcohol
Purell Instant Hand Sanitizer	Ethanol	Alcohol
Pine-Sol	Pine oil and surfactant	Aldehydes, alcohols
Allergan Eye Drops	Sodium chlorite	Halogen

CASE STUDY Part 2

On January 27, the same day that Aaron Young was undergoing his ERCP procedure, DNA analysis revealed that many of the CRE infections at UCLA were caused by the same strain of the bacterium, indicating spread within the hospital. Dr. Rubin returned to the medical records and asked one of his infectious disease fellows to once again review the available information, focusing solely on those patients infected with the outbreak strain of the bacterium. A pattern began to emerge.

More than 2 weeks before Aaron Young entered the hospital, a woman being evaluated for a liver transplant underwent an ERCP procedure using endoscope number 47. The same scope was used on Aaron 17 days later. In many cases, CRE infections could be traced to scope number 47, and a second scope, number 26, was linked to most of the others. The scopes were just 7 months old and had been cleaned in accordance with the manufacturer's recommendations. Eight patients were confirmed to have been infected, and three of them died.

In February, the Food and Drug Administration issued a safety alert to all U.S. hospitals, cautioning them to use extra care when reprocessing the scopes; it was thought that the elevator in the scope provided several nooks and crevices in which bacteria could become lodged. In March, Olympus, which makes 85% of the duodenoscopes used in the United States, provided new cleaning instructions and recommended a new cleaning brush, a warning that they had given to hospitals in Europe more than 2 years earlier. Both UCLA and Olympus are being sued by a number of patients or their families, including Aaron Young and his parents.

On April 3, after an additional 67 days in the hospital, Aaron Young was once again discharged, but he has continued to suffer bouts of infection.

- With such a worry about bacterial contamination, why aren't endoscopes simply steam sterilized between patients?
- The final step in reprocessing involves flushing the endoscope with 70% ethyl or isopropyl alcohol. Why was 70% alcohol specified?

Chapter Summary with Key Terms

11.1 Controlling Microorganisms
 A. **Decontamination** procedures involve the destruction or removal of contaminants. Contaminants are defined as microbes present at a given place and time that are undesirable or unwanted.
 B. **Sterilization** is a process that destroys or removes all microbes, including viruses.
 1. **A bacteri*cide*** is a chemical that destroys vegetative stages of bacteria. A **sporicide** can destroy bacterial endospores.
 2. **Bacterio*static*** agents inhibit or prevent the growth of bacteria on tissues or on other objects in the environment.

 3. A **germicide** or **microbicide** is a chemical that will kill any pathogenic microorganisms.
 C. **Disinfection** refers to a physical or chemical process that destroys vegetative pathogens but not bacterial endospores on objects. An **antiseptic** is a chemical applied to living tissues to render them free of pathogens.
 D. **Sanitization** is forceful cleaning that removes contaminants and makes objects hygienic and safe to use. **Degermation** is the same process applied to the body to remove potential pathogens.

E. Several factors influence the rate at which antimicrobial agents work. These factors are:
1. Exposure time to the agent
2. Numbers of microbes present
3. Relative resistance of microbes (for example, endospores versus vegetative forms)
4. Activity of the agent (microbicidal versus microbistatic)
F. How antimicrobial agents work: their **modes of action.** Agents affect cell wall synthesis, membrane permeability, and protein and nucleic acid synthesis and function.

11.2 Physical Methods of Control: Heat
A. **Moist heat** denatures proteins and DNA while destroying membranes.
1. *Sterilization:* **Autoclaves** utilize steam under pressure (121°C) to sterilize heat-resistant materials, whereas intermittent sterilization uses steam at 100°C to sterilize more delicate items.
2. *Disinfection:* **Pasteurization** subjects liquids to temperatures below 100°C and is used to lower the microbial load in liquids. Boiling water can be used to destroy vegetative pathogens in the home.
B. **Dry heat**, using higher temperatures than moist heat, can also be used to sterilize.
1. **Incineration** can be carried out using a Bunsen burner or incinerator. Temperatures range between 800°C and 6,500°C.
2. *Dry ovens* operate at temperatures of 150°C to 180°C.
C. Cold temperatures (refrigeration and freezing) are microbistatic and are commonly used to preserve food, media, and cultures.
D. Drying and **desiccation** lead to (often temporary) metabolic inhibition by reducing water in the cell.

11.3 Physical Methods of Control: Radiation and Filtration
A. *Radiation:* Energy in the form of **radiation** can be used for **cold sterilization,** which works by killing microbes without heat.
1. **Ionizing radiation,** such as gamma rays and X-rays, has deep penetrating power and works by causing breaks in the DNA of target organisms.
2. **Nonionizing radiation** uses **ultraviolet** waves with very little penetrating power and works by creating dimers between adjacent pyrimidines, which interferes with replication.
B. *Using Filtration to Remove Microbes:* Filtration involves the physical removal of microbes by passing a gas or liquid through a fine filter, and can be used to sterilize air as well as heat-sensitive liquids.

11.4 Chemical Agents in Microbial Control
A. Chemicals are divided into **disinfectants, antiseptics, sterilants, sanitizers,** and **degermers** based on their level of effectiveness and the surfaces to which they are applied.

B. Antimicrobial chemicals are found as solids, gases, and liquids. Liquids can be either **aqueous** (water based) or **tinctures** (alcohol based).
C. **Halogens** are chemicals based on elements from group VII of the periodic table.
1. Chlorine gas, hypochlorites, and chloramines all work by disrupting disulfide bonds and, given adequate time, are sporicidal.
2. Iodine compounds include free iodine (I_2) and **iodophors.** Iodine has a mode of action similar to chlorine and can also be sporicidal.
D. **Phenolics** work by disrupting cell membranes and precipitating proteins. They are bactericidal, fungicidal, and virucidal but not sporicidal. Bisphenols are mild forms for disinfection and antisepsis.
E. **Chlorhexidine** (Hibiclens, Hibitane) is a surfactant and protein denaturant with broad microbicidal properties, although it is not sporicidal. Solutions of chlorhexidine are used as skin degerming agents for preoperative scrubs, skin cleaning, and burns.
F. Ethyl and isopropyl **alcohol,** in concentrations of 50% to 90%, are useful for microbial control. Alcohols act as **surfactants,** dissolving membrane lipids and coagulating proteins of vegetative bacterial cells and fungi. They are not sporicidal.
G. **Hydrogen peroxide** produces highly reactive hydroxyl free radicals that damage protein and DNA while also decomposing to O_2 gas, which is toxic to anaerobes. Strong solutions of H_2O_2 are sporicidal.
H. Aldehydes such as **glutaraldehyde** kill microbes by alkylating protein and DNA molecules and can be used as sterilants.
I. Gases and aerosols such as **ethylene oxide (ETO),** propylene oxide, and chlorine dioxide are strong alkylating agents, all of which are sporicidal.
J. **Detergents** and **soaps**
1. Cationic detergents known as **quaternary ammonium compounds (quats)** act as surfactants that alter the membrane permeability of some bacteria and fungi. They are not sporicidal.
2. Soaps function by removing grease and soil that contain microbes.
K. **Heavy metals:** Compounds containing silver or mercury kill vegetative cells (but not spores) despite being highly diluted **(oligodynamic action)** by inactivating proteins.
L. **Dyes, acids,** and **alkalis** can also inhibit or destroy microbes but are limited in use.

 Assess Your Knowledge

Level I. These questions require a working knowledge of the concepts in the chapter and the ability to recall and understand the information you have studied.

Developing a Concept Inventory

Select the correct answer from the answers provided. For questions with blanks, choose the combination of answers that most accurately completes the statement.

1. A microbicidal agent has what effect?
 a. sterilizes
 b. inhibits microorganisms
 c. is toxic to human cells
 d. destroys microorganisms

2. Microbial control methods that kill _____ are able to sterilize.
 a. viruses c. endospores
 b. the tubercle bacillus d. cysts

3. Any process that destroys the non-spore-forming contaminants on inanimate objects is
 a. antisepsis c. sterilization
 b. disinfection d. degermation

4. Sanitization is a process by which
 a. the microbial load on objects is reduced
 b. objects are made sterile with chemicals
 c. utensils are scrubbed
 d. skin is debrided

5. An example of an agent that lowers the surface tension of cells is
 a. phenol c. alcohol
 b. chlorine d. formalin

6. High temperatures _____ and low temperatures _____.
 a. sterilize, disinfect
 b. kill cells, inhibit cell growth
 c. denature proteins, burst cells
 d. speed up metabolism, slow down metabolism

7. The primary action of _____ heat is to _____.
 a. dry, destroy cell walls
 b. moist, kill vegetative cells
 c. dry, dissolve lipids
 d. moist, denature proteins

8. The standard temperature-pressure combination for an autoclave is
 a. 100°C and 4 psi c. 131°C and 9 psi
 b. 121°C and 15 psi d. 115°C and 3 psi

9. Microbe(s) that is/are the target(s) of pasteurization include(s)
 a. *Clostridium botulinum* c. *Salmonella* species
 b. *Mycobacterium* species d. both b and c

10. Ionizing radiation like _____ removes _____ from atoms.
 a. UV, protons c. gamma rays, electrons
 b. X-rays, the charge d. cathode rays, ions

11. The primary mode of action of nonionizing radiation is to
 a. produce superoxide ions
 b. make pyrimidine dimers
 c. denature proteins
 d. break disulfide bonds

12. The most versatile method of sterilizing heat-sensitive liquids is
 a. UV radiation c. beta propiolactone
 b. exposure to ozone d. filtration

13. _____ is the iodine antiseptic of choice for wound treatment.
 a. 8% tincture c. 5% Iodophor
 b. 5% aqueous d. 7.5% potassium iodide solution

14. A chemical with sporicidal properties is
 a. phenol c. quaternary ammonium compound
 b. alcohol d. glutaraldehyde

15. Silver sulfadiazine is used
 a. in antisepsis of burns c. to treat genital gonorrhea
 b. as a mouthwash d. to disinfect water

16. Detergents are
 a. high-level germicides
 b. surfactants
 c. excellent antiseptics
 d. used in disinfecting surgical instruments

17. Which of the following is an approved sterilant?
 a. chlorhexidine c. ethylene oxide
 b. betadyne d. ethyl alcohol

Case Study Analysis

1. Based on the relative resistance scheme seen in Section 11.1, the CRE bacteria in this case would be classified as
 a. highest resistance
 b. moderate resistance
 c. least resistance

2. Many medical instruments are reprocessed and used on multiple patients. Why were duodenoscopes so integral to this outbreak?
 a. Technicians were inadvertently passing bacteria from one duodenoscope to another.

 b. They had areas that were difficult to effectively clean.
 c. They likely were contaminated with large numbers of bacteria.
 d. Duodenoscopes were not being cleaned according to the manufacturer's instructions.

3. After receiving far more rigorous protocols for duodenoscope reprocessing, one of the first things UCLA did was to purchase an additional 40 duodenoscopes. Why do you think they did this?

On the Test

These questions will help to prepare you to successfully answer similar questions you'll see on the TEAS (Test of Essential Academic Skills) and NCLEX (National Council Licensure Examination).

1. What type of molecule can be denatured by heat or changes in pH?
 a. carbohydrate c. protein
 b. lipid d. simple sugar

2. Which molecule is composed of long chains of nucleic acids?
 a. protein c. DNA
 b. lipid d. carbohydrate

Writing Challenge

For each question, compose a one- or two-paragraph answer that includes the factual information needed to completely address the question. Practice questions can also be used for writing-challenge exercises.

1. What is wrong with this statement: "Prior to vaccination, the patient's skin was sterilized with alcohol"? What would be the more correct wording?

2. Would it be proper to say that a patient has been disinfected? Why or why not?

3. Why are antimicrobials inhibited in the presence of organic matter?

4. Think of three situations in which the same microbe would be considered a serious contaminant in one case and completely harmless in another.

5. Explain what features of endospores make them so resistant to microbial control, and what sterilizing techniques could destroy them.

6. Explain some of the problems involved in sterilizing delicate and heat-sensitive instruments such as endoscopes, syringes, needles, catheters, and other instruments.

7. The shelf life and keeping qualities of fruit and other perishable foods are greatly enhanced through irradiation, saving industry and consumers billions of dollars. How would you personally feel about eating irradiated fruit? How about spices that had been sterilized with ETO?

Concept Mapping

On Connect you can find an Introduction to Concept Mapping that provides guidance for working with concept maps, along with concept-mapping activities for this chapter.

 Application, Analysis, Evaluation, and Synthesis

Level II. These problems go beyond just restating facts and require higher levels of understanding and an ability to interpret, problem solve, transfer knowledge to new situations, create models, and predict outcomes.

Critical Thinking

Critical thinking is the ability to reason and solve problems using facts and concepts. These questions can be approached from a number of angles and, in most cases, they do not have a single correct answer.

1. For each item on the following list, propose a reasonable method of sterilization. You cannot use the same method more than three times for the whole list. The method must sterilize, not just disinfect; and the method must not destroy the item or render it useless unless there is no other choice. After considering a workable method, think of a method that would not work. Note: Where an object containing something is given, you must sterilize everything (for example, both the jar and the petroleum jelly [Vaseline] in it). Some examples of sterilizing methods are autoclave, ethylene oxide gas, dry oven, and ionizing radiation.

room air

serum

a pot of soil

plastic Petri dishes

heat-sensitive drugs

cloth dressings

leather shoes from a thrift shop

a cheese sandwich

a flask of nutrient agar

an entire room (walls, floor, etc.)

rubber gloves

disposable syringes

carcasses of cows with "mad cow" disease

inside of a refrigerator

wine

a jar of Vaseline

fruit in plastic bags

milk

orchid seeds

metal instruments

mail contaminated with anthrax spores

2. Using pasteurization techniques as a model, compare the TDTs and explain the relationships between temperature and length of exposure.

3. It may seem contradictory that lyophilization can be used to preserve foods yet also be used to keep cultures of microbes viable. Explain how these applications can be reconciled.

4. A supermarket/drugstore assignment: Look at the labels of 10 different products used to control microbes, and make a list of their active ingredients, their suggested uses, and information on toxicity and precautions.

5. Devise an experiment that will differentiate between bactericidal and bacteriostatic effects.

6. There is quite a bit of concern that chlorine used as a water purification chemical presents serious dangers. What alternative methods covered by this chapter could be used to purify water supplies and keep them safe from contamination?

7. Explain why surfactant chemicals are more effective against gram-negative bacteria than against gram-positive bacteria.

Visual Assessment

1. From chapter 2, figure 2.21. Study this illustration of a cell membrane. In what ways could alcohol damage this membrane? How would that harm the cell?

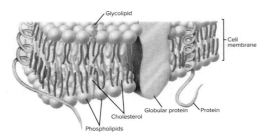

2. From figure 3.20. Why did three bacteria on this plate grow so well while growth of the fourth species (on the bottom) is nearly invisible?

Lisa Burgess/
McGraw-Hill Education

Drugs, Microbes, Host—The Elements of Chemotherapy

In This Chapter...

(prescription pills): wwing/Getty Images; (soil bacteria): Kathy Park Talaro; (Vancomycin) Lisa Burgess/McGraw-Hill Education; (E-test penicillin): Sirirat/Shutterstock

I Felt Better When I Was Sick

For a young person in good health, a few episodes of diarrhea do not normally warrant a doctor's visit, but for the 23-year-old engineer, the persistence of her **traveler's diarrhea,** along with the constant jokes about Montezuma's revenge and Delhi belly, drove her to seek treatment. Her medical history was unremarkable, and she was prescribed **ciprofloxacin** for 10 days, a broad-spectrum antibiotic commonly used to treat gastrointestinal infections.

Over the course of treatment, she began to suffer **nausea, dizziness, tachycardia** (rapid heart rate), **memory loss,** and extreme difficulty concentrating, which she described to her doctor as "brain fog." The ciprofloxacin was discontinued but the brain fog remained and was joined by a host of other symptoms over the next month—diarrhea, food intolerance leading to gastrointestinal pain, **migraines, chronic fatigue,** and frequent upper respiratory infections. She returned to work, despite the continued side effects.

Seven years after the first infection, the patient again visited the doctor, this time with a sore throat and fever. She was prescribed a 5-day course of a different antibiotic, **moxifloxacin.** She again began to suffer severe side effects, this time including **convulsions,** multiple gastrointestinal symptoms, tachycardic episodes in which her heart rate rose to 140 beats per minute for hours, **hypotension, dilated pupils,** incapacitating fatigue, insomnia, pain, and difficulty breathing. The moxifloxacin was discontinued after the third day, yet once again the symptoms persisted. Over the next month her weight dropped from 112 to 98 pounds and she was losing, by her own reckoning, several handfuls of hair each day. Extreme dry eye led to the development of a **corneal ulcer** 3 months after treatment had stopped, while at the same time she began to suffer joint and muscle pain in her neck, shoulders, hands, knees, and ankles. At 9 months post-treatment she developed **Achilles tendonitis.**

According to the patient's husband, she was now bedridden most of the time, finding it difficult to walk across the room, and often needing to sit on a stool to shower. She rationed her energy, having to choose between visiting her doctor or her 90-year-old grandmother, as her constant fatigue did not allow for both. Even talking on the telephone was enough to exhaust her, causing her to lead a more and more ostracized life. She was unable to continue working.

A barrage of tests led to a diagnosis of **autonomic polyneuropathy,** a condition in which the nerves that control involuntary bodily functions are damaged. The most common effects of the disorder, changes in blood pressure, temperature control, digestion, and bladder function, were all seen in the patient.

- *What is a broad-spectrum antibiotic?*

- *Can you think of a reason that the patient had similar reactions to two different drugs?*

To continue the Case Study, go to Case Study Part 2 at the end of the chapter.

(anthrax attacks): Scott J. Ferrell/Congressional Quarterly/Getty Images

12.1 Principles of Antimicrobial Therapy

 Learn

1. State the goals of antimicrobial therapy.
2. Discuss the origins of antimicrobial drugs.
3. Differentiate between antibiotics, synthetic drugs, and semisynthetic drugs.
4. Describe some of the special strategies of antimicrobial therapy.
5. Explain what is meant by a drug's spectrum and how narrow- and broad-spectrum drugs differ.
6. Summarize the five modes of action of antimicrobial drugs, with specific examples of their effects.

TABLE 12.1	Characteristics of the Ideal Antimicrobial Drug

- Selectively toxic to the microbe but nontoxic to host cells
- Microbicidal rather than microbistatic
- Remains potent long enough to act and is not broken down or excreted prematurely
- Is not subject to the development of antimicrobial resistance
- Complements or assists the activities of the host's defenses
- Remains active even when diluted in body fluids and tissues
- Readily delivered to the site of infection
- Reasonably priced
- Does not disrupt the host's health by causing allergies or predisposing the host to other infections

More than a century ago in the United States, one out of three children was expected to die of an infectious disease before the age of 5. Early death or severe lifelong debilitation from scarlet fever, diphtheria, tuberculosis, meningitis, and many other bacterial diseases was a fearsome yet undeniable fact of life to most of the world's population.

The introduction of modern drugs to control infections in the 1930s was a medical revolution that has added significantly to the life span and health of humans. It is no wonder that for many years, antibiotics in particular were regarded as miracle drugs. Although antimicrobial drugs have greatly reduced the incidence of certain infections, they have definitely not eradicated infectious disease and probably never will. In fact, in some parts of the world, mortality rates from infectious diseases are as high as before the arrival of antimicrobial drugs. Nevertheless, humans have been taking medicines to try to control diseases for thousands of years (**12.1 Making Connections**).

Quick Search
Look for "Antibiotics, Seven Wonders of the Microbe World" on the Internet.

The goal of **antimicrobial chemotherapy**[1] is deceptively simple: administer to an infected person a drug that destroys the infectious agent without harming the host's cells. In actuality this goal is rather difficult to achieve, because many often-contradictory factors must be taken into account. The ideal drug should be easily administered and able to reach the infectious agent anywhere in the body. It should be able to kill the infectious agent rather than merely inhibit its growth, and remain active in the body as long as needed, yet be safely and easily broken down and excreted. In short, the perfect drug does not exist, but by balancing drug characteristics against one another, a satisfactory compromise can usually be achieved (**table 12.1**).

The Origins of Antimicrobial Drugs

Modern antimicrobial drugs are highly varied in their origins. The type of drugs traditionally termed **antibiotics** are substances produced by the natural metabolic processes of certain microorganisms that can inhibit or destroy other microorganisms (**figure 12.1a**). Nature is a prolific producer of antimicrobial drugs. Many thousands

(a)

(b)

Figure 12.1 Mining for antibiotic-producing microbes.
(a) One strategy is to seed a plate with a sample (here, soil) and then spray its surface with a fine mist of bacteria and incubate it. Zones of inhibition (clear areas with no growth) surrounding several colonies indicate colonies that produce antibiotics. **(b)** Two colonies with antibiotic secretions on their surfaces. Left is *Penicillium chrysogenum,* with yellow droplets of penicillin; right is *Streptomyces coelicolor,* with blue droplets of actinorhodin, an experimental antibiotic. This release of the antibiotics is an important factor in the isolation and production of the drugs.
(a, b left): Kathy Park Talaro; (b right): Photo courtesy of Dr. Ramón Santamaría/ IMB. CSIC/USAL. Salamanca, Spain

1. The word *chemotherapy,* meaning the use of chemicals in therapy, is often associated with the treatment of cancer, but its official meaning also includes antimicrobial treatment.

12.1 MAKING CONNECTIONS

From Witchcraft to Wonder Drugs

Early human cultures relied on various types of primitive medications concocted from plant, animal, and mineral products that had been found, usually through trial and error or accident, to have some curative effect upon ailments. In one ancient Chinese folk remedy, a fermented soybean curd was applied to skin infections. The Greeks used wine and plant resins (myrrh and frankincense), rotting wood, and various mineral salts to treat diseases. Some folk medicines were effective, but others either had no effect or were harmful. It is interesting that the Greek word *pharmakeutikos* originally meant the practice of witchcraft. These ancient remedies were handed down from generation to generation, but it was not until the Middle Ages that a specific disease was first treated with a specific chemical. Dosing syphilitic patients with inorganic arsenic and mercury compounds may have proved the ancient axiom: *Graviora quaedum sunt remedia periculus* ("Some remedies are worse than the disease").

In the late 1800s Paul Ehrlich was the first scientist to formulate basic theoretical concepts in chemotherapy. Ehrlich had observed that certain dyes affixed themselves to specific microorganisms and not to animal tissues. This observation led to the profound idea that if a drug was properly selective in its actions, it would zero in on and destroy a microbial target and leave human cells unaffected. His first discovery was an arsenic-based drug that was very toxic to the spirochete of syphilis but, unfortunately, was toxic to humans as well. After 606 attempts, he arrived at a compound he called *salvarsan*. This drug had some therapeutic merit and was used for a few years, but it eventually had to be discontinued because it was still not selective enough in its toxicity. Ehrlich's work had laid important foundations for many of the developments to come.

Another pathfinder in early drug research was Gerhard Domagk, whose discoveries in the 1930s launched a breakthrough in therapy that marked the true beginning of broad-scale usage of antimicrobial drugs. Domagk showed that the red dye prontosil was chemically changed by the body into a compound with specific activity against bacteria. This substance was sulfonamide—the first *sulfa* drug. Once the structure of this drug was determined, it became possible to synthesize it on a wide scale and to develop scores of other sulfonamide drugs. Although these drugs had immediate applications in therapy (and still do), still another fortunate discovery ushered in the "age of antibiotics."

The discovery of antibiotics dramatically demonstrates how developments in science and medicine often occur through a combination of accident, persistence, collaboration, and vision. In 1928 in the London laboratory of Sir Alexander Fleming, a plate of *Staphylococcus aureus* became contaminated with the mold *Penicillium* (*notatum*) *chrysogenum* (see figure 12.1). Observing these plates, Fleming noted that the colonies of *Staphylococcus* were evidently being destroyed by some

A pioneer in the discovery of antibiotics. A Scottish physician, Sir Alexander Fleming, accidentally discovered penicillin in a culture plate contaminated with mold. From this mold he extracted the antibiotic, setting the scene for the development of the drug 10 years later.
Davies/Getty Images

activity of the nearby mold colonies. Struck by this curious phenomenon, he extracted from the fungus a compound he called penicillin and showed that it was responsible for the inhibitory effects.

A decade after his discovery, English chemists Howard Florey and Ernst Chain worked out methods for industrial production of penicillin to help in the war effort. Clinical trials conducted in 1941 ultimately proved penicillin's effectiveness, and by 1945 the drug had been used to save hundreds of thousands of lives. This event paved the way for an era of drug research and development that soon made penicillin only one of a large assortment of antimicrobial drugs. But in time, because of extreme overuse and misunderstanding of its capabilities, penicillin also became the model for one of the most serious drug problems—namely, drug resistance.

Once the first significant antibiotic was developed, the world immediately witnessed a scientific scramble to find more. Hundreds of investigators began searching for antibiotic-producing bacteria and fungi by screening of samples from soil, dust, muddy lake sediments, rivers, oceans, plant surfaces, compost heaps, sewage, skin, and even the hair and skin of animals. Finding a new antimicrobial substance is only a first step. The complete pathway of drug development from discovery to therapy can take more than a dozen years and cost several billion dollars.

Name some potential "therapies" you could employ to prevent and treat infections if you were a castaway on a desert island.

of antibiotics have been discovered (although, surprisingly, only a relatively small number have actually been used clinically). Antibiotics are made primarily by aerobic spore-forming bacteria and fungi. The antibiotics appear to have some survival value for these microbes, because the genes for antibiotic production are preserved in evolution. Some experts theorize that microorganisms synthesize

antibiotics to inhibit or destroy nearby competitors or predators (antagonism); others propose that antibiotics are connected to the formation of spores.

The greatest numbers of antibiotics are derived from bacteria in the genera *Streptomyces* and *Bacillus* and molds in the genera *Penicillium* and *Cephalosporium* (**figure 12.1***b* and **table 12.2**). Of

TABLE 12.2	Selected Microbial Sources of Antibiotics	
Producer Genus	**Type of Microbe**	**Drugs Formed**
Penicillium	Mold	Penicillins Griseofulvin
Cephalosporium	Mold	Cephalosporins
Micromonospora	Bacteria	Gentamicin
Bacillus	Bacteria	Bacitracin Polymyxin B
Chromobacterium	Bacteria	Aztreonam
Streptomyces	Filamentous bacteria	Streptomycin Erythromycin Tetracycline Vancomycin Chloramphenicol Amphotericin B

TABLE 12.3	Terminology of Chemotherapy
Chemotherapeutic drug	Any chemical used in the treatment, relief, or prophylaxis of a disease.
Antimicrobials	All-inclusive term for any antimicrobial drug, regardless of its origin
Antibiotics	Substances produced by the natural metabolic processes of some microorganisms that can inhibit or destroy other microorganisms
Semisynthetic drugs	Drugs that are chemically modified in the laboratory after being isolated from natural sources
Synthetic drugs	Antimicrobial compounds synthesized entirely in the laboratory through chemical reactions
Narrow spectrum (limited spectrum)	Antimicrobials effective against a limited array of microbial types; for example, a drug effective mainly on gram-positive bacteria
Broad spectrum (extended spectrum)	Antimicrobials effective against a wide variety of microbial types; for example, a drug effective against both gram-positive and gram-negative bacteria
Prophylaxis	Use of a drug to prevent potential for future infection in a person at risk.
Antimicrobial chemotherapy	The use of chemotherapeutic drugs to control infection
Combined therapy (combination therapy)	Taking multiple drugs at the same time to fight an infection.
Synergy (synergistic effect)	The enhanced effectiveness that occurs when certain drugs are used in combination.

these, species of *Streptomyces* are the most fertile producers. Nearly 9,000 different bioactive compounds have been isolated from them, and they are currently the source of one-third of all prescribed antibiotics. The pharmaceutical industry has harnessed the power of these microbes by growing them in vast quantities and harvesting their products to be sold as drugs. Researchers have facilitated the work of nature by selecting mutant species that yield more abundant or effective products, by varying the growth medium, or by altering the procedures for large-scale industrial production.

A few classes of antimicrobial drugs, termed **synthetic,** are not considered antibiotics because they are synthesized entirely through chemical processes and not secreted by microorganisms. Synthetic drugs include sulfa drugs, quinolones, quinines, azoles, and most antiviral drugs.

Probably the most common approach to drug production is the **semisynthetic** method, combining both natural and synthetic methods. Think of it as improving on nature by using chemical reactions to combine the basic antibiotic made by microorganisms with various preselected functional groups that tailor the action of the drug. Drugs produced in this way are designed to have new and improved functions over the original antibiotic. We can see examples of this technology in the design of the semisynthetic penicillins (see figure 12.7), cephalosporins, and tetracyclines. The potential for using bioengineering techniques to design drugs seems almost limitless, and, indeed, several drugs have already been produced by manipulating the genes of antibiotic producers.

Antimicrobial drugs can be organized by their origin, range of effectiveness, and whether they are naturally produced or chemically synthesized. A few of the more important terms you will encounter are found in **table 12.3.**

Interactions between Drugs and Microbes

The goal of antimicrobial drugs is either to disrupt the cell processes or structures of bacteria, fungi, and protozoa or to inhibit the virus multiplication cycle. Most of the drugs used in chemotherapy interfere with the function of enzymes required to synthesize or assemble macromolecules, but a few destroy structures already formed in the cell. Above all, drugs should be **selectively toxic,** which means they can kill or inhibit the growth of microbes without simultaneously damaging host tissues. This concept of selective toxicity is central to chemotherapy. The best drugs are those that act specifically on microbial structures or functions not found in vertebrate cells. Examples of drugs with excellent selective toxicity are those that block the synthesis of the cell wall in bacteria (penicillins). They have low toxicity and few direct effects on human cells, because human cells lack a cell wall. Among the most toxic to human cells are drugs that act upon a structure common to both the infectious agent and the host cell, such as the cell membrane (for example, amphotericin B used to treat fungal infections). As the characteristics of the pathogen become more similar to those of the host cell, selective toxicity becomes more difficult to achieve and undesirable side effects are more likely to occur. We will cover the subject of toxicity in section 12.5.

Mechanisms of Drug Action

The primary basis of chemotherapy is to target an infectious agent with a chemical that irreversibly damages or inhibits it. This

TABLE 12.4 General Actions of Drugs on Microbial Groups

Microbe Type	Drug Groups/ Examples	Effects of Drugs	Microbe Type	Drug Groups/ Examples	Effects of Drugs
Bacteria	Penicillins	Cell wall damage and lysis	Fungi	Amphotericin B	Loss of membrane permeability
	Cephalosporins	Cell wall damage and lysis		Azoles	Loss of membrane permeability
	Bacitracin	Cell wall damage and lysis		Flucytosine	Inhibits DNA and RNA synthesis
	Aminoglycosides	Inhibits protein synthesis	Protozoa	Quinines	Buildup of toxic wastes in the parasite's cells
	Macrolides				
	Erythromycin	Inhibits protein synthesis		Metronidazole	Buildup of toxic free radicals
	Vancomycin	Cell wall damage and lysis	Helminths	Bendazoles	Inhibit glucose metabolism
	Tetracyclines	Inhibits protein synthesis		Diethylcarbamide	Kills larval forms
	Chloramphenicol	Inhibits protein synthesis		Piperazine	Paralyzes muscular system
	Fluoroquinolones	Block replication of DNA		Niclosamide	Loosens worm hold
	Rifampin	Stops mRNA synthesis		Ivermectin	Inhibits neuromuscular system
	Sulfa drugs	Inhibit folic acid metabolism	Viruses	Oseltamivir	Prevents viral budding
	Trimethoprim	Inhibits folic acid metabolism		Cyclovirs	Stop viral replication
				Azidothymidine	Blocks formation of DNA from RNA strand

knowledge guides drug development as well. Most classes of antimicrobial drugs are active against some unique feature of microbial structure or metabolism. Observe **table 12.4** and take note of the diversity of cell types and possible effects of drug action. Overall, drugs may work in five ways **(figure 12.2)** to slow or stop the growth of an actively dividing cell:

1. inhibition of cell wall synthesis,
2. breakdown of the cell membrane structure or function,
3. interference with functions of DNA and RNA,
4. inhibition of protein synthesis, and
5. blockage of key metabolic pathways.

These targets are not completely discrete, and some have overlapping effects. For example, if DNA transcription is inhibited, protein synthesis will be as well. Viruses are a special case and have very specialized targets for drugs (see table 12.6).

The Spectrum of an Antimicrobial Drug One result of drugs acting upon a particular microbial structure or function is that each drug has a given range of activity. This has been termed the drug's **spectrum.** Traditionally, **narrow-spectrum** drugs are effective over a limited range of cell types. This is usually because they target a specific component that is found only in certain bacteria. For

Figure 12.2 Major targets of drugs acting on bacterial cells.

| TABLE 12.5 | Spectrum of Effectiveness for Antibacterial Drugs | | | | | |
|---|---|---|---|---|---|

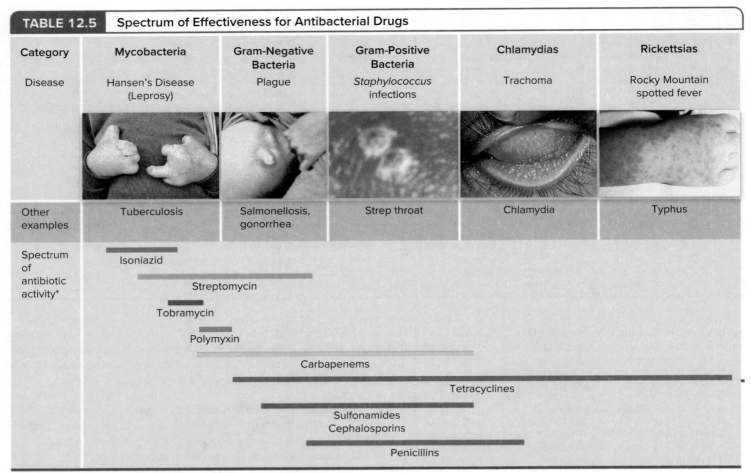

*Resistant strains of bacteria may occasionally be encountered, meaning that an antibiotic may not always be effective, even for bacteria that seem to fall within its spectrum of action.

(Tuberculosis): NikomMaelao Production/Shutterstock; (Salmonellosis): *Source:* CDC; (Strep throat): McGraw-Hill Education *Source:* Susan Lindsley/CDC; (Chlamydia): Susan Lindsley is the source for Chlamydia (Typhus): *Source:* CDC

instance, bacitracin blocks the elongation of the peptidoglycan in gram-positive bacteria but has no effect on most gram-negative bacteria because of the outer membrane on their cell wall that serves as a barrier to the drug. Polymyxin breaks down the outer membrane on gram-negative cells but does not target gram-positive cells because they lack this structure.

Drugs that are effective against a wider range of microbes are termed extended or broad spectrum, depending on the particular drug. For example, the **extended-spectrum** drug ampicillin is effective on both gram-positive and gram-negative bacteria, but not a wide range of them. **Broad-spectrum** drugs, such as tetracycline, have the greatest range of activity. They work on most gram-negative and gram-positive bacteria, rickettsias, mycoplasmas, and spirochetes. The broad-spectrum drugs usually exert their effects on common cell components such as ribosomes, which are found in all cells and mitochondria. Consult **table 12.5** to see an array of antibacterial drugs and their spectra.

Antimicrobial Drugs that Affect the Bacterial Cell Wall

The cell walls of most bacteria contain a rigid girdle of peptidoglycan, which protects the cell against rupture from hypotonic environments. Active cells must constantly synthesize new peptidoglycan

and transport it to its proper place in the cell envelope. Drugs such as penicillins and cephalosporins react with one or more of the enzymes required to complete this process, causing the cell to develop weak points at growth sites and to become osmotically fragile **(figure 12.3)**. Antibiotics that produce this effect are considered bactericidal, because the weakened cell usually undergoes **lysis**. However, cells that are old, inactive, or dormant and are not synthesizing peptidoglycan may resist these effects. (One exception is a class of antibiotics abbreviated as "-penems.")

Penicillins and cephalosporins bind and block peptidases that cross-link the glycan molecules, thereby interrupting the completion of the cell wall **(figure 12.3b)**. Narrow-spectrum penicillins do not penetrate the outer membrane and are therefore less effective against gram-negative bacteria. Many broad-spectrum penicillins (ampicillin) and cephalosporins (ceftriaxone) can pass into the cell walls of gram-negative species. Cycloserine inhibits the formation of the basic peptidoglycan subunits, and vancomycin hinders the elongation of the peptidoglycan.

Antimicrobial Drugs that Disrupt Cell Membrane Function

A cell with a damaged membrane invariably dies from disruptions in metabolism or complete breakdown and lysis. It does not even

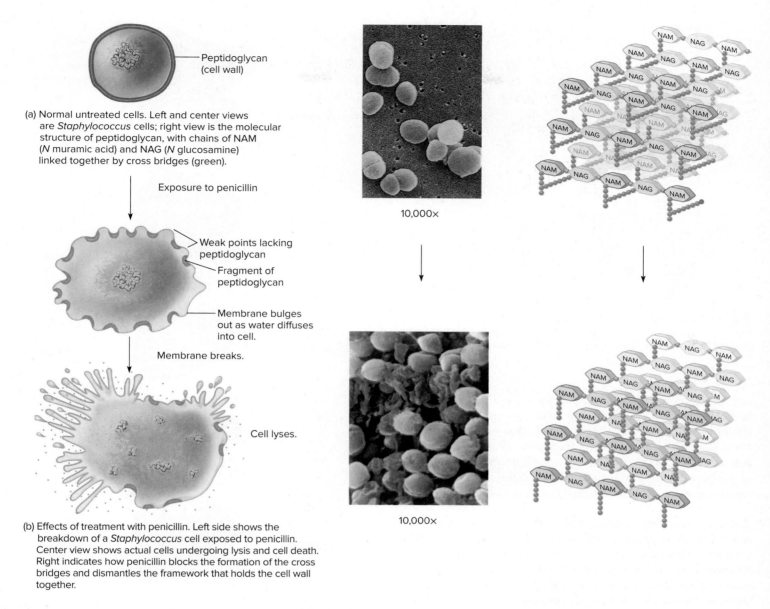

(a) Normal untreated cells. Left and center views are *Staphylococcus* cells; right view is the molecular structure of peptidoglycan, with chains of NAM (*N* muramic acid) and NAG (*N* glucosamine) linked together by cross bridges (green).

Exposure to penicillin

Peptidoglycan (cell wall)

Weak points lacking peptidoglycan

Fragment of peptidoglycan

Membrane bulges out as water diffuses into cell.

Membrane breaks.

Cell lyses.

10,000×

10,000×

(b) Effects of treatment with penicillin. Left side shows the breakdown of a *Staphylococcus* cell exposed to penicillin. Center view shows actual cells undergoing lysis and cell death. Right indicates how penicillin blocks the formation of the cross bridges and dismantles the framework that holds the cell wall together.

Figure 12.3 Effects of penicillin on gram-positive cell walls.
photos: (Top): *Source:* Janice Carr/CDC; (Bottom): CNRI/Science Source

have to be actively dividing to be destroyed. The antibiotic classes that damage cell membranes usually have specificity for particular microbial groups, based on differences in the types of lipids in their cell membranes.

Polymyxins interact with membrane phospholipids and cause leakage of proteins and nitrogen bases, particularly in gram-negative bacteria **(figure 12.4).** Daptomycin shows selectivity for gram-positive cells, but occasionally causes serious side effects that limit its use. The polyene antifungal antibiotics (amphotericin B and nystatin) form complexes with the sterols on fungal membranes, which causes abnormal openings and seepage of small ions. Unfortunately this selectivity is not exact, and the similarities in membranes of microbial and animal cells means that most of these antibiotics have greater toxicity to humans cells.

Antimicrobial Drugs that Affect Nucleic Acid Synthesis

As you learned in chapter 9, the pathway that generates DNA and RNA involves an extensive series of enzyme-catalyzed reactions. Like any complicated process, it is subject to breakdown at many different points along the way, and inhibition at any point in the sequence can block subsequent events. Antimicrobial drugs interfere with nucleic acid synthesis by blocking synthesis of nucleotides, inhibiting replication, or stopping transcription. Because functioning DNA and RNA are required for proper translation as well, the effects on protein metabolism can be far-reaching.

Several antimicrobials inhibit DNA synthesis. The broad-spectrum quinolones inhibit DNA-unwinding enzymes or helicases, thereby stopping DNA replication and repair. Certain

Figure 12.4 **Effects of drugs on membranes.** Polymyxin binds to the outer and cell membranes of gram-negative bacteria and creates abnormal openings that cause leakage and lysis.

Figure 12.5 **Sites of inhibition on the prokaryotic ribosome and major antibiotics that act on these sites.** All have the general effect of blocking protein synthesis. Blockage actions are indicated by X.

antiviral drugs are **analogs*** of purines and pyrimidines that will insert in the viral nucleic acid in place of a normal base. When this abnormal base stops synthesis, viral replication will be blocked (see table 12.6). The antifungal drug flucytosine is an analog of uracil that creates dysfunctional RNA. By inhibiting an enzyme that acts in purine synthesis, it also stops DNA replication. This double assault shuts down metabolism and causes cell death.

Antimicrobial Drugs that Block Protein Synthesis Most drugs that inhibit protein synthesis react with the ribosome-mRNA complex. Although human cells also have ribosomes, the ribosomes of eukaryotes are different in size and structure from those of prokaryotes, so these antimicrobials usually have a selective action against bacteria. One potential therapeutic consequence of drugs that bind to the prokaryotic ribosome is the damage they can do to eukaryotic mitochondria, which contain a prokaryotic type of ribosome.

Two possible targets of ribosomal inhibition are the 30S subunit and the 50S subunit **(figure 12.5).** Aminoglycosides (streptomycin, gentamicin, for example) insert on sites on the 30S subunit and cause the misreading of the mRNA, leading to abnormal proteins. Tetracyclines block the attachment of tRNA on the A acceptor site and effectively stop further synthesis of that protein. Other antibiotics attach to sites on the 50S subunit in a way that prevents the formation of peptide bonds and blocks protein synthesis (chloramphenicol). A few inhibit translocation of the subunit during translation (erythromycin). The oxazolidinones are a newer drug class that

> **Quick Search**
> Search for the video "Antibiotic and Protein Interactions" on YouTube to see an animation of the effects of antibiotics on ribosomes.

affects the assembly of the completed ribosome by blocking the attachment site for the 50S and 30S subunits.

Antimicrobial Drugs that Affect Metabolic Pathways Some drugs act by mimicking the normal substrate of an enzyme through a process called **competitive inhibition.** These drugs, termed **metabolic analogs,** are structurally similar to the natural substrate and compete with it for the active site on the enzyme. When the drug is

* *analog* (an'-uh-log) A compound whose configuration closely resembles another compound required for cellular reactions.

(a) The metabolic pathway needed to synthesize tetrahydrofolic acid (THFA) contains two enzymes that are chemotherapeutic targets. Under normal circumstances, PABA acts as a substrate for the enzyme pteridine synthetase, the product of which is needed for the eventual production of folic acid.

(b) Left: Formula of a sulfanilamide molecule compared alongside one of PABA. Note that, despite a similarity in overall shape, sulfa drugs cannot be used to make folic acid. Right: The sulfa drug molecules can insert into the active site in the enzyme that would ordinarily fit the PABA. This will work only when the sulfa molecules are more prevalent and can outcompete with the PABA and keep the enzyme sites filled. Since little or no PABA can bind, the synthesis of folic acid will be inhibited.

Figure 12.6 Competitive inhibition as a mode of action. This example shows how sulfa drugs block a metabolic pathway used by bacteria to synthesize folic acid.

supplied to a target cell in high concentrations, it will occupy the active site and displace the normal substrate. But the metabolic analog drug is a "dead end" and cannot function as required. As the enzyme is no longer able to produce a needed product, cellular metabolism slows or stops. Antibacterial drugs called sulfonamides and trimethoprim provide an example of this mode of action. Some antiviral drugs (example: retrovir) discussed in section 12.3 also function as competitive inhibitors.

Sulfonamides and trimethoprim interfere with folate metabolism by blocking enzymes required for the synthesis of tetrahydrofolate, which is needed by bacterial cells for the synthesis of folic acid and the eventual production of DNA and RNA and amino acids. Trimethoprim and sulfonamides are often given simultaneously to achieve a synergistic effect so that a lower dosage of each drug can be used. **Figure 12.6** illustrates sulfonamides' competition with PABA for the active site of the enzyme that synthesizes the folic acid precursor. The selective toxicity of these compounds is explained by the fact that mammals derive folic acid from their diet and so do not possess this enzyme system. This makes it possible to inhibit bacterial and protozoan parasites, which must synthesize folic acid, while leaving the human host unaffected.

Practice SECTION 12.1

1. Differentiate between antibiotics and synthetic drugs.
2. Differentiate between narrow-spectrum and broad-spectrum antibiotics.
3. Can you determine why some drugs have narrower spectra than others? (Hint: Look at their mode of action.)
4. What is the major source of antibiotics, and what appears to be the natural function of antibiotics in microbes that produce them?
5. What drug characteristics are most important to consider in therapy?
6. Why is it better for a drug to be microbicidal than microbistatic?
7. Explain the major modes of action of antimicrobial drugs, and give an example of each.
8. Explain the concept of competitive inhibition, and describe how a metabolic analog molecule inhibits metabolism.
9. What would be the extended effects of drugs that block transcription?

12.2 Survey of Major Antimicrobial Drug Groups

 Learn

7. Describe the classes of antibacterial drugs that act on the cell wall and membrane, and list some of their applications.

8. Describe the classes of antibacterial drugs that act on DNA or RNA, and characterize their uses.

9. Indicate which types of antibacterial drugs block protein synthesis, and explain how they are used.

10. Describe some new classes of antibacterial drugs and their applications.

Scores of antimicrobial drugs are marketed in the United States. Although the medical and pharmaceutical literature contains a wide array of names for antimicrobials, most of them are variants of a small number of drug families. About 280 different antimicrobial drugs are currently classified in about 24 drug families. Drug reference books may give the impression that there are 10 times that many, because various drug companies assign different trade names to the very same generic drug. Ampicillin, for instance, is listed under 50 different names. Most antibiotics are useful in controlling bacterial infections, although we shall also consider a number of antifungal, antiviral, and antiprotozoan drugs in the section to follow.

Antibacterial Drugs that Act on the Cell Wall

The **beta-lactam*** group of antibiotics all contain a 3-carbon, 1-nitrogen ring that is highly reactive. Its primary mode of action is to interfere with proteins involved in synthesis of the cell wall, leading to lysis and cell death. More than half of all antimicrobial drugs are beta-lactams, with the penicillins and cephalosporins being the most prominent representatives.

Beta-lactam ring

Structure of penicillin G

Penicillin and Its Relatives

The **penicillin** family of antibiotics, named for the parent compound, is a large, diverse group of compounds, most of which end in the suffix *-cillin*. Although penicillins could be completely synthesized in the laboratory from simple raw materials, it is more practical and economical to obtain natural penicillin through microbial fermentation. The major source of the drug is a unique strain of *Penicillium chrysogenum* that has been manipulated experimentally to synthesize 1,000 times more penicillin than the original strain. The natural product can then be used either in unmodified form or to make semisynthetic derivatives. All penicillins consist of three parts: a

beta-lactam ring, a thiazolidine ring, and a variable side chain that dictates its microbicidal activity (**figure 12.7**).

Penicillin G was the first antibiotic and is the parent compound for all "-cillin" drugs. It is narrow spectrum and cannot be given by mouth. It is often considered the drug of choice for infections by sensitive gram-positive bacteria (streptococci) and some gram-negative bacteria (meningococci). A close relative, *penicillin V*, has similar uses but has been modified to be stable in the stomach acid and so can be taken orally. The narrow-spectrum penicillins *dicloxacillin* and *nafcillin* are often given in place of penicillin G or V. So many pathogens have become resistant to *methicillin* that it has largely been replaced by newer varieties.

Other semisynthetic penicillins such as *ampicillin* and *amoxicillin* have been chemically altered with side chains that help them move across the outer membrane of gram-negative cell walls. This increases their spectrum and makes them useful in treating many types of gram-negative infections. *Ticarcillin* and *piperacillin* have such an extended spectrum that they can be substituted for combinations of antibiotics.

Many bacteria produce enzymes that are capable of severing the beta-lactam ring of some penicillins, thereby destroying the mode of action. The enzymes are referred to as **penicillinases** or **beta-lactamases**, and they confer resistance on the bacteria that possess them. One way to bypass this problem was to develop penicillinase-resistant penicillins such as nafcillin and cloxacillin for treating infections caused by penicillinase-producing bacteria. Another strategy for reducing drug resistance has been to pair a beta-lactamase inhibitor with the penicillin to increase the longevity of the antibiotic in the presence of resistant bacteria. For example, clavulanic acid is often added to broad-spectrum penicillins to augment their effectiveness. *Clavamox* is a combination of amoxicillin and clavulanate marketed under the trade name Augmentin. *Zosyn,* a similar combination of the beta-lactamase inhibitor tazobactam and piperacillin, is used for a wide variety of systemic infections. These combined medications show an extended spectrum because of the synergy of the two drugs working together.

All of the "-cillin" drugs are relatively mild and well tolerated because of their specific mode of action on cell walls (which humans lack). The primary problems in therapy include resistant strains of pathogens and allergy (which is altogether different from toxicity). Showing an allergy to any of the penicillin drugs will require avoidance of all of them, regardless of the type.

The Cephalosporin Group of Drugs

The **cephalosporin** antibiotics currently account for one-third of all antibiotics administered. Cephalosporins are similar to penicillins; they have a beta-lactam structure that can be synthetically altered (**figure 12.8**) and have a similar mode of action. The generic names of these compounds are often recognized by the presence of the root *cef, ceph,* or *kef* in their names.

The cephalosporins are versatile. They are relatively broad spectrum, resistant to most penicillinases, and cause fewer allergic reactions than penicillins. Although some cephalosporins are given orally, many are poorly absorbed from the intestine and must be administered **parenterally,*** by injection into a muscle or a vein.

* *beta-lactam* (bey'-tuh-lak'-tam) The chemical name of a molecular group found in a number of drug families.

* *parenterally* (par-ehn'-tur-ah-lee) Gr. *para*, beyond, and *enteron*, intestine. A route of drug administration other than the gastrointestinal tract.

Figure 12.7 Chemical structure and functions of semisynthetic penicillins. All penicillins start with a central molecule called a nucleus that forms the basic framework (blue box). The nucleus is an inactive penicillin derivative—aminopenicillanic acid—which has a bonding site on the nitrogen on the beta-lactam ring for addition of a side chain or R group. This "fine-tunes" the end product to create finished molecules with a specialized desired action. Here we see penicillins that have resistance to penicillinase (methicillin, nafcillin), a broader-activity spectrum (ticarcillin, ampicillin), and acid resistance (penicillin V).

Four generations of cephalosporins exist, with each group being more effective against gram-negative organisms than the generation before it. In addition, succeeding generations typically have improved dosing schedules and fewer side effects. First-generation cephalosporins (cephalothin and cefazolin) are most effective against gram-positive cocci and a few gram-negative bacteria. Second-generation forms (*cefaclor* and *cefonicid*) are more effective than the first-generation forms in treating infections by gram-negative bacteria such as *Enterobacter, Proteus,* and *Haemophilus.* Third-generation cephalosporins, such as *cephalexin* (Keflex) and *ceftriaxone* (Rocephin), are broad spectrum with especially well-developed activity against enteric bacteria that produce beta-lactamases. Fourth-generation drugs, such as *cefepime,* have the widest range of antimicrobial properties. They are effective with both gram-negative and gram-positive bacterial infections and are rapidly microbicidal.

Some recent additions to this drug family are two combination drugs that pair a broad spectrum cephalosporin with a beta-lactamase inhibitor. *Zerbaxa* is a combination of *ceftolozene* with *tazobactam* for treating resistant urinary tract and abdominal infections. *Avycaz,* which combines *ceftizadime* and *avibactam,* is being limited to the most life-threatening cases of kidney and abdominal infections.

Carbapenems and Monobactams Other beta-lactam drugs are the carbapenems or "penems" and aztreonam. *Imipenem* and *ertapenem* are broad-spectrum antibiotics with a mode of action similar to penicillin but with greater resistance to beta-lactamases. They are active in very low concentrations and can be taken by mouth with few side effects except for allergies. Starting in 2001, some carbapenem-resistant strains of gram-negative enteric bacteria began to emerge in hospital outbreaks. These pathogens, termed *CRE,* have continued to increase in numbers and are currently causing concern in some clinical settings (see the chapter 11 Case Study).

Aztreonam, a monobactam, is a narrow-spectrum antibiotic for treating pneumonia, septicemia, and urinary tract infections by

R Group 1	Basic Nucleus	R Group 2
		Cephalothin (first generation*)
	2nd	Cefotiam (second generation)
	3rd	Moxalactam (third generation)
	4th	Cefepime (fourth generation)

*New, improved versions of drugs are referred to as new "generations."

Figure 12.8 **The structure of cephalosporins.** Like penicillin, their main nucleus consists of a beta-lactam ring (red) and a second ring (yellow). However, unlike penicillins, they have two sites for placement of R groups (at positions 3 and 7). This makes possible several generations of molecules with greater versatility in function and complexity in structure.

Isoniazid (INH) works by interfering with the synthesis of mycolic acid, a necessary component of the cell wall of acid-fast organisms. It is used to treat infections with *Mycobacterium tuberculosis* but is effective only against growing cells. It is often prescribed along with rifampin and other drugs to treat tuberculosis. In late 2019, a new drug, Pretomanid, was approved for the treatment of some strains of drug resistant tuberculosis, the first new TB drug in more than 40 years. Ethambutol, a closely related compound, is another antituberculosis drug added to treatment regimens.

Antibiotics that Damage Bacterial Cell Membranes

Bacillus polymyxa is the source of the **polymyxins,** narrow-spectrum peptide antibiotics with a unique fatty acid component that contributes to their detergent activity (see figure 12.4). Only two polymyxins—B and E (also known as colistin)—have any routine applications, and even these are limited by their toxicity to the kidney. Either drug is indicated to treat drug-resistant infections caused by gram-negative rods such as *Pseudomonas aeruginosa* and *Acinetobacter baumannii*. It is also one of the topical agents in ointments to prevent skin infections, such as Neosporin.

gram-negative aerobic bacilli. Aztreonam is especially useful when treating persons who are allergic to penicillin, because it is chemically different and does not cross-react with antibodies made to penicillin.

Miscellaneous Cell Wall Inhibitors (Non–Beta-Lactam) *Vancomycin* is a narrow-spectrum antibiotic most effective in treating staphylococcal infections in cases of penicillin and methicillin resistance or in patients with an allergy to penicillins. It has also been chosen to treat *Clostridium* infections in children and endocarditis (infection of the lining of the heart) caused by *Enterococcus faecalis*. Because it is very toxic and hard to administer, vancomycin is usually restricted to the most serious, life-threatening conditions. Two relatives of vancomycin—Dalavancin and Orbactive—were recently introduced as alternative choices for skin and structure infections, especially those caused by MRSA.

Bacitracin is a narrow-spectrum peptide antibiotic produced by a strain of *Bacillus subtilis*. Its primary effect is to block the elongation of the peptidoglycan in gram-positive bacteria. Since it was first isolated, its greatest claim to fame has been as a major ingredient in a common drugstore antibiotic ointment (Neosporin) for combating superficial skin infections by streptococci and staphylococci. For this purpose, bacitracin is usually combined with neomycin (an aminoglycoside) and polymyxin.

Drugs that Act on DNA or RNA

Fluoroquinolones work by binding to DNA gyrase and a related enzyme, topoisomerase IV—both of which are essential for replication of the bacterial DNA. While DNA gyrase tends to be the primary target in gram-negative organisms, topoisomerase is targeted in gram-positive cells. It is not known how these drugs target different enzymes in different cell types, but this mode of action ensures that fluoroquinolones provide broad-spectrum effectiveness. In addition to being broad spectrum and highly potent, the drugs are readily absorbed from the intestine.

Since their introduction, quinolones have gone through four generations of development. There are currently about two dozen different types. Two of the more commonly used quinolones, *norfloxacin* and *ciprofloxacin* (Cipro), are prescribed in many cases of urinary tract infections, sexually transmitted diseases, gastrointestinal infections, osteomyelitis, respiratory infections, and soft tissue infections. Newer drugs in this category are *sparfloxacin* and *levofloxacin*. Side effects that can limit the use of quinolones include damage to tendons, an increased risk of aortic aneurysm, and brain disturbances. The FDA now requires fluoroquinolones to carry a **black box** label to warn consumers of these serious side effects.

Another drug that disrupts nucleic acids is *rifampin*. The primary action of this drug is to block the action of RNA polymerase, thereby preventing transcription. It is somewhat limited in spectrum

Figure 12.9 **The structure of an aminoglycoside: Streptomycin.** Colored portions of the molecule are found in all numbers of this drug class.

because the molecule cannot pass through the cell envelope of many gram-negative bacilli. It is mainly used to treat infections by selected gram-positive rods and cocci and a few gram-negative bacteria. Rifampin figures most prominently in treating mycobacterial infections, especially tuberculosis and leprosy, but it is usually given in combination with other drugs to prevent development of resistance. Rifampin is also recommended for prophylaxis in *Neisseria meningitidis* carriers and their contacts, and it is occasionally used to treat *Legionella, Brucella,* and *Staphylococcus* infections.

Drugs that Interfere with Protein Synthesis

The Aminoglycoside Drugs

Antibiotics composed of one or more amino sugars and an aminocyclitol (6-carbon) ring are referred to as **aminoglycosides** (**figure 12.9**). These complex compounds are exclusively the products of various species of soil **actinomycetes** in the genera *Streptomyces* and *Micromonospora.*

Subgroups and Uses of Aminoglycosides The aminoglycosides have a relatively broad antimicrobial spectrum because they inhibit protein synthesis by binding to one of the ribosomal subunits. They are especially useful in treating infections caused by aerobic gram-negative rods and certain gram-positive bacteria. *Streptomycin* is one of the oldest drugs but has gradually been replaced by newer forms with less mammalian toxicity. It is still the antibiotic of choice for treating bubonic plague and tularemia, and is considered an effective antituberculosis agent. *Gentamicin* is less toxic and is widely administered for infections caused by gram-negative rods (*Escherichia, Pseudomonas, Salmonella,* and *Shigella*). Two relatively new aminoglycosides, tobramycin and amikacin, are also used for gram-negative infections; tobramycin is especially useful for treating *Pseudomonas* infections in cystic fibrosis patients.

(a) **Tetracyclines**

(b) **Chloramphenicol**

(c) **Erythromycin**

Figure 12.10 **Structures of three antibiotics that act on prokaryotic ribosomes. (a)** Tetracyclines. These are named for their regular group of four rings. The several types vary in structure and activity by substitution at the four R groups. **(b)** Chloramphenicol, a broad-spectrum drug with potentially serious side effects. **(c)** Erythromycin, an example of a macrolide drug. Its central feature is a large lactone ring to which two hexose sugars are attached.

Tetracycline Antibiotics

The first antibiotic in this class was *aureomycin.* It was used to synthesize terramycin, tetracycline, and several semisynthetic derivatives, commonly known as the **tetracyclines** (**figure 12.10a**). Their action of binding to ribosomes and blocking protein synthesis accounts for the broad-spectrum effects in the group.

Subgroups and Uses of Tetracyclines The scope of microorganisms inhibited by tetracyclines is very broad. It includes gram-positive and gram-negative rods and cocci, aerobic and anaerobic bacteria, mycoplasmas, rickettsias, and spirochetes. Tetracycline compounds such as *doxycycline* and *minocycline* are administered orally to treat several sexually transmitted diseases, Rocky Mountain spotted fever, Lyme disease, typhus, *Mycoplasma* pneumonia, cholera, leptospirosis, acne, and even some protozoan infections. A newer derivative of minocycline—*tigecycline*—was developed to treat serious hospital skin and soft tissue infections in cases of drug resistance (*Acinetobacter* and MRSA). Although generic tetracycline is low in cost and easy to administer, its use can be limited by its side effects. In addition

to gastrointestinal disruption due to changes in the normal microbiota and staining of the teeth, ingestion during pregnancy can interfere with fetal bone development (see table 12.9).

Chloramphenicol

Chloramphenicol is a potent broad-spectrum antibiotic with a unique nitrobenzene structure **(figure 12.10*b*).** Its primary effect on cells is to block peptide bond formation and protein synthesis. It is one type of antibiotic that is no longer derived from the natural source but is entirely synthesized through chemical processes. Although this drug is as broad spectrum as the tetracyclines, it is so toxic to human cells that its uses are restricted. A small number of people undergoing long-term therapy with this drug incur irreversible damage to the bone marrow that usually results in a fatal form of aplastic anemia.[2] Its administration is now limited to typhoid fever, brain abscesses, and rickettsial and chlamydial infections for which an alternative therapy is not available. Chloramphenicol should never be given in large doses repeatedly over a long time period, and the patient's blood must be monitored during therapy.

Macrolides and Related Antibiotics

Erythromycin is a representative of antibiotics termed *macrolides*.[3] Its structure consists of a large lactone ring with sugars attached **(figure 12.10*c*).** This drug has a moderate spectrum and fairly low toxicity. Its mode of action is to block protein synthesis by attaching to the 50S subunit of the ribosome. It is administered orally for *Mycoplasma* pneumonia, legionellosis, *Chlamydia* infections, pertussis, and diphtheria, and as a prophylactic drug prior to intestinal surgery. It also offers a useful substitute for dealing with penicillin-resistant streptococci and gonococci and for treating syphilis and acne. Newer semisynthetic macrolides include *clarithromycin* and *azithromycin* (Zithromax). Both drugs are useful for middle ear, respiratory, and skin infections and have been approved for *Mycobacterium* (MAC) infections in AIDS patients. Clarithromycin has additional applications in controlling infections and gastric ulcers caused by *Helicobacter pylori*. Azithromycin is one of the most prescribed antibiotics in the world. It is used to treat respiratory, gastrointestinal, and sexually transmitted infections. One serious side effect it causes in some people is heart arrhythmias, which limits its use in sensitive people.

Clindamycin is a broad-spectrum antibiotic derived from lincomycin. The tendency of clindamycin to cause adverse reactions in the gastrointestinal tract limits its applications to (1) serious infections in the large intestine and abdomen due to anaerobic bacteria (*Bacteroides* and *Clostridium*), (2) infections with penicillin-resistant staphylococci, and (3) acne medications applied to the skin.

Drugs that Block Metabolic Pathways

Several of the drugs that interfere with metabolism are synthetic. These antimicrobials as a group do not originate from bacterial or fungal fermentations. Some were synthesized from aniline dyes, and others were

Figure 12.11 **The structures of some sulfonamides.** Boxed side chains attach at the —ONH group of the nucleus. **(a)** Sulfacetamide, **(b)** sulfadiazine, and **(c)** sulfisoxazole.

originally isolated from plants. Although they have been largely replaced by antibiotics, a few of them remain essential to chemotherapy.

The most important drugs in this class are the **sulfonamides,** or **sulfa drugs.** Their name is derived from sulfanilamide, an early form of the drug **(figure 12.11).** These drugs function as metabolic analogs to block the synthesis of folic acid by bacteria (see figure 12.6). Dozens of these drugs have been developed, most of them narrow spectrum. Because of its solubility, sulfisoxazole is an effective choice for treating shigellosis, urinary tract infections, and certain protozoan infections. Silver sulfadiazine ointment and solution are prescribed for treatment of burns and eye infections. Another drug, *trimethoprim,* inhibits a second enzymatic step in the synthesis of folic acid. Because of this, trimethoprim is often given in combination with sulfamethoxazole to take advantage of the synergistic effect of the two drugs (Septra, Bactrim). This combination is one of the primary treatments for *Pneumocystis jiroveci* pneumonia (PCP), urinary tract infections, and otitis media.

Sulfones are compounds chemically related to the sulfonamides but lacking their broad-spectrum effects. They still remain important as key drugs in treating Hansen's disease (leprosy). The most active form is dapsone, usually given in combination with rifampin and clofazimine (an antibacterial dye) over long periods.

Newly Developed Classes of Antibiotics

Although most new antibiotics are formulated from the drug classes that already exist, a few classes of drugs with novel actions against bacteria have been added to drug regimens. Medical experts are urging physicians to prescribe these medications only when no other drugs are available to slow the development of drug resistance.

Fosfomycin trimethamine is a phosphoric acid agent effective as an alternative treatment for urinary tract infections caused by enteric bacteria. It works by inhibiting an enzyme necessary for cell wall synthesis.

2. A failure of the blood-producing tissue that results in very low levels of blood cells.
3. Macrolide antibiotics get their name from the type of chemical ring structure (macrolide ring) they all possess.

Synercid is an antibiotic from the streptogramin group of drugs that contains two active chemicals (quinupristin and dalfopristin) that together exert a synergistic action on certain bacteria. It has bactericidal effects against *Staphylococcus* and *Enterococcus* species that cause endocarditis and surgical infections and against resistant strains of *Streptococcus.* It is one of the main choices when other drugs are ineffective due to resistance. Synercid works by binding to sites on the 50S ribosome, inhibiting peptide transfer and elongation.

Daptomycin (Cubicin) is a lipopeptide directed mainly against gram-positive bacteria, acting to disrupt multiple aspects of membrane function.

Another new class of drugs, the ketolides, is similar to macrolides like erythromycin but has a different ring structure. The main representative, *telithromycin* (Ketek), is used for respiratory tract infections caused by macrolide-resistant bacteria.

The *oxazolidinone* class of drugs operates using a unique mechanism, namely to inhibit the *initiation* of protein synthesis. It does this by interfering with the interaction between the mRNA and the two ribosomal subunits necessary for the initiation of translation. The two drugs in this class are *linezolid* (sold under the trade name Zyvox) and *tedizolid* (Sivextro). They are important alternative choices to treat infections caused by two prominent clinical pathogens, methicillin-resistant *Staphylococcus aureus* (MRSA) and vancomycin-resistant *Enterococcus* (VRE). Because they are synthetic and not found in nature, it is hoped that drug resistance will be slow to develop.

Drugmakers have developed a new antituberculosis drug for the first time in 40 years. Called bedaquiline (Sirturo), this drug will be restricted to use only for multidrug-resistant and extremely drug-resistant TB cases that are currently on the rise.

 Practice SECTION 12.2

10. Construct a chart that summarizes the modes of action and applications of the major groups of antibacterial drugs (antibiotics and synthetics).

11. Why do the penicillin and cephalosporin groups of drugs have milder toxicity than other antibiotics? What are their primary side effects?

12.3 Drugs to Treat Fungal, Parasitic, and Viral Infections

 Learn

11. Categorize antimicrobial drugs that are effective against fungi, and describe how they are used.

12. Discuss the categories of drugs used to treat parasite infections, and describe their applications.

13. Discuss some of the difficulties in giving antiviral drug treatments.

14. Identify several categories of antiviral drugs, and explain how they are used.

Antifungal Drugs

Because the cells of fungi are eukaryotic, they present special problems in chemotherapy. The great majority of chemotherapeutic drugs are designed to act on bacteria and are generally ineffective in combating fungal infections. And because fungal and human cells are so similar, drugs toxic to fungal cells are also capable of harming human tissues. A few agents with special antifungal properties have been developed for treating systemic and superficial fungal infections. Five main drug groups currently in use are the macrolide polyene antibiotics, griseofulvin, synthetic azoles, flucytosine, and echinocandins **(figure 12.12).**

Polyenes bind to fungal membranes and cause loss of selective permeability. They are specific for fungal membranes because fungal membranes contain a particular sterol component called *ergosterol,* which human membranes do not contain. The toxicity of polyenes is not completely selective, however, because mammalian cell membranes contain compounds similar to ergosterol that bind polyenes to a small extent.

Macrolide polyenes, represented by *amphotericin B* (Fungizone) (named for its acidic and basic—amphoteric—properties) and *nystatin* (for New York State, where it was discovered), have a structure that mimics the lipids in some cell membranes. Amphotericin B is by far the most versatile and effective of all antifungals. Not only does it work on most fungal infections, including skin and mucous membrane lesions caused by *Candida albicans,* but it is one of the few drugs that can be injected to treat systemic fungal infections such as histoplasmosis and cryptococcus meningitis. A significant drawback to the widespread use of amphotericin centers on its serious side effects, which can include fatigue and irregular heartbeat. Nystatin (Mycostatin) is used only topically or orally to treat mycoses of the skin and mucous

(a)

(b) (c)

Figure 12.12 Some antifungal drug structures. (a) Polyenes. The example shown is amphotericin B, a complex steroidal antibiotic that inserts into fungal cell membranes. **(b)** Azoles, complex cyclic (ringed) compounds, such as ketoconazole which inhibits synthesis of ergosterol, a component of the fungal cell membrane. **(c)** Flucytosine, a structural analog of cytosine that inhibits DNA and protein synthesis.

membranes, but it is not useful for subcutaneous or systemic fungal infections or for ringworm.

Griseofulvin is an antifungal product especially active in treating certain dermatophyte infections such as athlete's foot. The drug is deposited in the epidermis, nails, and hair, where it inhibits fungal growth. Because complete eradication requires several months and griseofulvin is relatively nephrotoxic, this therapy is given only for the most stubborn cases. A newer drug for treatment of ringworm and athlete's foot, *terbinifine* (Lamisil), is an inhibitor of ergosterol synthesis that is readily deposited in skin and nails. Unfortunately, it must also be taken for an extended period and has a number of side effects, including hepatotoxicity.

The **azoles** are broad-spectrum antifungal agents with a complex ringed structure that also inhibits ergosterol and cell membrane synthesis. They have fewer adverse side effects when compared with other antifungal drugs. The most effective drugs are *ketoconazole* (Nizoral), *fluconazole* (Diflucan), *clotrimazole* (Gyne-Lotrimin), *miconazole* (Monistat), *voriconazole* (VFEND), and *itraconazole* (Sporanox). Ketoconazole is used orally and topically for cutaneous mycoses, vaginal and oral candidiasis, and some systemic and invasive mycoses. Fluconazole can be used in selected patients for AIDS-related mycoses such as aspergillosis and cryptococcus meningitis. Clotrimazole and miconazole are used mainly as topical ointments for infections in the skin, mouth, and vagina. Itraconazole is generally used orally for fungal infections of the nails and systemic candidiasis. Because voriconazole crosses the blood-brain barrier, it is the treatment of choice for fungal meningitis. A new member of the azole family, Cresemba, is designated for severe systemic mycoses such as aspergillosis and mucormycosis.

Flucytosine is an analog of the nucleotide cytosine that has antifungal properties. It is rapidly absorbed after oral therapy, and it is readily dissolved in the blood and cerebrospinal fluid. Alone, it can be used to treat certain cutaneous mycoses. Many fungi are resistant to flucytosine, so it is usually combined with amphotericin B to effectively treat systemic mycoses.

After many years of testing, a new antifungal drug category has been introduced. Echinocandins, such as *Caspofungin,* damage the cell walls of several types of fungi, thereby making them sensitive to lysis. A significant advantage of this mode of action is that it cannot target human cells.

Antiparasitic Chemotherapy

The enormous diversity among protozoan and helminth parasites and their corresponding therapies reaches far beyond the scope of this textbook; however, a few of the more common drugs are surveyed here. Presently a small number of approved and experimental drugs are used to treat malaria, leishmaniasis, trypanosomiasis, amebic dysentery, and helminth infections, but the need for new and better drugs has spurred considerable research in this area.

Antimalarial Drugs: Quinine and Its Relatives

Quinine, a toxic chemical extracted from the bark of the cinchona tree, was the principal treatment for malaria for hundreds of years, but it has largely been replaced by the synthesized quinolines, mainly *chlo-*

roquine and *primaquine,* which have less toxicity to humans. Because of the several species of *Plasmodium* (the malaria parasite) and many stages in its life cycle, no single drug is universally effective for every species and stage, and each drug is restricted in application. For instance, primaquine eliminates the liver phase of infection, and chloroquine suppresses acute attacks associated with infection of red blood cells. It is also given as a prophylactic treatment in endemic regions. Chloroquine is usually taken in combination with another drug to reduce the chances of parasite resistance.

Structure of quinine

Mefloquine is a semisynthetic analog of quinine used to treat infections caused by chloroquine-resistant strains of *Plasmodium,* an increasing problem in Southeast Asia. The latest drug approved for treating uncomplicated malaria is a combination of artimisinin and lumefantrine called *Coartem.* It was designed to prevent drug resistance and has become the drug of choice in many parts of the world.

Chemotherapy for Other Protozoan Infections

A widely used amoebicide, metronidazole (Flagyl), is effective in treating intestinal infections and hepatic disease caused by *Entamoeba histolytica.* It appears to inactivate essential metabolic enzymes of the pathogens. Given orally, it also has applications for infections by *Giardia lamblia* and *Trichomonas vaginalis.* Other drugs with antiprotozoan activities are quinacrine (a quinine-based drug), sulfonamides, and tetracyclines.

Antihelminthic Drug Therapy

Treating helminthic infections has been one of the most challenging of all chemotherapeutic tasks. Flukes, tapeworms, and roundworms are much larger parasites than other microorganisms and, being animals, have greater similarities to human physiology. Also, the usual strategy of using drugs to block their reproduction is usually not successful in eradicating the adult worms. The most effective drugs immobilize, disintegrate, or inhibit the metabolism of all stages of the life cycle.

Mebendazole and *thiabendazole* are broad-spectrum antiparasitic drugs used to treat several types of roundworm infections. These drugs work locally in the intestine to inhibit the function of the microtubules of worms, eggs, and larvae, which blocks a key step in glucose metabolism and disables them. The compounds *pyrantel* and *piperazine* paralyze the muscles of intestinal roundworms. Niclosamide destroys the scolex and the adjoining proglottids of tapeworms, thereby loosening the worm's holdfast. In these forms of therapy, the worms are unable to maintain their grip on the intestinal wall and are expelled along with the feces by the normal peristaltic action of the bowel. A drawback can be the severe abdominal cramps that often accompany treatment. Two newer antihelminthic drugs are *praziquantel,* a treatment for various tapeworm and fluke

infections, and *ivermectin,* a veterinary drug now used for strongyloidiasis and oncocercosis in humans.

Antiviral Chemotherapeutic Agents

The chemotherapeutic treatment of viral infections presents unique challenges. Throughout our discussion of infections caused by bacteria, fungi, protozoa, and helminths, we've emphasized differences in structure and metabolism that guide drug choice. With viruses, we are dealing with an infectious agent that relies upon the host cell for the vast majority of its metabolic functions. Disrupting viral function may require that we disrupt the metabolism of the host cell to a much greater extent than is desirable. Put another way, selective toxicity with regard to viral infection can be difficult to achieve because a single metabolic system is responsible for the well-being of both virus and host. A few viral diseases, such as measles, mumps, and hepatitis, are routinely prevented by effective vaccinations. Unfortunately, vaccines are unavailable for many serious viral diseases, creating a real need for antiviral medications.

Over the past few years several antiviral drugs have been developed that target specific points in the infectious cycle of certain types of viruses. But due to marked differences among viruses, antiviral compounds tend to be limited in their spectrum.

Most antiviral drugs are designed to block a step in completion of the virus cycle. Major modes of action include

1. barring penetration of the virus into the host cell;
2. blocking replication, transcription, and/or translation of viral genetic material; and
3. preventing the normal maturation of viral particles.

Although antiviral drugs protect uninfected cells by keeping viruses from being synthesized and released, most are unable to eliminate extracellular viruses or those in a latent or persistent state within the host's DNA. A summary covering the actions of several antiviral drugs appears in **table 12.6.**

Drugs for Treating Influenza

Zanamivir (*Relenza*) and oseltamivir (*Tamiflu*) are broader-spectrum anti-influenza medications that block neuraminidase actions in both influenza A and influenza B viruses. Without the functions of neuraminidase, the virus cannot be budded off and released from the host cell, so cells cannot produce active viruses. Both types of drugs may be used prophylactically and must be given early in an infection to be most effective (table 12.6).

In late 2018, the FDA approved baloxavir marboxil (Xofluza), a new anti-influenza medication that blocks the initiation of viral RNA synthesis, preventing replication of the influenza virus. Like Relenza and Tamiflu, Xofluva must be taken early in the course of infection to receive any benefit.

Quick Search

See an animation of Relenzas's action by searching for "Relenza 2008WM" on YouTube.

Antiherpes Drugs

Many antiviral agents mimic the structure of nucleotides (i.e., act as *analogs*) and compete for sites on replicating DNA. Once one of these nucleotide analogs is incorporated into the growing chain of DNA, replication of that strand stops, interrupting the viral life cycle.

Acyclovir (Zovirax) and the related compounds *valacyclovir* (Valtrex), *famciclovir* (Famvir), and *penciclovir* (Denavir) all work in this manner and (with small exceptions from drug to drug) can be used either orally or topically to treat common herpesvirus infections such as oral and genital herpes, chickenpox, and shingles. A related drug, *ganciclovir* (Cytovene), is used parenterally to treat cytomegalovirus infection in patients with compromised immune systems.

An interesting aspect of some of these antiviral agents (specifically valacyclovir and famciclovir) is that they are activated by an enzyme encoded by the virus itself, making the drug active only in virally infected cells. The enzyme thymidine kinase is used by the virus to process nucleosides before incorporating them into viral RNA or DNA. When the inactive drug enters a virally infected cell, the virus's own thymidine kinase converts it to a working antiviral agent. In cells without viruses, the drug is never activated and normal DNA replication is allowed to continue.

Antihepatitis C Drugs

Increased understanding of the viral life cycle has led to the virtual cure of hepatitis C, a disease affecting about 2.4 million people in the United States. A treatment regimen of two drugs, *sofosbuvir* and *ledipavir,* sold together under the brand name *Harvoni,* has led to a cure rate of 94% to 99% of persons infected with the most common form of the virus. Sofosbuvir is a nucleotide analog which targets the RNA polymerase responsible for replication of the hepatitis C genome, preventing synthesis of the RNA strand. Ledipasvir interferes with the function of a protein called NS5A (non-structural protein 5A) that is required for the RNA polymerase to function properly. Together, the two drugs have a synergistic effect. The primary drawback is its cost, which can amount to nearly $100,000 per treatment series, but many medical experts feel that the cure rate is worth the cost.

Drugs for Treating HIV Infection and AIDS

The global epidemic of HIV-related disease has been a powerful stimulus for drug discovery. Most of the newer drugs being introduced are designed to treat HIV infection and AIDS. There is now a considerable array of drugs and drug combinations to manage HIV, which can complicate treatment. All of the antiretrovial drugs target a specific part of the multiplication cycle of HIV. Currently, there are drugs that can inhibit or block every strategic step in the virus cycle (table 12.6).

One of the most important targets is the **reverse transcriptase (RT)** enzyme that HIV brings into the host cell. Recall from chapter 9 that HIV is a retrovirus with an RNA genome. Upon entering a host, the RNA is used as a template by reverse transcriptase to produce a DNA copy of this RNA. This activity offers two types of targets for anti-HIV drugs. One type of anti-RT drugs, *nucleoside* or *nucleotide reverse transcriptase analogs* (NRTIs), directly stops DNA synthesis through competitive inhibition. *Zidovudine* was the first NRTI and the first drug developed to treat HIV and AIDS. It is an analog of thymine that becomes incorporated into the DNA strand of HIV but terminates synthesis because it does not offer the correct sites for binding additional nucleotides. Other examples are stavudine and lamivudine.

TABLE 12.6 Actions of Selected Antiviral Drugs*

I. Inhibition of Virus Entry or Release

(1) Enfuvirtide (Fuzeon)

Anti-HIV drug prevents binding of viral GP-41 receptors to cell and blocks fusion of virus with cell

(2) Maraviroc

Covers up the cell receptors; HIV cannot adhere and remains inactive

(3) Oseltamivir (Tamiflu), zanamivir (Relenza)

Drugs do not stop the early influenza cycle involving entry, uncoating, and replication; they block the action of neuraminidase that is required for final budding and release of new viruses

Labels in figure: Host cell membrane — HIV virus — Drug — No fusion/no entry — Cell receptors — Nucleus — Influenza virus — Virus cannot leave vesicle

II. Inhibition of Nucleic Acid Synthesis

(4) Acyclovir (Zovirax), other "cyclovirs"

Nucleotide analogs that terminate DNA replication in herpesviruses

(5) Nucleoside analog reverse transcriptase (RT) inhibitors (zidovudine, epivir)

Stop the action of reverse transcriptase in HIV, blocking viral DNA synthesis

(6) Nonnucleoside reverse transcriptase inhibitors (nevirapine)

Attach to HIV RT binding site, stopping its action

Labels in figure: Herpesvirus — DNA polymerase — Virus DNA — Drug — No viral DNA replication — HIV virus — HIV RNA — No HIV DNA — RT — No reverse transcription

III. Inhibition of HIV Insertion, Assembly, Release

(7) Integrase inhibitor (raltegravir)

This interacts with integrase and blocks its action; HIV DNA is not spliced into host chromosome.

(8) Protease inhibitors (amprenavir, saquinavir)

These insert onto HIV protease, an enzyme that clips viral proteins into functional pieces. Viruses are defective and unable to infect other cells.

Labels in figure: HIV virus — HIV RNA — HIV DNA — RT — HIV integrase — Host DNA — Drug — HIV protease — Virus is unable to infect host cell. — Defective virus is released. — HIV protein not clipped

*Details of viral cycles are omitted for ease in observing drug effects.

TABLE 12.7 Overview of Anti-HIV Drugs, Effects, and Examples

Category of Anti-HIV Drug	Effect of Drug on Virus	Examples of Drugs
Binding inhibitors	Drugs prevent binding of virus to receptors needed for entry into the host cell. Maraviroc covers the CCR5 receptor and ibalizumab blocks CD4 receptors.	Maraviroc (Selzentry) Ibalizumab (Trogarzo)
Fusion inhibitor	Drug prevents fusion of HIV with host cell membrane.	Enfuvirtide (Fuzeon)
Nucleoside reverse transcriptase inhibitors (NRTIs)	Drugs are chemical analogs that insert into the HIV DNA and prevent further addition of new bases. This terminates DNA synthesis and stops viral replication. This is a type of competitive inhibition.	azidothymidine (AZT, Retrovir) lamivudine (3TC, Epiver)
Nonnucleoside reverse transcriptase inhibitors (NNRTIs)	Drugs interact with reverse transcriptase and block its active site, a type of noncompetitive inhibition.	Doravirine (Pifeltro) Etravirine (Intelence) Rilpivirine (Endurant)
Integrase inhibitors	Drugs interact with HIV integrase, which is required for the viral DNA to be inserted (integrated) into the host cell chromosome.	Dolutegravir (Tivicay) Raltegravir (Isentress)
Protease inhibitors	HIV protease that completes viral assembly is blocked, leading to incomplete and dysfunctional viruses.	Atazanavir (Reyataz) Darunavir (Prezista) Saquinavir (Invirase)
Pharmacokinetic enhancers	Work synergistically to increase the effectiveness of other anti-HIV medications	Cobicicast (Tybost)

The second type of anti-RT drugs are *nonnucleoside reverse transcriptase inhibitors* (NNRTIs) that attach to a site on the reverse transcriptase enzyme itself and alter its shape—a type of noncompetitive inhibition (see table 12.7). NNRTIs accomplish a similar goal in preventing reverse transcription of the HIV RNA, but they bind to the enzyme itself and prevent its reactive site from synthesizing DNA. They are usually given together or in combination with NRTIs.

Another enzyme essential to the virus's release is HIV protease, which is involved in cutting the proteins that are an essential part of the virus structure (capsids, enzymes). The class of drugs called *protease inhibitors* has the effect of blocking this enzyme and causing the assembly of faulty viruses that are not infective.

Newer classes of anti-HIV drugs are two that block entry or fusion of the virus at the beginning of its invasion and one that prevents viral integration into the host genome. The drug *maraviroc* keeps HIV out of cells by preventing the viruses from adhering to host cells, and without this step, they cannot invade. Enfuvirtide (*Fuzeon*) prevents infection when it stops the envelope of the virus from fusing with the host cell after it has attached. Another important enyzme targeted for HIV therapy is *HIV integrase*. This enzyme is essential for the final step in HIV DNA processing. Integrase inhibitors prevent this viral DNA from being incorporated or integrated into a host cell's chromosome. Because this step must occur for full viral function, the cycle is terminated by this action.

The strategy for HIV and AIDS treatment currently involves antiretroviral therapy (ART), which uses combinations of two,

three, or four drugs in a single pill to reduce the development of drug resistance. Most have at least one NRTI and one NNRTI, and some have protease inhibitors and an integrase inhibitor. In 2018, Biktarvy, which contains two NRTIs and an integrase inhibitor, was approved to treat ongoing HIV infection. A few years earlier, in 2015, Truvada, another combination drug, was approved for both ongoing infection along with **pre-exposure*** and postexposure **prophylaxis (PrEP)**. **Table 12.7** summarizes HIV drug types, their modes of action, and examples.

Interferons A sensible alternative to artificial antiviral drugs has been the human-based substance **interferon (IFN)**. Interferon is a glycoprotein produced primarily by fibroblasts and leukocytes in response to various immune stimuli. It has numerous biological activities, including antiviral and anticancer properties. Studies have shown that it is a versatile part of animal host defenses, having a major role in natural immunities. Its mechanism is discussed in chapter 14.

The first investigations of interferon's antiviral activity were limited by the extremely minute quantities that could be extracted from human blood. Several types of interferon (Betaseron, Roferon) are currently produced by the recombinant DNA technology techniques outlined in chapter 10. Extensive clinical trials have tested

*Pre-exposure prohylaxis (PrEP)—treatment given to uninfected persons to prevent infection, such as a daily dose of anti-HIV medication given to a person who is HIV negative—is now considered a viable way to prevent infection in people whose lifestyles may increase the risk of infection.

interferon's effectiveness in viral infections and cancer. Some of the known therapeutic benefits of interferon include

1. reducing the time of healing and some of the complications in certain infections (mainly of herpesviruses);
2. preventing or reducing some symptoms of cold and papilloma-viruses (warts);
3. slowing the progress of certain cancers, including bone cancer and cervical cancer, and certain leukemias and lymphomas; and
4. treating a rare cancer called hairy-cell leukemia, hepatitis C (a viral liver infection), genital warts, and Kaposi's sarcoma in AIDS patients.

 Practice SECTION 12.3

12. Construct a chart to outline the applications of major groups of antifungal drugs, antiparasitic drugs, and antiviral drugs.
13. Explain why there are fewer antifungal, antiparasitic, and antiviral drugs than antibacterial drugs.
14. List the targets of antiviral drugs and their modes of action. What is the strategy behind taking several different types of drugs to treat HIV?
15. Summarize the origins and biological actions of interferon-based drugs.

12.4 Interactions between Microbes and Drugs: The Acquisition of Drug Resistance

 Learn

15. Describe the development of microbial drug resistance, and explain how it is acquired.
16. Explain the major mechanisms by which microbes become resistant to drugs.
17. Review some of the ways to reduce levels of drug resistance.
18. Discuss how drug resistance spreads through a population of microbes and the long-term effects of this.

One unfortunate outcome of the use of antimicrobials is the development of microbial **drug resistance,** an adaptive response in which microorganisms begin to tolerate an amount of drug that would previously have been inhibitory. The development of mechanisms for resisting antimicrobial drugs is a result of the genetic versatility and adaptability of microbial populations. The property of drug resistance can be an intrinsic characteristic as well as acquired. Intrinsic drug resistance would be found in bacteria that must be resistant to any antibiotic that they produce or bacteria that have natural barriers that block the drug (the outer membrane of gram-negative bacteria, for example). This type of resistance is not the main problem with regard to antimicrobial chemotherapy. Of much greater importance is the acquisition of resistance by a microbe that was previously sensitive to the drug. In our context, the term *drug resistance* will refer to this type of acquired resistance.

How Does Drug Resistance Develop?

Contrary to popular belief, antibiotic resistance is not a recent phenomenon. Resistance to penicillin developed in some bacteria as early as 1940, 3 years before the drug was even approved for public use. The scope of the problem became apparent in the 1980s and 1990s when scientists and physicians observed treatment failures on a large scale.

Microbes become newly resistant to a drug after one of the following events occurs: (1) spontaneous mutations in critical chromosomal genes or (2) acquisition of entirely new genes or sets of genes via transfer from another species. Chromosomal drug resistance usually results from spontaneous random mutations in bacterial populations. The chance that such a mutation will be advantageous is minimal, and the chance that it will confer resistance to a specific drug is lower still. Nevertheless, given the huge numbers of microorganisms in any population and the constant rate of mutation, such mutations do occur. The end result varies from slight changes in microbial sensitivity, which can be overcome by larger doses of the drug, to complete loss of sensitivity.

Resistance through intermicrobial transfer originates from chromosomal genes and plasmids called **resistance (R) factors** being transferred through the processes we considered in chapter 9: conjugation, transformation, or transduction (**figure 12.13**). Studies have shown that plasmids encoded with drug resistance are naturally

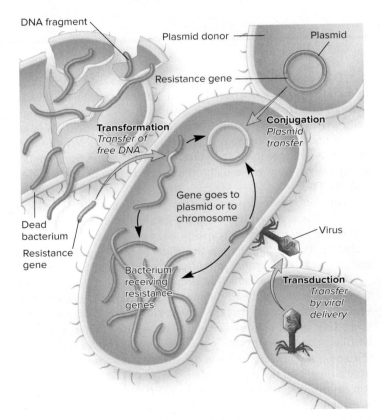

Figure 12.13 Transfer of drug resistance. Bacteria transmit R factors, often containing numerous genes for drug resistance by means of conjugation, transduction, and transformation. The widespread occurrence of such exchanges accounts for the rapid spread of drug resistance.

present in microorganisms before they have been exposed to the drug. Such traits are "lying in wait" for an opportunity to be expressed and to confer adaptability on the species. Many bacteria also maintain transposable drug-resistance sequences (transposons) that are duplicated and inserted from one plasmid to another or from a plasmid to the chromosome. Chromosomal genes and plasmids containing codes for drug resistance are faithfully replicated and inherited by all subsequent progeny. This sharing of resistance genes accounts for the rapid proliferation of drug-resistant species. A growing body of evidence points to the ease and frequency of gene transfers in biofilms between totally unrelated bacteria living in the body's microbiota and the environment.

Specific Mechanisms of Drug Resistance

Inside a bacterial cell, the net effect of these genetic transfers is one of the following, which actually causes the bacterium to be resistant (note that the numbers that follow correspond to the numbers seen in **figure 12.14**):

Quick Search

Explore this topic by going to "Animation of Antibiotic Resistance" on YouTube.

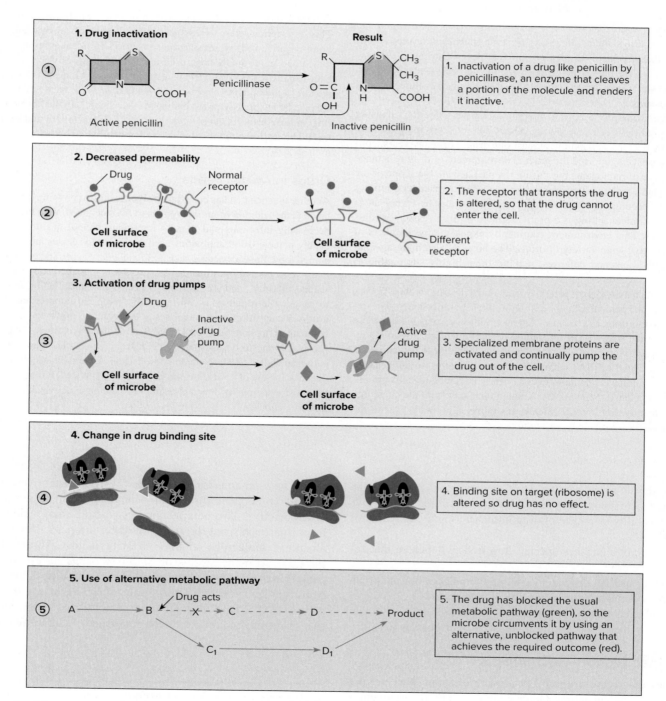

Figure 12.14 Examples of mechanisms of acquired drug resistance.

12.2 MAKING CONNECTIONS

Are We Losing the Drug Resistance Race?

"The rise of antibiotic resistance is a global health crisis. Antimicrobial resistance is on the rise in every region of the world. We are losing first line antibiotics. This makes a broad range of common infections much more difficult to treat, and replacement treatments are most costly, more toxic, and need much longer durations of treatment."

Margaret Chan, MD, WHO Director General

It is a fact of nature that, when a large number of microbes are exposed to a variety of drugs, there will always be some genetically favored strains or types that survive in the presence of those drugs. One could even say that microbes are merely practicing what they do best—adapt and survive. Our very use of drugs is a catalyst that speeds their evolution toward drug resistance.

Approximately 2 million hospital-acquired infections causing 90,000 fatalities occur every year. About 70% of these infections are caused by bacteria resistant to at least one drug. For many years, concerned observers reported the gradual development of drug resistance in a number of pathogens, but during the past decade the scope of the problem has escalated. It is now a common event to discover microbes that have become resistant to relatively new drugs in a very short time. The clinical setting is a prolific source of drug-resistant strains of bacteria. This environment continually exposes large numbers of pathogens to a wide variety of drugs. The hospital also maintains patients with weakened defenses, making them highly susceptible to infections.

We can readily see the pattern by examining the case of *Staphylococcus aureus* and penicillin. In the 1950s, hospital strains began to show resistance to this drug, and because of indiscriminate use of penicillin, these strains became nearly 100% resistant to penicillin within 25 years. In response, drugmakers created methicillin as an alternative to penicillin, but within a few years MRSA (methicillin-resistant *S. aureus*) strains began to appear that ultimately came to tolerate nearly all antibiotics. To complicate this problem, strains of MRSA found their way from the clinic into the community. Fortunately MRSA was universally treatable with the

drug vancomycin—at least for a while. Then there arose reports of VISA (Vancomycin intermediate *Staphylococcus aureus*) strains that were less sensitive, followed by reports of VRSA strains with complete resistance to this drug, all within a few years. It is this creeping pattern of drug resistance to newer replacement drugs that has health officials most concerned.

One of the more urgent alerts has arisen over carbapenem-resistant Enterobacteriaceae (CRE), featured in the Case Study for chapter 11. This description refers to resistance among members of this family of gram-negative rods to the carbapenem drugs (imipenem, ertapenem), which had traditionally been used in cases of drug resistance to other beta-lactam drugs. Many new resistant strains of *Klebsiella pneumoniae, Enterobacter cloacae,* and *Escherichia coli* have emerged as significant hospital-acquired pathogens (see figure). In the hospital setting, enteric bacteria cause infections of the bloodstream and urinary tract. The fatality rate for compromised or debilitated patients can be as high as 50%.

Drugs in Animal Feeds

Another practice that has contributed significantly to growing drug resistance is the addition of antimicrobials to livestock feed, with the idea of decreasing infections and thereby improving animal health and size. Eighty percent of all antibiotics used in the United States are added to animal food. Enteric bacteria such as *Salmonella, E. coli,* and enterococci that live as normal intestinal residents of these animals readily share resistance plasmids and are constantly selected and amplified by exposure to drugs. These pathogens subsequently "jump" to humans and cause drug-resistant infections, oftentimes at epidemic proportions. In a 2018 outbreak of *Salmonella* in the United States, linked to chicken, the pathogen was found to be resistant to 12 different drugs. The opportunistic pathogen called VRE (vancomycin-resistant Enterococcus) has been traced to the use of a vancomycin-like drug in cattle feed. It is now one of the most tenacious of hospital-acquired infections, for which there are few drug choices.

1. The development of alternative enzymes that inactivate the drug (occurs only when new genes are acquired).
2. Permeability or uptake of drug into bacterium is decreased or eliminated.
3. The microbe engages special drug transport pumps that remove the drug.
4. Binding sites for drug are decreased in number or affinity (can occur via mutation or acquisition of new genes).
5. An affected metabolic pathway is shut down or an alternate pathway is used (occurs due to mutation of original enzyme[s]).

Drug Inactivation Mechanisms

Microbes inactivate drugs by producing enzymes that permanently alter drug structure. One example, bacterial exoenzymes

called *beta-lactamases,* hydrolyze the beta-lactam ring structure of some penicillins and cephalosporins, rendering the drugs inactive. Two beta-lactamases—penicillinase and cephalosporinase—disrupt the structure of certain penicillin or cephalosporin molecules so their activity is lost **(figure 12.14, part 1).** So many strains of *Staphylococcus aureus* produce penicillinase that regular penicillin is rarely a possible therapeutic choice. Now that some strains of *Neisseria gonorrhoeae,* called PPNG,[4] have also acquired penicillinase genes, alternative drugs are required to treat gonorrhea. A large number of

4. Penicillinase-producing *Neisseria gonorrhoeae.*

Worldwide Drug Resistance

The drug dilemma has become a widespread problem, affecting all countries and socioeconomic groups. In general, the majority of infectious diseases, whether bacterial, fungal, protozoan, or viral, are showing increases in drug resistance. In parts of India, the main drugs used to treat cholera (furazolidone, ampicillin) have gone from being highly effective to essentially useless in 10 years. In Southeast Asia, 98% of gonococcus infections are multidrug resistant. Many strains of the malaria parasite have become resistant to the mainstay drug chloroquine, which means that it must be combined with an alternative drug or not given at all. The influenza drugs amantadine and rimantadine had to be discontinued because the virus had become almost completely resistant to these medications. In some parts of Africa, strains of the TB bacillus have developed such extreme resistance that there are no effective treatments available. To add to the problem, global travel and globalization of food products mean that drug-resistant pathogens can be spread around the world in a short time.

In the United States alone, the extra cost for treating drug-resistant infections is around $10 billion per year. In many developing countries, drugs are mishandled by overuse and underuse, either of which can contribute to drug resistance. Many countries that do not regulate the sale of prescription drugs make them readily available to purchase over the counter. For example, the antituberculosis drug INH (isoniazid) is sometimes used as a "lung vitamin" to improve health, and antibiotics are often taken in the wrong dose for undiagnosed conditions. These countries serve as breeding grounds for drug resistance that can eventually be carried to other countries.

"Bad Bugs—No Drugs"

The development of new antimicrobial drugs is considered an urgent goal. Medical experts are seeing an increase in the incidence of the "bad bugs—no drugs" dilemma. A case in point is the alarming trend of pathogens known collectively as ESKAPE. This acronym comes from the first letters of their generic names, but it also tells us that these six pathogens are very successful at escaping the effects of drugs and are getting better at it all the time. The bacteria—*Enterococcus*, *Staphylococcus aureus*, *Klebsiella*, *Acinetobacter*, *Pseudomonas*, and *Enterobacter*—make up the majority of hospital-acquired infections, and are also the most drug-resistant. It is not unusual to isolate extremely drug-resistant strains or "superbugs" for which there are only two, one, and sometimes no drugs available. To avert a public health crisis, a number of governments are actively working with pharmaceutical companies on drug discovery and development, sometimes called the "new bugs–new drugs" approach.

To see an excellent documentary addressing this crisis, go to the PBS Frontline website and search for "Hunting the Nightmare Bacteria."

What are some of the reasons microbes develop drug resistance so rapidly?

Plates comparing sensitivity test results for two bacterial cultures exposed to 12 different antibiotic discs. The plate on the left shows large, uniform zones of inhibition, indicating complete sensitivity of the culture to all 12 drugs. On the right is a sample of a CRE pathogen (here, *Enterobacter*) that has slight sensitivity to two of the drugs but is resistant to all of the rest.
Source: James Gathany/CDC

other gram-negative species are inherently resistant to some of the penicillins and cephalosporins because of naturally occurring beta-lactamases.

Decreased Drug Permeability or Increased Drug Elimination

The resistance of some bacteria can be due to a mechanism that prevents the drug from entering the cell and acting on its target. For example, the outer membrane of the cell wall of certain gram-negative bacteria is a natural blockade for some of the penicillin drugs. Aminoglycoside resistance is known to develop through changes in drug permeability caused by point mutations in proteins of the transport system or outer membrane **(figure 12.14, parts 2 and 3).**

Many bacteria possess multidrug-resistant (MDR) pumps that actively transport drugs and other chemicals out of cells. These pumps are proteins encoded by plasmids or chromosomes. They are stationed in the cell membrane and expel molecules by a proton-motive force similar to ATP synthesis **(figure 12.14, part 3).** They confer drug resistance on many gram-positive pathogens (*Staphylococcus, Streptococcus*) and gram-negative pathogens (*Pseudomonas, E. coli*). Because MDRs lack selectivity, one type of pump can expel a broad array of antimicrobial drugs, detergents, and other toxic substances.

Change of Drug Receptors

As most drugs act on a specific target such as protein, RNA, DNA, or membrane structure, microbes can circumvent drugs by altering the nature of this target. Bacteria can become resistant to aminoglycosides when point mutations in ribosomal proteins arise **(figure 12.14, part 4)**. Erythromycin and clindamycin resistance is associated with an alteration on the 50S ribosomal binding site. Penicillin resistance in *Streptococcus pneumoniae* and methicillin resistance in *Staphylococcus aureus* are related to an alteration in the binding proteins in the cell wall. Several species of enterococci have acquired resistance to vancomycin through a similar alteration of cell wall proteins. Some bacteria may become resistant by shedding their cell wall entirely, converting to a cell-wall-deficient form (L-form) that is unaffected by penicillin. Fungi can become resistant by decreasing their synthesis of ergosterol, the principal receptor for certain antifungal drugs.

Changes in Metabolic Patterns

The action of antimetabolites can be circumvented if a microbe develops an alternative metabolic pathway or enzyme **(figure 12.14, part 5)**. Sulfonamide and trimethoprim resistance develops when microbes deviate from the usual patterns of folic acid synthesis. Fungi can acquire resistance to flucytosine by completely shutting off certain metabolic activities.

Biofilms and Drug Resistance

It is estimated that about 60% of infections involve biofilms, complex communities of microorganisms growing within an extracellular matrix (first discussed in chapter 4). Biofilms add another level of complexity to thoughts of bacterial resistance. Always a problem on natural tissues—for example, bacterial infections of the heart valves, middle ear, and teeth—the increased use of indwelling medical devices has created yet another habitat in which biofilms may become tenaciously attached. Catheters, artificial valves, and prosthetic devices can harbor persistent biofilms that are difficult to treat or remove.

Microbes in infectious biofilms may be hundreds of times more drug resistant than the same free, unattached microbes. Most obviously, microbes are protected by the impenetrable nature of the extracellular matrix, drugs may simply be blocked from entry. We also know that microbes within the biofilm communicate with one another and are more likely to engage in the transfer of drug-resistant plasmids and genes. And of course, if one microbe in a biofilm can inactivate a particular drug, nearby microbes may benefit from the drug-free environment.

Natural Selection and Drug Resistance

So far we have been considering drug resistance at the cellular and molecular levels, but its full impact is felt only if this resistance occurs throughout the cell population. Let us examine how this might happen and its long-term therapeutic consequences.

Any large population of microbes is likely to contain a few individual cells that are already drug resistant because of prior mutations or transfer of plasmids **(figure 12.15a)**. As long as the drug is not present in the habitat, the numbers of these resistant forms will remain low because they have no particular growth advantage. But if the population is subsequently exposed to this drug **(figure 12.15b)**, sensitive individuals are inhibited or destroyed, and resistant forms survive and proliferate. As the population continues to grow, offspring

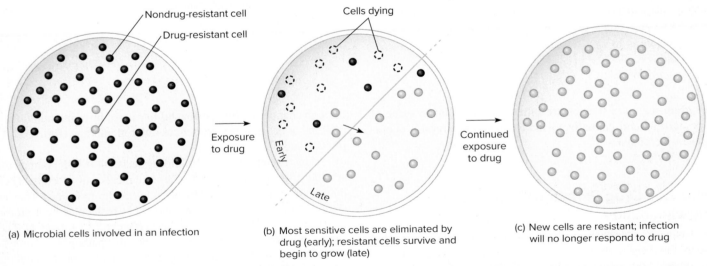

(a) Microbial cells involved in an infection (b) Most sensitive cells are eliminated by drug (early); resistant cells survive and begin to grow (late) (c) New cells are resistant; infection will no longer respond to drug

Figure 12.15 A model of natural selection for drug resistance. (a) Generally, any population of microbes will harbor a few cells carrying a prior mutation that confers drug resistance. **(b)** Environmental pressure (here, exposure to the drug) selects for survival of these cells. **(c)** In time, the resistant cells become the dominant cells.

TABLE 12.8	**Strategies to Limit Drug Resistance of Microorganisms**

Drug Usage

- Physicians have the responsibility for making an accurate diagnosis and prescribing the correct drug therapy.
- Compliance with physicians' guidelines: The patient should take the correct dosage, by the best route, for the appropriate period. This diminishes the selection for mutants that can resist low drug levels and ensures elimination of the pathogen.
- Combined therapy with two or more drugs together increases the chances that at least one of the drugs will be effective and that a strain resistant to one drug will be eliminated by the other.

Drug Research

- Research focuses on developing shorter-term, higher-dose antimicrobials that are more effective, less expensive, and have fewer side effects.
- Pharmaceutical companies continue to seek new antimicrobial drugs with structures that are not readily inactivated by microbial enzymes or drugs with modes of action that are not readily circumvented.

Long-Term Strategies

- Proposals to reduce the abuse of antibiotics range from educational programs for medical workers to requiring justification for prescribing certain types of antibiotics.
- Especially valuable antimicrobials may be restricted in their use to only one or two types of infections.
- The addition of antimicrobials to animal feeds must be curtailed worldwide.
- Government programs that make effective therapy available to low-income populations should be increased.
- Vaccines should be used whenever possible to provide alternative protection.

of these resistant microbes will inherit this drug resistance. In time, the replacement population will have more of the drug-resistant forms and can eventually become completely resistant **(figure 12.15c)**. In ecological and evolutionary terms, the environmental factor (in this case, the drug) has put selection pressure on the population, allowing the better adapted microbe (the drug-resistant one) to survive and grow. The end result is a population that has evolved to a condition of drug resistance.

Natural selection for drug-resistant forms is apparently a common phenomenon. It takes place most frequently in various natural habitats, medical environments, and it also can occur within the bodies of humans and animals during drug therapy. See **12.2 Making Connections** to find out some of the current implications of drug resistance. **Table 12.8** summarizes a number of actions that are being considered to slow its development.

Practice SECTION 12.4

16. Explain the phenomenon of drug resistance from the standpoint of microbial genetics (include a description of R factors).

17. Describe the five basic mechanisms of drug resistance.

18. Outline several situations or events that increase the development of drug-resistant microbes.

19. Name several ways drug resistance can be prevented by medical personnel and patients (see table 12.8).

12.5 Interactions between Drugs and Hosts

Learn

19. Summarize the adverse effects of drugs on the human body.

20. Describe some of the toxic effects of drugs on organs and tissues.

21. Discuss how drugs can cause damaging immune responses.

22. Explain the ways in which drugs alter the normal microbiota and the results.

Until now, this chapter has focused on the interactions between antimicrobial drugs and the microorganisms they target. During an infection, the microbe is living in or on a host, which means that the drug is administered to the host, even though its target is the microbe. Because of this, the effect of the drug on the host must always be considered.

Although selective antimicrobial toxicity is the ideal constantly being sought, chemotherapy by its very nature involves contact with foreign chemicals that can harm human tissues. In fact, estimates indicate that at least 5% of all persons taking an antimicrobial drug experience some type of serious adverse reaction to it. Antibiotics cause one out of five emergency visits due to adverse drug reactions. The major **side effects** of drugs fall into one of three categories: direct damage to tissues through toxicity, allergic reactions, and disruption in the balance of normal microbial flora. The damage incurred by antimicrobial drugs can be

short term and reversible or permanent, and it ranges in severity from cosmetic to lethal effects.

Toxicity to Organs

Drugs are chemicals whose primary purpose is to slow or stop the growth of a living organism. With this in mind, it is unsurprising that drugs can in some way adversely affect nearly every tissue in the body.

Two organs that bear the brunt of chemotherapy are the liver and kidney. Because the liver is responsible for metabolizing and detoxifying foreign chemicals in the blood, it can be damaged by a drug or its metabolic products. Injury to liver cells can result in enzymatic abnormalities, fatty liver deposits, hepatitis, and liver failure. The kidney is involved in excreting drugs and their metabolites. Some drugs irritate the nephron tubules, creating changes that interfere with their filtration abilities. Drugs such as sulfonamides can crystallize in the kidney and form stones that obstruct the flow of urine.

The most common complaint associated with oral antimicrobial therapy is diarrhea, which can progress to severe intestinal irritation or colitis. Although some drugs directly irritate the intestinal lining, the usual gastrointestinal complaints are caused by disruption of the intestinal microbiota (shown in figure 12.17).

Many drugs given for parasitic infections are toxic to the heart, causing irregular heartbeats and even cardiac arrest in extreme cases. Chloramphenicol can severely depress blood-forming cells in the bone marrow, resulting in either a reversible or a permanent (fatal) anemia. Some drugs hemolyze the red blood cells, others reduce white blood cell counts, and still others damage platelets or interfere with their formation, thereby inhibiting blood clotting.

> **Quick Search**
> Find the video "Important Side Effects and Toxicities" on YouTube.

Certain antimicrobials act directly on the brain and cause seizures. Others, such as aminoglycosides, damage nerves (very commonly, the eighth cranial nerve), leading to dizziness, deafness, or motor and sensory disturbances. When drugs block the transmission of impulses to the diaphragm, respiratory failure can result.

The skin is a frequent target of drug-induced side effects. The skin response can be a symptom of drug allergy or a direct toxic

Figure 12.16 **Drug-induced side effect.** An adverse effect of tetracycline given to young children is the permanent brownish discoloration of tooth enamel continuing into adulthood.
Biophoto Associates/Science Source

CLINICAL CONNECTION

Clinical Testing, When Is Enough, Enough?

A common argument when discussing drugs is how much testing is enough. Should drugs be tested for years before approval, leaving a patient to die because an experimental drug wasn't approved fast enough to treat her condition? Or, should we streamline the approval process, leaving a patient to die from drug effects that could have been avoided if only we would have tested more thoroughly? As with most things, the truth lies somewhere in the middle.

Any new drug is first tested, in the laboratory, on bacterial cells and animals. These early tests focus primarily on the safety of the drug and, if successful, allow the drug company (known as the sponsor) to apply to the Food and Drug Administration (FDA) to begin a clinical trial. During a clinical trial, the drug is tested on healthy people and patients to monitor its safety and effectiveness, and if the benefits of the drug outweigh the risks—for there has never been a drug with zero risk—the FDA will typically approve it for manufacture and sale.

Once the drug is approved, post-marketing surveillance begins. This period is often informative, as the number of people being treated jumps from a few hundred to, perhaps, hundreds of thousands, and rare adverse reactions—like the tendonitis seen with fluoroquinolones, which affects 2 people per 1,000—may become apparent. Reports of adverse events are collected and stored within the FDA Adverse Event Reporting System (FAERS). When a problem arises, like a patient not taking a drug as prescribed, the drug company, with input from the FDA, may issue a letter to health care providers, often referred to as a "Dear Doctor" letter, alerting them to the issue. In other cases, the FDA may require a change to the prescribing information or to the label of the drug itself. The strictest of these requirements is a "black box warning," so named because the warning must be enclosed by a black outline to draw attention. This warning is reserved for drugs that have serious or life-threatening risks.

Finally, after months or years, the FDA may reassess its approval of a drug. In these cases, the nature and frequency of adverse events may suggest that the benefits of the drug no longer outweigh its risks, and the FDA will ask the manufacturer to withdraw the drug from the market.

What type of problem may have spurred the development of extended-release drugs, which are designed to allow a drug to enter the system slowly over time?

effect. Some drugs interact with sunlight to cause photodermatitis, a skin inflammation. Tetracyclines are contraindicated (not advisable) for children from birth to 8 years of age because they bind to the enamel of the teeth, creating a permanent gray to brown discoloration (**figure 12.16**). Pregnant women should avoid tetracyclines because they cross the placenta and can be deposited in the developing fetal bones and teeth. As seen in this chapter's Case Study, fluoroquinolones, like ciprofloxacin, may cause serious side effects

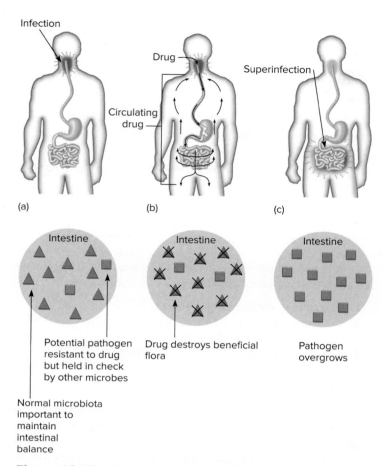

Figure 12.17 **The role of antimicrobials in disrupting microbiota and causing superinfections. (a)** A primary infection in the throat is treated with an oral antibiotic. **(b)** The drug is carried to the intestine and is absorbed into the circulation. **(c)** The primary infection is cured, but drug-resistant pathogens have survived and create an intestinal superinfection.

in several tissues including nerve damage, loss of mental acuity, swollen joints, and ruptured tendons.

Allergic Responses to Drugs

One of the most frequent drug reactions is heightened sensitivity, or **allergy.** This reaction occurs because the drug acts as an antigen (a foreign material capable of stimulating the immune system) and stimulates an allergic response. This response can be provoked by the intact drug molecule or by substances that develop from the body's metabolic alteration of the drug. In the case of penicillin, for instance, it is not the penicillin molecule itself that causes the allergic response but a product, *benzylpenicilloyl.* Allergic reactions have been reported for every major type of antimicrobial drug, but the penicillins account for the greatest number of antimicrobial allergies, followed by the sulfonamides.

People who are allergic to a drug become sensitized to it during the first contact, usually without symptoms. Once the immune system is sensitized, a second exposure to the drug can lead to a

reaction such as a skin rash (hives); respiratory inflammation; and, rarely, anaphylaxis—an acute, overwhelming allergic response that develops rapidly and can be fatal. This topic is discussed in greater detail in chapter 16.

Suppression and Alteration of the Microbiota by Antimicrobials

Most normal, healthy body surfaces, such as the skin, large intestine, outer openings of the urogenital tract, and oral cavity, provide numerous habitats for a virtual "garden" of microorganisms. These normal colonists or residents, called the microbiota, consist mostly of harmless or beneficial bacteria, but a small number of them can potentially be pathogens. We defer a more detailed discussion of this topic to chapter 13 and later chapters. Here we focus on the general effects of drugs on this population.

If a broad-spectrum antimicrobial drug is administered to treat infection, it will destroy microbes regardless of their roles in maintaining a balance, affecting not only the targeted infectious agent but also many others in sites far removed from the original infection **(figure 12.17).** When this therapy destroys beneficial resident species, resistant microbes that were once in small numbers begin to overgrow and cause disease. This complication is called a **superinfection.**

Some common examples demonstrate how a disturbance in the microbiota leads to replacement pathogens and superinfection. A broad-spectrum cephalosporin used to treat a urinary tract infection by *E. coli* will cure the infection, but it will also destroy the lactobacilli in the vagina that normally maintain a protective acidic environment there. The drug has no effect, however, on *Candida albicans,* a yeast that also resides in normal vaginas. Released from the inhibitory environment provided by lactobacilli, the yeasts proliferate and cause symptoms. *Candida* can cause similar superinfections of the oropharynx (thrush) and the large intestine.

Oral therapy with tetracyclines, clindamycin, and broad-spectrum penicillins and cephalosporins is associated with a serious and potentially fatal condition known as *antibiotic-associated colitis* (pseudomembranous colitis). This condition is due to the overgrowth in the bowel of *Clostridioides difficile,* an endospore-forming bacterium that is resistant to the antibiotic. It invades the intestinal lining and releases toxins that induce diarrhea, fever, and abdominal pain.

Refer to **table 12.9** for a general summary of major drug groups and their side effects.

Practice SECTION 12.5

20. Why do drugs that act on bacterial and fungal membranes generally have high toxicity?

21. Describe the series of events that gives rise to a superinfection, using an example.

22. What characteristic of antibiotics and other drugs causes hypersensitivity and allergic reactions?

23. Explain why it is better to use a narrow-spectrum drug instead of a broad-spectrum one, if possible.

TABLE 12.9	Major Adverse Toxic Reactions to Common Drug Groups
Antimicrobial Drug	**Primary Damage or Abnormality Produced**
Antibacterials	
Penicillin G	Skin allergy
Ampicillin	Diarrhea and enterocolitis
Cephalosporins	Inhibition of prothrombin synthesis
	Decreased circulation
	Nephritis
Tetracyclines	Diarrhea and enterocolitis
	Discoloration of tooth enamel
	Reactions to sunlight (photosensitization)
Chloramphenicol	Injury to red and white blood cell precursors
Aminoglycosides (streptomycin, gentamicin)	Diarrhea and enterocolitis; loss of hearing, dizziness, kidney damage
Azithromycin	Heart arrhythmias
Isoniazid	Hepatitis
	Seizures
	Dermatitis
Sulfonamides	Formation of kidney crystals; blockage of urine flow
	Hemolysis
	Reduction in number of platelets
Polymyxin	Damage to membranes of kidney tubules
	Weakened muscular responses
Quinolones (floxacins)	Headache, dizziness, GI distress, tendinitis
Rifampin	Damage to hepatic cells
	Dermatitis
Antifungals	
Amphotericin B	Disruption of kidney filtration
Flucytosine	Decreased number of white blood cells
Antiprotozoan Drugs	
Metronidazole	Nausea, vomiting
Chloroquine	Vomiting
	Headache
	Itching
Antihelminthics	
Niclosamide	Nausea, abdominal pain
Pyrantel	Irritation
	Headache, dizziness
Antivirals	
Acyclovir	Seizures, confusion
	Skin rash
Amantadine	Nervousness, light-headedness
	Nausea
AZT	Immunosuppression, anemia
Protease inhibitors	Hepatic damage
	Abnormal deposition of fats
	Diabetes

12.6 The Process of Selecting an Antimicrobial Drug

 Learn

23. Outline some important factors to consider in drug therapy.
24. Describe the principles behind sensitivity testing for infectious agents.
25. Explain the uses of the minimum inhibitory concentration and the therapeutic index in drug selection.
26. Discuss medical considerations in final drug selection.
27. Summarize the problems in managing antimicrobial drugs.

Before actual antimicrobial therapy can begin, consideration must be given to at least three factors:

1. the nature of the microorganism causing the infection,
2. the degree of the microorganism's susceptibility (also called sensitivity) to various drugs, and
3. the overall medical condition of the patient.

Identifying the Agent

Identification of infectious agents from body specimens should be attempted as soon as possible. It is especially important that such specimens be taken before any antimicrobial drug is given to prevent loss of the infectious agent. Direct examination of body fluids, sputum, or stool can provide a rapid detection method for bacteria or fungi. Newer methods of molecular diagnosis have greatly improved the speed of identification in many cases. A doctor often begins the therapy on the basis of such immediate findings. The choice of drug will be based on experience with drugs that are known to be effective against the microbe. For instance, if a sore throat appears to be caused by *Streptococcus pyogenes,* the physician may prescribe penicillin, because this species seems to be almost universally sensitive to it so far. If the infectious agent is not or cannot be isolated, epidemiological statistics may be required to predict the most likely agent in a given infection. For example, *Streptococcus pneumoniae* accounts for the majority of cases of meningitis in children, followed by *Neisseria meningitidis* and *Haemophilus influenzae.*

Testing for the Drug Susceptibility of Microorganisms

Testing is essential in those groups of bacteria commonly showing resistance, primarily *Staphylococcus* species, *Neisseria gonorrhoeae, Streptococcus pneumoniae, Enterococcus faecalis,* and the aerobic gram-negative enteric bacilli. However, not all infectious agents require antimicrobial sensitivity testing. When certain groups, such as group A streptococci and most anaerobic bacteria, are known to be uniformly susceptible to penicillins, testing may not be necessary unless the patient is allergic to penicillin. Testing methods are available for fungi (see figure 12.21), protozoa, and viruses, although testing might not be done as often for these groups.

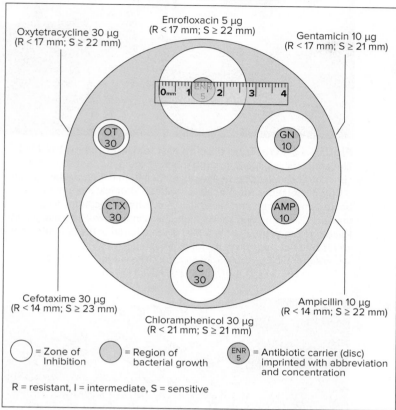

Kirby-Bauer Disc Diffusion Test

Oxytetracycline 30 µg
(R < 17 mm; S ≥ 22 mm)

Enrofloxacin 5 µg
(R < 17 mm; S ≥ 22 mm)

Gentamicin 10 µg
(R < 17 mm; S ≥ 21 mm)

Cefotaxime 30 µg
(R < 14 mm; S ≥ 23 mm)

Chloramphenicol 30 µg
(R < 21 mm; S ≥ 21 mm)

Ampicillin 10 µg
(R < 14 mm; S ≥ 22 mm)

○ = Zone of Inhibition ● = Region of bacterial growth (ENR 5) = Antibiotic carrier (disc) imprinted with abbreviation and concentration

R = resistant, I = intermediate, S = sensitive

(a) Example and evaluation of an agar diffusion sensitivity test. If the test bacterium is sensitive to a drug, a zone of inhibition develops around its disc. The larger the size of this zone, the greater is the bacterium's sensitivity to the drug. The diameter of each zone is measured in millimeters and evaluated for susceptibility or resistance by means of a comparative standard (R, I, or S).

Figure 12.18 Techniques for preparation and interpretation of disc diffusion tests.
(b): Lisa Burgess/McGraw-Hill Education; (c): Lisa Burgess/McGraw-Hill Education

(b) *Staphylococcus aureus,* displaying a zone of inhibition around a vancomycin-containing disk. The zone of inhibition is always measured across its diameter, in this case, 18 mm.

(c) Three different pieces of information can be seen in this comparison of Kirby-Bauer tests of *Pseudomonas aeruginosa* (gram-negative, left) and *Staphylococcus aureus* (gram-positive, right). 1) The larger-sized zones of inhibition on the right plate indicate that, in general, gram-positive bacteria tend to be more susceptible to antimicrobics than gram-negative bacteria. 2) Vancomycin (VA 30, center) is a narrow-spectrum antibiotic, showing effectiveness against *S. aureus* but not *P. aeruginosa.* 3) This strain of *Pseudomonas* displays resistance to the normally broad-spectrum antibiotics tetracycline (TE 30) and Chloramphenicol (C 30). *Pseudomonas* is well known for its resistance to multiple drugs.

Selection of a proper antimicrobial agent begins by demonstrating the in vitro activity of several drugs against the infectious agent by means of standardized methods. In general, these tests involve exposing a pure culture of the bacterium to several different drugs and observing the effects of the drugs on growth.

The *Kirby-Bauer* technique is an agar diffusion test that provides useful data on antimicrobial susceptibility. In this test, the surface of a plate of special medium is spread with the test bacterium, and small discs containing a premeasured amount of antimicrobial are dispensed onto the bacterial lawn. After incubation, the zone of inhibition surrounding the discs is measured and compared with a standard for each drug **(figure 12.18).** The profile of antimicrobial sensitivity, or *antibiogram,* provides data for drug selection. The Kirby-Bauer procedure is less effective for

bacteria that are anaerobic, highly fastidious, or slow-growing (*Mycobacterium*).

An alternative system that provides a quantitative rating of drug effectiveness is the *Etest®* **(figure 12.19).** In addition to providing a precise numerical rating (discussed in the next paragraph), this method allows testing for a wide variety of drugs and microbial types, including anaerobes, mycobacteria, and fungi.

More sensitive and quantitative results can also be obtained with tube dilution tests. First the antimicrobial is diluted serially in tubes of broth, and then each tube is inoculated with a small uniform sample of pure culture, incubated, and examined for growth (turbidity). The smallest concentration of drug in the series that visibly inhibits growth is called the **minimum inhibitory concentration,** or **MIC.** The MIC is useful in determining the smallest

Figure 12.19 **Etest®: A quantitative method for determining sensitivity.** This test uses a plastic strip that contains a premeasured gradient of a drug and is labeled with a scale that indicates varying concentrations of the drug. The concentration ranges from higher at the top of the strip to lower toward the bottom. When the strip is placed on a plate swabbed with the test microbe and incubated, an oval area called the ellipse of inhibition develops adjacent to the strip. The lowest point on the scale where the ellipse begins to form corresponds with the minimum inhibitory concentration (MIC). In this test, for benzylpenicillin, the MIC is 0.094 µg/ml.
Sirirat/Shutterstock

Figure 12.20 **Tube dilution test for determining the MIC.** The antibiotic is diluted through tubes of liquid nutrient so that the concentration in successive tubes ranges from 6.4 µg/ml (far right) to 0.1 µg/ml. All tubes are inoculated with an identical amount of a test bacterium and then incubated. The first tube on the left is a control that lacks the drug and shows cloudiness indicative of normal growth. Reading from left to right, the MIC is the dilution of the first tube in the series that has no growth (is not cloudy).
© Copyright AB BIODISK 2008. Re-printed with permission of AB BIODISK

Figure 12.21 **Microbroth dilution in a multiwell plate adapted for a pathogenic yeast.** Drugs being tested are amphotericin B (AmB), flucytosine (5FC), fluconazole (Fluc), azole drugs (itraconazole [itra], ketoconazole [Keto], Voriconazole [vori], and caspofungin [caspo]). Pink indicates growth; blue indicates no growth. Reading across, numbers 2–12 are increasing concentrations of the drugs in µg/ml. Row 1 has no drug. The first dilution with no growth is crossed out, indicating the MIC for that drug. Results are given in the box on the left.
Kathy Park Talaro

effective dosage of a drug and in providing a comparative index against other antimicrobials (**figures 12.20** and **12.21,** and **table 12.10**). In many clinical laboratories, these antimicrobial testing procedures are performed in automated machines that can test dozens of drugs and microbes simultaneously.

The MIC and the Therapeutic Index

The results of antimicrobial sensitivity tests guide the physician's choice of a suitable drug. If therapy has already commenced, it is imperative to determine if the tests bear out the use of that particu-

TABLE 12.10	Comparative MICs (µg/ml) for Common Drugs and Pathogens				
Bacterium	**Penicillin G**	**Ampicillin**	**Sulfamethoxazole**	**Tetracycline**	**Cefaclor**
Staphylococcus aureus	4.0	0.05	3.0	0.3	4.0
Enterococcus faecalis	3.6	1.6	100.0	0.3	60.0
Neisseria gonorrhoeae	0.5	0.5	5.0	0.8	0.2
Escherichia coli	100.0	12.0	3.0	1–4.0	3.0
Pseudomonas aeruginosa	>500.0	>200.0	>100.0	>100.0	4.0
Salmonella species	12.0	6.0	10.0	1.0	0.8
Clostridium perfringens	0.16	NA	NA	3.0	12.0

NA = not available

lar drug. Once therapy has begun, it is important to observe the patient's clinical response, because the in vitro activity of the drug is not always correlated with its in vivo effect. When antimicrobial treatment fails, the failure is usually due to

1. the inability of the drug to diffuse into that body compartment (the brain, joints, skin);
2. a few resistant cells in the culture that did not appear in the sensitivity test; or
3. an infection caused by more than one pathogen (mixed), some of which are resistant to the drug.

If therapy does fail, a different drug, combined therapy, or a different method of administration must be considered.

Many factors influence the choice of an antimicrobial drug besides microbial sensitivity to it. The nature and spectrum of the drug, its potential adverse effects, and the condition of the patient can be critically important. When several antimicrobial drugs are available for treating an infection, final drug selection advances to a new series of considerations. In general, it is better to choose the narrowest-spectrum drug of those that are effective if the causative agent is known. This decreases the potential for superinfections and other adverse reactions.

Because drug toxicity is of concern, it is best to choose the drug with high selective toxicity for the infectious agent and low human toxicity. The **therapeutic index (TI)** is defined as the ratio of the dose of the drug that is toxic to humans as compared to its minimum effective (therapeutic) dose. The closer these two figures are (the smaller the ratio), the greater the potential for toxic drug reactions. For example, a drug that has a therapeutic index of

$$\frac{10\,\mu g/ml: \text{toxic dose}}{9\,\mu g/ml\,(\text{MIC})} \quad \boxed{\text{TI} = 1.1}$$

is a riskier choice than one with a therapeutic index of

$$\frac{10\,\mu g/ml}{1\,\mu g/ml} \quad \boxed{\text{TI} = 10}$$

Drug companies recommend dosages that will inhibit the microbes but not adversely affect patient cells. When a series of drugs being considered for therapy have similar MICs, the drug with the highest therapeutic index usually has the widest margin of safety.

Patient Factors in Choosing an Antimicrobial Drug

The physician must also take a careful history of the patient to discover any preexisting medical conditions that will influence the activity of the drug or the response of the patient. A history of allergy to a certain class of drugs should preclude the administration of that drug and any drugs related to it. Underlying liver or kidney disease will ordinarily necessitate the modification of drug therapy, because these organs play such an important part in metabolizing or excreting the drug. Infants, the elderly, and preg-

nant women require special precautions. For example, age can diminish gastrointestinal absorption and organ function, and most antimicrobial drugs cross the placenta and could affect fetal development.

The intake of other drugs must be carefully scrutinized, because incompatibilities can result in increased toxicity or failure of one or more of the drugs. For example, the combination of aminoglycosides and cephalosporins increases nephrotoxic effects, antacids reduce the absorption of isoniazid, and the interaction of tetracycline or rifampin with oral contraceptives can abolish the contraceptive's effect. Some drugs (penicillin with certain aminoglycosides, or amphotericin B with flucytosine) act synergistically, so that reduced doses of each can be used. Other concerns in choosing drugs include any genetic or metabolic abnormalities in the patient, the site of infection, the route of administration, and the cost of the drug.

 CLINIC CASE

Never Give These Drugs Together. Maybe We Should Give These Drugs Together. The patient, a 45-year-old male with a history of bipolar disease, arrived by ambulance. Found unresponsive at home, he was intubated by first responders before being transported. To control his bipolar disease, he had been prescribed valproic acid (VPA), and it was thought that his current state was the result of a suicide attempt involving an overdose of the drug. Based on prescription records, physicians estimated he consumed about 10 grams of VPA, roughly 15 times a normal dose.

Immediately upon admission, doctors administered the antibiotics cefepime and metronidazole with the goal of preventing aspiration pneumonia—lung infection caused by inhaling the contents of the gastrointestinal tract—a serious consequence of valproic acid overdose. Despite giving the patient activated charcoal to adsorb toxins in the gastrointestinal tract, his VPA level continued to rise.

Valproic acid is normally used to treat seizures, bipolar disorders, and migraines. Physicians are cautioned against prescribing carbapenem antibiotics to these patients, as an interaction can occur between the two drugs, lowering the concentration of VPA in the bloodstream. Usually this would be an unwanted side effect, leaving the patient with less protection against seizures, migraines, etc., but in this case, it was thought that the drug interaction could work to the patient's advantage.

Doctors discontinued the two drugs initially used to protect against pneumonia and replaced them with meropenem, a broad-spectrum carbapenem antibiotic. Over the next 14 hours, the patient's valproic acid level declined dramatically, he became more alert, and he was extubated the following day. Four days later, he was discharged to the inpatient psychiatry service.

Patients taking nifedipine (Procardia®) to lower blood pressure are cautioned against drinking grapefruit juice while on the medication. How is the nifedipine/grapefruit effect fundamentally different than the VPA/meropenem effect? (A trip to the Internet will be in order.)

Even when all the information is in, the final choice of a drug is not always straightforward. Consider the case of an elderly alcoholic patient with pneumonia caused by *Klebsiella* and complicated by diminished liver and kidney function. All drugs must be given parenterally because of prior damage to the gastrointestinal lining and poor absorption. Drug tests show that the infectious agent is sensitive to fourth-generation cephalosporins, gentamicin, imipenem, and ticarcillin. The patient's history shows previous allergy to the penicillins, so these would be ruled out. Cephalosporins are associated with serious bleeding in elderly patients, so this may not be a good choice. Aminoglycosides such as gentamicin are nephrotoxic and poorly cleared by damaged kidneys. Imipenem is probably the best choice because of its broad spectrum and low toxicity.

Practice SECTION 12.6

24. How are dilution susceptibility tests and disc diffusion tests used to determine microbial drug sensitivity?

25. Briefly describe the Kirby-Bauer test and its purpose.

26. If a technician examined a Kirby-Bauer assay and found individual colonies of the plated microbe growing within the zone of inhibition for a drug, what should her conclusion be?

27. Explain the relationship between the minimum inhibitory concentration and the therapeutic index. What is optimum for each?

28. Discuss the general factors to consider in selecting an appropriate antimicrobial drug.

CASE STUDY Part 2

Despite a reputation as an effective, broad-spectrum antibiotic, fluoroquinolones have a long list of potential side effects, also referred to as adverse reactions. Most commonly, these reactions are minor annoyances (nausea, vomiting, diarrhea, and headache) that generally have no lasting effects and are not much different from those seen with other types of drugs. In a few cases though, fluoroquinolones, like ciprofloxacin and moxifloxacin, have been linked to an increased risk of severe tendonitis (on the order of 1–2 people per 1,000) and, even more rarely, to disturbances of the central nervous system. In 2016, the Food and Drug Administration said,

> An FDA safety review has shown that fluoroquinolones when used systemically (i.e., tablets, capsules, and injectable) are associated with disabling and potentially permanent serious side effects that can occur together. These side effects can involve the tendons, muscles, joints, nerves, and central nervous system. . . . We have determined that fluoroquinolones should be reserved for use in patients who have no other treatment options. . . . because the risk of these serious side effects generally outweighs the benefits in these patients. For some serious bacterial infections, the benefits of fluoroquinolones outweigh the risks, and it is appropriate for them to remain available as a therapeutic option.

Fluoroquinolones, though they remain on the market, now carry a black box warning, the FDA's most stringent advisory label for any drug. In 2018, the verbiage of the black box warning was strengthened to emphasize that fluoroquinolones may cause neurological impairment and cause significant decreases in blood sugar, possibly leading to coma and death.

The reason for the adverse effects attributed to fluoroquinolones is not known but may be due to mitochondrial toxicity. People whose mitochondria are already stressed, due to strenuous physical activity, or who are taking drugs known to affect mitochondria (certain HIV protease inhibitors, cholesterol-lowering statin drugs, and cancer chemotherapies), are more likely than others to suffer adverse reactions to fluoroquinolone antibiotics.

Said the husband of the patient in this case, "I fortunately never took a fluoroquinolone, but I witnessed, firsthand, the devastation they cause. . . . Her life has been completely torn apart by these drugs. All she can do is just try to warn others about the dangers of fluoroquinolones."

- Why, in general, is a narrow-spectrum antibiotic a better therapeutic choice than a broad-spectrum one?

- Why would an antibiotic, meant to work against bacterial cells, cause damage to mitochondria?

Chapter Summary with Key Terms

12.1 Principles of Antimicrobial Therapy

A. **Chemotherapeutic drugs** are used to control microorganisms in the body. Depending on their source, these drugs are described as **antibiotics**. Antibiotics are produced naturally by microorganisms, while semisynthetic or synthetic drugs are produced partially or completely through a chemical process.

B. Based on their mode and spectrum of action, they are described as **broad spectrum** or **narrow spectrum** and microbistatic or microbicidal.

C. Strategic approaches to the use of chemotherapeutics include

1. **Prophylaxis,** where drugs are administered to *prevent* infection in susceptible people.

2. **Combined therapy,** where two or more drugs are given simultaneously, either to prevent the emergence of resistant species or achieve **synergism.**

D. *Interactions between Drugs and Microbes*

1. The ideal antimicrobial is **selectively toxic,** highly potent, stable, and soluble in the body's tissues and fluids.

2. It does not disrupt the immune system or microbiota of the host and is exempt from drug resistance.

12.2 Survey of Major Antimicrobial Drug Groups
 A. *Drugs that Act on the Cell Envelope*
 1. **Penicillins** are beta-lactam-based drugs originally isolated from the mold *Penicillium chrysogenum*. The natural form is penicillin G, although various semisynthetic forms, such as ampicillin and methicillin, vary in their spectrum and applications.
 a. Penicillin is bactericidal, blocking completion of the cell wall, which causes eventual rupture of the cell.
 b. Major problems encountered in penicillin therapy include allergic reactions and bacterial resistance to the drug through **beta-lactamase.**
 2. **Cephalosporins** include both natural and semisynthetic drugs initially isolated from the mold *Cephalosporium*. Cephalosporins inhibit peptidoglycan synthesis (like penicillin) but have a much broader spectrum.
 3. Bacitracin and **polymyxin** are narrow-spectrum antibiotics.
 a. Bacitracin prevents cell wall synthesis in gram-positive organisms and is used in antibacterial skin ointments.
 b. Polymyxin interferes with the cell membrane. It is added to skin ointments and can be used to treat *Pseudomonas* infections.
 4. Vancomycin interferes with the early stages of cell wall synthesis and is used for life-threatening, methicillin-resistant staphylococcal infection.
 5. Isoniazid (INH) blocks the synthesis of cell wall components in *Mycobacteria*. It is used in the treatment of tuberculosis.
 B. *Drugs that Affect Nucleic Acid Synthesis*
 1. Fluoroquinolones (ciprofloxacin) class of broad-spectrum synthetic drugs that have proven useful in a variety of infections, but occasionally produce severe side effects.
 2. Rifampin interferes with RNA polymerase (thereby affecting transcription) and is primarily used for tuberculosis and Hansen's disease (leprosy) infections.
 C. *Drugs that Inhibit Protein Synthesis*
 1. **Aminoglycosides** include several narrow-spectrum drugs isolated from unique bacteria found in the genera *Streptomyces*. Examples include streptomycin, gentamicin, tobramycin, and amikacin.
 2. **Tetracyclines** and chloramphenicol are very broad-spectrum drugs isolated from *Streptomyces*. Both interfere with translation but their use is limited by adverse effects.
 3. Erythromycin and clindamycin both affect protein synthesis. Erythromycin is a broad-spectrum alternative for use with penicillin-resistant bacteria, while clindamycin is used primarily for intestinal infection by anaerobes.
 D. *Antimetabolite Drugs*
 1. **Sulfonamides** are synthetic drugs that act as **metabolic analogs, competitively inhibiting** enzymes needed for nucleic acid synthesis.
 2. Trimethoprim is often used in combination with sulfa drugs.
 3. Dapsone is a narrow-spectrum drug used (often in combination with rifampin) to treat leprosy.

 E. *Newly Developed Antibiotics* are useful when bacteria have developed resistance to more traditional drugs.
 1. Fosfomycin inhibits cell wall synthesis and is effective against gram-negative organisms.
 2. Synercid inhibits translation and is most effective against gram-positive cocci.
 3. Ketek is a new ketolide antibiotic with broad-spectrum effects.
 4. Oxazolidinones are another class of synthetic drug that work by inhibiting the start of protein synthesis. They are useful for treatment of staphylococci that are resistant to other drugs (MRSA and VRE).

12.3 Drugs to Treat Fungal, Parasitic, and Viral Infections
 A. *Antifungal Drugs*
 1. Amphotericin B and nystatin disrupt fungal membranes by detergent action.
 2. **Azoles** are synthetic drugs that interfere with membrane synthesis. They include ketoconazole, fluconazole, and miconazole.
 3. Flucytosine inhibits DNA synthesis. Due to fungal resistance, flucytosine must usually be used in conjunction with amphotericin.
 B. *Drugs for Protozoan Infections*
 1. Quinine or the related compounds chloraquine, primaquine, or mefloquine are used to treat infections by the malarial parasite *Plasmodium*.
 2. Other antiprotozoan drugs include metronidazole, suramin, melarsopral, and nitrifurimox.
 C. *Drugs for Helminth Infections* include mebendazole, thiabendazole, praziquantel, pyrantel, piperizine, and niclosamide.
 D. *Drugs for Viral Infections* inhibit viral penetration, multiplication, or assembly. Because viral and host metabolism are so closely related, toxicity is a potential adverse reaction.
 1. **Acyclovir,** valacyclovir, famciclovir, and ribavirin act as nucleoside analogs, inhibiting viral DNA replication, especially in herpesviruses.
 2. Tamiflu acts to stop uncoating of the influenza A virus. Another anti-influenza drug, **Xofluza**, works by blocking the initiation of RNA synthesis.
 3. Two varieties of reverse transcriptase inhibitors, protease inhibitors, integrase inhibitors, and entry/fusion inhibitors are the main categories of anti-HIV drugs, usually given in combinations of two or three.
 4. **Interferon** is a naturally occurring protein with both antiviral and anticancer properties.

12.4 Interactions between Microbes and Drugs: The Acquisition of Drug Resistance
 A. Microbes can lose their sensitivity to a drug through the acquisition of **resistance (R) factors.** Drug resistance takes the form of drug inactivation, decreased permeability to drug or increased elimination of drug from the cell, change in drug receptors, or change of metabolic patterns.
 B. Microbes living within biofilms show much greater resistance to most drug regimens.

12.5 Interactions between Drugs and Hosts
Side effects of chemotherapy include organ toxicity, allergic responses, and alteration of microflora.

12.6 The Process of Selecting an Antimicrobial Drug
A. Rapid identification of the infectious agent is important.
B. The pathogenic microbe should be tested for its susceptibility to different antimicrobial agents. This involves using standardized methods such as the ***Kirby-Bauer*** and **minimum inhibitory concentration (MIC)** techniques. The **therapeutic index** factors in the toxicity of a drug

as compared with its MIC so as to guide proper drug selection.
C. Medical conditions of the patient such as age, allergy, disease, and pregnancy are also important guides.
D. The inappropriate use of drugs on a worldwide basis has led to numerous medical and economic problems.

 ## Assess Your Knowledge

 Level I. These questions require a working knowledge of the concepts in the chapter and the ability to recall and understand the information you have studied.

Developing a Concept Inventory

Select the correct answer from the answers provided. For questions with blanks, choose the combination of answers that most accurately completes the statement.

1. A compound synthesized by bacteria or fungi that destroys or inhibits the growth of other microbes is a(n)
 a. synthetic drug
 b. antibiotic
 c. antimicrobial drug
 d. competitive inhibitor

2. Which statement is *not* an aim in the use of drugs for antimicrobial chemotherapy? The drug should
 a. have selective toxicity
 b. be active even in high dilutions
 c. be broken down and excreted rapidly
 d. be microbicidal

3. Microbial resistance to drugs is acquired through
 a. conjugation
 b. transformation
 c. transduction
 d. all of these

4. R factors are _____ that contain a code for _____.
 a. genes, replication
 b. plasmids, drug resistance
 c. transposons, interferon
 d. plasmids, conjugation

5. When a patient's immune system becomes reactive to a drug, this is an example of
 a. superinfection
 b. drug resistance
 c. allergy
 d. toxicity

6. An antibiotic that disrupts the normal microbiota can cause
 a. the teeth to turn brown
 b. aplastic anemia
 c. a superinfection
 d. hepatotoxicity

7. Most antihelminthic drugs function by
 a. weakening the worms so they can be flushed out by the intestine
 b. inhibiting worm metabolism
 c. blocking the absorption of nutrients
 d. inhibiting egg production
 e. all of these

8. Select a drug or drugs that can prevent a viral nucleic acid from being replicated.
 a. retrovir
 b. acyclovir
 c. saquinavir
 d. both a and b

9. Which of the following effects do antiviral drugs *not* have?
 a. destroying extracellular viruses
 b. stopping virus synthesis
 c. inhibiting virus maturation
 d. blocking virus receptors

10. Which of the following modes of action would be most selectively toxic?
 a. interrupting ribosomal function
 b. dissolving the cell membrane
 c. preventing cell wall synthesis
 d. inhibiting DNA replication

11. The MIC is the _____ of a drug that is required to inhibit growth of a microbe.
 a. largest concentration
 b. standard dose
 c. smallest concentration
 d. lowest dilution

12. An antimicrobial drug with a _____ therapeutic index is a better choice than one with a _____ therapeutic index.
 a. low, high
 b. high, low

13. **Matching.** Select the mode of action for each drug in the left column; all but one choice is used.

 _____ sulfonamides
 _____ zidovudine
 _____ penicillin
 _____ tetracycline
 _____ erythromycin
 _____ quinolone
 _____ relenza
 _____ polymyxin

 a. reverse transcriptase inhibitor
 b. blocks the attachment of tRNA on the ribosome
 c. interferes with viral budding and release
 d. interferes with synthesis of folic acid
 e. breaks down cell membrane integrity
 f. prevents the ribosome from translocating
 g. blocks synthesis of peptidoglycan
 h. inhibits DNA gyrase

Case Study Analysis

1. While this case focuses on rare side effects, a patient could *reasonably* expect to suffer from _____ as a result of treating an infection with ciprofloxacin.
 a. temporary hearing loss
 b. an allergic reaction
 c. an alteration in microbiota
 d. kidney damage

2. What other drug could have potentially substituted for ciprofloxacin in this case?
 a. penicillin
 b. erythromycin

 c. vancomycin
 d. bacitracin

3. Even though the potential serious side effects associated with ciprofloxacin are well known, the FDA has allowed the drug to remain on the market. Why do you think this is?

On the Test

These questions will help to prepare you to successfully answer similar questions you'll see on the TEAS (Test of Essential Academic Skills) and NCLEX (National Council Licensure Examination).

1. A client has been diagnosed with drug-sensitive tuberculosis. The physician plans to treat the client with a first-line medication. Which medication should the nurse prepare to administer?
 a. ketoconazole
 b. rifampin
 c. ciprofloxacin
 d. penicillin

2. A client has been diagnosed with oral candidiasis and prescribed fluconazole (Diflucan). The client asks what the medicine is used for and the nurse correctly replies,
 a. "This is a medication used to treat bacterial infections."
 b. "This medication relieves pain, so you will be better able to eat."
 c. "This medication is used to treat fungal infections."
 d. "This medication prevents replication of viruses."

Writing Challenge

For each question, compose a one- or two-paragraph answer that includes the factual information needed to completely address the question. Practice questions can also be used for writing-challenge exercises.

1. Using the diagram as a guide, briefly explain how the three factors in drug therapy interact.

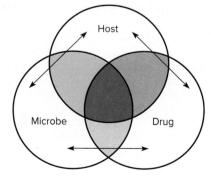

2. Observe table 12.4 with regard to type of microbe and structures or functions that are affected by drugs. Write a paragraph or two that explains the different ways in which drugs can affect microbes and how this affects selectivity of drugs and their spectrum.

3. Drugs are often given to patients before going into surgery, to dental patients with heart disease, or to healthy family members exposed to contagious infections.
 a. What word would you use to describe this use of drugs?
 b. What is the purpose of this form of treatment?
 c. Explain some potential undesired effects of this form of therapy.
 d. Define *probiotics* and list some ways they are used.

4. Write an essay covering some of the main concerns in antimicrobial drug therapy, including resistance, allergies, superinfections, and other adverse effects.

5. a. Explain the basis for combined therapy.
 b. What are some reasons it could be helpful to use combined therapy in treating HIV infection?

6. Explain the kinds of tests that would differentiate between a broad- or narrow-spectrum antibiotic.

7. Summarize the primary reasons that we find ourselves in a "drug dilemma" with regard to antimicrobial drugs.

Concept Mapping

On Connect you can find an Introduction to Concept Mapping that provides guidance for working with concept maps, along with concept-mapping activities for this chapter.

 ## Application, Analysis, Evaluation, and Synthesis

Level II. These problems go beyond just restating facts and require higher levels of understanding and an ability to interpret, problem solve, transfer knowledge to new situations, create models, and predict outcomes.

Critical Thinking

Critical thinking is the ability to reason and solve problems using facts and concepts. These questions can be approached from a number of angles and, in most cases, they do not have a single correct answer.

1. In 2015, the WHO surveyed 10,000 people on the subject of drug resistance. Seventy-five percent of them said that antibiotic resistance is due to the body becoming resistant to the drug. Explain how you would respond to someone having this misconception.

2. Explain a simple test one could do to determine if drug resistance is developing in a culture.

3. a. Your pregnant neighbor has been prescribed a daily dose of oral tetracycline for acne. Do you think this therapy is advisable for her? Why or why not?
 b. A woman has been prescribed a broad-spectrum oral cephalosporin for a strep throat. What are some possible consequences in addition to cure of the infected throat?
 c. A man has a severe case of sinusitis that is negative for bacterial pathogens. A physician prescribes an oral antibacterial drug for treatment. What is right or wrong with this therapy?

4. You have been directed to take a sample from a growth-free portion of the zone of inhibition in the Kirby-Bauer test and inoculate it onto a plate of nonselective medium.
 a. What does it mean if growth occurs on the new plate?
 b. What if there is no growth?

5. From the results shown in figure 12.21, determine which drugs could be used to treat the yeast infection. Taking into account their adverse side effects, which drug would probably be the best choice?

6. Explain why drugs that interfere with the prokaryotic ribosome can have harmful side effects on a human patient.

7. In cases in which it is not possible to culture or drug-test an infectious agent (such as middle ear infection), how would the appropriate drug be chosen?

8. Reviewing drug characteristics, choose an antimicrobial for each of the following situations (explain your choice):
 a. for an adult patient suffering from *Mycoplasma* pneumonia
 b. for a child with bacterial meningitis (drug must enter into cerebrospinal fluid)
 c. for a patient who has chlamydiosis and an allergy to azithromycin
 d. for PPNG drug-resistant gonorrhea

9. a. Using table 12.10 as a reference, find and explain the differences between the results for *Staphylococcus* and *Pseudomonas*. Are any of these drugs broad spectrum?
 b. Explain the difference in the MIC of *E. coli* for penicillin versus ampicillin.
 c. Refer to figure 12.18*a*, take measurements, and interpret the results.

Visual Assessment

For the following figures a–e, research the chapter and book to find an appropriate drug to treat an infection with the microbe shown, and explain what the drug's effects on the microbe will be.

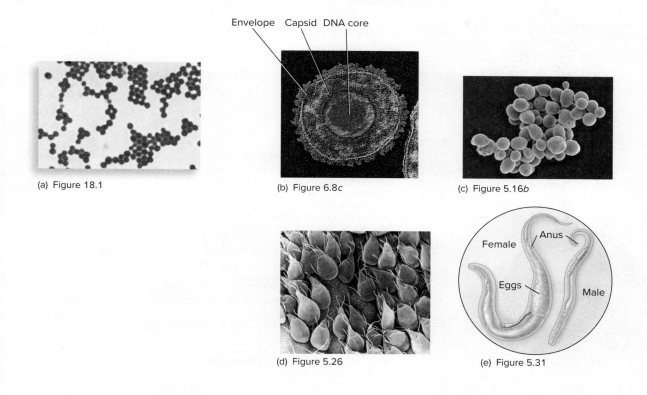

Envelope Capsid DNA core

(a) Figure 18.1

(b) Figure 6.8*c*

(c) Figure 5.16*b*

(d) Figure 5.26

Female Anus

Eggs Male

(e) Figure 5.31

(a, b): © Eye of Science/Science Source; (c) *Source:* Robert Simmons/Janice Haney Carr/CDC; (d) *Source:* Dr. Stan Erlandsen/CDC

Microbe–Human Interactions:
Infection, Disease, and Epidemiology

In This Chapter...

Reported Cases of Lyme Disease—United States, 2019

In late December 2013, an 18-month-old child in a remote village in Guinea, West Africa, came down with an **acute** **illness** marked by high **fever,** severe **diarrhea,** and **vomiting.** He died 2 days later without being diagnosed. Within 2 weeks several family members and other villagers developed a similar illness that also led to fatalities. New **cases** began to appear in health care workers who had treated some of the sick patients. Local medical officers began to suspect a cholera **outbreak** based on the condition of the patients. This mystery **disease** escaped more serious notice until a member of the dead child's family traveled to a larger city, became ill, and died in the hospital. Local authorities were concerned but made no attempt to formally report it. When they suspected the unidentified disease might be **Lassa fever,** an outreach center for the **World Health Organization (WHO)** tested a blood sample and identified a **filovirus.** It took until March 2014 for them to finally clarify the diagnosis as **Ebola virus disease;** by then there had been 49 cases and 29 deaths.

Unfortunately, the **virulence** of this virus, its small **infectious dose,** and the unpredictability of the **incubation period** were working against the patients and their caretakers. Very little attempt had been made to **isolate** the patients, and many people in both the clinics and the communities had been exposed. What had started as a local outbreak was becoming primed to explode into an Ebola **epidemic.** And that is precisely what happened. Within a month, cases appeared in the small African nations of Liberia and Sierra Leone, and by early summer of 2014 the disease had spread to several other countries and even beyond the continent of Africa. With thousands of cases and hundreds of deaths, a public health emergency was finally declared by officials in August 2014. Even with great attention being focused on stopping the spread of Ebola, there were not enough safeguards to prevent it from finding other exit routes.

In late September 2014 a Liberian citizen, Thomas Duncan, traveled to Texas to visit family. Although he arrived in a healthy state, within a few days he began to have nonspecific **symptoms** of fever, abdominal pain, and nasal drainage and sought treatment at a hospital. He was given antibiotics and sent home, but he was not tested for infection or questioned about his recent **travel history.** Soon after, he returned to the hospital with more severe symptoms of vomiting, diarrhea, muscle pain, and weakness. Once medical personnel learned he had flown in from Africa, he was placed in **strict isolation** and tested for Ebola virus. When the result came back as positive, the hospital immediately initiated protocols as required by the **Centers for Disease Control and Prevention (CDC)** to use personal protective gear (masks, gowns, gloves, biosafety suits) and **universal precautions,** but workers were not fully trained in techniques specific to Ebola. After a week of constant care, Mr. Duncan died. At some time during his stay, caretakers were exposed directly to his **infectious fluids.**

■ *Explain why it took so long for the African outbreak to be recognized and acted upon.*

■ *Give some reasons the protective gear did not prevent infection in the American nurses.*

To continue the Case Study, go to Case Study Part 2 at the end of the chapter.

(Ebola virus): Source: National Institute of Allergy and Infectious Diseases (NIAID)/CDC

13.1 We Are Not Alone

Learn

1. Describe some of the major interactions between humans and the microbes that share our habitats.

2. Identify and define the terms associated with infectious diseases.

3. Discuss the characteristics of the normal microbiota and the types of functions they serve.

4. Briefly relate the sources and conditions that influence the development of microbiota in the major body systems.

5. Identify which bodily sites remain free of living organisms, and explain why this is necessary.

6. Explain the germ-free condition and how it is important to microbiologists.

The human body exists in a state of dynamic equilibrium with microorganisms. The healthy individual is able to maintain a balanced coexistence with them. But on occasion the balance is disrupted, allowing microorganisms to cause an infection or disease. In this chapter we explore each component of the human–microbe relationship, beginning with the nature and function of normal microbial residents, moving to the stages of infection and disease, and closing with a study of epidemiology and the patterns of disease in populations. These topics will set the scene for chapters 14 and 15, which deal with host defenses and the protections we use to fight off the agents of infectious disease.

Many of the interactions between the human body and microorganisms involve the development of biofilms. These associations result from the binding of microbial cells to our cells and to those of other microorganisms to form complex partnerships. As we discuss topics in this chapter, keep in mind that colonization of the body involves a constant "give and take" between us and them. The most significant of these interactions can be summarized as follows:

- Microbes provide a protective and stabilization effect on body surfaces by establishing themselves as normal residents.
- Microbes are involved in maturation of host defenses and development of the immune system.
- Microbes can invade and grow in sterile tissues, where they cause disease by damaging tissues and organs.

Contact, Colonization, Infection, Disease

In chapter 7, we first considered several of the basic interrelationships between humans and microorganisms. Most of the microbial inhabitants benefit from the nutrients and protective habitat the body provides. Our microbial partnerships run the gamut from mutualism to commensalism to parasitism and can have beneficial, neutral, or harmful effects.

Microbes that engage in mutual or commensal associations with humans belong to the **normal resident microbiota.** Other terms commonly used to refer to these residents are **indigenous***

*indigenous (in-dih´-juh-nus) Belonging or native to.

microflora, normal flora, and commensals. Even though these microbes have colonized the body, they are more or less restricted to the outer surfaces without penetrating into sterile tissues or fluids. When a microbe has penetrated the host defenses, invaded sterile tissues, and multiplied, the result is an **infection,** and the microbe is considered an infectious agent or **pathogen.** If the infection causes damage or disruption to tissues and organs, it is now considered an **infectious disease.** Note that the term *disease* is defined as any deviation from health. There are hundreds of diseases caused by such factors as infections, diet, genetics, and aging. In this chapter, however, we discuss only diseases arising from the disruption of a tissue or organ caused by microbes or their products.

Figure 13.1 provides a diagrammatic view of the potential phases in infection and disease. Because of numerous factors relating to host resistance and degree of pathogenicity, not all contacts lead to infection and not all infections lead to disease. In fact, contact without infection and infection without disease are the rule. Before we consider further details of infection and disease, let us examine what happens when microbes colonize the body, thereby establishing a long-term, usually beneficial, relationship.

Resident Microbiota: The Human as a Habitat

The human body offers a seemingly endless variety of microenvironments and niches, with variations in temperature, pH, nutrients, moisture, and oxygen tension from one area to another. With such a wide range of habitats, it should not be surprising that the body supports an abundance of microbes. In fact, it is so favorable that our bodies hold three times more microbes than our own cells. The importance of this relationship has recently become the focus of a comprehensive initiative **(13.1 Making Connections).**

As shown in **table 13.1,** most areas of the body in contact with the outside environment harbor resident microorganisms. Mucosal surfaces provide a particularly attractive surface for attachment. Most other body sites, including internal organs, tissues, and the fluids they contain, are generally microbe-free **(table 13.2).** In fact, the presence of microbes in these areas is usually indicative of infection.

The vast majority of microbes that come in contact with the body are removed or destroyed by the host's defenses long before they are able to colonize a particular area. Those organisms that occupy the body for only short periods are known as **transients.** The remaining microbes that do become established more permanently are considered **residents.** One of their most important adaptations is to avoid the attention of the body's defenses. The resident organisms have coevolved along with their human hosts toward a complex relationship in which the effects of normal microbiota are generally not harmful to the host, and vice versa.

Although generally stable, the microbiota fluctuates with general health, age, variations in diet, hygiene, hormones, and drug therapy. In many cases the microbiota actually benefits

> **Quick Search**
> Seek out the video "The Human Microbiome and What We Do to It" on YouTube.

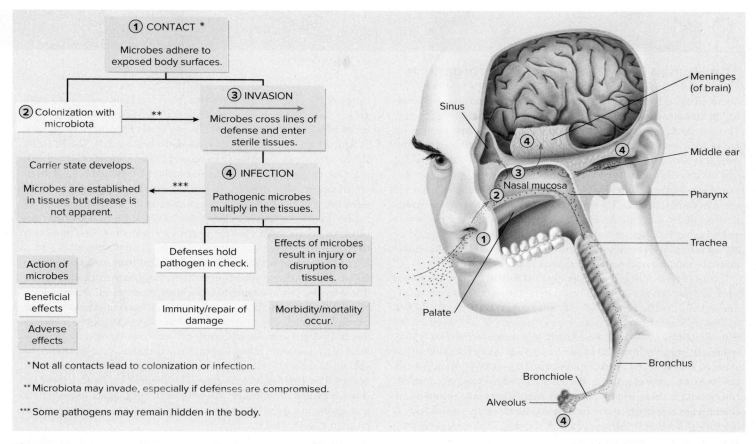

Figure 13.1 Associations between microbes and humans. Effects of contact with microbes can progress in a variety of directions, ranging from no effect to colonization, and from infection to disease and immunity. The example shown here follows the possible events in the case of contact with a pathogen such as *Streptococcus pneumoniae* (the pneumococcus). This bacterium can be harbored harmlessly in the upper respiratory tract, but it may also invade and infect the ear, cranium, and lower respiratory tract.

TABLE 13.1	Sites that Harbor Normal Resident Microbes

- Skin and its contiguous mucous membranes
- Upper respiratory tract (oral cavity, pharynx, nasal mucosa)
- Gastrointestinal tract (mouth, colon, rectum, anus)
- Outer opening of urethra
- External genitalia
- Vagina
- External ear and canal
- External eye (lids, lash follicles)

TABLE 13.2	Sterile (Microbe-Free) Anatomical Sites and Fluids

All Internal Tissues and Organs

Heart and circulatory system	Bones
Liver	Ovaries/testes
Kidneys and bladder	Glands (pancreas, salivary)
Lungs	Sinuses
Brain and spinal cord	Middle and inner ear
Muscles	Internal eye

Fluids Within an Organ or Tissue

Blood
Urine in kidneys, ureters, bladder
Cerebrospinal fluid
Saliva prior to entering the oral cavity
Semen prior to entering the urethra

the human host by preventing the overgrowth of harmful microorganisms. A common example is the fermentation of glycogen by lactobacilli, which keep the pH in the vagina acidic enough to prevent the overgrowth of the yeast *Candida albicans* and other pathogens. A second example is seen in the large intestine, where a protein produced by *Escherichia coli* can prevent the growth of pathogenic bacteria such as *Salmonella* and *Shigella.*

The generally antagonistic effect that "good" microbes have against intruder microorganisms is called **microbial antagonism.** Microbiota that exists in an established biofilm is unlikely to be displaced by incoming microbes. This antagonistic protection

13.1 MAKING CONNECTIONS

The Human Microbiome—A Superorganism

Microbiologists have recognized for many years that the microbes residing on the human body exert profound effects on our health and disease. This is to be expected, because they outnumber our cells many times over and occupy about 2% to 5% of our body's mass. Knowledge of this intimate coexistence inspired the concept of a superorganism—the merger of humans and their microbiota into a single, functioning, interactive unit that shares nutrients, metabolism, and genetic information and stays in constant communication. Up until recently we had an incomplete understanding of the scientific details of our interactions with our microbiota and many of their functions. A complete picture has been hampered by having to rely on knowledge of cultured microbes, and many species that cannot be cultured have not been explored to any extent.

This all began to change when the National Institutes of Health launched a massive program to study the superorganism from a different perspective. The project, called the **Human Microbiome Project (HMP),** uses advanced technology in metagenomics to analyze the genomes of as many of the microbial residents as possible. Researchers took samples from 300 healthy volunteers, primarily from such locations as the oral cavity, skin, nose, digestive tract, and vagina. By extracting and sequencing the DNA, it was possible to identify a number of microbes that we already knew were part of the microbiota and to tabulate many others that were entirely new and unknown. After 5 years of analysis, the researchers estimated that the human body is home to at least 10,000 different species of microbes. Even more astonishing was the isolation of 8 million distinct microbial genes, which is 360 times more than our own genome holds. This means that, genetically, we are more microbe than we are human! The collective total of genetic material from all microbiota has been termed the human **microbiome.**

Preliminary results of the study provide some interesting insights. Representatives of all microbial groups were isolated, including bacteria (the largest group), archaea (the smallest group), fungi, protozoa, and viruses. Most of the microbes have a mutualistic relationship and do not cause disease, although a few pathogens, such as *Staphylococcus aureus* and *Helicobacter pylori,* were among the isolates. Although many bacteria were common to all volunteers, the precise content of microbiota is apparently unique to each individual, begins developing even before birth, and varies with age and sex. Because of these studies, we now know that many unculturable bacteria will not grow on artificial media because they have lost genes required for certain metabolic processes that are now derived from their hosts.

Approximately 500 species of bacteria and yeasts were associated with the skin, with notable differences depending on the location sampled. For example, the skin of the hands and body creases had much greater microbial diversity than areas such as the ear and navel. Most bacterial isolates are members of four phyla: Actinobacteria, Firmicutes, Proteobacteria, and Bacteroidetes (discussed in chapter 4). See the figure for the sites sampled and the proportion of bacterial groups found in each site. One finding suggests that the skin harbors a large number and diversity of viruses. Most of the viruses appear to be bacteriophages, probably those that accompany bacteria also residing on the skin, but a number of human and other eukaryotic viruses were also discovered. Obviously this aspect of the microbiota has far greater complexity than was previously thought.

The intestinal microbiota is the largest and most varied, containing 500 to 1,000 different species of bacteria, fungi, archaea, and protozoa. The dominant phyla in this habitat are the Firmicutes and Bacteroidetes. Most of them occupy the colon, where they influence a number of physiological activities. The most common member is a species of *Bacteroides* that helps digest complex carbohydrates and contributes to the development of the protective mucous layer. There is evidence that these bacteria also signal intestinal cells to regulate development of the intestine in newborns. Other types of bacteria apparently communicate with cells of the immune system and assist in its development. Some newer research findings appear to suggest that microbes affect even brain development, biochemistry, and behavior.

The HMP has reemphasized the idea that a balanced microbiota is protective, and that a disturbed microbiota increases the susceptibility to a number of diseases. A well-established example can be seen with the colitis caused by *Clostridioides difficile,* which arises when the normal intestinal residents have been eliminated by antibiotic therapy. Several studies are investigating the impact of an altered microbiota on other intestinal diseases such as irritable bowel syndrome, Crohn's disease, and colorectal cancer. Some findings indicate that composition of the microbiome can influence fat cell metabolism and can be a factor in obesity in certain individuals. There are also new data to show that the skin microbiota in diseases such as psoriasis, eczema, and acne differs significantly from that found in normal subjects. As hundreds of researchers continue to unravel the secrets of the microbiome, they are already on a quest for new strategies and therapies that may prevent these and many other diseases linked to our microbial passengers.

What effects on the development of our microbiome might be expected from excessive cleanliness in our habits and habitats?

may simply be a result of a limited number of attachment sites in the host site, all of which are stably occupied by normal microbiota. Antagonism may also result from the chemical or physiological environment created by the resident microbiota, which is hostile to other microbes.

In experiments performed with mice, scientists discovered that a species of the intestinal bacterium *Bacteroides* controlled the host's production of a defense compound that suppressed other microbes in the area. This is an extreme case of microbial antagonism, but the general phenomenon is of great importance to human health.

Generally the normal residents will have beneficial or benign effects only if the host is in good health with a fully functioning immune system, and if the microbiota remain in their

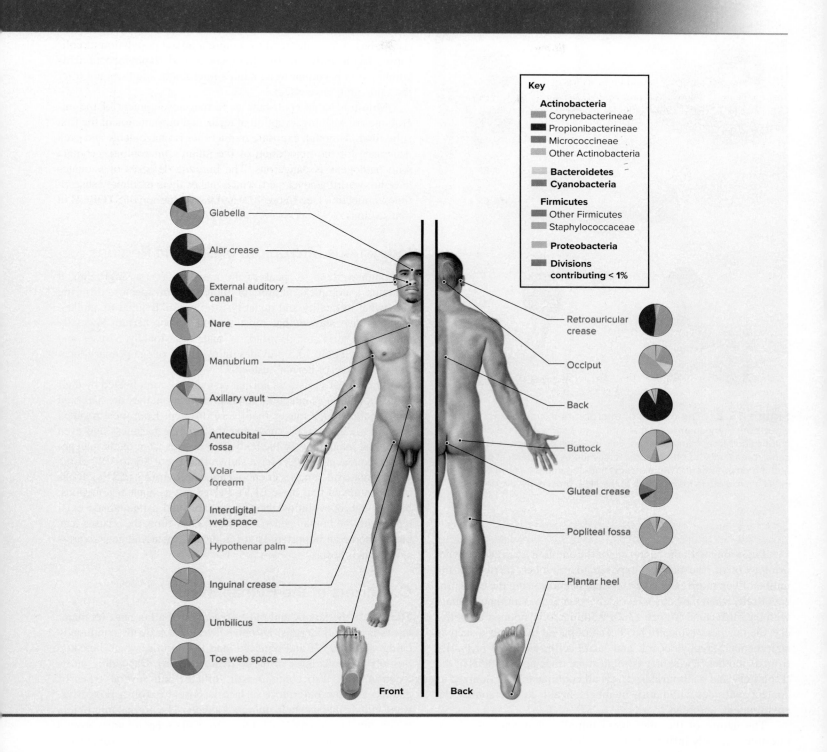

natural microhabitats within the body. Hosts with compromised immune systems could very easily be infected by these residents (see table 13.4). We see this outcome when AIDS patients develop recurring bouts of pneumonia from *Streptococcus pneumoniae,* often carried as normal residents in the nasopharynx. Other microbiota-associated infections can occur when residents are introduced to a site that was previously sterile, as when

E. coli from the large intestine gets into the bladder, resulting in a urinary tract infection.

Initial Colonization of the Fetus and Newborn

It has long been the consensus that the uterus and its contents are normally sterile during embryonic and fetal development and remain essentially germ-free until just before birth.

Figure 13.2 **The origins of microbiota in newborns.** Once a newborn baby emerges, it goes through a second phase of colonization from many sources. This includes exposure to the birth canal, breast milk or other foods, family members, medical personnel, and the environment. Within a short time the infant has developed its initial microbiota in major areas of the skin, oral cavity, and intestine.

Beginning with the rupturing of the amniotic sac several hours prior to birth, the baby is exposed to microbes carried by the mother. Even more extensive exposure occurs during the birth process itself, when the baby unavoidably comes into intimate contact with the birth canal **(figure 13.2).** Within 8 to 12 hours after delivery, the newborn typically has been colonized by bacteria such as streptococci, staphylococci, and lactobacilli, acquired primarily from its mother. The skin, gastrointestinal tract, and portions of the respiratory and genitourinary tracts all continue to be colonized as contact continues with family members, health care personnel, the environment, and food.

The nature of the microbiota initially colonizing the large intestine is greatly influenced by whether the baby receives breast milk or formula. Milk and breast tissues contain their own microbiomes that seed the baby's digestive tract with beneficial bacteria. A surprising part of neonatal research has revealed that mother's milk contains short carbohydrate chains (oligosaccharides) that cannot be digested by the infant. Only certain species of *Bifidobacterium* (*infantis*) produce enzymes to break them down. This ensures that the milk selects for the growth of these beneficial bacteria, and the baby's GI tract will become populated almost

exclusively by them. It is likely that these bacteria provide protection against colonization by potentially harmful species and invasion by pathogens. In contrast, bottle-fed infants (receiving milk or a milk-based formula) tend to acquire a mixed population of coliforms, lactobacilli, enteric streptococci, and staphylococci. This combination is similar to an adult's microbiota and does not offer the same protective effect.

Milestones that contribute to further development of the microbiota are weaning, eruption of teeth, and introduction of the first solid food. Although exposure to microbes is unavoidable and even necessary for the maturation of the infant's microbiome, contact with pathogens is dangerous. The immune defenses of neonates have not yet fully developed, which makes them extremely susceptible to infection (see figure 13.9 and the discussion of STORCH in that section).

Indigenous Microbiota of Specific Regions

Although we tend to speak of the microbiota as a single unit, it contains a complex mixture of thousands of species, differing somewhat in quality and quantity from one individual to another. Studies have shown that most people harbor certain specially adapted bacteria, fungi, protozoa, and, occasionally, viruses and arthropods. **Table 13.3** provides an overview of the primary locations and types of normal residents.

The role of viruses as normal residents is complicated by their usual reputation as infectious agents. In addition, they are harbored inside cells, which makes them very different from most resident microbes. But we now know that they can be harmless and even beneficial inhabitants of the body. Discoveries from the human genome sequencing project have shown that about 8% to 10% of the genetic material consists of endogenous retroviruses (ERVs). It has been postulated that these ERVs started out as ancient infections, but through coevolution the virus established a mutualistic existence with the human genetic material. Over time, the viruses may have become an important factor in development and gene expression of their hosts.

Colonizers of the Human Skin

The skin is the largest and most accessible of all organs. Its major layers are the epidermis, an outer layer of dead cells continually being sloughed off and replaced, and the dermis, which lies atop the subcutaneous layer of tissue **(figure 13.3a).** Depending on its location, skin also contains hair follicles and several types of glands; and the outermost surface is covered with a protective, waxy cuticle that can help microbes adhere. The normal microbiota reside only in or on the dead cell layers, and except for areas around follicles and glands, it does not extend into the dermis or subcutaneous levels. The nature of the population varies according to site. Oily, moist skin supports a more prolific microbiota than dry skin. Humidity, occupational exposure, and clothing also influence its character. Transition zones where the skin joins with the mucous membranes of the nose, mouth, and external genitalia harbor a particularly rich set of microbial colonists.

Ordinarily there are two cutaneous populations. The **transients** cling to the skin surface but do not ordinarily grow there. They are

TABLE 13.3	Life on Humans: Sites Containing Well-Established Microbiota and Representative Examples	
Anatomic Sites	**Common Genera**	**Remarks**
Skin	**Bacteria:** *Pseudomonas, Micrococcus, Corynebacterium, Propionibacterium, Staphylococcus, Streptococcus*	Microbes live only in upper dead layers of epidermis, glands, and follicles; dermis and layers below are sterile.
	Fungi: *Candida, Malassezia, Rhodotorula*	Dependent on skin lipids for growth.
	Arthropods: *Demodex* mite	Present in sebaceous glands and hair follicles.
GI Tract Oral cavity	**Bacteria:** *Streptococcus, Neisseria, Veillonella, Fusobacterium, Lactobacillus, Bacteroides, Actinomyces, Eikenella, Treponema, Haemophilus*	Colonize the epidermal layer of cheeks, gingiva, pharynx; surface of teeth; found in saliva in huge numbers; some members involved in dental caries and periodontal diseases.
	Fungi: *Candida*	*C. albicans* can cause thrush.
	Protozoa: *Entamoeba gingivalis*	Inhabit the gingiva of persons with poor oral hygiene.
Large intestine and rectum	**Bacteria:** *Bacteroides, Fusobacterium, Bifidobacterium, Clostridium*, fecal streptococci and staphylococci, *Lactobacillus*, coliforms (*Escherichia, Enterobacter*), *Proteus* spp.	Areas of lower gastrointestinal tract other than large intestine and rectum have sparse or nonexistent residents. Microbiota consist predominantly of strict anaerobes; other microbes are aerotolerant or facultative.
	Fungi: *Candida*	Yeast can survive this habitat, but not molds.
	Protozoa: *Entamoeba coli, Trichomonas hominis*	Feed on waste materials in the large intestine.
Upper Respiratory Tract	Microbial population exists in the nasal passages, throat, and pharynx; owing to proximity, microbes are similar to those of oral cavity.	Trachea may harbor a sparse population; bronchi, bronchioles, and alveoli are essentially sterile due to local host defenses.
Genital Tract	**Bacteria:** *Lactobacillus, Streptococcus,* diphtheroids (*Corynebacterium* and relatives) *Escherichia, Gardnerella*	In females, microbes occupy the external genitalia and vaginal and cervical surfaces; internal reproductive structures normally remain sterile. Vaginal colonists respond to hormonal changes during life.
	Fungi: *Candida*	Cause of yeast infections.
Urinary Tract	**Bacteria:** *Staphylococcus, Streptococcus, Corynebacterium, Lactobacillus*	In females, microbiota exist only in the first portion of the urethral mucosa; the remainder of the tract is sterile. In males, the entire reproductive and urinary tract is sterile except for a short portion of the anterior urethra.
Eye	**Bacteria:** coagulase-negative staphylococci, *Streptococcus, Neisseria*	The lids and follicles harbor similar microbes as skin; the conjunctiva has a transient population; deep tissues are sterile.
Ear	**Bacteria:** Staphylococci, diphtheroids	The external ear is similar to the skin in content; areas internal to the tympanum are generally sterile.
	Fungi: *Aspergillus, Penicillium, Candida*, yeasts	

(b)

Figure 13.3 **The landscape of the skin.** **(a)** The epidermis, along with associated glands and follicles (colored), provides rich and diverse habitats. Noncolored regions (dermis and subcutaneous layers) are free of microbes. **(b)** A highly magnified view (7,500×) of skin layers reveals rod- and coccus-shaped bacteria adhering to skin cells (blue).
(b): *Source:* Janice Haney Carr/CDC

acquired by routine contact and vary markedly from person to person and over time. The transients include any microbe a person has picked up, often species that do not ordinarily live on the body, and are greatly influenced by the hygiene of the individual.

The **resident populations** live and multiply in deeper layers of the epidermis and in glands and follicles **(figure 13.3b).** The composition of the resident microbiota is more stable, predictable, and less influenced by hygiene than are the transients. The normal skin residents consist primarily of bacteria (notably *Staphylococcus, Corynebacterium,* and *Propionibacterium*) and yeasts. Moist skin folds, especially between the toes, tend to harbor fungi, whereas lipophilic mycobacteria and staphylococci are prominent in sebaceous[1] secretions of the axilla, external genitalia, and external ear canal. One species, *Mycobacterium smegmatis,* lives in the waxy secretion, or *smegma,* on the external genitalia of men and women.

Microbial Residents of the Gastrointestinal Tract

The gastrointestinal (GI) tract receives, moves, digests, and absorbs food and removes waste. It encompasses the oral cavity, esophagus, stomach, small intestine, large intestine, rectum, and anus. Stating that the GI tract harbors residents may seem to contradict our earlier statement that internal organs are generally sterile, but it is not an exception to the rule. How can this be true? In reality, the GI tract is a long, hollow tube (with numerous pockets and curves), bounded by the mucous membranes of the oral cavity on one extreme and those of the anus on the other. Because the innermost surface of this tube is exposed to the environment, it is topographically outside the body, so to speak.

The shifting conditions of pH and oxygen tension and differences in the microscopic anatomy of the GI tract are reflected by the variations in or distribution of the microbiota **(figure 13.4).** Some microbes remain attached to the mucous epithelium or its associated structures, and others dwell in the **lumen.*** Although the abundance of nutrients invites microbial growth, the only areas that harbor appreciable permanent microbes are the oral cavity, large intestine, and rectum. The esophagus contains an extremely light load of microbiota, primarily bacteria swallowed with saliva. The stomach acid inhibits most microbes, although small numbers of lactobacilli and *Helicobacter pylori* (associated with stomach ulcers) can become established there. The small intestine has a sparse population of lactobacilli and streptococci except for its terminal segment, which has microbiota more similar to that of the adjacent large intestine.

Microbiota of the Mouth

The oral cavity has unique residents that are some of the most diverse and abundant of the body. Microhabitats, including the cheek epithelium, gingiva, tongue, floor of the mouth, and tooth enamel, provide numerous adaptive niches. By one estimate, there are more than 600 species residing there. The most common residents are aerobic *Streptococcus* species—*S. sanguinis, S. salivarius, S. mitis*—that colonize the smooth superficial epithelial surfaces. Two

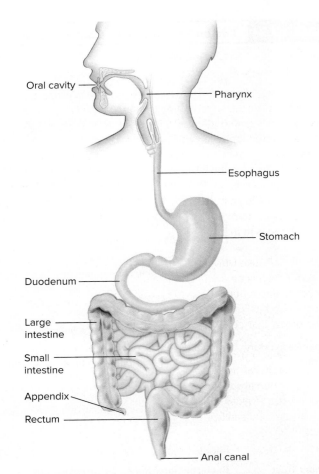

Figure 13.4 **Distribution of microbes in the GI tract.** Areas of the gastrointestinal tract that shelter major communities of resident microbes are highlighted in color. Noncolored areas do not harbor residents in significant numbers.

species, *S. mutans* and *S. sanguinis,* make a major contribution to dental caries by forming sticky dextran slime layers in the presence of simple sugars. The adherence of dextrans to the tooth surface establishes the basis for a biofilm that attracts other bacteria.

Eruption of the teeth establishes an anaerobic habitat in the gingival crevice that favors the colonization by anaerobic bacteria that can be involved in dental caries and periodontal[2] infections. The instant that saliva is secreted from ducts into the oral cavity, it becomes laden with resident and transient bacteria. Saliva normally has a high bacterial count (up to 5×10^9 cells per milliliter), a fact that tends to make mouthwashes rather ineffective and a human bite quite dangerous.

Microbiota of the Large Intestine

Microbes inhabiting the intestinal tract have complex and profound interactions with the host. The large intestine (cecum and colon) and the rectum harbor a huge population of microbes (10^8–10^{11} per gram of feces). So abundant and prolific are these microbes that they constitute 30% or more of the fecal volume. Even an individual on a long-term fast passes feces consisting primarily of bacteria.

1. From *sebum,* a lipid material secreted by glands in the hair follicles.

* *lumen* (loo′-men) The space within a tubular structure.

2. Situated or occurring around the tooth.

CLINICAL CONNECTIONS

The Appendix: A Safe Haven for Microbiota?

The appendix, a 4-inch-long wormlike pouch that sprouts from the junction between the small and large intestine, had been written off for years as a lingering remnant of tissue without any real functions. Evidence offered for its uselessness is that it can be removed without real medical consequences. In recent times, the medical establishment has been reconsidering the accuracy of this claim. For one thing, immunologists have known for some time that the appendix contains a significant population of white blood cells, and they consider it a modest form of lymphatic organ that protects the intestines from pathogens in the same way that tonsils protect the respiratory tract.

Studies at Duke University have produced strong evidence that the appendix has an additional role to play—that of harboring and supporting the normal resident microbiota. Researchers uncovered an extensive biofilm of beneficial microbes on the internal surfaces of the organ that periodically reinoculates the large intestine and maintains the correct composition necessary for normal colon function—enabling rapid replacement of the colon's own biofilms after a case of diarrhea or other intestinal disruption. These experts reason that humans can function normally without an appendix because we don't need it as much today, in light of our improved medical care and sanitation, which greatly reduce the incidence of intestinal infections.

An unusual but effective therapy for a serious form of diarrhea caused by *Clostridioides difficile* involves the transplantation of fecal microbiota. The idea behind this has been around for hundreds of years, but it involves implanting a fecal sample from a healthy donor directly into the infected colon or swallowing a pill containing normal microbiota. This technique is often more successful than taking antibiotics alone for this disease. It likely restores the normal microbial residents of the colon and the appendix, which inhibits the growth of the pathogen.

There are thousands of microbial species in a "normal" intestine. What could be some unintended but harmful consequences of implanting one person's intestinal microbiota into another person's colon?

The appendix has been considered an organ without much use, but recent research is verifying its importance in replenishment of the normal microbiota (see **Clinical Connections**). The lack of oxygen within the large intestine favors strictly anaerobic bacteria (*Bacteroides, Bifidobacterium, Fusobacterium,* and *Clostridium*). **Coliforms*** such as *E. coli, Enterobacter,* and *Citrobacter* are present in smaller numbers. Many species ferment waste materials in the feces, generating vitamins (B_{12}, K, pyridoxine, riboflavin, and thiamine) and acids (acetic, butyric, and propionic) of potential value to the host. Occasionally significant are bacterial digestive enzymes that convert disaccharides to monosaccharides or promote steroid metabolism.

Intestinal bacteria contribute to intestinal odor by producing **skatole,*** amines, and gases (CO_2, H_2, CH_4, and H_2S). Intestinal gas is known in polite circles as *flatus,* and the expulsion of it as *flatulence.* Some of the gas arises through the action of bacteria on dietary carbohydrate residues from vegetables such as cabbage, corn, and beans. The bacteria produce an average of 8.5 liters of gas daily, but only a small amount is ejected in flatus. Combustible gases occasionally form an explosive mixture in the presence of oxygen that has reportedly ignited during intestinal surgery and ruptured the colon!

Late in childhood many people lose the ability to secrete the enzyme lactase, a condition known as lactase deficiency or intolerance. Difficulties arise when an individual with this condition ingests milk or other lactose-containing dairy products. Lactose is a disaccharide that cannot be absorbed, and when lactose lies undigested, it increases the osmotic pressure in the gut, resulting in cramps, diarrhea, and intestinal distress. To complicate matters, the lactose can be digested by intestinal bacteria, which release gas and intestinal irritants. The recommended treatment for this deficiency is avoiding these foods or eating lactose-free substitutes.

Inhabitants of the Respiratory Tract

The first microorganisms to colonize the upper respiratory tract (nasal passages and pharynx) are predominantly oral streptococci. *Staphylococcus aureus* preferentially resides in the nasal entrance, nasal vestibule, and anterior nasopharynx, and *Neisseria* species take up residence in the mucous membranes of the nasopharynx behind the soft palate **(figure 13.5).** Lower in the tract are assorted

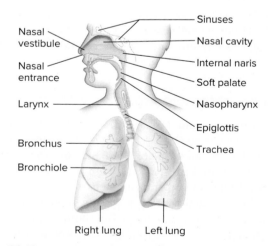

Figure 13.5 **Colonized regions of the respiratory tract.** The moist mucous blanket of the nasopharynx has well-entrenched resident microbes (indicated by color). Some colonization occurs in the upper trachea, but lower regions (bronchi, bronchioles, and lungs) lack resident microbes.

* *coliform* (koh'-lih-form) L. *colum,* a sieve. Gram-negative, facultatively anaerobic, and lactose-fermenting microbes.

* *skatole* (skat'-ohl) Gr. *skatos,* dung. One chemical that gives feces their characteristic stench.

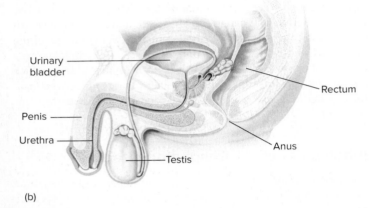

Figure 13.6 **Microbiota of the reproductive tract. (a)** Female and **(b)** male genitourinary residents (location indicated by color).

streptococci and species of *Haemophilus* that colonize the tonsils and lower pharynx. Conditions even lower in the respiratory tree (bronchi and lungs) are unfavorable habitats for permanent residents.

Microbiota of the Genitourinary Tract

The regions of the genitourinary tract that harbor resident microbes are the vagina and outer opening of the urethra in females and the anterior urethra in males **(figure 13.6)**. The internal reproductive organs are kept sterile through physical barriers such as the cervical plug and other host defenses. The kidney, ureter, bladder, and upper urethra are presumably kept sterile by urine flow and regular bladder emptying. The shortness of the urethra in women (about 3.5 cm long), frequently leads to urinary tract infections. The principal residents of the urethra are nonhemolytic streptococci, staphylococci, corynebacteria, and occasionally, coliforms.

The vagina presents a notable example of how changes in physiology can greatly influence the composition of the normal microbiota. An important factor influencing these changes in women is the hormone estrogen. Estrogen normally stimulates the vaginal mucosa to secrete glycogen, which certain bacteria

(primarily *Lactobacillus* species) ferment, thus lowering the pH to about 4.5. Before puberty a girl produces little estrogen and little glycogen and has a vaginal pH of about 7. These conditions favor the establishment of diphtheroids,[3] staphylococci, streptococci, and some coliforms. As hormone levels rise at puberty, the vagina begins to deposit glycogen, and the microbiota shift to the acid-producing lactobacilli. It is thought that the acidic pH of the vagina during this time prevents the establishment and invasion of microbes with potential to harm a developing fetus. The estrogen-glycogen effect continues, with minor disruption, throughout the childbearing years until menopause, when the microbiota return to a mixed population similar to that of prepuberty. These transitions are not abrupt but occur over several months to years.

Maintenance of the Normal Microbiota

There is no question that the normal residents are essential to the health of humans and other animals. When living in balance with their host, the microbiota create an environment that may prevent infections and can enhance certain host defenses. In general, the microbes replace themselves naturally on a regular basis to maintain the types and numbers in their zones. However, because the exact content of the microbiota is not fixed, a number of changes can disrupt this balance. Use of broad-spectrum antibiotics, changes in diet, and underlying disease all have the potential to alter the makeup of the microbiota and tilt the system toward disease. A growing trend in therapy is the use of live cultures of known microbes in the form of **probiotics.** This essentially involves introducing pure cultures of known microbes into the body through ingestion or inoculation. The microbes chosen for this process are known to be beneficial and are considered nonpathogenic.

For a look into laboratory studies that address the effects of microbiota, see **13.2 Making Connections.**

![Practice icon] ***Practice*** SECTION 13.1

1. Describe the significant relationships that humans have with microbes.
2. Explain what is meant by *microbiota* and *microbiome* and summarize their importance to humans.
3. Differentiate between contamination, colonization, infection, and disease, and explain some possible outcomes in each.
4. How are infectious diseases different from other diseases?
5. Outline the general body areas that are sterile and those regions that harbor normal resident microbiota.
6. Differentiate between transient and resident microbes.
7. Explain the factors that cause variations in the microbiota of the newborn intestine and the vaginal tract.

3. Any nonpathogenic species of *Corynebacterium.*

13.2 MAKING CONNECTIONS

A Germ-Free Existence

For years, questions lingered about how essential the microbiota are to normal life and what functions they might serve. The need for animal models to further investigate these questions led eventually to development of laboratory strains of *germ-free,* or **axenic,*** mammals and birds. After the young mammals are taken from the mother aseptically by cesarean section, they are immediately transferred to a sterile isolator or incubator. The newborns must be fed by hand through gloved ports in the isolator until they can eat on their own, and all materials entering their chamber must be sterile. Mice, rats, rabbits, guinea pigs, monkeys, and dogs are some of the mammals raised in the germ-free state.

Experiments with germ-free animals are of two basic varieties: (1) general studies on how the lack of normal microbial residents influences the nutrition, metabolism, and anatomy of the animal; and (2) **gnotobiotic*** studies, in which the germ-free subject is inoculated either with a single type of microbe to determine its individual effect or with several known microbes to determine interrelationships. Results are validated by comparing the germ-free group with a conventional, normal control group. **Table 13.A** summarizes some major conclusions arising from studies with germ-free animals.

A dramatic characteristic of germ-free animals is that they live longer and have fewer diseases than normal controls, as long as they remain in a sterile environment. From this standpoint, it seems that the microbiota are not absolutely necessary for survival and may even be the source of infectious agents. But it is also clear that axenic life is highly impractical for humans and will probably never be an option. We will have to rely on germ-free animals for valuable insights into the powerful influence microbiota exert on development, biochemistry, and behavior.

Additional studies have revealed that microbiota contribute significantly to the development of the immune system. When germ-free animals are placed in contact with normal control animals, they gradually develop resident microbes similar to those of the controls. However, germ-free subjects are less tolerant of these microorganisms and can die when infected by relatively harmless species. This susceptibility is due to

the immature character of the immune systems of germ-free animals. These animals have a reduced number of certain types of white blood cells and slower immune responses.

One puzzling observation revolved around the fact that germ-free mice had as much as 42% less body fat than their normal counterparts. Later experiments revealed that indigenous bacteria acted to increase the body fat of mice in two ways. First, certain bacteria in the gut helped to digest complex carbohydrates, making extra calories available to the mice. Second, these same bacteria secreted a substance that, by acting on mouse hormones, caused the animal to store more fat than it otherwise would.

Gnotobiotic experiments have clarified the dynamics of several infectious diseases. For years, the precise involvement of microbes in dental caries had been ambiguous. Studies with germ-free rats, hamsters, and beagles confirmed that caries' development is influenced by heredity, a diet high in sugars, and poor oral hygiene. Even when all these predisposing factors are present, however, germ-free animals still remain free of caries unless they have been inoculated with specific bacteria.

* *axenic* (aye-zeen′-ik) Gr. *a,* not, and *xeno,* strange or foreign.
* *gnotobiotic* (noh″-toh-by-aw′-tik) Gr. *gnotos,* known, and *biosis,* life.

Laboratory technician handles germ-free mouse being reared in a sterile isolator. Most gnotobiotic studies are based on specially created strains of mice.
LookatSciences/Phototake

TABLE 13.A	**A Sampling of Effects of the Germ-Free State**
Germ-Free Animals Display	**Significance**
Enlargement of the cecum; other degenerative diseases of the intestinal tract of rats, rabbits, chickens	Microbes are needed for normal intestinal development.
Vitamin deficiency in some animals	Microbes can be a significant nutritional source of vitamins.
Underdevelopment of immune system in most animals	Microbes are needed to stimulate development of certain host defenses.
Absence of dental caries and periodontal disease in dogs, rats, hamsters	Microbes are key players in caries' formation and gum disease.
Heightened susceptibility to enteric pathogens (*Shigella, Salmonella, Vibrio cholerae*) and to fungal infections	Normal bacterial residents are antagonistic against pathogens.
Lessened susceptibility to amebic dysentery	Normal resident microbes facilitate the completion of the life cycle of the amoeba in the gut.
Less body fat	Normal microbiota help to break down indigestible carbohydrates and increase fat storage in the body.
Increased anxiety and nervousness	Mice are much more sensitive to stressful conditions and produce increased levels of stress hormones.

Why is a cesarean section necessary for developing axenic mammals?

13.2 Major Factors in the Development of an Infection

Learn

7. Review the main stages in the development of an infection.

8. Categorize the different types and degrees of pathogens and differentiate pathogenicity from virulence.

9. Describe the differences among the portals of entry, and give examples of pathogens that invade by these means.

10. Explain what is meant by the infectious dose, using examples.

11. Describe the process of adhesion and various mechanisms by which microbes use it to gain entry.

12. Identify and discuss invasive factors and virulence factors.

13. Compare and contrast the major characteristics of exotoxins and endotoxins.

In this section we trace the course or "chain" of infection, a sequence of events that is summarized in **figure 13.7.** Pathogens are parasitic microbes whose relationship with a host results in infection and disease. The type and severity of infection depend on both the **pathogenicity** of the organism and the condition of the host. Pathogenicity, you will recall, is a broad concept that describes an organism's potential to cause infection or disease and is used to divide pathogenic microbes into one of two general groups.

True pathogens (primary pathogens) are capable of causing disease in healthy persons with normal immune defenses. They are generally associated with a specific, recognizable disease, which may vary in severity from mild (colds) to severe (malaria) to fatal (rabies). Other examples of true pathogens are the influenza virus, plague bacillus, and meningococcus.

Opportunistic pathogens cause disease when the host's defenses are compromised[4] or when they become established in a part of the body that is not natural to them. Opportunists are not considered pathogenic to a normal healthy person and, unlike primary pathogens, do not generally possess well-developed virulence

TABLE 13.4	Factors that Weaken Host Defenses and Increase Susceptibility to Infection*

- Old age and extreme youth (infancy, prematurity)
- Genetic defects in immunity and acquired defects in immunity
- Surgery and organ transplants
- Organic disease: cancer, liver malfunction, diabetes
- Chemotherapy/immunosuppressive drugs
- Physical and mental stress
- Other infections

*These conditions compromise defense barriers or immune responses.

properties. Examples of opportunistic pathogens include *Pseudomonas* species and *Candida albicans*. Factors that greatly predispose a person to infections, both primary and opportunistic, are shown in **table 13.4.**

As with many concepts, the idea of a pathogen being true or opportunistic is a convenience to simplify discussion. In reality, pathogenicity extends along a range from low to high. To recognize this, the CDC has adopted a system of biosafety categories for pathogens based on their degree of pathogenicity and the relative danger in handling them. This system assigns microbes to one of four levels or classes. Microbes not known to cause disease in humans are assigned to class 1, and highly contagious viruses that pose an extreme risk to humans are classified as class 4. Microbes of intermediate virulence are assigned to class 2 or 3. Details of this system are presented in more detail in appendix B.

The relative severity of the disease caused by a particular microorganism depends on its **virulence.*** Although the terms *pathogenicity* and *virulence* are often used interchangeably, virulence is the accurate term for describing the degree of pathogenicity. The virulence of a microbe is determined by its ability to establish itself in the host and cause damage. There is much involved in both of these steps. To invade, microbes must enter the host, attach firmly to host tissues, and survive the host defenses. To cause damage, microbes must grow in tissues, produce toxins, or induce a host response that is more injurious than protective. Any characteristic or

4. People with weakened immunity are often termed *immunocompromised*.

* *virulence* (veer-yoo-lents) L. *virulentia*, virus, poison.

Finding a Portal of Entry	Attaching Firmly	Surviving Host Defenses	Causes of Damage and Disease	Exiting Host
Skin	Fimbriae	Avoiding phagocytosis	Direct damage	Portals of exit
GI tract	Capsules	Avoiding death inside phagocyte	Toxins, enzymes, lysis	Respiratory tract, salivary glands
Respiratory tract	Surface proteins	Evading actions of the immune system	Indirect damage	Skin cells
Urogenital tract	Viral spikes		Host response is inappropriate and excessive.	Fecal matter
Endogenous biota	Hooks			Urogenital tract
				Blood

Figure 13.7 A flow diagram that relates the events in entry, establishment, and exit of infectious agents.

Plague Is Not an Opportunistic Infection, Unless... The patient was Malcolm Casadaban, a 60-year-old professor at the University of Chicago who was well known for his work with *Yersinia pestis*, the bacterium that causes bubonic plague. A primary pathogen responsible for the death of more than 100 million people in the 1300s, outbreaks of plague were still seen from time to time, and Casadaban was working to develop a vaccine to protect against the disease. But even plague researchers get the flu from time to time, and this is what compelled Dr. Casadaban to visit his primary care physician.

Not surprisingly, given his occupation, the first question the doctor asked was, "Do you work with *Yersinia pestis*?" Casadaban assured his doctor that he worked exclusively with an attenuated strain of the bacterium that required excess iron—more than was normally found in the human body—to reproduce. While it grew well in the lab, there was no chance this strain could cause disease. Assured that he wasn't dealing with the "Black Death," the doctor diagnosed a viral infection and sent Dr. Casadaban home with instructions to rest. Three days later, he returned to the hospital, very sick, and soon thereafter died.

An autopsy revealed the supposedly innocuous strain of *Yersinia pestis* in his system, but the researcher's demise remained a mystery. How could such a weakened strain of *Yersinia pestis* cause death? Analysis of the doctor's blood finally solved the puzzle. Unbeknownst to him, Dr. Casadaban suffered from hemochromatosis, a genetic disorder in which people accumulate high levels of iron in their blood. This excess of iron allowed the usually iron-starved *Yersinia pestis* to assume its original virulence. Dr. Casadaban's condition increased his susceptibility to a single bacterial species, the one he had been working with for years.

Drugs meant to reduce stomach acid (to combat heartburn) may make the patient more susceptible to infection by bacteria that pass through the gastrointestinal tract. How is this situation similar to what happened to Dr. Casadaban?

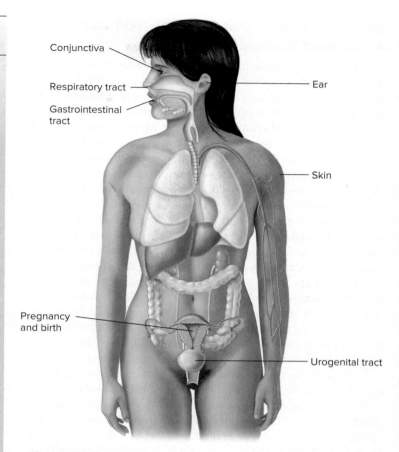

Figure 13.8 Portals of entry. Infectious microbes first enter the body through characteristic routes. Most microbes have adapted to a specific means of entry. Only one of these (the uterus) is an internal portal of entry as it may allow microbes to access a developing fetus.

structure of the microbe that contributes to the infection or disease state is called a **virulence factor.** Virulence can be due to a single factor or to multiple factors. In some microbes, the causes of virulence are clearly established, but in others, they are not as well understood. In the following section, we examine the effects of virulence factors and their roles in the progress of an infection.

Becoming Established: Phase 1—Portals of Entry

To initiate an infection, a microbe enters the tissues of the body by a characteristic route, the **portal of entry (figure 13.8),** usually some sort of cutaneous or membranous boundary. The source of the infectious agent can be **exogenous,** originating from a source outside the body such as the environment or another person or animal, or **endogenous,** already existing on or in the body from microbiota or a latent infection.

For the most part, the portals of entry are the same anatomical regions that also support resident microbes: the skin, gastrointestinal tract, respiratory tract, and urogenital tract. The majority of pathogens have adapted to a specific portal of entry, one that provides a habitat for further growth and spread. This adaptation can be so restrictive that if certain pathogens enter the "wrong" portal, they will not be infectious. For instance, inoculation of the nasal mucosa with the influenza virus invariably gives rise to the flu, but if this virus contacts only the skin, no infection will result. Likewise, contact with athlete's foot fungi in small cracks in the toe webs can induce an infection, but inhaling the spores from this same fungus will not infect a healthy individual.

Occasionally an infectious agent can enter by more than one portal. For instance, *Mycobacterium tuberculosis* enters through both the respiratory and gastrointestinal tracts, and pathogens in the genera *Streptococcus* and *Staphylococcus* have adapted to invasion through several portals of entry such as the skin, urogenital tract, and respiratory tract. Understand that the same pathogen entering different portals of entry will likely lead to different infections or diseases. Infection of a skin follicle by *Staphylococcus aureus* will produce an abscess, but its invasion of the respiratory tract causes a serious form of pneumonia.

Infectious Agents that Enter the Skin and Associated Mucous Membranes

The skin is a very common portal of entry. The actual sites of entry are usually nicks, abrasions, and punctures (many of which are tiny and inapparent) rather than smooth, unbroken skin. *Staphylococcus aureus* (the cause of boils), *Streptococcus pyogenes* (an agent of impetigo), the fungal dermatophytes, and agents of gangrene and tetanus gain access through damaged skin. The cold sore virus (herpes simplex) enters through the mucous membranes near the lips.

Some infectious agents create their own passageways into the skin using digestive enzymes. For example, certain helminth worms burrow through the skin directly to gain access to the tissues. Other infectious agents enter through bites. The bites of insects, ticks, and other animals offer an avenue to a variety of viruses, rickettsias, and protozoa. An artificial means for breaching the skin barrier is contaminated hypodermic needles by intravenous drug abusers. Users who inject drugs are predisposed to a disturbing list of well-known diseases: hepatitis, HIV/AIDS, tetanus, tuberculosis, osteomyelitis, and malaria. A resurgence of some of these infections is directly traceable to drug use. Contaminated needles often contain bacteria from the skin or environment that induce heart disease (endocarditis), lung abscesses, and chronic infections at the injection site.

Although the conjunctiva, the outer protective covering of the eye, is a relatively good barrier to infection, bacteria such as *Chlamydia trachomatis* (trachoma) and *Neisseria gonorrhoeae* readily attach to this membrane. Many childhood viruses (measles, mumps, rubella) can gain access through the eye. As was described in this chapter's Case Study, the Ebola virus readily invades the eye surface and other membranes through direct contact with infectious fluids.

The Gastrointestinal Tract Portal of Entry

The gastrointestinal tract is the portal of entry for pathogens contained in food, drink, and other ingested substances. These pathogens are adapted to survive digestive enzymes and abrupt pH changes. Most enteric pathogens possess specialized mechanisms for entering and localizing in the mucosa of the small or large intestine. The best-known enteric agents of disease are gram-negative rods in the genera *Salmonella, Shigella,* and *Vibrio* and in certain strains of *Escherichia coli.* Viruses that enter through the gut are poliovirus, hepatitis A virus, echovirus, and rotavirus. Important enteric protozoans are *Entamoeba histolytica* (amebiasis) and *Giardia lamblia* (giardiasis). Although the anus is not a typical portal of entry, it becomes one in people who practice anal sex.

The Respiratory Portal of Entry

The oral and nasal cavities are also the gateways to the respiratory tract, the portal of entry for the greatest number of pathogens. Because there is a continuous mucous membrane surface covering the upper respiratory tract, the sinuses, and the auditory tubes, microbes are often transferred from one site to another. The extent to which an agent is carried into the respiratory tree is based primarily on its size. In general, small cells and particles are inhaled more deeply than larger ones.

Infectious agents with this portal of entry include the bacteria of streptococcal sore throat, meningitis, diphtheria, and whooping

TABLE 13.5	Incidence of Common Sexually Transmitted Infections/Diseases in the United States*
STI/STD	**Estimated Number of New Cases per Year (Incidence)**
Human papillomavirus	14,000,000
Trichomoniasis	2,230,000
Chlamydiosis**	1,708,569
Herpes simplex	522,000
Gonorrhea**	555,608
Hepatitis B**	20,900
New HIV infections	39,782
Sphilis**	30,644

*Data from CDC, 2017, based on reported statistics and clinical data.
**These are the only STDs that are officially reported by health authorities to the CDC.

cough and the viruses of influenza, measles, mumps, rubella, chickenpox, and the common cold. Pathogens that are inhaled into the lower regions of the respiratory tract (bronchioles and lungs) can cause pneumonia, an inflammatory condition of the lung. Bacteria (*Streptococcus pneumoniae, Klebsiella, Mycoplasma*) and fungi (*Cryptococcus* and *Pneumocystis*) are a few of the agents involved in pneumonias. Other agents causing unique recognizable lung diseases are *Mycobacterium tuberculosis* and fungal pathogens such as *Histoplasma.*

Urogenital Portals of Entry

The urogenital tract is the portal of entry for pathogens that are contracted by sexual means (intercourse or intimate direct contact). These conditions are termed **sexually transmitted infections (STIs)** or **sexually transmitted diseases (STDs).** The term *sexually transmitted infections* may be preferred in some cases because it recognizes the fact that many of the sexually related conditions are asymptomatic and do not lead to symptoms of disease, even though they are still transmissible. STIs and STDs account for an estimated 4% of infections worldwide, with approximately 20 million new cases each year, caused by just eight bacteria and viruses. **Table 13.5** provides the most recent available statistics and estimates of the most common sexually related infections and diseases.

The microbes of STI/STDs enter the skin or mucosa of the penis, external genitalia, vagina, cervix, and urethra. Some can penetrate an unbroken surface; others require a cut or abrasion. Once-predominant STDs such as syphilis and gonorrhea have been surpassed by a growing list led by genital warts (HPV), chlamydia, and trichomoniasis. Evolving sexual practices have increased the incidence of STI/STDs that were once uncommon, and diseases that were not originally considered sexually acquired are now so classified.[5] Other common sexually transmitted agents include HIV, herpes simplex virus, *Candida albicans* (a yeast), and hepatitis B virus.

> **Quick Search**
> See the videos "STD Symptoms" on the Internet and on YouTube.

5. Amebic dysentery, scabies, salmonellosis, and *Strongyloides* worms are examples.

Figure 13.9 **Transplacental infection of the fetus. (a)** Fetus in the womb. **(b)** In a closer view, microbes are shown penetrating the maternal blood vessels and entering the blood pool of the placenta. They subsequently travel into the fetal circulation by way of the umbilical vein.

TABLE 13.6	Estimated Infectious Doses of Selected Pathogens*	
Agent of	**Infectious Dose Estimate**	**Primary Route of Infection**
Measles	1 virus	Respiratory
Shigellosis	1–10 cells	Ingestion
Norovirus gastroenteritis	18 viruses or less	Ingestion
Tuberculosis	10–50 cells	Various
Smallpox	10–100 viruses	Respiratory
Brucellosis	10–100 cells	Various
Viral encephalitis	10–100 viruses	Mosquito bite
Plague	100–500 cells	Flea bite
Gonorrhea	1,000 cells	Sexual contact
Anthrax	8,000–50,000 spores	Respiratory, cutaneous
Salmonellosis	10,000 cells	Ingestion
Cholera	100,000,000 cells	Ingestion

*Several of these agents are considered potential bioterror pathogens.

Not all urogenital infections are transmitted sexually. Some of these infections are caused by displaced organisms, as when normal microbiota from the gastrointestinal tract cause urinary tract infections, or by opportunistic overgrowth of normal microbiota ("yeast infections").

Pathogens that Infect During Pregnancy and Birth

The placenta is an exchange organ formed by maternal and fetal tissues that separate the blood of the developing fetus from that of the mother yet permit diffusion of dissolved nutrients and gases to the fetus. The placenta is ordinarily an effective barrier against pathogens that have entered the maternal circulation. However, a few microbes, such as the syphilis spirochete, can cross the placenta, enter the umbilical vein, and spread by the fetal circulation into the fetal tissues **(figure 13.9).**

Not all neonatal infections occur through the placenta. Some, such as herpes simplex and chlamydiosis, develop perinatally when the infant is contaminated by the birth canal. The most prominent infections of fetus and neonate are grouped together in a unified cluster known by the acronym **STORCH** that medical personnel are on the alert to detect. STORCH stands for **s**yphilis, **t**oxoplasmosis, **o**ther diseases (hepatitis B, HIV, and chlamydia), **r**ubella, **c**ytomegalovirus, and **h**erpes simplex virus. The most serious complications of STORCH infections are spontaneous abortion, congenital abnormalities, brain damage, prematurity, and stillbirths.

The Requirement for an Infectious Dose

Another factor crucial to the course of an infection is the quantity of microbial cells or particles that enters the portal of entry. For most agents, infection will proceed only if a minimum number, called the **infectious dose (ID),** is present. This number has been determined experimentally for many microbes. It is theorized that microbes with lower IDs tend to act locally and immediately, whereas those with higher IDs produce substances that must travel through the body to have their effect. **Table 13.6** presents examples of dose sizes for a number of pathogens, ranging from small to large infectious doses. Certain microbes (cholera, salmonellosis) have a significantly higher ID because they are inhibited or destroyed by acid as they pass through the stomach on their way into the lower GI tract. If the number of microbes entering a portal is below an infectious dose, infection and disease will generally not result. But if the quantity is far in excess of the ID, the onset of disease can be extremely rapid. Even weakly pathogenic species can be rendered more virulent with a large inoculum. Much of our knowledge of modes of infection and infectious dose has come from human and animal experimentation **(13.3 Making Connections).**

Attaching to the Host: Phase 2

Once a pathogen has penetrated the portal of entry in adequate numbers, it next must establish a stable association with the host's cells through **adhesion.** Such a firm attachment is almost always a prerequisite for invasion, because the body has so many mechanisms for flushing microbes and foreign materials from its tissues. Adhesion is dependent on binding between specific molecules on both the host and the pathogen, so a particular pathogen is limited to only those cells (and organisms) to which it can bind. Once attached, the pathogen is poised advantageously to invade the body compartments. Bacterial, fungal, and protozoal pathogens attach most often by appendages and surface structures such as fimbriae, pili, or flagella, and adhesive slimes or capsules; viruses attach by means of specialized receptors **(figure 13.10).** Larger pathogens like parasitic worms are mechanically fastened to the portal of entry by suckers, hooks, and barbs. Adhesion methods of various microbes and the diseases they cause are shown in **table 13.7.**

Human Guinea Pigs

These days, human beings are not used as subjects for determining the effects of infectious disease, but in earlier times they were. The tradition of human experimentation dates well back into the eighteenth century, and the subject frequently was the experimenter himself. In some studies, mycologists inoculated their own skin and even that of family members with scrapings from fungal lesions to demonstrate that the disease was transmissible. In the early days of parasitology, it was not uncommon for a brave researcher to swallow worm eggs in order to study the course of his infection and the life cycle of the worm.

In a sort of reverse test, one of Robert Koch's German colleagues, named Max von Petenkofer, believed so strongly that cholera was *not* caused by a bacterium that he and his assistant swallowed cultures of *Vibrio cholerae*. Fortunately for them, they acquired only a mild form of the disease. Many self-experimenters have not been so fortunate.

One of the most famous cases is that of Jesse Lazear, a Cuban physician who worked with Walter Reed on the etiology of yellow fever in 1900. Dr. Lazear was convinced that mosquitoes were directly involved in the spread of yellow fever; and by way of proof, he allowed himself and two volunteers to be bitten by mosquitoes infected with the blood of yellow fever patients. All three became ill as a result of this exposure; Dr. Lazear's sacrifice was the ultimate one: he died of yellow fever.

A remarkable, more recent use of human guinea pigs occurred from 1954 to 1973, when the U.S. government staged 153 separate tests using biological warfare agents. The scientists in charge of so-called "Operation Whitecoat" wanted to determine the infectivity of certain agents and how readily they could be acquired through airborne or other means. A group of about 2,000 courageous volunteers agreed to be exposed to some highly virulent pathogens, including the agents of Q fever, tularemia, and leishmaniasis. None of the deadliest pathogens (anthrax, plague, smallpox) was tested on humans. The test subjects all shared some important characteristics: they were young, male draftees, and they belonged to the Seventh-Day Adventist religion.

What made them uniquely suited to this highly secret study was their status as conscientious objectors—opposed to service as combat

A specially constructed chamber with vents for exposing test subjects to pathogens
Source: US Army

soldiers on religious grounds. Many of them were assigned to other military positions of a medical or clerical type. One of the expectations was that they would consent to be subjects for experiments. The tests, run by the biological warfare program at Fort Detrick, Maryland, involved direct exposure to airborne pathogens released inside special chambers, or in some cases breathing aerosols of pure cultures released into the air. Frequently, monkeys and actual guinea pigs were exposed simultaneously as a way to track the same infectious agent in animals for comparison.

A number of important discoveries were made. The infectious doses of several pathogens were determined by these studies, as were the effects of particle size. Other tests helped determine the effectiveness of vaccines. It is quite extraordinary that none of the men experienced long-term diseases as a result of these studies, given the high risks involved. It is very unlikely that this sort of testing would be sanctioned in the present era, but there is no doubt that the sacrifices of these men greatly advanced our understanding of the risks of biological warfare.

What are some reasons epidemiologists might have needed to use human subjects to test for the effects of pathogens?

Figure 13.10 **Mechanisms of adhesion by pathogens. (a)** Illustration of *Salmonella* cells covered in minute fimbriae, which they use to attach to the intestinal epithelium. **(b)** Bacterial cells using capsules to adhere to the surface of a tooth. **(c)** Coronavirus particles displaying spikes used to adhere to cells of the respiratory tract.
(a): *Source:* Melissa Brower/CDC; (b): Science Photo Library/Alamy Stock Photo; (c): *Source:* Dr. Fred Murphy/Sylvia Whitfield/CDC

TABLE 13.7	Adhesion Properties of Microbes	
Microbe	**Disease**	**Adhesion Mechanism**
Neisseria gonorrhoeae	Gonorrhea	Type IV pili attach to genital epithelium.
Escherichia coli	Diarrhea	Well-developed fimbriae adhere to intestinal cells.
Shigella and *Salmonella*	Gastroenteritis	Fimbriae attach to intestinal epithelium.
Vibrio cholerae	Cholera	Glycocalyx anchors to intestinal epithelium.
Treponema	Syphilis	Tapered hook embeds in host cell.
Mycoplasma	Pneumonia	Specialized tip fuses to lung epithelium.
Pseudomonas aeruginosa	Lung infections	Fimbriae and slime layer stick to host cells.
Streptococcus mutans	Dental caries	Dextran slime layer glues cocci to tooth surface.
Influenza virus	Influenza	Viral spikes dock to respiratory receptors.
Poliovirus	Polio	Capsid attaches to receptors on target cells.
HIV	AIDS	Viral spikes adhere to white blood cell receptors.
Giardia lamblia	Giardiasis	Suction disc on underside attaches to intestinal surface.
Trypanosoma	Trypanosomiasis	Flagellum assists in penetration of host cell.

Invading the Host and Becoming Established: Phase 3

Microbes have numerous properties that improve their invasiveness, that is, their capacity to evade host defenses and enter into deeper tissues where they will grow and become established. These properties all contribute to virulence and thus are considered some type of **virulence factor.** These same factors determine the degree of tissue damage that occurs and hence the severity of the disease. The effects of a pathogen's virulence factors on tissues vary greatly. Cold viruses, for example, invade and multiply but cause relatively little damage to their host. At the other end of the spectrum, pathogens such as the tetanus bacillus or rabies virus can severely damage or even kill their host.

Most of the common virulence factors fall into one or more of three categories: antiphagocytic effects, exoenzymes, and toxins. **Figure 13.11** illustrates the workings of some of these factors.

Antiphagocytic Factors

Microbes are likely to encounter resistance from host defenses when first entering the portal of entry. The initial response comes from white blood cells called **phagocytes.** These cells can ordinarily engulf pathogens and destroy them by means of enzymes and antimicrobial chemicals (see chapter 14).

Antiphagocytic factors are a type of virulence factor used by some pathogens to avoid phagocytes or to circumvent some part of the phagocytic process **(figure 13.11c).** The most aggressive strategy involves bacteria that kill phagocytes outright. Species of both *Streptococcus* and *Staphylococcus* produce **leukocidins,** substances that are toxic to white blood cells. Some microorganisms secrete an extracellular surface layer (slime or capsule) that makes it physically difficult for the phagocyte to engulf them. *Streptococcus pneumoniae, Salmonella typhi, Neisseria meningitidis,* and *Cryptococcus neoformans* are notable examples. Some bacteria are well adapted to survival inside phagocytes after ingestion. For instance, pathogenic species of *Legionella* and *Mycobacterium* are readily engulfed but are capable of

avoiding further destruction. This survival inside phagocytes has special significance because it provides a place for the microbes to hide, grow, and be spread throughout the body.

Getting Inside Host Cells Intracellular pathogens in particular must gain entrance to a host cell to complete their life cycles. Rickettsias, chlamydias, and viruses have evolved specific virulence mechanisms for entering a cell through some variation of engulfment or fusion. Some bacterial pathogens invade their target cells by using a secretion system that inserts specialized virulence proteins directly into them **(figure 13.11d).** In the case of *Salmonella* and *E. coli,* the virulence proteins disrupt the actin cytoskeleton of an intestinal cell and force the cell surface to form ruffles that pull the pathogens into the cell interior. Once inside, they multiply within vacuoles and use the cell as a passageway to break out into the underlying layers of tissues. Other pathogens (*Listeria* and *Shigella*) collect actin filaments and use them as motility organelles to move about in the cells.

Quick Search

Search on "*Salmonella* video HHMI Biointeractive" to view a short animation of this process.

Extracellular Enzymes

Many pathogenic bacteria, fungi, protozoa, and worms secrete **exoenzymes** that disrupt the structure of tissues. Other enzymes dissolve the host's defense barriers and promote the spread of microbes to deeper regions of the body. A few examples include:

1. mucinase, which digests the protective coating on mucous membranes and is a factor in amoebic dysentery;
2. keratinase, which digests the principal component of skin and hair and is secreted by fungi that cause ringworm;
3. collagenase, which digests the protein fibers of connective tissue and is an invasive factor for *Clostridium* species and some parasitic worms; and
4. hyaluronidase, which digests hyaluronic acid, the ground substance that cements animal cells together. This enzyme is an important virulence factor in staphylococci, clostridia, streptococci, and pneumococci **(figure 13.11a).**

Some enzymes react with components of the blood. Coagulase, an enzyme produced by pathogenic staphylococci, causes clotting of blood or plasma. By contrast, the bacterial kinases (streptokinase, staphylokinase) activates a pathway that breaks down fibrin clots, which expedites the invasion of damaged tissues by the pathogen. In fact, a drug containing streptokinase (Streptase) is administered to patients with life-threatening thrombi and emboli.[6]

6. These conditions are intravascular blood clots that can cause circulatory obstructions.

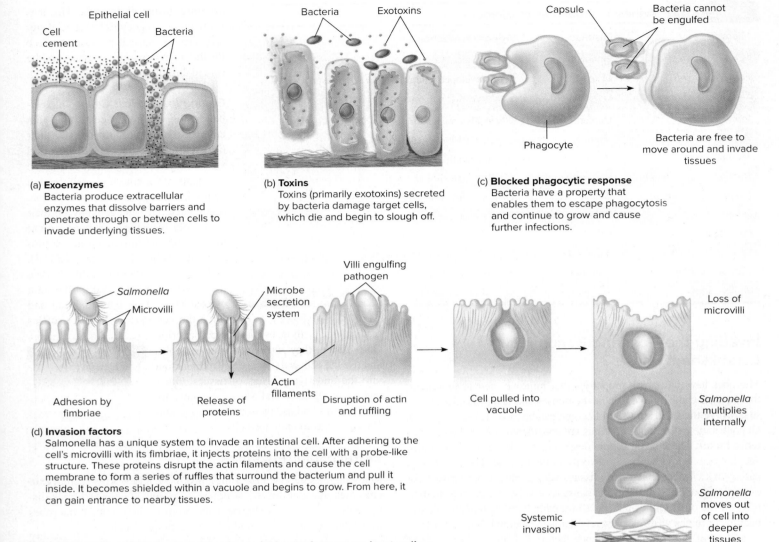

Figure 13.11 **Pathological effects of virulence factors on host cells.**

(a) **Exoenzymes**
Bacteria produce extracellular enzymes that dissolve barriers and penetrate through or between cells to invade underlying tissues.

(b) **Toxins**
Toxins (primarily exotoxins) secreted by bacteria damage target cells, which die and begin to slough off.

(c) **Blocked phagocytic response**
Bacteria have a property that enables them to escape phagocytosis and continue to grow and cause further infections.

(d) **Invasion factors**
Salmonella has a unique system to invade an intestinal cell. After adhering to the cell's microvilli with its fimbriae, it injects proteins into the cell with a probe-like structure. These proteins disrupt the actin filaments and cause the cell membrane to form a series of ruffles that surround the bacterium and pull it inside. It becomes shielded within a vacuole and begins to grow. From here, it can gain entrance to nearby tissues.

Bacterial Toxins: Poisonous Products

A **toxin** is a specific chemical product of microbes, plants, and some animals that has poisonous effects on other organisms. **Toxigenicity,** the power to produce toxins, is a genetically controlled characteristic of many bacterial species and is responsible for the adverse effects of a variety of diseases generally called **toxinoses.** Toxinoses in which the toxin is spread by the blood from the site of infection are called **toxemias** (tetanus and diphtheria, for example), whereas those caused by ingestion of toxins are **intoxications** (botulism). A toxin is named according to its specific target of action: neurotoxins act on the nervous system; enterotoxins act on the intestine; hemotoxins damage red blood cells; and nephrotoxins target the kidneys.

A more traditional scheme classifies bacterial toxins according to their origins **(figure 13.12).** A toxin molecule secreted by a living bacterial cell into the infected tissues is an **exotoxin.** A toxin that is not secreted but is released only after the cell is damaged or lysed is an **endotoxin.** Other important differences between the two groups are summarized in **table 13.8.**

Exotoxins are proteins with a strong specificity for a target cell and extremely powerful, sometimes deadly, effects. They generally affect cells by damaging the cell membrane and initiating lysis or by disrupting intracellular function **(figure 13.11b). Hemolysins*** are a class of bacterial exotoxins that disrupt the cell membrane of red blood cells (and some other cells, too). This damage causes the red blood cells to hemolyze—to burst and release hemoglobin pigment. Hemolysins that increase pathogenicity include the streptolysins of *Streptococcus pyogenes* and the alpha (α) and beta (β) toxins of *Staphylococcus aureus.* When colonies of bacteria growing on blood agar produce hemolysin, distinct zones appear around the colony **(figure 13.13).** The pattern of hemolysis is one characteristic used to identify bacteria and determine their degree of pathogenicity.

The exotoxins of diphtheria, tetanus, and botulism, among others, attach to a target cell, become internalized, and interrupt an essential cell pathway. This type of exotoxin is specified as an A-B

hemolysin (hee-mahl'-uh-sin) Gt. *hemo,* blood, and *lysin,* to split.

(a) Target organs are damaged; heart, muscles, blood cells, intestinal tract show dysfunctions.

(b) General physiological effects— fever, malaise, aches, shock

Figure 13.12 **The origins and effects of circulating exotoxins and endotoxin. (a)** Exotoxins, given off by live cells, have highly specific targets and physiological effects. **(b)** Endotoxin, given off when the cell wall of gram-negative bacteria disintegrates, has more generalized physiological effects.

TABLE 13.8	Differential Characteristics of Bacterial Exotoxins and Endotoxin	
Characteristic	**Exotoxins**	**Endotoxin**
Toxicity	Toxic in small amounts	Toxic in higher quantities
Effects on the Body	Specific to a cell type (blood, liver, nerve)	Systemic and less specific: fever, inflammation, weakness, shock
Chemical Composition	Small proteins	Lipopolysaccharide of cell wall
Heat Denaturation at 60°C	Unstable	Stable
Toxoid Formation	Can be converted to toxoid*	Cannot be converted to toxoid
Immune Response	Stimulate antitoxins**	Does not stimulate antitoxins
Fever Stimulation	Usually not	Yes
Manner of Release	Secreted from live cell	Released from cell wall during lysis
Typical Sources	A few gram-positive and gram-negative bacteria	All gram-negative bacteria
Examples of Diseases	Tetanus, diphtheria, cholera, anthrax	Meningitis, endotoxic shock, salmonellosis

*A toxoid is an inactivated toxin used in vaccines.

**An antitoxin is an antibody that reacts specifically with a toxin.

toxin because it consist of two parts: an A (active) component and a B (binding) component. The B component binds to a specific receptor molecule on the surface of the host cell, allowing the A component to move across the host cell membrane. Once it has entered the cell, the A component interferes with cellular processes, damaging specific targets within the cell.

Examples include a toxin of *Clostridium tetani* that blocks the action of certain spinal neurons; the toxin of *Clostridium botulinum* that interferes with transmission of nerve-muscle stimuli; pertussis toxin that inactivates the respiratory cilia; and cholera toxin that provokes profuse salt and water loss from intestinal cells.

Unlike exotoxins, of which there are many specific examples, there is just a single type of endotoxin. It is chemically a substance called lipopolysaccharide (LPS), which is part of the outer membrane of gram-negative cell envelopes. When gram-negative bacteria cause infections, some of the bacteria eventually lyse and release these LPS molecules into the infection site or into the circulation. Endotoxin differs from exotoxins in having a variety of systemic effects on tissues and organs. Depending upon the amounts present, endotoxin can cause fever, inflammation, hemorrhage, and diarrhea. Blood infection by gram-negative bacteria such as *Salmonella, Shigella, Neisseria meningitidis,* and *Escherichia coli* is particularly dangerous. It can lead to fatal endotoxic shock caused by large amounts of endotoxins being released into the bloodstream.

Effects of Infection on Organs and Body Systems

In addition to the adverse effects of enzymes, toxins, and other factors, multiplication by a pathogen frequently weakens host tissues. Pathogens can obstruct tubular structures such as blood vessels, lymphatic channels, fallopian tubes, and bile ducts. Accumulated damage can lead to cell and tissue death, a condition called **necrosis.** Although viruses do not produce toxins or destructive enzymes, they destroy cells by multiplying in and lysing them. Many of the cytopathic effects of viral infection arise from the impaired metabolism and death of cells (see chapter 6).

The direct effects of virulence factors such as enzymes and toxins can cause significant harm to cells, tissues, and organs. It is important to note that many microbial diseases are actually the result of indirect damage, or the host's excessive or inappropriate response to a microorganism. This means that pathogenicity is not a trait inherent in microorganisms alone but is really a consequence of the interplay between microbe and host. The capsule of *Streptococcus pneumoniae* is a good example. It prevents the bacterium from being cleared from the lungs by phagocytic cells, leading to a powerful inflammatory response by white blood cells and a continuous influx of fluids into the lung spaces—a condition we know as pneumonia.

Figure 13.13 **Patterns of hemolysis.** The effect of the hemolysin can be seen as a halo surrounding bacterial growth that is partially or completely cleared of red blood cells. Alpha hemolysis refers to a partial lysing of red blood cells. (Note the greenish halo surrounding growth on the right.) Beta hemolysis refers to a complete lysing, as seen in the completely clear halo surrounding the growth of the left and bottom samples. Gamma hemolysis (top) is synonymous with a lack of hemolytic activity.
Lisa Burgess/McGraw-Hill Education

Of course, it is easier to study and characterize the microbes that cause direct damage through toxins or enzymes. For this reason, these true pathogens were the first to be fully understood as the science of microbiology progressed. But in the last 15 to 20 years, microbiologists have come to appreciate exactly how important the relationship between microbe and host is, and this has greatly expanded our understanding of infectious diseases.

 Practice SECTION 13.2

8. Explain several ways in which true pathogens differ from opportunistic pathogens.

9. Distinguish between pathogenicity and virulence.

10. Explain the concept of portal of entry, and list the major portals of entry with examples of associated infections.

11. Differentiate between exogenous and endogenous infections.

12. What factors possibly affect the size of the infectious dose?

13. Describe several components of pathogens that are involved in microbial adhesion.

14. Define *virulence factors* and give examples of them in gram-positive and gram-negative bacteria, viruses, and parasites.

15. Discuss the effects of several virulence factors that help microbes invade hosts and evade host defenses.

16. Define *toxigenicity,* and summarize the main features of exotoxins and endotoxins.

17. Which body cells or tissues are affected by hemolysins, leukocidins, hyaluronidase, kinases, tetanus toxin, pertussis toxin, and enterotoxin?

13.3 The Outcomes of Infection and Disease

Learn

14. Describe the clinical stages of infection.

15. Use key terms to describe different patterns of infection.

16. Use correct terminology to explain the manifestations of infections and inflammation.

17. Discuss the major portals of exit and how they influence the end stages of infection and disease.

The Stages of Clinical Infections

As the body of the host responds to the invasive and toxigenic activities of a pathogen, it passes through four distinct phases of infection and disease: the incubation period, the prodromal stage, the period of invasion, and the convalescent period **(figure 13.14).**

The **incubation period** is the time from initial contact with the infectious agent (at the portal of entry) to the appearance of the first symptoms. During the incubation period, the agent is multiplying at the portal of entry but has not yet caused enough damage to elicit symptoms. Although this period is relatively well defined and predictable for each microorganism, it does vary according to host resistance, degree of virulence, and distance between the target organ and the portal of entry (the farther apart, the longer the incubation period). Overall, an incubation period can range from several hours in pneumonic plague to several years in leprosy. The majority of infections, however, have incubation periods ranging between 2 and 30 days.

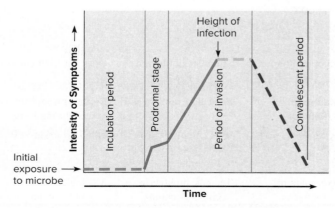

Figure 13.14 **Stages in the course of infection and disease.** Dashed lines represent periods with a variable length.

Figure 13.15 The occurrence of infections with regard to location and sequence. (a) A localized infection, in which the pathogen is restricted to one specific site. (b) Systemic infection, in which the pathogen spreads through circulation to many sites. (c) A focal infection occurs initially as a local infection, but circumstances cause the microbe to be carried to other sites systemically. (d) A mixed infection, in which the same site is infected with several microbes at the same time. (e) In a primary-secondary infection, an initial infection is complicated by a second one in the same or a different location and caused by a different microbe.

The earliest notable symptoms of infection appear as a vague feeling of discomfort, such as head and muscle aches, fatigue, upset stomach, and general malaise. This short period (1–2 days) is known as the **prodromal stage.** The infectious agent next enters a **period of invasion,** during which it multiplies at high levels, exhibits its greatest toxicity, and becomes well established in its target tissues and organs. This period is often marked by fever and other prominent and more specific signs and symptoms, which can include cough, skin lesions, diarrhea, loss of muscle control, swelling, jaundice, discharge of exudates, or severe pain, depending on the pathogen. The length of this period is extremely variable.

As the patient begins to respond to the infection, the symptoms decline—sometimes dramatically, other times slowly. During the recovery that follows, called the **convalescent period,** the patient's strength and health gradually return as the immune response begins to clear the infectious agent and restore normal function to damaged tissues. In the event that the patient does not recover and dies, the infection is considered *terminal.*

The transmissibility of the microbe during these four stages must be considered on an individual basis. A few agents are released mostly during incubation (measles, for example); many are released during the invasive period (*Shigella*); and others can be transmitted during all of these periods (hepatitis B virus, norovirus).

Patterns of Infection

Patterns of infection are many and varied. In the simplest situation, a **localized infection,** the microbe enters the body and remains confined to a specific tissue (**figure 13.15a**). Examples of localized infections are boils, fungal skin infections, and warts.

Many infectious agents do not remain localized but spread from the initial site of entry to other tissues. In fact, spreading is necessary for pathogens such as rabies and hepatitis A virus, whose target tissue may be some distance from the site of entry. The rabies virus travels from a bite wound along nerve tracts to its target in the brain, and the hepatitis A virus moves from the intestine to the liver via the circulatory system. When an infection spreads to several sites and tissue fluids, usually in the bloodstream, it is called a **systemic infection** (**figure 13.15b**). Examples of systemic infections are viral diseases (measles, rubella, chickenpox, and AIDS); bacterial diseases (brucellosis, anthrax, typhoid fever, and syphilis); and fungal diseases (histoplasmosis and cryptococcosis). Infectious agents can also travel to their targets by means of nerves (as in rabies) or cerebrospinal fluid (as in meningitis).

A **focal infection** is said to exist when the infectious agent breaks loose from a local infection and is seeded or *disseminated* into other tissues (**figure 13.15c**). This pattern is exhibited by tuberculosis or by streptococcal pharyngitis, which gives rise to scarlet fever. In the condition called **toxemia,**[7] the infection itself remains localized at the portal of entry, but the toxins produced by the pathogens are carried by the blood to the actual target tissue. In this way, the cells initially infected by the bacterial cells can be

7. Not to be confused with toxemia of pregnancy, which is a metabolic disturbance and not an infection.

13.4 MAKING CONNECTIONS

A Guide to the Terminology of Infection and Disease

Words in medicine have great power and economy. A single technical term can often replace a whole phrase or sentence, thereby saving time and space in charting. It is not uncommon to feel overwhelmed by what seems like a mountain of new words. However, having a grasp of a few root words and a fair amount of anatomy can help you learn many of these words and even deduce the meaning of unfamiliar ones. Some examples of medical shorthand follow.

The suffix *-itis* means an inflammation and, when affixed to the end of an anatomical term, indicates an inflammatory condition in that location. Thus, meningitis is an inflammation of the meninges surrounding the brain; encephalitis is an inflammation of the brain itself; hepatitis involves the liver; gastroenteritis, the intestine; and otitis media, the middle ear. Although not all inflammatory conditions are caused by infections, many infectious diseases inflame their target organs.

The suffix *-emia* is derived from the Greek word *haeima,* meaning blood. When added to a word, it means "associated with the blood." Thus, septicemia means sepsis (infection) of the blood; bacteremia, bacteria in the blood; viremia, viruses in the blood; and fungemia, fungi in the blood. It is also applicable to specific conditions such as toxemia, gonococcemia, and spirochetemia.

The suffix *-osis* means "a disease or morbid process." It is frequently added to the names of pathogens to indicate the disease they cause: for example, listeriosis, histoplasmosis, toxoplasmosis, shigellosis, salmonellosis, and borreliosis. A variation of this suffix is *-iasis*, as in trichomoniasis and candidiasis.

The suffix *-oma* comes from the Greek word *onkomas* (swelling) and means tumor. Although the root is often used to describe cancers (lymphoma, melanoma), it is also applied in some infectious diseases that cause masses or swellings (tuberculoma, leproma).

different from the targets of their toxin. Examples include diphtheria and some staphylococcal diseases.

An infection is not always caused by a single microbe. In a **mixed infection,** several agents establish themselves simultaneously at the infection site (**figure 13.15d**). In some mixed infections, the microbes cooperate in breaking down a tissue. In other cases, one microbe creates an environment that enables another microbe to invade. Gas gangrene, wound infections, dental caries, and human bite infections tend to be mixed. These are sometimes called **polymicrobial** diseases and may be the result of biofilm formation at the site of infection.

Some diseases are described according to the sequence of occurrence. When an initial, or **primary,** infection is complicated by another infection caused by a different microbe, this subsequent infection is termed a **secondary infection** (**figure 13.15e**). This pattern is seen in a child whose chickenpox (primary infection) becomes infected with *Staphylococcus aureus* (secondary infection). Another significant combination is seen in patients who develop secondary pneumonia as a complication of influenza. The secondary infection need not be in the same site as the primary infection, and it usually indicates weakened host defenses.

Infections that come on rapidly, with severe but short-lived effects, are called **acute infections.** Infections that progress and persist over a long period of time are **chronic infections.** Read **13.4 Making Connections,** for other common words used to describe infectious diseases.

Signs and Symptoms: Warning Signals of Disease

When an infection causes pathologic changes leading to disease, it is often accompanied by a variety of signs and symptoms. A **sign** is any objective evidence of disease as noted by an observer; a **symptom** is the subjective evidence of disease as sensed by the patient. Signs tend to be more precise than symptoms and are often measured. Both can be the result of the same underlying cause. For example, an infection of the brain may present with the sign of bacteria in the spinal fluid and the symptom of headache. Or a streptococcal infection may produce a sore throat (symptom) and inflamed pharynx (sign). Disease indicators that can be sensed and observed can qualify as either a sign or a symptom depending upon how they are reported. When a disease can be identified or described by a defined collection of signs and symptoms, it is termed a **syndrome.** Signs and symptoms with considerable importance in diagnosing infectious diseases are shown in **table 13.9.**

| TABLE 13.9 | Common Signs and Symptoms of Infectious Diseases | |
|---|---|
| **Signs*** | **Symptoms** |
| Fever | Chills |
| Septicemia | Pain, irritation |
| Microbes in tissue fluids that should be sterile | Nausea |
| Abnormal chest sounds | Malaise, fatigue |
| Skin eruptions | Chest tightness |
| Leukocytosis | Itching |
| Leukopenia | Headache |
| Swollen lymph nodes | Weakness |
| Abscesses | Abdominal cramps |
| Tachycardia (increased heart rate) | Anorexia (lack of appetite) |
| Antibodies in serum | Sore throat |

*The technical terms for signs are defined in the body of the text.

Signs and Symptoms of Inflammation

The earliest manifestations of disease generally result from the activation of the defense process called **inflammation.*** The inflammatory response includes cells and chemicals that are activated when there has been damage to tissues by a microbe or its products. This subject is discussed in greater detail in chapter 14, but as noted earlier, many symptoms and signs of infection are caused by the mobilization of this system. Inflammation is always a likely cause of symptoms such as redness, pain, soreness, and swelling. A general term for a noticeable sign of infection or disease is **lesion.*** Some lesions typical of inflammation include **edema,*** the accumulation of fluid in an afflicted tissue; **granulomas** and **abscesses,** walled-off collections of inflammatory cells and microbes in the tissues; and **lymphadenitis,** swollen lymph nodes.

Rashes and other skin eruptions are some of the most common lesions in many diseases, and because they tend to mimic each other, it can be difficult to differentiate among diseases on this basis alone. Skin lesions can be restricted to the epidermis and its glands and follicles, or they can extend into the dermis and subcutaneous regions. The lesions of some infections (boils, chickenpox, athlete's foot, warts) undergo characteristic changes in appearance and location during the course of disease and thus fit more than one category.

Signs of Infection in the Blood

Changes in the number of circulating white blood cells, as determined by blood cell counts, are considered to be a significant sign of possible infection. **Leukocytosis*** is an increase in the level of white blood cells, whereas **leukopenia*** is a decrease. Other signs of infection revolve around the occurrence of a microbe or its products in the blood. The clinical term for blood infection, **septicemia,** refers to a general state in which microorganisms are multiplying in the blood and are present in large numbers. When small numbers of bacteria or viruses are found in the blood, the correct terminology is **bacteremia** or **viremia,** which means that these microbes are present in the blood but are not necessarily multiplying.

During infection, a normal host will invariably show signs of an immune response in the form of antibodies in the serum or some type of sensitivity to the microbe. This fact is the basis for several serological tests used in diagnosing infectious diseases such as HIV infection or syphilis. Such specific immune reactions indicate the body's attempt to develop specific immunities against pathogens. We concentrate on this role of the host defenses in chapters 14 and 15.

Infections that Go Unnoticed

It is rather common for an infection to produce no noticeable or typical symptoms, even though the microbe is active in the host tissue. In these cases, the person does not show overt indications of infection. Infections of this nature are known as **asymptomatic,**

subclinical, or *inapparent* because the patient experiences no symptoms usually associated with disease and does not seek medical attention. However, it is important to note that most infections are attended by some sort of detectable *sign*. In section 13.4 we further address the significance of subclinical infections in the transmission of infectious agents.

The Portal of Exit: Vacating the Host

Earlier we introduced the idea that a parasite is considered *unsuccessful* if it does not have a provision for leaving its host and moving to other susceptible hosts. With few exceptions, pathogens depart by a specific avenue called the **portal of exit (figure 13.16).** In most cases the pathogen is shed or released from the body through secretion, excretion, discharge, or sloughed tissue. The high number of pathogens in these materials increases both virulence and the likelihood that the pathogen will reach other hosts. One of the most dramatic examples of this is the Ebola virus (Case Study), which is at its most transmissible late in the disease and is released in massive numbers in every bodily fluid. In many cases, the portal of exit is the same as the portal of entry, but a few pathogens use a different route. As we will see in section 13.4, the portal of exit concerns epidemiologists because it greatly influences the dissemination of infection in a population.

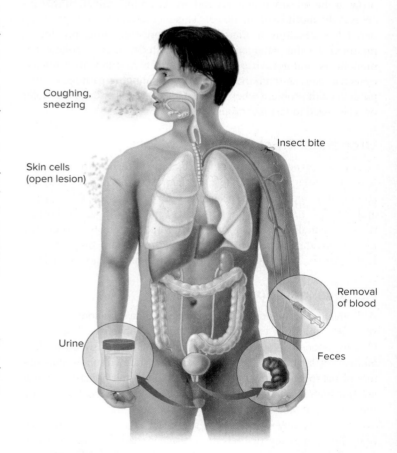

Coughing, sneezing

Insect bite

Skin cells (open lesion)

Removal of blood

Urine

Feces

Figure 13.16 Major portals of exit of infectious diseases. Pathogens are released from the body through secretion, excretion, discharge, or shedding.

*inflammation (in-flam-aye'-shun) L. *inflammation,* to set on fire.
*lesion (lee'-zhun) L. *laesio,* to hurt.
*edema (uh-dee'-muh) Gr. *oidema,* swelling.
* leukocytosis (loo"-koh'-sy-toh'-sis) From *leukocyte,* a white blood cell, and the suffix *-osis.*
* leukopenia (loo"-koh'-pee'-nee-uh) From *leukocyte* and *penia,* a loss or lack of.

Respiratory and Salivary Portals

Mucus, sputum, nasal drainage, and other moist secretions are the fluids of escape for the pathogens that infect the lower or upper respiratory tract. The most forceful means of releasing these secretions are coughing and sneezing (see figure 13.19), although they can also be released during talking and laughing. Tiny particles of liquid released into the air form aerosols or droplets that can spread the infectious agent to other people. The agents of tuberculosis, influenza, measles, and chickenpox most often leave the host through airborne droplets. Droplets of saliva are also the exit route for several viruses, including those of mumps, rabies, and infectious mononucleosis.

Epithelial Cells

The outer layers of the skin and scalp are constantly being shed into the environment. A large proportion of household dust is actually composed of skin cells. A single person can shed several billion skin cells a day, and some persons, called shedders, disseminate massive numbers of bacteria into their immediate surroundings. Skin lesions and their exudates can serve as portals of exit in warts, fungal infections, boils, herpes simplex, smallpox, and syphilis.

Fecal Exit

Feces are a very common portal of exit. Some intestinal pathogens grow in the intestinal mucosa and create an inflammation that increases the motility of the bowel. This increased motility speeds up peristalsis, resulting in diarrhea. The more-fluid stool provides a rapid exit for the pathogen, as we see with dysentery, cholera, salmonellosis, and noroviruses. A number of helminth worms release cysts and eggs through the feces. Feces containing pathogens are a public health problem when allowed to contaminate drinking water or when used to fertilize crops.

Urogenital Tract

A number of agents involved in sexually transmitted infections leave the host in vaginal discharge or semen. This is also the source of neonatal infections such as herpes simplex, *Chlamydia,* and *Candida albicans,* which infect the infant as it passes through the birth canal. Less commonly, certain pathogens that infect the kidney are discharged in the urine; examples are the agents of leptospirosis, typhoid fever, tuberculosis, and schistosomiasis.

Removal of Blood or Bleeding

Although the blood does not have a direct route to the outside, it can serve as a portal of exit when it is removed or released through a vascular puncture made by natural or artificial means. Blood-feeding animals such as ticks, fleas, and mosquitoes are common transmitters of pathogens. Human immunodeficiency and hepatitis viruses are transmitted by shared needles or through small abrasions in a mucous membrane during sexual intercourse.

Because many microbes can be transferred through blood donation, the monitoring of both donors and donated blood has to be scrupulous. In the mid-1980s, several thousand people suffering from hemophilia were infected with HIV as a result of receiving blood-clotting factors contaminated with the virus. The current risk for transfusion-transmitted infections is about one case in 10 million transfusions. One factor that increases risk is the presence of emerging disease agents in the blood supply that have not yet been detected. This has already happened with West Nile virus and Chagas disease.

The Persistence of Microbes and Pathologic Conditions

The apparent recovery of the host does not always mean that the microbe has been completely removed or destroyed by the host defenses. After the initial symptoms in certain chronic infectious diseases, the infectious agent retreats into a state called chronic **persistence** or **latency.** In some cases of latency, the microbe can periodically become active and produce recurrent disease. The viral agents of herpes simplex, herpes zoster, hepatitis B, AIDS, and Epstein-Barr can persist in the host for long periods. The agents of syphilis, typhoid fever, tuberculosis, and malaria also enter into latent stages. The person harboring a persistent infectious agent may or may not shed it during the latent stage. If it is shed, such persons are chronic carriers who serve as sources of infection for the rest of the population.

Some diseases leave **sequelae*** in the form of long-term or permanent damage to tissues or organs. For example, meningitis can result in deafness, a strep throat can lead to rheumatic heart disease, Lyme disease can cause arthritis, and hepatitis B can initiate cirrhosis and liver cancer.

 Practice SECTION 13.3

18. Explain what is happening during each stage of infection. Compare and contrast: systemic, local, and focal infections; primary versus secondary infections; infection versus intoxication.
19. Discuss the distinguishing features of signs and symptoms, using examples.
20. Name some examples of infections and their portals of exit.
21. Using terminology from 13.4 Making Connections, define *urethritis, endotoxemia, chlamydiosis,* and *lymphoma.*

* *sequelae* (su-kwee′-lee) L. *sequi,* to follow.

13.4 Epidemiology: The Study of Disease in Populations

 Learn

18. Define *epidemiology,* and summarize the major goals of its studies.
19. Relate the significant factors involved in the transmission of infectious diseases.
20. Explain the concept of carriers and describe several types.
21. Use examples to distinguish between the types of vectors, and discuss the importance of zoonoses.
22. Differentiate between communicable and noncommunicable infectious diseases.
23. Characterize the patterns of transmission for communicable diseases.

So far our discussion has revolved primarily around the impact of an infectious disease in individuals. We now turn our attention to the effects of diseases on the community—the realm of **epidemiology.*** By definition, this term involves the study of the frequency and distribution of disease and other health-related factors in defined human populations. It involves many disciplines—not only microbiology but also anatomy, physiology, immunology, medicine, psychology, sociology, ecology, and statistics—and it considers many diseases other than infectious ones, including heart disease, cancer, drug addiction, and mental illness.

The epidemiologist is a medical sleuth who collects clues on the causative agent, pathology, and sources and modes of transmission and tracks the numbers and distribution of cases of disease in the community. In fulfilling these demands, the epidemiologist looks for the "chain of infection" involving the who, when, where, how, why, and what that surrounds the spread of diseases. The outcome of these studies helps public health departments develop prevention and treatment programs and establish a basis for predictions.

Origins and Transmission Patterns of Infectious Microbes

Reservoirs: Where Pathogens Persist

One of the important concerns of epidemiology is discovering where pathogens originate and how they are transmitted. As we saw in the Case Study, these aspects are intensely scrutinized from the very first signs of an outbreak.

For an infectious agent to continue to exist and be spread, it must have a permanent place to reside. The **reservoir** is the primary habitat in the natural world from which a pathogen originates. Often it is a human or animal carrier, although soil, water, and plants are also reservoirs. The reservoir can be distinguished from the infection **source,** which is the individual or object from which an infection is actually acquired. An infectious agent that does not survive well outside of its host and is usually transmitted directly tends to have the same reservoir and source, whereas one that can remain viable outside of the host can have a different reservoir and source. For example, gonorrhea has the same reservoir and source (the human body), whereas hepatitis A usually has a different reservoir (a human carrier) and source (contaminated food).

Living Reservoirs

Many pathogens continue to exist and spread because they are harbored by members of a host population. A person or animal with an obvious or *overt* symptomatic infection is clearly a source of infection, as opposed to a **carrier** who is, by definition, an individual who *inconspicuously* shelters a pathogen and spreads it to others unknowingly. Although human carriers are occasionally detected through routine screening (blood tests, cultures) and other epidemiological devices, they are unfortunately very difficult to discover and control. As long as a pathogenic reservoir is maintained, the disease will continue to exist in that population or location, and the potential for epidemics will be a constant threat. The duration of

* *epidemiology* (ep″-ih-dee-mee-alh′-uh-gee) Gr. *epidemios,* prevalent.

 CLINIC CASE

Wash Your Hands. And Your Nose. The patient was only a few days old, born the previous week in a Chicago hospital via cesarean section. Before being discharged, a number of blisters and pustules were noted on his skin. Clinical and laboratory diagnosis determined that the infant was infected with methicillin-resistant *Staphylococcus aureus* (MRSA), a strain of the bacterium resistant to all the first-line antibiotics commonly used to treat it. Complicating matters in this case was the fact that many of the alternative antibiotics for *S. aureus* infection are contraindicated for use in newborns. Because of their immature immune systems and potential for rapid deterioration, any infection in newborns is especially worrisome and is generally treated aggressively. Fortunately, an effective combination of topical and systemic antibiotic therapy resolved the infection and the baby was discharged without complication.

Unfortunately, this was not an isolated event. The hospital had seen 10 similar cases in the previous 6 months, prompting infection-control specialists to launch an investigation. Nasal cultures were obtained from 135 health care workers in the labor and delivery, postnatal, and newborn nursery wards who were likely to have had direct contact with one of the patients. One doctor and one nurse were found to be asymptomatic carriers of MRSA, and DNA profiling determined that the isolates they carried were the same as those seen in five of the patients. The two MRSA-colonized health care workers were restricted from work until they had completed a full course of antibiotics and a repeat nasal culture tested negative for MRSA. Additionally, increased enforcement of standard infection-control measures, hand hygiene, and environmental cleaning was begun.

Only half of the infections in the nursery could be connected to health care providers in the nursery. Where could the other infections have originated?

the carrier state can be short or long term, and the carrier may or may not have experienced disease due to the microbe.

Several situations can produce the carrier state. **Asymptomatic** (apparently healthy) carriers are infected, but as previously indicated, they show no outward symptoms **(figure 13.17a).** A few asymptomatic infections (such as gonorrhea and genital warts) can carry out their entire course without overt manifestations. **Figure 13.17b** demonstrates three types of carriers who show no indications of infection at the time they transmit the pathogen. *Incubation carriers* spread the infectious agent during the incubation period before symptoms have appeared. For example, patients with HIV infection can harbor and spread the virus for months and years before their infection is evident. Recuperating patients without symptoms are considered *convalescent carriers* when they continue to shed viable microbes and convey the infection to others after symptoms have subsided. Norovirus, the most common cause of gastroenteritis, can be transmitted for weeks after an infection is resolved.

An individual who continues to shelter the infectious agent for a long period after recovery is a *chronic carrier.* Patients who have

Asymptomatic **Incubation** **Convalescent** **Chronic**

Stages of release during infection

Time

(a) (b)

Passive

(c) Transfer of infectious agent through contact ✳ Infectious agent

Figure 13.17 Involvement of carriers in transmission of infectious agents. (a) An asymptomatic carrier is infected without symptoms. **(b)** Incubation, convalescent, and chronic carriers can transmit the infection either before or after the period of symptoms. **(c)** A passive carrier is contaminated but not infected and spreads the pathogen through physical contact.

recovered from tuberculosis, hepatitis, and herpes infections frequently carry the agent chronically. About one in 20 victims of typhoid fever harbors *Salmonella typhi* in the gallbladder for several years and sometimes for life. The most infamous of these was "Typhoid Mary," a cook who spread the infection to hundreds of victims in the early 1900s.

The **passive carrier** state is of great concern during patient care (see the discussion of healthcare–associated infections in section 13.5). Medical and dental personnel who must constantly handle materials that are heavily contaminated with body fluids and blood are at risk of picking up pathogens mechanically and accidentally transferring them to other patients **(figure 13.17c).** Proper hand washing, handling of contaminated materials, and aseptic techniques greatly reduce this likelihood.

Animals as Reservoirs and Sources Up to now we have lumped animals with humans in discussing living reservoirs or carriers, but animals deserve special consideration as vectors of infections. The word **vector** is used by epidemiologists to indicate a live

animal that transmits an infectious agent from one host to another. (The term is sometimes misused to include any object that spreads disease.) The majority of vectors are arthropods such as fleas, mosquitoes, flies, and ticks, although larger animals can also spread infection; for example, mammals (rabies), birds (ornithosis), or lower vertebrates (salmonellosis).

By tradition, vectors are placed into one of two categories, depending upon the animal's relationship with the microbe. A **biological vector** actively participates in a pathogen's life cycle, serving as a site in which it can multiply or complete its development. A biological vector communicates the infectious agent to the human host by biting, aerosol formation, or touch. In the case of biting vectors, the animal can inject infected saliva into the blood (mosquito), defecate around the bite wound (flea), or regurgitate blood into the wound (tsetse fly).

Mosquito

Mechanical vectors are not necessary to the life cycle of an infectious agent and merely transport it without being infected. The

external body parts of these animals become contaminated when they come into physical contact with a source of pathogens. The agent is subsequently transferred to humans indirectly by an intermediate such as food or occasionally by direct contact (as in certain eye infections). Houseflies are notorious mechanical vectors. They feed on decaying garbage and feces, and while they are feeding, their feet and mouthparts easily become contaminated. They also regurgitate juices onto food to soften and digest it. Flies spread more than 20 bacterial, viral, protozoan, and worm infections. Other non-biting flies transmit tropical ulcers, yaws, and trachoma. Cockroaches, which have unsavory habits similar to those of flies, play a role in the mechanical transmission of fecal pathogens, as well as contributing to allergy attacks in asthmatic children.

Housefly

Many vectors and animal reservoirs spread their own infections to humans. An infection indigenous to animals but naturally transmissible to humans is a **zoonosis.*** In these types of infections, the human is essentially a dead-end host and does not contribute to the natural persistence of the microbe. Some zoonotic infections (rabies, for instance) can have multihost involvement, and others (such as plague) can have very complex cycles in the wild. Zoonotic spread of disease is promoted by close associations of humans with animals, and people in animal-oriented or outdoor professions are at greatest risk. At least 150 zoonoses exist worldwide; the most common ones are listed in **table 13.10.** Zoonoses make up a full 70% of all new emerging diseases worldwide. It is worth noting that zoonotic infections are impossible to completely eradicate without also eradicating the animal reservoirs. Attempts have been made to eradicate mosquitoes and certain rodents. During influenza epidemics, millions of chickens and thousands of pigs are slaughtered in the attempt to control its spread.

One technique that can provide an early warning signal for the occurrence of certain mosquito-borne zoonoses has been the use of *sentinel animals.* These are usually domestic animals (most often

* *zoonosis* (zoh″-uh-noh′-sis) Gr. *zoion,* animal, and *nosos,* disease.

TABLE 13.10	Common Zoonotic Infections	
Disease/Agent	**Primary Animal Reservoirs**	**Mode of Infection**
Viruses		
Rabies	All mammals	Bite; aerosol
Yellow fever	Wild birds, mammals, mosquitoes	Mosquito bite
Viral fevers	Wild mammals	Various mosquitoes
Hantavirus	Rodents	Airborne wastes
Influenza	Chickens, swine	Airborne secretions
West Nile virus	Wild birds, mosquitoes	Mosquito bite
Bacteria		
Rocky Mountain spotted fever	Dogs, ticks	Tick bite
Psittacosis	Birds	Airborne secretions
Leptospirosis	Domestic animals	Animal wastes (urine)
Anthrax	Domestic animals	Airborne spores, cutaneous contact
Brucellosis	Cattle, sheep, pigs	Air- and food-borne
Plague	Rodents, fleas	Flea bite; aerosol
Salmonellosis	Variety of mammals, birds, and rodents	Food-borne
Tularemia	Rodents, birds, arthropods	Tick bite, airborne
Miscellaneous		
Ringworm	Domestic mammals	Cutaneous contact
Toxoplasmosis	Cats, rodents, birds	Food-borne, contact
Trypanosomiasis	Domestic and wild mammals	Tsetse fly; reduviid bug
Trichinosis	Swine, bears	Ingestion of cysts
Tapeworm	Cattle, swine, fish	Ingestion of eggs
Scabies	Domestic animals	Cutaneous contact

chickens or horses) that can serve as hosts for diseases such as West Nile fever, various viral encephalitides, and malaria. Sentinel animals are placed at various sites throughout the community, and their blood is monitored periodically for antibodies to the infectious agents that

Figure 13.18 **Summary of how communicable infectious diseases are acquired.**
(1): Igormakarov/Shutterstock; (2): Custom Medical Stock Photo/Alamy Stock Photo; (3): Monkeybusinessimages/Getty Images; (4): *Source:* Frank Hadley Collins, Dir, Center for Global Health and Infectious Diseases; University of ND/CDC; (5): Frank Rosenstein/Getty Images; (7): AlexRaths/Getty Images; (8): *Source:* James Gathany/CDC

would indicate a recent infection by means of a mosquito bite. The presence of infected animals provides useful data on the potential for human exposure, and it also helps establish the epidemiological pattern of the zoonosis, including where it may have spread.

Nonliving Reservoirs

Clearly, microorganisms have adapted to nearly every habitat in the biosphere. They thrive in soil and water and often find their way into the air. Although most of these microbes are saprobic and cause little harm and considerable benefit to humans, some are opportunists and a few are regular pathogens. Because human hosts are in regular contact with these environmental sources, acquisition of pathogens from natural habitats is of diagnostic and epidemiological importance.

Soil harbors the vegetative forms of bacteria, protozoa, helminths, and fungi, as well as their resistant or developmental stages such as spores, cysts, ova, and larvae. Bacterial pathogens that live in soil include the anthrax bacillus and species of *Clostridium* that are responsible for gas gangrene, botulism, and tetanus. Pathogenic fungi in the genera *Coccidioides* and *Blastomyces* are spread by spores in the soil and dust. The invasive stages of the hookworm *Necator* occur in the soil. Natural bodies of water carry fewer nutrients than soil does but still support pathogenic species such as *Legionella, Cryptosporidium,* and *Giardia.*

The Acquisition and Transmission of Infectious Agents

Infectious diseases can be categorized on the basis of how they are acquired. A disease is **communicable** when an infected host can transmit the infectious agent to another host and establish infection in that new host. Although this terminology is standard, one must realize that it is not the disease that is communicated but the microbe. The transmission of the agent can be direct or indirect, and the ease with which the disease is transmitted varies considerably from one agent to another. If the agent is highly communicable, especially through direct contact, the correct term to use is **contagious.** Influenza and measles move readily from host to host and thus are contagious, whereas leprosy is only weakly communicable. Because they can be spread through the population, communicable diseases are our main focus in the following sections.

In contrast, a **noncommunicable** infectious disease does *not* arise through transmission of the infectious agent from host to host. The infection and disease are acquired through some other, special circumstance. Noncommunicable infections occur primarily when a compromised person is invaded by his or her own microbiota (as with certain pneumonias, for example) or when an individual has accidental contact with a facultative parasite that exists in a nonliving reservoir such as soil. Some examples are certain mycoses, acquired through inhalation of fungal spores, and tetanus, in which *Clostridium tetani* spores from a soiled object enter a cut or wound. Persons thus infected do not become a source of infection.

Patterns of Transmission in Communicable Diseases

The routes or patterns of disease transmission are many and varied. The spread of diseases is by direct or indirect contact with animate or inanimate objects and can be horizontal or vertical. The term *horizontal* means the disease is spread through a population from one infected individual to another; *vertical* signifies transmission from parent to offspring via the ovum, sperm, placenta, or milk. Although exact transmission patterns can vary, a general system of organization divides microorganisms into two major groups, as shown in **figure 13.18**: those transmitted by direct routes or those transmitted by indirect routes, which involve some sort of vehicle to transport them.

Modes of Direct Transmission For microbes to be directly transferred, some type of contact must occur between the skin or mucous membranes of the infected person and those of the infectee. It may help to think of this route as the portal of exit meeting the portal of entry without the involvement of an intermediate object or substance. Included in this category are fine droplets sprayed directly upon a person during sneezing or coughing (as distinguished from droplet nuclei that are transmitted some distance by air). Most sexually transmitted diseases are spread directly. In addition, infections that result from kissing or bites by biological vectors are direct. Most obligate parasites are far too sensitive to survive for long outside the host and can be transmitted only through direct contact. Diseases transmitted vertically from mother to baby fit in this contact category as well.

Routes of Indirect Transmission For microbes to be indirectly transmitted, the infectious agent must pass from an infected host to an intermediate conveyor and from there to another host. This form of communication is especially pronounced when the infected individuals contaminate inanimate objects, food, or air through their activities. The transmitter of the infectious agent can be either openly infected or a carrier.

Indirect Spread by Vehicles: Contaminated Materials The term **vehicle** specifies any inanimate material commonly used by humans that can transmit infectious agents. A **common vehicle** or **source** is a single material that serves as the source of infection for many individuals. Some specific types of vehicles are food, water, various biological products (such as blood, serum, and tissue), and fomites.

A **fomite** is an inanimate object that harbors and transmits pathogens. The list of possible fomites is as long as your imagination allows. Probably highest on the list would be objects commonly in contact with the public, such as doorknobs, telephones, push buttons, and faucet handles that are readily contaminated by touching. Shared bed linens, handkerchiefs, toilet seats, toys, eating utensils, clothing, personal articles, and syringes are other examples. Although paper money is impregnated with a disinfectant to inhibit microbes, pathogens are still isolated from bills as well as coins.

Outbreaks of food poisoning often result from the role of food as a common vehicle. The source of the agent can be soil, the handler, or a mechanical vector. Because milk provides a rich growth medium for microbes, it is a significant

> **Quick Search**
> View a short video on the effect of climate change on infectious diseases by searching for "Infectious Disease-Changing Planet."

means of transmitting pathogens from diseased animals, infected milk handlers, and environmental sources of contamination. The agents of brucellosis, Q fever, salmonellosis, and listeriosis are transmitted by contaminated milk. Water that has been contaminated by excretions can carry *Salmonella, Vibrio* (cholera), viruses (hepatitis A, polio), *Leptospira*, and pathogenic protozoans (*Giardia, Cryptosporidium*).

The **oral-fecal route** is a special category of indirect transmission, which specifies that a vehicle first becomes contaminated through contact with fecal material and is then transported to someone's mouth. A common scenario would involve a fecal carrier contaminating food during handling and an unsuspecting person ingesting it. Hepatitis A, amebic dysentery, shigellosis, and typhoid fever are often transmitted this way. Oral-fecal transmission can also involve contaminated materials such as toys, diapers, and other inanimate objects. An example would be the norovirus, which is readily picked up through contact with public facilities touched by an infected person. Handwashing anyone?

Indirect Spread by Vehicles: Air as a Vehicle Unlike soil and water, outdoor air cannot provide nutritional support for most microbial growth and is less likely to transmit airborne pathogens. On the other hand, indoor air (especially in a closed space) can serve as an important medium for the suspension and dispersal of certain respiratory pathogens via droplet nuclei and aerosols.

Droplet nuclei are dried microscopic residues created when microscopic pellets of mucus and saliva are ejected from the mouth and nose. They are generated forcefully in an unstifled sneeze or cough (**figure 13.19**) or mildly during other vocalizations. Although the larger beads of moisture settle rapidly, smaller particles evaporate and remain suspended for longer periods and can be drawn deeply into the lungs. Droplet nuclei are implicated in the spread of hardier pathogens such as the tubercle bacillus and the influenza virus.

Figure 13.19 **The explosiveness of a sneeze.** Special photography dramatically captures droplet formation in an unstifled sneeze. Even the merest attempt to cover a sneeze with one's hand will reduce this effect considerably. When such droplets dry and remain suspended in air, they become droplet nuclei.
Source: James Gathany/CDC

Aerosols are suspensions of fine dust or moisture particles in the air that contain live pathogens. Q fever is spread by dust from animal quarters, and psittacosis by aerosols from infected birds. Outbreaks of coccidioidomycosis (a lung infection) often occur in areas where soil is disturbed by wind or digging, releasing clouds of dust bearing the spores of *Coccidioides*.

Practice SECTION 13.4

22. Explain the differences between communicable and noncommunicable infectious diseases and between (direct) contact and indirect modes of transmission.
23. Distinguish between reservoirs and sources, using examples.
24. State the primary differences between mechanical and biological vectors.
25. Define *zoonosis* and describe the difficulties in controlling zoonotic infections.
26. Explain what it means to be a carrier of infectious disease, and describe four ways in which humans can be carriers.
27. What is epidemiologically and medically important about carriers in the population?

13.5 The Work of Epidemiologists: Investigation and Surveillance

 ## Learn

24. Explain the primary methods of tracking infections and diseases in a population.
25. Differentiate among the patterns of disease outbreaks according to frequency, number, and location.
26. Summarize the steps in Koch's postulates, and explain their importance to microbiologists.
27. Discuss important aspects of healthcare-associated infections and their impact on patients in clinical settings.
28. Explain what is meant by universal precautions, and discuss how they are implemented.

Epidemiologists are concerned with all of the factors covered earlier in this chapter: virulence, portals of entry and exit, and the course of disease. But they are also interested in **surveillance;** that is, collecting, analyzing, and reporting data on the rates of occurrence, mortality, morbidity, and transmission of infections. A well-developed network of individuals and agencies at the local, district, state, national, and international levels keeps constant track of infectious diseases. Surveillance involves monitoring data for a large number of diseases observed in the medical setting and reported to public health authorities. By law, certain **reportable diseases** must be reported to authorities; **notifiable** diseases are reported on a voluntary basis. Physicians and hospitals must contact the appropriate agency for all reportable diseases that are

brought to their attention. Case reporting can focus on a single individual or collectively on group data.

Local public health agencies first receive the case data and determine how the data will be handled. In most cases, health officers investigate the history and movements of patients to trace their prior contacts and to control the further spread of the infection as soon as possible through drug therapy, immunization, and education. In sexually transmitted diseases, patients are asked to name their partners so that these persons can be notified, examined, and treated. It is very important to maintain the confidentiality of the persons in these reports. The principal government agency responsible for keeping track of infectious diseases nationwide is the Centers for Disease Control and Prevention (CDC) in Atlanta, Georgia, which is home to the **National Notifiable Diseases Surveillance System (NNDSS).** The CDC publishes a weekly notice of diseases (the *Morbidity and Mortality Weekly Report*) that provides weekly and cumulative summaries of the case rates and deaths for about 50 notifiable and 65 reportable diseases, highlights important and unusual diseases, and presents data concerning disease occurrence in the major regions of the United States. This notice is available to anyone at http://www.cdc.gov/mmwr/. Ultimately the CDC shares its statistics on diseases with the World Health Organization (WHO) for worldwide tabulation and control.

Epidemiological Statistics: Frequency of Cases

The **prevalence** of a disease is the accumulated total of existing cases with respect to the entire population. It is usually reported as the percentage of the population having a particular disease and provides an indicator of how commonly a disease occurs in a population. Disease **incidence** measures the number of new cases over a certain time period, as compared with the general healthy population. This statistic, also called the case rate or morbidity rate, indicates both the rate and the risk of infection at the time of reporting. The equations used to figure these rates follow:

$$\text{Prevalence} = \frac{\text{Total number of cases in population}}{\text{Total number of persons in population}} \times 100 = \%$$

$$\text{Incidence} = \frac{\text{Number of new cases}}{\text{Total number of susceptible persons}} \quad \text{(Usually reported per 100,000 persons)}$$

(a)

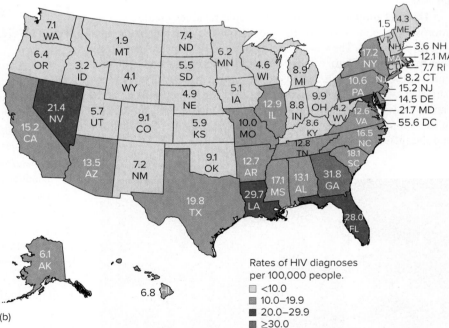

(b)

Figure 13.20 Samples of epidemiological data as analyzed by the CDC. **(a)** FluView is a CDC application that displays influenza statistics. Here, the 2017–2018 flu season is displayed by infections per week, and age of patient. **(b)** HIV diagnosis, by state, 2016.

(a): *Source:* Fluview, Centers for Disease Control and Prevention; (b): *Source:* Centers for Disease Control and Prevention

As an example, let us use a classroom of 50 students exposed to a new strain of influenza. Before exposure, the prevalence and incidence in this population are both zero (0/50). If in a week, 5 out of the 50 people contract the disease, the prevalence is 5/50 = 10%, and the incidence is 1 in 10 (10 is used instead of 100,000 due to smaller population). If within a month 25 more people acquire the flu, the prevalence becomes 30/50 or 60%, and the incidence (the number of new infections) is 25/50, or 5 in 10. Using reported cases of HIV infection as a real-life example, the most recent statistics show a cumulative total of cases (prevalence) between 1981 and 2015 of 1,007,000 cases, or 0.31% of the population. The incidence of 38,500 cases for just the year 2015 averages out to 11.8 cases per 100,000 people.

The changes in incidence and prevalence are usually followed over a seasonal, yearly, and long-term basis and are helpful in predicting trends **(figure 13.20).** Statistics of concern to the epidemiologist are the rates of disease with regard to sex, race, or geographic region. Also of importance is the **mortality rate,** which measures the total number of deaths in a population due to a certain disease. Over the past century, the overall death rate from infectious diseases has dropped, although the **morbidity*** rate, or the number of persons afflicted with infectious diseases, has remained relatively high.

* *morbidity* (mor-bih′-dih-tee) L. *morbidis,* sick. A condition of being diseased.

Monitoring statistics also makes it possible to define how often a disease appears in a given population. An infectious disease that exhibits a relatively steady and predictable frequency over a long time period and is tied to a particular geographic locale is **endemic (figure 13.21a).** Often the reason for endemicity is the presence of a reservoir restricted to that location. For example, Lyme disease is endemic to certain areas of the United States where the tick vector is found. New cases are expected to appear in these areas every year. For a disease to be considered **sporadic,** occasional cases are reported at irregular intervals in widely dispersed locations **(figure 13.21b).** Tetanus and typhoid fever are reported sporadically in the United States (fewer than 500 cases a year in a random distribution).

When statistics indicate that the number of new cases of an endemic or sporadic disease is increasing beyond what is expected for that population, this trend is known as an **epidemic (figure 13.21c).** The time period is not defined. It can range from hours in food poisoning to years in STDs, such as gonorrhea or chlamydiosis. The term **outbreak** is often used interchangeably with *epidemic,* but an outbreak is usually on a smaller scale in a more limited area. In this chapter's Case Study, the Ebola cases in Africa started as outbreaks, but as time went on, the numbers of cases and regions affected rose to the level of an epidemic. There is no exact percentage of increase required before an outbreak can qualify as an epidemic. Several diseases are at epidemic levels in the United States, the most recent examples being hepatitis C and pertussis.

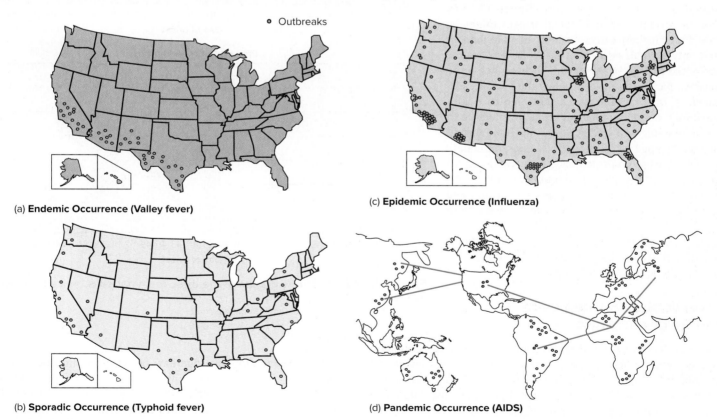

● Outbreaks

(a) **Endemic Occurrence (Valley fever)**

(c) **Epidemic Occurrence (Influenza)**

(b) **Sporadic Occurrence (Typhoid fever)**

(d) **Pandemic Occurrence (AIDS)**

Figure 13.21 **Patterns of infectious disease occurrence. (a)** In endemic occurrence, cases are concentrated in one region at a relatively stable rate. **(b)** In sporadic occurrence, a few cases occur randomly over a wide area. **(c)** An epidemic is an increased number of cases that often appear in geographic clusters. The clusters may be local, as in the case of a restaurant-related food-borne epidemic, or nationwide, as is the case with influenza. **(d)** A pandemic results when an epidemic ranges across continents and borders.

One useful way to analyze data from outbreaks is to graph the number of cases over time in an **epicurve** format **(figure 13.22).** The pattern of epidemics will ordinarily follow one of three patterns. The first, a **point-source epidemic,** indicates that the infectious agent came from a single source more or less simultaneously, as when a single batch of contaminated food is served at a BBQ, sickening everyone. The curve begins abruptly and gradually diminishes. A **common-source epidemic** occurs when all cases came from exposure to the same source, which continues to infect others over time. The epicurve in this case will have irregular peaks corresponding to the timing and extent of exposure. An example is a restaurant worker with poor hygiene who infects diners every time he works. A **propagated epidemic** occurs when a disease is transmitted from person to person, as when a microbiology instructor with influenza infects several students during lecture, who in turn infect other students as they attend other classes. The curve in this case shows a sustained increase over time, indicating that it is being communicated from person to person.

The spread of an epidemic across continents or international borders is a **pandemic,** as exemplified by AIDS and influenza **(figure 13.21d).** One important epidemiological truism might be called the "iceberg effect," which refers to the fact that only a small portion of an iceberg is visible above the surface of the ocean, with a much more massive part lying unseen below the surface. Regardless of case reporting and public health screening, a large number of cases of infection in the community go undiagnosed and unreported. In the instance of salmonellosis, approximately 40,000 cases are reported each year. Epidemiologists estimate that the actual number of infections is more likely somewhere between 1 million and 2 million. The iceberg effect can be even more lopsided for sexually transmitted diseases or for infections that are not reported to agencies. For a list of reportable diseases in the United States, refer to the appendix on Connect.

(a)

(b)

(c)

Figure 13.22 **Epicurve graphs of the three main patterns typically shown by epidemics.**
Source: UNC Gillings School Of Global Public Health

Investigative Strategies of the Epidemiologist

Initial evidence of a new disease or an epidemic in the community is fragmentary. A few sporadic cases are seen by health care providers and are eventually reported to authorities. It can take several reports before any alarm is registered. Epidemiologists and public health departments play the part of medical detectives who must piece together odds and ends of data from similar cases and attempt to find any connections they may have. This often involves working backward to reconstruct factors that could play some part in the outbreak or epidemic. A completely new disease requires even greater preliminary investigation, because the infectious agent must be isolated and linked directly to the disease **(13.5 Making Connections).** An early piece of information that drives an investigation is the **index case,** defined as the first case to bring the infection or disease to the attention of medical authorities. It may not even be the first case, but it is the first one reported. Usually other cases will follow, and the ensuing statistics will help fine-tune the investigation.

13.5 MAKING CONNECTIONS

Koch's Postulates: Solving the Puzzle of New Diseases

An essential aim in the study of infection and disease is determining the precise **etiologic,** or causative, **agent.** In our modern technological age, we take it for granted that a certain infection is caused by a certain microbe, but such has not always been the case. More than 130 years ago, Robert Koch realized that in order to support the germ theory of disease, he would have to develop a standard for determining causation that would stand the test of scientific scrutiny. Out of his experimental observations on the transmission of anthrax in cows came a series of proofs, called **Koch's postulates,** that established the principal criteria for etiologic studies. A summary of these postulates is as follows:

1. find evidence of a particular microbe in every case of a disease,
2. isolate that microbe from an infected subject and cultivate it artificially in the laboratory,
3. inoculate a susceptible healthy animal with the laboratory isolate and observe the same resultant disease in that animal, and
4. re-isolate the agent from the diseased animal.

Valid application of Koch's postulates involves several critical details. Each culture must be pure, observed microscopically, and identified by means of characteristic tests; the first and second isolate must be identical; and the pathologic effects, signs, and symptoms of the disease in the first and second subject must be the same. Once established, these postulates were rapidly put to the test. Within a short time, they had helped determine the causative agents of tuberculosis, diphtheria, and plague. Today, most infectious diseases have been directly linked to a known agent.

Many infectious agents such as viruses and obligately parasitic bacteria can be difficult to culture or cannot be cultured. For these pathogens, the postulates have been modified to take this into account. It is now considered significant to repeatedly observe the infectious agent in tissue samples taken from people with the same disease. A good case in point is Whipple disease, a chronic intestinal infection that for many years could not be tied to a known causative agent. Finally medical researchers had sufficient evidence of a bacterium being consistently present in infected tissues to give an identity to the mystery pathogen, which they named *Tropheryma whipplei*. Modern sequencing techniques to analyze unculturable microbes and their genes have added a new type of evidence for fulfilling the postulates.

Koch's original postulates—or a modified version—continue to play an essential role in modern epidemiology. Nearly every year, new diseases arise or old ones spread out of their usual range. Notable examples include dengue fever, influenza, SARS, and West Nile fever. Viral diseases require some modifications to the postulates. These include that the virus must be cultivated in cell culture, it must be filterable through bacteriological filters, and it must cause a detectable specific immune response.

Explain how we can be so certain that HIV causes AIDS even though there is no effective animal model for it.

(1) Specimen from patient ill with infection of unknown etiology is carried through an isolation procedure.

(2) A pure culture of the suspected agent is made.

Full microscopic and biological characterization

(3) Inoculation of test animal

Observe animal for disease characteristics

Specimen taken

(4) Pure culture and identification procedures

The microbe in the initial and second isolations and the disease in the patient and experimental animal must match for the postulates to be satisfied.

All factors possibly impinging on the disease are scrutinized. Investigators search for *clusters* of cases indicating transmission between persons or a public (common) source or vehicle. They also look at possible contact with animals, contaminated food, water, and public facilities and at human interrelationships or changes in community structure. Out of this maze of case information, the investigators hope to recognize a pattern that indicates the source of infection so that they can quickly move to control it.

Hospital Epidemiology and Healthcare-Associated Infections

Infectious diseases that are acquired or develop during a stay in a medical facility are known as **healthcare-associated infections (HAIs)**. This concept seems incongruous at first thought, because a hospital or clinic is regarded as a place to get treatment for a medical problem, not a place to acquire one. Yet it is not uncommon for a surgical incision to become infected or a patient with a catheter to develop a urinary tract infection after being treated in a hospital or clinic. The rate of hospital-acquired infections can be as low as 0.1% or as high as 20% of all admitted patients, depending on the clinical setting or hospital. The average rate is about 3% (1 out of 31 patients). In light of the number of admissions, this adds up to 1 million to 2 million cases a year, which result in around 72,000 deaths. By one estimate, they amount to 8 million additional days of hospitalization a year and an increased cost of $5 billion to $10 billion.

So many factors unique to the hospital environment create conditions that favor HAIs that a certain number of them are virtually unavoidable. After all, the hospital both attracts and creates compromised patients, and it serves as a collection point for opportunistic pathogens. Some patients become infected when surgical procedures or lowered defenses permit resident microbes to invade their bodies. Other patients acquire infections directly or indirectly from contaminated catheters or ventilators and other medical equipment, other patients, medical personnel, visitors, air, and water.

The healthcare process itself increases the likelihood that infectious agents will be transferred from one patient to another. Treatments using reusable instruments such as respirators and endoscopes constitute a possible source of infectious agents (see the Case Study in chapter 11). Indwelling devices such as catheters, prosthetic heart valves, grafts, and tracheostomy tubes form a ready portal of entry and habitat for infectious agents. Because such high numbers of the hospital population receive antimicrobial drugs during their stay, drug-resistant microbes are selected for at a much greater rate compared to outside the hospital.

The most common HAIs involve surgical incisions and the respiratory tract, GI tract, skin, urinary tract, and blood (sepsis) **(figure 13.23)**. Gram-negative intestinal bacteria (*Escherichia coli, Klebsiella, Pseudomonas*) are cultured in more than half of patients with HAIs. Gram-positive bacteria (staphylococci and streptococci) and yeasts (*Candida*) make up most of the remainder. True pathogens such as the tubercle bacillus, *Salmonella,* hepatitis B, and influenza virus can be transmitted in the clinical setting as well.

The potential seriousness and impact of healthcare-associated infections have required hospitals to develop committees that monitor infectious outbreaks and develop guidelines for infection control and aseptic procedures. *Medical asepsis* includes practices that lower the microbial load in patients, caregivers, and the hospital environment. These practices include proper hand washing, disinfection, and sanitization, as well as patient isolation. **Table 13.11** summarizes guidelines for the major types of isolation. The goal of these procedures is to limit the spread of infectious agents from person to person. The most rigorous level of precautions is associated with *surgical asepsis,* which involves all of the strategies listed previously plus ensuring that all surgical procedures are conducted under sterile conditions. This includes sterilization of surgical instruments, dressings, sponges, and the like, as well as clothing personnel in sterile garments and scrupulously disinfecting the room surfaces and air.

Hospitals generally employ an *infection control officer* who not only implements proper practices and procedures throughout the hospital but also is charged with tracking potential outbreaks, identifying breaches in asepsis, and training other healthcare workers in aseptic technique. Among those most in need of this training are nurses and other caregivers whose work, by its very nature, exposes them to

Figure 13.23 **Prevalence of healthcare-associated infections (HAIs).** Relative frequency by body site. These are the most common isolates out of the nearly 500 pathogens that are known to cause HAIs. *Source:* National Health Safety Network, a unit of the CDC.
Source: Centers for Disease Control and Prevention

TABLE 13.11	Levels of Isolation Used in Clinical Settings	
Type of Isolation*	**Protective Measures****	**To Prevent Spread Of**
Enteric Precautions	Gowns and gloves must be worn by all persons having direct contact with patient; masks are not required; special precautions are taken for disposing of feces and urine.	Diarrheal diseases; *Shigella, Salmonella, E. coli,* and *Clostridioides difficile;* cholera; hepatitis A; rotavirus; and giardiasis
Respiratory Precautions	Private room with closed door is necessary; gowns and gloves are not required; masks are usually indicated; items contaminated with secretions must be disinfected.	Tuberculosis, measles, mumps, meningitis, pertussis, rubella, chickenpox
Drainage and Secretion Precautions	Gowns and gloves are required; masks are not needed; contaminated instruments and dressings require special precautions.	Staphylococcal and streptococcal infections; gas gangrene; herpes zoster; burn infections
Strict Isolation	Private room with closed door is required; gowns, masks, and gloves must be worn; contaminated items must be wrapped and decontaminated.	Mostly highly virulent or contagious microbes; includes tuberculosis, some types of pneumonia, extensive skin and burn infections, herpes simplex and zoster
Reverse Isolation (Also Called Protective Isolation)	Same guidelines as for strict isolation are required; room may be ventilated by laminar airflow filtered through a high-efficiency particulate (HEPA) filter that removes airborne pathogens; infected persons must be barred.	Used to protect patients extremely immunocompromised by cancer therapy, surgery, genetic defects, burns, prematurity, or AIDS and therefore vulnerable to opportunistic pathogens

*Precautions are based upon the primary portal of entry and communicability of the pathogen.

**In all cases, visitors to the patient's room must report to the nurses' station before entering the room; all visitors and personnel must wash their hands upon entering and leaving the room.

needlesticks, infectious secretions, blood, and physical contact with the patient. The same practices that interrupt the routes of infection in the patient can also protect the healthcare worker. It is for this reason that most hospitals have adopted universal precautions that recognize that all secretions from all persons in the clinical setting are potentially infectious and that transmission can occur in either direction.

Universal Blood and Body Fluid Precautions

Medical and dental settings require stringent measures to prevent the spread of infectious agents from patient to patient, from patient to worker, and from worker to patient. But even with precautions, the rate of such infections can be rather high. An established body of evidence indicates that more than one-third of health-care-acquired infections could be prevented by consistent and rigorous infection control methods.

Previously control guidelines were disease-specific, and clearly identified infections were managed with particular restrictions and techniques. With this arrangement, personnel tended to handle materials labeled *infectious* with much greater care than those that were not so labeled. The AIDS epidemic spurred a reexamination of that policy. Because of the potential for patients with undiagnosed infections, the CDC laid down more-stringent guidelines for handling patients and body substances. These guidelines have been termed **universal precautions (UPs),** because they are based on the assumption that all patient specimens could harbor infectious agents and so must be

treated with the same degree of care. They also include body substance isolation (BSI) techniques to be used in known cases of infection.

It is worth mentioning that these precautions are designed to protect all individuals in the clinical setting—patients, workers, and the public alike. In general, they include techniques designed to prevent contact with pathogens and contamination and, if prevention is not possible, to take purposeful measures to decontaminate potentially infectious materials. See appendix B for a more detailed list of UPs.

 Practice SECTION 13.5

28. Outline the science of epidemiology and the work of an epidemiologist.

29. What types of information do epidemiologists require to differentiate between incidence and prevalence of infectious diseases?

30. Distinguish between point-source, common-source, and propagated epidemics, and explain what is meant by an index case.

31. List the main features of Koch's postulates and explain why it is so difficult to prove them for some diseases.

32. Health-care-associated infections can arise from what general sources?

33. Outline the major factors involved in healthcare–associated infections and describe the levels of precaution that are followed to prevent HAIs.

CASE STUDY | Part 2

Despite the attempts to prevent transmission of the virus, two people acquired Ebola infections from contact with Mr. Duncan. Both were nurses who had provided round-the-clock care during the time he was hospitalized. First, Nina Pham began to register a low-grade fever 4 days after his death. She was immediately tested for Ebola virus and moved into an isolation unit. Two days later, Amber Vinson reported a fever and was also isolated. Both women tested positive for the virus. They were continuously monitored and provided intensive medical support at other hospitals, but they received no antiviral medicines because specific drugs were not yet available. Within 2 weeks both nurses recovered, were found to be free of the virus, and were released from isolation.

Even though these cases were the only ones that originated in the United States, they still fostered a wave of fear in the populace that this epidemic could evolve into a pandemic. In addition to the anguish of the two nurses and their families, repercussions were felt in the lives of many other people. In this situation, a carrier in the prodromal phase can actively transmit the virus, so it was necessary for public health officers to implement tracing, monitoring, and quarantining of all contacts. This included all hospital workers and their families, crews and passengers on Mr. Duncan's airline flight, and Mr. Duncan's family and contacts, which eventually totaled over 200 people. Several other American health care workers came down with Ebola, but all of them were infected while caring for patients in West Africa, and all but one of them survived.

The story of Ebola virus outbreaks is not a new one. The first cases, originally termed *Ebola hemorrhagic fever,* occurred near the Ebola River of Zaire (now the Central

African Republic) in 1976. Since then, there have been 24 additional outbreaks, but the one in 2014–2015 was by far the most severe. It affected 28,638 people and killed 11,315 in Africa, with the mortality rate varying from 25% to 90% (average is 50%). The epidemic was declared over in January 2016, following a period with no new case reports. As of late 2019, an ongoing Ebola outbreak in the Democratic Republic of the Congo has affected more than 3,000 people and taken nearly 2,000 lives.

Virologists who have been studying the origins of the Ebola virus for 4 decades have long considered it a zoonosis transmitted by biological vectors. It has been isolated from primates such as great apes and monkeys, but it causes a deadly infection in these animals, which means they are probably not reservoir hosts. The current consensus is that species of fruit bats and insectivorous bats are the most likely reservoirs. We know that the source of most human infections is other humans and animals, especially forest animals that are butchered for meat. In humans it is transmitted only by direct contact with patient fluids such as blood, feces, vomit, saliva, urine, breast milk, and semen. It is likely that infections occur when these body fluids contaminate portals of entry such as exposed skin; cuts; and mucous membranes of the mouth, nose, and eyes. There is little evidence that infection occurs through airborne droplet nuclei, coughing, sneezing, food (except wild meat), fomites, or mosquitoes.

■ Explain why this epidemic of Ebola virus disease was not considered a pandemic.

■ Provide some explanations why Ebola virus would be transmitted by fresh droplets but not droplet nuclei.

Chapter Summary with Key Terms

13.1 We Are Not Alone

A. The human body is in contact with microbes that are constantly present in the environment. Microbes are classified as either part of the normal residents of the body or as **pathogens,** depending on whether or not their colonization of the body results in infection.

B. *Resident Microbiota: The Human as Habitat*

1. **Normal resident microbiota** consist of a huge and varied population of microbes that reside permanently on all surfaces of the body exposed to the environment.

2. Colonization begins prior to birth and continues throughout life. Variations in normal residents occur in response to changes in an individual's age, diet, hygiene, and health.

3. Normal residents often provide some benefit to the host but are also capable of causing disease, especially when the immune system of the host is compromised or when they invade a normally sterile area of the body.

4. An important benefit provided by microbiota is **microbial antagonism.**

C. *Indigenous Microbiota of Specific Regions* Resident microbes include bacteria, fungi, and protozoa. They occupy the skin, mouth, gastrointestinal tract, large intestine, respiratory tract, and genitourinary tract.

13.2 Major Factors in the Development of an Infection

A. **Pathogenicity** is the ability of microorganisms to cause infection and disease; **virulence** refers to the degree to which a microbe can invade and damage host tissues.

1. **True pathogens** are able to cause disease in a normal healthy host with intact immune defenses.
2. **Opportunistic pathogens** can cause disease only in persons whose host defenses are compromised by *predisposing conditions.*

B. *Becoming Established: Phase 1—Portals of Entry*
 1. Microbes typically enter the body through a specific **portal of entry.** Portals of entry are generally the same as those areas of the body that harbor microbiota.
 2. The minimum number of microbes needed to produce an infection is termed the **infectious dose,** and these pathogens may be classified as **exogenous** or **endogenous,** based on their source.

C. *Attaching to the Host: Phase 2* Microbes attach to the host cell, a process known as **adhesion,** by means of fimbriae, capsules, or receptors.

D. *Invading the Host and Becoming Established: Phase 3* Microbes that persist in the human host have developed mechanisms of disabling early defensive strategies.

E. *How Virulence Factors Contribute to Tissue Damage and Disease* **Virulence factors** are structures or properties of a microbe that lead to pathologic effects on the host. Some virulence factors are those that enable entry or adhesion, but many virulence factors lead directly to damage. These fall in three categories: enzymes, toxins, and the inhibition or destruction of phagocytes.
 1. **Exoenzymes** digest epithelial tissues and permit **invasion** of pathogens.
 2. **Toxigenicity** refers to a microbe's capacity to produce **toxins** at the site of multiplication. Toxins are divided into **endotoxins** and **exotoxins,** and diseases caused by toxins are classified as **intoxications, toxemias,** or **toxinoses.**

13.3 The Outcomes of Infection and Disease

A. **Infectious diseases** follow a typical pattern consisting of an **incubation period, prodromal stage, period of invasion,** and **convalescent period.** Each stage is marked by symptoms of a specific intensity.

B. Infections are classified by
 1. whether they remain localized at the site of inoculation **(localized infection, systemic infection, focal infection);**
 2. the number of microbes involved in an infection, and the order in which they infect the body **(mixed infection, primary infection, secondary infection);** and
 3. the persistence of the infection **(acute infection, chronic infection,** subacute infection).

C. **Signs** of infection refer to *objective* evidence of infection, and **symptoms** refer to *subjective* evidence. A **syndrome** is a disease that manifests as a predictable complex of symptoms.

D. After the initial infection, pathogens may remain in the body in a **latent** state and may later cause recurrent infections. Long-term damages to host cells are referred to as **sequelae.**

E. Microbes are released from the body through a specific **portal of exit** that allows them access to another host.

13.4 Epidemiology: The Study of Disease in Populations *Origins and Transmission Patterns of Infectious Microbes*

A. The **reservoir** of a microbe refers to its natural habitat; a pathogen's **source** refers to the immediate origin of an infectious agent.

B. **Carriers** are individuals who inconspicuously shelter a pathogen and spread it to others. Carriers are divided into **asymptomatic carriers,** incubation carriers, convalescent carriers, chronic carriers, and **passive carriers.**

C. **Vectors** refer to animals that transmit pathogens.
 1. **Biological vectors** are animals that are involved in the life cycle of the pathogen they transmit; **mechanical vectors** transmit pathogens without being involved in the life cycle.
 2. **Zoonoses** are diseases that can be transmitted to humans but are normally found in animal populations.

D. Agents of disease are either **communicable** or **noncommunicable,** with highly communicable diseases referred to as **contagious.**
 1. Direct transmission of a disease occurs when a portal of exit meets a portal of entrance.
 2. Indirect transmission occurs when an intermediary such as a **vehicle, fomite,** or **droplet nuclei** connects portals of entrance and exit.

13.5 The Work of Epidemiologists: Investigation and Surveillance

A. Epidemiologists are involved in the surveillance of **reportable** and notifiable diseases in populations.

B. Infectious diseases are tabulated with regard to their **prevalence** and **incidence.**

C. Populations are analyzed with regard to **morbidity, mortality,** age, sex, and geographic region.

D. Disease patterns are described as being **endemic, sporadic, epidemic,** or **pandemic** based on the frequency of their occurrence in a population.

E. Epidemiologists look for **index cases** and changes in the occurrence of diseases such as clusters of new cases. They compile evidence and **trace back** to the original source or reservoir.

F. **Healthcare–associated infections (HAIs)** are diseases acquired in a hospital or other clinical setting. Special vigilance is required to reduce their occurrence. Most HAIs involve the respiratory tract, surgical incisions, the GI tract, urinary tract, skin, and blood. Infectious agents may originate from the microbiota, medical devices, patients, healthcare workers, and the environment.

Assess Your Knowledge

Level I. These questions require a working knowledge of the concepts in the chapter and the ability to recall and understand the information you have studied.

Developing a Concept Inventory

Select the correct answer from the answers provided. For questions with blanks, choose the combination of answers that most accurately completes the statement.

1. The best descriptive term for the resident microbes is
 a. commensals
 b. parasites
 c. pathogens
 d. contaminants

2. Resident microbiota are commonly found in the
 a. liver
 b. kidney
 c. salivary glands
 d. urethra

3. Normal resident microbes are absent from the
 a. pharynx
 b. lungs
 c. intestine
 d. hair follicles

4. Virulence factors include
 a. toxins
 b. exoenzymes
 c. capsules
 d. all of these

5. The specific action of hemolysins is to
 a. damage white blood cells
 b. cause fever
 c. damage red blood cells
 d. cause leukocytosis

6. The _____ is the time that lapses between encounter with a pathogen and the first symptoms.
 a. prodrome
 b. period of invasion
 c. period of convalescence
 d. period of incubation

7. A short period early in a disease that manifests with general malaise and achiness is the
 a. period of incubation
 b. prodrome
 c. sequela
 d. period of invasion

8. The presence of a few bacteria in the blood is termed
 a. septicemia
 b. toxemia
 c. bacteremia
 d. a secondary infection

9. A _____ infection is acquired through exposure in a hospital setting.
 a. subclinical
 b. focal
 c. HAI
 d. secondary

10. A(n) _____ is a passive animal transporter of pathogens.
 a. zoonosis
 b. biological vector
 c. mechanical vector
 d. asymptomatic carrier

11. An example of a noncommunicable infection is
 a. measles
 b. leprosy
 c. tuberculosis
 d. tetanus

12. A general term that refers to an increased white blood cell count is
 a. leukopenia
 b. inflammation
 c. leukocytosis
 d. leukemia

13. The occurrence of Lyme disease mainly in areas where certain species of ticks live would define it as a(n) _____ disease.
 a. epidemic
 b. pandemic
 c. endemic
 d. sporadic

14. A positive antibody test for HIV would be a _____ of infection.
 a. sign
 b. symptom
 c. syndrome
 d. sequela

15. Which of the following would *not* be a portal of entry?
 a. the meninges
 b. the placenta
 c. skin
 d. small intestine

16. Which of the following is *not* a condition of Koch's postulates?
 a. isolate the causative agent of a disease
 b. cultivate the microbe in a lab
 c. inoculate a test animal to observe the disease
 d. test the effects of a pathogen on humans

Case Study Analysis

1. Which of these would be the index case for the Ebola epidemic?
 a. Nina Pham
 b. the baby in Guinea
 c. Thomas Duncan
 d. a dead monkey
2. Ebola virus is a(n) ___ virus classified in the ___ family.
 a. enveloped RNA, rhabdovirus
 b. naked DNA, adenovirus
 c. enveloped DNA, herpesvirus
 d. enveloped RNA, filovirus

3. Explain what features of the virulence, infectious dose, and incubation period of Ebola virus increase its transmission from person to person.

On the Test

These questions will help to prepare you to successfully answer similar questions you'll see on the TEAS (Test of Essential Academic Skills) and NCLEX (National Council Licensure Examination).

1. A nurse is working with her hospital's infection control officer to reduce healthcare-associated infections (HAIs). Which strategy would likely reduce HAIs to the greatest extent?
 a. ensuring adequate nutrition and hydration of her clients
 b. limiting the use of urinary catheters
 c. making certain that her client's immunizations are up to date
 d. requiring the use of walkers for those patients with limited mobility

2. A client who is 22 weeks' pregnant asks the nurse about infections that may lead to miscarriage or birth defects. The nurse answers that all of the following except _____ are of particular concern for pregnant women.
 a. *Staphylococcus aureus*
 b. herpes simplex virus
 c. rubella
 d. cytomegalovirus

Writing Challenge

For each question, compose a one- or two-paragraph answer that includes the factual information needed to completely address the question. Practice questions can also be used for writing-challenge exercises.

1. What are the important clinical implications of blood or cerebrospinal fluid that tests positive for microbes?
2. What is the expected result if a compromised person is exposed to a true pathogen?
3. Explain how endotoxin gets into the bloodstream of a patient with endotoxic shock.
4. Give a brief description of how the A-B type of toxin works.
5. For each portal of entry, give a vehicle that carries the pathogen and the course it must travel to invade the tissues.
6. What are some important considerations about the portal of exit?
7. What does it mean for salmonellosis to have an iceberg effect?

8. a. Outline the five types of clinical isolation.
 b. Describe the work of an infection control officer.
9. Complete the following table.

	Exotoxins	Endotoxins
Chemical makeup		
General source		
Degree of toxicity		
Effects on cells		
Symptoms in disease		
Examples		

Concept Mapping

On Connect you can find an Introduction to Concept Mapping that provides guidance for working with concept maps, along with concept-mapping activities for this chapter.

Application, Analysis, Evaluation, and Synthesis

Level II. These problems go beyond just restating facts and require higher levels of understanding and an ability to interpret, problem solve, transfer knowledge to new situations, create models, and predict outcomes.

Critical Thinking

Critical thinking is the ability to reason and solve problems using facts and concepts. These questions can be approached from a number of angles and, in most cases, they do not have a single correct answer.

1. Discuss the relationship between the vaginal residents and the colonization of the newborn.

2. Can you think of some medical consequences of this relationship?

3. How could the microbiome cause some infections to be more severe and other infections to be less severe?

4. Each of the nine patient specimens listed below has produced a positive culture when inoculated and grown on appropriate media. Indicate whether this result is indicative of infection and explain why or why not.

 Urine from urethra Liver biopsy Blood
 Lung biopsy Throat Urine from bladder
 Saliva Cerebrospinal fluid Semen

5. Use the following formula to explain the relationships among the several factors and what happens when they change:

$$\frac{\text{Infection}}{\text{(infectious disease)}} = \frac{\text{No. of organisms} \times \text{Virulence}}{\text{Host resistance}}$$

6. Assume that you have been given the job of developing a colony of germ-free chickens.
 a. What will be the main steps in this process?
 b. What possible experiments can you do with these animals?

7. Describe each of the following infections using correct technical terminology. (Descriptions may fit more than one category.)
 Use terms such as *primary, secondary, nosocomial, STD, mixed, latent, toxemia, chronic, zoonotic, asymptomatic, local, systemic, -itis, -emia.*

 Caused by needlestick in dental office
 Pneumocystis pneumonia in AIDS patient
 Bubonic plague from rat flea bite
 Diphtheria
 Undiagnosed chlamydiosis
 Acute necrotizing gingivitis
 Syphilis of long duration
 Large numbers of gram-negative rods in the blood
 A boil on the back of the neck
 An inflammation of the meninges

8. a. Suggest several reasons why respiratory, surgical, and gastrointestinal infections are the most common healthcare–associated infections.
 b. Name several measures that health care providers must exercise at all times to prevent or reduce these types of infections.

9. Look at figure 13.20*a*; which pattern of epicurve does it show?

Visual Assessment

1. Briefly compare the two vectors seen below.

Mosquito

Housefly

2. Compare the two maps in (a) and (b). What pattern of spread (endemic, sporadic, epidemic) is represented by each map, and based on the illnesses involved, why does each map look as it does?

Reported cases of lyme disease—United States, 2017

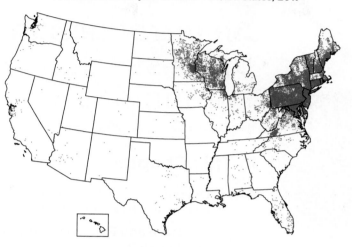

1 dot placed randomly within county of residence for each confirmed case

(a) *Source:* Centers for Disease Control and Prevention

2017–18 Influenza Season Week 10 ending Mar 10, 2018

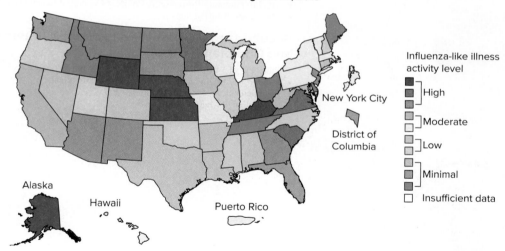

(b) *Source:* Centers for Disease Control and Prevention

3. What type of outbreak is indicated by the epicurve seen here?

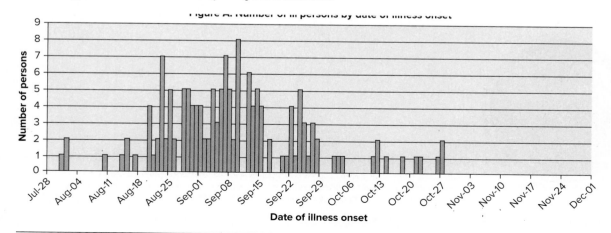

Figure A. Number of ill persons by date of illness onset

An Introduction to Host Defenses and Innate Immunities

In This Chapter...

(MRI scan): Plush Studios/Blend Images LLC; Trachea (wind pipe): Science Photo Library/Alamy Stock Photo; (Neutrophil): Courtesy of Harold Benson; (Paronychia): Robert Kirk/Getty Images; (Human neutrophil): Source: National Institute of Allergy and Infectious Diseases (NIAID)

CASE STUDY **Part 1** | When a Body Can't Get Out of Its Own Way

Certain combinations of **signs** and **symptoms** are guaranteed to garner the attention of an emergency room physician, because they signal a serious, **emergent situation.** So, when a young woman seen by emergency room doctors displayed **tachypenea** (rapid breathing), a depressed level of consciousness, and **fever,** she was immediately admitted to the hospital for further examination. She also exhibited low blood pressure, had not passed any urine that day, and had a blueish tinge to her fingers and toes, a clinical presentation compatible with **sepsis.** Sepsis is a serious complication of infection that occurs when chemicals released by the body trigger an overwhelming inflammatory response. Without rapid, aggressive treatment, sepsis can quickly lead to death.

Laboratory tests were also consistent with sepsis, as the patient had a **low platelet count** and a decreased number of infection-fighting **leukocytes.** Elevated levels of C-reactive protein indicated widespread inflammation throughout the body, while blood tests showed damage to the liver and kidneys, along with intravascular coagulation. Sepsis was causing her body to shut down.

The patient, though only 15 years old, was no stranger to the hospital. She had been diagnosed with **systemic lupus erythematosus (SLE,** or simply lupus) at the age of 6 and had an extensive medical history. Lupus is an autoimmune disorder in which the body's immune system attacks itself by producing **antibodies** against the nuclei of its own cells. **Inflammation** due to lupus can affect the skin, joints, kidneys, liver, heart, and lungs, with symptoms ranging from mild to severe, and fluctuating greatly over time. In less than 9 years, the patient had already experienced nephritis, pancreatitis, hemolytic anemia, and arterial hypertension, all due to a particularly aggressive form of the disease. Her lupus was being treated with corticosteroids along with multiple **immunosuppressive drugs,** including methotrexate and cyclophosphamide. She was last seen at the hospital 3 months previously, where she displayed no clinical manifestations of SLE.

A chest X-ray was unremarkable, while a computed tomography (CT) scan revealed sinusitis, likely not enough to cause the symptoms seen in the patient. *Streptococcus pneumoniae* was cultured from both the blood, indicating a **systemic infection,** and cerebrospinal fluid, indicating **meningitis.** *Streptococcus pneumoniae* is a gram-positive, heavily **encapsulated** bacterium, commonly responsible for infections of the sinuses, lungs, blood, and meninges. An MRI (magnetic resonance imaging) scan was performed, the results of which were remarkable not for what was seen, but for what was absent. The patient did not have a spleen.

- *Inflammation is normally part of what line of defense?*
- *If the immune system functioned properly, what type of white blood cell would be increased in number in this case?*

To continue the Case Study, go to Case Study Part 2 at the end of the chapter.

(Group C Streptococcus): Janice Haney Carr/CDC

14.1 Overview of Host Defense Mechanisms

 Learn

1. Summarize the characteristics of basic host defenses.
2. Differentiate between the three lines of defense, describing examples of each.
3. Explain the nature of the different types of innate, nonspecific defenses.

In chapter 13, we explored the human–microbe relationship, with emphasis on the role of microorganisms in disease. In this chapter, we examine the other side of the relationship—that of the host defending itself against microorganisms. As previously stated, in light of the unrelenting microbial contact with and colonization of humans, it is something of a miracle that we are not constantly infected and diseased. Our ability to overcome this continual assault on our bodies is the result of a fascinating, highly complex system.

To protect the body against pathogens, the immune system relies on an overlapping network of **host defenses** that operate on several levels. These include **innate, natural defenses** present at birth that provide nonspecific resistance to infection and **adaptive immunities** that are specific and must be acquired. These levels of protection are sometimes divided into categories called the *first, second,* and *third lines of defense* (**table 14.1**).

The *first line of defense* includes any barrier that blocks invasion at the portal of entry. This mostly nonspecific line of defense limits access to the internal tissues of the body. However, it is not considered a true immune response because it does not involve recognition of a specific foreign substance and is very general in its actions.

The *second line of defense* is a more internalized system of protective cells and fluids, which includes inflammation and phagocytosis. It acts rapidly at both the local and systemic levels once the first line of defense has been circumvented, and in most reactions it is also nonspecific.

The highly specific *third line of defense* is adaptive and acquired on an individual basis as each foreign substance is encountered by white blood cells called lymphocytes. Responses directed toward each different microbe produce unique protective substances and memory cells that can come into play if that microbe is encountered again. Details of how this third line of defense provides

long-term immunity are discussed in chapter 15, whereas this chapter focuses on the first and second lines of defense.

The various levels of defense do not operate in a completely separate fashion; most defenses overlap and are even redundant in some of their effects. This cooperative reaction targets invading microbes on several different fronts simultaneously, making their survival unlikely. To present the interactive nature of host defenses, we start with basic concepts that will build a foundation for understanding the more complex reactions of the immune system to come later.

Barriers at the Portal of Entry: An Inborn First Line of Defense

A number of defenses are a normal part of the body's anatomy and physiology. These inborn, nonspecific defenses can be divided into physical, chemical, and genetic barriers that impede the entry of not only microbes but any foreign agent, whether living or not (**figure 14.1**).

Physical or Anatomical Barriers at the Body's Surface

The skin and mucous membranes of the respiratory and digestive tracts have several built-in defenses. The outermost layer (stratum corneum) of the skin is composed of epithelial cells that have become compacted, cemented together, and impregnated with an insoluble protein, keratin. The result is a thick, tough layer that is impervious and waterproof. Few pathogens can penetrate this unbroken barrier, especially in regions such as the soles of the feet or the palms of the hands, where the stratum corneum is much thicker than on other parts of the body. Other cutaneous barriers include hair follicles and skin glands. The hair shaft is periodically extruded, and the follicle cells are **desquamated,*** or shed. The flushing effect of sweat glands also helps remove microbes.

The mucocutaneous membranes of the digestive, urinary, and respiratory tracts and of the eye are moist and permeable. Despite the normal wear and tear upon these epithelia, damaged cells are rapidly replaced. The mucous coat on the free surface of some membranes impedes the entry and attachment of bacteria. Blinking and tear production (lacrimation) flush the eye's surface with tears and rid it of irritants. The constant flow of saliva helps carry

* *desquamate* (des´-kwuh-mayt) L. *desquamo,* to scale off. The casting off of epidermal scales.

TABLE 14.1	General Features of Host Defenses

Line of Defense	Innate/ Acquired	Specific or Nonspecific	Development of Immunologic Memory	Examples
First	Innate	Nonspecific	No	Physical barriers: skin, tears, coughing, sneezing Chemical barriers: low pH, lysozyme, digestive enzymes Genetic barriers: resistance inherent in genetic makeup of host (pathogen cannot invade)
Second	Innate	Mostly nonspecific	No	Phagocytosis, inflammation, fever, interferon, complement
Third	Acquired	Specific	Yes	T lymphocytes, B lymphocytes, antibodies

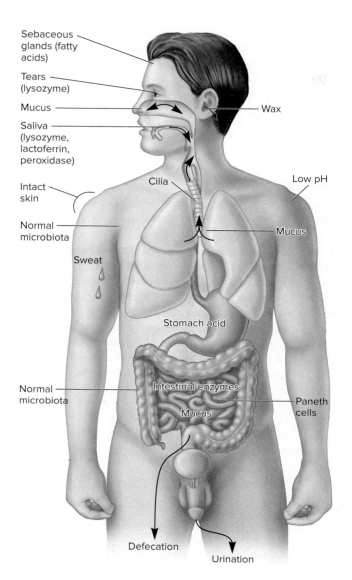

Sebaceous glands (fatty acids)

Tears (lysozyme)

Mucus

Saliva (lysozyme, lactoferrin, peroxidase)

Intact skin

Cilia

Wax

Low pH

Normal microbiota

Mucus

Sweat

Stomach acid

Normal microbiota

Intestinal enzymes

Mucus

Paneth cells

Defecation

Urination

Figure 14.1 **Defenses.** Some nonspecific defense barriers that help prevent entry of microorganisms into the host's tissues.

The composition of microbiota and its protective effect were discussed in chapter 13. Even though the normal microbial residents do not constitute a physical or anatomical barrier, their presence can block the access of pathogens to epithelial surfaces. They may also compete with pathogens for limited resources or alter the environment of the body, making it less welcoming for pathogens. Some bacterial residents of the large intestine, for instance, secrete bacteriocins or antibiotics, which can inhibit or kill other bacteria.

Nonspecific Chemical Defenses

The skin and mucous membranes offer a variety of chemical defenses. Sebaceous secretions exert an antimicrobial effect, and specialized glands such as the meibomian glands of the eyelids lubricate the conjunctiva with an antimicrobial secretion. Other defenses in tears and saliva include **lysozyme** and **defensins.** Lysozyme is an enzyme that hydrolyzes the peptidoglycan in the cell wall of bacteria. Defensins are peptides produced by various cells and tissues that damage cell membranes and lyse bacteria and fungi. Skin cells produce a defensin called dermicidin that helps eliminate bacteria, and paneth cells in the intestine secrete defensins that can destroy or inhibit several types of infectious agents. The high concentrations of lactic acid and electrolytes in sweat and the skin's acidic pH and fatty acid content are also inhibitory to many microbes.

Internally, the hydrochloric acid content of the stomach renders protection against many pathogens that are swallowed. The intestine's digestive juices and bile are also potentially destructive to microbes. Even semen contains an antimicrobial chemical that inhibits bacteria, and the vagina has a protective acidic pH maintained by lactobacilli that are part of the microbiota.

Genetic Resistance to Infection

In certain cases, the genetic makeup of an individual is different enough to ensure protection from some pathogens. One explanation for this phenomenon is that some pathogens have such great specificity for one host species that they are incapable of infecting other

microbes into the harsh conditions of the stomach. Vomiting and defecation also evacuate noxious substances or microorganisms from the body.

The respiratory tract is constantly guarded from infection by elaborate and highly effective adaptations. Nasal hair traps larger particles. Rhinitis, the inflammation of the nasal mucosa often seen with allergy and colds, creates a copious flow of mucus and fluids that helps to flush out the nasal passageways. In the respiratory tree (primarily the trachea and bronchi), a ciliated epithelium (called the ciliary escalator) conveys foreign particles entrapped in mucus toward the pharynx to be removed **(figure 14.2).** Irritation of the nasal passage reflexively initiates a sneeze, which expels a large volume of air at high velocity. Similarly, the acute sensitivity of the bronchi, trachea, and larynx to foreign matter triggers coughing, which ejects irritants.

The genitourinary tract derives partial protection from the continuous trickle of urine through the ureters and from periodic bladder emptying that flushes the urethra.

Figure 14.2 **The ciliary defense of the respiratory tree.** Epithelial cells in the trachea are covered in tufts of cilia that sweep mucus, filled with small particles and microbes, up and away from the lungs.
Science Photo Library/Alamy Stock Photo

species. This specificity is particularly true of viruses, which can invade only by attaching to a specific host receptor. Newcastle virus may kill your parrot while you remain safe, and it is perfectly okay to cuddle with your dog while recovering from the mumps. Both viruses have a limited host range. But this defense does not hold true for zoonotic infectious agents that attack a broad spectrum of animals. Genetic differences in susceptibility can also exist within members of one species. Humans carrying a mutation responsible for sickle-cell disease are resistant to malaria. Genetic differences also exist in susceptibility to tuberculosis, leprosy, and certain systemic fungal infections.

The vital contribution of barriers is clearly demonstrated in people who have lost them or never had them. Patients with severe skin damage due to burns are extremely susceptible to infections; those with blockages in the salivary glands, tear ducts, intestine, and urinary tract are also at greater risk for infection. But as important as it is, the first line of defense alone cannot provide adequate protection. Because many pathogens find a way to circumvent the barriers by using their virulence factors (discussed in chapter 13), a whole new set of defenses—inflammation, phagocytosis, specific immune responses—is ready to react to them.

 Practice SECTION 14.1

1. Explain the functions of the three lines of defense and indicate which are the most essential to survival.
2. What is the difference between nonspecific host defenses and immune responses?
3. Differentiate innate defenses and acquired immunity. What are the general characteristics of each? Discuss the advantages of having multiple defenses (innate and acquired) against the same microbe.
4. List four innate defensive responses present in the body, and explain how each type functions to combat infection.

14.2 Structure and Function of the Organs of Defense and Immunity

 Learn

4. Describe the primary functions and organs of the immune system.
5. Describe several features of the recognition system of host defenses.
6. Characterize pattern recognition receptors and pathogen-associated molecular patterns.
7. Describe the microscopic anatomy of body compartments and how they interconnect.
8. Outline the anatomy and functions of the mononuclear phagocyte system.
9. Outline the origin and composition of the blood, and characterize the types of blood cells and their functions.
10. Explain the behavior of white blood cells with regard to the blood circulation and tissues.
11. Describe the characteristics and functions of the lymphatic system.

Immunology encompasses the study of all features of the body's second and third lines of defense. Although this chapter is concerned primarily with infectious microbes, be aware that immunology is central to the study of fields as diverse as cancer and allergy.

The primary functions of a healthy immune system can be summarized as

1. surveillance of organs, tissues, and other compartments;
2. recognition and differentiation of normal components of the body and foreign material such as pathogens; and
3. attack against and destruction of foreign invaders.

Because infectious agents could potentially enter through any number of portals, the cells of the immune system constantly move about the body, surveying the tissues for potential pathogens (see figure 14.3). This process is carried out primarily by **white blood cells (WBCs)** or **leukocytes,** which have an innate capacity to recognize and differentiate any foreign material in the body, such as invading bacterial cells. Such foreign matter is often referred to as **nonself.** Normal cells of the body, called **self,** are monitored and recognized and are usually not attacked by the immune system. The ability to differentiate nonself and thus spare self from attack is central to the effectiveness of the immune system. In chapter 16, we will see how autoimmune diseases can arise when this system goes awry. Foreign cells must be recognized as a potential threat and dealt with appropriately, but normal, healthy cells should not come under attack by the immune defenses. Exceptions to this would be abnormal or damaged self such as cancer cells.

How Do White Blood Cells Carry Out Recognition and Surveillance?

White blood cells are motile, migratory cells that move about the tissues and body compartments in search of any foreign matter that may have gotten through the first line of defense. Even though each type of blood cell has a particular role to play in defense, most of them have some capacity to locate and interact with foreign matter **(figure 14.3).** They display special molecules on their membranes, known as **pattern recognition receptors (PRRs),** which are like "feelers" for sensing pathogens. Several different types of PRRs are involved in this recognition, including kinases, lectins, and mannose-type molecules. The best-understood PRRs are the **toll-like receptors (TLRs),** which reside within the membranes of early responders such as phagocytes.

Although PRRs and TLRs are not specific to a particular microbe, they can immediately recognize and interact with molecules on the surface of many pathogens called **pathogen-associated molecular patterns,** or **PAMPs.** PAMPs are molecules shared by many microorganisms that act like "red flags" that signal white blood cells involved in innate immunity. The detection of PAMPs on pathogens by PRRs and TLRs provides an early alert of invasion, and triggers reactions that help to control pathogens before they can invade further. Examples of PAMPs include peptidoglycan, lipoteichoic acid, and lipopolysaccharide from bacterial cell walls, double-stranded RNA found in some viruses, zymosan from fungal cell walls, and bacterial flagellin. We will return to this topic again in section 14.4 on phagocytes.

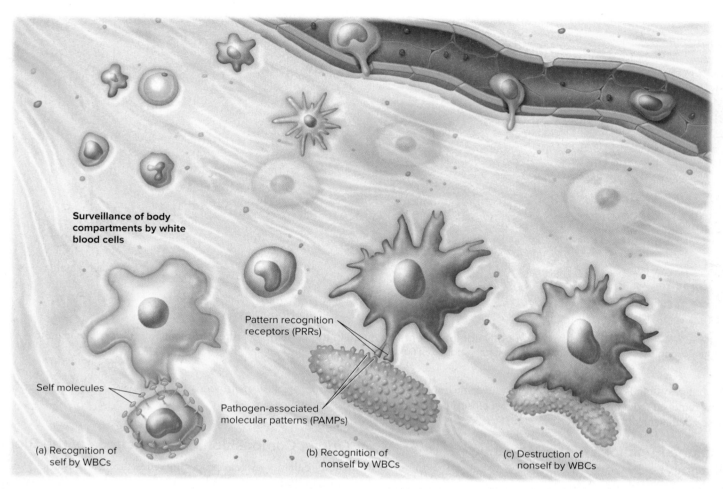

Surveillance of body compartments by white blood cells

Pattern recognition receptors (PRRs)

Self molecules

Pathogen-associated molecular patterns (PAMPs)

(a) Recognition of self by WBCs

(b) Recognition of nonself by WBCs

(c) Destruction of nonself by WBCs

Figure 14.3 To search, to recognize, and to eliminate are the functions of the immune system. White blood cells (WBCs) as seen in this view are equipped with a highly developed sense of "touch." **(a, b)** As they sort through the tissues, they "feel" the surrounding environment by means of their pattern recognition receptors (PRRs), which detect what is foreign or nonself. **(c)** When nonself molecules called PAMPs are detected, WBCs mount a reaction to eliminate the microbes that carry them. PAMPs are pathogen-associated molecular patterns that many pathogens display. Self molecules do not trigger these reactions.

Because these components are shared among many pathogens and not specific to a single cell type, only a small number of TLRs are needed to recognize a very wide variety of microbes. It is important to emphasize that this type of recognition is not specific or selective for a single type of microbe, making it a type of nonspecific, innate immunity that should not be confused with the specific acquired immunity from the third line of defense.

Compartments and Connections of the Immune System

Unlike many body systems, the immune system does not exist in a single, well-defined organ. Instead, it encompasses a large, complex, and diffuse network of cells and fluids that penetrate into every organ and tissue. It is this very arrangement that promotes the surveillance and recognition processes that help screen the body for microbes and harmful substances.

The body is partitioned into several fluid-filled spaces called the intracellular, extracellular, lymphatic, cerebrospinal, and circulatory compartments. Although these compartments are physi-

cally separated, they have numerous connections. Their structure and position permit extensive interchange and communication. The most extensive body compartments that participate in immune function are

1. the **mononuclear phagocyte system,**
2. the spaces surrounding tissue cells that contain **extracellular fluid (ECF),**
3. the **bloodstream,** and
4. the **lymphatic system.**

For effective immune responsiveness, the activities in one fluid compartment must be conveyed to other compartments. At the microscopic level **(figure 14.4),** clusters of tissue cells are in direct contact with the reticular fibers that are part of the mononuclear phagocyte system, along with blood and lymphatic capillaries. Bathing all of the cells and structures is the extracellular fluid (ECF), which is an important site of exchange for nutrients and gases. Regardless of which compartment is first exposed, an immune reaction in any one of them will be communicated to the others at the microscopic level. An obvious benefit of such an

(a)

(b)

Figure 14.4 **Connections between body compartments involved in the immune system.** The meeting of the major compartments at the microscopic level allows for continuous exchange of cells, fluids, and molecules (arrows).

integrated system is that no cell of the body, even the most isolated, is far removed from protection. Let us take a closer look at each of these compartments separately.

Immune Functions of the Mononuclear Phagocyte System

Connective tissue fibers called the reticular system permeate the body. These fibers originate in the cellular basal lamina, interconnect nearby cells, and mesh with the massive connective tissue network surrounding all organs. This network, or mononuclear phagocyte system (MPS) **(figure 14.5),** is critical to immune

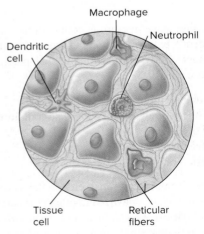

Figure 14.5 **The mononuclear phagocyte system occurs as a continuous connective tissue framework throughout the body.** This system begins at the microscopic level with a fibrous support network (reticular fibers) enmeshing each cell. This web connects one cell to another within a tissue or organ and provides a niche for phagocytic white blood cells, which can move within and between tissues.

function because it provides a passageway within and between tissues and organs.

Origin, Composition, and Functions of the Blood

The circulatory system proper includes the heart, arteries, veins, and capillaries that circulate blood, and the lymphatic system, which includes lymphatic vessels and lymphatic organs (lymph nodes) that circulate lymph. As you will see, these two circulations parallel, interconnect with, and complement one another.

The substance that courses through the arteries, veins, and capillaries is **whole blood,** a liquid connective tissue consisting of **blood cells** (formed elements) suspended in **plasma.** One can see these two components with the naked eye when a tube of unclotted blood is allowed to sit or is spun in a centrifuge. The cells' density causes them to settle into an opaque layer at the bottom of the tube, leaving the plasma, a clear, yellowish fluid, on top **(figure 14.6). Serum** is essentially the same as plasma, except it is the clear fluid from clotted blood so it lacks the clotting proteins that plasma contains. Serum is often used in immune testing and therapy (chapter 15).

Fundamental Characteristics of Plasma Plasma contains hundreds of different chemicals produced by the liver, white blood cells, endocrine glands, and nervous system and absorbed from the digestive tract. The main component of this fluid is water (92%), and the remainder consists of proteins such as albumin and globulins (including antibodies); other immunochemicals; fibrinogen and other clotting factors; hormones; nutrients; ions and electrolytes; dissolved gases (O_2 and CO_2); and waste products (urea). These substances support the normal physiological functions of nutrition, development, protection, homeostasis, and immunity.

Figure 14.6 The macroscopic composition of whole blood.
(a) When uncoagulated blood sits in a tube, it stratifies into a clear layer of plasma, a thin layer of off-white material called the buffy coat (which contains the white blood cells), and a layer of red blood cells in the bottom. **(b)** Serum is the clear fluid that separates from clotted blood. Clotting causes the red and white cells to clump in the bottom of the tube in a single mass.
Source: National Cancer Institute; Created by; Bruce Wetzel and Harry Schaefer (Photographers)

A Survey of Blood Cells The production of blood cells, known as **hemopoiesis** or **hematopoiesis,*** begins early in embryonic development in the yolk sac (an embryonic membrane). Later it is taken over by the liver and lymphatic organs, and it is finally assumed entirely and permanently by the red bone marrow. Although much of a newborn's red marrow is devoted to hematopoietic function, the active marrow sites gradually recede, and by the age of 4 years, only the ribs, sternum, pelvic girdle, flat bones of the skull and spinal column, and proximal portions of the humerus and femur are devoted to blood cell production.

The relatively short life of blood cells demands a rapid turnover that is continuous throughout a human life span. The primary precursor of new blood cells is a pool of undifferentiated cells called pluripotential **stem cells**[1] maintained in the marrow. During development, these stem cells proliferate and *differentiate*—meaning that immature or unspecialized cells develop the specialized form and function of mature cells. The primary lines of cells that arise from this process produce red blood cells (RBCs), white blood cells (WBCs, or leukocytes), and platelets (thrombocytes). The white blood cell lines are programmed to develop into several secondary lines of cells during the final process of differentiation **(figure 14.7).** These committed lines of WBCs are largely responsible for immune function.

> **Quick Search**
> To learn more, search the Internet for the videos "How White Blood Cells Are Formed" and "How White Blood Cells Work."

The **leukocytes*** traditionally are evaluated by their reactions with a hematologic stain that contains a mixture of dyes and can differentiate cells by color and morphology. When this stain is used on blood smears and evaluated using the light microscope, the leukocytes appear either with or without noticeable colored granules in the cytoplasm; on that basis they are divided into two groups: **granulocytes** and **agranulocytes.** Greater magnification reveals that even the agranulocytes have tiny granules in their cytoplasm, so some hematologists also use the appearance of the nucleus to distinguish them. Granulocytes have a lobed nucleus, and agranulocytes have an unlobed, rounded nucleus (figure 14.7).

Granulocytes The types of granular leukocytes present in the bloodstream are neutrophils, eosinophils, and basophils. All three are known for prominent cytoplasmic granules that stain with some combination of acidic dye (eosin) or basic dye (methylene blue). Although these granules are useful diagnostically, they also function in numerous physiological events.

Neutrophils* are distinguished from other leukocytes by their conspicuous lobed nuclei and their fine, pale lavender granules. In cells newly released from the bone marrow, the nuclei are horseshoe-shaped, but as they age, they form multiple lobes (up to five). These cells, also called polymorphonuclear neutrophils (PMNs), make up 55% to 90% of the circulating leukocytes— about 25 billion cells in the circulation at

Neutrophil
Courtesy of Harold Benson

any given moment. The main work of the neutrophils is in phagocytosis. Their high numbers in both the blood and the tissues suggest that there is a constant challenge from resident microbiota and environmental sources. Most of the cytoplasmic granules carry digestive enzymes and other chemicals that degrade the phagocytosed materials (see the discussion of phagocytosis in section 14.4). The average neutrophil lives only about 2 days, spending much of this time in the tissues and only about 4 to 10 hours in circulation.

Eosinophils* are readily distinguished in a stain preparation by their larger, orange to red (eosinophilic) granules and bilobed nucleus. They are much more numerous in the bone marrow and the spleen than in the circulation, contributing only 1% to 3% of the total WBC count. Their granules contain peroxidase, lysozyme, and other digestive enzymes, as well as toxic proteins and inflammatory chemicals.

Eosinophil
Courtesy of Harold Benson

* *hematopoiesis* (hem″-mat-o-poy-ee′-sis) Gr. *haima,* blood, and *poiesis,* a making.

1. Pluripotential stem cells can develop into several different types of blood cells; unipotential cells have already committed to a specific line of development.

* *leukocyte* (loo′-koh-syte) Gr. *leukos,* white, and *kytos,* cell. The whiteness of unstained WBCs is best seen in the white layer, or buffy coat, of sedimented blood.

* *neutrophil* (noo′-troh-fil) L. *neuter,* neither, and Gr. *philos,* to love. The granules are neutral and do not react markedly with either acidic or basic dyes. In clinical reports, they are often called "polys" or PMNs for short.

* *eosinophil* (ee″-oh-sin′-oh-fil) Gr. *eos,* dawn, rosy, and *philos,* to love. Eosin is a red, acidic dye attracted to the granules.

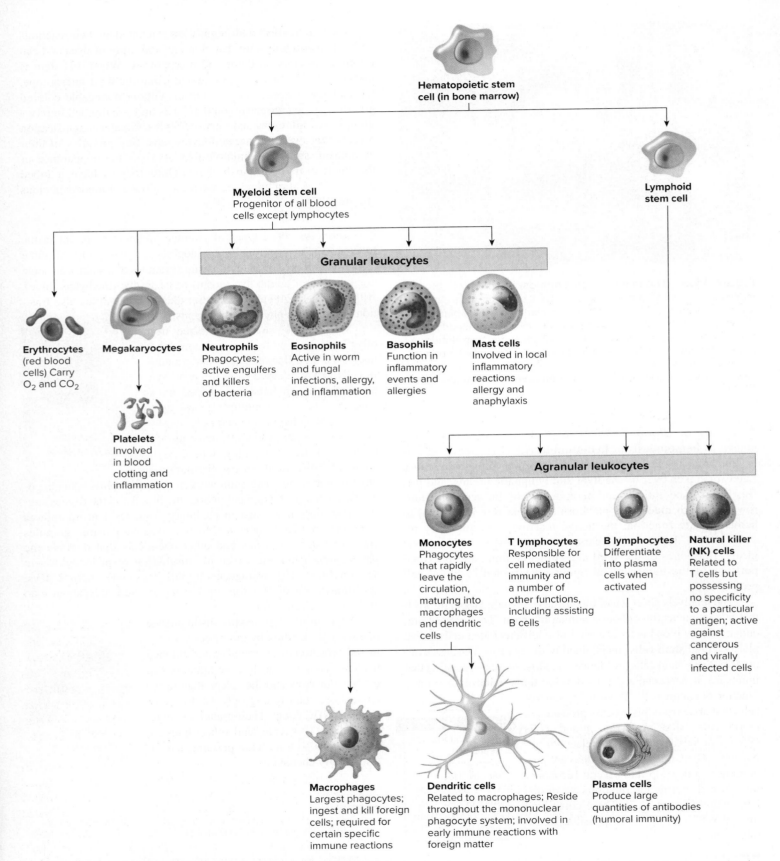

Figure 14.7 **Simplified diagram of blood cell and platelet development.** The details of several intermediate steps have been omitted. Undifferentiated stem cells in the red marrow give rise to several different cell lines that become increasingly specialized until mature cells are released into circulation.

The main protective action of eosinophils is their ability to attack and destroy large eukaryotic pathogens. They are also involved in inflammation and allergic reactions. Among their most important targets are the larval forms of worm parasites that cause ascariasis, filariasis, and schistosomiasis. The binding of eosinophils to the larval surface and the release of toxic compounds into their cells causes disintegration of the larvae. Eosinophils are among the earliest cells to accumulate near sites of inflammation and allergic reactions, where they attract other leukocytes and release chemical mediators.

Basophils* are characterized by pale-stained, two-lobed nuclei and very prominent dark blue to black granules. They are the scarcest type of leukocyte, making up less than 0.5% of the total circulating WBCs in a normal individual. Basophils share some morphological and functional similarities with widely distributed tissue cells called **mast* cells.** Mast cells are nonmotile elements bound to connective tissue around blood vessels, nerves, and epithelia, and basophils are motile elements that migrate within and between compartments. Both cell types originate from the same bone marrow stem cell line.

Basophil
Courtesy of Harold Benson

Basophils parallel eosinophils in many of their actions, because they also contain granules with potent chemical mediators. These mediators act on other cells and tissues of the body. For example, they may attract white blood cells toward the site of an infection or cause blood vessels to dilate in response to an injury. Mast cells are first-line defenders against the local invasion of pathogens; they recruit other inflammatory cells; and they are directly responsible for the release of histamine and other allergic stimulants during immediate allergies.

Agranulocytes

Agranular leukocytes have globular, nonlobed nuclei and lack prominent cytoplasmic granules when viewed with the light microscope. The two general types are monocytes and lymphocytes.

Although lymphocytes are the cornerstone of the third line of defense, which is the subject of chapter 15, their origin and morphology are described here so their relationship to the other blood components is clear. **Lymphocytes** are the second most common WBC in the blood, comprising 20% to 35% of the total circulating leukocytes. The fact that their overall number throughout the body is among the highest of all cells indicates how important they are to immunity. One estimate suggests that about one-tenth of all adult body cells are lymphocytes, exceeded only by erythrocytes and fibroblasts.

Lymphocytes
Courtesy of Harold Benson

In a stained blood smear, most lymphocytes appear as small, spherical cells with a uniformly dark, rounded nucleus surrounded by a thin fringe of clear cytoplasm, although in tissues they can become much larger and can even mimic monocytes in appearance. Two

* *basophil* (bay'-soh-fil) Gr. *basis,* foundation. The granules attract to basic dyes.
* *mast* From Ger. *mast,* food. Early cytologists thought these cells were filled with food vacuoles.

CLINIC CASE

Personally, I'd Go for Well-Done The patients were a couple who arrived together at the emergency room in Claiborne County, Tennessee, exhibiting a similar collection of signs and symptoms: fever, chills, and headache, along with muscle and joint pain. At first assuming a simple case of the flu, they became worried when they began to experience facial swelling. A white blood cell count revealed 24% eosinophils in the man and 28% in the woman; far above normal levels.

Suspecting a parasitic infection, doctors asked about travel or any exotic food the couple may have consumed. The man volunteered that several months previously he had shot a black bear in Canada and had much of the meat shipped on ice to his home in the United States. Weeks later, he and a small group of friends enjoyed a meal of Canadian black bear. Probing deeper, the doctor learned that the meat was barbecued, medium-rare for the couple and well-done for the friends (none of whom became ill). The remaining meat was packaged for storage in the kitchen freezer and eaten over the next several weeks.

Serological testing revealed that both patients had developed antibodies to *Trichinella,* a parasitic worm. *Trichinella* was once routine in domestic pigs but is now more commonly found in game meat, especially wild boar and bear. Histological examination revealed the presence of *Trichinella* larvae encysted in the muscle of the bear (350–400 larvae per gram of muscle), and PCR was used to identify the worms as *Trichinella nativa,* a species found in northern latitudes that (unlike other species of the genus) is resistant to freezing. *T. nativa* is more commonly found in polar bears and walruses, which are occasionally hunted and eaten by the indigenous people of Alaska and Canada.

The patients were started on a course of albendazole and corticosteroids, and both fully recovered.

If the species of worm in the bear was the more commonly encountered *Trichinella spiralis,* what likely would have been the outcome for the couple in this case?

types of lymphocytes exist, **B lymphocytes (B cells,** for short) and **T lymphocytes (T cells,** for short). B cells were named for the bursa of Fabricus, the organ in birds in which they develop. In humans, who have no bursa, B cells are produced in the bone marrow. T cells are also produced in the bone marrow but mature in the thymus gland. Both populations of cells are transported by the bloodstream and lymph and move about freely between lymphoid organs and connective tissue. **Natural killer (NK) cells** develop from the same precursor as T and B cells but follow a different developmental path.

B and T lymphocytes are the key cells of the third line of defense, the specific immune response. When stimulated by foreign substances (antigens), lymphocytes are transformed into activated cells that neutralize and destroy those foreign substances. Activated B cells form specialized **plasma cells,** which in turn produce **antibodies.*** Antibodies are proteins that bind to foreign cells or molecules and participate in their destruction. Because of these

* *antibody* (an'-tih-bahd"-ee) Gr. *anti,* against, and O.E., *bodig,* body.

			TABLE 14.2	Characteristics of Leukocytes	

Cell Type	Prevalence in Circulation	Primary Function	Features	Appearance*
Neutrophils	55%–90% of white blood cells	General phagocytosis	Life span of 2 days, with only 4–10 hours spent in the circulation	Multilobed nuclei; small purple granules containing digestive enzymes
Eosinophils	1%–3% of white blood cells	Destruction of parasitic worms; mediators of allergy	Found in much higher numbers in the spleen and bone marrow	Bilobed nucleus with large orange granules containing toxic proteins, inflammatory mediators, and digestive enzymes
Basophils	0.5% of white blood cells	Active in allergy, inflammation, parasitic infections	Cytoplasmic granules contain histamines, prostaglandins, and other chemical mediators of the allergic response.	Pale-staining, constricted nuclei with dark blue to black granules
Monocytes	3%–7% of white blood cells	Phagocytosis, followed by final differentiation into macrophages and dendritic cells	Monocytes also secrete several chemicals that moderate the functions of the immune system.	Largest WBC; nuclei large, ovoid, and often indented—no cytoplasmic granules visible using a light microscope
Lymphocytes	20%–35% of white blood cells	Specific (acquired) immunity	Two types of lymphocytes exist. T cells are responsible for cell-mediated immunity, whereas B cells are responsible for humoral immunity.	Small, spherical cells with uniformly staining dark, round nuclei
Natural killer cells	2–3% of white blood cells	Innate immunity	Natural killer cells are active against body cells that have been infected by viruses or have become cancerous.	Small, spherical cells with dark, round nuclei

*See examples in figure 14.7.

actions, B cells are said to contribute to **antibody-mediated immunity** (also referred to as humoral immunity). Activated T cells engage in a spectrum of immune functions—called **cell-mediated immunity**—which include killing foreign cells directly and exerting control over immune function. Both classes of lymphocytes display specificity and memory, key characteristics of the immune system. Unlike B and T cells, natural killer cells never develop specificity for a single antigen and are generally not considered part of the third line of defense. The specific immune response modulated by lymphocytes is so important that most of chapter 15 is devoted to their reactions.

Monocytes* are generally the largest of all white blood cells and the third most common in the circulation (3% to 7%). As a monocyte matures, its nucleus becomes oval- or kidney-shaped—indented on one side, off center, and often contorted with fine wrinkles. The cytoplasm holds many fine vacuoles containing digestive enzymes. Monocytes are discharged by the bone marrow into the bloodstream, where they live as phagocytes for a few days. Later they leave the circulation to undergo final differentiation into **macrophages.*** Macrophages are key players in immunity, in general, responsible for

Monocyte

Courtesy of Harold Benson

1. many types of specific and nonspecific phagocytic and killing functions (they assume the job of cellular housekeepers, "mopping up the messes" created by infection and inflammation);
2. processing foreign molecules and presenting them to lymphocytes; and
3. secreting biologically active compounds that assist, mediate, attract, and inhibit immune cells and reactions.

We touch upon these functions in several ensuing sections.

Another product of the monocyte cell line is **dendritic cells,** named for their long, thin cell processes. Immature dendritic cells move from the blood to the mononuclear phagocyte system and lymphatic tissues, where they trap pathogens. Ingestion of bacteria and viruses stimulates dendritic cells to migrate to lymph nodes and the spleen to participate in reactions with lymphocytes.

Some of the major characteristics of leukocytes are summarized in **table 14.2.**

Erythrocyte and Platelet Lines These elements stay in the circulatory system proper and are not generally considered part of the immune system. Their development is also shown in figure 14.7.

Erythrocytes are produced by stem cells that go through several stages of differentiation and lose their nucleus just prior to entering the circulation. The resultant red blood cells are simple, biconcave sacs of hemoglobin that transport oxygen and carbon dioxide to and from the tissues. These are the most numerous of circulating blood cells, appearing in stains as small pink circles. Red blood cells do not ordinarily have immune functions, though they can be the target of immune reactions.

* *monocyte* (mon′-oh-syte) From *mono,* one, and *cytos,* cell.
* *macrophage* (mak′-roh-fayj) Gr. *macro,* large, and *phagein,* to eat. They are the "large eaters" of the tissues.

Right lymphatic duct

Right subclavian vein

Axillary lymph nodes

Lymphatics of breast

(b)

Bone marrow

Lymphatic vessels

(a)

Tonsils (MALT)

Thymus

Axillary lymph node

MALT (mucosal-associated lymphoid tissue) in breast

Spleen

GALT (Peyer's patches in small intestine)

Inguinal lymph node

Figure 14.8 **General components of the lymphatic system, showing drainage patterns and connections with the regular circulation. (a)** A general depiction of the lymphatic system, a branching network of specialized vessels that extend into most regions of the body. It includes several types of supportive tissues and organs, including the lymph nodes, MALT, spleen, GALT, thymus gland, tonsils, and bone marrow. **(b)** Expanded view of the right breast and axillary lymphatic circulation. The right lymphatic duct receives lymph from the right axillary and head region and drains into the regular blood circulation at the right subclavian vein. On the left side of the body, there is a similar arrangement in which the thoracic lymphatic duct returns lymph from the remainder of the body at the left subclavian vein. Through these direct connections, all lymph eventually makes its way into circulating blood.

Platelets are formed elements in circulating blood that are *not* whole cells. They are formed by the disintegration of a large, multinucleate cell, the megakaryocyte. In stains, platelets are blue-gray with fine red granules and are readily distinguished from cells by their small size. Platelets function primarily in hemostasis (plugging broken blood vessels to stop bleeding) and in releasing chemicals that act in blood clotting and inflammation.

Components and Functions of the Lymphatic System

The lymphatic part of the circulatory system is a compartmentalized network of vessels, cells, and specialized accessory organs **(figure 14.8).** It begins in the farthest reaches of the tissues as tiny capillaries that transport a special fluid (lymph) through an increasingly larger system of vessels and filters (lymph nodes). It eventually connects to major vessels that drain back into the regular circulatory system. Some major functions of the **lymphatic** or **lymphoid system** relating to immune defenses are:

1. to provide an additional route for the return of extracellular fluid to the circulatory system;
2. to help drain fluid that has accumulated due to the inflammatory response; and

3. to render surveillance, recognition, and protection against foreign materials through a system of lymphocytes, phagocytes, and antibodies.

Lymphatic Fluid **Lymph** is a plasmalike liquid carried by the lymphatic circulation. It is formed when certain blood components move out of the blood vessels into the extracellular spaces and diffuse or migrate into the lymphatic capillaries. Because of this, the composition of lymph parallels that of plasma in many ways. It is made up of water, dissolved salts, and 2% to 5% protein (especially antibodies and albumin). Like blood, it also transports numerous white blood cells (especially lymphocytes) and miscellaneous materials such as fats, cellular debris, and infectious agents that have gained access to the tissue spaces. Unlike blood, red blood cells are not normally found in lymph.

Lymphatic Vessels The system of vessels that transport lymph is constructed along the lines of blood vessels **(figure 14.9).** The tiniest vessels, **lymphatic capillaries,** accompany the blood capillaries. The lymphatic capillaries permeate all parts of the body except the central nervous system and certain organs such as bone, placenta, and thymus. Their thin walls have a single layer of epithelial cells similar to blood capillaries, with loose junctions that

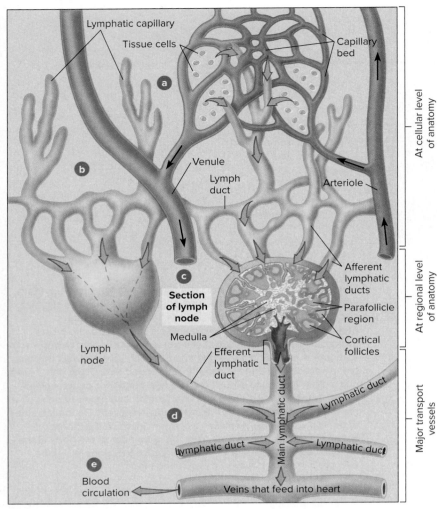

At cellular level of anatomy

At regional level of anatomy

Major transport vessels

(a) The finest level of lymphatic circulation begins with blind capillaries (green) that pick up foreign matter from the surrounding tissues and transport it in lymph away from the extremities via a system of small ducts.

(b) The ducts carry lymph into a circuit of larger ducts that ultimately flow into clusters of filtering organs, the lymph nodes.

(c) A section through a lymph node reveals the afferent ducts draining lymph into sinuses that house several types of white blood cells. Here, foreign material is filtered out and processed by lymphocytes, macrophages, and dendritic cells.

(d) and (e) Lymph continues to trickle from the lymph nodes via efferent ducts into a system of larger drainage vessels, which ultimately connect with large veins near the heart. In this way, cells and products of immunity continually enter the regular circulation.

Figure 14.9 Scheme of circulation in the lymphatic vessels and lymph nodes.

Figure 14.10 **Comparison of the circulation patterns of the regular circulatory and lymphatic systems.** The movement of lymphatic flow is in one direction (green) from lymphatic capillaries to collecting vessels and ducts to large lymphatic trunks to subclavian veins to the heart. The flow of blood, on the other hand, is cyclic, with blood continuously flowing through arteries to capillaries to veins to the heart and back around. With this combined system the lymphatics can collect excess tissue fluid and return it to the bloodstream. The two systems can also participate together in surveillance of the tissues for foreign invaders. Note: The lymphatic flow (green) is shown on only one side to keep the comparison uncluttered.

allow free entry of extracellular fluid that collects from the circulatory system (see figure 14.4). Lymphatic vessels are found in particularly high numbers in the hands and feet and around the areolae of the breast.

Two important differences between the bloodstream and the lymphatic system should be mentioned **(figure 14.10).** First, given that one of the main functions of the lymphatic system is returning lymph to the circulation, lymph flows only in one direction, moving from the extremities toward the heart. Eventually it will be returned to the bloodstream through the thoracic duct and the right lymphatic duct near the base of the neck (see figure 14.8). The second difference concerns how lymph travels through the vessels of the lymphatic system. Whereas blood is transported through the body by means of a dedicated pump (the heart), lymph is moved only through the contraction of skeletal muscles that surround the lymphatic ducts. This dependence on muscle movement helps to

explain the swelling of the hands and feet that sometimes occurs during the night (when muscles are inactive) yet goes away soon after waking.

The parasitic infection filariasis presents a dramatic example of what happens when the lymphatic drainage is blocked by infectious agents. Filarial worms from the infection become caught in the lymph nodes and channels of the extremities and plug them up. This prevents lymph from flowing into the accessory ducts and back to the circulation. The buildup of lymph massively distorts limbs and other body parts such as the scrotum and breasts.

> **Quick Search**
> To witness the devastation of this disease, type "filarial elephantiasis" into a search engine and click on images.

Lymphoid Organs Lymphatic organs and tissues with immune functions can be classified as primary and secondary, as summarized here:

Primary organs
 Thymus gland
 Bone marrow

Secondary organs and tissues
 Lymph nodes
 Spleen
 MALT—mucosal-associated lymphoid tissue
 GALT—gut-associated lymphoid tissue (Peyer's patches)

The **primary lymphoid organs** include the thymus and bone marrow, locations where lymphocytes are formed or reside. They are the sites of origin and maturation of lymphocytes—white blood cells with specific immune function. They subsequently release these cells to populate the secondary lymphatic sites.

Secondary lymphoid organs, such as the spleen and lymph nodes, are circulatory-based locations where encounters with microbes and immune responses often take place. Associated lymphoid tissues are collections of cells widely dispersed throughout body tissues such as the skin and mucous membranes, ready to react with any locally entering infectious agents.

The Thymus Gland The **thymus** originates in the embryo as two lobes in the pharyngeal region that fuse into a triangular structure. It is located in the thoracic cavity near the tip of the sternum. The size of the thymus is greatest proportionately at birth **(figure 14.11),** and it continues to exhibit high rates of activity and growth until puberty, after which it begins to shrink gradually through adulthood.

Children born without a complete thymus (DiGeorge syndrome, see chapter 16) or who have had their thymus surgically removed are severely immunodeficient and fail to thrive. Adults have developed enough mature T cells that removal of the thymus or reduction in its function has milder effects. Do not confuse the thymus with the thyroid gland, which is located in the cervical region near the larynx and has an entirely different function.

Lymph Nodes Lymph nodes are small, encapsulated, bean-shaped organs stationed, usually in clusters, along lymphatic channels and large blood vessels of the thoracic and abdominal cavities (see figure 14.8). Major aggregations of nodes occur in the loose connective tissue of the armpit (axillary nodes), groin (inguinal nodes), and neck (cervical nodes). Both the location and the architecture of these nodes clearly specialize them for filtering out materials that

Figure 14.11 The thymus gland. Immediately after birth, the thymus is a large organ that nearly fills the region over the midline of the upper thoracic region. In the adult, however, it is proportionately smaller. Section shows the main anatomical regions of the thymus. Immature T cells enter through the cortex and migrate into the medulla as they mature.
BJI/Blue Jean Images/Getty Images; *(Inset):* Alvin Telser/McGraw-Hill Education

have entered the lymph and providing appropriate cells and niches for immune reactions.

Spleen The spleen is a lymphoid organ in the upper portion of the abdominal cavity nestled below the diaphragm and left of the stomach. It is somewhat similar to a lymph node except that it serves as a filter for blood instead of lymph. While the spleen's primary function is to remove worn-out red blood cells from circulation, its most important immunologic function centers on the filtering of pathogens from the blood and their subsequent phagocytosis by resident macrophages. Adults whose spleens have been surgically removed can live a relatively normal life, but children who have failed to develop or lost their spleen are severely immunocompromised.

Associated Lymphoid Tissue Embedded throughout systems lined with mucous membranes are discrete bundles of lymphocytes and other white blood cells termed the **mucosal-associated lymphoid tissue,** or **MALT.** The positioning of this widespread system provides a local, rapid mechanism for responding to the constant influx of microbes entering via the gastrointestinal, respiratory, urinary, and other portals of entry. The pharynx houses a prominent source of MALT in the form of tonsils. The breasts of pregnant and lactating women also become temporary sites of lymphoid tissues that add protective antibodies to breast milk.

MALT is further divided into more than a dozen categories, based on where the specific lymphoid tissue is found. The most important example of this is the gut-associated lymphoid tissue, or GALT. GALT includes the appendix and **Peyer's patches,** compact aggregations of lymphocytes in the ileum of the small intestine. GALT provides immune functions against intestinal pathogens and is a significant source of some types of antibodies. Other, less well-organized collections of secondary lymphoid tissue include *skin-associated lymphoid tissue* and *bronchial-associated lymphoid tissue.*

 Practice SECTION 14.2

5. How is surveillance of the tissues carried out, and what is responsible for it?

6. Describe the processes through which the immune system distinguishes self from foreign cells and particles.

7. What does the term *nonself* mean in reference to the immune system?

8. What are the main components of the mononuclear phagocyte system?

9. How does the mononuclear phagocyte system communicate with tissues and the vascular system?

10. Explain the functions of stem cells, and summarize the stages of hematopoiesis.

11. Differentiate between granulocytes and agranulocytes.

12. Describe the main types of granulocytes and agranulocytes, their functions, and their incidence in the circulation.

13. Describe the principal function of the two lymphocyte types, and differentiate between humoral and cell-mediated immunity.

14. What is lymph, and how is it formed?

15. Outline the functions of the lymphatic system and describe the actions of associated lymphatic tissues such as MALT and GALT.

Figure 14.12 The response to inflammations. The classic indicators of inflammation, whether due to infection or injury, are rubor (redness), calor (warmth), tumor (swelling), and dolor (pain). Each of the events is an indicator of one of the mechanisms of inflammation described in this section.
Robert Kirk/Getty Images

14.3 Second-Line Defenses: Inflammation

Learn

12. Describe the main events in the inflammatory reaction, and explain what is occurring in each.

13. Summarize the functions of cytokines, chemokines, and other inflammatory mediators.

14. Describe the mechanism behind fever, and explain its beneficial and harmful effects.

Now that we have introduced the principal anatomical and physiological framework of the immune system, we address some mechanisms that play important roles in host defenses: (1) inflammation, (2) phagocytosis, (3) interferon, and (4) complement. Because of the generalized nature of these defenses, they are primarily nonspecific in their effects, but they also support and interact with the specific immune responses described in chapter 15.

The Inflammatory Response: A Complex Concert of Reactions to Injury

At its most general level, **inflammation** is a reaction to any traumatic event in the tissues that attempts to restore homeostasis: It is a normal and necessary process that helps to clear away invading microbes and cellular debris left by immune reactions. Most people manifest inflammation in some way every day. It appears in the flare of a cut, the

blistering of a burn, the painful lesion of an infection, and the symptoms of allergy, and at times it can even go unnoticed.

Inflammation is readily identifiable by a classic series of signs and symptoms characterized succinctly by four Latin terms: *rubor, calor, tumor,* and *dolor*. Rubor (redness) is caused by increased circulation and vasodilation in the injured tissues; calor (warmth) is the heat given off by the increased flow of blood; tumor (swelling) is caused by increased extracelluar fluid accumulating in the tissues; and dolor (pain) is caused by the stimulation of nerve endings from the pressure of swelling or by chemical mediators **(figure 14.12)**. A fifth symptom, *loss of function,* is sometimes added for a complete picture of effects that can accompany inflammation. Although these manifestations are often unpleasant, they serve an important warning that injury has taken place and will set in motion responses that can save the body from further injury.

Factors that can elicit an inflammatory response include trauma from infection (the primary emphasis here), tissue injury or death, and specific immune reactions. Although the details of inflammation are very complex, its chief functions can be summarized as follows:

1. to mobilize and attract immune cells and chemicals to the site of the injury,
2. to set in motion mechanisms to repair tissue damage and localize and clear away harmful substances, and
3. to destroy and block microbes from further invasion (see process figure 14.13).

The inflammatory response is a powerful defensive reaction, a means for the body to maintain stability and restore itself after an

injury. But when it is chronic, it has the potential to actually *cause* tissue injury, destruction, and disease (see 14.2 Making Connections, "The Downside of Inflammation").

The Stages of Inflammation

The inflammatory response is a dynamic sequence of events that can be acute (lasting from a few minutes or hours) to chronic (lasting for days, weeks, or years). Once the initial injury has occurred, a chain reaction takes place at the site of damaged tissue, summoning beneficial cells and fluids into the injured area. To envision this process in action, we start with an injury and observe the flow of major events at the microscopic level (**process figure 14.13**).

Vascular Changes: Early Inflammatory Events

Following an injury, some of the earliest changes occur in the vasculature (arterioles, capillaries, venules) in the vicinity of the damaged tissue. These changes are controlled by nervous stimulation, **chemical mediators,** and **cytokines*** released by blood cells, tissue cells, and platelets in the injured area. Vasoactive mediators affect the smooth muscle cells surrounding veins and arteries, changing the flow of blood to the area by causing constriction or dilation of vessels. Others are **chemotactic factors,** also called **chemokines,** that affect white blood cells. Inflammatory mediators cause fever, stimulate lymphocytes, prevent infection spread, and cause allergic symptoms (**14.1 Making Connections**). Although the constriction of arterioles is stimulated first, it lasts for only a few seconds or minutes. Once a clot has formed to prevent blood loss, it is followed in quick succession by the opposite reaction, **vasodilation.** The overall effect of vasodilation is to increase the flow of blood into the area, which facilitates the influx of immune components and also causes redness and warmth (rubor and calor).

An Early Chemical Indicator of Inflammation

C-reactive protein* (**CRP**) is a pattern recognition receptor that is an early indicator of inflammation. It is a large protein synthesized by the liver that circulates in the blood. CRP is released in response to cytokines produced by macrophages during infections and other pathologic conditions. It attaches to PAMPs and other receptors on dead or injured body cells and infectious agents, an action that increases phagocytosis and promotes the complement system (see next section). In this way it serves as another source of localized, immediate, innate protection. Because it can be detected within the first few hours of the onset of inflammation, it is an effective marker for inflammation and can be measured with blood tests. Elevated levels of CRP can also be found in cardiovascular disease, cancer, tissue injury, and necrosis, and are often used to diagnose risks for these conditions.

Postcapillary venules, small veins that drain blood from the capillary beds, are important in several aspects of inflammation. When they constrict, this causes a slowing of circulation and a pooling of extracellular fluid at the site. Some vasoactive substances cause the

(a) **Injury/Immediate Reactions:** Blood vessels narrow (vasoconstriction); blood clots; and mast cells release chemokines and cytokines into injured area.

- Bacteria in wound
- Mast cells release chemical mediators
- Vasoconstriction

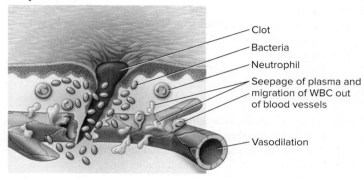

(b) **Vascular Reactions:** Nearby blood vessels dilate; increased blood flow; increased vascular permeability; increased leakage of fluid forms exudate.

- Clot
- Bacteria
- Neutrophil
- Seepage of plasma and migration of WBC out of blood vessels
- Vasodilation

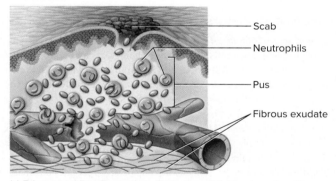

(c) **Edema and Pus Formation:** Collection of fluid; edema/swelling; infiltration by neutrophils and formation of pus.

- Scab
- Neutrophils
- Pus
- Fibrous exudate

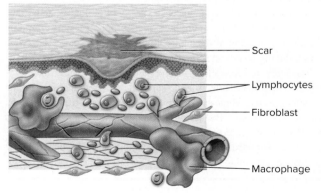

(d) **Resolution/Scar Formation:** Macrophages, lymphocytes, and fibroblasts migrate in; initiate immune response and repair of injury; scar and loss of normal tissue.

- Scar
- Lymphocytes
- Fibroblast
- Macrophage

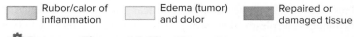

| Rubor/calor of inflammation | Edema (tumor) and dolor | Repaired or damaged tissue |

⚙ Process Figure 14.13 The major events in inflammation.

cytokine (sy′-toh-kyne) Gr. *cytos,* cell, and *kemein,* to move. A protein or polypeptide produced by WBCs that regulates host defenses.

* Not to be confused with the complement system.

14.1 MAKING CONNECTIONS

The Dynamics of Inflammatory Mediators

Just as the nervous system is coordinated by a complex communications network, so, too, is the immune system. Hundreds of small, active molecules are constantly being secreted to regulate, stimulate, suppress, and otherwise control the many aspects of cell development, inflammation, and immunity. These substances are the products of several types of cells, including monocytes, macrophages, lymphocytes, fibroblasts, mast cells, platelets, and endothelial cells of blood vessels. Their effects may be local or systemic, short term or long lasting, nonspecific or specific, protective or pathologic.

The field of cytokines has become so increasingly complex that we can include here only an overview of the major groups of important cytokines and other mediators. The major functional types can be categorized into

1. cytokines that mediate nonspecific immune reactions such as inflammation and phagocytosis,
2. cytokines that regulate the growth and activation of lymphocytes,
3. cytokines that activate immune reactions during inflammation,
4. hematopoiesis factors for white blood cells,
5. vasoactive mediators, and
6. miscellaneous inflammatory mediators.

Nonspecific Mediators of Inflammation and Immunity

- *Tumor necrosis factor (TNF)*, a substance from macrophages, lymphocytes, and other cells. It increases chemotaxis and phagocytosis and stimulates other cells to secrete inflammatory cytokines. It also triggers fever (is an endogenous pyrogen) and stimulates blood coagulation. Unfortunately, it has the potential to cause damage to tissues when produced in excess.
- *Interferon alpha and interferon beta*, produced by leukocytes and fibroblasts, inhibit virus replication and cell division and increase the action of certain lymphocytes that kill other cells.
- *Interleukin* is a term that refers to a group of small peptides originally isolated from leukocytes. There are currently more than 50 known interleukins. We now know that other cells besides leukocytes can synthesize them and that they have a variety of biological activities.
 - *Interleukin-1 (IL-1)*, a product of macrophages and epithelial cells. It has many of the same biological activities as TNF, such as inducing fever and activating certain white blood cells.
 - *Interleukin-6*, secreted by macrophages, lymphocytes, and fibroblasts. Its primary effects are to stimulate the growth of B cells and to increase the synthesis of liver proteins such as C-reactive protein.
- *Various chemokines.* By definition, chemokines are cytokines that stimulate the movement and migration of white blood cells (chemotactic factors). Included among these are complement $C5_a$, interleukin-8, and platelet-activating factor.

Cytokines that Regulate Lymphocyte Growth and Activation

- *Interleukin-2*, the primary growth factor from T cells. Interestingly, it acts on the same cells that secrete it. It stimulates cell division and secretion of other cytokines. In B cells, it is a growth factor and stimulus for antibody synthesis.
- *Interleukin-4*, a stimulus for the development of B cells and production of antibodies that mediate allergies. It inhibits macrophage actions.
- *Granulocyte colony-stimulating factor (G-CSF)*, produced by T cells, macrophages, and neutrophils. It stimulates the activation and differentiation of neutrophils.
- *Macrophage colony-stimulating factor (M-CSF)*, produced by a variety of cells. M-CSF promotes the growth and development of stem cells that differentiate into macrophages.
- *Interferon gamma*, a T-cell-derived mediator whose primary function is to activate macrophages. It also promotes the differentiation of T and B cells, activates neutrophils, and stimulates diapedesis.

Vasoactive Mediators

- *Histamine*, a vasoactive mediator produced by mast cells and basophils. It causes vasodilation, increased vascular permeability, and mucus production. It functions primarily in inflammation and allergy.
- *Serotonin*, a mediator produced by platelets and intestinal cells. It causes smooth muscle contraction, inhibits gastric secretion, and acts as a neurotransmitter.
- *Bradykinin*, a vasoactive amine from the blood or tissues. It stimulates smooth muscle contraction and increases vascular permeability, mucus production, and pain. It is particularly active in allergic reactions.

Miscellaneous Inflammatory Mediators

- *Prostaglandins*, produced by most body cells, are complex chemical mediators that can have opposing effects (for example, dilation or constriction of blood vessels) and are powerful stimulants of inflammation and pain.
- *Leukotrienes* stimulate the contraction of smooth muscle and enhance vascular permeability. They are implicated in the more severe manifestations of immediate allergies (constriction of airways).
- *Platelet-activating factor*, a substance released from basophils, causes the aggregation of platelets and the release of other chemical mediators during immediate allergic reactions.

Which inflammatory mediators would be involved in rubor? In tumor? In dolor? In calor?

endothelial cells in the walls of these venules to separate and form gaps through which blood-borne components exude into the extracellular spaces. Capillaries also become leaky under the influence of cytokines. The plasma that escapes from small vessels into the tissues is called the *exudate*. Accumulation of this fluid gives rise to local swelling and hardness known as **edema.** The edematous exudate contains varying amounts of plasma proteins, such as globulins, albumin, the clotting protein fibrinogen, blood cells, and cellular debris. Depending upon its content, the exudate may be clear (called *serous*), or it may contain red blood cells or **pus.** Pus is composed mainly of white blood cells, microbes, and the debris generated by phagocytosis. In some types of edema, the fibrinogen is converted to

Figure 14.14 **Formation of a blood clot.** After an injury, fibrinogen is converted to insoluble fibrin threads that cover an injury site. Platelets (not seen) soon adhere to the fibrin fibers, forming the clot.
Juan Gaertner/Shutterstock

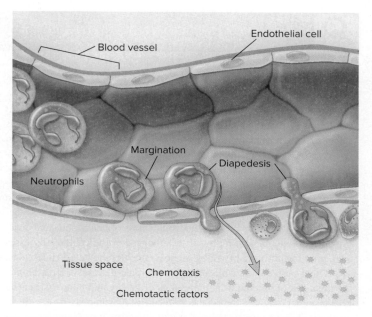

Figure 14.15 **Diapedesis and chemotaxis of leukocytes.** Cross section of a venule depicts white blood cells squeezing themselves between spaces in the vessel wall through diapedesis. This process also indicates how the pool of leukocytes adheres to receptors in the endothelial wall. From this site, they are poised to migrate out of the vessel into the tissue space and respond to chemotactic factors released as part of the generalized inflammatory process.

fibrin threads that enmesh the injury site (**figure 14.14**). Within an hour multitudes of neutrophils, responding chemotactically to special signaling molecules, converge on the injured site.

Unique Dynamic Characteristics of White Blood Cells In order for WBCs to leave the blood vessels and enter the tissues, they adhere to the inner walls of the smaller blood vessels such as capillaries and venules. From this position, they are poised to migrate out of the blood into the tissue spaces by a process called **diapedesis.***

Diapedesis, also known as transmigration, is aided by several related characteristics of WBCs. For example, they are actively motile and readily change shape. Their migration is assisted by the nature of the endothelial cells lining venules. Venules contain complex adhesive receptors that develop increased "stickiness" under the influence of inflammatory mediators. This causes WBCs to adhere or marginate at the endothelial cells. From this location, they can readily crawl into the extracellular spaces (**figure 14.15**).

Another factor in the migratory habits of these WBCs is **chemotaxis,*** defined as the tendency of cells to migrate in response to a specific chemical stimulus released at a site of injury or infection. Through this means, cells swarm from many compartments to the site of infection and remain there to perform general functions such as phagocytosis, repair, and specific immune reactions. These basic properties are absolutely essential for the sort of intercommunication and deployment of cells required for most immune reactions.

The Benefits of Edema and Chemotaxis The influx of fluids and the infiltration of neutrophils are physiologically beneficial activities. Fluids dilute toxic substances, and the fibrin clot can

effectively trap microbes and prevent their further spread. The neutrophils that aggregate in the inflamed site are immediately involved in phagocytosing and destroying microbes, dead tissues, and particulate matter (by mechanisms discussed in section 14.4 on phagocytosis). In some types of inflammation, accumulated phagocytes contribute to pus. Certain bacteria (streptococci, staphylococci, gonococci, and meningococci) are especially powerful attractants for neutrophils and are thus termed **pyogenic,** or pus-forming, bacteria.

Late Reactions of Inflammation Sometimes a mild inflammation can be resolved by edema and phagocytosis. Inflammatory reactions that last more than a few days attract a collection of monocytes, lymphocytes, and macrophages to the reaction site. Clearance of pus, cellular debris, dead neutrophils, and damaged tissue is performed by macrophages, the only cells that can engulf and dispose of such large masses. At the same time, specific immune reactions of acquired immunity are brought into play. B lymphocytes react with foreign molecules and cells by producing specific antimicrobial proteins (antibodies), and T lymphocytes kill intruders directly. Late in the process, the tissue undergoes various levels of repair and may be replaced by connective tissue in the form of a scar (see process figure 14.13*d*). If the inflammation cannot be relieved or resolved in this way, it can become chronic and create long-term pathologic conditions discussed in **14.2 Making Connections,** "The Downside of Inflammation."

Fever: An Adjunct to Inflammation

An important systemic component of inflammation is fever, defined as an abnormally elevated body temperature. Although fever is a

* *diapedesis* (dye"-ah-puh-dee′-sis) Gr. *dia,* through, and *pedan,* to leap.

* *chemotaxis* (kee-moh-tak′-sis) NL. *chemo,* chemical, and *taxis,* arrangement.

14.2 MAKING CONNECTIONS

The Downside of Inflammation

Not every aspect of inflammation is protective or results in the proficient resolution of tissue damage. As one looks over a list of diseases, it is rather striking how many of them are due in part or even completely to an overreactive or dysfunctional inflammatory response.

Some *-itis* reactions mentioned in chapter 13 are a case in point. Inflammatory exudates that build up in the brain in African trypanosomiasis, cryptococcosis, and other brain infections can be so injurious to the nervous system that impairment is permanent. Inflammatory reactions frequently lead to abscess, a swollen mass of neutrophils and dead, liquefied tissue that can harbor live pathogens in the center. Abscesses are a prominent feature of staphylococcal, amebic, and enteric infections.

Other pathologic manifestations of chronic diseases—for example, the tubercles of tuberculosis, the lesions of late syphilis, the disfiguring nodules of leprosy, and the cutaneous ulcers of leishmaniasis—are due to an aberrant tissue response called *granuloma formation*. Granulomas develop in response not only to microbes but also to inanimate foreign bodies that are difficult to break down. This condition is initiated when neutrophils and macrophages ineffectively and incompletely phagocytose the pathogens or materials involved in an inflammatory reaction. This failure to manage the debris of inflammation is sometimes referred to as "frustrated phagocytosis." Macrophages respond by storing ingested materials in vacuoles and becoming inactive. Over a given time period, macrophages fuse into giant, inactive multinucleate cells called foreign body giant cells. These sites are further infiltrated with lymphocytes. The resultant collections make the tissue appear granular—hence the name. A granuloma can exist in the tissue for months, years, or even a lifetime.

One common cytokine, tumor necrosis factor (TNF), is a potent inflammatory mediator. It regulates a wide variety of early immune activities such as phagocytosis, and it is a powerful pyrogen. Unfortunately, the overproduction of TNF is also involved in a number of diseases, such as septic shock, psoriasis, asthma, and autoimmunity. Several drugs (adalimumab [Humira] and etanercept [Enbrel], for example) have been developed as therapy to counteract the damaging effects of TNF.

Medical science is rapidly searching for additional applications based on new information about inflammatory mediators. One highly promising area appears to be the use of chemokine inhibitors that could reduce chemotaxis and the massive, destructive influx of leukocytes. Such therapy could ultimately be used to treat certain cancers, hardening of arteries, and Alzheimer disease.

Explain how inflammatory mediators stimulate tissue injury and disease.

nearly universal symptom of infection, it is also associated with certain allergies, cancers, and other organic illnesses. Fevers whose causes are undiagnosed are called fevers of unknown origin, or FUOs.

The body temperature is normally maintained by a control center in the hypothalamus region of the brain. This thermostat regulates the body's heat production and heat loss and sets the core temperature at around 37°C (98.6°F), with slight fluctuations (1°F) during a daily cycle. Fever is initiated when a circulating substance called **pyrogen*** resets the hypothalamic thermostat to a higher setting. This change signals the musculature to increase heat production and peripheral arterioles to decrease heat loss through vasoconstriction. Fevers range in severity from low-grade (37.7°C to 38.3°C, or 100°F to 101°F) to moderate (38.8°C to 39.4°C, or 102°F to 103°F) to high (40.0°C to 41.1°C, or 104°F to 106°F).

Pyrogens are described as *exogenous* (coming from outside the body) or *endogenous* (originating internally). Exogenous pyrogens are products of infectious agents such as viruses, bacteria, protozoans, and fungi. One well-characterized exogenous pyrogen is endotoxin, the lipopolysaccharide found in the cell walls of gram-negative bacteria. Blood, blood products, vaccines, or injectable solutions can also contain exogenous pyrogens. Endogenous pyrogens are liberated by monocytes, neutrophils, and macrophages during the process of phagocytosis and appear to be a natural part of the immune response. Two potent pyrogens released by macrophages are interleukin-1 (IL-1) and tumor necrosis factor (TNF).

Fever is usually accompanied by chills. What would cause a febrile (feverish) person to periodically feel cold and tremble uncontrollably? The explanation lies in how the brain reacts to pyrogen and the natural physiological interaction between the the hypothalamus and the temperature of the blood. For example, if the thermostat has been reset (by pyrogen) at 102°F but the blood temperature is 99°F, the muscles are stimulated by the brain to contract involuntarily (shivering) as a means of producing more heat. In addition, the vessels in the skin constrict, creating a sensation of cold, and the piloerector muscles in the skin cause goose bumps to form.

Benefits and Treatment of Fever Medical experts have abundant evidence that fever serves an important biological function. Work with tissue cultures showed that increased temperatures stimulate the activities of T cells and increase the effectiveness of interferon. Artificially infected rabbits and pigs allowed to remain febrile survive at a higher rate than those given suppressant drugs. Fever appears to enhance phagocytosis of staphylococci by neutrophils in many mammalian species. The appearance of fever during infections strongly suggests that it is normal and beneficial reaction to invading microbes. Some other effects of fever include:

- It inhibits multiplication of temperature-sensitive microorganisms, such as the poliovirus, cold viruses, herpes zoster virus, systemic and subcutaneous fungal pathogens, *Mycobacterium* species, and the syphilis spirochete.
- It impedes the nutrition of bacteria by reducing the availability of iron. Research has demonstrated that during fever, the

* *pyrogen* (py'-roh-jen) Gr. *pyr,* fire, and *gennan,* produce. Same origin as *funeral pyre* and *pyromaniac.*

macrophages stop releasing their iron stores, which could retard several enzymatic reactions needed for pathogen growth.

- It increases metabolism and stimulates immune reactions and naturally protective physiological processes. It speeds up hematopoiesis, phagocytosis, and specific immune reactions.

Understanding that fever is possibly more beneficial than harmful, deciding whether to suppress it is an important medical question. Some advocates feel that a slight to moderate fever (99–101°F) in an otherwise healthy person should be allowed to run its course in light of its potential as an immune stimulant and its minimal side effects. All medical experts do agree that high and prolonged fevers or fevers in children or patients with cardiovascular disease, seizures, and respiratory ailments are risky and must be treated immediately with fever-suppressant drugs. The classic therapy for fever is an antipyretic drug such as aspirin or acetaminophen (Tylenol) that lowers the setting of the hypothalamic center and restores normal temperature. Any physical technique that increases heat loss (tepid baths, for example) can also help reduce the core temperature.

 Practice SECTION 14.3

16. Describe the major events in the inflammatory response, including the stimuli, physiological reactions, and signs and symptoms.
17. Of rubor, calor, dolor, and tumor, which are signs and which are symptoms?
18. What actions of the inflammatory and immune defenses account for swollen lymph nodes and leukocytosis?
19. What causes pus, and what does it indicate?
20. In what ways can edema be beneficial and in what ways is it harmful?
21. Describe the physiological events leading to fever and review the ways in which fever is naturally beneficial.
22. Explain the processes of diapedesis and chemotaxis, and show how they interrelate.
23. Briefly account for the origins and actions of the major types of inflammatory mediators and cytokines.

14.4 Second-Line Defenses: Phagocytosis, Interferon, and Complement

 Learn

15. Define *phagocytosis*, and identify which cells serve this function.
16. Indicate the major stages of phagocytosis, and describe what is happening at each stage.
17. Explain how phagocytes kill pathogens.
18. Describe the origin of interferon, and explain its role in controlling viruses and other immune functions.
19. Characterize the complement system, its origins, and its basic functions.

Phagocytosis: Ingestion and Destruction by White Blood Cells

By any standard, a phagocyte represents an impressive piece of living machinery, meandering through the tissues to seek, capture, and destroy a target. The following is a summary of the major activities of phagocytes:

1. to survey the tissue compartments and target microbes, particulate matter (dust, carbon particles, antigen–antibody complexes), and injured or dead cells;
2. to ingest and eliminate these materials; and
3. to extract immunogenic information (antigens) from foreign matter.

Major Categories of Phagocytes

It is generally accepted that all cells have some capacity to engulf materials, but professional phagocytes do it for a living. The main types of phagocytes are neutrophils, monocytes, macrophages, and dendritic cells.

Neutrophils and Eosinophils As previously stated, neutrophils are general-purpose phagocytes that react early in the inflammatory response to bacteria and other foreign materials and to damaged tissue. A common sign of bacterial infection is a high neutrophil count in the blood (neutrophilia), and neutrophils are also a primary component of pus. Eosinophils are attracted to sites of parasitic infections and antigen–antibody reactions, though they play only a minor phagocytic role.

Extended Functions of Neutrophils Neutrophils are truly one of the "workhorses" of innate immunity. In addition to their phagocytic functions, they have a distinct system for capturing pathogens called *neutrophil extracellular traps,* or NETS. Neutrophils are programmed to die after they have gone through their regular engulfment and killing of bacteria and other pathogens. But their death does not end their protective actions. Dying neutrophils throw out a fibrous matrix composed of DNA, enzymes, histones, and other cell contents that continue to stop invading microbes even after the neutrophils are completely lysed. The NET works at several levels to trap and immobilize bacteria and fungi, degrade their virulence factors, kill them with microbicidal chemicals, and ultimately, prevent them from spreading.

Macrophages: Dynamic Scavengers After emigrating out of the bloodstream into the tissues, monocytes are transformed by various inflammatory mediators into macrophages. This process is marked by an increase in size and by enhanced development of lysosomes and other organelles **(figure 14.16).** At one time macrophages were classified as either fixed (adherent to tissue) or wandering, but this terminology can be misleading. All macrophages retain the capacity to move about. Whether they reside in a specific organ or wander depends upon their stage of development and the immune stimuli they receive. Specialized macrophages called histiocytes migrate to a certain tissue and remain there during their life span. Examples are alveolar (lung)

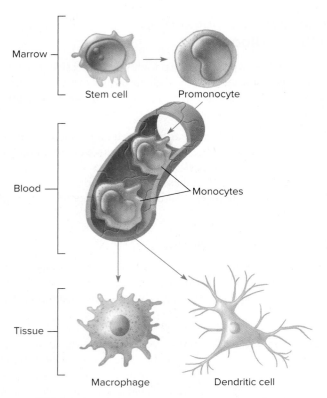

Figure 14.16 **The developmental stages of monocytes and macrophages.** The cells progress through maturational stages in the bone marrow and peripheral blood. Once in the tissues, macrophage and dendritic cells can remain nomadic or take up residence in a specific organ.

macrophages; Kupffer cells in the liver; Langerhans cells in the skin; and macrophages in the spleen, lymph nodes, bone marrow, kidney, bone, and brain. Other macrophages do not reside permanently in a particular tissue but instead drift nomadically throughout the reticuloendothelial system. Dendritic cells—another product of the monocyte line—are concentrated in skin and the linings of mucous membranes, where they process foreign substances and prepare them for reactions with selected lymphocytes (see chapter 15).

Mechanisms of Phagocytic Recognition, Engulfment, and Killing

The term **phagocytosis** literally means "eating cell process." But phagocytosis is more than just the physical act of engulfment, because phagocytes also actively attack and dismantle foreign cells using a wide array of antimicrobial substances. Phagocytosis can occur as an isolated event performed by a lone phagocytic cell responding to a minor irritant in its area or as part of the orchestrated events of inflammation described in section 14.3. The events in phagocytosis include chemotaxis, ingestion, phagolysosome formation, destruction, and elimination **(process figure 14.17).**

> **Quick Search**
> Observe a video of active phagocytes by accessing "Bacterial Phagocytosis by Neutrophils" on YouTube.

Chemotaxis, Binding, and Ingestion Phagocytes migrate into a region of inflammation with a deliberate sense of direction, attracted by a gradient of stimulant products from the pathogen and host tissue at the site of injury.

Once a phagocyte encounters the pathogen, it uses its toll-like receptors to make contact with the pathogen (figure 14.17). Recall that TLRs are receptors that recognize and bind the pathogen-associated molecular pattern (PAMP) receptors of various microbes. There are about 10 different TLRs in the membranes of phagocytes. The exposed end of a receptor hooks on to a PAMP and immediately dimerizes, or joins, with a second TLR to encase the molecule **(figure 14.18).** This relays a signal into the nucleus that stimulates the intracellular phagocytic processes and the release of chemical mediators.

Phagolysosome Formation On the scene of an inflammatory reaction, phagocytes often trap cells or debris against the fibrous network of connective tissue or the wall of blood and lymphatic vessels. Once the phagocyte has "caught" its prey, it extends pseudopods that enclose the cells or particles in a pocket and internalize them in a vacuole called a **phagosome.**

In a short time, **lysosomes** migrate to the scene of the phagosome and fuse with it to form a **phagolysosome.** Other granules containing antimicrobial chemicals are released into the phagolysosome, forming a potent brew designed to poison and then dismantle the ingested material (see process figure 14.17). The destructiveness of phagocytosis is evident by the death of bacteria within 30 minutes after contacting this battery of antimicrobial substances.

Destruction and Elimination Systems Destructive chemicals await the microbes in the phagolysosome. The oxygen-dependent system known as the **respiratory burst,** or oxidative burst, elaborates products of oxygen metabolism called **reactive oxygen intermediates (ROIs).** Myeloperoxidase, an enzyme found in granulocytes, forms halogen ions (OCl^-) that are strong oxidizing agents. Other products of oxygen metabolism such as hydrogen peroxide, the superoxide anion (O_2^-), activated or singlet oxygen ($^1O^-$), and the hydroxyl free radical (HO) separately and together have formidable killing power. This series of reactive oxygen products delivers a "knockout" punch necessary to kill aerobic pathogens such as fungi and many bacteria. Other chemicals that come into play are lactic acid, lysozyme, and *nitric oxide* (NO), a powerful mediator that kills bacteria and inhibits viral replication. Cationic proteins that injure bacterial cell membranes and a number of **hydrolytic** enzymes complete the job. The bits of undigestible debris are released from the macrophage by exocytosis. As we shall see in chapter 15, macrophages and dendritic cells combine phagocytosis with further processing of microbial antigens required for specific immune responses with lymphocytes.

Interferon: Antiviral Cytokines and Immune Stimulants

Interferon (IFN) was described in chapter 12 as a small protein produced naturally by certain white blood and tissue cells. It is used in therapy against certain viral infections and cancer and can be used as

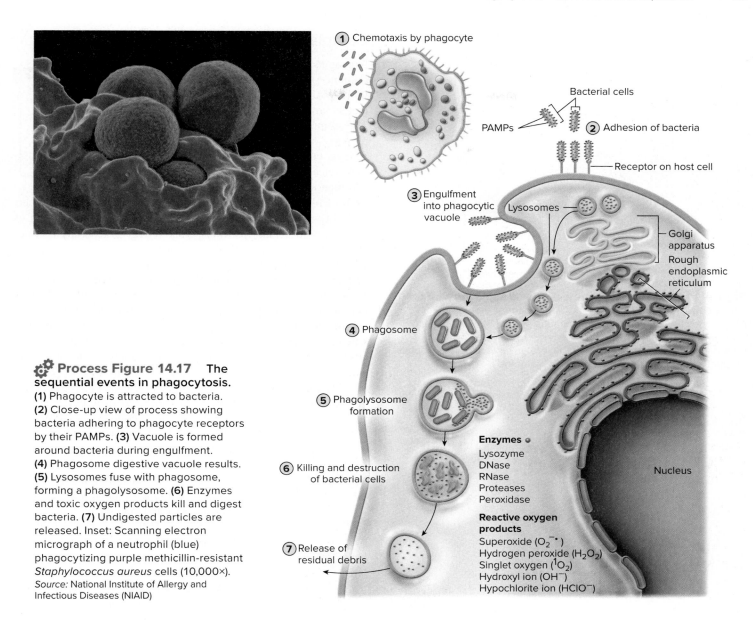

1 Chemotaxis by phagocyte

Bacterial cells

PAMPs

2 Adhesion of bacteria

Receptor on host cell

3 Engulfment into phagocytic vacuole

Lysosomes

Golgi apparatus

Rough endoplasmic reticulum

4 Phagosome

5 Phagolysosome formation

Enzymes
Lysozyme
DNase
RNase
Proteases
Peroxidase

6 Killing and destruction of bacterial cells

Nucleus

Reactive oxygen products
Superoxide ($O_2^{-\bullet}$)
Hydrogen peroxide (H_2O_2)
Singlet oxygen (1O_2)
Hydroxyl ion (OH^-)
Hypochlorite ion ($HClO^-$)

7 Release of residual debris

Process Figure 14.17 The sequential events in phagocytosis.
(1) Phagocyte is attracted to bacteria.
(2) Close-up view of process showing bacteria adhering to phagocyte receptors by their PAMPs. **(3)** Vacuole is formed around bacteria during engulfment.
(4) Phagosome digestive vacuole results.
(5) Lysosomes fuse with phagosome, forming a phagolysosome. **(6)** Enzymes and toxic oxygen products kill and digest bacteria. **(7)** Undigested particles are released. Inset: Scanning electron micrograph of a neutrophil (blue) phagocytizing purple methicillin-resistant *Staphylococcus aureus* cells (10,000×).
Source: National Institute of Allergy and Infectious Diseases (NIAID)

an immune enhancer. Although the interferon system was originally thought to be directed exclusively against viruses, it is now known to be involved also in defenses against other microbes and in immune regulation and intercommunication. Three major types are *interferon alpha,* a product of lymphocytes and macrophages; *interferon beta,* a product of fibroblasts and epithelial cells; and *interferon gamma,* a product of T cells. See 14.1 Making Connections for a summary of interferon actions.

All three classes of interferon are produced in response to viruses, RNA, immune products, and a variety of foreign molecules. Their biological activities are extensive. In all cases, they bind to cell surfaces and induce changes in genetic expression, but the exact results vary. In addition to antiviral effects, discussed next, all three IFNs can inhibit the expression of cancer genes and have tumor suppressor effects. Interferon alpha and IFN beta stimulate phagocytes, and IFN gamma is an immune regulator of macrophages and T and B cells.

Characteristics of Antiviral Interferon

When a virus binds to the receptors on a host cell, a signal is sent to the nucleus that directs the cell to synthesize interferon. After transcription and translation of the interferon gene, newly synthesized interferon molecules are rapidly secreted by the cell into the extracellular space, where they bind to other host cells. The binding of interferon to a second cell induces the production of another class of proteins that inhibit viral multiplication by preventing the translation of viral proteins **(figure 14.19).** Interferon is not virus-specific, so its synthesis in response to one type of virus will also protect against other types. Because this protein is an inhibitor of viruses, it has been a valuable treatment for a number of viral infections.

Other Roles of Interferon

Interferons are also important immune regulatory cytokines that activate or instruct the development of white blood cells. For

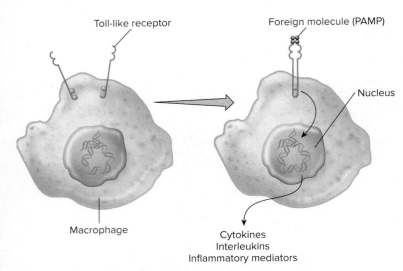

Figure 14.18 **Phagocyte detection and signaling with toll-like receptors.** Toll-like receptors (TLRs) span the membrane of phagocytes and other cells of the immune system. When a molecule such as a PAMP on a particular pathogen is recognized by this receptor, the TLRs merge and bind the foreign molecule. This induces production of chemicals and triggers engulfment.

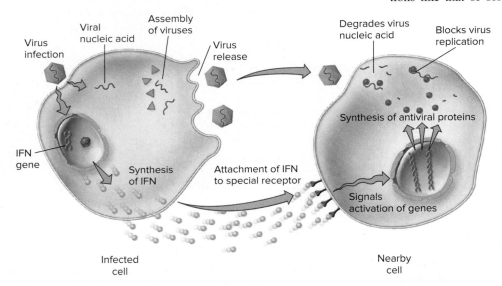

Figure 14.19 **The antiviral activity of interferon.** When a cell is infected by a virus, its nucleus is triggered to transcribe and translate the interferon (IFN) gene. Interferon diffuses out of the cell and binds to IFN receptors on nearby uninfected cells, where it induces production of proteins that eliminate viral genes and block viral replication. Note that the initial cell is not protected by its own IFN and that IFN does not prevent recipient cells from being invaded by viruses, but the viruses are inactivated before they can start replicating.

example, interferon alpha produced by T lymphocytes activates a subset of cells called natural killer (NK) cells. In addition, one type of interferon beta plays a role in the maturation of B and T lymphocytes and in inflammation. Interferon gamma inhibits cancer cells, stimulates B lymphocytes, activates macrophages, and enhances the effectiveness of phagocytosis.

Complement: A Versatile Backup System

Among its many overlapping functions, the immune system has another complex and multiple-duty system called **complement** that is brought into play at several levels. The complement system, named for its property of "complementing" immune reactions, consists of at least 30 blood proteins released by liver cells, lymphocytes, and monocytes. Complement factors are a form of pattern recognition receptor (PRR) that works in concert with inflammation and phagocytosis to destroy a wide variety of bacteria, viruses, and parasites. This system is generally nonspecific and innate, but it can also play a role in acquired immune responses. The three primary defensive features of the complement system are (1) the **membrane attack complex (MAC),** which kills pathogens directly; (2) the coating of pathogens with molecules that make them more attractive to phagocytes **(opsonization);** and (3) the recruitment of inflammatory cells and triggering of cytokine release. Having introduced the second and third topics previously, we will focus here on the main mechanisms of the membrane attack complex.

The membrane attack function of complement is a series of reactions like that of blood clotting, in which the first substance in a chemical series activates the next substance, which activates the next, and so on, until a desired end product is reached. Three different versions of the complement pathways exist **(process figure 14.20).** Their main distinguishing features are how they are activated, major participating factors, and specificity. The end stages of all three converge at the same point and yield a similar end result, that is, destruction of a microbe or infected cell. Because the focus of damage is on the cell membrane, this portion of the complement defense is not as effective on microbes whose outer walls block access to the membrane, but is is effective on cells and viruses with exposed membranes.

The *classical pathway* is the most specific, activated mainly by the presence of antibody bound to microorganisms. It is this pathway that links complement to reactions of acquired immunity. The other two pathways are nonspecific and triggered by common foreign molecules on the surfaces of microbes. In the *lectin pathway,* a host serum protein or lectin binds a sugar called mannan present in the walls of bacteria and other microbes. The *alternative pathway* is initiated by complement proteins that bind to certain surface molecules of microbes (PAMPS), although it may also be triggered spontaneously. Note that because the complement numbers (C1 to C9) are based on the order of their discovery, some factors are not activated in numerical order.

> **Quick Search**
>
> For a dynamic look at the complement system, look up "Animation: Activation of Complement" online.

(a) **Initiation**

Classical Pathway	MB-Lectin Pathway	Alternative Pathway
Complement-fixing antibodies have rapid, specific effects	Mannose-binding lectin (MBL) binds mannose on pathogen surfaces; nonspecific for bacteria and viruses	Molecules on surfaces of bacteria, viruses, and parasites; nonspecific
C1q, C1r, C1s, Factors C4, C2, **C3**	MBL, MASP-1, MASP-2, Factors C4, C2, **C3**	Factors B, D, and **C3**

C3 convertase converts the C3 molecule to an activator of the cascade—$C3_b$.

C3 convertase enzyme

Gram-negative bacterial cell

C5

$C5_b$ C3 $C3_b$

$C3_a$ $C5_a$

(b) **Cascade and Amplification.** C5 factor is acted on by $C3_b$, which converts it to $C5_b$. $C5_b$ becomes bound to the membrane and serves as the starting molecule for the chain of events that assemble the complex in (c) and (d).

Two products of the cascade reaction—$C3_a$ and $C5_a$—have additional inflammatory functions. Both molecules stimulate mast cell degranulation, enhance chemotaxis of white blood cells, and act as inflammatory mediators.

C8 C9

C6 $C5_b$

C7

(c) **Polymerization.** $C5_b$ is a reactive site for the final assembly of an attack complex. In series, C6, C7, and C8 aggregate with $C5_b$ and become integrated into the membrane. They form a substrate upon which the final component, C9, can bind. Up to 15 of these C9 units ring the central core of the final membrane attack complex (MAC).

Completed MAC Lysis

(d) **Membrane Attack.** Insertion of MACs produces hundreds of tiny holes in the cell membrane. This can cause lysis and death of eukaryotic cells and many gram-negative bacteria.

Lysis of bacterial cell

Process Figure 14.20 **Overview of the complement pathways leading to membrane attack. (a)** All three pathways have different triggers and starting points, but they all converge at the same place, C3 convertase. This enzyme begins the series of reactions **(b, c, d)** that give rise to the membrane attack complex characteristic of the complement "machinery." The final result is the formation of tiny openings in the cell membrane and the destruction of the target pathogen.

Stages in the Complement Cascade

In general, the complement pathways go through four stages: initiation, amplification and cascade, polymerization, and membrane attack. The starting reaction requires some type of initiator molecule such as antibodies, lectins, or microbial surface receptors **(process figure 14.20a)**, depending on the pathway. The presence of this initiator on the pathogen's membrane propels the chain of actions involving complement chemicals C1 through C4, with each step serving a dual purpose. We are omitting the fine details of the amplification part of the complement system, but the end result is a molecule, **C3**, that is a key factor in subsequent polymerization of the remaining complement factors in the membrane of the target cell. C3 is acted on by a convertase enzyme that splits it into factors $C3_a$ and $C3_b$. $C3_b$ forms the recognition site and anchor for the final series of reactions to come **(process figure 14.20b)**. $C3_b$ by itself is also an important factor in opsonization and thus facilitates phagocytosis. More information on opsonization can be found in chapter 15.

$C3_b$ moves the cascade reaction forward by splitting factor C5 into $C5_a$ and $C5_b$. One of these molecules—$C5_b$—is key to finishing up polymerization of the remaining complement factors described next. You will notice that the two cleavage products that do not continue in the cascade reaction—$C3_a$ and $C5_a$—still have a number of immune functions (process figure 14.20—right side

of *b*). Both of them are chemotactic factors that recruit white blood cells and trigger the release of inflammatory mediators such as histamine.

The final events in the complement series involve factors $C5_b$, C6, C7, and C8, which join together and give rise to an anchoring complex within the membrane **(process figure 14.20c)**. This is followed by the insertion of several **C9** molecules in the pattern of a ring-shaped formation that is the membrane attack complex (MAC) **(process figure 14.20d)**. The MAC is the primary destructive force of the complement system. It effectively perforates and lyses the membranes of gram-negative bacteria, some parasitic protozoans, enveloped viruses, and virally infected host cells. Except for the classical pathway, these reactions are nonspecific and can be active against a wide spectrum of microbes.

An Outline of Major Host Defenses

At this point, it should be apparent that the body's defenses often work in both parallel and redundant ways to fight pathogens. The result is a constant onslaught of defenses functioning at many levels. This can be illustrated by **figure 14.21**, organized by the three lines of defense that started out our discussion and that lead us naturally into chapter 15.

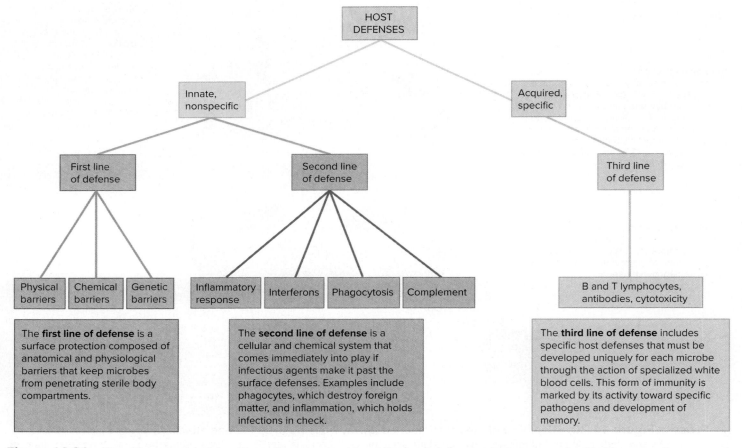

Figure 14.21 **Flowchart summarizing the major components of the host defenses.** Defenses are classified into one of two general categories: (1) innate and nonspecific or (2) acquired and specific. These can be further subdivided into the first, second, and third lines of defense, each being characterized by a different level and type of protection. The third line of defense, the most varied, is responsible for specific immunity. It is covered in greater detail in chapter **15.**

Practice SECTION 14.4

24. Describe the events that give rise to macrophages.

25. What are the types of macrophages, and what are their principal functions?

26. Outline the major phases of phagocytosis.

27. Briefly describe the three major types of interferon, their sources, and their biological effects.

28. Describe the mechanism by which interferon acts as an antiviral compound.

29. Describe the general actions of the complement system.

30. What are some factors that trigger the complement cascade?

31. Using figure 14.21 as a guide, give examples for each category shaded brown, purple, and orange.

CASE STUDY | **Part 2**

The patient's MRI showed only a thin strand of tissue where the spleen should have been located, and the absence of the spleen most likely led to her infection. Roughly 5% of cases of SLE result in functional asplenia, a condition where the spleen is mostly or completely absent due to attack by autoantibodies. Splenic macrophages (those macrophages sequestered in the spleen) are the body's primary defense against encapsulated bacteria, like *Streptococcus pneumoniae*. Patients who are asplenic—due to disease or, more often, trauma—are susceptible to overwhelming post-splenectomy infection (OPSI), which can progress from mild illness to full sepsis in just a few hours.

The patient was treated in the intensive care unit for 9 days, with 4 of those spent on a respirator to aid her breathing. Dopamine and epinephrine were used to stabilize her blood pressure, and antibiotics were administered to treat the *S. pneumoniae* infection. Before being discharged, she was prescribed prophylactic penicillin and vaccinated with Pneumovax, a vaccine which protects against 23 different strains of pneumococcal pneumonia. Among healthy adults, the Centers for Disease Control normally recommends this vaccine only for those over 65 years of age.

Lupus is not the only genetic disease that can wreak havoc with the immune system. Sickle-cell disease is a genetic condition in which, during periods of low oxygen saturation, erythrocytes may change shape. Normally, erythrocytes are round and flexible, but when oxygen is low, these same cells become rigid and sickle shaped, and are unable to pass through small capillaries of the body, blocking the red blood cells behind them. As these trapped red blood cells lose oxygen, they, too, begin to sickle, resulting in a sickling crisis, a painful episode that may include swelling of the hands and feet, delayed growth, vision problems, and stroke.

Sickled erythrocytes also damage the spleen, generally in the first year of life. Over time, the spleen becomes fibrous, smaller, and nonfunctional, and patients are said to have undergone a functional autosplenectomy. These patients, like the young woman in this case, are immune deficient, especially with regard to encapsulated organisms like *Streptococcus pneumoniae,* and face an increased risk of sepsis.

■ Outline the normal interaction between an *S. pneumoniae* cell and a sequestered macrophage in a healthy spleen.

■ Why was the patient prescribed prophylactic penicillin?

Chapter Summary with Key Terms

14.1 Overview of Host Defense Mechanisms

The *first line of defense* is an inborn, nonspecific system composed of anatomical, chemical, and genetic barriers that block microbes at the portal of entry. The *second line of defense* is also inborn and nonspecific and includes protective cells and fluids in tissues, and the *third line of defense* is acquired and specific and is dependent on the function of T and B cells.

14.2 Structure and Function of the Organs of Defense and Immunity

A. **Immunology** is the study of **immunity,** which refers to the development of resistance to infectious agents by white blood cells (WBCs). WBCs conduct surveillance of the body, recognizing and differentiating **nonself** (foreign) cells by means of molecules or **pattern recognition receptors (PRRs)** in their membranes. PRRs recognize a number of indicators carried on foreign cells called **pathogen-associated molecular patterns (PAMPs).** Under normal conditions, **self** cells are left alone but nonself cells are destroyed by the concerted efforts of several types of immune reactions.

B. For purposes of immunologic study, the body is divided into three compartments: the blood, lymphatics, and the **mononuclear phagocyte system.** A fourth component, the extracellular fluid, surrounds the first three and allows constant communication between all areas of the body.

C. **Circulatory System: Blood and Lymphatics**

1. **Whole blood** consists of **blood cells** (formed by **hematopoiesis** in the bone marrow) dispersed in **plasma. Stem cells** in the bone marrow differentiate to produce white blood cells (**leukocytes**), red blood cells

(erythrocytes), and megakaryocytes, which give rise to **platelets.**

2. Leukocytes are the primary mediators of immune function and can be divided into **granulocytes** (**neutrophils, eosinophils,** and **basophils**) and **agranulocytes** (**monocytes, lymphocytes,** and natural killer cells) based on their appearance. Monocytes later differentiate to become **macrophages.** Lymphocytes are divided into **B cells,** which produce **antibodies** as part of **humoral immunity,** and **T cells,** which participate in **cell-mediated immunity.** Natural killer cells act nonspecifically against cancerous and virally infected cells. Leukocytes display both **chemotaxis** and **diapedesis** in response to chemical mediators of the immune system.

D. *Lymphatic System*

1. The **lymphatic system** parallels the circulatory system and transports lymph while also playing host to cells of the immune system. Lymphoid organs and tissues include **lymph nodes,** the spleen, and the **thymus,** as well as areas of less well-organized immune tissues such as **GALT** and **MALT.**

14.3 Second-Line Defenses: Inflammation

A. The inflammatory response is a complex reaction to tissue injury marked by *redness, heat, swelling,* and *pain* (rubor, calor, tumor, and dolor).

1. Blood vessels narrow and then dilate in response to **chemical mediators, cytokines,** and **chemokines.**
2. **Edema** swells tissues as blood supply to the area of infection is increased.
3. WBCs, microbes, debris, and fluid collect to form **pus.**
4. **Pyrogens** may induce fever.

14.4 Second-Line Defenses: Phagocytosis, Interferon, and Complement

A. Phagocytosis: Partner to Inflammation

1. Macrophages and neutrophils engage in **phagocytosis,** engulfing microbes in a phagosome. Uniting the phagosome with a **lysosome** results in destruction of the phagosome contents.
2. Phagocytes use a type of PRR called **toll-like receptors (TLRs)** to recognize and adhere to foreign markers on microbes such as PAMPs.

B. **Interferon (IFN)** is a family of proteins produced by leukocytes and fibroblasts that inhibit the reproduction of viruses by degrading viral RNA or blocking the synthesis of viral proteins.

C. **Complement** is an innate defense system that plays a role in the destruction of bacteria, viruses, and parasites. It causes reactions on the surfaces of cells which result in the formation of a **membrane attack complex (MAC)** that kills microbial cells by creating holes in their membranes. It also plays roles in inflammation and phagocytosis.

Assess Your Knowledge

Level I. These questions require a working knowledge of the concepts in the chapter and the ability to recall and understand the information you have studied.

Developing a Concept Inventory

Select the correct answer from the answers provided. For questions with blanks, choose the combination of answers that most accurately completes the statement.

1. An example/examples of a nonspecific chemical barrier to infection is/are
 a. unbroken skin
 b. lysozyme in saliva
 c. cilia in respiratory tract
 d. all of these

2. Which nonspecific host defense is associated with the trachea?
 a. lacrimation
 b. ciliary lining
 c. desquamation
 d. lactic acid

3. Which of the following blood cells function primarily as phagocytes?
 a. eosinophils
 b. basophils
 c. lymphocytes
 d. neutrophils

4. Which of the following is *not* a lymphoid tissue?
 a. spleen
 b. thyroid gland
 c. lymph node
 d. GALT

5. What is included in GALT?
 a. thymus
 b. Peyer's patches
 c. tonsils
 d. breast lymph nodes

6. A signaling molecule from microbes recognized by phagocytes is
 a. pyrogen
 b. PAMP
 c. complement
 d. lectin

7. Monocytes are _____ leukocytes that develop into _____.
 a. granular, phagocytes
 b. agranular, mast cells
 c. agranular, macrophages
 d. granular, T cells

8. Which of the following inflammatory signs specifies pain?
 a. tumor
 b. calor
 c. dolor
 d. rubor

9. Toll-like receptors are proteins on _____.
 a. phagocytes that recognize foreign molecules
 b. viruses that stimulate immune reactions
 c. skin cells that provide barriers to infection
 d. lymphocytes that damage parasitic worms

10. An example of an inflammatory mediator that stimulates vasodilation is
 - a. histamine
 - b. collagen
 - c. complement C5$_a$
 - d. interferon

11. _____ is an example of an inflammatory mediator that stimulates chemotaxis.
 - a. Endotoxin
 - b. Serotonin
 - c. A fibrin clot
 - d. Interleukin-2

12. An example of an exogenous pyrogen is
 - a. interleukin-1
 - b. complement
 - c. interferon
 - d. endotoxin

13. _____ interferon, produced by T lymphocytes, activates cells called _____ and is involved in destroying viruses.
 - a. Gamma, fibroblasts
 - b. Beta, lymphocytes
 - c. Alpha, natural killer cells
 - d. Beta, fibroblasts

14. In what process is tumor necrosis factor (TNF) *not* involved?
 - a. chemotaxis of phagocytes
 - b. fever
 - c. the inflammatory response
 - d. the classic complement pathway

15. Which of the following substances is *not* produced by phagocytes to destroy engulfed microorganisms?
 - a. hydroxyl radical
 - b. superoxide anion
 - c. hydrogen peroxide
 - d. bradykinin

16. Which of the following is the end product of the complement system?
 - a. properdin
 - b. cascade reaction
 - c. membrane attack complex
 - d. complement factor C9

Case Study Analysis

1. The spleen is considered a
 - a. primary lymphoid tissue
 - b. secondary lymphoid tissue
 - c. tertiary lymphoid tissue
 - d. quaternary lymphoid tissue

2. Which type of cell normally matures to become the splenic macrophages that were absent in the patient?
 - a. neutrophil
 - b. lymphocyte
 - c. megakaryocyte
 - d. monocyte

3. Explain why the patient in the Case Study could have an overactive immune response (as manifested by her lupus) yet still be prone to infection.

On the Test

These questions will help to prepare you to successfully answer similar questions you'll see on the TEAS (Test of Essential Academic Skills) and NCLEX (National Council Licensure Examination).

1. A client is known to have consumed food contaminated with disease-causing bacteria but has not become ill. The nurse explains to the client that the acidity of the stomach can kill some organisms. This type of protection would be classified as
 - a. innate immunity, which provides specific protection
 - b. innate immunity, which provides nonspecific protection
 - c. acquired immunity, which provides specific protection
 - d. acquired immunity, which provides nonspecific protection

2. The mother of a client asks which cells in the body are responsible for humoral immunity. The pediatric nurse correctly answers
 - a. neutrophils
 - b. natural killer cells
 - c. B lymphocytes
 - d. platelets

Writing Challenge

For each question, compose a one- or two-paragraph answer that includes the factual information needed to completely address the question. Practice questions can also be used for writing-challenge exercises.

1. Use the lines on the figure to the right to locate and describe the eight components of the first line of defense.

2. What effects do these defenses have on microbes? Describe the initial steps taken by the primary responders to foreign matter.

3. Explain what PRRs and TLRs are and the nature of their interaction with PAMPs.

4. Make a simple drawing of the functions of toll-like receptors.

5. Describe the mechanisms by which leukocytes migrate from the bloodstream into an area of infection. What chemical factors are they reacting to?

6. Prepare a simplified outline of the cell lines of hematopoiesis.

7. Differentiate between the functions of primary and secondary lymphoid organs.

8. In what ways is a phagocyte a tiny container of disinfectants?

9. Macrophages perform the final job of removing tissue debris and other products of infection. Indicate some of the possible effects when these scavengers cannot successfully complete the work of phagocytosis.

10. Briefly outline what leads to the result shown in the figure on the right. Give the name and actions of this structure.

Concept Mapping

On Connect you can find an Introduction to Concept Mapping that provides guidance for working with concept maps, along with concept-mapping activities for this chapter.

 ## Application, Analysis, Evaluation, and Synthesis

Level II. These problems go beyond just restating facts and require higher levels of understanding and an ability to interpret, problem solve, transfer knowledge to new situations, create models, and predict outcomes.

Critical Thinking

Critical thinking is the ability to reason and solve problems using facts and concepts. These questions can be approached from a number of angles and, in most cases, they do not have a single correct answer.

1. Suggest some reasons that there is so much redundancy of action and there are so many interacting aspects of immune responses.

2. a. What are some possible elements missing in children born without a functioning lymphocyte system?
 b. What is the most important component extracted in bone marrow transplants?

3. A patient's chart shows an increase in eosinophil levels.
 a. What does this cause you to suspect?
 b. What does it mean if the basophil levels are very high?
 c. What if the neutrophil levels are very high?

4. How can adults continue to function relatively normally after surgery to remove the thymus, tonsils, spleen, or lymph nodes?

5. An obsolete treatment for syphilis involved inducing fever by deliberately infecting patients with the agent of relapsing fever. An experimental AIDS treatment involved infecting patients with malaria to induce high fevers. Can you provide some possible explanations behind these peculiar forms of treatment?

6. Patients with a history of tuberculosis often show scars and other lesions in the lungs and experience recurrent infection. Account for these effects on the basis of the inflammatory response.

7. *Shigella, Mycobacterium,* and numerous other pathogens have developed mechanisms that prevent them from being killed by phagocytes.
 a. Suggest two or three factors that help them avoid destruction by the powerful antiseptics in macrophages.
 b. Suggest the potential implications that these infected macrophages can have on the development of disease.

8. Account for the several inflammatory symptoms that occur in the injection site when one has been vaccinated against influenza and tetanus.

9. What is the specific target of fever-suppressing drugs? Knowing that fever is potentially both harmful and beneficial, what are some possible guidelines for deciding whether to suppress it or not?

10. Discuss the multiple, overlapping functions of the immune system. Which tissues and organs are involved in the immune response, and how does each function?

Visual Assessment

1. Each numbered figure 1–3 represents a cell that provides an immune defense. Each lettered figure A–C shows a pathogenic microbe. Name the type of defense and match it with its primary target microbe and effects.

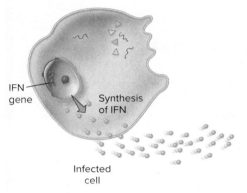

IFN gene

Synthesis of IFN

Infected cell

(1) Figure 14.19

(2)
Courtesy of Harold Benson

(3)
Courtesy of Harold Benson

(A) Figure 18.8
Kathy Park Talaro

(B) Figure 23.21
Source: Oregon State Public Health Laboratory/ CDC-DPDx

(C) Table 6.2

Adaptive, Specific Immunity, and Immunization

In This Chapter...

Not to Worry, It's Just a Flesh Wound

Most big things start small, and a minor cut seemed no reason to interrupt a ski vacation. So, when a 33-year-old man received just such a cut, he cleaned and dressed the **wound** himself, and thought little else of it. Over the next several days, though, the wound on his calf grew larger and more painful, leading him to seek professional treatment. Believing the wound to be **infected**, doctors prescribed cefuroxime, a **cephalosporin antibiotic** primarily directed against *Staphylococcus aureus* and *Streptococcus pyogenes*. Despite antibiotic treatment, the infection worsened, and the patient was admitted to the hospital for surgical **debridement** (the removal of dead and damaged tissue).

The bacterial infection continued to spread through the patient's leg, leaving dead and damaged soft tissue in its wake, a condition known to medical professionals as **necrotizing fasciitis** and to headline writers as **flesh-eating bacteria**. Necrotizing fasciitis causes local tissue death and can lead to septic shock, an **inflammatory** reaction in which multiple organs systems fail, blood pressure plummets and, as often as not, the patient dies. Medical treatment for necrotizing fasciitis relies on surgically removing the infected tissue, often **necessitating amputation**, while the infection itself is treated with broad-spectrum antibiotics. Due to his worsening condition, the patient was transferred to a specialized hospital and his antibiotic regimen was changed to clindamycin and tazobactam, a far more potent combination, and one that is especially effective against **anaerobic infections**. During his first 2 days in the new hospital, surgeons removed large swaths of necrotic tissue, trying to stay ahead of the infection.

The patient complained of **severe pain** and had swelling of the **lymph nodes** in his groin and both axillae (armpits). Laboratory results were consistent with infection—an elevated white blood cell (WBC) count and high C-reactive protein (CRP), a marker of inflammation—and antibiotics were once again changed, in the hope of finding something that would successfully combat the infection before the patient died. On the fourth day after admission, a **fasciotomy**—a long incision along a muscle, used to relieve pressure, restore blood flow, and prevent the need for amputation—was performed on the patient's left thigh, and both axillae were surgically debrided.

During each surgical procedure, tissue samples and swabs were taken from each affected area, but no **pathogen** could be cultured. The **polymerase chain reaction** detected the presence of DNA from *Corynebacterium tuberculostearicum* and *Acinetobacter baumannii*, two very different bacteria. In the absence of a culturable pathogen, doctors had no choice but to guess at an effective treatment. A CT (computed tomography) scan revealed a buildup of fluid in both lungs; the patient was placed on a respirator, as he was unable to breathe on his own.

- *Would the DNA of* Corynebacterium tuberculostearicum *and* Acinetobacter baumannii *detected by polymerase chain reaction make an easily recognized antigen?*

- *What happens when an antigen encounters an antigen-presenting cell (APC)?*

To continue the Case Study, go to Case Study Part 2 at the end of the chapter.

(Scanning electron micrograph): Brand X/Getty Images

15.1 Specific Immunities: The Adaptive Line of Defense

 Learn

1. Summarize the general features of adaptive, acquired immunity.

2. Define *immunocompetence, antigens, specificity,* and *memory* as they relate to the immune system.

3. Outline the overall phases in a specific immune response.

4. Explain the functions and types of immune receptors, including where and how they develop.

5. Describe the major events in the origin of diversity of the immune system and features of the clonal selection theory.

6. Describe the development of antigen receptors on lymphocytes.

7. Discuss the events in B-cell and T-cell maturation and how they differ.

In chapter 14, we described the capacity of the immune system to survey, recognize, and react to foreign cells and molecules. Our main focus in that chapter was to overview innate host defenses such as anatomical and physiological barriers, phagocytosis, and inflammation. We also provided essential background for the main systems involved, such as blood cells and lymphatic tissues. Refer to figure 14.21 and use the flowchart to refresh yourself on the relationships among various host defenses. An essential system of defense that is not innate but must be acquired will be the main subject of this chapter.

Normal humans have an extremely specific and powerful system for resisting infectious agents. This system is called **adaptive** or **acquired immunity,** sometimes known as the third line of defense. It is responsible for the long-term protection we develop through infections or vaccinations. The absolute need for adaptive immunity is impressively documented in children with genetic defects in this system or in AIDS patients who have lost it. Even with heroic measures to isolate the patient, combat infections, or restore lymphoid tissue, immunodeficient people are constantly vulnerable to life-threatening infections.

Acquired adaptive immunity is the product of a dual system of specialized leukocytes—the B and T lymphocytes. During fetal development, these lymphocytes undergo a selective process that prepares them to react only to one specific antigen. During this time, **immunocompetence,** the ability of the body to interact with a wide spectrum of foreign substances, begins to develop. Through this process, an infant is born with the theoretical *potential* to produce an immune response to hundreds of millions of different foreign molecules or antigens. But the completion of this immunocompetence takes many years, extending into late puberty.

Antigens figure very prominently in specific immunity. They are defined as any molecules that can stimulate a response by T and B cells. They consist of protein, polysaccharide, and other compounds from cells and viruses. Environmental chemicals can also be antigens, as we shall see in section 16.2 dealing with allergy. In fact, any exposed or released substance is potentially an antigen, even those from our own cells. For reasons we discuss later, our own antigens do not usually evoke a response from our own immune systems, but they may do so in other persons.

In chapter 14, we discussed pathogen-associated molecular patterns (PAMPs) that stimulate responses by phagocytic cells during an innate defense response. PAMPs are molecules shared by many types of microbes that stimulate a nonspecific response. In contrast, antigens are molecules unique to a microbe that stimulate specific immune responses. The two kinds of molecules do share two characteristics: (1) they are "parts" of foreign cells (microbes) and (2) they provoke a reaction by the white blood cells of the host.

Two features that make adaptive immunity very different from innate immunity are **specificity** and **memory.** Unlike mechanisms such as anatomical barriers or phagocytosis, acquired immunity is selective. For example, the antibodies produced against the chicken-pox virus during an infection will protect against that virus but not against the measles virus. Demonstrating memory means that lymphocytes have been programmed to "recall" their first engagement with an invader and respond rapidly to that same invader during subsequent exposures, which is a critical feature of immunity. These topics will be covered in greater depth in several later sections.

An Overview of Specific Immune Responses

Immune responses are highly complex and regulated, and they represent one of the most elegant and coordinated networks of cells and chemicals in the body. To present this system in an organized manner, we have found it helpful to divide it into separate but related sections, each detailing some event in development of the immune response. The sections of coverage are as follows:

I. Development and differentiation of the immune system (section 15.1)

II. Lymphocyte maturation and the nature of antigens (section 15.2)

III. Immune reactions to antigens and the activities of T cells (section 15.3)

IV. Immune activities of B cells and the production and actions of antibodies (section 15.3)

As we explore the information contained in these sections, we will be following a "map" of sorts. **Process figure 15.1** lays out the flow of the main stages and will serve to coordinate the presentation. It also includes figure numbers that enlarge on the topics in that section.

Development of the Immune Response System

Before we examine lymphocyte development and function in greater detail, we must initially review concepts such as the unique structure of molecules (especially proteins), the characteristics of cell surfaces (membranes and envelopes), the ways that genes are expressed, immune recognition, and identification of self and nonself. Ultimately the shape and function of protein receptors and markers protruding from the surfaces of certain white blood cells are the result of genetic expression, and these molecules are responsible for specific immune recognition and, thus, immune reactions.

Markers on Cell Surfaces Involved in Recognition of Self and Nonself

Chapter 14 touched on the fundamental idea that cell surface receptors confer specificity and identity. A given cell can express several

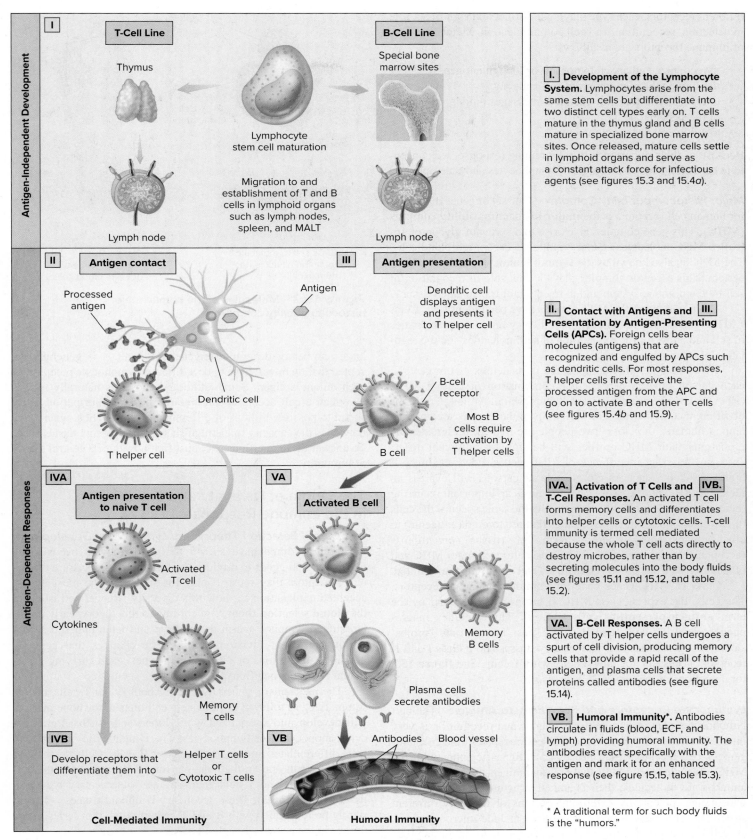

I. **Development of the Lymphocyte System.** Lymphocytes arise from the same stem cells but differentiate into two distinct cell types early on. T cells mature in the thymus gland and B cells mature in specialized bone marrow sites. Once released, mature cells settle in lymphoid organs and serve as a constant attack force for infectious agents (see figures 15.3 and 15.4a).

II. **Contact with Antigens and III. Presentation by Antigen-Presenting Cells (APCs).** Foreign cells bear molecules (antigens) that are recognized and engulfed by APCs such as dendritic cells. For most responses, T helper cells first receive the processed antigen from the APC and go on to activate B and other T cells (see figures 15.4b and 15.9).

IVA. **Activation of T Cells and IVB. T-Cell Responses.** An activated T cell forms memory cells and differentiates into helper cells or cytotoxic cells. T-cell immunity is termed cell mediated because the whole T cell acts directly to destroy microbes, rather than by secreting molecules into the body fluids (see figures 15.11 and 15.12, and table 15.2).

VA. **B-Cell Responses.** A B cell activated by T helper cells undergoes a spurt of cell division, producing memory cells that provide a rapid recall of the antigen, and plasma cells that secrete proteins called antibodies (see figure 15.14).

VB. **Humoral Immunity*.** Antibodies circulate in fluids (blood, ECF, and lymph) providing humoral immunity. The antibodies react specifically with the antigen and mark it for an enhanced response (see figure 15.15, table 15.3).

* A traditional term for such body fluids is the "humors."

⚙ **Process Figure 15.1** Overview of the origins and events of adaptive immune responses. This summary lays out the plan of sections 15.2, 15.3, and 15.4.

different receptors, each type playing a distinct and significant role in detection, recognition, and cell communication. Major functions of immune receptors are as follows:

- to recognize and attach to nonself or foreign antigens,
- to promote the recognition of self antigens,
- to receive and transmit chemical messages among other cells of the system, and
- to aid in cellular development.

Because of their importance in the immune response, we concentrate here on the major receptors of lymphocytes and macrophages.

Major Histocompatibility Complex One set of genes that codes for human cell receptors is the **major histocompatibility complex (MHC).** This gene complex gives rise to a series of glycoproteins (called MHC molecules) found on all cells except red blood cells. The MHC is also known as the **human leukocyte antigen (HLA)** system. This receptor complex plays a vital role in recognition of self by the immune system and in rejection of transplanted tissues.

The functions of the MHC groups have been identified. **Class I MHC** genes code for markers that display unique characteristics of self and allow for the recognition of self molecules and the regulation of immune reactions.

The system is rather complicated in its details, but in general, each person inherits a particular combination of class I MHC (HLA) genes in a relatively predictable fashion. Although millions of different combinations and variations of these genes are possible among humans, the closer two people are related, the greater the probability their MHC profiles will be similar. Individual differences in the exact inheritance of MHC genes, however, make it highly unlikely that even closely related persons will express an identical MHC profile. This fact introduces an important recurring theme: Although humans are genetically the same species, the cells of each individual express molecules that are foreign (antigenic) to other humans. This is where the term *histo-* (tissue) *compatibility* (acceptance) originated. This fact necessitates testing for MHC and other antigens when blood is transfused and organs are transplanted.

Class II MHC genes code for immune regulatory receptors. The cells that express class MHC II are grouped together by the term **antigen-presenting cells (APCs).** This includes macrophages, dendritic cells, and B cells. These are the only "professional" antigen presenters, in that they possess both class I and II receptors necessary for interactions with T cells. See **figure 15.2** for depictions of the two MHC classes.

Lymphocyte Receptors and Specificity to Antigen The part lymphocytes play in immune surveillance and recognition is very much a function of their receptors. B-cell receptors bind free antigens; T-cell receptors bind processed antigens together with the MHC molecules on the cells that present antigens to them. Because antigens are molecules, their chemical structures can vary over a wide range, potentially exhibiting billions of uniquely different structures. The many sources of antigens include microorganisms as well as an awesome array of chemical compounds in the environment. One of the most fascinating questions in immunology is: How can the lymphocyte receptors be varied to react with such a

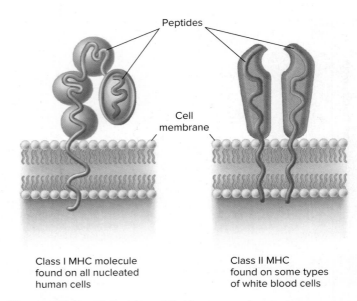

Class I MHC molecule found on all nucleated human cells

Class II MHC found on some types of white blood cells

Figure 15.2 Molecules of the human major histocompatibility complex.

large number of different antigens? After all, it is generally accepted that there will have to be a different lymphocyte receptor for each unique antigen. Some additional questions naturally follow: How can a cell accommodate enough genetic information to respond to possibly billions of different antigens? When, where, and how does the capacity to distinguish self from foreign tissue arise? To answer these questions, we must first introduce a central theory of immunity.

The Origin of Diversity and Specificity in the Immune Response

The Clonal Selection Theory and Lymphocyte Development Research findings have shown that lymphocytes use slightly more than 500 genes to produce the tremendous repertoire of specific receptors they must display for antigens. The most widely accepted explanation for how this diversity is generated is called the **clonal selection theory.** According to this theory, early undifferentiated lymphocytes in the embryo and fetus undergo a continuous series of divisions and genetic changes that generate hundreds of millions of different cell types, each carrying a particular receptor specificity.

The mechanism, generally true for both B and T cells, can be summarized as follows: Certain stem cell lines in the bone marrow will develop into specialized white blood cells such as granulocytes, monocytes, or lymphocytes. The lymphocytic line of stem cells differentiates into either T cells or B cells. Cells destined to become B cells stay in the bone marrow; T cells move to the thymus. Mature B and T cells then migrate to secondary lymphoid tissues **(figure 15.3).** These secondary lymphoid tissues will constantly be resupplied with B and T cells through this series of activities in the primary lymphoid tissues.

By the time T and B cells reach the lymphoid tissues, each one is already equipped to respond to a single unique antigen. This

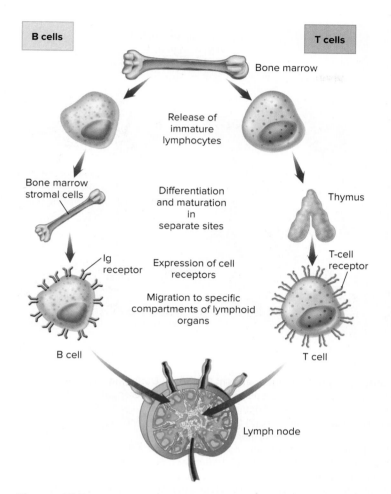

Figure 15.3 Major stages in the development of B and T cells.

caused by a loss of immune tolerance that can lead to immune reactions directed at self (covered in chapter 16).

The second stage of development—**clonal selection and expansion**—does require stimulation by antigens, such as those that come from microbes. When an antigen enters the body, it encounters specific lymphocytes ready to recognize it. Such contact stimulates that clone to undergo mitotic divisions and expands it into a larger population of lymphocytes, all bearing the same specificity. This increases the capacity of the immune response for that antigen.

Two important generalities one can derive from the clonal selection theory are (1) that lymphocyte specificity is preprogrammed, existing in the genetic makeup before an antigen has ever entered the tissues; and (2) that each genetically distinct lymphocyte expresses only a single specificity and can react to only one type of antigen. Other important features of the lymphocyte response system are detailed in later sections.

The Specific B-Cell Receptor: An Immunoglobulin Molecule

In the case of B lymphocytes, the receptor genes that undergo the recombination process are those governing **immunoglobulin* (Ig)** synthesis. Immunoglobulins are large glycoprotein molecules that serve as the specific receptors of B cells and as antibodies. The immunoglobulin molecule is a composite of four protein chains: a pair of identical heavy (H) chains and a pair of identical light (L) chains **(figure 15.5a)**. Each light chain binds to a heavy chain, and the two heavy chains bind to each other with disulfide bonds, creating a symmetrical, Y-shaped arrangement.

The ends of the forks formed by the light and heavy chains contain pockets called the **antigen binding sites.** These sites can be highly variable in shape to fit a wide range of antigens. This extreme versatility is due to **variable (V) regions,** where amino acid composition is highly varied from one clone of B lymphocytes to another **(figure 15.5b)**. The remainder of the light chains and heavy chains consist of **constant (C) regions** whose amino acid content does not vary greatly from one antibody to another. Process figure 15.14 provides further details of antibody structure.

Development of B-Lymphocyte Receptors During Maturation

The genes that code for immunoglobulins lie on three different chromosomes. An undifferentiated lymphocyte has about 150 different genes that code for the variable region of light chains and about 250 genes for the **variable (V)** and **diversity (D) regions** of the heavy chains. The **constant (C)** regions and the **joining (J) regions** that link segments of the final molecule are represented by only a small number of genes. A result of the extensive genetic recombination that occurs during development is that only a single V and D gene segments are active in the mature cell, and all the other V and D genes have been deleted (figure 15.5b).

One can envision this process by comparing it to a molecular "cut and paste." The gene segments lie in an established sequence along a chromosome. A complex enzyme system randomly selects and cuts out particular blocks of DNA and splices them together. All remaining unused gene segments are permanently removed

amazing diversity is generated by rearrangements of the gene segments that code for the antigen receptors on the T and B cells **(process figure 15.4a).** These extensive genetic recombinations give rise to a huge assortment of lymphocytes.[1] Each genetically unique line of lymphocytes arising from this process is termed a **clone.** All of the cells in a clone display identical protein receptors on their surface, and because of this will react with one specific antigen.

This *proliferative* stage of lymphocyte development does not require the actual presence of foreign antigens. But it does require another important action—namely, the removal of clones of lymphocytes that can react against *self* MHC antigens. The presence of such "forbidden clones" could cause severe damage if the immune system mistakenly identifies self molecules as foreign and mounts a response against the host's own tissues. Thus, part of the clonal selection theory says that some clones are eliminated during development through clonal *deletion.* The removal of such potentially harmful clones is one basis of **immune tolerance** or tolerance to self. Some diseases (such as autoimmunity) are thought to be

1. Estimates of the theoretical number of possible variations that may be created vary from 10^{14} to 10^{18} different specificities—clearly enough to react with all potential antigens that might be encountered.

* *immunoglobulin* (im″-yoo-noh-glahb′-yoo-lin)

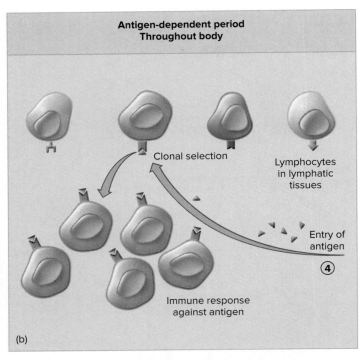

⚙️ Process Figure 15.4 **Lymphocyte development and maturation. (a) Antigen-Independent Period. (1)** During development of early lymphocytes from stem cells, a given stem cell undergoes rapid cell division to form numerous progeny. As cells differentiate, random rearrangement of the genes that code for cell surface protein receptors results in a large array of genetically distinct cells, called clones. Each clone bears a different receptor that reacts with only a single type of foreign molecule or antigen. **(2)** Lymphocyte clones with receptors that recognize self molecules and could be harmful are eliminated (clonal deletion). T cells undergo further selection in the thymus, where cells that do not recognize self MHC (and are therefore nonfunctional) are also deleted. **(3)** Each surviving lymphocyte that exits the thymus is specific for a single antigen molecule. The result is an enormous pool of mature but naive lymphocytes that are ready to further differentiate under the influence of their "home" organs and immune stimuli. **(b) Antigen-Dependent Period. (4)** Lymphocytes migrate to the lymphatic organs where they are situated to encounter antigens. Entry of a specific antigen selects only the lymphocyte clone or clones that carry surface receptors matching the antigen. This will trigger an immune response, which varies according to the type of lymphocyte involved.

from the genome of this cell, leaving only the selected segments, which will code for a specific polypeptide receptor. A summary of the steps in the process is as follows:

- For a heavy chain, a variable region gene segment and diversity region gene segment are selected from among the hundreds available and spliced to one joining region gene and one constant region gene.
- For a light chain, one variable, one joining, and one constant gene segment are spliced together.
- After transcription and translation of each gene complex into a polypeptide, a heavy chain combines with a light chain to form half an immunoglobulin; two of these combine to form a completed protein (figure 15.5b).

Once synthesized, the immunoglobulin product is transported to the cell membrane and inserted there to act as a receptor that expresses the specificity of that cell and to react with an antigen, as shown in figure 15.5. It is notable that for each lymphocyte, the genes that were selected for the variable region, and thus for its specificity, will be locked in for the rest of the life of that lymphocyte and its progeny. But the constant region may be altered to provide different functional properties. We discuss the different classes of Ig molecules further in section 15.4.

T-Cell Receptors for Antigen The T-cell receptor for antigen belongs to the same protein family as the B-cell receptor. It is similar to B cells in being formed by genetic modification, having variable and constant regions, being inserted into the membrane, and having an antigen binding site formed from two parallel polypeptide chains (**figure 15.6**). Unlike the immunoglobulins, the T-cell receptor is relatively small. It is equivalent to one fork of the B-cell receptor and is not secreted. Additional receptors of T cells are described in section 15.3.

With a working knowledge of some factors in the development of immune specificity, we can now continue our coverage of the immune response as outlined in process figure 15.1.

Specific Events in T-Cell Maturation

The further development and maturation of T cells are directed by the thymus gland and its hormones. The complexity of T-cell function, discussed in section 15.3, is partly due to different classes of T-cell surface molecules termed **clusters of differentiation** or **CD receptors** added during maturation. CD molecules serve multiple roles as cell receptors and may be involved in cell adhesion and communication in a variety of cells. They are denoted with a number—CD1, CD2, and so on. Our focus will be primarily on two CD groups found on T cells:

① The heavy-chain genes are composed of four separate segments (V, D, J, and C) that are ② transcribed and translated to form two copies of the heavy polypeptide chain.

③ The light-chain genes are put together like heavy ones, except that the final gene is spliced from three gene groups (V, J, and C), making smaller polypeptides.

Precisely shaped binding sites

④ During final assembly, first the heavy and light chains are bound, and then the two halves are connected to form the immunoglobulin molecule.

Figure 15.5 **The basic structure and genetics of immunoglobulins. (a)** Simple model of an immunoglobulin molecule. The main components are four polypeptide chains—two identical light chains and two identical heavy chains bound by disulfide bonds as shown. Each chain consists of a variable region (V) and a constant region (C). The variable regions of light and heavy chains form a binding site for antigen. **(b)** The final gene that codes for a heavy or light chain is assembled by splicing blocks of genetic material from several regions (1, 2, 3). These genes are transcribed and translated into the polypeptides that join to form the final molecule (4). **(c)** Space-filling model of an immunoglobulin molecule. Heavy chains are blue and light chains are teal. The intricate configuration of the proteins where the light and heavy chains come together at the tips of the "Y" provide each antibody with a unique antigen binding site.
(c): molekuul_be/Shutterstock

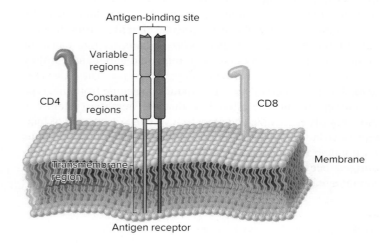

Figure 15.6 **Structure of the T-cell receptor (TCR) for antigen and CD receptors.** The structure of the TCR is similar to that of an immunoglobulin. It consists of two polypeptides that mimic the structure of one "arm" of an immunoglobulin. The TCR has variable regions (orange and teal) that can show high levels of diversity for antigens, and constant regions (green and yellow) that do not greatly vary. Another class of T-cell receptors, called CD receptors, function in cell signaling. The CD4 and CD8 receptors will be discussed in section 15.3.

TABLE 15.1	Contrasting Properties of T Cells and B Cells							
	Site of Maturation	Immune Surface Markers	Circulation in Blood	Receptors for Antigen	Distribution in Lymphatic Organs	Require Antigen Presented with MHC	Product of Antigenic Stimulation	General Functions
T Cells	Thymus gland	T-cell receptor, CD molecules, MHC I receptors	High numbers	T-cell receptor (TCR)	Paracortical sites (interior to the follicles)	Yes	Helper and cytotoxic T cells and memory cells	Regulate immune functions, kill foreign and infected cells, synthesize cytokines
B Cells	Bone marrow	Immunoglobulin MHC I and MHC II receptors	Low numbers	Immunoglobulins D and M	Cortex (in follicles)	No	Plasma cells and memory cells	Produce antibodies to target, inactivate, and neutralize antigens

CD4 receptors on T helper cells and CD8 receptors on T cytotoxic cells. These CD receptors interact with a particular MHC marker on other white blood cells during immune reactions. As was shown in figure 15.3, mature T cells migrate to specific sites in lymphoid organs and constantly circulate from there. It is estimated that 25×10^9 T cells pass between the lymphatic and general circulation per day.

Specific Events in B-Cell Maturation

The sites of B-cell maturation exist in certain bone marrow regions that harbor *stromal cells.* These huge cells nurture the lymphocyte stem cells and provide chemical signals that initiate B-cell development. The result of gene modification and selection is the development of hundreds of millions of distinct B cells (see process figure 15.4a). Just as T cells do, these naive B lymphocytes travel to specific sites in the lymph nodes, spleen, and mucosal-associated lymphoid tissue (MALT), where they adhere to specific binding molecules. Here they will come into contact with antigens throughout life. B cells display immunoglobulins as surface receptors for antigens (see table 15.3).

Table 15.1 summarizes the main differences in the structure, functions, and actions of B cells and T cells.

Practice SECTION 15.1

1. Discuss what is meant by immunocompetence, immune specificity and memory, and adaptive immunity.
2. What function do receptors play in specific immune responses and how can they be made to vary so widely?
3. Describe the major histocompatibility complex, and explain how it participates in immune reactions.
4. Explain the clonal selection theory of receptor specificity and diversity in lymphocytes.
5. Why must the body develop tolerance to self?
6. Trace the origin and development of T lymphocytes and of B lymphocytes.
7. What is happening during lymphocyte maturation?
8. Describe three ways in which B cells and T cells are similar and at least five major ways in which they are different.

15.2 The Nature of Antigens and Antigenicity

 Learn

8. Explain the characteristics of antigens, the property of antigenicity, and epitopes.
9. Discuss the main categories of antigens, based on function.

Characteristics of Antigens and Immunogens

Earlier we encountered the concept of an **antigen,*** which can now be more fully defined as any molecule or fragment of a molecule that has the *potential* to trigger a specific immune response by lymphocytes. This property is known as **antigenicity.** For a substance to be antigenic, it must meet several criteria related to foreignness, size, shape, and accessibility that are discussed next. A related set of more specific terms are **immunogen** and *immunogenicity.* An immunogen is a type of antigen that actually *does* induce a specific immune response when introduced into the body.

The difference between these terms is subtle and addresses the fact that some antigens may not fit all of the actual conditions to stimulate an immune reaction, whereas immunogens do. One example involves the small **polysaccharides** from the capsule of the bacterium *Haemophilus influenzae,* one cause of meningitis. These molecules are foreign and antigenic, but they are too small to trigger a lymphocyte response: They are antigenic but not immunogenic. To produce a vaccine from this type of antigen, it must be altered so that the immune system can more readily recognize and react to it (see the discussion of haptens later in this section). In most of the succeeding discussions on immune responsiveness, we will use the more general term *antigen* because it encompasses all possibilities of eliciting immune reactions.

antigen* (an′-tih-jen) Means, literally, an **antibody **gen**erator.

Figure 15.7 Characteristics of antigens. (a) Whole cells of bacteria, fungi, and viruses make good immunogens. So do plant parts and animal cells. **(b)** Complex molecules with several epitopes make good immunogens, including antibodies, which can also act as antigens. **(c)** Poor immunogens include small, simple molecules not attached to a carrier molecule (1, 2) and larger molecules with repetitive chains of monomers that have less complexity (3, 4).

One important characteristic of an antigen is that the immune cells react to it as nonself or as foreign, meaning that it is not a "normal" constituent of the body. Whole microbes or their parts, cells, or substances that arise from other humans, animals, plants, and various molecules all possess this quality of foreignness and thus are potentially antigenic to the immune system of an individual **(figure 15.7).** Molecules of complex composition such as proteins and protein-containing compounds prove to be more immunogenic than repetitive polymers composed of a single type of unit. Most materials that serve as antigens fall into these chemical categories (with examples):

- proteins and large polypeptides (enzymes, cell surface receptors, hormones, exotoxins);

- molecules that contain two or more different macromolecules bound together. Examples of these include:
 - lipoproteins (combinations of lipids and proteins) and lipopolysaccharides (combinations of lipids and carbohydrates). These substances originate from the cell membranes or cell walls of microbes.
 - nucleoproteins (DNA complexed to proteins); unbound DNA is too regular and repetitive in structure to be antigenic;
 - polysaccharides (certain bacterial capsules) and glycolipids (mycolic acid of *M. tuberculosis*).

Effects of Molecular Shape and Size on Antigenicity

To initiate an immune response, a substance must also be large enough to "catch the attention" of the surveillance cells. Molecules with a molecular weight (MW) of less than 1,000 are seldom complete antigens, and those between 1,000 MW and 10,000 MW are weakly so. Complex macromolecules of at least 100,000 MW are the most immunogenic, a category also dominated by large proteins. Note that large size alone is not sufficient for antigenicity. Glycogen, a polymer of glucose with a highly repetitious structure, has a MW over 100,000 and is not normally antigenic, whereas insulin, a protein with a MW of 6,000, can be antigenic.

A lymphocyte's capacity to discriminate differences in molecular shape is so fine that it recognizes and responds to only a portion of the antigen molecule. This molecular fragment, called the **epitope** or antigenic determinant, provides the primary signal that the molecule is foreign (figure 15.7*b*). The shape of this determinant fits like a key to the receptor "lock" of the lymphocyte, which then recognizes and responds to it. Certain amino acids accessible at the surface of proteins or carbohydrate side chains protruding from a protein receptor are typical examples. Many foreign cells and molecules are very complex antigenically, with numerous determinants, each of which will elicit a separate and different lymphocyte response. Examples of these multiple, or *mosaic,* antigens include bacterial cell wall, membrane, flagellar, capsular, and toxin antigens; and viruses, which express various surface and core antigens.

Small foreign molecules that are too small by themselves to elicit an immune response are called **haptens.** However, if a hapten is linked to a larger carrier molecule, the combination develops immunogenicity **(figure 15.8).** The carrier group contributes to the size of the complex and enhances the orientation of the antigen, while the hapten serves as the epitope. Haptens include such molecules as vaccine antigens, drugs, metals, and a variety of chemicals. Many haptens develop immunogenicity in the body by combining with large carrier molecules such as serum proteins (see section 16.2).

Functional Categories of Antigens

Because each human being is genetically and biochemically unique (except for identical twins), the proteins and other

Figure 15.8 The hapten-carrier phenomenon. (a) Haptens are antigens that are too small to be discovered by an animal's immune system and do not elicit a response. **(b)** When a hapten binds to a large molecule, the hapten serves as an epitope and stimulates a response and an antibody that is specific for it.

molecules of one person can be antigenic to another. **Alloantigens** are cell surface markers and molecules that occur in some members of the same species but not in others. Alloantigens are the basis for an individual's blood group and major histocompatibility profile, and they are responsible for incompatibities that can occur in blood transfusion or organ grafting.

Some bacterial proteins, called **superantigens,** are potent stimuli for T cells. Notable examples of these types of antigens are toxic shock toxin and enterotoxin of *Staphylococcus.* Reactions with superantigens may cause the massive release of cytokines, leading to cell death. The role of these compounds is covered in section 15.3.

Antigens that evoke allergic reactions, called **allergens,** will be characterized in detail in chapter 16.

On occasion, even a normal part of self can take on the character of an antigen. During lymphocyte differentiation, immune tolerance to self tissue occurs, but a few anatomical sites can contain sequestered (hidden) molecules that escape this assessment. Such molecules, called **autoantigens,** can occur in tissues (of the eye and thyroid gland, for example) that are walled off early in embryonic development before the surveillance system is in complete working order. Because tolerance to these substances has not yet been established, they can subsequently be mistaken as foreign; this mechanism appears to account for some types of autoimmune diseases such as rheumatoid arthritis (chapter 16).

With a working knowledge of some factors in the development of immune specificity, we can now continue our coverage of the immune response as outlined in figure 15.1.

 Practice SECTION 15.2

9. What are antigens, immunogens, and epitopes, and what role do they play in immune reactions?
10. How do foreignness, size, and complexity contribute to antigenicity?
11. Compare five unique types of antigens, and explain their functions or actions.

15.3 Immune Reactions to Antigens and the Activities of T Cells

 Learn

10. Describe the cooperative interactions between antigen-presenting cells, T cells, and B cells.
11. Discuss the actions of interleukins in the early reactions of recognition and activation.
12. Outline the main activities of cell-mediated immunities.
13. Analyze the relationships between the types of T cells and their receptors, and how they are activated.
14. Describe the primary functions of helper T cells and cytotoxic T cells.
15. Explain the concepts of natural killer cells and superantigens.

The basis for most immune responses is the encounter between antigens and white blood cells. Microbes and other foreign substances enter most often through the respiratory or gastrointestinal mucosa and less frequently through other mucous membranes or the skin. Antigens introduced intravenously become localized in the liver, spleen, bone marrow, kidney, and lung. If introduced by some other route, antigens are carried in lymphatic fluid and concentrated by the lymph nodes. The lymph nodes and spleen are important in concentrating antigens in areas where they will come in contact with antigen-presenting cells (APCs) and lymphocytes. APCs and lymphocytes can subsequently circulate into fluid compartments to seek out the antigens for which they are specific.

The Role of Antigen Processing and Presentation

In most immune reactions, the antigen is in a "raw" state and must be further acted upon by **antigen-presenting cells (APCs)** before it is ready for contact with T cells. Three different cells can serve as

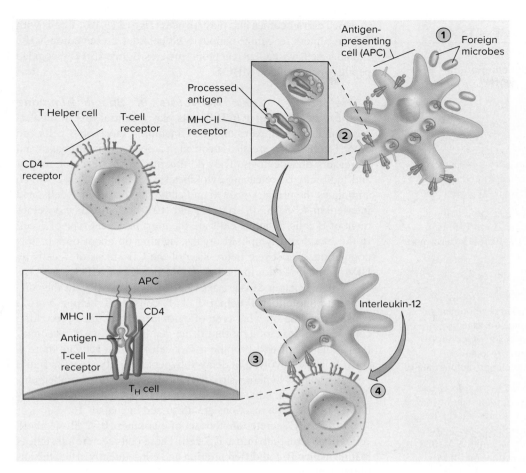

Process Figure 15.9
Interactions between antigen-presenting cells (APCs) and T helper (CD4) cells required for T-cell activation. (1) APCs (here a dendritic cell) are found in large numbers in lymphatic tissues, where they frequently encounter complex antigens such as microbes. APCs engulf the microbes, take them into intracellular vesicles, and degrade them into smaller, simpler peptides. (2) The antigen peptides are combined with MHC-II receptors and displayed on the surface of the APC. From its location on the cell membrane, the combination antigen/MHC-II receptor is easily recognized by a T helper cell with a complementary receptor. (3) The MHC-II/antigen complex on the APC is recognized by two receptors on the T helper cell, the T-cell receptor and the CD4 coreceptor. Together, the two receptors recognize both the MHC receptor (self) and the antigen (nonself) simultaneously. (4) Physical binding, along with the release of Interleukin-12 by the APC, activate the T helper cell, stimulating it to release interleukins and assist other lymphocytes in their functions.

APCs: **macrophages, dendritic* cells,** and B cells, although dendritic cells are the most common APC in the first contact with an antigen. Antigen-presenting cells modify the antigen so that it will be more immunogenic and recognizable. After processing is complete, the antigen is moved to the surface of the APC and bound to an MHC class II receptor to make it readily accessible to T cells during presentation **(process figure 15.9).**

Before a T cell can respond to APC-bound antigens, certain conditions must be met. *T-cell-dependent antigens,* usually protein-based, require recognition steps between the APC, antigen, and lymphocytes. The first cells on the scene to assist in activating B cells and other T cells are a special class of **T helper cells (T_H).** The T-cell receptor (TCR) of this class of T cell will bind simultaneously with the class II MHC receptor on the APC and with the antigen (process figure 15.9). A second interaction involves the binding of the T-cell CD4 receptor to the MHC of the APC. Once this identification step has occurred, a cytokine, **interleukin-12 (IL-12),** produced by the APC, activates this T helper cell. The T_H cell, in turn, produces a different cytokine, **interleukin-2 (IL-2),** which stimu-

Quick Search
To learn more about this topic, go to "Our Immune System" on YouTube.

lates a general increase in activity of committed B and T cells. The manner in which B and T cells subsequently become activated by the APC–T helper cell complex and their individual responses to antigen are addressed below and in section 15.4.

A few antigens can trigger a response from B lymphocytes without the cooperation of APCs or T helper cells. These *T-cell–independent antigens* are usually simple molecules such as carbohydrates with many repeating and invariable determinant groups. Examples include lipopolysaccharide from the cell wall of *Escherichia coli,* polysaccharide from the capsule of *Streptococcus pneumoniae,* and molecules from rabies and Epstein-Barr virus. Because so few antigens are of this type, most B-cell reactions require assistance from T helper cells.

T-Cell Responses and Cell-Mediated Immunity (CMI)

The responses of T cells, referred to as **cell-mediated immunities (CMIs),** are among the most complex and diverse in the immune system. They involve several subsets of T cells that differ in their types of CD receptors and the precise ways they react against foreign antigens and cells **(table 15.2).** T cells are restricted, meaning that before they can be activated, they must have the antigen

* *dendritic* (den′-drih-tik) Gr. *dendron,* branching like a tree.

TABLE 15.2	Characteristics of Subsets of T Cells	
Types	**Primary Receptors on T Cell**	**Functions/Important Features**
T helper cell 1 (T_H1)	CD4	Activates other CD4 and CD8 cells; secretes IL-2, tumor necrosis factor, and interferon gamma; responsible for delayed hypersensitivity; interacts with MHC-II receptors
T helper cell 2 (T_H2)	CD4	Drives B-cell proliferation; secretes IL-4, IL-5, IL-6, IL-9, IL-10, IL-13; can dampen T_H1 activity
T helper 17	CD4	Promotes inflammation; secretes IL-17
T regulatory cell (T_{reg})	CD4, CD25	Involved in development of immune tolerance; suppression of harmful immune responses, inflammation, autoimmunity
T cytotoxic cell (T_C)	CD8	Destroys a target foreign cell by lysis; important in destruction of cancer cells, virus-infected cells; graft rejection; requires MHC I for function; may have some regulatory functions

offered by an MHC complex on an APC (figure 15.9) to ensure recognition of self. All produce cytokines that, working together, carry out a spectrum of biological effects and immune functions. T cells differ notably from B cells in function. We will see that B cells combat foreign antigens by secreting molecules into the circulation, but in the case of T cells, the whole cell reacts directly in contact with target cells. T cells also stimulate other T cells, B cells, and phagocytes.

A T cell is initially sensitized by the binding of antigen/MHC to its receptors, and the release of cytokines (principally interleukin-12) from the antigen-presenting cell. These events activate the T cell, preparing it for mitotic divisions, and causing it to form effector cells and memory cells that can interact with the antigen if it is encountered. Memory T cells are some of the longest-lived blood cells known (decades, rather than weeks or months for other lymphocytes).

The Activation of T Cells and Their Differentiation into Subsets

Mature T cells in lymphoid organs are primed to react with antigens that have been processed and presented to them by dendritic cells and macrophages. They recognize an antigen only when it is presented in association with a particular MHC carrier, but they differ

in which carrier comes into play (**process figure 15.10**). T cells with CD4 receptors recognize endocytosed peptides presented on MHC II, and T cells with CD8 receptors (**process figure 15.11**) recognize peptides presented on MHC I.

T Helper (T_H) Cells: Activators of Specific Immune Responses **T helper (CD4) cells** play a central role in regulating immune reactions to antigens, including those of B cells and other T cells. They are also involved in activating macrophages and increasing phagocytosis. They do this directly by receptor contact and indirectly by releasing cytokines such as interleukin-2, which stimulates the primary growth and activation of B and T cells, and interleukin-4, -5, -6, -9, -10, -11, and -13 which stimulate development of B cells. T helper cells are the most prevalent type of T cell in the blood and lymphoid organs, making up about 65% of this population. The severe depression of the CD4 class of T cells by HIV is a major factor in the immunopathology of AIDS.

When T helper cells are activated by antigen/MHC II, they differentiate into either **T helper 1** (T_H1) cells, or **T helper 2** (T_H2) cells, depending on what type of cytokines the antigen-presenting cells secrete. It is thought that if the dendritic cell (APC) secretes IL-12, the T cell will become a T_H1 cell that can activate more T cells. It is also involved in delayed hypersensitivity (process figure 15.10). Delayed hypersensitivity is a type of response to allergens, distinct from immediate allergies such as hay fever and anaphylaxis. Both of these reactions are discussed in chapter 16.

If the APC secretes another set of cytokines (IL-2, IL-4), the T cell will differentiate into a T_H2 cell. These cells secrete substances that influence B-cell differentiation and consequently affect the antibody response.

Cytotoxic T (T_C) Cells: Cells that Kill Other Cells When CD8 cells are activated by antigen/MHC I, they differentiate into **T cytotoxic cells (T_C or killer T cells). Cytotoxicity** is the capacity of certain T cells to kill a specific target cell. It is a fascinating and powerful property that accounts for much of our immunity to foreign cells and cancer; and yet, under some circumstances, it can lead to disease. For a cytotoxic T cell to become activated, it must recognize a foreign peptide carried by an MHC-I receptor and mount a direct attack upon the target cell. The T_C cell severely injures the target cell by secreting **perforins**[2] and **granzymes** (process figure 15.11). Perforins are proteins that can punch holes in the membranes of target cells, and granzymes are enzymes that digest proteins. First the perforins cause ions to leak out of target cells and create a passageway for granzymes to enter. Granzymes induce the loss of selective permeability followed by target cell death through a process called *apoptosis.** The apoptosis is genetically programmed and results in destruction of the nucleus and complete cell lysis and death.

Target cells that can be destroyed by T_C cells include the following:

- Virally infected cells (process figure 15.11). Cytotoxic cells recognize and react against other cells that carry virus peptide

2. *Perforin* is taken from the term *perforate*, to make holes in.

 * *apoptosis* (ah-pop-toh′-sis) Gr. *apo,* away from, and *ptosis,* falling or dropping.

Process Figure 15.10 **Activation and differentiation of T cell.** **(1)** Antigen-presenting cells (APCs) present a combination of MHC II markers and antigenic peptides to T cells bearing CD4 markers. **(2)** The APC releases one or more cytokines (primarily interleukins). **(3)** Depending on the type of cytokine secreted by the APC, the CD4 cell will differentiate to become T helper 1 (T_H1), T helper 2 (T_H2), T helper 17 (T_H17), T regulatory cells (T_{reg}), or memory CD4 T cells. **(4)** T_H1 cells, by secreting tumor necrosis factor (TNF) and interferon gamma (IF-γ) stimulate macrophages or T_H2 cells. **(5)** T_H2 cells, by releasing IL-4, IL-5, IL-6, IL-9, IL-10, or IL-13, stimulate the antibody-mediated immune response by activating B cells. **(6)** The secretion of still other combinations of interleukins and growth factors by the APC cause the CD4 cell to differentiate into T_H17 cells, which increase inflammation or T regulatory cells, which lessen the immune response.

Process Figure 15.11 **Activation and differentiation of CD8 cells.** **(1)** Antigen-presenting cells (APCs) present a combination of MHC I markers and antigenic peptides to T cells bearing CD8 markers. **(2)** T_H1 cells secrete interleukin-2. **(3)** The CD8 cell differentiates into cytotoxic T cells (T_C cells) and memory CD8 cells. **(4)** Cytotoxic T cells bind to self cells that have become cancerous or are virally infected, and secrete proteins called perforins and granzymes. **(5)** Perforins and granzymes attack the target cell, eventually leading to its destruction.

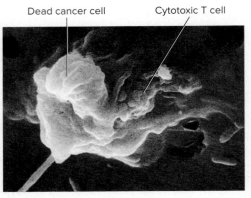

Cytotoxic T cells Cancer cell Dead cancer cell Cytotoxic T cell

Figure 15.12 Attack of the cytotoxic T cells. (Left) T cells recognize and bind to a cancer cell, which they perforate with many small holes. **(Right)** The cancer cell collapses and dies by apoptosis and the T cell remains alive and active.
(left, right): *Source:* Susan Arnold, Dr. Raowf Guirguis/National Cancer Institute

MHC combinations expressed on their surface. Cytotoxic defenses are an essential protection against viral infections.

- Cancer cells. T cells constantly survey the tissues and immediately attack any abnormal cells they encounter **(figure 15.12).** The importance of this function is clearly demonstrated in the susceptibility of T-cell–deficient people to cancer (chapter 16).
- Cells from other animals and humans. Cytotoxic CMI is the most important factor in graft rejection. In this instance, the T_C cells attack the foreign tissues that have been implanted into a recipient's body.

T Regulatory (T_{reg}) Cells: Modulators of Immune Function

As we'll explore further in chapter 16, an overactive immune system can be as bad as an underactive one. **Regulatory T cells,** or T_{regs}, express CD4 and CD25 receptors (see table 15.2) and prevent the immune system from overreacting. They play important roles in moderating inflammation, allergy, autoimmunity, and helping to ensure that the immune system doesn't target the body's normal microbiota.

Gamma-Delta T Cells: Specific and Nonspecific Activity

Gamma-Delta T cells have attributes of both the nonspecific and specific immune responses. They bind to certain PAMPs on microorganisms in a manner similar to nonspecific WBCs like macrophages or dendritic cells. But they also display characteristics of a specific response, as the cells possess T-cell receptors which are rearranged to recognize a wide variety of antigens and produce memory cells when activated, acting like a "traditional" T cell. The biology of these cells is unclear for now, but they are known to be especially active against certain bacterial pathogens and tumor cells.

Natural Killer (NK): Defense against Cancer and Viral Infection

Natural killer cells are a type of lymphocyte related to T cells. They circulate through the spleen, blood, and lungs, and are probably the first killer cells to attack cancer cells and virus-infected cells. They destroy these cells by mechanisms similar to those seen in cytotoxic T cells **(figure 15.13).** Because they lack antigen receptors, they are not specific for a single antigen, and so are not considered part of the specific, cell-mediated immune response.

Natural Killer T Cells (NKT Cells): A Hybrid of T Cells and NK Cells

Natural killer T cells, a recently identified cell type, have properties of both T cells and NK cells. They express T-cell receptors and NK cell markers and are stimulated by both self and nonself lipids (recall that lipids are a primary component of cell membranes). Once stimulated, they produce cytokines (like T cells) along with granzymes and perforins (like NK cells). Recent evidence shows an important role for these cells in the regulation of immune reactions against pathogens and tumors, as well as autoimmune and metabolic disorders.

T Cells and Superantigens

Most of the T-cell responses we have covered so far are primarily beneficial and protective. But there is one type of reaction that often has drastic consequences and may lead to serious diseases. Such is the case in exposure of T cells to **superantigens.** These antigens, found primarily in bacteria and viruses, are actually a form of virulence factor. Examples include enterotoxin given off by pathogenic staphylococci, certain toxins of group A streptococci, and proteins of Epstein-Barr virus. They can provoke overwhelming immune responses by large numbers of T cells regardless of specificity. Superantigen molecules are structured so that they can span both MHC-II receptors and some antigen receptors (TCR) on T cells. This event can "trick" large numbers of T cells into releasing massive amounts of cytokines such as tumor necrosis factor and interleukins-1 and -6. The overwhelming influx of such potent mediators leads to blood vessel damage, toxic shock, and multiorgan failure. This is thought to be the underlying mechanism of toxic shock syndrome and other serious infections.

↻ *Practice* SECTION 15.3

12. Describe the actions of an antigen-presenting cell.
13. Explain the difference between a T-cell–dependent and a T-cell–independent response.
14. Trace the immune response system, beginning with the entry of a T-cell–dependent antigen, antigen processing, presentation, the cooperative response among the macrophage and lymphocytes, and the reactions of activated B cells.
15. What are the actions of interleukins -2, -4, and -12?
16. Why are the immunities involving T cells called cell-mediated?
17. Explain how the different types of T cells are activated and their responses.
18. What are the targets of cytotoxic cells and how do they destroy them?
19. Discuss how superantigens are different from other antigens and how they contribute to pathology.

Figure 15.13 **The action of natural killer (NK) cells. (a) (1)** NK cell releases perforins, which polymerize and form a hole in the membrane of a foreign cell. **(2)** Granzymes from the NK cell enter the cell through the newly formed hole in the membrane. **(3)** The foreign cell dies by apoptosis. **(4)** Macrophage engulfs and digests the dead cell. **(b)** Scanning electron micrograph of a natural killer cell.
(b): Science History Images/Alamy Stock Photo

15.4 Immune Activities of B Cells

 Learn

16. List and analyze the stages in activation of B lymphocytes, clonal expansion, and antibody formation.

17. Describe the structure and basic functions of the five major types of immunoglobulins.

18. Explain the actions of antibodies in protective immune reactions.

19. Analyze the primary and secondary responses to antigens and immunogens, including the importance of the anamnestic response and boosters.

Events in B-Cell Responses

Activation of B Lymphocytes: Clonal Selection, Expansion, and Antibody Production

The immunologic activation of most B cells requires a series of events as outlined in the numbered steps that follow and illustrated in **process figure 15.14.**

1. **Clonal selection and binding of antigen.** In this case, a precommitted B cell of a particular clonal specificity picks up the antigen on its Ig receptors and processes it into small peptide determinants. The antigen is then bound to the MHC-II receptors on the B cell. The MHC/Ag complex on the B cell is bound by T-cell receptors.

> **Quick Search**
> Watch "B Cells & Antibody" on YouTube to see this process animated.

2. **Induction by chemical mediators.** The B cell receives developmental signals from macrophages and T cells (interleukin-2 and interleukin-6) and other growth factors, especially IL-4 and IL-5.

3. The combination of these stimuli on the membrane receptors causes a signal to be transmitted internally to the B-cell nucleus.

4. These events trigger B-cell activation. An activated B cell—referred to as a *lymphoblast*—enlarges and increases its synthesis of DNA and protein in preparation for entering the cell cycle and mitosis.

5–6. **Clonal expansion.** The stimulated B cell multiplies through successive mitotic divisions and produces a large population of genetically identical daughter cells. Some cells that stop short of becoming fully differentiated are **memory cells,** which remain for long periods to react with that same antigen at a later time. This reaction also expands the clone size, so that subsequent exposure to that antigen provides more cells with that specificity. This expansion of the clone size is one factor in the increased memory response. The more numerous progeny are large, specialized, terminally differentiated B cells called **plasma cells.**

7. **Antibody production and secretion.** The primary action of plasma cells is to secrete copious amounts of antibodies with the same specificity as the original receptor into the surrounding tissues **(process figure 15.14, step 7).** Although an individual plasma cell can produce around 2,000 antibodies per second, production does not continue indefinitely. The plasma cells do not survive for long, and they deteriorate after they have synthesized antibodies.

Products of B Lymphocytes: Antibody Structure and Functions Earlier we saw that a basic **immunoglobulin (Ig)**[3] molecule contains four polypeptide chains connected by disulfide bonds. Because antibodies are a type of immunoglobulin, they all feature this same basic structure. Let us review it using an IgG molecule as a model. Two functionally distinct segments called *fragments* can be differentiated. The two "arms" that bind antigen are termed **antigen binding fragments (Fabs),** and the rest of the molecule is the **crystallizable fragment (Fc),** so called because it can be crystallized in pure form. The amino-terminal end of each

3. *Ig* is a shorthand term. Immunoglobulins are proteins found in the globulin fraction of the serum and have immune function as antibodies.

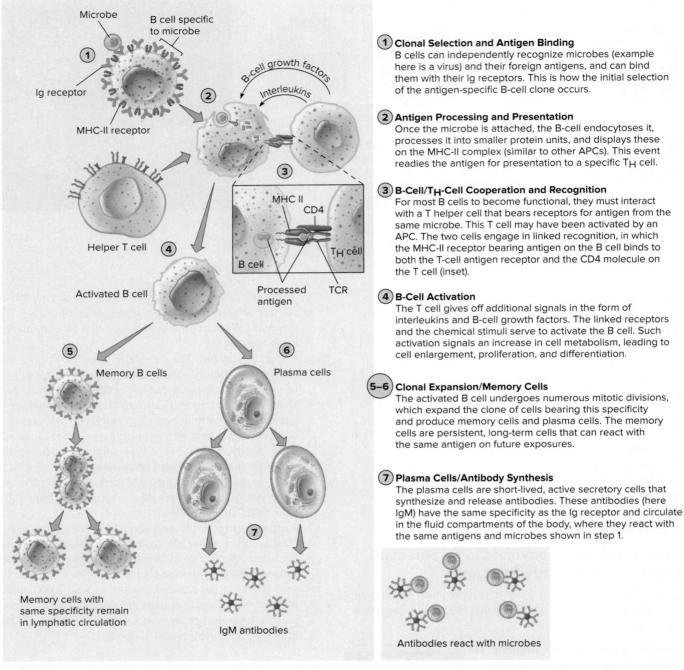

1 Clonal Selection and Antigen Binding
B cells can independently recognize microbes (example here is a virus) and their foreign antigens, and can bind them with their Ig receptors. This is how the initial selection of the antigen-specific B-cell clone occurs.

2 Antigen Processing and Presentation
Once the microbe is attached, the B-cell endocytoses it, processes it into smaller protein units, and displays these on the MHC-II complex (similar to other APCs). This event readies the antigen for presentation to a specific T$_H$ cell.

3 B-Cell/T$_H$-Cell Cooperation and Recognition
For most B cells to become functional, they must interact with a T helper cell that bears receptors for antigen from the same microbe. This T cell may have been activated by an APC. The two cells engage in linked recognition, in which the MHC-II receptor bearing antigen on the B cell binds to both the T-cell antigen receptor and the CD4 molecule on the T cell (inset).

4 B-Cell Activation
The T cell gives off additional signals in the form of interleukins and B-cell growth factors. The linked receptors and the chemical stimuli serve to activate the B cell. Such activation signals an increase in cell metabolism, leading to cell enlargement, proliferation, and differentiation.

5–6 Clonal Expansion/Memory Cells
The activated B cell undergoes numerous mitotic divisions, which expand the clone of cells bearing this specificity and produce memory cells and plasma cells. The memory cells are persistent, long-term cells that can react with the same antigen on future exposures.

7 Plasma Cells/Antibody Synthesis
The plasma cells are short-lived, active secretory cells that synthesize and release antibodies. These antibodies (here IgM) have the same specificity as the Ig receptor and circulate in the fluid compartments of the body, where they react with the same antigens and microbes shown in step 1.

Process Figure 15.14 Events in B-cell activation and antibody synthesis. These steps are tied to the numbered text. Only key receptors for these reactions are shown in the inset.

antigen binding fragment (consisting of the variable regions of the heavy and light chains) folds into a groove that will accommodate one epitope of the antigen. The presence of a special hinge region at the site of attachment between the Fabs and the Fc allows swiveling of the Fabs. In this way, they can change their angle to accommodate nearby antigen sites that vary slightly in distance and position. The Fc portion is involved in binding to various cells and molecules of the immune system itself. **Figure 15.15** shows a schematic view of an antibody (see figure 15.5 for a quick review of antibody genetics).

Antibody-Antigen Interactions and the Function of the Fab The site on the antibody where the antigenic determinant binds is composed of *hypervariable regions* with an extremely variable amino acid content. The groove of this antigen binding site has a specific three-dimensional fit for the antigen (**figure 15.16**).

Figure 15.15 **Working models of antibody structure. (a)** Diagrammatic view of IgG depicts the principal regions (Fabs and Fc) of the molecule. Note that the Fabs can swivel at the hinge region and provide flexibility in position. **(b)** Three-dimensional model of immunoglobulin shows the tertiary and quaternary structure achieved by intrachain and interchain bonds and the positioning of the light- and heavy-chain components.
(b): *Source:* Dr. Timothy Vickers

Because the specificity of the two Fab sites is identical for each antigen, an Ig molecule can bind antigenic determinants on the same cell or on two separate cells and thereby link them.

The principal activity of secreted antibodies is to unite with, immobilize, call attention to, or neutralize the antigen that initiated the antibody's formation **(figure 15.17)**. Antibodies called opsonins stimulate **opsonization,*** a process in which microorganisms or other particles are coated with specific antibodies so that they will be more readily recognized by phagocytes, which dispose of

* *opsonization* (awp″-son-uh-zay′-shun) L. *opsonium,* food or provisions, and *izare,* to become.

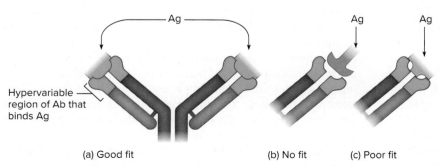

Figure 15.16 **Antigen-antibody binding.** The union of antibody (Ab) and antigen (Ag) is characterized by a certain degree of fit and is supported by a multitude of weak linkages, especially hydrogen bonds and electrostatic attraction. A better fit (i.e., antigen in **(a)** vs antigen in **(c)**) provides greater lymphocyte stimulation during the activation stage.

them. Opsonization has been likened to putting handles on a slippery object to provide a better grip.

Antibodies can aggregate or **agglutinate** cells by cross-linking them into large clumps. Agglutination renders microbes immobile and enhances their phagocytosis. **Precipitation** is a similar reaction that occurs with small, free antigen molecules. Both processes provide a basis for certain immune tests discussed in chapter 17. The interaction of an antibody with complement can result in the specific rupturing of cells and some viruses. This is seen in complement fixation, which refers to the classical pathway of complement activation (see figures 14.20 and 17.14).

In **neutralization** reactions, antibodies fill the surface receptors on a virus or the active site on a bacterial protein, which prevents them from attaching to their target cells. **Antitoxins** are special types of antibodies that neutralize bacterial exotoxins.

Functions of the Crystallizable Fragment Although the Fabs bind antigen, the Fc has a different binding function. In most classes of immunoglobulin, the end of the Fc contains an effector that can bind to the membrane of cells, such as macrophages, neutrophils, eosinophils, mast cells, basophils, and lymphocytes. The effect of an antibody's Fc binding to a cell depends upon that cell's role. In the case of opsonization, the attachment of antibody to foreign cells and viruses exposes the Fcs to phagocytes.

Certain antibodies have regions on the Fc portion for fixing complement, and in some immune

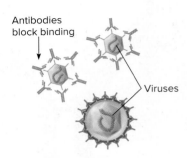

Complement fixation
Antibodies bound to the surface of a microorganism can activate the complement system, leading to lysis of the cell, and some viruses.

Opsonization
When coated with antibodies (opsinized) microorganisms or other particles are more readily recognized by phagocytes, which engulf and dispose of them.

Neutralization
Antibodies fill the surface receptors on a virus or the active site on a bacterial protein, which prevents them from attaching to their target cells.

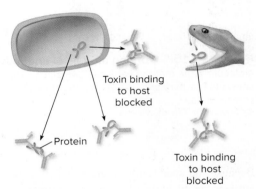

Agglutination
Because each antibody has two identical binding sites, cells can be bound together to form large clumps. Agglutination renders microbes immobile and increases the speed with which they are phagocytized.

Precipitation
Antigens much smaller than a cell (typically proteins), can be bound by antibodies, increasing the speed with which they are phagocytized.

Antitoxin
In a special case of precipitation, antibodies can be used to bind to bacterial exotoxins or animal toxins, intercepting them before they have had a chance to cause damage to cells.

Figure 15.17 **Summary of antibody functions.** Complement fixation, agglutination, and precipitation are covered further in chapter 17.

reactions, the binding of the Fc causes the release of cytokines. For example, the Fc end of the antibody of allergy (IgE) binds to basophils and mast cells, which causes the release of allergic mediators such as histamine.

Accessory Molecules on Immunoglobulins All antibodies contain molecules other than the basic polypeptides. Varying amounts of carbohydrates are affixed to the constant regions in most instances (see figure 15.15*b* and **table 15.3**). Two additional accessory molecules are the *J chain,* which helps keep the monomers of IgA and IgM together, and the *secretory component,* which helps move IgA across mucous membranes. These proteins occur only in certain immunoglobulin classes.

The Classes of Immunoglobulins Immunoglobulins exist as structural and functional classes called *isotypes* (compared and contrasted in table 15.3). The differences in these classes are due primar-

ily to variations in the Fc. The classes are differentiated with shorthand names—Ig, followed by a letter: IgG, IgA, IgM, IgD, IgE.[4]

The structure of **IgG** has already been presented. It is a monomer[5] produced by a plasma cell late in a primary response and by memory cells responding the second time to a given antigenic stimulus. It is by far the most prevalent antibody circulating throughout the blood, lymph, and extracellular fluids. It has numerous functions: It neutralizes toxins, opsonizes, and fixes complement, and it is the only antibody that crosses the placenta and provides protection to the fetus.

The two forms of **IgA** are (1) a **monomer** that circulates in small amounts in the blood, and (2) a **dimer** that is a significant

4. The letters correspond to the Greek letters gamma, alpha, mu, delta, and epsilon, which also refer to the distinct structures of their constant regions.

5. *Monomer* means "one unit" or "one part." Accordingly, *dimer* means "two units," *pentamer* means "five units," and *polymer* means "many units."

TABLE 15.3	Characteristics of the Immunoglobulin (Ig) Classes

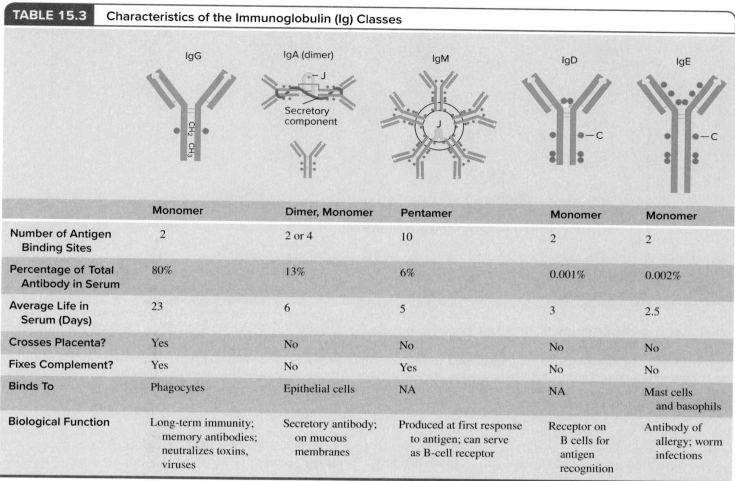

	IgG	IgA (dimer)	IgM	IgD	IgE
	Monomer	Dimer, Monomer	Pentamer	Monomer	Monomer
Number of Antigen Binding Sites	2	2 or 4	10	2	2
Percentage of Total Antibody in Serum	80%	13%	6%	0.001%	0.002%
Average Life in Serum (Days)	23	6	5	3	2.5
Crosses Placenta?	Yes	No	No	No	No
Fixes Complement?	Yes	No	Yes	No	No
Binds To	Phagocytes	Epithelial cells	NA	NA	Mast cells and basophils
Biological Function	Long-term immunity; memory antibodies; neutralizes toxins, viruses	Secretory antibody; on mucous membranes	Produced at first response to antigen; can serve as B-cell receptor	Receptor on B cells for antigen recognition	Antibody of allergy; worm infections

C = carbohydrate. J = J chain.

component of the mucous and serous secretions of the salivary glands, intestine, nasal membrane, breast, lung, and genitourinary tract. The dimer, called secretory IgA, is formed in a plasma cell by two monomers held together by a J chain. To facilitate the transport of IgA across membranes, a secretory piece is later added by the epithelial cells of the mucosa. IgA coats the surface of these membranes and appears free in saliva, tears, colostrum, and mucus. It confers essential immunity against enteric, respiratory, and genitourinary pathogens by excluding foreign intruders on mucosal membranes. Its contribution in protecting newborns who derive it passively from nursing is the focus of Clinical Connections.

IgM is a huge molecule composed of five monomers (making it a pentamer) attached by the Fc portions to a central J chain. With its 10 binding sites, this molecule has tremendous capacity for binding antigen. IgM is the first class synthesized following the host's first encounter with antigen. Its ability to agglutinate and fix *complement* make it an important antibody in many immune reactions. It circulates mainly in the blood and is far too large to cross the placental barrier.

IgD is a monomer found in minuscule amounts in the serum, and it does not fix complement, opsonize, or cross the placenta.

Its main function is to serve as a receptor for antigen on B cells, usually along with IgM, and it is the triggering molecule for B-cell activation.

IgE is also a less common blood component unless one is allergic or has a parasitic worm infection. Its Fc region interacts with receptors on mast cells and basophils. Its biological significance is to stimulate an inflammatory response through the release of potent physiological substances by the basophils and mast cells. Because inflammation would enlist blood cells such as eosinophils and lymphocytes to the site of infection, it would certainly be one defense against parasites. Unfortunately, IgE has another, more insidious effect—that of mediating anaphylaxis, asthma, and certain other allergies (see chapter 16).

Evidence of Antibodies in Serum

Regardless of the site where antibodies are first secreted, a large quantity eventually ends up in the blood by way of the body's communicating networks. If one subjects a sample of **antiserum** (serum containing specific antibodies) to electrophoresis, the major groups of proteins migrate in a pattern consistent with their mobility and size. The albumins show up in one band, and the globulins

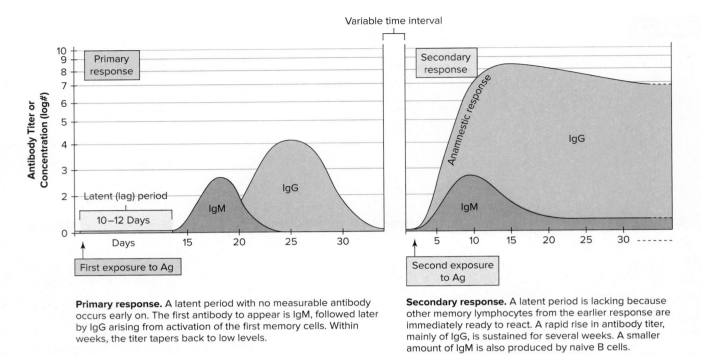

Variable time interval

Primary response. A latent period with no measurable antibody occurs early on. The first antibody to appear is IgM, followed later by IgG arising from activation of the first memory cells. Within weeks, the titer tapers back to low levels.

Secondary response. A latent period is lacking because other memory lymphocytes from the earlier response are immediately ready to react. A rapid rise in antibody titer, mainly of IgG, is sustained for several weeks. A smaller amount of IgM is also produced by naive B cells.

Figure 15.18 A graphic view of the primary and secondary immune responses to antigenic stimuli. Monitoring the antibody titer or concentration throughout the initial (primary) response and the second (secondary) response produces a distinct pattern. Note that the anamnestic response yields an amount of antibody that is nearly 1,000 times that of the primary response (the scale is logarithmic). This in effect "boosts" this defense to even more effective levels.

in four bands called alpha-1 (α_1), alpha-2 (α_2), beta (β), and gamma (γ) globulins. Most of the globulins represent antibodies, which explains how the term *immunoglobulin* was derived. **Gamma globulin** is composed primarily of IgG, whereas β and α_2 globulins are a mixture of IgG, IgA, and IgM.

Monitoring Antibody Production over Time: Primary and Secondary Responses to Antigens

We can learn a great deal about how the immune system reacts to an antigen by studying the levels of antibodies in serum over time **(figure 15.18).** This level is expressed quantitatively as the **titer,**[6] or concentration, of antibodies. Upon the first exposure to an antigen or immunogen, the system undergoes a **primary response.** The earliest part of this response, the *latent period,* is marked by a lack of antibodies for that antigen, but much activity is occurring. During this time, the antigen is being concentrated in lymphoid tissue and is being processed by the correct clones of B lymphocytes. As plasma cells synthesize antibodies, the serum titer increases to a certain plateau and then tapers off to a low level over a few weeks or months.

When the class of antibodies produced during this response is tested, an important characteristic of the response is uncovered. It turns out that, early in the primary response, most of the antibodies are the IgM type, which is the first class to be secreted by plasma cells. Later, the class of the antibodies (but not their specificity) is switched to IgG or some other class (IgA or IgE).

When the immune system is exposed again to the same antigen or immunogen within weeks, months, or even years, a **secondary response** occurs. The rate of antibody synthesis, the peak titer, and the length of antibody persistence are greatly increased over the primary response. The rapidity and amplification seen in this response are attributable to the memory B cells that were formed during the primary response. Because of its association with recall, the secondary response is also called the **anamnestic* response.** The recall effect shortens the latent or lag period and yields a faster, stronger, and longer-lasting antibody response. The main factors in creating the anamnestic effect are that the memory B cells do not have to go through the early steps in activation, and they do not require as many signals to form plasma cells.

The advantage of this response is evident: It provides a quick and potent strike against subsequent exposures to infectious agents. This memory effect is the fundamental basis for **vaccine boosters,** which we discuss in section 15.6.

Monoclonal Antibodies: Specificity in the Extreme

The value of antibodies as tools for locating or identifying antigens is well established. For many years, antiserum extracted

6. *Titer* (ty′-tur) Fr. *titre,* standard. One method for determining titer is shown in figure 17.9.

* *anamnestic* (an-am-ness′-tik) Gr. *anamnesis,* a recalling.

TABLE 15.4	Selected Monoclonal Antibody–Based Therapies	
Drug Names (Chemical and Trade)		**Used in Therapy For**
Cancer Drugs		
Trastuzumab	Herceptin	Breast cancer
Rituximab	Rituxan	B-cell disorders (lymphomas, leukemias)
Alemtuzumab	Campath	Chronic T-cell leukemia and lymphoma
Pembrolizumab	Keytruda	Metastatic melanoma and lung cancer
Other Applications		
Omalizumab	Xolair	Asthma
Belimumab	Benlysta	Systemic lupus erythematosus
Daclizumab	Biogen	Multiple sclerosis
Ibalizumab	Trogarza	HIV
Erenumab	Aimovig	Migraine
Adalimumab	Humira	Rheumatoid arthritis, psoriasis

Note that the chemical names are coded to end in *mab*—short for monoclonal antibody.

from human or animal blood was the main source of antibodies for tests and therapy, but most antiserum has a basic problem. It contains **polyclonal antibodies,** meaning that it is a mixture of different antibodies because it reflects dozens of immune reactions from a wide variety of B-cell clones. This characteristic is to be expected, because multiple immune reactions may be occurring simultaneously. Also, even a single species of microbe has many epitopes and will induce the expression of antibodies with different specificities. Antibodies produced from a single B-cell clone, and that therefore recognize a single antigen, are called **monoclonal antibodies (MABs).** These antibodies are used to target specific cells in the body that may differ only slightly from other cells; for instance, cancerous lung cells from healthy lung cells. With the advancement of genetic engineering techniques discussed in chapter 10, the creation of MABs has become far easier than it once was, and therapies relying on the use of monoclonal antibodies have grown exponentially, with more than 80 in current use **(table 15.4).**

Practice SECTION 15.4

20. How are B cells activated, what events are involved in this process, and what happens after B cells are activated?

21. What are the functions of plasma cells, clonal expansion, and memory cells?

22. Describe the structure of immunoglobulin and the functions of the Fab and Fc portions.

23. Describe four or five ways that antibodies function in immunity

24. Describe the attachment of antibodies to antigens. What eventually happens to the antigens?

25. Contrast the primary and secondary response to antigens.

26. Explain the type, order of appearance, and amount of immunoglobulin in each response in figure 15.16 and what causes the differences.

27. What causes the latent period and the anamnestic response?

15.5 A Classification Scheme for Specific, Acquired Immunities

 Learn

20. Outline the major categories of adaptive immunity.

21. Differentiate between natural and artificial immunities and between active and passive immunities.

22. Expand on the four combinations of the defining categories, using examples.

Humans develop their adaptive immunity by several general routes, as summarized in **figure 15.19.** These categories are based on the source of the immunity and whether the protection is produced by one's own immune system or whether it is received from another person. This classification system is a useful medical guide that can rapidly identify and explain the sources of immunity.

Defining Categories by Mode of Acquisition

Active immunity occurs when an individual receives an immune stimulus (microbe) that activates specific lymphocytes, causing an immune response such as production of antibodies. Active immunity is marked by several characteristics: (1) it is an essential attribute of an immunocompetent individual; (2) it creates a memory that renders the person ready for quick action upon reexposure to that same microbe; (3) it requires several days to develop; and (4) it can last for a relatively long time, sometimes for life. Active immunity can be stimulated by natural or artificial means.

Passive immunity occurs when an individual receives immune substances (primarily antibodies) that were produced actively by the immune system of another human or animal donor. Recipients are protected for a time even though they have not had actual exposure to the microbe. It is characterized by (1) lack of memory for the original antigen, (2) no production of new antibodies against that disease, (3) immediate onset of protection, and (4) short-term effectiveness because antibodies have a limited period of function. Ultimately, the recipient's body disposes of them. Passive immunity can also be natural or artificial in origin.

Natural immunity encompasses immunity that is acquired during any normal biological experiences of an individual but not through medical intervention.

Acquired Immunity

Natural Immunity
acquired through the normal life experiences
not induced through medical means

Artificial Immunity
produced purposefully through
medical procedures (immunization)

Active Immunity
results when a person
develops his own immune
response to a microbe
through infection.

Passive Immunity
results when a person
receives preformed
immunity through the
placenta or nursing.

Active Immunity (vaccination)
results when a person
develops his own
immune response to a
prepared microbial antigen.

Passive Immunity
results when a person is
given selected immune
substances made by
another individual.

Figure 15.19 **Categories of acquired immunities.** Natural immunities, which occur during the normal course of life, are either active (acquired from an infection and then recovering) or passive (antibodies donated by the mother to her child). Artificial immunities are acquired through medical practices and can be active (vaccinations with antigen, to stimulate an immune response) or passive (immune therapy with a serum containing antibodies).
(left): Rido/Shutterstock; (left-center): EyeWire Collection/Getty Images; (center-right): Source: Amanda Mills/CDC; (right): Arthur Tilley/Getty Images

Artificial immunity is protection from infection obtained through medical procedures. This type of immunity is induced by immunization with vaccines and immune serum.

Putting together all combinations of these categories, we arrive at four possible examples of origins of immunity.

Natural Active Immunity: Getting an Infection

After recovering from infectious disease, a person may be actively resistant to reinfection for a period that varies according to the disease. In the case of childhood viral infections such as measles, mumps, and rubella, this natural active stimulus provides nearly lifelong immunity. Other diseases result in a less extended immunity of a few months to years (such as pneumococcal pneumonia and shigellosis), and reinfection is possible. Even a subclinical infection can stimulate natural active immunity. This probably accounts for the fact that some people are immune to an infectious agent without ever having been noticeably infected with or vaccinated for it.

Natural Passive Immunity: Mother to Child

Natural, passively acquired immunity occurs as a result of the prenatal and postnatal, mother–child relationship. During fetal life,

IgG antibodies circulating in the maternal bloodstream are small enough to pass or be actively transported across the placenta. Antibodies against tetanus, diphtheria, pertussis, and several viruses regularly cross the placenta. This natural mechanism provides an infant with a mixture of many maternal antibodies that can protect it for the first few critical months outside the womb, while its own immune system is gradually developing active immunity. Depending upon the microbe, passive protection lasts anywhere from a few months to a year, but it eventually wanes. Most childhood vaccinations are timed so that there is no lapse in protection against common childhood infections.

Another source of natural passive immunity comes to the baby by way of mother's milk (**Clinical Connections**). Although the human infant acquires most natural passive immunity in utero and some through nursing, the milk-borne antibodies provide IgA antibodies that react against microbes entering the intestine. This unique protection is not available from transplacental antibodies.

Artificial Immunity: Immunization

Immunization is any clinical process that produces immunity in a subject. Because it is often used to give advance protection against infection, it is also called *immunoprophylaxis*. The details of this form of immunity are presented in section 15.6.

CLINICAL CONNECTIONS

The Immunological Benefits of Breast-Feeding

An advertising slogan from the past claims that cow's milk is "nature's most nearly perfect food." One could go a step farther and assert that human milk is nature's *perfect* food for young humans. Clearly, it is loaded with essential nutrients, not to mention being available on demand from a readily portable, hygienic container that does not require refrigeration or warming. But there is another and perhaps even greater benefit. During lactation, the breast becomes a site for the proliferation of lymphocytes that produce IgA antibodies that protect the mucosal surfaces from local invasion by microbes. The very earliest secretion of the breast, a thin, yellow milk called **colostrum,** is very high in these antibodies. They form a protective coating in the gastrointestinal tract of a nursing infant that guards against infection by a number of enteric pathogens (*Escherichia coli, Salmonella,* poliovirus, rotavirus). Protection at this level is especially critical because an infant's own antibodies and natural intestinal barriers are not yet developed. As with immunity in utero, the necessary antibodies will be donated only if the mother herself has active immunity to the microbe through a prior infection or vaccination.

International symbol for breast-feeding
Lukasz Stefanski/Shutterstock

A critical benefit of breast-feeding that has not been given adequate credit is the connection between nursing, the breast microbiome, and the neonatal microbiome. For many years, milk was thought to be sterile unless the mother's breasts were infected. Now we know from studies on the human microbiome that breast milk and tissues harbor a diverse bacterial community that is distinct from that of the skin or the mouth. This discovery acknowledges that, in addition to its nutritional and immunological support, breast milk is an important early source of microbes that populate the newborn intestine and other body sites. A related function of the breast microbiome could be to supply bacterial stimuli for the continuing development of the baby's immune system.

For a number of years, the ready availability of artificial formulas and the changing lifestyles of women have reduced the incidence of breast-feeding. According to UNICEF, only about 38% of mothers worldwide breast-feed their babies for 6 months or more. Where adequate hygiene and medical care prevail, bottle-fed infants get through the critical period with few problems because the foods given them are relatively free of pathogens and they have received protection against some childhood infections in utero. Mothers in developing countries with untreated water supplies or poor medical services are strongly discouraged from using prepared formulas, because they can actually inoculate the baby's intestine with pathogens from the formula. Millions of neonates suffer from severe and life-threatening diarrhea that could have been prevented by sustained breast-feeding. The use of formula has been so damaging to infant health that the World Health Organization issued an *International Code on the Marketing of Breast Milk Substitutes,* discouraging the use of formula in the developing world.

Explain the reasons donated antibodies (either placental or in breast milk) are only a temporary protection.

Artificial Active Immunization: Vaccination

The term *vaccination* originated from the Latin word *vacca* (cow), because the cowpox virus was used in the first preparation for active immunization against smallpox (see 15.1 Making Connections). Vaccination exposes a person to a specially prepared microbial (antigenic) stimulus, which then triggers the immune system to produce antibodies and memory cells to protect the person upon future exposure to that microbe. As with natural active immunity, the degree and length of protection vary. Commercial vaccines are currently available for many diseases.

Artificial Passive Immunization: Immunotherapy

In immunotherapy, a patient at risk for acquiring a particular infection is administered a preparation that contains specific antibodies against that infectious agent. Pooled human serum from donor blood (gamma globulin) and immune serum globulins containing high quantities of antibodies are the usual sources. Immune serum globulins are used to protect people who have been exposed to certain diseases such as hepatitis A, rabies, and tetanus.

Practice SECTION 15.5

28. Contrast active and passive immunity in terms of how each is acquired, how long it lasts, whether memory is triggered, how soon it becomes effective, and what immune cells and substances are involved.

29. Name at least two major ways in which natural and artificial immunities are different.

30. Explain why the passive transfer of T-cell immunities would be highly unlikely.

15.6 Immunization: Providing Immune Protection through Therapy

 Learn

23. Explain the purposes of immunotherapy and immunization.

24. Describe the sources and uses of artificial passive immunization and artificial active immunization or vaccination.

25. Discuss which factors are involved in vaccine development and new strategies for developing vaccines.

26. Identify the major categories of vaccine antigens, citing examples.

27. Describe the medical guidelines for vaccination, its side effects, and how it relates to herd immunity.

Methods that actively or passively immunize people are widely used in disease prevention and treatment. The use of these terms is sometimes imprecise; thus, it should be stressed that active immunization, in which a person is administered some form of antigen, is synonymous with vaccination. Passive immunization, in which a person is given antibodies, is a type of **immunotherapy.**

Artificial Passive Immunization

The first attempts at passive immunization involved the transfusion of horse serum containing antitoxins to prevent tetanus and to treat patients exposed to diphtheria. Since then, antisera from animals have been largely replaced with products of human origin that function with various degrees of specificity. **Immune serum globulin (ISG),** sometimes called *gamma globulin,* contains immunoglobulin extracted from the pooled blood of at least 1,000 human donors. The method of processing ISG concentrates the antibodies to increase potency and eliminates potential pathogens (such as the hepatitis B and HIV viruses). It is a treatment of choice in preventing measles and hepatitis A and in replacing antibodies in immunodeficient patients. Most forms of ISG are injected intramuscularly to minimize adverse reactions, and the protection they provide lasts 2 to 3 months.

A serum product called **specific immune globulin (SIG)** is derived from a more defined group of donors. SIG preparations are made with serum from patients who are in a hyperimmune state after being vaccinated or infected by pertussis, tetanus, chickenpox, and hepatitis B. These globulins are preferable to ISG because they contain higher titers of specific antibodies obtained from a smaller pool of patients. Although useful for prophylaxis in persons who may be exposed to infectious agents, these sera can be limited in availability.

When a human immune globulin is not available, antisera and antitoxins of animal origin can be effective. Sera produced in horses are available for diphtheria, botulism, rabies, and spider and snake bites. Unfortunately, horse antigens often stimulate allergies such as serum sickness or anaphylaxis (chapter 16). With the development

of monoclonal therapies, many of these older sources are being replaced by pure antibody drugs that have been tailored to just one specific pathogen, Although all of these passive immunities only last a relatively short time, they act immediately and can protect patients for whom no other useful medication or vaccine exists, such as immunocompromised patients who cannot be vaccinated.

Artificial Active Immunity: Vaccination

Active immunity can be conferred artificially by **vaccination**—exposing a person to material that is immunogenic but not pathoenic. The discovery of vaccination was one of the furthest-reaching and most important developments in medical science **(15.1 Making Connections).** The basic principle behind vaccination is to stimulate a primary response that primes the immune system for future exposure to a pathogen. If this pathogen enters the body, the secondary immune response will be immediate, powerful, and sustained. Second or additional doses of vaccines can also stimulate the anamnestic response.

Vaccines have profoundly reduced the prevalence and impact of many infectious diseases that were once common and often deadly. In this section, we survey the principles of vaccine preparation and important considerations surrounding vaccine indication and safety. Vaccines are also given specific consideration in later chapters on infectious diseases and organ systems.

Principles of Vaccine Preparation

A vaccine must be considered from the standpoints of immunogen selection, effectiveness, ease in administration, safety, and cost. In natural immunity, an infectious agent stimulates a relatively long-term protective response. In artificial active immunity, the objective is to obtain this same response with a modified version of the microbe or its components. Most vaccine preparations are based on one of the following antigen preparations **(process figure 15.20):**

1. killed whole cells or inactivated viruses;
2. live, attenuated bacterial cells or viruses;
3. antigenic molecules derived from bacterial cells or viruses; or
4. genetically engineered microbes or microbial antigens.

The main qualities of an effective vaccine are listed in **table 15.5.**

TABLE 15.5	**Checklist of Requirements for an Effective Vaccine**

- It should have a low level of adverse side effects or toxicity and not cause serious harm.
- It should protect against exposure to natural, wild forms of pathogen.
- It should stimulate both antibody (B-cell) response and cell-mediated (T-cell) response.
- It should have long-term, lasting effects (produce memory cells).
- It should work with minimal doses or boosters.
- It should be inexpensive, have a relatively long shelf life, and be easy to administer.

15.1 MAKING CONNECTIONS

The Lively History of Active Immunization

The basic notion of immunization has existed for thousands of years. It probably stemmed from the observation that persons who had recovered from certain communicable diseases rarely, if ever, got a second case of it. The earliest crude vaccination attempts involved bringing a susceptible person into contact with a diseased person or animal. The first recorded attempt occurred in sixth-century China. It consisted of drying and grinding up smallpox scabs and blowing them with a straw into the nostrils of vulnerable family members.

By the tenth century, this practice had changed to the deliberate inoculation of dried pus from the smallpox pustules of one patient into the arm of a healthy person, a technique later called **variolation** (variola is the smallpox virus). This method was used in parts of Asia for centuries before it was first brought to England in 1721. Although the principles of the technique had some merit, unfortunately many recipients and their contacts died of smallpox. This outcome vividly demonstrates a cardinal rule for a workable vaccine: It must contain an antigen that will provide protection but not cause the disease. Variolation was so controversial that any English practitioner caught doing it was charged with a felony.

Eventually this human experimentation paved the way for the first really effective vaccine, developed by the English physician Edward Jenner in 1796. Jenner conducted the first scientific test of a vaccine, one that had a tremendous impact on the advance of medicine. His work gave rise to the words *vaccine* and *vaccination* (from L., *vacca,* cow), which now apply to any immunity obtained by inoculation with selected antigens. Jenner was inspired by the case of a milkmaid who had been infected by a pustular infection called cowpox. This related virus afflicts cattle but causes a milder condition in humans. She explained that she and other milkmaids had remained free of smallpox. To test the effectiveness of this cross protection, Jenner prepared material from human cowpox lesions and inoculated a young boy. When challenged 2 months later with an injection of crusts from a smallpox patient, the boy was immune to it.

Jenner's discovery—that a less pathogenic agent could confer protection against a more pathogenic one—is especially remarkable in view of the fact that microscopy was still in its infancy and the nature of viruses was unknown. When Jenner's method proved successful and word of its significance spread, it was eventually adopted in many other countries. Eventually the original virus mutated into a unique strain

A modern setup for smallpox vaccination; note the two-pronged needle used to scratch the vaccine into the skin.
Source: James Gathany/CDC

(*vaccinia* virus) that became the basis of the current vaccine. In 1979, the World Health Organization declared that smallpox had been eradicated. As a result, smallpox vaccination had been discontinued until recently, due to the threat of bioterrorism.

Other historical developments in vaccination included using heat-killed bacteria in vaccines for typhoid fever, cholera, and plague, and techniques for using neutralized toxins for diphtheria and tetanus. Throughout the history of vaccination, there have been vocal opponents and minimizers, but one fact seems clear: Whenever a vaccine has been introduced, the prevalence of that disease has declined dramatically (look back at figure 1.10). The number of cases of childhood diseases such as diphtheria, measles, mumps, rubella, and polio have declined 98% to 100% when compared to the numbers reported for these diseases prior to the development of vaccines.

Using principles of immunology, explain how a vaccine based on one type of microbe (vaccinia) could produce an effective immunity to a different microbe (variola).

Large, complex antigens such as whole cells or viruses are very effective immunogens. Depending on the vaccine, these are either killed or attenuated. **Killed or inactivated vaccines** are prepared by cultivating the desired strain or strains of a bacterium or virus and treating them with formalin, radiation, heat, or some other agent that kills the microbe but does not change its antigenic structure. One type of vaccine for the bacterial disease cholera is of this type. The IPV polio vaccine and some forms of influenza vaccine contain inactivated viruses. Because the microbe does not multiply, killed vaccines often require a larger dose and more boosters to be effective.

A number of vaccines are prepared from **attenuated** microbes. Attenuation is any process that substantially lessens the virulence of viruses or bacteria. It is usually achieved by modifying the growth conditions or manipulating microbial genes in a way that eliminates virulence factors. Attenuation methods include long-term cultivation, selection of mutant strains that grow at colder temperatures (cold mutants), passage of the microbe through unnatural hosts or tissue culture, and removal of virulence genes. The vaccine for tuberculosis (BCG) was obtained after 13 years of subculturing the agent of bovine tuberculosis. Vaccines for measles, mumps, polio (oral vaccine),

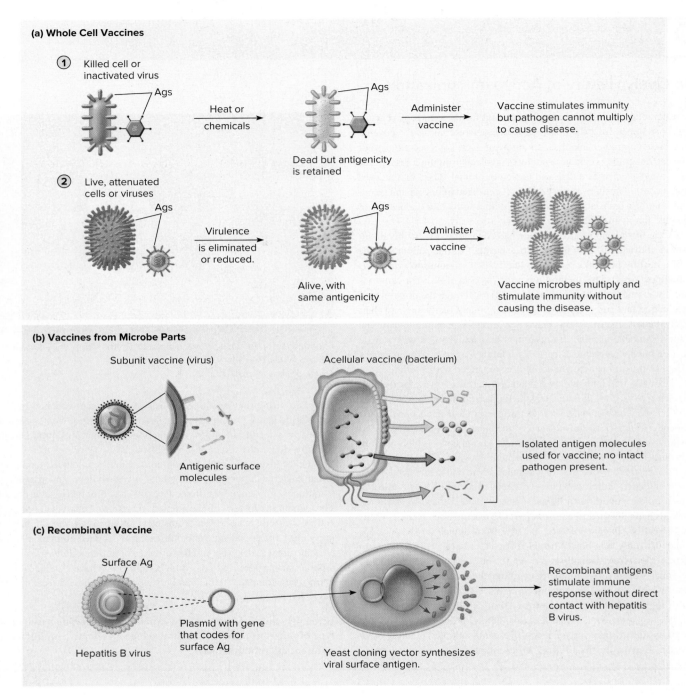

(a) Whole Cell Vaccines

① Killed cell or inactivated virus

Ags

Heat or chemicals →

Dead but antigenicity is retained

Administer vaccine →

Vaccine stimulates immunity but pathogen cannot multiply to cause disease.

② Live, attenuated cells or viruses

Ags

Virulence is eliminated or reduced. →

Alive, with same antigenicity

Administer vaccine →

Vaccine microbes multiply and stimulate immunity without causing the disease.

(b) Vaccines from Microbe Parts

Subunit vaccine (virus)

Acellular vaccine (bacterium)

Antigenic surface molecules

Isolated antigen molecules used for vaccine; no intact pathogen present.

(c) Recombinant Vaccine

Surface Ag

Hepatitis B virus

Plasmid with gene that codes for surface Ag

Yeast cloning vector synthesizes viral surface antigen.

Recombinant antigens stimulate immune response without direct contact with hepatitis B virus.

Process Figure 15.20 **Strategies in vaccine design. (a)** Whole cells or viruses, killed or attenuated. **(b)** Acellular or subunit vaccines are made by disrupting the virus or cell to release antigenic molecules or components that can be isolated and purified. **(c)** Recombinant vaccines are made by isolating a gene for the antigen from the pathogen (here a hepatitis virus) and splicing it into a plasmid. Insertion of the recombinant plasmid into a cloning host (yeast) results in the production of large amounts of viral surface antigen to use in vaccine preparation.

and rubella contain active, nonvirulent viruses. The primary advantages of these preparations are that (1) viable microorganisms can multiply and produce infection (but not disease) like the natural organism, (2) they confer long-lasting protection, and (3) they usually require fewer doses and boosters than other types of vaccines.

Disadvantages of using live microbes in vaccines are that they require special storage facilities, can be transmitted to other people, and can conceivably mutate back to a virulent strain.

If the exact antigenic determinants that stimulate immunity are known, these substances can be isolated from microorganisms and serve as the basis for a vaccine **(process figure 15.20b).**

Vaccines made from bacterial cell parts are called **acellular** or **subcellular vaccines.** If isolated from viruses, they are called **subunit vaccines.** The antigen used in these vaccines may be extracted from cultures of the microbes, produced by genetic engineering, or synthesized chemically.

Examples of extracted antigens currently in use are the capsules of the pneumococcus and meningococcus, the protein surface antigen of anthrax, and the surface proteins of hepatitis B virus. A special type of vaccine is the **toxoid,** which consists of a purified fragment of bacterial exotoxin that has been inactivated. By eliciting the production of antitoxins that can neutralize the natural toxin, toxoid vaccines provide protection against toxinoses such as diphtheria and tetanus.

> **Quick Search**
>
> To see a list of all vaccines approved for use in the United States, search for "FDA licensed vaccines."

Development of New Vaccines

Despite considerable successes, dozens of bacterial, viral, protozoan, and fungal diseases still remain without a functional vaccine. No reliable vaccines are available for, HIV/AIDS, various diarrheal diseases (*E. coli, Shigella*), a number of respiratory diseases, and worm infections, which affect over 200 million people per year worldwide. Of all of the challenges facing vaccine specialists, probably the most difficult has been choosing a vaccine antigen that is safe and that properly stimulates immunity. Currently much attention is being focused on newer strategies for vaccine preparation that employ antigen synthesis, recombinant DNA, and gene cloning technology.

When the exact composition of an antigenic determinant is known, it is sometimes possible to artificially synthesize it. This ability permits preservation of antigenicity while greatly increasing antigen purity and concentration. Mosquirex, the first malaria vaccine to show relative success against the disease, is known by the initials of the three peptides of which it is composed: RTS,S (the S fragment appears twice in the vaccine). Several biotechnology companies are using plants to mass-produce vaccine antigens. Tests are underway to grow tomatoes, potatoes, and bananas that synthesize proteins from cholera, hepatitis, papillomavirus, and *E. coli* pathogens. This strategy aims to economically harvest vaccine antigens and make vaccines for populations that otherwise would not have access to them.

Genetically Engineered Vaccines

Some of the genetic engineering concepts introduced in chapter 10 offer novel approaches to vaccine development. These methods are particularly effective in designing vaccines for obligate parasites that are difficult or expensive to culture, such as the syphilis spirochete or the malaria parasite. Recombinant DNA technology provides a means of isolating the genes that encode various microbial antigens, inserting them into plasmid vectors, and cloning them in appropriate hosts. The outcome of recombination can be as varied

CLINICAL CONNECTIONS

Has Vaccination Become a Victim of Its Own Success?

Vaccination has always been considered one of humanity's triumphs, one that has made an enormous contribution to health and well-being. Most people are no longer at risk for such life-threatening diseases as tetanus, diphtheria, polio, and others. But lately, vaccination's good reputation is being tarnished. It began with a poorly designed 1998 British study that hinted at a link between autism and the MMR (mumps, measles, and rubella) vaccine. The publicity from this report spurred a controversy that led some parents to stop vaccinating their children against the usual childhood diseases. The study's results have since been thoroughly refuted, but the vaccine phobia persists. More than a dozen separate epidemiologic studies have discounted any connection between the MMR vaccine and autism, and additional studies show that the preservative thimerosal is also not correlated with autism (MMR is a live attenuated vaccine and would not contain this substance anyway). Recently the CDC reported findings of the latest in-depth study that found no correlation between vaccine type or vaccine number and the development of autism. In fact, the study identified a significant number of unvaccinated children who were diagnosed with some form of autism.

Many decisions not to vaccinate are based on misconceptions and emotion rather than science, yet consequences are being felt in some populations. Recent outbreaks of measles, mumps, meningitis, and pertussis have been tied to inadequate vaccinations. The reality is that these diseases are still around, and they pose a greater risk for young children than the possibility of a vaccine reaction. In fact, 1% of babies develop a severe brain condition from measles virus, and mumps, meningitis, and pertussis all have their own serious complications. Any reduction in vaccinations will lead to less herd immunity and create pockets where children lack protection. Now more than ever before, health care workers have a responsibility to educate and counsel patients about the importance of routine immunizations for both individuals and the community.

Explain how vaccination has been responsible for the worldwide eradication of smallpox and the near elimination of polio and many other infectious diseases.

as desired. For instance, the cloning host can be stimulated to synthesize and secrete a protein product (antigen), which is then harvested and purified **(figure 15.20c)**. Vaccines for hepatitis and human papillomavirus are currently being prepared in this way. Antigens from the agents of syphilis, *Schistosoma,* and influenza have been similarly isolated and cloned and are currently being considered as potential vaccine material.

Another technique using genetic recombination has been nicknamed the *Trojan horse* vaccine. The term derives from an

ancient legend in which the Greeks sneaked soldiers into the fortress of their Trojan enemies by hiding them inside a large, mobile wooden horse. In the microbial equivalent, genetic material from a selected infectious agent is inserted into a live carrier microbe that is nonpathogenic. In theory, the recombinant microbe will multiply and express the foreign genes, and the vaccine recipient will be immunized against the microbial antigens. Vaccinia, the virus originally used to vaccinate for smallpox, and adenoviruses have proved practical agents for this technique. Vaccinia has been used as the carrier in experimental vaccines for HIV, herpes simplex 2, leprosy, and tuberculosis.

DNA vaccines are another promising approach to immunization. The technique in these formulations is very similar to gene therapy, as described in chapter 10, except in this case, microbial (not human) DNA is inserted into a plasmid vector and inoculated into a recipient **(figure 15.21).** The expectation is that the human cells will take up some of the plasmids and express the microbial DNA in the form of proteins. Because these proteins are foreign, they will be recognized during immune surveillance and cause B and T cells to be sensitized and form memory cells. It should be noted that even though the DNA is from a microbe, it will not cause an immune response because the structure of the DNA molecule by itself is not highly immunogenic.

Experiments with animals have shown that these vaccines are very safe and that only a small amount of the foreign antigen need be expressed to produce effective immunity. Another advantage to this method is that any number of potential microbial proteins can be expressed, making the antigenic stimulus more complex and improving the likelihood that it will stimulate both antibody and cell-mediated immunity. At the present time, vaccines for Lyme disease, hepatitis C, herpes simplex, influenza, Ebola, tuberculosis, papillomavirus, malaria, and SARS are undergoing trials.

Routes of Administration and Side Effects of Vaccines

Most vaccines are injected by subcutaneous, intramuscular, or intradermal routes. Oral vaccines are available for only a few diseases, but they have some distinct advantages. An oral dose of a vaccine can stimulate protection (IgA) on the mucous membrane of the portal of entry. Oral vaccines are also easier to give, more readily accepted, and well tolerated. Other methods that show promise are an intranasal vaccine delivered into the nose by aerosol or drops (FluMist for influenza, for example) and skin patches.

Some vaccines are made more effective by adding an **adjuvant.*** An adjuvant is any compound that enhances immunogenicity and prolongs antigen retention at the injection site. The adjuvant precipitates the antigen and holds it in the tissues so that it will be released gradually. Its gradual release presumably facilitates contact with antigen-presenting cells and lymphocytes. Common adjuvants are alum (aluminum hydroxide salts), Freund's complete adjuvant (emulsion of mineral oil, water, and extracts of mycobacteria), and beeswax.

Vaccines must go through many years of trials in experimental animals and human volunteers before they are licensed for general use. Even after they have been approved, like all therapeutic products, they are not without complications. The most common of these are local reactions at the injection site, fever, allergies, and other adverse reactions. Relatively rare reactions (about one case out of 300,000 vaccinations) are panencephalitis (from measles vaccine), back-mutation to a virulent strain (from polio vaccine), disease due to contamination with dangerous viruses or chemicals, and neurological effects of unknown cause

* *adjuvant* (ad′-joo-vunt) L. *adjuvans,* a thing that helps or aids.

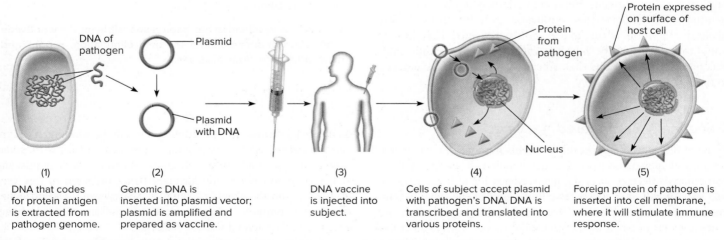

(1)	(2)	(3)	(4)	(5)
DNA that codes for protein antigen is extracted from pathogen genome.	Genomic DNA is inserted into plasmid vector; plasmid is amplified and prepared as vaccine.	DNA vaccine is injected into subject.	Cells of subject accept plasmid with pathogen's DNA. DNA is transcribed and translated into various proteins.	Foreign protein of pathogen is inserted into cell membrane, where it will stimulate immune response.

Figure 15.21 DNA vaccine preparation. DNA vaccines contain all or part of the pathogen's DNA, which is used to "infect" a recipient's cells. Processing of the DNA leads to production of an antigen protein that can stimulate a specific response against that pathogen.

CLINIC CASE

But I've Heard Bad Things Over the course of 3 days, the Minnesota Department of Health confirmed measles in three patients, all under 3 years of age. The patients attended the same day care center, and two were siblings. None had been vaccinated against measles. Within 2 months, 75 persons had been infected by the virus, with one-third requiring hospitalization. Patients who had never received the MMR (measles, mumps, rubella) vaccine accounted for 95% of cases, and 85% of cases occurred in children of Somali descent. Hennepin County, Minnesota, has the largest Somali population in the United States.

Working with attendance rosters from day care centers and schools in the area, epidemiologists identified people who may have been exposed to measles, and the vaccination status of each one. Susceptible contacts—unvaccinated, immunocompromised, or pregnant—were offered postexposure prophylaxis consisting of MMR vaccine or immune globulin against measles virus. Those who accepted treatment were allowed to return to school or day care immediately, whereas others were excluded for 21 days and were counseled not to be a part of public gatherings during that time.

Prior to 2008, MMR vaccine coverage among Minnesota-born Somali children exceeded 90%, but declined each year afterward. By the time of the outbreak in 2017, coverage was only 35.6%, leaving the community highly susceptible to measles. The decline in vaccination coverage was the result of two mistaken beliefs: that there was a link between the MMR vaccine and autism and that the Somali community had a higher rate of autism than other groups.

Health care officials, working with Somali medical professionals, faith leaders, and community officials, were able to address questions, concerns, and misinformation about the MMR vaccine. Within a month of the outbreak, the average number of MMR vaccine doses administered per week in Minnesota had more than tripled, from 2,700 doses before the outbreak to 9,964.

Health care providers decided whether susceptible contacts were offered MMR vaccine or immune globulin. Would there be a disadvantage to providing the vaccine and immune globulin simultaneously?

(from pertussis and swine flu vaccines). Some patients experience allergic reactions to the medium (eggs or tissue culture) rather than to vaccine antigens.

When known or suspected adverse effects have been detected, vaccines are altered or withdrawn. For example, the whole-cell pertussis vaccine was replaced by the acellular capsule (aP) form when it was associated with adverse neurological effects. The Lyme disease vaccine was withdrawn when recipients developed arthritis and other side effects. Polio vaccine was switched from live to inactivated when too many cases of paralytic disease occurred from back-mutated vaccine stocks. Vaccine companies have also phased out certain preservatives, such as thimerosal, that could cause allergies and other medical problems in some patients.

Professionals involved in giving vaccinations must understand their inherent risks but also realize that the risks from the infectious disease almost always outweigh the chance of an adverse vaccine reaction. The greatest caution must be exercised in giving live vaccines to immunocompromised or pregnant patients, the latter because of possible risk to the fetus.

To Vaccinate: Why, Whom, and When?

Vaccination confers long-lasting, sometimes lifetime, protection in the individual, but an equally important effect is to protect public health. Vaccination is a proven method of establishing **herd immunity** in the population. According to this concept, individuals immune to a communicable infectious disease will not harbor it, thus reducing the occurrence of that pathogen. With a larger number of immune individuals in a population (herd), it will be less likely that an unimmunized member of the population will encounter the agent and become infected. In effect, collective immunity through mass immunization confers indirect protection on the nonimmune members (such as infants too young to be vaccinated). The most effective herd immunity outcome occurs when the healthiest members are vaccinated. Because most vaccine programs target the youngest and oldest (and thus weaker) people instead, herd immunity in many populations is not complete. Herd immunity maintained through immunization is considered a valuable factor in preventing epidemics.

> **Quick Search**
> "Get the Picture: Childhood Immunizations" on the CDC-TV website emphasizes the importance of vaccinations.

To encourage vaccination, those involved in our health care—whether doctors, politicians, or representatives of the pharmaceutical industry—have attempted to make the process as easy as possible. Most routine vaccines can be obtained at pharmacies, and vaccines have been combined in many cases. These combination vaccines, such as the measles, mumps, rubella (MMR) vaccine are simply mixtures of antigens from several pathogens given in the same injection. This reduces the number of shots for an anxious 4-year-old, along with the number of doctor visits for mom or dad that must be squeezed into the daily schedule. It is common for several vaccines to be given simultaneously, as occurs in military recruits who receive as many as 15 injections within a few minutes and children who receive boosters for DTaP and polio at the same time they receive the MMR vaccine. Experts doubt that immune interference (inhibition of one immune response by another) is a significant problem in these instances. The main problem with simultaneous administration is that side effects can be amplified.

> **Quick Search**
> To see all of the recommended immunization schedules, search for "CDC vaccine schedule."

Practice SECTION 15.6

31. Describe the preparation of killed vaccines; live, attenuated vaccines; subunit vaccines; recombinant vaccines; and DNA vaccines. Explain the advantages and disadvantages of each.

32. Explain the purposes of boosters, adjuvants, Trojan horse vaccines, and toxoids.

33. Describe the concept of herd immunity, and explain how vaccination contributes to its development in a community.

34. List some possible adverse side effects of vaccination.

CASE STUDY Part 2

Once again, doctors changed the chemotherapeutic regimen of the patient, which now included levofloxacin and daptomycin for bacteria, caspofungin for fungi, and acyclovir for viruses. Still, the patient's condition declined. With seemingly no options left, and death imminent, physicians treated the patient with hydrocortisone, a steroid, along with injections of immune serum globulin (ISG). The patient responded immediately, with significant drops in WBC count and CRP level; after 6 days of treatment, he was weaned from the respirator. On the tenth day, inflammation had subsided to the point that the wounds on the leg and both axillae could be partially closed, and the patient was moved from the ICU on day 32. A week later, his wounds were closed completely, using a skin graft from his right thigh. Forty-eight days after admission to the hospital, the patient was discharged.

At first glance, it would seem that the action of the immune serum globulin was straightforward; one of the millions of different antibodies infused into the patient specifically targeted the pathogen, helping to clear the infection. In fact, the action of ISG is more complex than it would at first appear. The ability of blood to opsonize bacteria, marking pathogenic cells for later destruction by macrophages, is enhanced by ISG. Also, ISG binds to and neutralizes superantigens and toxins, bacterial proteins that stimulate the massive release of cytokines by T cells. Cytokines in turn lead to inflammation, blood vessel damage, and organ failure. Finally, in necrotizing soft tissue infections, like the one seen in this case, ISG is thought to bind to the exotoxins produced by staphylococcal and streptococcal species, limiting the inflammatory response.

- Why was the patient treated with immune serum globulin (ISG), and not specific immune globulin (SIG)?

- ISG consists of antibodies collected from a large pool (1,000 or more) of healthy people. Why is ISG collected from such a large pool of donors?

Chapter Summary with Key Terms

15.1 Specific Immunities: The Adaptive Line of Defense
Development of Lymphocyte Specificity/Receptors Acquired immunity involves the reactions of B and T lymphocytes to foreign molecules, or **antigens.** Before they can react, each lymphocyte must undergo differentiation into its final functional type by developing protein receptors for antigen, the specificity of which is randomly generated and unique for each lymphocyte.
 A. Development of the Immune Response System
 1. Genetic recombination and mutation during embryonic and fetal development produce billions of different lymphocytes, each bearing a different receptor. The process by which diversity is generated is **clonal selection.**
 2. **Immune tolerance** or tolerance to self occurs during this time.

 3. The receptors on B cells are **immunoglobulin (Ig)** molecules, and receptors on T cells are smaller unrelated glycoprotein molecules called **CD** markers.
 4. T-cell receptors bind antigenic determinants on **MHC** molecules, which in humans are called **human leukocyte antigens (HLAs).**

15.2 The Nature of Antigens and Antigenicity
An antigen (Ag) is any substance that stimulates an immune response.
 A. Requirements for **antigenicity** include foreignness (recognition as nonself), large size, and complexity of cell or molecule.
 B. Foreign molecules less than 1,000 MW (**haptens**) are not antigenic unless attached to a larger carrier molecule.

C. The epitope is the small molecular group of the foreign substance that is recognized by lymphocytes. Cells, viruses, and large molecules can have numerous epitopes.

D. Other antigens are mosaic alloantigens, superantigens, allergens, and autoantigens.

15.3 Immune Reactions to Antigens and the Activities of T Cells

A. T-cell-dependent antigens must be processed by large phagocytes such as dendritic cells or macrophages called **antigen-presenting cells (APCs).**

B. The presentation of a single antigen involves a direct collaboration between an APC, a T helper (T_H), and an antigen-specific B or T cell.

C. Cytokines involved are **interleukin-12** from the APC, which activates the T_H cells, and **interleukin-2** produced by the T_H cell, which activates B cells and other T cells.

D. **T helper cells (T_H or CD4)** are the dominant T cells.
 1. They regulate immune reactions to antigens and require interaction with MHC-II receptors on host cells.
 2. They activate macrophages, B cells, and other T cells by means of secreted interleukins.
 a. T_H1 cells function as T-cell activators and stimulate delayed hypersensitivity.
 b. T_H2 cells modulate B-cell functions and may suppress certain undesirable T cells' actions.

E. **Cytotoxic T cells (T_C or CD8)** are responsive to MHC-I receptors on host cells and are sometimes called killer T cells.
 1. They recognize and react to foreign cells, cancer cells, and graft tissues and secrete chemicals that directly damage and kill these cells.

F. T regulatory cells (T_{reg}) cells express CD4 and CD25 receptors and function to suppress inappropriate immunological reactions.

G. Gamma-Delta T cells have attributes of both specific and nonspecific immune responses, and are active against bacterial pathogens and tumors cells.

H. Natural killer (NK) cells are T-cell relatives that function nonspecifically. They are responsible for early killing of infected cells and cancer cells in response to various cytokines.

15.4 Immune Activities of B Cells

1. Once B cells process the antigen, interact with T_H cells, and are stimulated by B-cell growth and differentiation factors, they enter the cell cycle in preparation for mitosis and clonal expansion.

2. Divisions give rise to **plasma cells** that secrete antibodies and **memory cells** that can react to that same antigen later.
 a. *Nature of antibodies* (immunoglobulins): A single immunoglobulin molecule (monomer) is a large Y-shaped protein molecule consisting of four polypeptide chains. It contains two identical regions with ends that form the **antigen binding fragments (Fabs)** that bind with a unique specificity to an antigen. The **crystallizable fragment (Fc)** determines the location and the function of the antibody molecule.

b. *Antigen-antibody (Ag-Ab) reactions* include **opsonization, neutralization, agglutination,** and complement fixation.

c. The five **antibody** or **immunoglobulin classes,** which differ in size and function, are **IgG, IgA** (secretory Ab), **IgM, IgD,** and **IgE.**

3. *Antibodies in serum* **(antiserum)**
 a. The first introduction of an Ag to the immune system produces a **primary response,** with a gradual increase in Ab titer.
 b. The second contact with the same Ag produces a **secondary,** or **anamnestic, response** due to memory cells produced during initial response.
 c. **Monoclonal antibodies (MABs)** are pure forms of immunoglobulins. They may be tailored to high specificities and have numerous applications in medicine and research.

15.5 A Classification Scheme for Specific, Acquired Immunities
Immunities acquired through B and T lymphocytes can be classified by a simple system.

A. **Active immunity** results when a person is challenged with antigen that stimulates production of antibodies. It creates memory, takes time, and is lasting.

B. In **passive immunity,** preformed antibodies are donated to an individual. It does not create memory, acts immediately, and is short term.

C. **Natural immunity** is acquired as part of normal life experiences.

D. **Artificial immunity** is acquired through medical procedures such as immunization.

15.6 Immunization: Providing Immune Protection through Therapy

A. Passive **immunotherapy** includes administering immune serum globulin and specific immune globulins pooled from donated serum to prevent infection and disease in those at risk; antisera and antitoxins from animals are occasionally used.

B. Active immunization is synonymous with **vaccination** and provides an antigenic stimulus that does not cause disease but can produce long-lasting, protective immunity. **Vaccines** are made with:
 1. **Killed** whole cells or **inactivated viruses** that do not reproduce but are antigenic
 2. Live, **attenuated** cells or viruses that are able to reproduce but have lost virulence
 3. **Acellular** or **subunit** components of microbes such as surface antigens or neutralized toxins **(toxoids)**
 4. Genetic engineering techniques, including cloning of antigens, recombinant attenuated microbes, and DNA-based vaccines
 5. Boosters (additional doses) are often required.

C. Vaccination increases **herd immunity,** protection provided by mass immunity in a population.

 Assess Your Knowledge

Level I. These questions require a working knowledge of the concepts in the chapter and the ability to recall and understand the information you have studied.

Developing a Concept Inventory

Select the correct answer from the answers provided. For questions with blanks, choose the combination of answers that most accurately completes the statement.

1. Which of these characteristics is not a major factor in adaptive or acquired immunity?
 a. specificity
 b. chemotaxis
 c. recognition
 d. memory

2. The primary B-cell receptor is
 a. IgD
 b. IgA
 c. IgE
 d. IgG

3. In humans, B cells mature in the _____ and T cells mature in the _____.
 a. GALT, liver
 b. bursa, thymus
 c. bone marrow, thymus
 d. lymph nodes, spleen

4. Small, simple molecules are _____ antigens.
 a. poor
 b. never
 c. effective
 d. mosaic

5. Which type of cell actually secretes antibodies?
 a. T cell
 b. macrophage
 c. plasma cell
 d. monocyte

6. CD4 cells are _____ cells and CD8 cells are _____ cells.
 a. killer, suppressor
 b. helper, cytotoxic
 c. cytotoxic, helper
 d. B, T

7. Helper T cells receive antigen from _____, and cytotoxic T cells receive antigen from _____.
 a. macrophages, B cells
 b. class II MHC, class I MHC
 c. viruses, bacteria
 d. class I MHC, class II MHC

8. The cross-linkage of antigenic cells by antibodies is known as
 a. opsonization
 b. a cross-reaction
 c. agglutination
 d. complement fixation

9. The greatest concentration of antibodies is found in the _____ fraction of the serum.
 a. gamma globulin
 b. albumin
 c. beta globulin
 d. alpha globulin

10. T _____ cells assist in the functions of certain B cells and other T cells.
 a. sensitized
 b. cytotoxic
 c. helper
 d. natural killer

11. Cytotoxic T cells are important in controlling
 a. virus infections
 b. allergy
 c. autoimmunity
 d. all of these

12. Vaccination is synonymous with _____ immunity.
 a. natural active
 b. artificial passive
 c. artificial active
 d. natural passive

13. Which of the following can serve as antigen-presenting cells (APCs)?
 a. T cells
 b. B cells
 c. macrophages
 d. dendritic cells
 e. b, c, and d

14. A living microbe with reduced virulence that is used for vaccination is considered
 a. a toxoid
 b. attenuated
 c. denatured
 d. an adjuvant

15. A vaccine that contains parts of viruses is called
 a. acellular
 b. recombinant
 c. subunit
 d. attenuated

16. Widespread immunity that protects the population from the spread of disease is called
 a. seropositivity
 b. cross-reactivity
 c. epidemic prophylaxis
 d. herd immunity

17. DNA vaccines contain _____ DNA that stimulates cells to make _____ antigens.
 a. human, RNA
 b. microbial, protein
 c. human, protein
 d. microbial, polysaccharide

18. What is the purpose of an adjuvant?
 a. to kill the microbe
 b. to stop allergic reactions
 c. to improve the contact between the antigen and lymphocytes
 d. to make the antigen more soluble in the tissues

19. **Multiple Matching.** Place all possible matches in the spaces at the left of each Ig.
 _____ IgG
 _____ IgA
 _____ IgD
 _____ IgE
 _____ IgM
 a. found in mucous secretions
 b. a monomer
 c. a dimer
 d. has greatest number of Fabs
 e. first antibody made during the primary response
 f. first antibody made during the secondary response
 g. crosses the placenta
 h. fixes complement
 i. involved in allergic reactions
 j. primarily a surface receptor on B cells

20. **Multiple Matching.** An outline summarizing the general host defenses covered in chapters 14 and 15 was presented in figure 14.21. You may want to use this resource to review major aspects of immunity and to guide you in answering this question. In the blanks on the left, place the letters of all of the host defenses and immune responses in the right column that can fit the description.

_____ vaccination for tetanus a. active
_____ lysozyme in tears b. passive
_____ immunization with horse serum c. natural
_____ in utero transfer of antibodies d. artificial
_____ booster injection for diphtheria e. acquired

_____ colostrum f. innate, inborn
_____ interferon g. chemical barrier
_____ action of neutrophils h. mechanical barrier
_____ injection of gamma globulin i. genetic barrier
_____ recovery from a case of mumps j. specific
_____ edema k. nonspecific
_____ humans having protection from l. inflammatory response
 canine distemper virus m. second line of defense
_____ stomach acid
_____ cilia in trachea

Case Study Analysis

1. The immune serum globulin administered to the patient in this case was a form of
 a. natural active immunity
 b. natural passive immunity
 c. artificial active immunity
 d. artificial passive immunity

2. The protection provided by immune serum globulin normally lasts
 a. 2–3 months
 b. a lifetime
 c. 48–72 hours
 d. years, if ISG antibodies encounter a pathogen; otherwise, less than a week

3. Why was the patient treated with steroids in this case, when they generally cause a reduction in the strength of the immune response?

On the Test

These questions will help to prepare you to successfully answer similar questions you'll see on the TEAS (Test of Essential Academic Skills) and NCLEX (National Council Licensure Examination).

1. During a well-baby visit, the baby receives a hepatitis B vaccine. What type of immunity will this vaccination provide?
 a. natural active immunity
 b. artificial passive immunity
 c. artificial active immunity
 d. artificial passive immunity

2. Before administration of the measles, mumps, rubella (MMR) vaccine, the nurse informs the client about which common side effects?
 a. fever
 b. blurred vision
 c. seizures
 d. injection site pain

Writing Challenge

For each question, compose a one- or two-paragraph answer that includes the factual information needed to completely address the question. Practice questions can also be used for writing-challenge exercises.

1. Using words and arrows, complete a flow outline of an immune response, beginning with entrance of antigen; include processing, cell interaction, involvement of cytokines, and the end results for B and T cells.

2. a. Explain why most immune reactions result in a polyclonal collection of antibodies.
 b. How do monoclonal antibodies differ from this?
 c. Describe several applications of monoclonals in medicine.

3. Give an immunological explanation as to why people can get influenza every year even though they have been vaccinated.

4. How can the anamnestic response be explained in immunologic terms?

5. Differentiate between humoral and cell-mediated immunity.

6. Combine information on the functions of different classes of Ig to explain the exact mechanisms of natural passive immunity (both transplacental and colostrum-induced).

Concept Mapping

On Connect you can find an Introduction to Concept Mapping that provides guidance for working with concept maps, along with concept-mapping activities for this chapter.

 Application, Analysis, Evaluation, and Synthesis

Level II. These problems go beyond just restating facts and require higher levels of understanding and an ability to interpret, problem solve, transfer knowledge to new situations, create models, and predict outcomes.

Critical Thinking

Critical thinking is the ability to reason and solve problems using facts and concepts. These questions can be approached from a number of angles and, in most cases, they do not have a single correct answer.

1. Cells contain built-in suicide genes to self-destruct by apoptosis under certain conditions. Can you explain why development of the immune system might depend in part on this sort of adaptation?

2. a. Describe what could be summarized as the three Rs of immunity: recognize, react, remember.

 b. Why would it be necessary for the T cells to bind both antigen and self (MHC) receptors?

3. Double-stranded DNA is a large, complex molecule, but it is not generally immunogenic unless it is associated with proteins or carbohydrates. Can you think why this might be so? (Hint: How universal is DNA?)

4. Explain how it is possible for people to give a false-positive reaction in blood tests for syphilis, AIDS, and infectious mononucleosis.

5. Describe the relationship between an antitoxin, a toxin, and a toxoid.

6. It is said that a vaccine does not prevent infection; rather, it primes the immune system to undergo an immediate response to prevent an infection from spreading. Explain what is meant by this statement, and outline what is happening at the cellular/molecular level from the time of vaccination until subsequent contact with the infectious agent actually occurs.

7. A study by the CDC reported that less than 80% of children in some areas of the United States are being adequately vaccinated. Several million children are at high risk for infections.

 a. Name some factors that account for this trend.

 b. Explain how the reduction in vaccination impacts herd immunity.

8. When traders and missionaries first went to the Hawaiian Islands, the natives there experienced severe disease and high mortality rates from smallpox, measles, and certain STDs. Explain what immunologic factors are involved in the devastating effects of new diseases in previously unexposed populations.

Visual Assessment

1. Using figure 15.14, label the lines and arrows, and explain what is happening at numbers 1, 2, and 3.

2. Examine figure 6.6*a* and determine which components would act as epitopes or antigens.

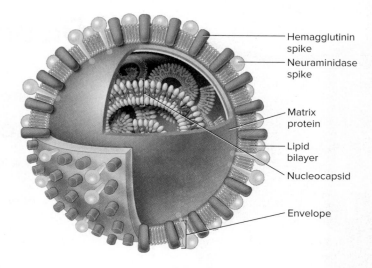

Hemagglutinin spike

Neuraminidase spike

Matrix protein

Lipid bilayer

Nucleocapsid

Envelope

Disorders in Immunity

In This Chapter...

(police car in side view mirror): YAY Media AS/Alamy Stock Photo; *(Abutilon pollen):* Science Photo Library/Alamy Stock Photo; *(Toxicodendron):* Source: Robert H. Mohlenbrock @ USDA-NRCS PLANTS Database/USDA SCS. 1991. Southern wetland flora: Field office guide to plant species. South National Technical Center, Fort Worth; *(rheumatoid arthritis):* Mediscan/Alamy Stock Photo; *(David Vetter):* ©Baylor College of Medicine, Public Affairs

Being **followed** on a dark road late at night brings all kinds of thoughts to the mind of a 19-year-old college student, none of them good, and this is exactly what was happening to Emily Gavigan. She became aware of being followed while on her way home after having coffee with some friends. Not knowing what else to do, Emily, a sophomore at Scranton College in Pennsylvania, kept driving, from Pennsylvania to New Jersey. She had no money with her and so passed through toll booths without paying. She called her parents and friends to warn them that something **terrible** was going to happen, and eventually detoured to her grandparents' house, where she told them about being followed. Her grandfather looked outside, searching for whoever it was that was stalking his granddaughter, before coming to the inescapable conclusion that Emily was having some sort of **psychotic episode.** No one was chasing her. Her parents arrived and took her to the hospital.

Over the next few months, Emily continued to **deteriorate.** She lost the ability to do simple math and had **trouble conversing.** At one point, she was placed in a psychiatric hospital that she believed to be a movie set. Doctors treated Emily with a variety of **antidepressants** and mood stabilizers, believing her behavior to be the initial manifestations of a psychological disorder like **schizophrenia** or **psychosis,** both of which commonly make their first appearance between the ages of 20 and 30. She continued to decline, suffering **numbness** in her face and hands, and experienced several **seizures.** Emily, an avid figure skater, forgot how to walk.

While doctors continued to search for an underlying cause for Emily's symptoms, her aunt saw a segment on the *Today* show that struck a chord. Susannah Cahalan, a journalist for the *New York Post,* was discussing a recent article she wrote, entitled *My Mysterious Lost Month of Madness,* in which she wrote about a month-long **neurologic episode.** Without warning, Cahalan became **paranoid,** suffered **seizures,** found it difficult to speak, and lost the ability to read. The first neurologist suggested **mononucleosis,** perhaps a **virus,** or maybe alcohol withdrawal (Cahalan rarely drank). On one trip to the hospital, Susannah's paranoia compelled her to jump from the car; once admitted, she was required to wear an orange wristband that proclaimed, "Flight Risk."

Over the next 2 weeks, Cahalan was subjected to an alphabet of tests, EEGs, MRIs, CAT scans, PET scans, and X-rays, all with no results. A **spinal tap** revealed increased numbers of **white blood cells** in her cerebrospinal fluid, an indication of **encephalitis** (inflammation of the brain). Samples of her blood and spinal fluid were sent to Dr. Josep Dalmau to test for the presence of rare **autoantibodies** that could be the source of the **inflammation.**

Emily's parents, having heard Cahalan's story, asked doctors to test Emily for the same rare antibodies seen in Cahalan's case. Doctors initially disagreed, telling her father, "You have to come to grips with the fact that you have a child with mental illness. You're not doing anybody any favors by grasping at these types of straws."

- *What type of disorder would cause a person to produce antibodies against their own cells?*

- *Is there any significance to the fact that both Emily Gavigan and Susannah Cahalan are female?*

To continue the Case Study, go to Case Study Part 2 at the end of the chapter.

16.1 The Immune Response: A Two-Sided Coin

 Learn

1. Summarize the main categories of immunopathology and their medical consequences.

2. Discuss the factors involved in allergies and hypersensitivities.

Our previous discussions of the immune response centered primarily around its numerous beneficial effects. The precisely coordinated system that recognizes and destroys invading microbes is clearly protective, but it also presents another side—a side that promotes rather than prevents disease. In this chapter, we survey **immunopathology,** the study of disease states associated with overreactivity or underreactivity of the immune response **(figure 16.1).** In the cases of **allergy** and **autoimmunity,** the tissues are innocent bystanders to immune attacks that do not distinguish between one's own cells and foreign antigens. In **grafts** and **transfusions,** a recipient reacts to the foreign tissues and cells of another individual. In **immunodeficiency** diseases, immune function is incompletely developed, suppressed, or destroyed. **Cancer** falls into a special category, because it is both a cause and an effect of immune dysfunction. As we shall see, one fascinating by-product of studies of immune disorders has been our increased understanding of the basic workings of the immune system.

Overreactions to Antigens: Allergy/Hypersensitivity

The term **allergy** means a condition of altered reactivity or exaggerated immune responsiveness that is manifested by inflammatory symptoms. Although it is sometimes used interchangeably with **hypersensitivity,** some experts use the term *allergy* in reference to immediate reactions (hay fever, asthma) and use *hypersensitivity* in reference to other forms of overreactions to antigens (contact dermatitis). Allergic and hypersensitive individuals are acutely sensitive to repeated contact with antigens called **allergens** that do not noticeably affect other "normal" individuals. Although the general effects of these immune pathologies are usually detrimental, we must emphasize that they involve the very same types of immune reactions as protective immunities. These include humoral and cell-mediated actions, the inflammatory response, phagocytosis, and complement. Such an association means that all humans have the potential to develop allergy or hypersensitivity under particular circumstances.

Originally allergies and hypersensitivities were defined as either immediate or delayed, depending upon the time lapse between contact with the allergen and onset of symptoms. Subsequently they were differentiated as humoral versus cell-mediated. But as

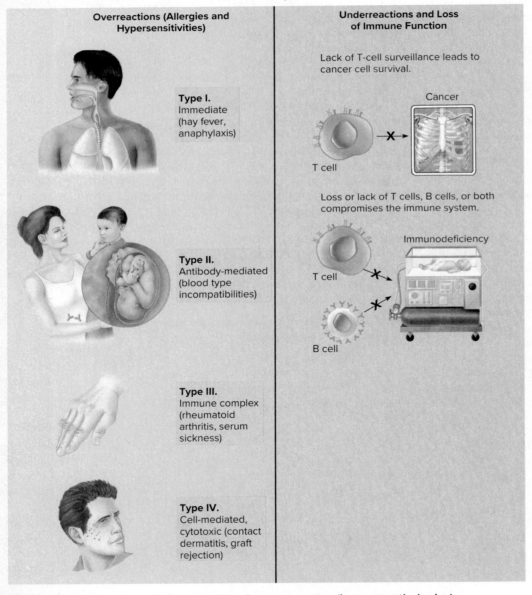

Figure 16.1 **Overview of diseases of the immune system (immunopathologies).** Just as the system of T cells and B cells provides necessary protection against infection and disease, the same system can cause serious and debilitating conditions by overreacting (pink) or underreacting (blue) to immune stimuli.

TABLE 16.1	Classification of Immunopathologies Caused by Overreactions to Antigens	
Type	**Systems and Mechanisms Involved**	**Examples**
I Immediate allergies	IgE-mediated; involves mast cells, basophils, and allergic mediators	Anaphylaxis, allergies such as hay fever, asthma
II Antibody-mediated incompatibilities	IgG, IgM antibodies act upon cells with complement and cause cell lysis; includes some autoimmune diseases	Blood group incompatibility, pernicious anemia; myasthenia gravis
III Immune complex diseases	Antibody-mediated inflammation; circulating IgG complexes deposited in basement membranes of target organs; includes some autoimmune diseases	Systemic lupus erythematosus; rheumatoid arthritis; serum sickness; rheumatic fever
IV T-cell-mediated hypersensitivities	Delayed hypersensitivity and cytotoxic reactions in tissues	Infection reactions; contact dermatitis; graft rejection; some types of autoimmunity

information accumulated on these types of dysfunctional immune responses, it became evident that, although useful, these schemes oversimplified what is really a very complex spectrum of reactions. The most widely accepted classification, first introduced by immunologists P. Gell and R. Coombs, includes four major categories of immune system pathologies involving overreactions to antigens: type I ("common" allergy and anaphylaxis), type II (IgG- and IgM-mediated cell damage), type III (immune complex diseases), and type IV (delayed hypersensitivity) **(table 16.1).** In general, types I, II, and III involve a B-cell–immunoglobulin response, and type IV involves a T-cell response. The antigens that elicit these reactions can be exogenous, originating from outside the body (microbes, pollen grains, and foreign cells and proteins) or endogenous, arising from self tissue (autoimmunities).

One of the reasons allergies and hypersensitivities are easily mistaken for infections is that both involve damage to the tissues and thus trigger the inflammatory response, as described in chapter 14. Many symptoms and signs of inflammation (redness, heat, skin eruptions, edema, and granuloma) are prominent features of allergies and are caused by some of the same chemical mediators.

 Practice SECTION 16.1

1. Explain what is meant by immunopathology and give some examples of this condition.
2. Define *allergy/hypersensitivity*, and explain what accounts for the reactions that occur in these conditions.
3. What is involved in the four categories of B-cell and T-cell–mediated immunopathologies outlined by Gell and Combs?
4. What does it mean for a reaction to be immediate or delayed?

16.2 Allergic Reactions: Atopy and Anaphylaxis

Learn

3. Describe general characteristics of allergic reactions.
4. Outline the major allergen categories, giving examples.

5. Explain the mechanism of immediate allergies, including the concepts of IgE, mast cells, sensitization, and provocation.
6. Summarize the physiological effects of allergies that cause major symptoms.
7. Define the types of atopic allergies, and describe their major features.
8. Explain the process of anaphylaxis and its outcome.
9. Relate the primary methods of diagnosing, treating, and preventing allergies.

Type I allergies share a similar physiological mechanism, are immediate in onset, and are associated with exposure to specific antigens. However, it is convenient to recognize two levels of severity: **Atopy*** is any chronic allergy, such as hay fever or eczema, whose effects are localized to a region and usually not life-threatening; and **anaphylaxis*** is a systemic, sometimes fatal reaction that involves airway obstruction and circulatory collapse. In the following sections we consider the allergens, routes of inoculation, mechanisms of disease, and specific syndromes involved in type I allergies.

Modes of Contact with Allergens

Allergies exert profound medical and economic impact. Allergists (physicians who specialize in treating allergies) estimate that about 10% to 30% of the population is prone to atopic allergy. It is generally acknowledged that self-treatment with over-the-counter medicines accounts for significant underreporting of cases. The 40 million people afflicted with hay fever (15% to 20% of the population) together spend about half a billion dollars annually for medical treatment. The monetary loss due to employee debilitation and absenteeism is immeasurable. The majority of allergies are relatively mild, but certain forms, such as asthma and anaphylaxis, may require hospitalization and can cause death.

The predisposition for atopic allergies has a strong familial association. Be aware that what is hereditary here is a generalized *susceptibility,* not an allergy to a specific substance. For example, a parent who is allergic to ragweed pollen can have a child who is allergic to cat hair. The prospect of a child's developing an atopic allergy is at least 25% if one parent is atopic, increasing up to 50%

* *atopy* (at′-oh-pee) Gr. *atop,* out of place.
* *anaphylaxis* (an″-uh-fih-lax′-us) Gr. *ana,* excessive, and *phylaxis,* protection.

CLINICAL CONNECTIONS

Are Some Allergies a Consequence of Clean Living?

Allergists have been observing an increased incidence of allergies such as asthma, allergic rhinitis, and other atopic allergies that is not tied to genetic factors or better diagnosis. Most of these increases have occurred in more affluent regions of the United States and Europe. Although this phenomenon cannot easily be explained, many medical experts think it is connected to something called the **hygiene or biodiversity hypothesis.** This explanation says that ultraclean lifestyles and living environments prevent the kind of contact with microbes that is required for the normal development of the immune system. The effects of modern housekeeping, lifestyles, and antimicrobial drugs mean that children have less exposure to noninfectious environmental microbes and viral and parasitic infections. The phenomenon was first hypothesized to explain the fact that children in large families, who were presumably exposed to more potential allergens, displayed fewer allergic symptoms. It was also noted that the levels of allergies are lower in developing countries and rural areas, where children have greater exposure to soil, infectious agents, and household pets.

Although the factors involved are complex, it is thought that contact with certain types of microbes initiates protective responses and shapes the future direction of immune system development. The immune systems of children who lack sufficient microbial contact become programmed to react to allergens such as household chemicals, animal and plant molecules, and even food, which sets the scene for long-term allergies. Because people are unlikely to return to less clean lifestyles, researchers are on the trail of finding out what kinds of stimuli can inoculate people against allergies. It may turn out that "a little dirt can't hurt" and may even be beneficial.

Explain how the hygiene hypothesis relates to the overuse of household disinfectants and antibiotics as discussed in chapters 11 and 12.

if grandparents or siblings are also afflicted. The actual basis for atopy appears to be the inheritance of genes that favor allergic antibody (IgE) production, increased reactivity of mast cells, and increased susceptibility of target tissue to allergic mediators. Allergic persons often exhibit a combination of syndromes, such as hay fever, eczema, and asthma.

Other factors that affect the onset of allergy are age, infection, and geographic locale. New allergies tend to crop up throughout an allergic person's life, especially as new exposures occur after moving or changing lifestyle. In some persons, atopic allergies last for a lifetime, others "outgrow" them, and still others suddenly develop them later in life. Some features of allergic pathology are not yet completely explained.

The Nature of Allergens and Their Portals of Entry

As with other antigens, allergens have certain immunogenic characteristics. Not unexpectedly, proteins are more allergenic than

carbohydrates, fats, or nucleic acids. Some allergens are haptens, nonproteinaceous substances with a molecular weight of less than 1,000 that can form complexes with carrier molecules in the body. Organic and inorganic chemicals found in industrial and household products, cosmetics, food, and drugs are commonly of this type. **Table 16.2** lists a number of common allergenic substances and their portal of entry.

Allergens typically enter through the epithelia of the respiratory tract, gastrointestinal tract, and skin. The mucosal surfaces of the gut and respiratory system present a thin, moist surface that is normally quite penetrable. The dry, tough keratin coating of skin is less permeable, but access still occurs through tiny breaks, glands, and hair follicles. It is worth noting that the organ of allergic expression may or may not be the same as the portal of entry.

Airborne environmental allergens such as pollen, house dust, dander (shed skin scales), or fungal spores are termed *inhalants*. Each geographic region harbors a particular combination of airborne substances; this combination varies with the season and humidity **(figure 16.2a)**. Pollen, the most common offender, is given off seasonally by the reproductive structures of pines and flowering plants (weeds, trees, and grasses). Unlike pollen, mold spores are released throughout the year and are especially profuse in moist areas of the home and garden. Airborne animal hair and dander (skin flakes), feathers, and the saliva of dogs and cats are common sources of allergens.

House dust is a complex mixture of organic debris, soil, human skin cells, and a wide array of bacteria and fungi. The component of house dust that appears to account for most dust allergies is not the debris or microbes but the decomposed skeletons of tiny mites that commonly live in this dust **(figure 16.2b)**. Some people are allergic to their work, in the sense that they are exposed to allergens on the job. Examples include florists, woodworkers, farmers, drug processors, and plastics manufacturers whose work can aggravate inhalant and contact allergies.

Allergens that enter by mouth, called *ingestants*, often cause food allergies. *Injectant* allergies are an important adverse side effect of injected drugs or other substances used in diagnosing, treating, or preventing disease. A natural source of injectants is venom from stings by hymenopterans, a family of insects that includes honeybees and wasps. *Contactants* are allergens that enter through the skin. Many contact allergies are of the type IV, delayed variety discussed in section 16.5.

TABLE 16.2	Common Allergens, Classified by Portal of Entry		
Inhalants	**Ingestants**	**Injectants**	**Contactants**
Pollen	Food (milk, peanuts,	Hymenopteran	Topical drugs
Dust	wheat, shellfish,	venom (bee,	Cosmetics
Mold spores	soybeans, nuts,	wasp)	Heavy metals
Dander	eggs, fruits)	Insect bites	Detergents
Animal hair	Food additives	Drugs	Formalin
Insect parts	Oral drugs	Vaccines	Rubber
Formalin	(aspirin,	Serum	Solvents
Aerosols	penicillin)	Enzymes	Dyes
		Hormones	

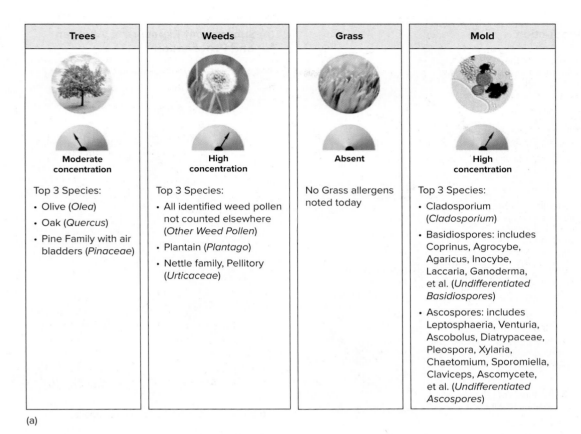

Trees	Weeds	Grass	Mold
Moderate concentration	**High concentration**	**Absent**	**High concentration**
Top 3 Species: • Olive (*Olea*) • Oak (*Quercus*) • Pine Family with air bladders (*Pinaceae*)	Top 3 Species: • All identified weed pollen not counted elsewhere (*Other Weed Pollen*) • Plantain (*Plantago*) • Nettle family, Pellitory (*Urticaceae*)	No Grass allergens noted today	Top 3 Species: • Cladosporium (*Cladosporium*) • Basidiospores: includes Coprinus, Agrocybe, Agaricus, Inocybe, Laccaria, Ganoderma, et al. (*Undifferentiated Basidiospores*) • Ascospores: includes Leptosphaeria, Venturia, Ascobolus, Diatrypaceae, Pleospora, Xylaria, Chaetomium, Sporomiella, Claviceps, Ascomycete, et al. (*Undifferentiated Ascospores*)

(a)

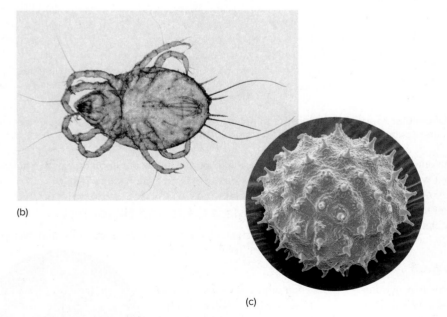

(b)

(c)

Figure 16.2 Monitoring airborne allergens. (a) The air in heavily vegetated places with a mild climate is especially laden with allergens such as pollen and mold spores. These counts vary seasonally and can be easily tracked on the Internet (www.pollen.aaaai.org). **(b)** An SEM of the dust mite *Dermatophagoides* (2,000×), which feeds primarily on human skin cells in house dust, and is found in abundance in bedding and carpets. Airborne mite feces and particles from their exoskeletons are an important source of allergies. **(c)** Scanning electron micrograph of a pollen grain from a flowering maple (1,000×). Millions of these are released from a single flower.

(a): American Academy of Allergy, Asthma & Immunology; (b): prill/123RF; (c): Science Photo Library/Alamy Stock Photo

Mechanisms of Allergy: Sensitization and Provocation

What causes some people to sneeze and wheeze every time they step out into the spring air, while others suffer no ill effects? We can answer this question by examining what occurs in the tissues of the allergic individual that does not occur in the normal person. What is not as easy to answer is the question of why allergy is so common, affecting over 40% of the world's population. What useful function, if any, can it possibly serve? See 16.1 Making Connections for some possible explanations.

In general, allergies develop in stages **(process figure 16.3).** The initial encounter with an allergen provides a **sensitizing dose** that primes the immune system for a subsequent encounter with that allergen but generally elicits no signs or symptoms. The memory cells and immunoglobulin produced during this encounter are then ready to react with a subsequent **provocative dose** of the same allergen. It is this dose that precipitates the first signs and

(a) Sensitization/IgE Production

① Allergens enter through mucous membrane and are picked up by a dendritic cell.

② Dendritic cell processes allergen and presents it to a T helper cell in lymph node.

③ B cell activated by T_H cell reacts to allergen.

④ B cell divides to form numerous plasma cells.

⑤ Synthesis of IgE specific to allergen

Fc fragments

⑥ IgEs bind with their Fc fragments to mast cell receptors.

IgE-primed mast cells remain in tissues for extended periods.

Granules with inflammatory mediators

Mast cell in tissue

(b) Subsequent Exposure to Allergen and Provocation

⑦ Allergen is encountered again and goes directly to primed mast cells.

⑧ Allergen attaches to IgE on mast cells and triggers degranulation and release of allergic mediators.

stimulates

⑨ Systemic distribution of mediators in bloodstream

⑩ End result: Symptoms in various organs

Red, itchy eyes

Hives

Runny nose

Process Figure 16.3 **A schematic view of cellular reactions during the allergic response. (a)** Sensitization (initial contact with sensitizing dose), includes steps 1–6. **(b)** Provocation (later contacts with provocative dose), steps 7–10.

symptoms that an allergy exists. Despite numerous anecdotal reports of people showing an allergy upon first contact with an allergen, it is generally believed that these individuals unknowingly had contact at some previous time. Fetal exposure to allergens from the mother's bloodstream is one possibility, and foods can be a prime source of "hidden" allergens such as penicillin.

The Physiology of IgE-Mediated Allergies

During primary contact and sensitization, the allergen penetrates the portal of entry **(process figure 16.3, steps 1–6).** When large particles such as pollen grains, hair, and spores encounter a moist membrane, they are first captured by dendritic cells, which process the allergen and present it to T helper cells in the lymph nodes. Here, the T cells interact with clones of B cells, which they activate to respond to the specific allergen. This causes proliferation of plasma cells, following a sequence similar to the typical immune response to an antigen. These plasma cells produce **immunoglobulin E (IgE),** the antibody of allergy. IgE is different from other immunoglobulins in having an Fc region with great affinity for mast cells and basophils. The binding of IgE to these cells in the tissues

sets the scene for the reactions that occur upon repeated exposure to the same allergen **(process figure 16.3, steps 7–10).**

The Role of Mast Cells and Basophils

The most important characteristics of mast cells and basophils relating to their roles in allergy are these:

1. Their ubiquitous location in tissues. Mast cells are located in the connective tissue of virtually all organs, but particularly high concentrations exist in the lungs, skin, gastrointestinal tract, and genitourinary tract. Basophils circulate in the blood but migrate readily into tissues.

2. Their capacity to bind IgE during sensitization (process

SEM of mast cell with ruffled membrane and receptors for IgE
Source: Bridget Wilson/University of New Mexico

figure 16.3). Each cell carries 30,000 to 100,000 cell receptors that bind 10,000 to 40,000 IgE antibodies.

3. Their cytoplasmic granules (secretory vesicles), which contain physiologically active cytokines (histamine, serotonin—introduced in chapter 14).

4. Their tendency to **degranulate** (process figure 16.3 and figure 16.4) or release the contents of the granules into the tissues when triggered by a specific allergen through the IgE bound to them.

Let us now see what occurs when sensitized cells are challenged with allergen a second time.

The Provocative Contact with Allergen

After sensitization, the IgE-primed mast cells can remain in the tissues for years. Even after long periods without contact, a person can retain the capacity to react immediately upon reexposure. The next time allergen molecules contact these sensitized cells, they bind across adjacent receptors and stimulate degranulation. As chemical mediators are released, they diffuse into the tissues and bloodstream. Cytokines give rise to numerous local and systemic reactions, many of which appear quite rapidly **(process figure 16.3, step 10).** Thus, the symptoms of allergy are caused, not by the direct action of allergen on tissues, but by the physiological effects of mast cell mediators on target organs.

Cytokines, Target Organs, and Allergic Symptoms

Numerous substances involved in mediating allergy (and inflammation) have been identified. The principal chemical mediators produced by mast cells and basophils are histamine, serotonin, leukotriene, platelet-activating factor, prostaglandins, and bradykinin **(figure 16.4).** These chemicals, acting alone or in combination, account for the tremendous scope of allergic symptoms. Targets of these mediators include the skin, upper respiratory tract, gastrointestinal tract, and conjunctiva. The general responses of these organs include rashes, itching, redness, rhinitis, sneezing, diarrhea, and shedding of tears. Systemic targets include smooth muscle, mucous glands, and nervous tissue. Because smooth muscle is responsible for regulating the size of blood vessels and respiratory passageways, changes in its activity can profoundly alter blood flow, blood pressure, and respiration. Pain, anxiety, agitation, and lethargy are also attributable to the effects of mediators on the nervous system.

Histamine* is the most profuse and fastest-acting allergic mediator. It is a potent stimulator of smooth muscle, glands, and eosinophils. Histamine's actions on smooth muscle vary with location. It *constricts* the smooth muscle layers of the bronchioles and intestine, thereby causing labored breathing and increased intestinal motility. In contrast, histamine *relaxes* vascular smooth muscle and dilates arterioles and venules. It is responsible for the **wheal*** **and**

flare reaction in the skin (see figure 16.6), pruritis (itching), and headache. More severe reactions such as anaphylaxis can be accompanied by edema and vascular dilation, which lead to hypotension, tachycardia, circulatory failure, and, frequently, shock. Salivary, lacrimal, mucous, and gastric glands are also histamine targets.

Although the role of **serotonin*** in human allergy is uncertain, its effects appear to complement those of histamine. In experimental animals, serotonin increases vascular permeability, capillary dilation, smooth muscle contraction, intestinal peristalsis, and respiratory rate, but it diminishes central nervous system activity.

A type of **leukotriene,*** known as the "slow-reacting substance of anaphylaxis," induces gradual contraction of smooth muscle. This leukotriene is responsible for the prolonged bronchospasm, vascular permeability, and mucous secretion of the asthmatic individual. Other leukotrienes stimulate the activities of polymorphonuclear leukocytes.

Platelet-activating factor is a lipid released by basophils, neutrophils, monocytes, and macrophages. The physiological response to this factor is similar to that of histamine, including increased vascular permeability, pulmonary smooth muscle contraction, pulmonary edema, hypotension, and a wheal and flare response in the skin.

Prostaglandins* are a group of powerful inflammatory agents. Normally these substances regulate smooth muscle contraction. For example, they stimulate uterine contractions during delivery. In allergic reactions, they are responsible for vasodilation, increased vascular permeability, increased sensitivity to pain, and bronchoconstriction. Certain anti-inflammatory drugs work by preventing the actions of prostaglandins.

Bradykinin* is related to a group of plasma and tissue peptides known as kinins that participate in blood clotting and chemotaxis. In allergy, it causes prolonged contraction of the bronchioles, dilation of peripheral arterioles, increased capillary permeability, and increased mucus secretion.

Specific Diseases Associated with IgE- and Mast-Cell–Mediated Allergy

The mechanisms just described are basic to hay fever, allergic asthma, food allergy, drug allergy, eczema, and anaphylaxis. In this section we cover the main characteristics of these conditions, followed by methods of detection and treatment.

Atopic Diseases

Hay fever is a generic term for **allergic rhinitis,*** a seasonal reaction to inhaled plant pollen or molds or a chronic, year-round reaction to a wide spectrum of airborne allergens or inhalants (see table 16.2). The targets are typically respiratory membranes, and the symptoms include nasal congestion; sneezing; coughing; profuse mucus secretion; itchy, red, and teary eyes; and mild bronchoconstriction.

* *histamine* (his´-tah-meen) Gr. *histio,* tissue, and amine.
* *wheal* (weel) A smooth, slightly elevated, temporary welt (wheal) that is surrounded by a flushed patch of skin (flare).

* *serotonin* (ser″-oh-toh´-nin) L. *serum,* fluid, and *tonin,* stretching.
* *leukotriene* (loo″-koh-try´-een) Gr. *leukos,* white blood cell, and *triene,* a chemical suffix.
* *prostaglandin* (pross″-tah-glan´-din) From prostate gland. The substance was originally isolated from semen.
* *bradykinin* (brad″-ee-kye´-nin) Gr. *bradys,* slow, and *kinein,* to move.
* *rhinitis* (rye-nye´-tis) Gr. *rhis,* nose, and *itis,* inflammation.

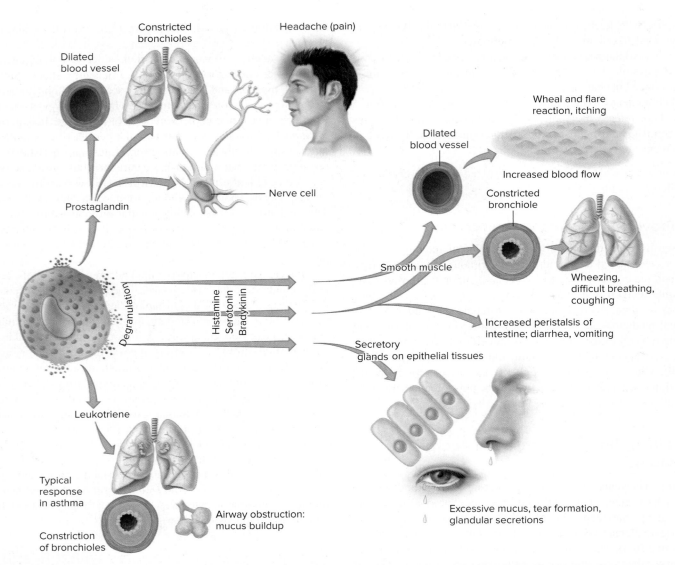

Figure 16.4 **The spectrum of reactions to inflammatory cytokines released by mast cells and the common symptoms they elicit in target tissues and organs.** Note the extensive overlapping effects.

Allergic asthma* is a respiratory disease characterized by episodes of impaired breathing due to severe bronchoconstriction. The airways of asthmatic people are exquisitely responsive to minute amounts of inhalant allergens, food, or other stimuli, such as infectious agents. The symptoms of asthma range from occasional, annoying bouts of difficult breathing to fatal suffocation. Labored breathing, shortness of breath, wheezing, cough, and ventilatory **rales*** are present to one degree or another. The respiratory tract of an asthmatic person is chronically inflamed and severely overreactive to allergy

> **Quick Search**
>
> For an overview, watch the video "Allergies—Hypersensitivity Type I" on YouTube.

chemicals, especially leukotrienes and serotonin from pulmonary mast cells. Other pathologic components are thick mucous plugs in the air sacs and lung damage that can result in long-term respiratory compromise. An imbalance in the nervous control of the respiratory smooth muscles is apparently involved in asthma, and the episodes are influenced by the psychological state of the person, which strongly supports a neurological connection.

The number of asthma sufferers in the United States is estimated at more than 20 million, with nearly one-third of them children. For reasons that are not completely understood, asthma and deaths from it have been increasing over the last 30 years, even though effective agents to control it are more available now than they have ever been before. Surprisingly, asthma is more common in developed regions of the world (the United States and parts of Europe) than in less developed countries in Asia and Africa, It has been suggested that

asthma (az'-muh) Greek word for gasping.
rales (rails) Abnormal breathing sounds.

16.1 MAKING CONNECTIONS

The Origins of Allergy

Why would humans and other mammals evolve an allergic response that is capable of doing so much harm and even causing death? It is unlikely that this limb of immunity exists merely to make people miserable; it must have a role in protection and survival. What are the underlying biological functions of IgE, mast cells, and the array of potent cytokines? Analysis has revealed that, although allergic persons have high levels of IgE, trace quantities are present even in the sera of nonallergic individuals, just as mast cells and inflammatory chemicals are also part of normal human physiology. In chapter 14, you learned that inflammatory mediators serve valuable functions, such as increasing blood flow and vascular permeability to summon essential immune components to an injured site. They are also responsible for increased mucus secretion, gastric motility, sneezing, and coughing, which help expel noxious agents. The difference is that, in allergic persons, the quantity and quality of these reactions are excessive and uncontrolled.

SEM of cockroach chitin exoskeleton and its complex allergenic surface.
Source: Janice Carr/CDC

Some surprising insights have emerged from studies at the University of California. It seems that a significant source of many allergies is the polysaccharide *chitin*. This ubiquitous compound is found in insect exoskeletons, fungal cell walls, and parasitic worms. The digestion of chitin by enzymes present in the human body causes the release of smaller antigen molecules. These set off powerful immune and inflammatory reactions. There is even a specific pathway in lymphocytes and other white blood cells for responding to chitin and its antigens. It is theorized that this system originally functioned in the attack against worms, fungi, and other pathogens containing chitin, but modern hygiene and therapy have greatly reduced these infections. The remnant of this formerly protective mechanism now actually causes "out of control" reactions such as asthma and other respiratory allergies. This appears to be one basis of allergies to cockroaches and dust mites and the increase in childhood asthma.

What are some potential benefits of allergy?

modern insulated buildings have created indoor conditions that harbor higher concentrations of airborne allergens and ozone. This suggests a pronounced influence of environmental factors on the development of allergies and asthma (**16.1 Making Connections**).

Atopic dermatitis is an intensely itchy inflammatory condition of the skin, also known as **eczema.*** Sensitization occurs through ingestion, inhalation, and, occasionally, skin contact with allergens. It usually begins in infancy with reddened, vesicular, weeping, encrusted skin lesions (**figure 16.5**). It then progresses in childhood and adulthood to a dry, scaly, thickened skin condition. Lesions can occur on the face, scalp, neck, and inner surfaces of the limbs and trunk. The itchy, painful lesions cause considerable discomfort, and they are often predisposed to secondary bacterial infections. An anonymous writer once aptly described eczema as "the itch that rashes" or "one scratch is too many but one thousand is not enough."

Food Allergy

The ordinary diet contains a vast variety of compounds that are potentially allergenic. Although food allergies have an intestinal mode of entry, they can affect the skin and respiratory tract as well. Gastrointestinal symptoms include vomiting, diarrhea, and abdominal pain. In severe cases, nutrients are poorly

absorbed, leading to growth retardation and failure to thrive in young children. Other manifestations of food allergies include rashes, hives (figure 16.5), rhinitis, asthma, and occasionally anaphylaxis. Classic food hypersensitivity involves IgE and degranulation of mast cells, but not all reactions involve this mechanism. The most common food allergens come from peanuts, fish, cow's milk, eggs, shellfish, and soybeans.[1] A recent investigation of babies who were considered at risk for peanut allergy concluded that eating a small amount of peanuts early in life greatly reduced their developing sensitivity to peanuts. Allergists are now thinking that in some cases, certain foods should be introduced earlier to prevent sensitization of children to that food.

Drug Allergy

Modern chemotherapy has been responsible for many medical advances. Unfortunately, it has also been hampered by the fact that drugs are foreign compounds capable of stimulating allergic reactions. In fact, allergy to drugs is one of the most common side effects of treatment (present in 5% to 10% of hospitalized patients). Depending upon the allergen, route of entry, and individual sensitivities, virtually any tissue of the body can be affected, and reactions range from mild atopy to fatal anaphylaxis. Compounds implicated most often are antibiotics (penicillin is number one in

Quick Search

Learn some fascinating facts from the video "Animation Describing Anaphylaxis" on YouTube.

* *eczema* (eks'-uh-mah; also ek-zeem'-uh) Gr. *ekzeo,* to boil over.

1. Do not confuse food allergy with food intolerance. Many people are lactose intolerant, for example, due to a deficiency in the enzyme that degrades the sugar in milk.

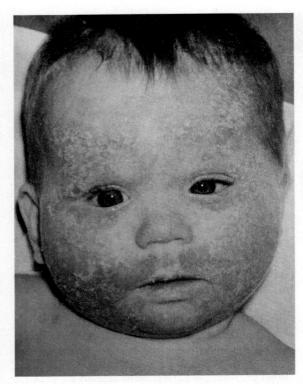

Figure 16.5 **Skin manifestations in atopic allergies.** Atopic dermatitis, or eczema. Vesicular, encrusted lesions are typical in afflicted infants. This condition is prevalent enough to account for 1% of pediatric care.
©DermNet New Zealand Trust

prevalence), synthetic antimicrobials (sulfa drugs), aspirin, opiates, and contrast dye used in X-rays. The actual allergen is not the intact drug itself but a hapten given off when the liver processes the drug. Some forms of penicillin sensitivity are due to the presence of small amounts of the drug in meat, milk, and other foods and to exposure to *Penicillium* mold in the environment.

Anaphylaxis: A Powerful Systemic Reaction to Allergens

The term **anaphylaxis** was first used to denote a reaction of animals injected with a foreign protein. Although the animals showed no response during the first contact, upon reinoculation with the same protein at a later time, they exhibited acute symptoms—itching, sneezing, difficult breathing, prostration, and convulsions—and many died in a few minutes. Two clinical types of anaphylaxis are seen in humans. **Cutaneous anaphylaxis** is the wheal and flare inflammatory reaction to the local injection of allergen. **Systemic anaphylaxis,** also called **anaphylactic shock,** is

Source: Rob Flynn/USDA

characterized by sudden respiratory and circulatory disruption that can be fatal in a few minutes. In humans, the allergen and route of entry are variable, though bee stings and injections of antibiotics or serum are implicated most often. Honeybee and other hymenopteran stings are one of the most frequent causes of anaphylactic shock. Bee venom often creates a sensitivity that can last for decades after exposure.

The underlying physiological events in systemic anaphylaxis parallel those of atopy, but the concentration of chemical mediators and the strength of the response are greatly amplified. The immune system of a sensitized person exposed to a provocative dose of allergen responds with a sudden, massive release of chemicals into the tissues and blood, which act rapidly on the target organs. The throat swells, respiration is compromised, blood pressure falls, and the heart may stop. Anaphylactic persons have been known to die within 15 minutes from complete airway blockage. Peanut allergies, the leading cause of death related to food allergy, are notorious for their rapid onset and tiny allergen dose. Fatal cases have occurred from merely kissing a person who had eaten peanuts or sharing a drinking glass that had been in contact with peanuts.

Diagnosis of Allergy

Because allergy mimics infection and other conditions, it is important to determine if a person is actually allergic. If possible or necessary, it is also helpful to identify the specific allergen or allergens. Allergy diagnosis involves several levels of tests, including nonspecific, specific, in vitro, and in vivo methods.

A test that can distinguish whether a patient has experienced an allergic attack measures elevated blood levels of tryptase, an enzyme released by mast cells. The enzyme level increases during an allergic response. Several types of specific in vitro tests can determine significant signs of allergy from a patient's blood sample. A differential blood cell count can indicate the levels of basophils and eosinophils—a higher level of these indicates allergy. The leukocyte histamine-release test measures the amount of histamine released from the patient's basophils when exposed to a specific allergen. Serological tests that reveal the quantity and type of IgE are also clinically helpful (see chapter 17).

Skin Testing

Skin testing can precisely detect atopic or anaphylactic sensitivities. With this technique, a patient's skin is injected, scratched, or pricked with a small amount of a pure allergen extract. Drug companies can supply a large battery of standard allergen extracts containing common airborne allergens (plant and mold pollen) and more unusual allergens (mule dander, theater dust, bird feathers). Unfortunately, skin tests for food allergies using food extracts are unreliable in most cases.

In patients with numerous allergies, the allergist maps the skin on the inner aspect of the forearms or back and injects the allergens intradermally according to this predetermined pattern **(figure 16.6a).** Approximately 20 minutes after antigenic challenge, each site is appraised for a wheal response indicative of histamine release. The

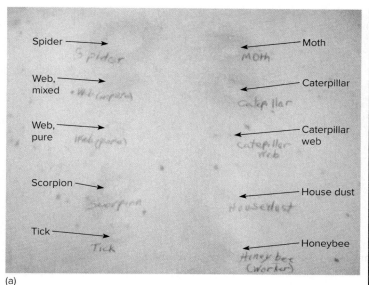

Figure 16.6 **A method for conducting a skin test for type I allergies.** The back (or forearm) is mapped and injected with a selection of allergen extracts. The allergist must be very aware of potential anaphylaxis attacks triggered by these injections. **(a)** View of skin prick test reactions for arthropod allergens, ranging from severe (spider) to 0 (caterpillar web). **(b)** A skin test record for some common environmental allergens in a patient with severe multiple allergies, some showing even more than 4+s. (a): *Source:* Dr. Frank Perlman, M.A. Parson/CDC

Environmental Allergens

No. 1 Standard Series

ID	
+++	1. Acacia gum
+++	2. Cat dander
++++	3. Chicken feathers
++++	4. Cotton lint
++	5. Dog dander
+	6. Duck feathers
+	7. Glue, animal
++	8. Horse dander
✕	9. Horse serum
+++	10. House dust #1
+	11. Kapok
+	12. Mohair (goat)
+	13. Paper
++++	14. Pyrethrum
+++	15. Rug pad, ozite
+	16. Silk dust
+	17. Tobacco dust
+	18. Tragacanth gum
+++++	19. Upholstery dust
+++	20. Wool

No. 2 Airborne Particles

ID	
+++	1. Ant
+++++	2. Aphid
++++	3. Bee
++++	4. Housefly
✕	5. House mite
+++	6. Mosquito
++++	7. Moth
+++	8. Roach
++	9. Wasp
0	10. Yellow jacket

Airborne mold spores

++	11. *Alternaria*
+++	12. *Aspergillus*
++	13. *Cladosporium*
+++	14. *Fonsecaea*
0	15. *Penicillium*
+	16. *Phoma*
+++	17. *Rhizopus*
	18.

✕ - not done ++ - mild reaction
0 - no reaction +++ - moderate reaction
+ - slight reaction ++++ - severe reaction
+++++ - extreme degree of this person's allergy

(b)

Treatment and Prevention of Allergy

diameter of the wheal is measured and rated on a scale of 0 (no reaction) to 4+ (greater than 15 mm). **Figure 16.6b** shows skin test results for a person with extreme inhalant allergies.

In general, the methods of treating and preventing allergy involve (1) avoiding the allergen, although this may be very difficult depending on the allergen, for example, it's easy to avoid limes and difficult to avoid dust; (2) taking drugs that block the action of lymphocytes, mast cells, or chemical mediators; and (3) undergoing allergen desensitization therapy.

For many years, common medical advice for avoiding the development of food allergies was to delay the introduction of solid food—especially allergenic foods like peanuts, eggs, soy, and fish—until a child was at least 1 year old. Recent studies have suggested that exactly the opposite is true. Introducing these foods at a young age is the best way to prevent allergies in the future.

Therapy to Counteract Allergies

The aim of antiallergy medication is to block the progress of the allergic response somewhere along the route between IgE production and the appearance of symptoms **(figure 16.7).** Oral anti-inflammatory

> **Quick Search**
> Find out more about this process by searching the Internet for videos, such as "Allergy Skin Tests—How They're Performed" on YouTube.

drugs such as corticosteroids inhibit the activity of lymphocytes and thereby reduce the production of IgE, but they also have dangerous side effects and should not be taken for prolonged periods. Some drugs block the degranulation of mast cells and reduce the levels of inflammatory cytokines. The most effective of these are diethylcarbamazine and cromolyn. Asthma and rhinitis sufferers can find relief with a drug that blocks synthesis of leukotriene (montelukast [Singulair]) and a monoclonal antibody that inactivates IgE (omalizumab [Xolair]).

Widely used medications for preventing symptoms of atopic allergy are **antihistamines,** the active ingredients in most over-the-counter allergy-control drugs. Antihistamines interfere with histamine activity by binding to histamine receptors on target organs. Although many of them have major side effects such as drowsiness, many of the newer antihistamines lack this side effect because they do not cross the blood-brain barrier. Other drugs that relieve inflammatory symptoms are aspirin and acetaminophen, which reduce pain by interfering with prostaglandin, and theophylline, a bronchodilator that reverses spasms in the respiratory smooth muscles. Persons who suffer from anaphylactic attacks are urged to carry at all times injectable epinephrine (adrenaline) and an identification tag indicating their sensitivity. An aerosol inhaler containing epinephrine can also provide rapid relief. Epinephrine reverses constriction of the airways and slows the release of allergic mediators.

Approximately 70% of allergic patients benefit from controlled injections of specific allergens as determined by skin tests. This

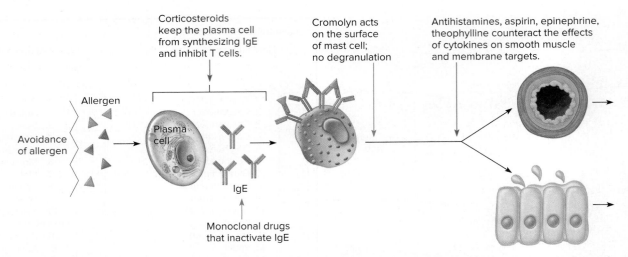

Figure 16.7 **Strategies for circumventing allergic attacks.** These range from avoidance of the allergen, inhibiting immune reactions, inhibiting IgE release, stopping degranulation, to preventing the effects of cytokines.

technique is a form of allergen immunotherapy called **desensitization**, or **hyposensitization**, that prevents reactions between allergen, IgE, and mast cells. The allergen preparations contain pure, preserved suspensions of plant antigens, venoms, dust mites, dander, and molds. A newer experimental method of hyposensitization involves **sublingual immunotherapy (SLIT)**, in which a tiny dose of premeasured allergen is placed under the tongue to be absorbed. The FDA has approved SLIT tablets for ragweed, certain grasses, and dust mites. Liquid allergen preparations (sublingual drops) are prescribed by some allergists, but this treatment has not been approved by the FDA.

A recent clinical study has shown success using peanut extracts to desensitize children with severe peanut allergies. Patients enrolled in the study consumed tiny but gradually increasing quantities of peanut protein over the course of 6 months, followed by a daily maintenance dose for an additional 6 months. By the end of the trial, most patients were able to safely tolerate 1,000 milligrams of peanut protein, the equivalent of three peanuts. The goal in this case is not to introduce a love of peanut butter sandwiches, but to protect the patients should they accidentally ingest food contaminated with small amounts of peanut protein.

The immunologic basis of desensitization treatment is open to differences in interpretation. One theory suggests that injected allergens stimulate the formation of high levels of allergen-specific IgG **(figure 16.8)** instead of IgE. It has been proposed that these IgG **blocking antibodies** remove allergen from the system before it can bind to IgE, thus preventing the degranulation of mast cells. It is also possible that allergen delivered in this fashion combines with the IgE itself and takes it from circulation before it can react with the mast cells.

Practice SECTION 16.2

5. Give some examples of allergens and explain their routes of access to the body.

6. Describe several factors that influence types and severity of allergic responses.

7. Describe the events in sensitization and provocation.

8. How are atopic allergies similar to anaphylaxis, and how are they different?

9. Trace the course of a pollen grain through sensitization and provocation in allergies. Include in the discussion the role of mast cells, basophils, IgE, and allergic mediators.

10. Relate the roles of major mediators to the signs and symptoms of allergy.

11. Outline the target organs and symptoms of the principal atopic diseases and their diagnosis and treatment.

12. Explain how hyposensitization is achieved, and suggest a credible mechanism by which it might work.

Figure 16.8 **The blocking antibody theory for allergic desensitization.** An injection of allergen causes IgG antibodies to be formed instead of IgE; these blocking antibodies cross-link and effectively remove the allergen before it can react with the IgE in the mast cell.

16.3 Type II Hypersensitivities: Reactions that Lyse Foreign Cells

Learn

10. Explain the requirements for developing a type II hypersensitivity.

11. Define what is meant by *blood groups*, explain how they are inherited and expressed, and relate the primary medical concerns of blood transfusions.

12. Discuss how blood is typed and notated.

13. Explain the special concerns about the Rh factor, the causes of hemolytic disease of the newborn, and how to prevent it.

The diseases termed type II hypersensitivities are a complex group of syndromes that involve complement-assisted destruction (lysis) of cells by antibodies (IgG and IgM) directed against those cells' surface antigens. This category includes transfusion reactions and some types of autoimmunities (discussed in section 16.6). The cells targeted for destruction are often red blood cells, but other cells can be involved.

Chapters 14 and 15 described the functions of unique surface markers on cell membranes. Ordinarily these molecules play essential roles in transport, recognition, and development, but they become medically important when the tissues of one person come in intimate contact with the body of another person. Blood transfusions and organ donations introduce **alloantigens** (molecules that differ in the same species) on donor cells that are recognized by lymphocytes of the recipient. These reactions are not really immune dysfunctions in the way that allergy and autoimmunity are. The immune system is in fact working normally, but it is not equipped to distinguish between the beneficial foreign cells of a transplanted tissue and the harmful cells of a microbe.

The Basis of Human ABO Antigens and Blood Types

The existence of human blood types was first demonstrated by an Austrian pathologist, Karl Landsteiner, in 1904. While studying incompatibilities in blood transfusions, he found that the serum of one person could clump the red blood cells of another. Landsteiner identified four distinct types, subsequently called the **ABO blood groups.**

Like the **MHC/HLA** antigens on white blood cells described in chapter 15, the ABO antigen markers on red blood cells are genetically determined and composed of glycoproteins. These ABO antigens are inherited as two (one from each parent) of three alternative **alleles***: A, B, or O. A and B alleles are dominant over O and codominant with one another. As **table 16.3** indicates, this mode of inheritance gives rise to four blood types (phenotypes), depending on the particular combination of genes (genotypes). Thus, a person with an *AA* or *AO* genotype has type A blood; genotype *BB* or *BO* gives type B; genotype *AB* produces type AB; and genotype *OO* produces type O. Some important points about the blood types are:

1. they are named for the dominant antigen(s);
2. the RBCs of type O persons lack the A and B antigens, but they do have other types of antigens; and
3. tissues other than RBCs carry A and B antigens, which can complicate organ transplantation.

A diagram of the AB antigens and blood types is shown in **figure 16.9.** The A and B genes each code for an enzyme that adds a terminal carbohydrate to RBC surface molecules during maturation. RBCs of type A contain an enzyme that adds *N*-acetylgalactosamine to the molecule; RBCs of type B have an enzyme that adds D-galactose; RBCs of type AB contain both enzymes that add both carbohydrates; and RBCs of type O lack the genes and enzymes to add a terminal molecule and are not antigenic.

Antibodies against A and B Antigens

Although an individual does not normally produce antibodies in response to his or her own RBC antigens, the serum can contain antibodies that react with blood of another antigenic type, even though contact with this other blood type has *never* occurred. These preformed antibodies account for the immediate and intense quality of transfusion reactions. As a rule, type A blood contains antibodies (anti-b) that react against the B antigens on type B and AB red blood cells. Type B blood contains antibodies (anti-a) that react with A antigen on type A and AB red blood cells. Type O blood contains antibodies against both A and B antigens. Type AB blood

* *allele* (ah-leel′) Gr. *allelon,* of one another. An alternate form of a gene for a given trait.

| TABLE 16.3 | Characteristics of ABO Blood Groups |

Genotype	Blood Type	Antigen Present on Erythrocyte Membranes	Antibody in Plasma	Incidence of Type in United States		
				Among Whites (%)	Among Asians (%)	Among Those of African and Caribbean Descent (%)
AA, AO	A	A	Anti-b	41	28	27
BB, BO	B	B	Anti-a	10	27	20
AB	AB	A and B	Neither anti-a nor anti-b	4	5	7
OO	O	Neither A nor B	Anti-a and anti-b	45	40	46

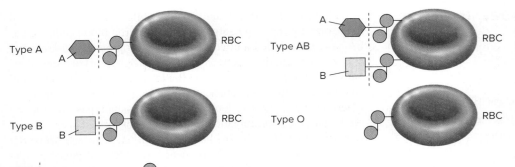

Figure 16.9 **The genetic/molecular basis for the A and B antigens (receptors) on red blood cells.** In general, persons with blood types A, B, and AB inherit a gene or genes for enzymes that add a terminal sugar to the basic RBC receptor. Type O persons do not have these enzymes and lack a terminal sugar.

does not contain antibodies against either A or B antigens (see table 16.3). Where do these anti-a and anti-b antibodies originate? Immunologists have evidence that they develop in early infancy through exposure to certain antigens that are widely distributed in nature. These antigens are surface molecules on bacteria and plant cells that mimic the structure of A and B antigens and stimulate the production of the antibodies that cause transfusion reactions. Once the immune system has been primed to form these antibodies, they will continue to circulate in the blood throughout life.

Clinical Concerns in Transfusions

Safe transfusions always begin by identifying the blood types of the recipient and potential donor. By use of a standard technique, drops of blood are mixed with **antisera** that contain antibodies against the A and B antigens and are then observed for the evidence of agglutination **(figure 16.10).**

Knowing the blood types involved makes it possible to determine which transfusions are safe to do. The general rule of compatibility is that the RBC antigens of the donor must not be agglutinated by antibodies in the recipient's blood **(figure 16.11).** The ideal practice is to transfuse blood that is a perfect match (A to A, B to B). But even in this event, blood samples must be cross-matched before the transfusion because other blood group incompatibilities can exist. This test involves mixing the blood of the donor with the serum of the recipient to check for agglutination.

Under certain circumstances (medical emergencies, the battlefield) the concept of universal transfusions can be used. To appreciate how this works, we must apply the rule stated in the previous paragraph. Type O blood lacks A and B antigens and will not be agglutinated by other blood types, so it could theoretically be used in any transfusion. We call a person with this blood type a **universal donor.** Because type AB blood lacks agglutinating antibodies, an individual with this blood could conceivably receive any type of blood. Type AB persons are consequently called **universal recipients.** Although both types of transfusions involve antibody incompatibilities, these are of less concern because of the dilution of the donor's blood in the circulatory system of the recipient. Additional RBC markers that can be significant in transfusions are the Rh, MN, and Kell antigens, but they do not create the same transfusion risks as ABO types.

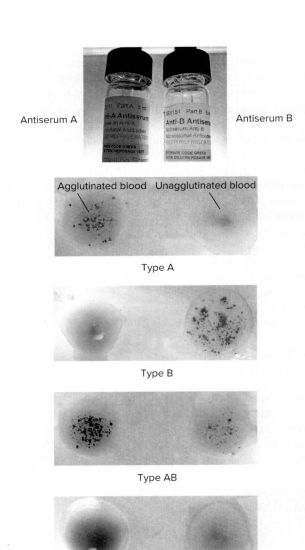

Figure 16.10 **Interpretation of blood typing.** In this test, a drop of blood is mixed with antiserum A, containing antibodies to type A antigen (blue), and antiserum B, containing antibodies to type B antigen (yellow). If that particular antigen is not present, the red blood cells in that droplet do not agglutinate, and form a uniform suspension. If that antigen is present, agglutination occurs and the RBCs form visible clumps (small red particles). The patterns and interpretations for the four blood types are shown.
Kathy Park Talaro

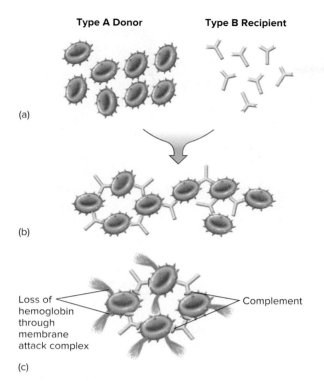

Type A Donor **Type B Recipient**

(a)

(b)

Loss of
hemoglobin
through
membrane
attack complex Complement

(c)

Figure 16.11 Microscopic view of a transfusion reaction.
(a) Incompatible blood types. The red blood cells of the type A donor contain antigen A, whereas the serum of the type B recipient contains anti-a antibodies that can agglutinate donor cells. (b) Agglutination complexes can block the circulation in vital organs. (c) Activation of the complement by antibody on the RBCs causes hemolysis and anemia. This sort of incorrect transfusion is very rare because of the great care taken by blood banks to ensure a correct match.

Transfusion of the wrong blood type causes differing degrees of adverse reactions. The severest reaction is massive hemolysis when the donated red blood cells react with recipient antibody and trigger the complement cascade (figure 16.11). The resultant destruction of red cells leads to systemic shock and kidney failure brought on by the blockage of glomeruli (blood-filtering apparatus) by cell debris. Death is a common outcome. Other reactions caused by RBC destruction are fever, anemia, and jaundice. A transfusion reaction is managed by immediately halting the transfusion, administering drugs to remove hemoglobin from the blood, and beginning another transfusion with red blood cells of the correct type.

The Rh Factor and Its Clinical Importance

Another RBC antigen of major clinical concern is the **Rh factor** (or D antigen). First discovered in rhesus monkeys, 85% of humans carry the Rh (for rhesus) factor on their red blood cells. The details of Rh inheritance are more complicated than those of ABO; but in simplest terms, a person's Rh type results from a combination of two possible alleles—a dominant one that codes for the factor and a recessive one that does not. A person inheriting at least one Rh

allele will be Rh⁺; only those persons inheriting no Rh allele are Rh⁻. The "+" or "−" appearing after a blood type refers to the Rh status of the person, as in O⁺ or AB⁻. However, unlike the ABO antigens, humans have no innate sensitivity to the Rh factor and only become sensitized after coming into contact with blood containing the factor.

Hemolytic Disease of the Newborn and Rh Incompatibility

The potential for placental sensitization occurs when a mother is Rh⁻ and her unborn child is Rh⁺. The obvious intimacy between mother and fetus makes it possible for fetal RBCs to leak into the mother's circulation during childbirth, especially when the detachment of the placenta creates avenues for fetal blood to enter the maternal circulation. The mother's immune system detects the foreign Rh factors on the fetal RBCs and is sensitized to them by producing antibodies and memory B cells. The first Rh⁺ child is usually not affected because the process begins so late in pregnancy that the child is born before maternal sensitization is completed. However, the mother's immune system has been strongly primed for a second contact with this factor in a subsequent pregnancy **(figure 16.12a).**

If a mother has been sensitized and becomes pregnant again with an Rh⁺ fetus, fetal blood cells escape into the maternal circulation late in pregnancy and elicit a memory response. The fetus is at risk when the maternal anti-Rh antibodies cross the placenta into the fetal circulation, where they affix to fetal RBCs and cause complement-mediated lysis. The outcome is a potentially fatal **hemolytic disease of the newborn (HDN)** called **erythroblastosis fetalis.*** This term is derived from the presence of immature nucleated RBCs called erythroblasts in the blood. They are released into the infant's circulation to compensate for the massive destruction of RBCs stimulated by maternal antibodies. Additional symptoms are severe anemia, jaundice, and enlarged spleen and liver.

Maternal-fetal incompatibilities are also possible in the ABO blood group, but adverse reactions occur less frequently than with Rh sensitization because the antibodies to these blood group antigens are IgM rather than IgG and are unable to cross the placenta in large numbers. The maternal-fetal relationship itself is a fascinating instance of foreign tissue not being rejected, despite the extensive potential for contact. It is thought that the placenta forms a barrier to keep the fetus isolated in its own antigen-free environment. The placenta is surrounded by a dense, many-layered envelope that prevents the passage of maternal cells; and it actively absorbs, removes, and inactivates circulating antigens.

Preventing Hemolytic Disease of the Newborn

Once sensitization of the mother to Rh factor has occurred, all other Rh⁺ fetuses will be at risk for hemolytic disease of the newborn. Prevention requires a careful family history of an Rh⁻

* *erythroblastosis fetalis* (eh-rith″-roh-blas-toh′-sis fee-tal′-is)

Figure 16.12 Rh factor incompatibility can result in RBC lysis and hemolytic disease of the newborn. (a) A naturally occurring blood cell incompatibility results when a Rh⁺ fetus develops within a Rh⁻ mother. Initial sensitization of the maternal immune system occurs when fetal blood crosses through the placenta near the time of birth. In most cases, the fetus develops normally and is born without illness. A subsequent pregnancy with an Rh⁺ fetus results in a severe hemolysis of fetal RBCs. **(b)** Control of incompatibility: Anti-Rh antibody (RhoGAM) can be administered to Rh⁻ mothers during pregnancy to help bind, inactivate, and remove any Rh factor that may be transferred from the fetus. In some cases, RhoGAM is administered before sensitization occurs.

pregnant woman. It can predict the likelihood that she is already sensitized or is carrying an Rh⁺ fetus. It must take into account other children she has had, their Rh types, and the Rh status of the father. If the father is also Rh⁻, the child will be Rh⁻ and free of risk, but if the father is Rh⁺, the probability that the child will be Rh⁺ is 50% or 100%, depending on the exact genetic makeup of the father. If there is any possibility that the fetus is Rh⁺, the mother must be passively immunized with antiserum containing antibodies against the Rh factor (Rh_0 [D] *immune globulin*, or RhoGAM[2]). This antiserum, injected at 28 to 32 weeks and again immediately after delivery, keeps the maternal immune system from recognizing fetal RBCs that have escaped into the mother's circulation. This prevents the sensitization of her immune system to Rh factor **(figure 16.12b).** Anti-Rh antibody must be given with each pregnancy that involves an Rh⁺ fetus. It is ineffective if the mother has already been sensitized by a prior Rh⁺ fetus or an incorrect blood transfusion, which can be determined by a serological test.

As in ABO blood types, the Rh factor should be matched for a transfusion, although it is acceptable to transfuse Rh⁻ blood if the recipient's Rh type is not known.

 Practice SECTION 16.3

13. What is the mechanism of type II hypersensitivity?

14. Explain why the tissues of some people are antigenic to others and why this would not be a problem except for transfusions and transplants.

15. What is the molecular basis of the ABO and Rh blood groups?

16. Where do we derive our natural hypersensitivities to the A or B antigens that we do not possess?

17. How does a person become sensitized to Rh factor?

18. Describe the sequence of events in an Rh incompatibility between mother and fetus.

19. Explain the rules of transfusion. Illustrate what will happen if type A blood is accidentally transfused into a type B person.

16.4 Type III Hypersensitivities: Immune Complex Reactions

 Learn

14. Describe the background features of immune complex reactions.

15. Differentiate between the major types of immune complex diseases, and discuss their physiological effects.

2. RhoGAM: Immunoglobulin fraction of human anti-Rh serum, prepared from pooled human sera.

Type III hypersensitivity involves the reaction of soluble antigen with antibody and the deposition of the resulting complexes in basement membranes of epithelial tissue. It is similar to type II because it involves the production of IgG and IgM antibodies after repeated exposure to antigens and the activation of complement. Type III differs from type II because its antigens are not attached to the surfaces of cells. The interaction of these antigens with antibodies produces free-floating complexes that can be deposited in the tissues, causing an **immune complex reaction** or disease. This category includes therapy-related disorders (serum sickness and the Arthus reaction) and a number of autoimmune diseases (such as glomerulonephritis and lupus erythematosus).

Mechanisms of Immune Complex Diseases

After initial exposure to a profuse amount of antigen, the immune system produces large quantities of antibodies that circulate in the fluid compartments. When this same antigen enters the system a second time, it reacts with the antibodies to form antigen-antibody complexes **(figure 16.13)**. These complexes summon the usual inflammatory components such as complement and neutrophils, which would ordinarily eliminate antibody-antigen (Ab-Ag) complexes as part of the normal immune response. In an immune complex disease, however, these complexes are so abundant that they deposit in the **basement membranes**[3] of epithelial tissues and become inaccessible. In response to these events, neutrophils release lysosomal granules that digest tissues and cause destructive inflammatory reactions at these sites. The symptoms of type III hypersensitivities are due in great measure to this pathology.

Types of Immune Complex Disease

During the early tests of immunotherapy using animals, hypersensitivity reactions to serum and vaccines were common. In addition to anaphylaxis, two syndromes, the **Arthus reaction**[4] and **serum sickness,** were identified. These syndromes are associated with certain types of passive immunization (especially with animal serum).

Serum sickness and the Arthus reaction are like anaphylaxis in requiring sensitization and preformed antibodies. Characteristics that set them apart from anaphylaxis are (1) they depend upon IgG, IgM, or IgA (precipitating antibodies) rather than IgE; (2) they require large doses of antigen (not the small dose required for anaphylaxis); and (3) their symptoms are delayed by a few hours to days. The Arthus reaction and serum sickness differ from each other in some important ways. The Arthus reaction is a *localized* dermal injury due to inflamed blood vessels in the vicinity of any injected antigen. Serum sickness is a *systemic* injury

initiated by antigen-antibody complexes that circulate in the blood and settle into membranes at various sites.

The Arthus Reaction

The Arthus reaction is usually an acute response to a second injection of vaccines (boosters) or drugs at the same site as the first injection. In a few hours, the area becomes red, hot to the touch, swollen, and very painful. These symptoms are mainly due to the destruction of tissues in and around the blood vessels and the release of histamine from mast cells and basophils. Although the reaction is usually self-limiting and rapidly cleared, intravascular blood clotting can occasionally cause necrosis and loss of tissue.

Serum Sickness

Serum sickness was named for a condition that appeared in soldiers after repeated injections of horse serum to treat tetanus. It can also be caused by injections of animal hormones and drugs. The immune complexes enter the circulation; are carried throughout the body; and are eventually deposited in blood vessels of the kidney, heart, skin, and joints (figure 16.13). The condition can become chronic, causing symptoms such as enlarged lymph nodes, rashes, painful joints, swelling, fever, and renal dysfunction.

Phases:

Antibody combines with excess soluble antigen, forming large quantities of Ab-Ag complexes.

Circulating immune complexes become lodged in the basement membranes of epithelia in blood vessels, kidney, skin, and other sites.

Complement factors trigger release of histamine and other inflammatory mediators.

Neutrophils migrate to sites of Ab-Ag complexes and release enzymes and chemokines that severely damage the target tissues and organs.

Immune complexes

Lodging of complexes in basement membrane

Neutrophils

Ab-Ag complexes

Basement membrane

Epithelial tissue

Blood vessels Heart/Lungs Joints Skin Kidney

Major organs where immune complexes are deposited

Figure 16.13 Pathology of immune complex disease. Deposition of circulating Ab-Ag complexes in tissues results in major organ damage.

3. **Basement membranes** are basal partitions of epithelia that normally filter out circulating antigen-antibody complexes.

4. Named after Maurice Arthus, the physiologist who first identified this localized inflammatory response.

Practice SECTION 16.4

20. Contrast type II and type III hypersensitivities with respect to type of antigen, antibody, and manifestations of disease.

21. Explain what occurs in immune complex diseases and give examples.

16.5 Immunopathologies Involving T Cells

Learn

16. Define what is meant by *type IV hypersensitivities.*

17. Describe the origins of allergies to infectious agents and contact dermatitis.

18. Outline the primary mechanisms in contact dermatitis.

19. Discuss the involvement of T cells in organ transplantation and the different ways that grafted tissues may be rejected.

20. Describe the categories of grafts and how rejection is prevented.

Type IV Delayed Hypersensitivity

The adverse immune responses we have covered so far are explained primarily by B-cell involvement and antibodies. A notable difference exists in type IV hypersensitivity, which involves primarily the T-cell branch of the immune system. Type IV immune dysfunction has traditionally been known as delayed hypersensitivity because the symptoms arise one to several days following the second contact with an antigen. In general, type IV diseases result when T cells respond to antigens displayed on self tissues or transplanted foreign cells. Examples of type IV hypersensitivity include delayed allergic reactions to infectious agents, contact dermatitis, and graft rejection.

Hypersensitivity Caused by Infections

A classic example of a delayed-type hypersensitivity occurs when a person sensitized by tuberculosis infection is injected with an extract (tuberculin) of the bacterium *Mycobacterium tuberculosis.* The so-called tuberculin reaction is an acute skin inflammation at the injection site appearing within 24 to 48 hours. So useful and diagnostic is this technique for detecting present or prior tuberculosis that it is the chosen screening device. Other infections that use similar skin testing are leprosy, syphilis, histoplasmosis, toxoplasmosis, and candidiasis. This form of hypersensitivity arises from a specific class of T cells (T_H1) that receive the processed allergens from dendritic cells. Activated T_H cells release cytokines that recruit inflammatory cells such as macrophages, neutrophils, and eosinophils. The buildup of fluid and cells at the site gives rise to a red papule characteristic of a positive tuberculin test. Other type IV reactions that occur in chronic infection

(tertiary syphilis, for example), cause granuloma formation that can lead to severe organ damage.

Contact Dermatitis

The most common delayed allergic reaction, **contact dermatitis,** is caused by exposure to resins in poison ivy or poison oak **(16.2 Making Connections),** to simple haptens in household and personal articles (jewelry, cosmetics, elasticized undergarments), and to certain drugs. Like immediate atopic dermatitis, the reaction to these allergens usually requires a sensitizing and a provocative dose. The allergen first penetrates the outer skin layers, is processed by Langerhans cells (skin dendritic cells), and is presented to T cells. When subsequent exposures attract CD8 lymphocytes and macrophages to this area, these cells give off enzymes and inflammatory cytokines that severely damage the epidermis in the immediate vicinity **(process figure 16.14a).** This response accounts for the intensely itchy papules and blisters that are the early symptoms **(process figure 16.14b).** As healing progresses, the epidermis is replaced by a thick layer. Depending upon the dose and the sensitivity of the individual, the time from initial contact to healing can take up to 2 weeks. Many allergists conduct a variation on skin testing called a patch test to detect delayed-type hypersensitivities to contact allergens **(figure 16.15).**

T Cells in Relation to Organ Transplantation

Transplantation or grafting of organs and tissues is a common medical procedure. Although it is life-giving, this technique is plagued by the natural tendency of lymphocytes to seek out foreign antigens and mount a campaign to destroy them through **graft rejection.** The bulk of the damage that occurs in graft rejections can be attributed to expression of cytotoxic T cells and other killer cells described in chapter 15. This section covers the mechanisms involved in graft rejection, tests for transplant compatibility, reactions against grafts, prevention of graft rejection, and types of grafts.

The Genetic and Biochemical Basis for Graft Rejection: T-Cell–Mediated Recognition of Foreign MHC Receptors

In chapter 15, we discussed the role of **major histocompatibility** (MHC or HLA) genes and surface markers in immune function. In general, the genes and markers in MHC classes I and II are extremely important in recognizing self and in regulating the immune response. These molecules also set the events of graft rejection in motion. The MHC genes of humans are inherited from among a large pool of genes, so the cells of each person can exhibit variability in the pattern of cell surface molecules. The pattern is identical in different cells of the same person and can be similar in related siblings and parents, but the more distant the relationship, the less likely that the MHC genes and markers will be similar. When donor tissue (a graft) displays surface molecules of a different MHC type than the recipient, the T cells of the recipient (also called the host) will recognize its foreignness and mount an immune attack against the donated tissue **(figure 16.16a).**

(a)

(b)

① Lipid-soluble catechols are absorbed by the skin.

② Dendritic cells close to the epithelium pick up the allergen, process it, and display it on MHC receptors.

③ Previously sensitized T_H1 (CD4$^+$) cells recognize the presented allergen.

④ Sensitized T_H1 cells are activated and secrete cytokines (IFN, TNF).

⑤ These cytokines attract macrophages and cytotoxic T cells to the site.

⑥ Macrophages release mediators that stimulate a strong, local inflammatory reaction. Cytotoxic T cells directly kill cells and damage the skin. Fluid-filled blisters result.

⚙ **Process Figure 16.14 Contact dermatitis. (a)** Stages in the development of of contact dermatitis. **(b)** Contact dermatitis caused by latex gloves.
(b): BW Folsom/Shutterstock

Figure 16.15 Patch testing for contact dermatitis. Most tests are done with household chemicals, cosmetics, plant materials, and metals. Small allergen-impregnated patches are applied to the skin and held in place for 48 hours.
SCIENCE PHOTO LIBRARY/age fotostock

Host Rejection of Graft When certain T cells of a host recognize foreign class I MHC markers on the surface of cells in grafted tissues or organs such as the heart, kidney, or liver, they release interleukin-2 as part of a general immune mobilization. The effect is to expand the helper and cytotoxic T cells specific to the antigens displayed by the donated cells. The cytotoxic cells bind to the grafted tissue and secrete lymphokines that begin the rejection process within 2 weeks of transplantation. Late in this process, antibodies formed against the graft contribute to immune damage. A final blow is the destruction of the vascular supply, promoting death of the grafted tissue or organ.

Graft Rejection of Host Some types of immunodeficiencies prevent the host from rejecting a graft. But this failure may not protect the host from serious damage, because graft incompatibility is a two-way phenomenon. Some grafted tissues (especially bone marrow) contain an indigenous population called passenger lymphocytes. This makes it quite possible for the graft to reject the host, causing **graft versus host disease (GVHD)** **(figure 16.16*b*).** Because any host tissue bearing MHC markers foreign to the graft can be attacked, the effects of GVHD are widely systemic and toxic. A papular, peeling skin rash is the most common symptom. Other organs affected are the liver, intestine, muscles, and mucous membranes. Previously, GVHD occurred in approximately 30% of bone marrow transplants within 100 to 300 days of the graft. This percentage is declining with the development of better screening and selection of tissues.

16.2 MAKING CONNECTIONS

Pretty, Pesky, Poisonous Plants

As a cause of allergic contact dermatitis (affecting about 10 million people a year), nothing can compare with a single family of plants belonging to the genus *Toxicodendron*. At least one of these plants—poison ivy, poison oak, or poison sumac—flourishes in the forests, woodlands, or along the trails of most regions of America. The allergen in these plants, an oil called urushiol, has such extreme potency that a pinhead-sized amount could spur symptoms in 500 people, and it is so long-lasting that botanists must be careful when handling 100-year-old plant specimens. Although degrees of sensitivity vary among individuals, it is estimated that 85% of all Americans are potentially hypersensitive to this compound. Some people are so acutely sensitive that even the most minuscule contact, such as handling pets or clothes that have touched the plant or breathing vaporized urushiol, can trigger an attack.

Humans first become sensitized by contact during childhood. Individuals at great risk (firefighters, hikers) are advised to determine their degree of sensitivity using a skin test, so that they can be adequately cautious and prepared. Some odd remedies include skin potions containing bleach, buttermilk, ammonia, hair spray, and meat tenderizer. Commercial products are available for blocking or washing away the urushiol. Allergy researchers have found that oral vaccines containing a form of urushiol could desensitize experimental animals. An effective method using poison ivy desensitization injection is currently available to people with extreme sensitivity.

Learning to identify these common plants can prevent exposure and sensitivity. One old saying that might help warns, "Leaves of three, let it be; berries white, run with fright." Search YouTube for videos that help you differentiate between these three poisonous plants.

Explain why a single, first-time exposure to poison oak can sometimes result in a dermatitis reaction.

Poison oak

Poison sumac

Poison ivy

(left, middle): *Source:* Robert H. Mohlenbrock @ USDA-NRCS PLANTS Database/USDA SCS. 1991. Southern wetland flora: Field office guide to plant species. South National Technical Center, Fort Worth; (right): *Source:* Jennifer Anderson. United States, IA, Scott Co., Davenport, Nahant Marsh. 2001

Classes of Grafts Grafts are generally classified according to the genetic relationship between the donor and the recipient. Tissue transplanted from one site to another on an individual's body is known as an **autograft.** Typical examples are skin replacement in burn repair and the use of a vein to fashion a coronary artery bypass. In an **isograft,** tissue from an identical twin is used. Because isografts do not contain foreign antigens, they are not rejected, but this type of grafting has obvious limitations. **Allografts** also called **allogeneic grafts,** the most common type of grafts, are exchanges between genetically different individuals belonging to the same species (two humans). A close genetic correlation is sought for most allograft transplants (see next section). A **xenograft** is a tissue exchange between individuals of different species. Until rejection can be better controlled, most xenografts are experimental or for temporary therapy only.

Avoiding and Controlling Graft Incompatibility

Graft rejection can be averted or lessened by directly comparing the tissue of the recipient with that of potential donors. Several tissue matching procedures are used. In the *mixed lymphocyte reaction (MLR),* lymphocytes of the two individuals are mixed and incubated. If an incompatibility exists, some of the cells will become activated and proliferate. *Tissue typing* is similar to blood typing, except that specific antisera are used to disclose the HLA antigens on the surface of lymphocytes. In most grafts (one exception is bone marrow transplants), the ABO blood type must also be matched. Although a small amount of incompatibility is tolerable in certain grafts (liver, heart, kidney), a closer match is more likely to be successful, so the closest match possible is sought.

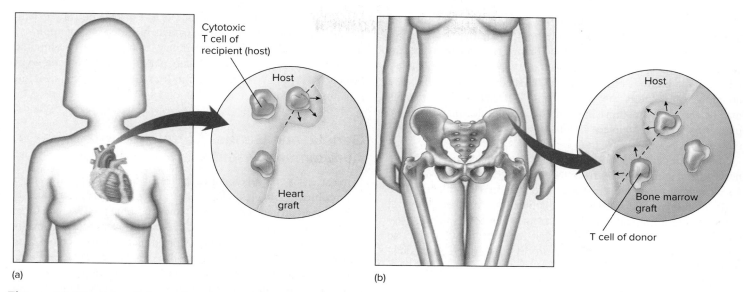

Figure 16.16 Potential reactions in transplantation. (a) In host rejection of graft, the host's immune system (primarily cytotoxic T cells) encounters the cells of the donated organ (heart in this case) and mediates the rejection of the organ. **(b)** Graft rejection of host occurs when transplanted tissue (bone marrow) contains endogenous T cells that recognize the host's tissues as foreign and mount an attack on many tissues and organs.

Practical Examples of Transplantation

Today, transplantation is a recognized medical procedure whose benefit is reflected in the fact that more than 200,000 transplants take place each year in the United States. It has been performed on every major organ, including parts of the brain. The most frequent transplant operations involve skin, liver, heart, kidney, coronary artery, cornea, and blood stem cells. The sources of organs and tissues are live donors (kidney, skin, bone marrow, liver), cadavers (heart, kidney, cornea), and fetal tissues. In the past decade, we have witnessed some unusual types of grafts. For instance, the fetal pancreas has been implanted as a potential treatment for diabetes and fetal brain tissues for Parkinson's disease.

Allogeneic hematopoietic stem cell transplantation is one of the most common medical procedures for patients suffering from immune deficiencies, aplastic anemia, leukemia and other cancers, and radiation damage. The three primary sources of stem cells used for this procedure are bone marrow, peripheral blood, and umbilical cord blood. These transplants are attempted in only the most severe cases because of a relatively high mortality rate associated with them. They are also costly, ranging from $100,000 to $250,000 for the entire process. For bone marrow transplants, a compatible donor with a closely matched MHC profile is sought. This person is sedated, and a bone marrow sample is aspirated by inserting a special needle into an accessible marrow cavity. The most favorable sites are the crest and spine of the ilium (major bone of the pelvis). During this procedure, between 500 and 800 ml of bone marrow are extracted with a special syringe. In a few weeks, the donor's marrow will naturally replace itself. Implanting the harvested bone marrow is rather convenient, because it is not necessary to place it directly into the marrow cavities of the recipient. Instead, it is dripped intravenously into the circulation, and the new marrow cells automatically settle in the appropriate bone marrow regions.

 CLINIC CASE

Transplanting More than Just an Organ Three weeks after receiving a new liver, a transplant recipient began to decompensate, exhibiting poor liver and kidney function, fever, rash, diarrhea, and clotting abnormalities. The patient died less than a week later. When three other organ recipients from the same donor began to show similar symptoms, and two of those three died, doctors suspected transplant-transmitted infection. Blood and tissue samples were sent to the Centers for Disease Control, where lymphocytic choriomenigitis virus (LCMV) was detected in all four patients. A rodent-borne virus, LCMV usually causes no more than mild symptoms in healthy people, but in immunosuppressed patients the disease can be severe.

To determine the source of the LCMV infection, epidemiologists investigated the hospitals involved in the procurement and transplant of the organs, the home and work sites of the donor, and the locations she frequented during the month preceding her death. They determined that exposure to wild rodents seemed unlikely but a family member of the donor had recently acquired a pet hamster that was kept in a shed on the donor's property. No illness consistent with LCMV was noted in any family members. Family members of the donor tested negative for antibodies to LCMV with the exception of the one person who cared for the hamster, who possessed both IgG and IgM antibodies against the virus. The hamster itself tested positive for LCMV virus by several methods.

While three of the four organ recipients died, the fourth, a kidney recipient, improved dramatically after being treated with intravenous ribavirin (an antiviral) and a reduction in his immunosuppressive drug regimen.

If reducing immunosuppressive drugs improved the condition of the living recipient, why not discontinue the drug completely?

To prepare recipients for the infusion procedure, they must be treated with chemotherapy and whole-body irradiation, a procedure designed to destroy their own blood stem cells and thus prevent rejection of the new stem cells. Within 2 weeks to a month after infusion, the grafted cells become established in the host. Because donor lymphoid cells can still cause GVHD, antirejection drugs may be necessary. A surprising consequence of bone marrow transplantation is that a recipient's blood type may change to the blood type of the donor.

Advances in stem cell technology have made it possible to harvest stem cells directly from the blood of donors by using *leukapheresis** to separate them and flow cytometry to identify and collect them (see discussion in chapter 7). Another potential source is the umbilical cord blood from a newborn infant. A decided advantage to cord blood is that its stem cells have yet to develop the donor's receptors and are less likely to cause transplant rejections.

* The process of selectively removing and collecting WBCs from the circulating blood, then returning the rest of the blood components back to the circulation.

 Practice SECTION 16.5

22. Explain the molecular/cellular basis for a host rejecting the graft and a graft rejecting the host.

23. Compare the four types of grafts.

24. What does it mean to say that tissues from two different individuals show a close match?

25. Describe the procedures involved in a bone marrow transplant and stem cell isolation.

16.6 Autoimmune Diseases: An Attack on Self

 Learn

21. Outline the pathology of autoimmune diseases.

22. Explain the origins of autoimmunity and describe which persons are most often targeted by it.

23. Review the major types of autoimmune diseases and the adverse medical effects they have.

The immune diseases we have covered so far are all caused by foreign antigens. In the case of autoimmunity, individuals actually develop hypersensitivity to their own cells. This pathologic process accounts for **autoimmune diseases,** in which **autoantibodies,** T cells, and in some cases both mount an abnormal attack against antigens that originate from one's own cells. The scope of autoimmune diseases is extremely varied. In general, they are either *systemic,* involving several major organs, or *organ-specific,* involving only one organ or tissue. They usually fall into categories II or III hypersensitivity, depending upon how the autoantibodies bring about injury. Some major autoimmune diseases, their targets, and basic pathology are presented in **table 16.4.** (For a reminder of the four Gell and Combs categories, refer to table 16.1.)

Genetic and Gender Correlation in Autoimmune Disease

In most cases the precipitating cause of autoimmune disease remains obscure, but we do know that susceptibility is determined by genetics and influenced by gender and environmental factors. Cases cluster in families, and even unaffected members tend to develop autoantibodies for that disease. More direct evidence comes from studies of the major histocompatibility gene complexes. Particular genes in the class I and class II major histocompatibility complexes coincide with certain autoimmune diseases. For example, autoimmune joint diseases such as rheumatoid arthritis and ankylosing spondylitis are more common in persons with the B-27 human leukocyte antigen (HLA) type; systemic lupus erythematosus, Graves' disease, and myasthenia gravis are associated with the B-8 HLA. Why autoimmune diseases (except ankylosing spondylitis) afflict more females than males also remains a mystery. Females are more susceptible during childbearing years than before puberty or after menopause, suggesting possible disruption of the immune system by hormones and pregnancy.

The Origins of Autoimmune Disease

Because otherwise healthy individuals show low levels of autoantibodies, it is suspected that there is a normal function for them. A moderate, regulated amount of autoimmunity is probably required to dispose of old cells and cellular debris. Disease apparently arises when this regulatory or recognition apparatus goes awry. Although there is not yet a complete explanation for autoimmune diseases, several theories have been proposed.

The **sequestered antigen theory** explains that during embryonic growth, some tissues are immunologically privileged; that is, they are sequestered behind anatomical barriers and cannot be surveyed by the immune system. Examples of these sites are regions of the central nervous system, which are shielded by the meninges and blood-brain barrier; the lens of the eye, which is enclosed by a thick sheath; and antigens in the thyroid and testes, which are sequestered behind an epithelial barrier. In time, the antigen becomes exposed by means of infection, trauma, or deterioration and is perceived by the immune system as a foreign substance.

According to the clonal selection theory, the immune system of a fetus develops tolerance to self by eradicating or silencing all self-reacting lymphocyte clones, called **forbidden clones,** while retaining only those clones that react to foreign antigens. Some of these forbidden clones may survive; and because they have not been subjected to this tolerance process, they can attack tissues carrying self molecules, which they mistake as antigens.

Disease	Target	Type of Hypersensitivity	Characteristics
Systemic lupus erythematosus (SLE)	Systemic	II and III	Inflammation of many organs; antibodies against red and white blood cells, platelets, clotting factors, nucleus DNA
Rheumatoid arthritis and ankylosing spondylitis	Systemic	III and IV	Vasculitis; frequent target is joint lining; antibodies against other antibodies (rheumatoid factor)
Scleroderma	Systemic	II	Excess collagen deposition in organs; antibodies formed against many intracellular organelles
Hashimoto's thyroiditis	Thyroid	II	Destruction of the thyroid follicles
Graves' disease	Thyroid	II	Antibodies against thyroid-stimulating hormone receptors
Pernicious anemia	Stomach lining	II	Antibodies against receptors prevent transport of vitamin B_{12}
Myasthenia gravis	Muscle	II	Antibodies against the acetylcholine receptors on the nerve-muscle junction alter function
Type I diabetes	Pancreas	II	Antibodies stimulate destruction of insulin-secreting cells
Multiple sclerosis	Myelin	II and IV	T cells and antibodies sensitized to myelin sheath destroy neurons
Goodpasture syndrome (glomerulonephritis)	Kidney	II	Antibodies to basement membrane of the glomerulus damage kidneys
Rheumatic fever	Heart	II	Antibodies to group A streptococci cross-react with heart valve tissue

TABLE 16.4 Selected Autoimmune Diseases

The **theory of immune deficiency** proposes (1) that mutations in the receptor genes of some lymphocytes render them reactive to self and (2) that T-cell regulatory cells that normally maintain tolerance to self have become dysfunctional. These would both set the scene for autoimmunity. Abnormal expression of MHC II markers on cells that don't normally express them has been found to cause other immune reactions against self. In a related phenomenon, T-cell activation has been known to mistakenly "turn on" B cells that can react with self antigens. This phenomenon is called the bystander effect.

Some autoimmune diseases appear to be caused by **molecular mimicry,** in which microbial antigens bear molecular determinants similar to normal human cells. An infection with this type of microbe could stimulate antibodies that can cross-react with tissues. This is one purported explanation for the pathology of rheumatic fever. Another probable example of mimicry leading to autoimmune disease is the skin condition psoriasis. Although the etiology of this condition is complex and involves the inheritance of certain types of MHC alleles, infection with group A streptococci also plays a role. Scientists report that T cells primed to react with streptococcal surface proteins also react with keratin cells in the skin, causing them to proliferate. For this reason, psoriasis patients often report flare-ups after a streptococcal throat infection.

Other autoimmune disorders such as type I diabetes and multiple sclerosis are likely triggered by *viral infection*. Viruses can noticeably alter cell receptors, thereby causing immune cells to attack the tissues bearing viral receptors.

Some researchers believe that many, if not most, autoimmune diseases will someday be found to have an underlying microbial cause or influence. The basis for this could be molecular mimicry, viral alteration of host antigens, or the presence of as yet undetectable microbes in the sites affected by the autoimmunity.

Examples of Autoimmune Disease

Systemic Autoimmunities

One of the most severe chronic autoimmune diseases is **systemic lupus erythematosus* (SLE),** or *lupus*. This name originated from the characteristic butterfly-shaped rash positioned across the nose and cheeks (**figure 16.17a**). Apparently ancient physicians thought

* *systemic lupus erythematosus* (sis-tem′-ik loo′-pis air″-uh-theem-uh-toh′-sis) L. *lupus,* wolf, and *erythema,* redness.

(a) (b)

Figure 16.17 Common autoimmune diseases. (a) Systemic lupus erythematosus. One symptom is a prominent rash extending across the nose, cheeks and forehead. Papules and blotches can also occur on the chest and limbs. **(b)** Rheumatoid arthritis commonly targets the synovial membranes of joints. Chronic inflammation thickens this membrane, erodes the articular cartilage, and fuses the joint. These effects severely limit motion and can swell and distort the joints. (a): ©DermNet New Zealand Trust; (b): ©Mediscan/Alamy Stock Photo

the rash resembled a wolf (*lupus* is Latin for "wolf"). Although the manifestations of the disease vary considerably, all patients produce autoantibodies against a great variety of organs and tissues. Antibodies to intracellular materials such as the nucleoprotein of the nucleus and mitochondria are an additional diagnostic feature. In addition to a facial rash, lesions occur on the skin of the limbs and body. Other affected organs are the kidneys, bone marrow, nervous system, joints, muscles, heart, and GI tract.

In SLE, autoantibody-autoantigen complexes appear to be deposited in the basement membranes of various organs. Kidney failure, blood abnormalities, lung inflammation, myocarditis, and skin lesions are the predominant symptoms. The disease often cycles between periods of flare-ups and remission. One form of chronic lupus (called discoid) is influenced by exposure to UV radiation and primarily afflicts the skin. The etiology of lupus is still not completely understood. It is not known how such a generalized loss of self-tolerance arises, though viral infection or loss of T-cell suppressor function is suspected. The fact that women of childbearing years account for 90% of cases indicates that immune suppression during pregnancy may be involved. The diagnosis of SLE can usually be made with a combination of symptoms and blood tests. Antibodies against nuclear DNA and RNA and various tissues (detected by indirect fluorescent antibody or radioimmune assay techniques) are common, and a positive test for the lupus factor (an antinuclear factor) is indicative of the disease. Treatment aims at controlling flare-ups with steroids, methotrexate, and the monoclonal antibody belimumab (Benlysta).

Rheumatoid arthritis (RA),* another systemic autoimmune disease, incurs progressive, debilitating damage to the joints. In some patients, the lung, eye, skin, and nervous systems are also involved. In the joint form of the disease, autoantibodies form immune complexes that bind to the synovial membrane of the joints and activate phagocytes and stimulate release of cytokines. Chronic inflammation leads to scar tissue and joint destruction. The joints in the hands and feet are affected first, followed by the knee and hip joints **(figure 16.17b)**. The precipitating cause in rheumatoid arthritis is not known, though infectious agents such as Epstein-Barr virus have been suspected. The most common feature of the disease is the presence of an IgM antibody, called rheumatoid factor (RF), directed against other antibodies. This does not cause the disease but is used mainly in diagnosis. More drugs have been developed to treat rheumatoid arthritis than other autoimmune diseases. They include methotrexate, TNF inhibitors (etanercept [Enbrel], adalimumab [Humira], infliximab [Remicade]), rituximab (Retuxan), abatacept (Orencia), and tocilizumab (Actrema). All of these inhibit some key immune cell or substance responsible for the pathology of RA.

Autoimmunities of the Endocrine Glands

On occasion, the thyroid gland is the target of autoimmunity. The underlying cause of **Graves' disease** is the attachment of autoantibodies to receptors on the follicle cells that secrete the hormone thyroxin. The abnormal stimulation of these cells causes the overproduction of this hormone and the symptoms of hyperthyroidism. In **Hashimoto's thyroiditis,** both autoantibodies and T cells are reactive to the thyroid gland, but in this instance, they reduce the levels of thyroxin by destroying follicle cells and by inactivating the hormone. As a result of these reactions, the patient suffers from hypothyroidism.

The pancreas and its hormone, insulin, are other autoimmune targets. Type I **diabetes mellitus** is caused by a dysfunction in insulin production by beta cells in the pancreas or its utilization by cells. This form is associated with autoantibodies and sensitized T cells that damage the beta cells. A complex inflammatory reaction leading to lysis of these cells greatly reduces the amount of insulin secreted. For several years it has been proposed that type I diabetes is linked to infection by the coxsackievirus, a common cause of colds and enteric infections, possibly due to molecular mimicry.

Neuromuscular Autoimmunities

Myasthenia gravis* is named for the pronounced muscle weakness that is its principal symptom. Although the disease afflicts all skeletal muscle, the first effects are usually felt in the muscles of the eyes and throat. In some cases, it can progress to complete loss of muscle function and death. Its cause is unknown, but it appears most often in females less than 40 years old and in males more than 60 years old, and it is often associated with having other autoimmune diseases. The classic syndrome is caused by autoantibodies binding to the receptors for acetylcholine, a chemical required to transmit a nerve impulse across the synaptic junction to a muscle. The immune attack so severely damages the muscle cell membrane that transmission is blocked and paralysis ensues. Treatment usually includes immunosuppressive drugs and therapy to remove the autoantibodies from the circulation. Experimental therapy using immunotoxins to destroy lymphocytes that produce autoantibodies shows some promise.

Multiple sclerosis (MS) is a paralyzing neuromuscular disease associated with lesions in the insulating myelin sheath that surrounds neurons in the white matter of the central nervous system. The underlying pathology involves damage to the sheath by both T cells and autoantibodies; this damage severely compromises the capacity of neurons to send impulses. The principal motor and sensory symptoms are muscular weakness and tremors, difficulties in speech and vision, and some degree of paralysis. Most MS patients first experience symptoms as young adults, and they tend to have remissions (periods of relief) alternating with recurrences of disease throughout their lives.

Despite years of research, no definitive cause for MS has been pinpointed. It appears to arise from a combination of genetics, environmental exposure, and possibly viral infections. It is immune-mediated, but the antigen that triggers the attack on the myelin sheath has not yet been identified. A number of studies have examined the involvement of viral infections of the brain such as measles, herpes, and rubella. The only one that has a verifiable connection to MS is Epstein-Barr virus, but isolating the virus alone is not enough to show causation.

The disease can be treated with oral medications that suppress immune functions of lymphocytes, including cortisone, beta interferon, and monoclonal antibody drugs (natalizumab or Tysabri). An unfortunate side effect of many of these therapies is that they compromise normal immune function and increase the risks for

* *rheumatoid arthritis* (roo′-muh-toyd ar-thry′-tis) Gr. *rheuma,* a moist discharge, and *arthron,* joint.

* *myasthenia gravis* (my-uss″-theen′-ee-uh grah′vis.) L. *myo,* muscle, and *aesthene,* weakness.

infections and cancer. There has been some interest in techniques to restore the normal immune system through autologous (self) stem cell transplants taken from the marrow of the MS patient, which would bypass some of these complications.

 Practice SECTION 16.6

26. Explain the pathologic process in autoimmunity.
27. Draw diagrams that explain five possible mechanisms for the development of autoimmunity.
28. Describe four major types of autoimmunity, comparing target organs and symptoms.

16.7 Immunodeficiency Diseases and Cancer: Compromised Immune Responses

 Learn

24. Outline the categories of immunodeficiency diseases.
25. Describe the origins and effects of primary immune diseases caused by B-cell, T-cell, or combined defects.
26. Relate examples of secondary immunodeficiencies.
27. Describe the characteristics of cancer, and explain the mechanism of oncogenesis.
28. Explain how immune function relates to the development of cancer.

It is a marvel that development and function of the immune system proceed as normally as they do. On occasion, however, an error occurs and a person is born with or develops weakened immune responses. In many cases, these "experiments of nature" have provided penetrating insights into the exact functions of certain cells, tissues, and organs because of the specific signs and symptoms shown by the immunodeficient individuals. The pronounced consequences of **immunodeficiencies** are recurrent, overwhelming infections, often with opportunistic microbes, and adverse effects on overall health. Dysfunctional immunities can be grouped into two general categories: **primary diseases,** present at birth (congenital) and usually stemming from genetic errors, and **secondary diseases,** acquired after birth and caused by natural or artificial agents **(table 16.5).**

Primary Immunodeficiency Diseases

Deficiencies affect both specific immunities such as antibody production and less-specific ones such as phagocytosis. Check out **figure 16.18** to survey the places in the normal sequential development of lymphocytes where defects can occur and the possible consequences. In many cases, the deficiency is due to an inherited abnormality, though the exact nature of the abnormality is not known for a number of diseases. Because the development of B cells and T cells departs at some point, an individual can lack one or both cell lines. It must be emphasized, however, that some deficiencies

TABLE 16.5	General Categories of Immunodeficiency Diseases with Selected Examples

Primary Immune Deficiencies (Genetic)

B-Cell Defects (Low Levels of B Cells and Antibodies)
Agammaglobulinemia (X-linked, non-sex-linked)
Hypogammaglobulinemia
Selective immunoglobulin deficiencies

T-Cell Defects (Lack of All Classes of T Cells)
Thymic aplasia (DiGeorge syndrome)
Chronic mucocutaneous candidiasis

Combined B-Cell and T-Cell Defects (Severe Combined Immunodeficiency Disease (SCID))
Adenosine deaminase (ADA) deficiency
X-SCID due to an interleukin defect
Wiskott-Aldrich syndrome
Ataxia-telangiectasia

Phagocyte Defects
Chédiak-Higashi syndrome
Chronic granulomatous disease of children
Lack of surface adhesion molecules

Complement Defects
Lacking one of C components
Hereditary angioedema
Associated with rheumatoid diseases

Secondary Immune Deficiencies (Acquired)

From Natural Causes
Infection: AIDS, leprosy, tuberculosis, measles
Other diseases: cancer, diabetes
Nutrition deficiencies
Stress
Pregnancy
Aging

From Immunosuppressive Agents
Irradiation
Severe burns
Steroids (cortisones)
Drugs to treat graft rejection and cancer
Removal of spleen

affect other cell functions. For example, a T-cell deficiency can affect B-cell function because of the role of CD4 T helper cells. In some deficiencies, the lymphocytes in question are completely absent or are present at very low levels, whereas in others, lymphocytes are present but do not function normally.

Clinical Deficiencies in B-Cell Development or Expression

Genetic deficiencies in B cells usually appear as an abnormality in immunoglobulin expression. In some instances, only certain

Figure 16.18 The stages of development and the functions of B cells and T cells, whose failure causes severe immunodeficiencies. Dotted lines represent the phases in development where breakdown can occur.

immunoglobulin classes are absent; in others, the levels of all types of immunoglobulins (Ig) are reduced. A significant number of B-cell deficiencies are X-linked (also called sex-linked) recessive traits, meaning that the gene occurs on the X chromosome and the disease appears primarily in male children.

The term **agammaglobulinemia** literally means the absence of gamma globulin, the fraction of serum that contains immunoglobulins (Ig). Because it is very rare for Ig to be completely absent, some physicians prefer the term **hypogammaglobulinemia.*** T-cell function in these patients is usually normal. The symptoms of recurrent, serious bacterial infections usually appear about 6 months after birth. The bacteria most often implicated are pyogenic cocci, *Pseudomonas,* and *Haemophilus influenzae;* and the most common infection sites are the lungs, sinuses, meninges, and blood. Many Ig-deficient patients can have recurrent infections with viruses and protozoa as well. Patients often manifest a wasting syndrome and may have a reduced life span, but modern therapy has improved their prognosis. About the only treatments available for this condition are passive immunotherapy with immune serum globulin and continuous antibiotic therapy.

The lack of a particular class of immunoglobulin is a relatively common condition. Although genetically controlled, its underlying mechanisms are not yet clear. IgA deficiency is the most prevalent, occurring in about 1 person in 600. Such persons have normal quantities of B cells and other immunoglobulins, but they are unable to produce IgA. Consequently, they lack protection against local microbial invasion of the mucous membranes and suffer recurrent respiratory and gastrointestinal infections. The usual treatment using Ig replacement does not work, because conventional preparations are high in IgG, not IgA.

Clinical Deficiencies in T-Cell Development or Expression

Due to T cells' critical role in immune defenses, a genetic defect in T cells results in a broad spectrum of disease, including severe opportunistic infections, wasting, and cancer. In fact, a dysfunctional T-cell line is usually more devastating than a defective B-cell line because T helper cells are required to assist in most specific immune reactions. The deficiency can occur anywhere along the developmental spectrum, from thymus to mature, circulating T cells.

Abnormal Development of the Thymus The most severe of the T-cell deficiencies involve a thymus gland that is underdeveloped (hypoplastic) or congenitally absent (aplastic). The disease associated with thymic dysfunction, **DiGeorge syndrome,** is

* *hypogammaglobulinemia* (hy′-poh-gem-ah-glob-yoo-lin-ee′-mee-ah) Gr. *hypo,* denoting a lowered level of Ig.

caused by failure in the embryonic development of the third and fourth pharyngeal pouches, and in most cases is associated with a deletion mutation in chromosome 22. The adverse effects on thymic function range from reduced immune activity to complete lack of cell-mediated immunity, especially of the CD4 or helper class of T cells. This makes makes children highly susceptible to persistent infections by fungi, protozoa, and viruses. Common, usually benign childhood infections such as chickenpox, measles, or mumps can be fatal if not diagnosed and treated right away. Even vaccinations using attenuated microbes pose a danger. Part of the severity of DiGeorge syndrome is the lack of antibodies resulting from deficiencies in helper T cells that are needed to activate B cells. Other symptoms of this syndrome are heart defects, reduced growth, wasting of the body, unusual facial characteristics, and an increased incidence of lymphatic cancer. The only therapy that could restore their immune system is a thymus transplant. Other conditions are alleviated by surgery and drugs to treat the recurrent infections.

Figure 16.19 An answer to the mystery of David. David Vetter, the best-known SCID child, lived all but the last 2 weeks of his life in a sterile environment to isolate him from the microorganisms that could have quickly ended his life. When David was 12, his doctors attempted a bone marrow transplant using his sister's bone marrow, but the marrow harbored Epstein-Barr virus. Because he lacked any form of protective immunities against this oncogenic virus, a cancer spread rapidly through his body.
©Baylor College of Medicine, Public Affairs

Severe Combined Immunodeficiencies: Dysfunction in B and T Cells

Severe combined immunodeficiencies (SCIDs) are the most dire and potentially lethal of the immunodeficiency diseases because they involve a loss of both T and B lymphocyte functions. Some SCIDs are due to the complete absence of the lymphocyte stem cell in the marrow; others are attributable to the dysfunction of B cells and T cells later in development. Infants with SCIDs usually manifest the T-cell deficiencies within days after birth by developing candidiasis, sepsis, pneumonia, or systemic viral infections. This debilitating condition appears to have several forms. In the two most common forms, Swiss-type agammaglobulinemia and thymic alymphoplasia, the numbers of all types of lymphocytes are extremely low, the blood antibody content is greatly diminished, and the thymus and cell-mediated immunity are poorly developed. Both diseases are due to a genetic defect in the development of the lymphoid cell line.

A rare form of SCID is **adenosine deaminase (ADA) deficiency,** which is caused by an autosomal recessive defect in the metabolism of adenosine. In this case, lymphocytes develop, but a metabolic product builds up to abnormal levels and selectively destroys the cells. Infants with ADA deficiency are subject to recurrent infections and severe wasting typical of severe deficiencies. Some SCID cases are due to a developmental defect in receptors for B and T cells. One of these, termed **X-SCID,** is a deficiency in interleukin receptors that occurs in about 1 in 50,000 to 100,000 births, Because it is X-linked, it occurs most often in male infants and was responsible for the disease of David, the child in the "plastic bubble" **(figure 16.19).** As heart-wrenching as David's life was, he also provided a means to study and understand the disease in a way that had never been possible. Later studies found that he had inherited a defective gene for essential molecules in several interleukin receptors. This prevented

> **Quick Search**
> See a slide show summarizing David's story at "Bubble Boy 40 Years Later" from *CBS News.*

both T and B cells from receiving signals that control growth, development, and responsiveness. Both cytotoxic and humoral immunities were shut down, leaving the body vulnerable to infections and cancers.

Because of their profound lack of specific adaptive immunities, children with SCID require the most rigorous kinds of aseptic techniques to protect them from opportunistic infections. Nowadays a better option for long-term survival is an immediate bone marrow or stem cell transplant right after the disease is diagnosed, rather than placing them into sterile bubbles. Because they lack functioning lymphocytes, the requirement for a bone marrow match is not as important with SCID children. Although transplanting bone marrow has been about 50% successful in curing the disease, it is complicated by graft versus host disease. This outcome can be corrected by selectively removing the reactive T cells from the donated marrow. Some infants have benefited from fetal liver or stem cell grafts, and some ADA-deficient patients can remain healthy through periodic transfusions of blood containing large amounts of the normal enzyme. A more lasting treatment for all types of SCID has emerged from gene therapy. So far, medical geneticists have cured two dozen children with SCID by inserting normal genes to replace the defective genes (see figure 10.16).

Secondary Immunodeficiency Diseases

Secondary acquired deficiencies in B cells and T cells are caused by one of four general agents: (1) infection, (2) organic disease, (3) chemotherapy, or (4) radiation.

The most recognized infection-induced immunodeficiency is **acquired immunodeficiency syndrome** or **AIDS.** This syndrome is caused when several types of immune cells, including T helper cells, monocytes, macrophages, and antigen-presenting cells, are infected by the human immunodeficiency virus (HIV). It is generally thought that the depletion of T helper cells and functional impairment of immune responses ultimately account for the cancers and opportunistic protozoan, fungal, and viral infections associated with this disease. (See chapter 25 for an extensive discussion of HIV and AIDS.) Other infections that can deplete immunities are tuberculosis, leprosy, and malaria.

Cancers that target the bone marrow or lymphoid organs can be responsible for extreme malfunction of both humoral and cellular immunity. In leukemia, the massive numbers of cancer cells compete for space and literally displace the normal cells of the bone marrow and blood. Plasma cell tumors produce large amounts of nonfunctional antibodies, and thymus gland tumors cause severe T-cell deficiencies.

The Role of the Immune System in Cancer

The term **cancer** comes from the Latin word for crab and presumably refers to the appendage-like projections that a spreading tumor develops. A cancer is defined as the new growth and spread of abnormal cells. The disease is also known by the synonym **neoplasm*** or by more specific terms that usually end in the suffix *-oma*. **Oncology*** is the field of medicine that specializes in cancer.

An abnormal growth or tumor is generally characterized as benign or malignant. A **benign tumor** is a self-contained mass within an organ that does not spread into adjacent tissues. The mass is usually slow-growing, rounded, and not greatly different from its tissue of origin. Benign tumors do not ordinarily cause death unless they grow into critical spaces such as the heart valves or brain ventricles. The feature that most distinguishes a **malignant tumor** (cancer) is uncontrolled growth of abnormal cells within normal tissue. As a general rule, cancer originates in cells such as skin and bone marrow cells that have retained the capacity to divide, whereas mature cells that have lost this power (some neurons, for instance) do not commonly become cancerous.

Research findings link cancers to genetic damage or inherited genetic predispositions that alter the function of certain genes called oncogenes found normally in all cells. These genetic alterations disrupt the normal cell division cycle and *transform* a normal cell into a cancer cell. Cancer development involves many complex interactions between genes, their products, and external signals received by the cell. There is no single mechanism. Consider the fact that at least eight different genetic defects lead to colon cancer and nearly that many are implicated in breast cancers.

It is increasingly evident that susceptibility to certain cancers is inherited. At least 30 neoplastic syndromes that run in families have been described. A particularly stunning discovery is that some cancers in animals are actually due to endogenous viral genomes

passed from parent to offspring in the gametes. Many cancers reflect an interplay of both hereditary and environmental factors. An example is lung cancer, which is associated mainly with tobacco smoking. But not all smokers develop lung cancer, and not all lung cancer victims smoke tobacco.

What is the role of the immune system in controlling cancer? To understand the connection, we need to review the actions of certain lymphocytes discussed in chapter 15. A concept that readily explains the detection and elimination of cancer cells is **immune surveillance.** Many experts postulate that cells with cancer-causing potential arise constantly in the body but that the immune system ordinarily discovers and destroys these cells, thus keeping cancer in check. Experiments with mammals have amply demonstrated that components of cell-mediated immunity interact with tumors and their antigens. The primary types of cells that operate in surveillance and destruction of tumor cells are cytotoxic T cells, natural killer (NK) cells, and macrophages. It appears that these cells recognize abnormal or foreign surface markers on the tumor cells and destroy them. Antibodies help destroy tumors by interacting with macrophages and natural killer cells. This involvement of the immune system in destroying cancerous cells has inspired a number of specific immunotherapies.

How do we account for the commonness of cancer in light of this powerful range of defenses against tumors? To an extent, the answer is simply that, as with infection, the immune system can and does fail. In some cases, the cancer may not be immunogenic enough; it may display self markers and not be targeted by the surveillance system. In other cases, the tumor antigens may have mutated to escape detection. As we saw earlier, patients with immunodeficiencies such as AIDS and SCID are more susceptible to various cancers because they lack essential T-cell or cytotoxic functions. It may turn out that most cancers are associated with some sort of immunodeficiency, even a slight or transient one. See the discussion of immune regulation by T cells in section 15.3.

An ironic outcome of lifesaving medical procedures is the possible suppression of a patient's immune system, which could leave them susceptible to cancer. Although radiation and anticancer drugs are the first line of therapy for many types of cancer, both agents are extremely damaging to the bone marrow and other body cells. Some immunosuppressive drugs that prevent graft rejection by T cells can likewise suppress responses against neoplastic cells.

Practice SECTION 16.7

29. In general, how do primary immunodeficiencies and acquired immunodeficiencies differ in their basic causes?
30. What kinds of symptoms accompany B-cell defects, T-cell defects, and combined defects, and why is this the case?
31. Give examples of specific diseases that involve each type of defect.
32. Define *cancer*, and differentiate between a benign tumor and a malignant tumor, using examples.
33. Describe the relationship between cancer and the immune system.

* *neoplasm* (nee´-oh-plazm) Gr. *neo.*, new, and *plasm*, formation.
* *oncology* (awn-kaw´-luh-gee″) Gr. *onkos*, cancer.

CASE STUDY Part 2

Dr. Josep Dalmau, a physician and researcher at the University of Pennsylvania's School of Medicine, detected a rare autoantibody in Susannah Cahalan's blood and spinal fluid. The antibody—anti-N-methyl-D-aspartic acid receptor, or anti-NMDAR—was first discovered by Dr. Dalmau in 2003. Instead of targeting foreign antigens, anti-NMDAR antibodies attack the brain, causing the "madness" Cahalan suffered. She was the first person in the history of NYU's Medical Center to be diagnosed with NMDAR encephalitis, but not the first to suffer from the disease. It is thought that 90% of those suffering from autoimmune encephalitis go undiagnosed, according to Dr. Souhel Najjar, the doctor at NYU who first thought to look for autoantibodies. "It's a death sentence while you're still alive," Najjar said. "Many are wasting away in a psych ward or nursing home."

Cahalan was treated with intravenous immune globulin and steroids to reduce inflammation, and plasmapheresis was used to selectively remove the autoantibodies from her bloodstream. When released from the hospital, she was

unable to read, write, or speak, but today Cahalan is back at work and her original article has been expanded to a book, entitled *Brain on Fire*. With sufficient prodding, Emily's doctors agreed to test her for autoimmune encephalitis, the results of which solved the mystery of her condition. Her treatment was similar to Cahalan's, and about a year after being released from the hospital, Emily returned to the ice rink for the first time.

Emily and Susannah appeared together on the *Today* show, along with Emily's father, Bill. He was quick to point out that without Susannah sharing her story, Emily would probably have never been diagnosed.

■ Autoantibodies are found in small amounts, even in healthy people. Why might they be necessary?

■ The median age of patients suffering autoantibody encephalitis is 20 years old, and three-quarters of those affected are female. What does this suggest might be a contributing factor of the disease?

Chapter Summary with Key Terms

16.1 The Immune Response: A Two-Sided Coin

The study of disease states involving malfunctions of the immune system is called immunopathology.

A. **Allergy** and hypersensitivity are terms for an exaggerated, misdirected expression of certain immune responses. "Allergy" is used mainly for immediate type reactions and "hypersensitivity" for other forms of overreactions to allergens.

B. Autoimmunity involves abnormal responses to self antigens. A deficiency or loss in immune function is called **immunodeficiency.**

C. Immediate-onset allergies involve contact with **allergens,** antigens that affect certain people; susceptibility is inherited.

D. Allergens enter through four portals: Inhalants are breathed in (pollen, dust); ingestants are swallowed (food, drugs); injectants are inoculated (drugs, bee stings); contactants react on skin surface (cosmetics, glue).

16.2 Allergic Reactions: Atopy and Anaphylaxis

A. On first contact with allergen, specific B cells react with allergen and form a special antibody class called IgE, which affixes by its Fc receptor to mast cells and basophils.

1. This **sensitizing dose** primes the allergic response system.

2. Upon subsequent exposure with a **provocative dose,** the same allergen binds to the IgE–mast cell complex.

3. This causes **degranulation,** release of intracellular granules containing mediators (**histamine, serotonin, leukotriene, prostaglandin),** with physiological effects such as vasodilation and bronchoconstriction.

4. Conditions that are common types of atopy are **eczema,** food allergies, and **asthma;** severe systemic reaction is **anaphylaxis.**

5. Other symptoms are rash, itching, redness, increased mucous discharge, pain, swelling, and difficulty in breathing.

B. Diagnosis of allergy can be made by a histamine release test on basophils; serological assays for IgE; and skin testing, which injects allergen into the skin and mirrors the degree of reaction.

C. Control of allergy involves drugs to interfere with the action of histamine, inflammation, and release of cytokines from mast cells. **Desensitization** or hyposensitzation therapy involves the administration of purified allergens.

16.3 Type II Hypersensitivities: Reactions That Lyse Foreign Cells

A. Type II reactions involve the interaction of antibodies, foreign cells, and complement, leading to lysis of the foreign cells. In transfusion reactions, humans may become sensitized to special antigens on the surface of the red blood cells of other humans.

B. The **ABO blood groups** are genetically controlled: Type A blood has A antigens on the RBCs; type B has B antigens; type AB has both A and B antigens; and type O has neither antigen. People produce antibodies against A or B antigens if they lack these antigens. Antibodies can react with antigens if the wrong blood type is transfused.

C. **Rh factor** is another RBC antigen that becomes a problem if an Rh^- mother is sensitized by an Rh^+ fetus. A second fetus can receive antibodies she has made against the factor and develop hemolytic disease of the newborn. Prevention involves therapy with Rh immune globulin.

16.4 Type III Hypersensitivities: Immune Complex Reactions
Exposure to a large quantity of soluble foreign antigens (serum, drugs) stimulates antibodies that produce small, soluble Ab-Ag complexes. These **immune complexes** are trapped in various organs and tissues, which incites a damaging inflammatory response.

16.5 Immunopathologies Involving T Cells
A. *Type IV Delayed Hypersensitivity*
 1. A delayed response to antigen involving the activation of and damage by T cells.
 2. Skin response to allergens, including infectious agents. Example is tuberculin reaction.
 3. Contact dermatitis is caused by exposure to plants (ivy, oak) and simple environmental molecules (metals, cosmetics).
 4. Cytotoxic T cells acting on allergen elicit a skin reaction.
B. **Graft Rejection:** Reaction of cytotoxic T cells directed against foreign cells of a grafted tissue; involves recognition of foreign human leukocyte antigens (HLA) by T cells and rejection of tissue.
 1. Host may reject graft; graft may reject host.
 2. Types of grafts include: **autograft,** from one part of body to another; **isograft,** between identical twins; **allograft,** between two members of same species; **xenograft,** between two different species.
 3. All major organs may be successfully transplanted.
 4. Allografts require tissue match (HLAs must correspond); rejection is controlled with drugs.

16.6 Autoimmune Diseases: An Attack on Self
A. In certain type II and type III hypersensitivities, the immune system has lost tolerance to self molecules (**autoantigens**) and forms **autoantibodies** and sensitized T cells against them. Disruption of function can be systemic or organ-specific.
B. **Autoimmune diseases** are genetically determined and more common in females.
C. Examples include **systemic lupus erythematosus, rheumatoid arthritis, diabetes mellitus,** and **multiple sclerosis.**

16.7 Immunodeficiency Diseases and Cancer: Compromised Immune Responses
I. Immunodeficiency Diseases
Components of the immune response system are absent. Deficiencies involve B and T cells, phagocytes, and complement.
A. Primary immunodeficiency is genetically based, congenital; defect in inheritance leads to lack of B-cell activity, T-cell activity, or both.
B. B-cell defect is called **agammaglobulinemia;** patient lacks antibodies; serious recurrent bacterial infections result. In Ig deficiency, one of the classes of antibodies is missing or deficient.
C. In T-cell defects, the thymus is missing or abnormal. In **DiGeorge syndrome,** the thymus fails to develop; afflicted children experience recurrent infections with eukaryotic pathogens and viruses; immune response is generally underdeveloped.
D. In **severe combined immunodeficiency (SCID),** both limbs of the lymphocyte system are missing or defective; no adaptive immune response exists; fatal without replacement of bone marrow or other therapies.
E. Secondary (acquired) immunodeficiency is due to damage after birth (infections, drugs, radiation). **HIV/AIDS** is the most common of these; T helper cells are main target; deficiency manifests in numerous opportunistic infections and cancers.
II. Cancer: The Role of the Immune System
A. **Cancer** is characterized by overgrowth of abnormal tissue, also known as a **neoplasm.** It can arise when normal **immune surveillance** by lymphocytes malfunctions and fails to detect and destroy tumors and cancers, allowing them to grow and spread.
 1. **Tumors** can be **benign** (a nonspreading local mass of tissue) or **malignant** (a cancer) that spreads (metastasizes) from the tissue of origin to other sites.
 2. Cancers occur in nearly every cell type (except mature, nondividing cells).
B. Cancer cells appear to share a common basic mechanism involving a genetic alteration that **transforms** a normally dividing cell into one that grows out of control.

Assess Your Knowledge

Level I. These questions require a working knowledge of the concepts in the chapter and the ability to recall and understand the information you have studied.

Developing a Concept Inventory

Select the correct answer from the answers provided. For questions with blanks, choose the combination of answers that most accurately completes the statement.

1. Pollen is which type of allergen?
 a. contactant c. injectant
 b. ingestant d. inhalant

2. B cells are responsible for which conditions?
 a. asthma c. tuberculin reactions
 b. anaphylaxis d. both a and b

3. Which hypersensitivities are T-cell mediated?
 a. type I c. type III
 b. type II d. type IV

4. The contact with allergen that results in symptoms is called the
 a. sensitizing dose c. provocative dose
 b. degranulation dose d. desensitizing dose

5. Production of IgE and degranulation of mast cells are involved in
 a. contact dermatitis
 b. anaphylaxis
 c. Arthus reaction
 d. both a and b

6. The direct, immediate cause of allergic symptoms is the action of
 a. the allergen directly on smooth muscle
 b. the allergen on B lymphocytes
 c. allergic mediators released from mast cells and basophils
 d. IgE on smooth muscle

7. Theoretically, type _____ blood can be donated to all persons because it lacks _____.
 a. AB, antibodies
 b. O, antigens
 c. AB, antigens
 d. O, antibodies

8. An example of a type III immune complex disease is
 a. serum sickness
 b. contact dermatitis
 c. graft rejection
 d. atopy

9. Type II hypersensitivities are due to
 a. IgE reacting with mast cells
 b. activation of cytotoxic T cells
 c. IgG-allergen complexes that clog epithelial tissues
 d. complement-induced lysis of cells in the presence of antibodies

10. Production of autoantibodies may be due to
 a. emergence of forbidden clones of B cells
 b. production of antibodies against sequestered tissues
 c. infection-induced change in receptors
 d. All of these are possible.

11. Rheumatoid arthritis is an _____ that affects the _____.
 a. immunodeficiency disease, muscles
 b. autoimmune disease, nerves
 c. allergy, cartilage
 d. autoimmune disease, joints

12. A positive tuberculin skin test is an example of
 a. a delayed-type allergy
 b. autoimmunity
 c. acute contact dermatitis
 d. eczema

13. Contact dermatitis can be caused by
 a. pollen grains
 b. chemicals absorbed by the skin
 c. microbes
 d. proteins found in foods

14. Which disease would be most similar to AIDS in its pathology?
 a. X-linked agammaglobulinemia
 b. SCID
 c. ADA deficiency
 d. DiGeorge syndrome

15. Which of these immunopathologies could be treated with a stem cell transplant?
 a. arthus reaction
 b. SCID
 c. anaphylaxis
 d. a and b only
 e. b and c only

16. How is the immune system involved in development of cancer?
 a. failure in immune surveillance
 b. mutation in cytotoxic T cells
 c. autoantibody formation
 d. overreaction to environmental chemicals

Case Study Analysis

1. The autoantibodies responsible for Emily and Susannah's condition were produced by
 a. plasma cells
 b. T cells
 c. macrophages
 d. bacteria that cross the blood-brain barrier

2. Which disease is caused in a manner most similar to anti-NMDAR encephalitis?
 a. cancer
 b. botulism
 c. adenosine deaminase deficiency
 d. myasthenia gravis

3. Women diagnosed with anti-NMDAR encephalitis are also commonly found to have an ovarian teratoma (an ovarian tumor). Postulate a connection between the tumor and the autoimmune disorder.

On the Test

These questions will help to prepare you to successfully answer similar questions you'll see on the TEAS (Test of Essential Academic Skills) and NCLEX (National Council Licensure Examination).

1. The nurse gives a primigravida (first pregnancy) client an injection of RhoGAM during the twenty-eighth week of her pregnancy. Why was the nurse required to take this action?
 a. The mother was Rh-negative while the father was Rh-positive.
 b. The mother was Rh-positive while the father was Rh-negative.
 c. The mother was O-negative while the father was Ab-positive.
 d. Both the mother and father were Rh-positive.

2. The nurse recognizes which of the following as a type III hypersensitivity?
 a. contact dermatitis after an encounter with poison sumac
 b. Arthus reaction
 c. an allergic reaction to shellfish
 d. hemolytic disease of the newborn

Writing Challenge

For each question, compose a one- or two-paragraph answer that includes the factual information needed to completely address the question. Practice questions can also be used for writing-challenge exercises.

1. Compare and contrast atopic allergy and type IV (delayed) hypersensitivity as to mechanism, symptoms, eliciting factors, and allergens.

2. Go through the sequence of events that gives rise to an anaphylactic response to peanuts.

3. How does a baby inherit Rh$^+$ blood from an Rh$^-$ mother?

4. Why is a hemolytic transfusion reaction considered a type of hypersensitivity?

5. Describe three circumstances that might cause antibodies to develop against self tissues.

6. Explain how people with autoimmunity could develop antibodies against intracellular components (nucleus, mitochondria, and DNA).

Concept Mapping

On Connect you can find an Introduction to Concept Mapping that provides guidance for working with concept maps, along with concept-mapping activities for this chapter.

 Application, Analysis, Evaluation, and Synthesis

Level II. These problems go beyond just restating facts and require higher levels of understanding and an ability to interpret, problem solve, transfer knowledge to new situations, create models, and predict outcomes.

Critical Thinking

Critical thinking is the ability to reason and solve problems using facts and concepts. These questions can be approached from a number of angles and, in most cases, they do not have a single correct answer.

1. Suggest some possible physiological benefits of allergy.

2. A 3-week-old neonate develops severe eczema after being given penicillin therapy for the first time. Explain what probably has happened.

3. Why would a person be allergic to strawberries when he eats them, but show a negative skin test to them?

4. a. Where in the course of type I allergies do antihistamine drugs, cortisone, and desensitization work? Exactly what do they do?

 b. Compare the sites of action of montelukast (Singulair) and omalizumab (Xolair).

5. Explain how cleaner living and medical advances could contribute to allergies.

6. Why would it be necessary for an Rh$^-$ woman who has had an abortion, miscarriage, or an ectopic pregnancy to be immunized against the Rh factor?

7. How can a person prevent becoming allergic to poison oak? What is the basis for infectious allergy?

8. Why are primary immunodeficiencies considered "experiments of nature"?

9. a. Explain why babies with agammaglobulinemia do not develop opportunistic infections until about 6 months after birth.

 b. Explain why people with B-cell deficiencies can benefit from artificial passive immunotherapy. Explain whether vaccination would work for them.

 c. Explain why T-cell deficiencies usually cause more severe effects than B-cell deficiencies.

10. In what ways can cancer be both a cause and a symptom of immunodeficiency?

Visual Assessment

1. Looking at figure 15.8, reproduced here, explain how this phenomenon pertains to allergies.

(a) Hapten X No antibody

(b) Hapten bound to carrier molecule Antibody formed in response to hapten

2. Observe the blood typing results shown here and label the blood types, including Rh. Which types are the most and least common?

Procedures for Identifying Pathogens and Diagnosing Infections

In This Chapter...

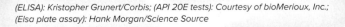
(ELISA): Kristopher Grunert/Corbis; (API 20E tests): Courtesy of bioMerioux, Inc.;
(Elsa plate assay): Hank Morgan/Science Source

Sometimes a Good Cat Is the Best Medicine

On April 20, 2015, after an illness lasting 5 days, a 15-year-old girl sought care from her pediatrician. She reported fever, myalgia, headache, and **photophobia.** Her erythrocyte sedimentation rate (which measures **inflammation**) and total white blood cell count (which can indicate **microbial infection**) were both normal. A test for influenza was negative. The three tests together pointed toward a noninfectious explanation for the girl's illness, and she was instructed to return home and treat her illness symptomatically.

Eight days after her initial visit to the pediatrician, the girl returned, reporting a recurrence of her headache and photophobia, and new onset of a stiff neck. She was admitted to the hospital with a fever of 39.4°C (102.9°F) and meningismus, an irritation of the meningeal membranes suggestive of **meningitis.** A computed tomography (CT) scan of the patient's head showed no abnormalities, while cerebrospinal fluid obtained via **lumbar puncture** revealed an elevated level of white blood cells, along with low levels of glucose, indicative of bacterial or fungal infection. The patient was treated simultaneously with antibacterial and antiviral drugs, a course of therapy not uncommon in cases of meningitis, where treatment is often begun before identification of an infectious agent is confirmed. Strictly speaking, meningitis is not a disease, but a condition—inflammation of the membranes surrounding the brain and spinal cord—that may be due to infection with any of four different agents: **bacteria, viruses, parasites,** or **fungi.**

A fifth variety, noninfectious meningitis, may be the result of **autoimmune disorders** like lupus, a head injury, cancer, or reaction to certain medications. Regardless of the cause, swelling of the meninges is uniformly bad, but to properly treat their young patient, doctors needed to know what was causing her meningitis.

Over the course of the next week, **CSF cultures** yielded no growth, and **polymerase chain reaction** (PCR) testing for the herpes simplex virus was negative. Testing for *Mycobacterium tuberculosis* using PCR, **acid-fast staining,** and culturing was negative, as was testing for human immunodeficiency virus; syphilis; Lyme disease; human herpesvirus 6 and 7; and species of *Babesia, Toxoplasma, Histoplasma, Cryptococcus, Blastomyces,* and *Brucella*. The patient recovered and was discharged on hospital day 11 with no apparent sequelae.

- *How would you classify each of the methods (phenotypic, genotypic, immunological) used in an attempt to identify the cause of the patient's meningitis.*

- *Why would an epidemiologist look at this case much differently than a doctor?*

To continue the Case Study, go to Case Study Part 2 at the end of the chapter.

(Black rat): Vitalii Hulai/Shutterstock

17.1 An Overview of Clinical Microbiology

 Learn

1. Describe what is involved in the main categories of laboratory identification of infectious agents.

2. Explain several techniques in specimen collection and the concerns in acquiring good cultures.

3. Summarize the main procedures in isolation, cultivation, and identification of pathogens.

In earlier chapters (3, 4, 5, 6, and 10) we introduced a variety of laboratory procedures used in cultivating and isolating microorganisms from samples. These techniques are an important part of studying and characterizing microbes, whether it be for research purposes or diagnosing infectious diseases. For many professionals and even beginning microbiology students, the most pressing concern is *how to identify unknown microbes* in specimens or **cultures.** The methods microbiologists use to identify bacteria to the level of genus and species fall into three main categories: **phenotypic,** which includes a consideration of morphology (microscopic and macroscopic) as well as physiology or biochemistry; **immunologic,** which entails analysis of the blood (serology) and other fluids; and **genotypic** (or genetic) techniques.

Data from a cross section of such tests can produce a unique profile of each isolate **(figure 17.1).** Increasingly, genetic means of identification are being used as a sole resource for identifying bacteria. As universally used databases of genetic profiles of microbes become more complete, these types of analyses provide a more accurate and speedy way of identifying microbes than was

possible even a decade ago. There are still many organisms, however, that must be identified through traditional means. Biochemical tests and rapid testing systems continue to be a mainstay of the clinical laboratory. Serology is a highly reliable procedure for some diseases, and is still favored as a way to screen large numbers of people rapidly and economically. In the next sections we emphasize cultural, serological, and genetic methods of analysis. Additional information on the methods for identifying bacteria can be found in appendix C. The specialized techniques required for identification and diagnosis of viruses and viral diseases are covered in section 17.6.

Phenotypic Methods

Microscopic Morphology

Traits that can factor in identification of bacteria are combinations of cell shape and size, Gram stain reaction, acid-fast reaction, and special structures, including endospores, granules, and capsules. Electron microscope studies can pinpoint additional structural features (such as the cell wall, flagella, pili, and fimbriae). Microscopic analysis is also used to evaluate specimen contents prior to culturing. This can often narrow the causative agent to bacterial, fungal, or protozoan.

Macroscopic Morphology

Cultural traits that can be assessed with the naked eye are also useful in diagnosis. These include the appearance of growth, including texture, size, shape, pigment of colonies, speed of growth, and reactions to special types of selective and differential media.

Physiological/Biochemical Characteristics

Physiological and biochemical characteristics have been the traditional mainstay of bacterial identification. Enzymes and other biochemical properties of bacteria are fairly reliable and stable expressions of the chemical identity of each species. Dozens of diagnostic tests exist for determining the presence of specific enzymes and for assessing nutritional and metabolic activities. Examples include tests for fermentation of sugars; capacity to digest or metabolize complex polymers such as proteins and polysaccharides; production of gas; presence of enzymes such as catalase, oxidase, and decarboxylases; and sensitivity to antimicrobic drugs. Special rapid identification test systems that record the major biochemical reactions of a culture have streamlined data collection and analysis.

Genotypic Methods

Examining the genetic material itself has revolutionized the identification and classification of bacteria. There are many advantages of genotypic methods over phenotypic methods, when they are available. The primary advantage is that actually culturing the microorganisms is not always necessary. In recent decades, scientists have come to realize that there are many more microorganisms that we can't grow in the lab compared with those that we can. Another advantage is that genotypic methods are increasingly automated, and results are obtained very quickly, often with more precision than with phenotypic methods.

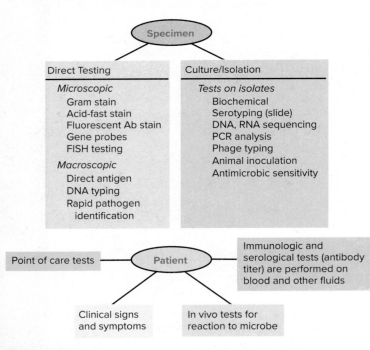

Figure 17.1 A scheme for specimen isolation and identification.

Immunologic Methods

Cells and viruses all have molecules that act as antigens and can be recognized by the immune system. One immune response to antigens is the production of antibodies that are designed to bind tightly to the antigens. The nature of the antibody response can be determined from a blood (or other tissue) sample. The presence of specific antibodies to a suspected pathogen usually indicates infection. This is often easier than testing for the microbe itself, especially in the case of viral infections. Most HIV testing entails examination of a person's blood for the presence of antibody to the virus. Laboratory kits based on this technique are available for immediate identification of a number of pathogens. These methods are covered in greater detail in section 17.4.

On the Track of the Infectious Agent: Specimen Collection

Regardless of the method of diagnosis, specimen collection is the common point that guides the health care decisions of every member of a clinical team. Indeed, the success of identification and treatment depends on how specimens are collected, handled, and stored. Specimens can be taken by a clinical laboratory scientist or medical technologist, nurse, physician, or even by the patient herself. However, it is imperative that general aseptic procedures be used, including sterile sample containers and other tools to prevent contamination from the environment or the patient. **Figure 17.2a** delineates the most common sampling sites and procedures.

In sites that normally contain resident microbiota, care should be taken to sample only the infected site and not surrounding areas. One common type of collection system is the sterile swab transport tube **(figure 17.2b)**. This allows for sampling, transporting, and maintaining the specimen in its original condition. When using a swab to take a sample from throat and nasopharyngeal regions, the swab should not touch the tongue, cheeks, or saliva. Saliva is an especially undesirable contaminant because it contains millions of bacteria per milliliter, most of which are normal microbiota. Sputum, the mucus secretion that coats the lower respiratory surfaces, especially the lungs, is discharged by coughing or taken by catheterization to avoid contamination with saliva. Depending on the nature of the lesion, skin can be swabbed or scraped with a scalpel to expose deeper layers. The mucous lining of the vagina, cervix, or urethra can be sampled with a swab or applicator stick.

If sterile urine is required, it is usually removed aseptically from the bladder with a thin tube called a catheter. Another method, called a "clean catch," is taken by washing the external urethra and collecting urine midstream during urination. The latter method inevitably incorporates a few normal microbiota into the sample, but these can usually be differentiated from pathogens in an actual infection. Sometimes diagnostic techniques require first-voided "dirty catch" urine.

Figure 17.2 **Specimen collection. (a)** Sampling sites and methods of collection for clinical laboratories. **(b)** Sterile transport swab with carrier—sometimes called a culturette. This example is a type of aerobic transport swab.

(b): Barry Chess

TABLE 17.1	General Guidelines for Specimen Collection*	
Type of Specimen	**Collection Method**	**Comments**
Abscess of skin or membrane or decubitus ulcer	Debride surface with sterile wipe; suction fluid with sterile needle and syringe.	Aspiration of tissue samples preferred to swab; transfer to anaerobic transport system.
Anaerobic cultures	Collect from deeper tissue below the surface, using sterile syringe.	Sample must not be exposed to air; transport immediately in anaerobic system to lab.
Blood	Prep area of skin with iodine; use Vacutainer or Bactec blood collection tubes.	Inoculate blood culture bottle immediately.
Bone marrow	Prepare site for surgical incision; extract sample with special needle.	Most samples taken from sternum or ilium; placed in blood bottle for culture.
Cerebrospinal fluid (CSF)	Remove CSF aseptically by lumbar puncture.	Place CSF into sterile tubes; do not refrigerate; transport immediately to lab for processing.
Feces	Take a small specimen into sterile container, cover and transport.	Refrigerate samples held over 1 hour; culture is mainly to rule out enteric pathogens; special kits available to detect cysts and trophozoites of protozoans and ova and larvae of intestinal worms.
Genital/urinary tract	Sterile swab of cervical mucus; swab urethral membrane or insert into lumen and twist.	Plate directly onto selective culture media with high CO_2 atmosphere or collect with anaerobic transport swab system; process immediately.
Respiratory tract, lower	Have patient cough to loosen phlegm and expectorate sputum into sterile cup for transport.	Patient should brush teeth and rinse mouth with water prior to any sampling. If coughing does not work, induce sputum by having patient inhale sterile saline from a nebulizer.
Respiratory tract, upper	Cleanse and debride oral cavity membranes; vigorously swab area of lesion; throat cultures are taken by swabbing the posterior pharynx, tonsils, and inflamed sites.	Tissue aspirates of infected tissue preferred; throat samples are processed for strep throat; culturing for other throat pathogens (except viruses) is done when specifically requested; care must be taken to avoid normal tissue and saliva.
Urine (two methods)	Sample by clean midstream catch into a sterile container.	Clean external genitalia, separate labia (female) or pull back foreskin (male) and urinate for a short time, followed by collection of 100- to 200-cc sample (midstream); samples not immediately processed must be refrigerated.
	Sample by sterile catheter inserted into bladder; urine is drained into sterile container.	Clean and rinse the urethral opening; only a specimen catheter should be used to sample for bladder infection; patients with indwelling catheters will always have microbes in their bladders.

*For a detailed account of collecting and managing specimens, log on to http://www.dshs.state.tx.us/LAB/bac_guidelines.shtm#guidelines.

Sterile materials such as blood, cerebrospinal fluid, and tissue fluids must be taken by sterile needle aspiration. Antisepsis of the puncture site is extremely important in these cases. Additional sources of specimens are the vagina, eye, ear canal, nasal cavity (all by swab), and diseased tissue that has been surgically removed (biopsied).

After proper collection, the specimen is promptly transported to a lab and stored appropriately (usually refrigerated) if it must be held for a time. Nonsterile samples in particular, such as urine, feces, and sputum, are especially prone to deterioration at room temperature. The overgrowth of normal microbiota in these samples could interfere with isolation of the pathogens. It could also alter the numbers and proportions of cells, making analysis more difficult. Many transport devices contain nonnutritive maintenance media (so the microbes do not grow), a buffering system, and

an aerobic or sometimes anaerobic environment as necessary for maintaining microbes that require oxygen or are damaged by it.

A summary of specimen collection guidelines can be found in **table 17.1.**

Quick Search

For a glimpse of the brave new world of the microbiology lab, search the Internet for "Work Cell Automation Concept."

↻ *Practice* SECTION 17.1

1. Summarize the major techniques in identifying and diagnosing pathogens and infections.
2. Describe the general principles in specimen collection.
3. Explain why it is important to prevent microbes from growing in specimens and why speed is so important in the clinical laboratory.
4. Summarize the kinds of tests that are used to identify microbes and detect signs of infection.

CLINICAL CONNECTIONS

The Changing Scene of Clinical Microbiology

Although it is true that most testing to identify pathogens must be carried out in a laboratory setting, medical researchers are continuing to look for ways to support the diagnosis of infections right at a patient's bedside or even at home. Such tests, called **point of care tests (POCTs),** have the benefits of speeding up treatment and giving patients greater charge of their own medical choices. These tests are usually performed in the presence of the patient and provide immediate feedback, similar to taking blood pressure or monitoring blood sugar, except that POC tests aim to detect infections or infectious agents.

POC tests range from nonspecific, over-the-counter kits that can help determine whether an infection is present (vaginal pH tests and ear checks that detect fluid in the middle ear, for example) to **rapid diagnostic tests (RDTs)** that identify specific microbes or diseases in a few minutes. Rapid *Staphylococcus* and *Streptococcus* kits used in clinics for several years to detect possible skin and throat infections were among the earliest examples. But these have been joined by dozens of other RDTs. There is now some type of RDT available for most major infectious agents, including Ebola virus and parasitic protozoa. Recent examples include an oral test for HIV; small inoculation modules for hepatitis C and B; and a panel for malaria **(figures *a, b, c*).** Depending on the particular microbe and site of infection, these tests can be performed directly from saliva, vaginal fluids, blood, urine, and food, and do not require isolation of the infectious agent or a great deal of technical skill to read. The accuracy of RDTs is not yet as high as that of

(a) An oral home test rapidly tests for HIV antibodies in saliva. *Kathy Park Talaro*

traditional cultural testing, but they are good early screening tools for possible infections.

An even more technologically advanced form of microbial identification (but not an RDT) is MALDI-TOF, an acronym for matrix associated laser desorption/ionization time-of-flight. MALDI-TOF uses a mass spectrometer to ionize the organic molecules in cells with a UV laser and analyze their content. In practice, a sample of microbe (like an isolated colony) is mixed on a small metal plate **(figure *d*)** with a matrix chemical and dried. The plate is placed in a spectrometer and bombarded by a UV laser until the sample has been completely ionized. Irradiation emits a specific spectrum of ions that is unique to each microbe, which can be graphically analyzed and displayed. When the pattern is compared with a computer data bank that compiles spectra of known microbes, an immediate identification is possible. It is limited only by the numbers of species that have been programmed into the data bank. This process can be completely automated and, except for the initial equipment costs, will greatly reduce the time and cost of testing. Although it has a relatively high level of accuracy, it is still not as accurate as traditional laboratory tests, but this is likely to change with increased usage.

Looking back at genome analysis in chapter 10, you will no doubt recall that the DNA or RNA profile of an organism is a powerful tool of identification and the most specific of all tests available. In this chapter, we cover the use of hybridization probes (FISH) and PCR. As more and more tests are developed, genome testing is gradually becoming the method of choice for many diseases. Companies are developing miniature "labs on a chip" or microarray biochips that can identify several pathogens at once. They consist of small platforms (like slides) that have been loaded with probes made to hybridize with specific genes of pathogens. When a sample of unknown nucleic acid is inserted onto the biochip and allowed to hybridize, any probes that have reacted with the nucleic acid will report by fluorescing. Fluorescence detectors create an image of the pattern that can identify the probable pathogen(s). So far, these have had the most extensive use in detecting some forms of enteric pathogens in food and water.

Do you expect that sometime in the future, the traditional microbiology labs, with media, Petri dishes, biochemical tests, microscopes, and the like, will no longer be needed? Base your answer on your own experiences and observations.

(b) Rapid diagnostic test uses a finger-prick blood drop to measure antibodies to hepatitis B and C viruses and HIV. *Courtesy of MedMira Inc.*

(c) A rapid diagnostic panel that identifies antigens from different species of *Plasmodium,* the agent of malaria, using a small drop of whole blood. *Courtesy of Alere, Inc.*

(d) A metal plate with tiny dots for placement of samples to be analyzed by MALDI-TOF technology. *MedSci/Alamy Stock Photo*

17.2 Phenotypic Methods

 Learn

4. Describe some direct methods of testing a specimen.

5. Summarize the aims in selection of culture techniques and media.

6. Explain the basis of biochemical and other methods of testing.

7. Describe how flowcharts and comparison tables are used in identification of bacterial pathogens.

Immediate Direct Examination of Specimen

Direct microscopic observation of a fresh or stained specimen is one of the most rapid methods of determining presumptive and sometimes confirmatory characteristics. Stains most often employed for bacteria are the Gram stain and the acid-fast stain. For many species, these ordinary stains can be useful, but they do not work with certain organisms. For these types of microbes, direct immunofluorescent antibody tests can highlight the presence of the microbe by means of antibodies labelled with fluorescent dyes **(figure 17.3)**. These tests are particularly useful for bacteria, such as the syphilis and Lyme disease spirochetes, that are not readily cultivated in the laboratory.

Another way that specimens can be analyzed is through *direct antigen testing*. This technique is similar to direct fluorescent antibody testing in that known antibodies are used to identify antigens on the surface of bacterial isolates. But in direct antigen testing, the reactions can be seen with the naked eye (see figure 17.9*b*). Quick test kits that greatly speed clinical diagnosis are available for *Staphylococcus aureus*, *Streptococcus* species, *Neisseria gonorrhoeae*, *Haemophilus influenzae*, *Neisseria meningitidis*, and *Salmonella*. However, when the microbe is very sparse in the specimen, direct testing is less effective, and identification will require more sensitive methods.

Cultivation of Specimen

Isolation Media

Such a wide variety of media exist for microbial isolation that a certain amount of preselection must occur, depending on the nature of the specimen. When the sample contains such small numbers of the pathogen that it could be easily lost or overgrown by competing microbes, the specimen is often cultured in enrichment media that can amplify the pathogen. In specimens such as feces, mucus, or urine that may have high bacterial counts and a diversity of species, selective media are chosen to make the target microbes more prominent by inhibiting microbes that are part of the normal microbiota. These media can be moderately inhibitory, such as those that grow only gram-positive or gram-negative bacteria, or highly inhibitory, being specific to a single group or species. One example is a medium used to screen clinical specimens that will grow only *Listeria monocytogenes*, a serious foodborne pathogen. This agar medium contains six selective agents, three of which are antibiotics. This type of media has the benefit of selecting the pathogen from the sample in a single step.

In most cases, specimens are also inoculated into differential media that define such characteristics as reactions in blood (blood

(a)

(b)

Figure 17.3 Direct immunofluorescent antibody testing.
(a) A setup that positively identifies the syphilis spirochete compared to a negative result. **(b)** Photomicrograph results for *Borrelia burgdorferi*, the spirochete of Lyme disease. Fluid from a lesion observed with a UV microscope reveals numerous fluorescing spirochetes. The two colors indicate different surface antigens reacting with antibodies specific to *B. burgdorferi*.
(b): *Source:* National Institute of Allergy and Infectious Diseases (NIAID)/CDC

agar) and fermentation patterns (mannitol salt and MacConkey agar). A patient's blood is usually cultured in a special bottle of broth that can be periodically sampled for growth. Numerous other examples of isolation, differential, and biochemical media were presented in chapter 3. So that subsequent steps in identification will be as accurate as possible, all work must be done from isolated colonies or pure cultures, because working with a mixed or contaminated culture gives misleading and inaccurate results. From such isolates, clinical microbiologists obtain information about a pathogen's microscopic morphology and staining reactions, cultural appearance, motility, oxygen requirements, and biochemical characteristics.

Biochemical Testing

The physiological reactions of bacteria to nutrients and other substrates provide useful indirect evidence of the types of enzyme

systems present in a particular species. Many of these tests are based on the following scheme:

The microbe is cultured in a medium with a special substrate and then tested for a particular end product. The presence of the end product indicates that the enzyme is expressed in that species; its absence means it lacks the enzyme.

Among the prominent biochemical tests are carbohydrate fermentation (acid and/or gas); hydrolysis of gelatin, starch, and other polymers; enzyme actions such as catalase, oxidase, and coagulase; and various by-products of metabolism. Many are presently performed with rapid, miniaturized systems that can simultaneously determine up to 23 characteristics in small individual cups or spaces

Figure 17.4 Rapid miniature tests for lab identification. The API 20E manual biochemical system for bacterial identification. Each cupule is inoculated with the same bacterial culture and the strip is incubated for a few hours. This cross section of biochemical tests can be sufficient to differentiate many common species of bacteria. Positive results are shown for a 20-test strip.
Courtesy of bioMerioux, Inc.

(figure 17.4). An important plus, given the complexity of biochemical profiles, is that such systems are readily adapted to computerized analysis.

Common schemes for identifying bacteria are somewhat artificial but convenient. They are based on easily recognizable characteristics such as motility, oxygen requirements, Gram stain reactions, shape, spore formation, and various biochemical reactions. Schemes can be set up as flowcharts **(figure 17.5)** or keys that trace a route of identification by offering pairs of opposing

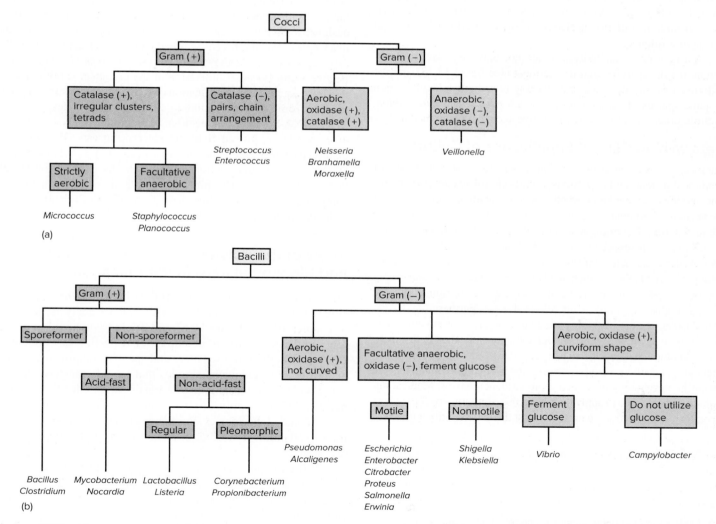

Figure 17.5 Flowchart key that separates genera of gram-positive and gram-negative bacteria often isolated from specimens. (a) Cocci and (b) bacilli of clinical interest.

characteristics (positive versus negative, for example) from which to select. Eventually, an endpoint is reached, and the name of a genus or species that fits that particular combination of characteristics appears. Diagnostic tables that provide more complete information are preferred by many laboratories because variations from the general characteristics used on the flowchart can be misleading. Both systems are used in this text.

Miscellaneous Tests

In many situations, morphological and biochemical tests are not definitive and need to be supplemented by other methods.

Bacteria host viruses called bacteriophages that are very species- and strain-specific. Such selection by a virus for its host is useful in typing some bacteria, primarily *Staphylococcus* and *Salmonella.* The technique of *phage typing* involves inoculating a lawn of cells onto a Petri dish, mapping it off into blocks, and applying a different phage to each block. Cleared areas corresponding to lysed cells indicate sensitivity to that phage. Phage typing is chiefly used for tracing strains of bacteria in epidemics.

Animals may be needed to cultivate bacteria such as *Mycobacterium leprae* and *Treponema pallidum,* whereas avian embryos and cell cultures are used to grow rickettsias, chlamydias, and viruses. Animal inoculation is also occasionally used to test bacterial or fungal virulence.

Antimicrobial sensitivity tests are not only important in determining the drugs to be used in treatment (see figure 12.18), but the patterns of sensitivity can also be used in presumptive identification of some species of *Streptococcus, Pseudomonas,* and *Clostridium.* Antimicrobials are also used as selective agents in many media.

Determining Clinical Significance of Cultures

Questions that can be difficult but necessary to answer in this era of debilitated patients and opportunists are: Is an isolate clinically important, and how can one know whether it is a contaminant or just part of the normal microbiota? The number of microbes in a sample is one useful criterion. For example, a few colonies of *Escherichia coli* in a urine sample can simply indicate normal microbiota, whereas several hundred can mean active infection. In contrast, the presence of a single colony of a true pathogen such as *Mycobacterium tuberculosis* in sputum or an opportunist in sterile sites such as cerebrospinal fluid or blood is highly suggestive of its role in disease. Furthermore, the repeated isolation of a relatively pure culture of any microorganism can mean it is an agent of disease, though care must be taken in this diagnosis. Another challenge facing the clinical laboratory is that of differentiating a pathogen from species in the normal microbiota that are similar in morphology from their more virulent relatives. Medical microbiologists are able to apply their expertise, supported by the tools of laboratory science, to solve even the most difficult identifications.

17.3 Genotypic Methods

 Learn

8. Explain the different variations on genetic testing and how they can be used in identification and diagnosis.

DNA Analysis Using Genetic Probes

The exact order of nucleotides in the DNA of an organism is unique. With a technique called *hybridization,* it is possible to identify a bacterial species by analyzing segments of its DNA. This requires small fragments of single-stranded DNA (or RNA) called **probes** that are known to be complementary to the specific sequences of DNA from a particular microbe. The test is conducted by extracting unknown test DNA from cells in specimens or cultures and binding it to special blotter paper. After several different probes have been added to the blotter, it is observed for visible signals that the probes have become fixed (hybridized) to the test DNA. The binding of probes onto several areas of the test DNA indicates close correspondence and makes positive identification possible. This forms the basis for certain DNA analysis techniques discussed in chapter 10.

A form of DNA hybridization with numerous applications for rapid identification of unknown bacteria is **fluorescent in situ hybridization,** or **FISH** (see figure 10.6). A sample from an uncultured specimen such as blood, a skin lesion, or a throat swab is applied to a slide and combined with a DNA probe chemically bound to a fluorescent dye (sometimes referred to as a peptide-nucleic acid probe, or PNA). The DNA sequence of the probe is designed to bind to a complementary sequence of nucleic acid found in a single organism. If cells within the unknown sample contain the target DNA or RNA, they will fluoresce under a UV microscope **(figure 17.6).** Because cultivation of the organism is not required, the time required for identification of septic blood cultures has been reduced from 24 hours or more to as little as 90 minutes.

A DNA-based technique often brought in to analyze outbreaks or epidemics is **pulsed-field gel electrophoresis (PFGE).** This method uses restriction endonucleases (see figure 10.1) to create a DNA profile of large sections of the bacterial genome, often millions of base pairs. The profiles of several isolates can then be compared to determine if they came from the same organism, especially useful in large outbreaks **(figure 17.7).**

Roles of the Polymerase Chain Reaction and Ribosomal RNA in Identification

The polymerase chain reaction (PCR) is one of the most valuable high technology tools for DNA and RNA analysis. A review of chapter 10 (see figure 10.8) will remind you how it can rapidly synthesize millions of copies of a particular segment of DNA. It is both highly sensitive and specific, amplifying minute quantities from unknown samples that would otherwise be lost. It is a widely used technique of forensics and molecular biology, but it can also be applied to the identification of microbes. With this method, laboratories can often completely dispense with traditional culturing techniques and go directly to diagnosis in a few hours.

PCR-based tests are used routinely for detecting a number of bacterial and viral infections. In many laboratories, the PCR or a similar rapid test is the method of choice for identifying gonorrhea and chlamydiosis. A version of this technique called real-time PCR can simultaneously pull DNA from a sample, register the amount that is amplified, and identify it.

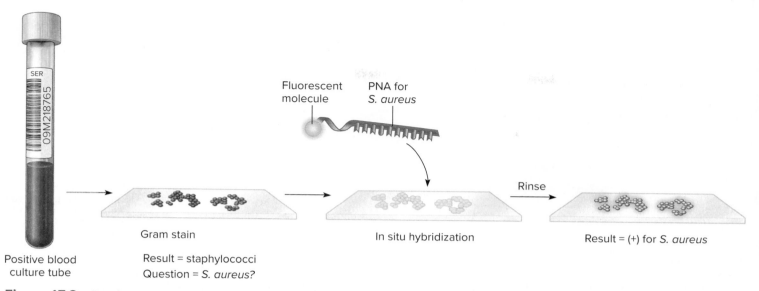

Figure 17.6 **Peptide-nucleic acid (PNA) FISH test for *Staphylococcus aureus* performed on a blood culture.** Once staphylococci are established by microscopic examination, a second slide is prepared and allowed to hybridize to a fluorescent peptide-nucleic acid combination probe. UV illumination reveals a positive reaction of fluorescing cocci in clusters.

One particularly versatile aspect to PCR is that it can be combined with other technologies for additional applications. For example, if the sample being analyzed contains mainly RNA (from an RNA virus or ribosome), the initial introduction of reverse transcriptase (RT) will convert the RNA in the sample to DNA, and this DNA can then be amplified by PCR. This technique—RT-PCR—is valuable for verifying RNA-based viruses

Figure 17.7 **Pulsed-field gel electrophoresis used to connect a strain of *E. coli* with food consumed by an ill child.** DNA from the sick child is seen in lanes 2 and 6 (the DNA in each lane was cut with a different restriction endonuclease), and DNA from the deer meat thought to be the source of the *E. coli* is seen in lanes 3 and 7. The fact that lanes 2 and 3 contain DNA bands of identical size, as do lanes 6 and 7, indicates that the two *E. coli* samples are identical. The other lanes are controls and molecular size standards. The size of each band, in kilobases, is indicated by the numbers on the right.
Source: Terry Rabatsky-Her, Comments to Author, Douglas Dingman, Ruthanne Marcus, Robert Howard, Aristea Kinney, and Patricia Mshar/CDC

⊕ CLINIC CASE

A Bad Day at Work . . . or Not The patient was a 75-year-old man who presented with chronic knee pain. To check for infection, fluid from the painful joint was withdrawn and cultured. A Gram stain revealed Gram-variable coccobacilli and an automated microbial identification system (AMIS) identified the isolate as *Francisella tularensis,* a bacterial species identified as a Tier 1 Select Agent. Microbes on this list are potential agents of bioterrorism, and their presence dictates the immediate implementation of specific protocols. Because the culture was handled in an open laboratory, as many as 24 people had been exposed to the pathogen (which is known to spread through the air). The Idaho Bureau of Laboratories and Eastern Idaho Public Health were called in to assist with the exposure and provide guidance. Among the 24 laboratory employees, 19 were determined to be at risk for exposure and immediately started on prophylactic antibiotics. The original culture was forwarded to the Idaho Bureau of Laboratories for confirmatory analysis, which was expected to take 48 hours.

Confirmatory testing at the Idaho State Reference Laboratory involved a number of non–culture-based techniques. Polymerase chain reaction was used to detect the DNA of *Francisella* or *Brucella,* a similar organism with bioterrorism potential, but no DNA from either species was identified. Sequencing of the 16S ribosomal RNA gene revealed the isolate to be *Veillonella parvula,* an organism with no bioterrorism potential. The laboratory workers were told to discontinue their antibiotic regimen, and the patient's antibiotics were switched to a combination specifically targeted to *Veillonella.*

If a rapid identification method like PCR or DNA sequencing was used prior to cultural testing, how might this scenario have been changed?

DNA reads

Reconstructed genome

1 Using chemicals to lyse cells of an unknown bacterial isolate, DNA is extracted and purified.

DNA extraction

Bacterial culture

2 DNA is cut into short fragments using restriction endonucleases or mechanical shearing.

DNA shearing

5 The millions of DNA reads are compared using a computer algorithm which, by looking for overlapping areas of sequence, assembles the genomic sequence of the unknown bacterial isolate.

DNA sequence analysis

DNA library preparation

3 PCR is used to amplify each DNA fragment (all within a single tube), creating a library of multiple overlapping DNA fragments, representing the entire genome.

DNA library sequencing

4 The sequence of each DNA fragment in the library (called a DNA read) is determined using an automatic DNA sequencer.

⚙ **Process Figure 17.8** **Whole genome sequencing.** Using this procedure, the genomic sequence of an unknown bacterial isolate can be quickly determined. Using different culturing methods, the sequence of any organism or virus can be determined.
Source: Centers for Disease Control and Prevention https://www.cdc.gov/pulsenet/pathogens/protocol-images.html#wgs; *(Isolation of bacteria):* Lisa Burgess/McGraw-Hill Education

such as rabies virus. DNA of PCR origin can be analyzed with the other tools of technology: it can be probed, hybridized, profiled, and sequenced.

One of the most powerful techniques for microbial identification is **whole-genome sequencing (WGS),** which uses the polymerase chain reaction along with automated DNA sequencing and analysis to determine the sequence of a bacterial genome in just a few hours, a feat that took years less than a decade ago. In this process, PCR, followed by DNA sequencing, produces many millions of DNA fragments, each of which is called a "read." The reads are analyzed using a computer algorithm that searches for two fragments with overlapping sequences, which are then joined together. Repeating this process millions of times allows the entire DNA sequence to be assembled (**process figure 17.8**).

The evolutionary relatedness of two organisms can be measured by comparing ribosomal RNA sequences (you should recall that rRNA makes up about half of each ribosome). Ribosomes have the same function (protein synthesis) in all cells, and their nucleic acid content tends to remain more or less stable over long periods. Thus, any major differences in the sequence of the rRNA is likely to indicate some distance in ancestry. This technique is powerful at two levels: It is effective for differentiating general group differences (it was used to separate the three superkingdoms of life discussed in chapter 1), and it can be fine-tuned to identify species.

 Practice SECTIONS 17.2–17.3

5. Describe what is involved in direct specimen testing, presumptive and confirmatory tests, cultivating and isolating the pathogen, biochemical testing, and gene probes.

6. Summarize the important aspects for determining if a clinical isolate is involved in infection.

7. Describe the applications of PCR in identification techniques.

17.4 Immunologic Methods

 Learn

9. Describe the background aims of immunologic testing.

10. Identify how antigen-antibody reactions are detected and quantified.

11. Differentiate between agglutination and precipitation, and describe how they are used in diagnosis.

12. Explain the basic methods behind the Western blot and complement fixation tests.

13. Interpret the outcome of direct and indirect immunofluorescent antibody testing.

14. Explain how in vivo testing differs from in vitro testing.

Patient's serum, antibody content *unknown*

Prepared *known* antigen

Macroscopic reaction

Molecular reaction

(a1) In serological diagnosis of disease, a blood sample is tested for the presence of antibody using an antigen of known specificity. A positive reaction is usually evident as some visible sign, such as color change or clumping, that indicates a specific interaction between antibody and antigen. (The reaction at the molecular level is rarely observed.)

Isolated colony, identity *unknown*

Antibodies of *known* identity

Macroscopic reaction

Molecular reaction

Ab Ag on microbe

(b1) An unknown microbe is mixed with serum containing antibodies of known specificity, a procedure known as serotyping. Macroscopic or microscopic clumping indicates a correct match between antibody and antigen and permits identification of the microbe.

(a2) Test of unknown serum on card with five different known antigens and a positive control. Clumps indicate precipitated antigens and a possible infection in the patient.

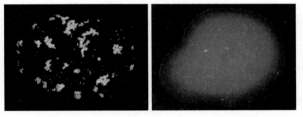

(b2) Unknown test colonies from streak plate mixed with antiserum against *Neisseria meningitidis;* agglutination on left is positive for that pathogen.

Figure 17.9 Basic principles of serological testing using antibodies and antigens. **(a)** Serological diagnosis. **(b)** Direct antigen testing.
(a2): Reproduced by kind permission of Thermo Fisher Scientific Inc.;
(b2): *Source:* Ortika BD, Habib H, Dunne EM, Porter BD, Satzke C: Production of latex agglutination reagents for pneumococcal serotyping. BMC Res Notes 2013, 6:49.

The antibodies formed during an immune reaction are important in combating infection, but they hold additional practical value. Characteristics of antibodies such as their quantity or specificity can reveal the history of a patient's contact with microorganisms or other antigens. This is the underlying basis of serological testing. **Serology** is the branch of immunology that traditionally deals with in vitro diagnostic testing of serum. Serological testing is based on the familiar concept that antibodies have extreme specificity for antigens, so when a particular **antigen** is exposed to its specific **antibody,** it will bind tightly to it. Being able to visualize this interaction provides a powerful tool for detecting, identifying, and quantifying antibodies—or, for that matter, antigens. The scheme works both ways, depending on the situation. One can detect or identify an unknown antibody using a known antigen, or one can use an antibody of known specific-

ity to help detect or identify an unknown antigen **(figure 17.9).** Modern serological testing has grown into a field that tests more than just serum. Urine, cerebrospinal fluid, whole tissues, and saliva can also be used to determine the immunologic status of patients. These and other immune tests are helpful in confirming a suspected diagnosis or in screening a certain population for disease.

General Features of Immune Testing

The strategies of immunologic tests are diverse, and they underline some of the brilliant and imaginative ways that antibodies and antigens can be used as tools. We summarize them under the headings of agglutination, precipitation, complement fixation, fluorescent antibody

Figure 17.10 Specificity and sensitivity in immune testing. (a) This test shows specificity in which an antibody (Ab) attaches to one type of antigen, while ignoring all others. **(b)** Sensitivity is demonstrated by the fact that Ab can detect antigens even when the antigen is present in very low numbers.

tests, and immunoassay tests. First, we overview the general characteristics of immune testing and then look at each type specifically.

The most effective serological tests are both highly specific and highly sensitive **(figure 17.10)**. **Specificity** is the property of a test to focus upon only a certain antibody or antigen and not to react with unrelated or distantly related ones. **Sensitivity** means that the test can detect even very small amounts of antibodies or antigens that are the targets of the test. A test with high sensitivity will diagnose even patients who are weakly positive. Modern systems using monoclonal antibodies have greatly improved specificity, and those using radioactivity, enzymes, and electronics have improved sensitivity.

Visualizing Antigen-Antibody Interactions

The primary basis of most tests is the binding of an antibody (Ab) to a specific molecular site on an antigen (Ag). Because this reaction cannot be readily seen without an electron microscope, tests involve some type of endpoint reaction visible to the naked eye or with regular magnification that tells whether the result is positive or negative. In the case of large antigens such as cells, Ab binds to Ag and creates large clumps or aggregates that are visible macroscopically or microscopically **(figure 17.11a)**. Smaller Ab-Ag complexes that do not result in readily observable changes will require special indicators in order to be visualized. Endpoints are often revealed by dyes or fluorescent reagents that can tag molecules of interest. Similarly, radioactive isotopes incorporated into antigens or antibodies constitute sensitive tracers that are detectable with photographic film.

An antigen-antibody reaction can be used to read a **titer,** or the concentration of antibodies in serum. Titer is determined by serially diluting a sample in tubes or in a multiple-welled microtiter plate and mixing it with antigen **(figure 17.11b).** It is determined by observing the highest dilution of serum that produces a visible reaction with an antigen. The titer is the denominator of this dilution. The more a sample can be diluted and yet still react with antigen, the greater the concentration of antibodies in that sample and the higher its titer. Possible interpretations of test results are discussed in **Clinical Connections, "When Positive Is Negative."**

Agglutination and Precipitation Reactions

The essential differences between agglutination and precipitation are in size, solubility, and location of the antigen. In agglutination, the antigens are whole cells such as red blood cells or bacteria with determinant groups on the surface. In precipitation, the antigen is a soluble molecule, such as a protein. In both instances, when Ag and Ab are optimally combined so that neither is in excess, one antigen is interlinked by several antibodies to form an insoluble, three-dimensional aggregate so large that it cannot remain suspended and it settles out.

Agglutination Tests

Agglutination refers to the cross-linking of antigens (by antibodies) into large clumps, which are visible to the naked eye. **Agglutination** tests are performed routinely by blood banks to determine ABO and Rh (Rhesus) blood types in preparation for transfusions. In this type of test, antisera containing antibodies against the blood group antigens on red blood cells are mixed with a small sample of blood and read for the presence or absence of clumping (see figure 16.10). The **Widal test** is an example of a tube agglutination test for diagnosing salmonelloses and undulant fever. In addition to detecting specific antibody, it gives the serum titer.

Numerous variations of agglutination testing exist. The rapid plasma reagin (RPR) test is one of several tests commonly used to test for antibodies to syphilis. The cold agglutinin test, named for antibodies that react only at lower temperatures (4°C to 20°C), was developed to diagnose *Mycoplasma* pneumonia. The *Weil-Felix reaction* is an agglutination test sometimes used in diagnosing rickettsial infections.

In some tests, agglutinating antigens are affixed to the surface of an inert particle. In **latex agglutination** tests, the inert particles are tiny latex beads. Kits based on agglutination are available for assaying pregnancy hormone in the urine; for identifying *Candida* yeasts, staphylococci, streptococci, and meningococci (see figure 17.9b2); and for diagnosing rheumatoid arthritis.

(a) Agglutination involves clumping of whole cells; precipitation is the formation of antigen-antibody complexes in cell-free solution. Both reactions can be observed by noticeable clumps or precipitates in test tubes (see (b) and figure 17.12).

(b) The tube agglutination test. A sample of patient's serum is serially diluted with saline. The dilution is made in a way that halves the number of antibodies in each subsequent tube. An equal amount of the antigen (here, blue bacterial cells) is added to each tube. The control tube has antigen, but no serum. After incubation and centrifugation, each tube is examined for agglutination clumps as compared with the control, which will contain unagglutinated cells and no clumps. The titer is equivalent to the denominator of the dilution of the last tube in the series that shows agglutination.

*Although IgG is shown as the Ab, IgM is also involved in these reactions.

Figure 17.11 **Antigen-antibody testing. (a)** Cellular/molecular view of agglutination and precipitation reactions that produce visible antigen-antibody complexes. **(b)** An agglutination test for determining the antibody titer of serum.

Precipitation Tests

In **precipitation** reactions, the soluble antigen is precipitated (made insoluble) by an antibody. This reaction is observable in a test tube in which an antigen sample has been carefully laid over an antiserum solution. At the point of contact, a cloudy or opaque zone forms. One example of this technique is the **VDRL** (Venereal Disease Research Laboratory) test that also detects antibodies to syphilis. Although it is a good screening test, it contains a heterophilic antigen (cardiolipin) that may give rise to false positive results.

Although precipitation is a useful detection tool, the precipitates are so easily disrupted in liquid media that most precipitation reactions are carried out in agar gels. These substrates are sufficiently soft to allow the reactants (Ab and Ag) to freely diffuse, yet firm enough to hold the Ab-Ag precipitate in place. One technique with applications in microbial identification and diagnosis of disease is the double diffusion (Ouchterlony) method **(figure 17.12)**. It is called double diffusion because it involves diffusion of both antigens and antibodies. The test is performed by punching a pattern of small wells into an agar medium and filling them with test antigens and antibodies. A band forming between two wells indicates that antibodies from one well have met and reacted with antigens from the other well. Variations on this technique provide a means of identifying unknown antibodies or antigens.

The Western Blot for Detecting Proteins

The **Western blot test** involves the **electrophoretic** separation of proteins, followed by an immunoassay to detect these proteins. This test is a counterpart of the Southern blot test for identifying DNA, described in chapter 10. It is a highly specific and sensitive method to identify or verify a particular protein (antibody or antigen) in a sample **(figure 17.13)**. First, the test material is electrophoresed in a gel to separate out particular bands. The gel is then transferred to a special membrane made of nylon or nitrocellulose, binding the proteins in place and creating a "blot." The blot is then incubated with a solution containing antibodies that have been labeled with radioactive, fluorescent, or luminescent molecules. Sites of specific binding will appear as a pattern of bands that can be compared with known positive and negative samples. This is usually the second test used to verify the status of people who are antibody-positive for HIV in the ELISA test (described in section 17.5), because it tests more types of antibodies and is less subject to misinterpretation and false positives than are other antibody tests. The technique has significant applications for detecting microbes and their antigens in specimens.

Complement Fixation

In chapter 14, we introduced the functions of complement as a defense system for destroying foreign cells (see figure 14.20). An antibody that requires the actions of complement to complete the lysis of its antigenic target cell is termed a **lysin** or cytolysin. When lysins act in conjunction with the intrinsic complement system on red

CLINICAL CONNECTIONS

When Positive Is Negative: How to Interpret Serological Test Results

What does it mean if a patient's serum gives a positive reaction—is **seropositive**—in a serological test? In most situations, it indicates that antibodies specific for a particular microbe have been detected in the serum sample. But one must be cautious in proceeding to the next level of interpretation. The mere presence of antibodies does not necessarily indicate that the patient has a disease, but only that he or she has possibly had contact with a microbe or its antigens through infection or vaccination. In screening tests for determining a patient's history (rubella, for instance), finding a measurable titer of antibodies can be significant, because it shows that the person has some protection against that infectious agent.

When the test is being used to diagnose ongoing infection or disease, however, it is necessary to show a rising titer of antibodies over time. The figure indicates how such a test can be used to diagnose patients who have nonspecific symptoms that could fit several diseases. Lyme disease, for instance, can be mistaken for arthritis or viral infections. In the first group, note that the antibody titer against *Borrelia burgdorferi,* the causative agent, increased steadily over a 6-week period. A control group that shared similar symptoms did not exhibit a rise in titer for antibodies to this microbe. Clinicians call samples collected early and late in an infection *acute* and *convalescent* sera.

Another important consideration in testing is the occasional appearance of **biological false positives**. These results show a positive reaction even though, in reality, the patients are not or have not been infected by the microbe. False positives, such as those in syphilis and HIV testing, arise when antibodies or other substances present in the serum cross-react with the test reagents, producing a positive result. Such false results may require retesting by a method that greatly minimizes cross-reactions.

Antibody titer against *Borrelia burgdorferi*	Patients with suspected Lyme disease	Control patients with arthritis

Weeks from onset of symptoms

Define a *false negative reaction*. What might cause such a reaction?

I.

Side view

I. In one method of setting up a double diffusion test, wells are punctured in soft agar, and antibodies (Ab) and antigens (Ag) are added in a pattern. As the contents of the wells diffuse toward each other, a number of reactions can result, depending on whether antibodies meet and precipitate antigens.

II.

Control Ab · Test serum 1 · Ag · Test serum 2 · Precipitation bands

II. Example of test pattern and results. Antigen (Ag) is placed in the center well and antibody (Ab) samples are placed in outer wells. The control contains known Abs to the test Ag. Note bands that form where Ab/Ag meet. The other wells (1, 2) contain unknown test sera. One is positive and the other is negative. Double bands indicate more than one antigen and antibody that can react.

III.

III. Actual test results for detecting infection with the fungal pathogen *Histoplasma.* Numbers 1 and 4 are controls and 2, 3, 5, and 6 are patient test sera. Can you determine which patients have the infection and which do not?

Figure 17.12 Precipitation reactions. The example shown here is a double diffusion (Ouchterlony) test in a semisolid matrix.
(III): Library Book Collection/Alamy Stock Photo

blood cells, the cells hemolyze (lyse and release their hemoglobin). This lysin-mediated hemolysis is the basis of a type of test called **complement fixation,** or **CF (figure 17.14).** Complement fixation tests are used to diagnose some viral, rickettsial, and fungal infections, but are often replaced by more sensitive and accurate ELISA and genetic tests.

Complement fixation testing uses four components—antibody, antigen, complement, and sensitized sheep red blood cells—and it is conducted in two stages.

In the first stage, the test antigen is allowed to react with the test antibody (at least one must be of known identity) in the absence of complement. If the antibody and antigen are specific for each other, they form complexes. To this mixture, purified complement proteins from guinea pig blood are added. If the antibody and antigen have complexed during the previous step, they attach, or fix, the complement to them, thus preventing it from participating in further reactions.

The extent of any complement fixation is determined in the second stage by means of sheep red blood cells (RBCs) with surface lysin molecules. The sheep RBCs serve as an indicator complex that can also fix complement. Contents of the stage 1 tube are mixed with the stage 2 tube and observed with the naked eye for hemolysis.

Successive tests on an HIV+ patient over 30 days reveals an increase in band intensity over time. This is due to continued formation of anti-HIV antibodies.

Figure 17.13 The Western blot procedure. Examples shown here test for antibodies to several HIV antigens. The test strips are prepared by electrophoresing the major HIV surface and core antigens and then blotting them onto special filters. The test strips are incubated with a serum sample and developed with radioactive or colorimetric labels. Sites where HIV antigens have bound antibodies show up as bands. A positive control strip (SRC) containing antibodies for all HIV antigens serves as a comparison.

Interpretation of bands to report a positive test

• Labels correspond with glycoproteins (gp) or proteins (p) that are part of HIV-1 antigen structure.

• The test is considered positive if bands occur at at least two locations: gp160 or gp120 and p31 or p24.

• The test is considered negative if no bands are present for any HIV antigen.

• The test is considered indeterminate if bands are present but not at the primary locations. This result may require retesting at a later date.

Genelabs Diagnostics Pte Ltd.

• If hemolysis *does not* occur, it means that the complement was used up by the first-stage Ab-Ag complex and that the unknown antigen or antibody was indeed present. This result is considered positive.

• If hemolysis *does* occur, it means that unfixed complement from tube 1 reacted with the RBC complex instead, thereby

causing lysis of the sheep RBCs. This result is negative for the antigen or antibody that was the target of the test.

A relative of the CF test, the antistreptolysin O (ASO) titer test, measures the levels of antibody against the streptolysin toxin, an important hemolysin of group A streptococci. A serum sample is exposed to known suspensions of streptolysin and then allowed to incubate with RBCs. Lack of hemolysis indicates antistreptolysin antibodies in the patient's serum that have neutralized the streptolysin and prevented hemolysis. This can be a useful procedure to verify scarlet fever, rheumatic fever, and other related streptococcal syndromes.

Miscellaneous Serological Tests

A test that relies on changes in cellular activity as seen microscopically is the ***Treponema pallidum* immobilization (TPI)** test for syphilis. The impairment or loss of motility of the *Treponema* spirochete in the presence of test serum and complement indicates that the serum contains anti–*Treponema pallidum* antibodies. In **toxin neutralization** tests, a test serum is incubated with the microbe that produces the toxin. If the serum inhibits the growth of the microbe, one can conclude that antitoxins to inactivate the toxin are present.

Serotyping is an antigen-antibody technique for identifying, classifying, and subgrouping certain bacteria into categories called serotypes, using antisera for cell antigens such as the capsule, flagellum, and cell wall. It is widely used in typing *Salmonella* species and strains and is the basis for identifying the numerous serotypes of streptococci (see figure 17.9, part *b*1). The Quellung test, which identifies serotypes of the pneumococcus, involves a precipitation reaction in which antibodies react with the capsular polysaccharide. Although the reaction makes the capsule seem to swell, it is actually creating a zone of Ab-Ag complexes on the cell's surface.

In Vivo Testing

Probably the first immunologic tests were performed not in a test tube but on the body itself. A classic example of one such technique is the **tuberculin test,** which uses a small amount of purified protein derivative (PPD) from *Mycobacterium tuberculosis* injected into the skin. The appearance of a red, raised, thickened lesion in 48 to 72 hours can indicate previous exposure to tuberculosis. In practice, in vivo tests employ principles similar to serological tests, except in this case, an antigen or an antibody is introduced into a patient to elicit some sort of visible reaction. Like the tuberculin test, some of these diagnostic skin tests are useful for evaluating infections due to fungi (coccidioidin and histoplasmin tests, for example) or allergens. Testing for allergic reactions was covered in chapter 16.

Fluorescent Antibody and Immunofluorescent Testing

The property of certain dyes to emit visible light in response to ultraviolet radiation was discussed in chapter 3. This property of fluorescence has found numerous applications in diagnostic immunology. The fundamental tool in immunofluorescent testing is a **fluorescent antibody**—a monoclonal antibody labeled by a fluorescent dye (fluorochrome).

Figure 17.14 **Complement fixation test.** In this example, two serum samples are being tested for antibodies to a certain infectious agent. In reading this test, one observes the cloudiness of the tube. If it is cloudy, the RBCs are not hemolyzed and the test is positive. If it is clear and pink, the RBCs are hemolyzed and the test is negative.

In **direct testing (figure 17.15)** an unknown test specimen or antigen is fixed to a slide and exposed to a fluorescent antibody solution of known composition. If the antibodies are complementary to antigens in the material, they will bind to it. After the slide is rinsed to remove unattached antibodies, it is observed with the fluorescent microscope. Fluorescing cells or specks indicate the presence of Ab-Ag complexes and a positive result. These tests are valuable for identifying and locating antigens on the surfaces of cells or in tissues and in identifying the disease agents of syphilis, gonorrhea, chlamydiosis, whooping cough, Legionnaires' disease, plague, trichomoniasis, meningitis, and listeriosis.

In **indirect testing (figure 17.16)** the fluorescent antibodies are antibodies made to react with the Fc region of another antibody (remember that antibodies are proteins and can be recognized as antigens themselves). In this scheme, an antigen of known identity (a bacterial culture, for example) is combined with a test serum of unknown antibody content. The fluorescent antibody solution that can react with the unknown antibody is applied and rinsed off to visualize whether the serum contains antibodies that have affixed to the antigen. A positive test shows fluorescing aggregates or cells, indicating that the fluorescent antibodies have combined with the unlabeled antibodies. In a negative test, no fluorescent complexes will appear. This technique is frequently used to diagnose syphilis and various viral infections.

Visible fluorescence

Unknown antigen (usually cell or tissue)

Antibody labeled with fluorescent dye

Fluorescent microscopy

Figure 17.15 **Immunofluorescent testing. Direct Testing:** Unidentified antigen (Ag) is directly tagged with fluorescent Ab. See figure 17.3 to view an example of actual test results.

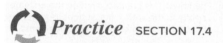

Ab2 fluorescently labeled; specific for Ab1

Ab1 in serum

No Ab in serum

Known Ag

Ab2 attaches to Ab1—visible fluorescence

Positive

Ab2 cannot attach—no fluorescence

Negative

(a)

(b)

Figure 17.16 **Immunofluorescent testing.** **Indirect Testing:** **(a)** Ag of known identity is used to assay unknown Ab; a positive reaction occurs when the second Ab (with fluorescent dye) affixes to the first Ab. **(b)** Indirect immunofluorescent stain of cells infected with two different viruses. Cells with green fluorescing nuclei contain cytomegalovirus; cells with yellow fluorescing nuclei contain adenovirus. (b): CHEMICON® International, Inc.

Practice SECTION 17.4

8. What is the basis of serology and serological testing?

9. Differentiate between specificity and sensitivity.

10. Describe several general ways that Ab-Ag reactions are detected.

11. What do *seropositivity* and *seronegativity* mean?

12. What is a false-positive test result, and what are some possible causes?

13. Explain how agglutination and precipitation reactions are alike and how they are different.

14. Give examples of several tests that employ agglutination and precipitation reactions.

15. What is meant by complement fixation? What are cytolysins?

16. Describe the principles behind direct and indirect fluorescent antibody tests.

17.5 Immunoassays: Tests with High Sensitivity

Learn

15. Describe the concepts behind the main types of immunoassays, and discuss their uses in diagnosis.

The elegant tools of the microbiologist and immunologist are being used increasingly in athletics, criminology, government, and business to test for trace amounts of substances such as hormones, metabolites, and drugs. But traditional techniques in serology are not refined enough to detect a few molecules of these chemicals. Extremely sensitive alternative methods that permit rapid and accurate measurement of trace antigens or antibodies are called **immunoassays.** Examples of the technology for detecting an antigen or antibody in minute quantities include radioactive isotope labels,

enzyme labels, and sensitive electronic sensors. Many of these tests are based on specifically formulated monoclonal antibodies.

Radioimmunoassay (RIA)

Antibodies or antigens labeled with a radioactive isotope can be used to pinpoint minute amounts of a corresponding antigen or antibody. Very complex in practice, these assays compare the amount of radioactivity present in a sample before and after incubation with a known, labeled antigen or antibody. The labeled substance competes with its natural, nonlabeled partner for a reaction site. Large amounts of a bound radioactive component indicate that the unknown test substance was not present. The amount of radioactivity is measured with an isotope counter or a photographic emulsion (autoradiograph). Radioimmunoassay has been employed to measure the levels of insulin and other hormones and to diagnose allergies, chiefly by the radioimmunosorbent test (RIST) for measurement of IgE in allergic patients and the radioallergosorbent test (RAST) to standardize allergenic extracts.

Enzyme-Linked Immunosorbent Assay (ELISA)

The **ELISA,** also known as enzyme immunoassay (EIA), relies on an enzyme-mediated color change to indicate the binding of antibody to antigen. The enzymes used most often are horseradish peroxidase and alkaline phosphatase, both of which release a dye (chromogen) when exposed to their substrate. This technique also relies on a solid support such as a plastic microtiter plate that can *adsorb* (attract on its surface) the reactants **(figure 17.17).**

The **indirect ELISA** can capture antibodies in a serum sample. As with other indirect tests, the final positive reaction is achieved by means of an antibody-antibody reaction. The indicator antibody is bound to an enzyme that produces a color change with positive serum samples **(figure 17.17a, b).** The starting reactant is a known antigen that is adsorbed to the surface of a well. To this,

Quick Search

To learn more about this topic, search the Internet for "Enzyme-Linked Immunosorbent Assay (ELISA)."

(a) Indirect ELISA.
Comparison of a positive (left) and negative (right) reaction. An indirect ELISA detects the presence of a specific antibody.

Well A Well B

Known antigen is adsorbed to well.

Serum samples with unknown antibodies.
A
B

Sample A Sample B

Well is rinsed to remove unbound antibodies.

Indicator antibody linked to enzyme attaches to any bound antibody.

Wells are rinsed to remove unbound indicator antibody. A colorless substrate for the enzyme is added.

Enzymes linked to indicator Ab react with the substrate. Wells that develop color are positive for the antibody; colorless wells are negative.

(+) (−)

(b) Capture or Antibody Sandwich ELISA.
Comparison of a positive (left) and negative (right) reaction. This type of ELISA detects the presence of a specific antigen.

Antibody specific to the antigen being sought is adsorbed to the well.

Solution (blood, CSF, etc.) potentially containing the antigen is added to the well. If the antigen is present (left) it will bind to an antibody.

Enzyme

The enzyme-linked antibody is added. If the antigen is present (left) an antibody "sandwich" is created, binding the enzyme tightly to the well. If the antigen is absent (right) the enzyme-linked antibody floats loosely in the well.

Rinsing the wells removes unbound antibody (right) while bound antibody remains attached to the antigen (left).

The enzyme's substrate is added (▫). If the enzyme is present (left) a color change occurs. If the enzyme is absent (right) no color change is seen.

+ −

(c) Microtiter ELISA Plate with 96 Tests for HIV Antibodies.
Colored wells indicate a positive reaction.

Figure 17.17 Methods of ELISA testing. (a) An indirect ELISA is used to detect the presence of an antibody in a clinical sample (blood, cerebrospinal fluid, urine etc.). **(b)** A sandwich ELISA is used to detect the presence of a specific antigen in a clinical sample. **(c)** Appearance of an ELISA plate holding 96 samples, displaying both positive (yellow) and negative (clear) results.
(c): Hank Morgan/Science Source

the unknown test serum is added. After rinsing, an enzyme-Ab reagent that can react with the unknown test antibody is placed in the well. The substrate for the enzyme is then added, and the wells are scanned for color changes. Color development indicates that the antibody was present in the patient's serum. This is the common screening test for the antibodies to HIV, various rickettsial species, hepatitis A and C, the cholera vibrio, and *Helicobacter*, a cause of gastric ulcers. Because false positives can occur, a verification test may be necessary (such as Western blot for HIV).

In **capture ELISA** (or sandwich) tests, a known antibody is adsorbed to the bottom of a well and incubated with a solution potentially containing the antigen being sought after **(figure 17.17)**. After excess components have been rinsed off, the enzyme-linked antibody, specific for the same sought-after antigen, is added. If the antigen is present, it will bind the enzyme-linked antibody, creating a "sandwich" with the antigen in between two antibodies. Most importantly, the enzyme-linked antibody will now be tightly bound to the bottom of the well. Next, the substrate for the enzyme is placed in the wells and incubated. Enzymes affixed to the antigen will hydrolyze the substrate and release a colored dye. Thus, any color developing in the wells is a positive result. Lack of color means that the antigen was not present and that the subsequent rinsing removed the enzyme-antibody complex. The capture technique is commonly used to detect antibodies to hantavirus, rubella virus, and *Toxoplasma*.

17.6 Viruses as a Special Diagnostic Case

 Learn

16. Summarize the protocols in identifying the causative agent in a viral infection.

All of the methods discussed so far—phenotypic, genotypic, and immunologic—are applicable to many different types of microorganisms. Viruses can present special difficulties because they are not cells and they are more labor intensive to culture in the laboratory. **Figure 17.18** presents an overview of various techniques available to diagnose viral infections. These range from observing symptoms, to direct microscopic examination, to cultivation, and to serological and genetic analysis.

Practice SECTIONS 17.5–17.6

17. Explain the differences between direct and indirect procedures in immunoassay tests, giving examples.

18. How does a positive reaction in an ELISA test appear? How many wells are positive in figure 17.17*c*?

19. Provide some reasons *in vivo* tests would not be as reliable as immunoassay tests.

20. Observing figure 17.18, indicate whether each method (a) through (f) is phenotypic, genotypic, or immunologic.

CASE STUDY | **Part 2**

The case was reported to the Minnesota Department of Health's Unexplained Critical Illnesses and Deaths Project, which provides testing for cases in which an infectious agent is suspected but has not been identified. Laboratory specimens collected during the patient's hospitalization were submitted to the project for further analysis, where one sample of serum was found to be positive for antibodies which recognized lymphocytic choriomeningitis virus (anti-LCMV antibodies).

Infection with LCMV most commonly results in asymptomatic or mild febrile disease. In persons who do become ill, the virus usually causes a biphasic illness, with the first set of flu-like symptoms (fever, malaise, lack of appetite, muscle aches, headache, nausea, and vomiting) lasting up to a week. After several days of recovery, a second phase, often marked by meningitis (fever, headache, stiff neck), encephalitis (drowsiness, confusion, sensory and motor disturbances), or meningoencephalitis (inflammation of the brain and meninges) may occur. Infection during pregnancy is especially worrisome, as the virus may be passed to the fetus, resulting in miscarriage—if infection occurs in the first trimester—or serious birth defects, including vision problems and mental retardation, if infection occurs later in pregnancy. The virus is most commonly carried by wild mice, rats, or other small rodents and occasionally by domestic rodents (hamsters, guinea pigs) who become infected through contact with wild rodents. Humans become infected through exposure to urine, droppings, saliva, or nesting materials from infected rodents via inhalation or introduction through the eyes, nose, mouth, or broken skin.

Because of the uncommon diagnosis, the CDC's Viral Special Pathogens Branch was consulted. Serological testing using enzyme-linked immunosorbent assay (ELISA) revealed an IgM titer of 6400, a level indicating recent infection. The Minnesota Department of Health initiated an investigation to identify the source of infection, determine whether additional persons were at risk, and develop recommendations to prevent additional cases. The patient's family had reported a rodent infestation to hospital personnel earlier, and mouse droppings found in the kitchen of the family's apartment tested positive for LCMV RNA using PCR, implicating the mouse infestation as the likely source of the patient's infection. The family was referred for integrated pest management services through the U.S. Department of Housing and Urban Development Healthy Homes program. The city housing inspector performed an urban rodent survey, and the property owner complied with orders to have professional exterminators treat the apartment within 30 days. Both households in the duplex were provided with educational materials concerning prevention of rodent reinfestation.

- What type of ELISA was used to detect exposure to lymphocytic choriomeningitis virus?

- Why couldn't optical microscopy be used to identify the pathogen in this case?

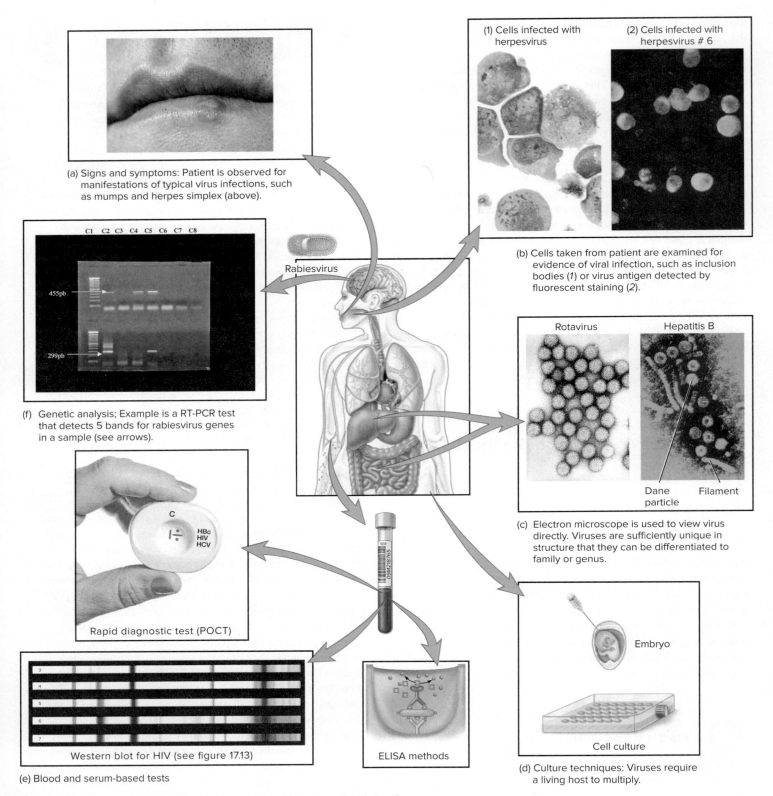

(a) Signs and symptoms: Patient is observed for manifestations of typical virus infections, such as mumps and herpes simplex (above).

(1) Cells infected with herpesvirus

(2) Cells infected with herpesvirus # 6

(b) Cells taken from patient are examined for evidence of viral infection, such as inclusion bodies (*1*) or virus antigen detected by fluorescent staining (*2*).

Rabiesvirus

(f) Genetic analysis; Example is a RT-PCR test that detects 5 bands for rabiesvirus genes in a sample (see arrows).

C1 C2 C3 C4 C5 C6 C7 C8

455pb

299pb

Rotavirus Hepatitis B

Dane particle Filament

(c) Electron microscope is used to view virus directly. Viruses are sufficiently unique in structure that they can be differentiated to family or genus.

C HBc HIV HCV

Rapid diagnostic test (POCT)

Embryo

Cell culture

Western blot for HIV (see figure 17.13)

ELISA methods

(d) Culture techniques: Viruses require a living host to multiply.

(e) Blood and serum-based tests

Figure 17.18 Summary of methods used to diagnose viral infections.

(a): *Source:* Dr. Hermann/CDC; (b1–2): *Source:* Zaki Salahuddin. Laboratory of Tumor Cell Biology/National Cancer Institute; (c, left): *Source:* Dr. Erskine Palmer/CDC; (c, right): *Source:* Bryon Skinner/CDC; (e): © Genelabs Diagnostics Pte Ltd.; (rapid diagnostic test): Courtesy of MedMira Inc.; (f): *Source:* 2008 Araújo et al. licensee BioMed Central Ltd.

Chapter Summary with Key Terms

17.1 An Overview of Clinical Microbiology

A. **Phenotypic** methods are those that assess microscopic morphology, macroscopic morphology, physiological and biochemical characteristics, and chemical composition.

B. **Genotypic** methods examine the genetic composition of a microorganism.

C. **Immunologic** methods exploit the host's antibody reaction to microbial antigens for purposes of diagnosis.

D. Diagnosis begins with accurate **specimen collection,** which means the sampling of body sites or fluids that are suspected to contain the infectious agent. Strategies vary depending on the source.

E. Laboratory methods yield either presumptive data or confirmatory data. Sometimes pathogens are diagnosed based solely on signs and symptoms in the patient. The route of diagnosis depends on the particular microbe and the technologies available to the lab.

17.2 Phenotypic Methods

A. The most obvious phenotypic characteristics of a microbe are gleaned from its **microscopic** and **macroscopic** appearance. Many infections can be diagnosed by microscopic examination of fresh or stained microorganisms from specimens. Direct antigen or antibody testing can also be performed on uncultured specimens.

B. Cultivation of specimens allows the examination of **cultural** characteristics such as colony morphology, growth characteristics, or both, which can be useful in identifying microbes.

C. **Biochemical** tests determine whether microbes possess particular enzymes or metabolic pathways that can serve to identify them.

D. Of utmost importance is the determination of whether an identified microbe is actually causing an infection or is simply a bystander, or member of the normal **microbiota.**

17.3 Genotypic Methods

A. Genetic methods of identification are being used increasingly in diagnostic microbiology.

B. **Probes** can detect specific genetic patterns, and advanced technology can characterize unique DNA sequences.

C. The polymerase chain reaction (PCR) can be used to quickly amplify specific DNA in a sample, which is often enough to fully identify an organism.

D. DNA hybridization probes can be used to detect the presence of a specific DNA sequence.

E. Whole genome sequencing relies on automation and computing power to completely sequence the genome of an organism in a matter of hours.

F. RNA in ribosomes and other cultures or specimens (RNA viruses) can be converted to DNA and treated with methods of DNA analysis.

17.4 Immunologic Methods

A. **Serology** is a science that tests a patient's serum to detect signs of infection, for example, finding specific antibodies for a particular microbe.

B. The basis of serological tests is that **antibodies (Abs)** bind to their specific **antigens (Ags)** in vitro. Known Ags can be used to react with Abs in an unknown serum sample. The reverse is also true; known Abs can be used to detect and type unidentified Ags.

C. These Ab-Ag reactions are visible in the form of obvious clumps and precipitates, color changes, or the release of radioactivity. Test results are read as positive or negative.

D. Desirable properties of tests are high **specificity** and **sensitivity.**

E. Types of Tests

1. In **agglutination** tests, antibody cross-links whole-cell antigens, forming complexes that settle out and form visible clumps in the test chamber.
 a. Examples are tests for blood type, some bacterial diseases, and viral diseases.
 b. These tests can determine the amount of antibody in serum, or **titer.**

2. Double diffusion **precipitation** tests involve the diffusion of Ags and Abs in a soft agar gel, forming zones of Ab/Ab complexes where they meet and react.

3. In **immunoelectrophoresis,** migration of serum proteins in gel is combined with precipitation by antibodies.

4. The **Western blot** test separates antigen into bands. After the gel is affixed to a membrane, it is allowed to hybridize with antibodies that have been labeled with radioactive or fluorescent molecules.

5. A **complement fixation** test detects **lysins**—antibodies that fix complement and can lyse target cells. It involves first mixing test Ag and Ab with complement and then with sensitized sheep RBCs. If the complement is fixed by the Ab-Ag, the RBCs remain intact, and the test is positive. If RBCs are hemolyzed, specific antibodies are lacking.

6. In direct assays, known marked Ab is used to detect unknown Ag (microbe).
 a. In indirect testing, known Ag reacts with unknown Ab, and the reaction is made visible by a second Ab that can affix to and identify the unknown Ab.
 b. **Immunofluorescent** testing uses **fluorescent antibodies** (FABs tagged with fluorescent dye) either directly or indirectly to visualize cells or cell aggregates that have reacted with the FABs.

17.5 Immunoassays: Tests with High Sensitivity
Immunoassays are highly sensitive tests for Ag and Ab.
 A. In *radioimmunoassay,* Ags or Abs are labeled with radioactive isotopes and traced.
 B. The **enzyme-linked immunosorbent assay (ELISA)** can detect unknown Ag or Ab by direct or indirect means. A positive result is visualized when a colored product is released by an enzyme-substrate reaction.

 C. With in vivo testing, Ags are introduced into the body directly to determine a patient's immunologic condition.

17.6 Viruses as a Special Diagnostic Case
 A. Viral diseases are diagnosed through patient observation supported by microscopic, cultural, serological, and genetic tests.

Assess Your Knowledge

Level I. These questions require a working knowledge of the concepts in the chapter and the ability to recall and understand the information you have studied.

Developing a Concept Inventory

Select the correct answer from the answers provided. For questions with blanks, choose the combination of answers that most accurately completes the statement.

1. **Matching.** Match each of the following culture results to the most likely interpretation, and explain your choice.
 a. probable infection
 b. normal microbiota
 c. environmental contaminant

 _____ Isolation of two colonies of *E. coli* on a plate streaked from the urine sample
 _____ Fifty colonies of *Streptococcus pneumoniae* on culture of sputum
 _____ A mixture of 80 colonies of various streptococci on a culture from a throat swab
 _____ Colonies of black bread mold on selective media used to isolate bacteria from stool
 _____ Blood culture bottle with heavy growth

2. Which of the following methods is most sensitive for identifying different strains of a microbe?
 a. microscopic examination
 b. hemolysis on blood agar
 c. DNA analysis
 d. agglutination test

3. In agglutination reactions, the antigen is a _____; in precipitation reactions, it is a _____.
 a. soluble molecule, whole cell
 b. whole cell, soluble molecule
 c. bacterium, virus
 d. protein, carbohydrate

4. Which reaction requires complement?
 a. hemagglutination
 b. precipitation
 c. hemolysis
 d. toxin neutralization

5. A patient with a _____ titer of antibodies to an infectious agent generally has greater protection than a patient with a _____ titer.
 a. high, low
 b. low, high
 c. negative, positive
 d. old, new

6. Direct immunofluorescent tests use a labeled antibody to identify
 a. an unknown microbe
 b. an unknown antibody
 c. fixed complement
 d. agglutinated antigens

7. The Western blot test can be used to identify
 a. unknown antibodies
 b. unknown antigens
 c. specific DNA
 d. both a and b

8. An example of an in vivo serological test is
 a. indirect immunofluorescence
 b. radioimmunoassay
 c. a tuberculin test
 d. complement fixation

9. Which of the following specimens must be removed using sterile techniques?
 a. feces
 b. urine
 c. upper respiratory tract
 d. blood

Case Study Analysis

1. Techniques used in this case to detect lymphocytic choriomeningitis virus (LCMV) included which of the following (choose all that apply)?
 a. serological testing to detect LCMV
 b. serological testing to detect antibodies against LCMV
 c. detection of LCMV RNA
 d. Gram stain of LCMV

2. Which technique would provide information like that acquired using the polymerase chain reaction in this case?
 a. indirect ELISA
 b. complement fixation
 c. whole-genome sequencing
 d. Western blot

3. The polymerase chain reaction (PCR) was used to detect LCMV RNA in mouse droppings. Why wasn't this same technique used to detect the presence of LCMV RNA in the patient?

On the Test

These questions will help to prepare you to successfully answer similar questions you'll see on the TEAS (Test of Essential Academic Skills) and NCLEX (National Council Licensure Examination).

1. A phlebotomist draws blood from a client and tells her that the physician has ordered an indirect ELISA to check for rubella. After the phlebotomist leaves, the client asks the nurse to clarify what the phlebotomist said. Which response by the nurse is most correct?
 a. The ELISA will identify the presence of the rubella virus in the patient's bloodstream.
 b. The ELISA will identify how serious rubella would be if the patient contracts the disease.
 c. The ELISA will identify the presence of antibodies against the rubella virus in the patient's bloodstream.
 d. The ELISA will reduce the pain associated with the rubella infection.

2. Serological tests rely on the action of which class of biomolecules?
 a. DNA
 b. proteins
 c. carbohydrates
 d. lipids

Writing Challenge

For each question, compose a one- or two-paragraph answer that includes the factual information needed to completely address the question. Practice questions can also be used for writing-challenge exercises.

1. Why do we interpret positive hemolysis in the complement fixation test to mean negative for the test substance?

2. What information can the antibody titer tell us about the immune status of a person?

3. Briefly describe the principles and give an example of the use of a specific test using immunoelectrophoresis, Western blot, complement fixation, fluorescent testing (direct and indirect), and immunoassays (direct and indirect ELISA).

4. Differentiate between the serological tests used to identify isolated cultures of pathogens and those used to diagnose disease from patients' serum, as shown in figure 17.9.

5. How would the staining and cultural tests have differed if *Staphylococcus* or *Clostridium* had been the cause of the outbreak of gastroenteritis described in this chapter's Case Study?

6. Explain what must be done to identify RNA viruses using genetic techniques.

Concept Mapping

On Connect you can find an Introduction to Concept Mapping that provides guidance for working with concept maps, along with concept-mapping activities for this chapter.

 Application, Analysis, Evaluation, and Synthesis

Level II. These problems go beyond just restating facts and require higher levels of understanding and an ability to interpret, problem solve, transfer knowledge to new situations, create models, and predict outcomes.

Critical Thinking

Critical thinking is the ability to reason and solve problems using facts and concepts. These questions can be approached from a number of angles and, in most cases, they do not have a single correct answer.

1. How would you explain to a biology class that in the next decade, some diseases currently thought to be noninfectious will probably be found to be caused by microbes?

2. In what way could the extreme sensitivity of the PCR method be a problem when working with clinical specimens?

3. Why do some tests for antibody in serum (such as for HIV and syphilis) require backup verification with additional tests at a later date?

4. a. Look at figure 17.11*b*. What is the titer as shown?
 b. If the titer had been 40, would a different interpretation be made as to the immune status of the patient?

c. Which patients are positive in figure 17.12, part III?

d. What would it mean if a test 2 weeks later revealed a titer of 280?

e. What would it mean if no agglutination had occurred in any tube?

5. Observe figure 17.16 and make note of the several steps in the indirect ELISA test. What four essential events are necessary to develop a positive reaction (besides having antibody A)? Hint: What would happen without rinses?

6. Distinguish between point of care tests that can be used to diagnose infection and those that can be used to identify pathogens, using examples.

Visual Assessment

1. From chapter 3, fig 3.18*a* (reproduced on the right) shows triple sugar iron agar. What biochemical characteristics does this figure illustrate? How could this medium be used to begin the identification of the isolated bacteria in this chapter's Case Study?

Lisa Burgess/McGraw-Hill Education

2. From chapter 15, figure 15.18, explain how determining the titer of IgM and IgG separately could help to distinguish between current exposure to a pathogen versus past exposure.

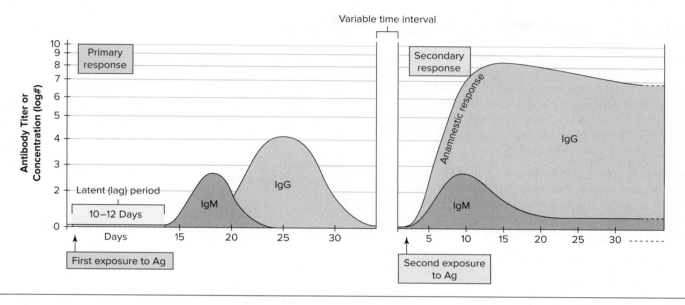

Detailed Steps in the Glycolysis Pathway

Steps in the Glycolysis Pathway The first portion of glycolysis involves activation of glucose, which is followed by oxidation reactions of the glucose fragments, the synthesis of ATP, and the formation of pyruvic acid. *Although each step of metabolism is catalyzed by a specific enzyme, we will not mention it for most reactions.* The following outline lists the principal steps of glycolysis. To see an overview of glycolysis, refer to figure 8.17.

1. **Glucose** is phosphorylated by means of an **ATP** acting with the enzyme hexokinase. The product is glucose-6-phosphate. (Numbers in chemical names refer to the position of the phosphate on the carbon skeleton.) This is a way of "priming" the system and keeping the glucose inside the cell.

2. Glucose-6-phosphate is converted to its isomer, fructose-6-phosphate, by phosphoglucoisomerase.

3. Another ATP is spent in phosphorylating the first carbon of fructose-6-phosphate, which yields fructose-1,6-diphosphate.

Up to this point, no energy has been released, no oxidation-reduction has occurred, and, in fact, 2 ATPs have been used. In addition, the molecules remain in the 6-carbon state.

4. Now doubly activated, fructose-1,6-diphosphate is split into two 3-carbon fragments: glyceraldehyde-3-phosphate (G3P) and dihydroxyacetone phosphate (DHAP).

5. DHAP is enzymatically converted to G3P, which is the more reactive form for subsequent reactions.

The effect of the splitting of fructose diphosphate is to double every subsequent reaction, because where there was once a single molecule, there are now two to be fed into the remaining pathways.

6. Each molecule of glyceraldehyde-3-phosphate becomes involved in the single oxidation-reduction reaction of glycolysis, a reaction that sets the scene for ATP synthesis. Two reactions occur simultaneously and are catalyzed by the same enzyme, called glyceraldehyde-3-phosphate dehydrogenase. The coenzyme **NAD$^+$** picks up electrons and a proton from G3P, forming **NADH.** This step is accompanied by the addition of an inorganic phosphate (PO_4^{3-}) to form an unstable bond on the third carbon of the G3P substrate. The product of these reactions is 1,3-bisphosphoglyceric acid.

In aerobic organisms, the NADH formed during step 6 will undergo further reactions in the electron transport system, where the final electron acceptor will be oxygen, and an additional 3 ATPs will be generated per NADH. In organisms that ferment glucose anaerobically, the NADH will be oxidized back to NAD$^+$, and the hydrogen acceptor will be an organic compound.

7. One of the high-energy phosphates of 1,3-bisphosphoglyceric acid is donated to ADP via substrate-level phosphorylation, resulting in a molecule of ATP. The product of this reaction is 3-phosphoglyceric acid.

8,9. During this phase, a substrate for the synthesis of a second ATP is made in two substeps. First, 3-phosphoglyceric acid is converted to 2-phosphoglyceric acid through the shift of a phosphate from the third to the second carbon. Then, the removal of a water molecule from 2-phosphoglyceric acid produces phosphoenolpyruvic acid, which is charged to release a high-energy phosphate.

10. In the final reaction of glycolysis, phosphoenolpyruvic acid gives up its high-energy phosphate to form a second ATP via substrate-level phosphorylation. This reaction, catalyzed by pyruvate kinase, also produces pyruvic acid (pyruvate), a compound with many roles in metabolism.

The 2 ATPs formed during steps 7 and 10 are examples of substrate-level phosphorylation, in that the high-energy phosphate is transferred directly from a substrate to ADP. These reactions are catalyzed by kinases. Because both molecules that arose in step 4 undergo these reactions, an overall total of **4** ATPs is generated in the partial oxidation of a glucose to 2 pyruvic acids. However, 2 ATPs were expended for steps 1 and 3, so the net number of ATPs available to the cell from these reactions is **2.**

TABLE A.1 | Twenty Amino Acids and Their Abbrevations*

Nonpolar

Glycine (Gly) Alanine (Ala) Valine (Val) Leucine (Leu) Isoleucine (Ile)

Tryptophan (Trp) Proline (Pro) Cysteine (Cys) Methionine (Met) Phenylalanine (Phe)

Polar

Asparagine (Asn) Glutamine (Gln) Tyrosine (Tyr) Serine (Ser) Threonine (Thr)

Electrically Charged

ACIDIC

BASIC

Aspartic Acid (Asp) Glutamic Acid (Glu) Arginine (Arg) Lysine (Lys) Histidine (His)

*The basic skeleton is in yellow; R groups are in purple, blue, or green, depending on the nature of their composition.

Tests and Guidelines

Methods for Testing Sterilization and Germicidal Processes

Most procedures used for microbial control in the clinical setting are either physical methods (heat, radiation) or chemical methods (disinfectants, antiseptics). These procedures are so crucial to the well-being of patients and staff that their effectiveness must be monitored in a consistent and standardized manner. Particular concerns include the time required for the process, the concentration or intensity of the antimicrobic agent being used, and the nature of the materials being treated. The effectiveness of an agent is frequently established through controlled microbiological analysis. In these tests, a biological indicator (a highly resistant microbe) is exposed to the agent, and its viability is checked. If this known test microbe is destroyed by the treatment, it is assumed that the less resistant microbes have also been destroyed. Growth of the test organism indicates that the sterilization protocol has failed. The general categories of testing include:

Heat The usual form of heat used in microbial control is steam under pressure in an autoclave. Autoclaving materials at a high temperature (121°C) for a sufficient time (15–40 minutes) destroys most bacterial endospores. To monitor the quality of any given industrial or clinical autoclave run, technicians insert a dried test strip of *Bacillus stearothermophilus,* a spore-forming bacterium with extreme heat resistance. After autoclaving, the ampule is incubated at 56°C (the optimal temperature for this species) and checked for growth.

Radiation The effectiveness of ionizing radiation in sterilization is determined by placing special strips of dried spores of *Bacillus sphaericus* (a common soil bacterium with extreme resistance to radiation) into a packet of irradiated material.

Filtration The performance of membrane filters used to sterilize liquids may be monitored by adding *Pseudomonas diminuta* to the liquid. Because this species is a tiny bacterium that can escape through the filter if the pore size is not small enough, it is a good indicator of filtrate sterility.

Gas sterilization Ethylene oxide gas, one of the few chemical sterilizing agents, is used on a variety of heat-sensitive medical and laboratory supplies. The most reliable indicator of a successful sterilizing cycle is the spore-former *Bacillus subtilis,* variety *niger.*

Germicidal assays U.S. hospitals and clinics commonly employ more than 250 products to control microbes in the environment, on inanimate objects, and on patients. Controlled testing of these products' effectiveness is usually performed not in the clinic itself but by the chemical or pharmaceutical manufacturer. A number of standardized in vitro tests are currently available to assess the effects of germicides. Most of them use a non-spore-forming pathogen as the biological indicator.

The Phenol Coefficient (PC)

The older disinfectant phenol has been the traditional standard by which other disinfectants are measured. In the PC test, a water-soluble phenol-based (phenolic) disinfectant (Amphyl, Lysol) is tested for its bactericidal effectiveness as compared with phenol. These disinfectants are serially diluted in a series of *Salmonella choleraesuis, Staphylococcus aureus,* or *Pseudomonas aeruginosa* cultures. The tubes are left for 5, 10, or 15 minutes and then subcultured to test for viability. The PC is a ratio derived by comparing the following data:

$$PC = \frac{\text{Greatest dilution of the phenolic that kills test bacteria in 10 min but not in 5 min}}{\text{Greatest dilution of phenol giving same result}}$$

The general interpretation of this ratio is that chemicals with lower phenol coefficients have greater effectiveness. The primary disadvantage of the PC test is that, because it is restricted to phenolics, it is inappropriate for the vast majority of clinical disinfectants.

Use Dilution Test

An alternative test with broader applications is the use dilution test. This test is performed by drying the test culture (one of those species used in the PC test) onto the surface of small stainless steel cylindrical carriers. These carriers are then exposed to varying concentrations of disinfectant for 10 minutes, removed, rinsed, and placed in tubes of broth. After incubation, the tubes are inspected for growth. The smallest concentration of disinfectant that kills the test organism on 10 carrier pieces is the correct dilution for use.

Filter Paper Disc Method

A quick measure of the inhibitory effects of various disinfectants and antiseptics can be achieved by the filter paper disc method. First, a small (½-inch) sterile piece of filter paper is dipped into a disinfectant of known concentration. This is placed on an agar medium seeded with a test organism (*S. aureus* or *P. aeruginosa*), and the plate is incubated. A zone devoid of growth (zone of inhibition) around the disc indicates the capacity of the agent to inhibit growth **(figure B.1).** Like the antimicrobic sensitivity test (see figure 12.18), this test measures the minimum inhibitory concentration of the chemical. In general, chemicals with wide zones of inhibition are effective even in high dilutions.

Guidelines for Universal Precautions in the Clinical Setting

The significance of these procedures for infection control is introduced in chapter 13.

1. Barrier precautions, including masks and gloves, should be taken to prevent contact of skin and mucous membranes with patients' blood or other body fluids. Because gloves can develop small invisible tears, double gloving further decreases the risk. For protection during surgery, venipuncture, or

FIGURE B.1 A filter paper disc containing hydrogen peroxide produces a broad clear zone of inhibition in a culture of *Staphylococcus aureus.*
Source: © Kathy Park Talaro

emergency procedures, gowns, aprons, and other body coverings should be worn. Dental workers should wear eyewear and face shields to protect against splattered blood and saliva.

2. More than 10% of health care personnel are pierced each year by sharp (and usually contaminated) instruments. These accidents carry risks not only for AIDS but also for hepatitis B, hepatitis C, and other diseases. Preventing inoculation infection requires vigilant observance of proper techniques.

 • All disposable needles, scalpels, or sharp devices from invasive procedures must immediately be placed in puncture-proof containers for sterilization and final discard.

 • Under no circumstances should a worker attempt to recap a syringe, remove a needle from a syringe, or leave unprotected and/or used syringes where they pose a risk to others.
 • Reusable needles or other sharp devices must be heat-sterilized in a puncture-proof holder before they are handled.
 • If a needlestick or other injury occurs, immediate attention to the wound, such as thorough degermation and application of strong antiseptics, can prevent infection.

3. Dental handpieces should be sterilized between patients, but if this is not possible, they should be thoroughly disinfected with a high-level disinfectant (peroxide, hypochlorite). Blood and saliva should be removed completely from all contaminated dental instruments and intraoral devices prior to sterilization.

4. Hands and other skin surfaces that have been accidentally contaminated with blood or other fluids should be scrubbed immediately with a germicidal soap. Hands should likewise be washed after removing rubber gloves, masks, or other barrier devices.

5. Because saliva can be a source of some types of infections, barriers should be used in all mouth-to-mouth resuscitations.

6. Health care workers with active, draining lesions of the skin or mucous membrane must refrain from handling patients or equipment that will come into contact with other patients. Pregnant health care workers risk infecting their fetuses and must pay special attention to these guidelines. Personnel should be protected by vaccination whenever possible.

Isolation procedures for known or suspected infections should still be instituted on a case-by-case basis. See table 13.11.

An additional consideration with regard to infectious agents is covered by the biosafety levels of microbes being handled in the laboratory, ranging from 1 (least level of pathogenicity) up to 4 (highest level of pathogenicity). This topic is also discussed in chapter 13. An overview of the containment levels and concerns are presented in **table B.1.**

TABLE B.1	Primary Biosafety Levels and Agents of Disease	
Personnel handling infectious agents in the laboratory must be protected from possible infection through special risk management or containment procedures.		
Biosafety Level	**Facilities and Practices**	**Risk of Infection and Class of Pathogens**
1	Standard, open bench, no special facilities needed; typical of most microbiology teaching labs; access may be restricted.	Low infection hazard; class 1 microbes not generally considered pathogens and will not invade the bodies of healthy persons; Examples include *Micrococcus luteus, Bacillus megaterium, Lactobacillus, Saccharomyces.*
2	At least Level 1 facilities and practices; plus personnel must be trained in handling pathogens; lab coats and gloves required; safety cabinets may be needed; biohazard signs posted; access restricted.	Agents with moderate potential to infect; class 2 pathogens can cause disease in healthy people but can be contained with proper facilities; pathogens that belong to class 2 include *Staphylococcus aureus, Escherichia coli, Salmonella* spp.; pathogenic helminths; hepatitis A, B, and rabies viruses; *Cryptococcus* and *Blastomyces;* HIV.
3	Minimum of Level 2 facilities and practices; manipulation performed in safety cabinets with special containment features; all personnel require protective clothing; no unsterilized materials can leave the lab; personnel are monitored and vaccinated.	Agents can cause severe or lethal disease especially when inhaled; BSL-3 microbes include *Mycobacterium tuberculosis, Francisella tularensis, Yersinia pestis, Brucella* spp., *Coxiella burnetii, Coccidioides immitis,* yellow fever, and western equine encephalitis.
4	Minimum of Level 3 facilities and practices; facilities have highest levels of controlled access; clothing changes and showers required for all people entering and leaving; materials must be autoclaved or gas-sterilized prior to entering and leaving lab.	Agents being handled are highly virulent microbes that pose extreme risk for morbidity and mortality when inhaled in droplet or aerosol form; class 4 microbes include flaviviruses, arenaviruses (Lassa fever virus), and filoviruses (Ebola and Marburg viruses).

TABLE B.2	Most Probable Number Chart for Evaluating Coliform Content of Water

The Number of Tubes in Series, with Positive Growth at Each Dilution							
10 ml	1 ml	0.1 ml	MPN* per 100 ml of Water	10 ml	1 ml	0.1 ml	MPN* per 100 ml of Water
0	1	0	0.18	5	0	1	3.1
1	0	0	0.20	5	1	0	3.3
1	0	0	0.40	5	1	1	4.6
2	0	0	0.45	5	2	0	4.9
2	0	1	0.68	5	2	1	7.0
2	2	0	0.93	5	2	2	9.5
3	0	0	0.78	5	3	0	7.9
3	0	1	1.1	5	3	1	11.0
3	1	0	1.1	5	3	2	14.0
3	2	0	1.4	5	4	0	13.0
4	0	0	1.3	5	4	1	17.0
4	0	1	1.7	5	4	2	22.0
4	1	0	1.7	5	4	3	28.0
4	1	1	2.1	5	5	0	24.0
4	2	0	2.2	5	5	1	35.0
4	2	1	2.6	5	5	2	54.0
4	3	0	2.7	5	5	3	92.0
5	0	0	2.3	5	5	4	160.0

*Most probable number of cells per sample of 100 ml.

Tests for Water Analysis

Figure B.2 and **table B.2** provide standards used in analyzing water samples using the most probable number (MPN) method, as described in chapter 26. The figure indicates the steps in the laboratory procedure, and the table provides estimated counts for coliforms, based on the number of tubes with growth.

FIGURE B.2 The most probable number (MPN) procedure for determining the coliform content of a water sample. In the presumptive test, each set of tubes of broth is inoculated with a water sample reduced by a factor of 10. After incubation, the sets of tubules are examined and rated for gas production (for instance, 0 means no tubes with gas, 1 means one tube with gas, 2 means two tubes with gas). Applying this result to table B.2 will indicate the probable number of cells present in 100 ml of the water sample. Confirmation of coliforms can be achieved by confirmatory tests on additional media, and complete identification can be made through selective and different media and staining (chapter 20).

General Classification Techniques and Taxonomy of Bacteria

TABLE C.1	Summary of Techniques Used in Bacterial Identification and Classification, Chapter 4, Section 4.6

- **Microscopic Morphology** Traits that can be valuable aids to identification are combinations of cell shape and size, Gram stain reaction, acid-fast reaction, and special structures, including endospores, granules, and capsules. Electron microscope studies can pinpoint additional structural features (such as the cell wall, flagella, pili, and fimbriae).

- **Macroscopic Morphology** Appearance of colonies, including texture, size, shape, pigment, and speed of growth and patterns of growth in broth and gelatin media.

- **Physiological/Biochemical Characteristics** Enzymes and other biochemical properties of bacteria are fairly reliable and stable expressions of the "chemical identity" of each species. Diagnostic tests determine the presence of specific enzymes and assess nutritional and metabolic activities. Examples include fermentation of sugars; digestion of complex polymers such as proteins and polysaccharides; presence of catalase, oxidase, and decarboxylases; sensitivity to antimicrobic drugs.

- **Chemical Analysis** Analyzing the types of specific structural substances that the bacterium contains, such as the chemical composition of peptides in the cell wall and lipids in membranes.

- **Serological Analysis** Bacteria display molecules called antigens that are recognized by the immune system. One immune response to antigens is to produce antibodies that are designed to bind tightly to the antigens. This response is so specific that antibodies can be used as a means of identifying bacteria in specimens and cultures.

- **Genetic and Molecular Analysis** Examining the genetic material itself has revolutionized the identification and classification of bacteria.

G + C Base Composition The overall percentage of guanine and cytosine (the G + C content as compared with A + T content) in DNA is a general indicator of relatedness because it is a trait that does not change rapidly. Bacteria with a significant difference in G + C percentage are less likely to be genetically related. See the revised classification scheme that is partly based on this percentage **(table C.2).**

DNA Analysis Using Genetic Probes It is possible to identify a bacterial species by analyzing its genetic material. This uses small fragments of DNA (or RNA) called probes that are complementary to the specific sequences of DNA from a particular microbe. Unknown test DNA from specimens or cultures is bound to a special surface. After several different probes have been added, the plate is observed for visible signs that the probes have become fixed to the test DNA. The binding of probes onto areas of the test DNA indicates close correspondence and makes identification possible.

Nucleic Acid Sequencing and rRNA Analysis One of the most valuable indicators of evolutionary relatedness is the sequence of nitrogen bases in ribosomal RNA, a major component of ribosomes. Ribosomes have the same function (protein synthesis) in all cells, and they tend to remain stable in their nucleic acid content over long periods. Thus, any major differences in the sequence, or "signature," of the rRNA is likely to indicate some distance in ancestry.

This technique is effective for differentiating general group differences (it was used to separate the three superkingdoms of life discussed in chapter 1), and it can identify species. Elements of these and other identification methods are presented in more detail in chapters 10, 16, and 17.

TABLE C.2	Organization of *Bergey's Manual of Systematic Bacteriology,* Second Edition

Taxonomic Rank	Representative Genera
Volume 1. The Archaea and the Deeply Branching and Phototrophic Bacteria	
Domain Archaea	
Phylum Crenarchaeota	*Thermoproteus, Pyrodictium, Sulfolobus*
Phylum Euryarchaeota	
Class I. Methanobacteria	*Methanobacterium*
Class II. Methanococci	*Methanococcus*
Class III. Halobacteria	*Halobacterium, Halococcus*
Class IV. Thermoplasmata	*Thermoplasma, Picrophilus*
Class V. Thermococci	*Ferroplasma*
Class VI. Archaeoglobi	*Thermococcus, Pyrococcus*
Class VII. Methanopyri	*Archaeoglobus*
	Methanopyrus

(continues)

TABLE C.2 *(continued)*

Taxonomic Rank	Representative Genera
Volume 1. The Archaea and the Deeply Branching and Phototrophic Bacteria *(continued)*	
Domain Archaea	
Phylum Aquificae	*Aquifex, Hydrogenobacter*
Phylum Thermotogae	*Thermotoga, Geotoga*
Phylum Thermodesulfobacteria	*Thermodesulfobacterium*
Phylum "Deinococcus-Thermus"	*Deinococcus, Thermus*
Phylum Chrysiogenetes	*Chrysogenes*
Phylum Chloroflexi	*Chloroflexus, Herpetosiphon*
Phylum Thermomicrobia	*Thermomicrobium*
Phylum Nitrospira	*Nitrospira*
Phylum Deferribacteres	*Geovibrio*
Phylum Cyanobacteria	*Prochloron, Synechococcus*
Phylum Chlorobi	*Pleurocapsa, Oscillatoria, Anabaena, Nostoc, Stigonema Chlorobium, Pelodictyon*
Volume 2. Domain Bacteria: The Proteobacteria	
Phylum Proteobacteria	
Class I. Alphaproteobacteria	*Rhodospirillum, Rickettsia, Bartonella, Caulobacter, Rhizobium, Brucella, Nitrobacter, Methylobacterium, Beijerinckia, Hyphomicrobium*
Class II. Betaproteobacteria	*Neisseria, Burkholderia, Alcaligenes, Comamonas, Nitrosomonas, Methylophilus, Thiobacillus*
Class III. Gammaproteobacteria	*Chromatium, Leucothrix, Legionella, Pseudomonas, Moraxella, Acinetobacter, Azotobacter, Vibrio, Escherichia, Klebsiella, Proteus, Salmonella, Shigella, Yersinia, Haemophilus*
Class IV. Deltaproteobacteria	*Desulfovibrio, Bdellovibrio, Myxococcus, Polyangium*
Class V. Epsilonproteobacteria	*Campylobacter, Helicobacter*
Volume 3. Domain Bacteria: The Low G + C Gram-Positive Bacteria	
Phylum Firmicutes	
Class I. Clostridia	*Clostridium, Peptostreptococcus, Eubacterium, Desulfotomaculum, Heliobacterium, Veillonella*
Class II. Mollicutes	*Mycoplasma, Ureaplasma, Spiroplasma, Acholeplasma Bacillus, Caryophanon, Paenibacillus*
Class III. Bacilli	*Thermoactinomyces, Lactobacillus, Streptococcus, Enterococcus, Listeria, Leuconostoc, Staphylococcus*
Volume 4. Domain Bacteria: The High G + C Gram-Positive Bacteria	
Phylum Actinobacteria	
Class Actinobacteria	*Actinomyces, Micrococcus, Arthrobacter, Corynebacterium, Mycobacterium, Nocardia, Actinoplanes, Propionibacterium, Streptomyces, Thermomonospora, Frankia, Actinomadura, Bifidobacterium*
Volume 5. Domain Bacteria: The Planctomycetes, Spirochaetes, Fibrobacteres, Bacteriodetes, and Fusobacteria	
Phylum Planctomycetes	*Planctomyces, Gemmata*
Phylum Chlamydiae	*Chlamydia, Chlamydiophila*
Phylum Spirochaetes	*Spirochaeta, Borrelia, Treponema, Leptospira*
Phylum Fibrobacteres	*Fibrobacter*
Phylum Acidobacteria	*Acidobacterium*
Phylum Bacteriodetes	*Bacteroides, Porphyromonas, Prevotella, Flavobacterium, Sphingobacterium, Flexibacter, Cytophaga*
Phylum Fusobacteria	*Fusobacterium, Streptobacillus*
Phylum Verrucomicrobia	*Verrucomicrobium*
Phylum Dictyoglomus	*Dictyoglomus*

Answers to End of Chapter Questions

Chapter 1
1. d
2. c
3. d
4. c
5. d
6. a
7. c
8. b
9. d
10. c
11. c
12. b
13. d
14. order top to bottom: 3, 7, 4, 2, 8, 5, 6, 1
15. c
16. d, not cellular and not alive

Case Study
1. b
2. b
3. Answer appears in online appendix

On the Test
1. c

Chapter 2
1. c
2. c
3. b
4. c
5. a
6. d
7. c
8. b
9. c
10. b
11. b
12. d
13. b
14. c
15. c
16. c
17. a
18. d
19. d
20. b

Case Study
1. a, b, d
2. c
3. Answer appears in online appendix

On the Test
1. c
2. d

Chapter 3
1. c
2. b
3. c
4. d
5. b
6. d
7. b
8. b
9. c
10. c
11. a
12. b
13. c
14. d
15. b
16. c
17. abf, df, abf, ef, def, af, bf, bf

Case Study
1. e
2. c, d
3. Answer appears in online appendix

On the Test
1. b
2. d

Chapter 4
1. a
2. d
3. d
4. a
5. c
6. a
7. c
8. b
9. d
10. b
11. b
12. b
13. d
14. c
15. c
16. c
17. c
18. d

Case Study
1. b
2. d
3. Answer appears in online appendix

On the Test
1. a
2. c

Chapter 5
1. b
2. d
3. d
4. a
5. b
6. c
7. c
8. b
9. b
10. c
11. a
12. c
13. b
14. c
15. d
16. b
17. b, e, c, h, g, j, i, d, a, f

Case Study
1. c
2. b
3. Answer appears in online appendix

On the Test
1. c
2. d

Chapter 6
1. c
2. d
3. d
4. b
5. d
6. a
7. a
8. d
9. b
10. b
11. c
12. d
13. a
14. d
15. d

Case Study
1. a
2. b
3. Answer appears in online appendix

On the Test
1. c
2. c

Chapter 7
1. c
2. a
3. a
4. c
5. c
6. b
7. a
8. a
9. b
10. b
11. c
12. d
13. c
14. c
15. b
16. c

Case Study
1. d
2. c
3. Answer appears in online appendix

On the Test
1. b
2. b

Chapter 8
1. b
2. a
3. c
4. d
5. d
6. b
7. b
8. b
9. b
10. a
11. c
12. a
13. d
14. b
15. c
16. d
17. b
18. c
19. c
20. c
21. c
22. c, a, abc, a, b, a, c, c

Case Study
1. c
2. b
3. Answer appears in online appendix

On the Test
1. a
2. c

Chapter 9
1. b
2. e
3. b
4. b
5. c
6. c
7. c
8. a
9. b
10. a
11. e
12. b
13. d
14. b
15. c
16. b
17. d
18. d, f, b, g, e, a, i, c/e/h

Case Study
1. c
2. c
3. Answer appears in online appendix

On the Test
1. a
2. d

Chapter 10
1. c
2. c
3. d
4. a
5. b
6. c
7. c
8. e
9. d
10. h, c, f, a, g, b, e, d

Case Study
1. d
2. b
3. Answer appears in online appendix

On the Test
1. d
2. a

Chapter 11
1. d
2. c
3. b
4. a
5. c
6. b
7. d
8. b
9. d
10. c
11. b
12. d
13. c
14. d
15. a
16. b
17. c

Case Study
1. c
2. b
3. Answer appears in online appendix

On the Test
1. c
2. c

Chapter 12
1. b
2. c
3. d
4. b
5. c
6. c
7. b
8. d
9. a
10. c
11. c
12. b
13. d, a, g, b, f, h, c, e

Case Study
1. c
2. b
3. Answer appears in online appendix

On the Test
1. b
2. c

Chapter 13
1. a
2. d
3. b
4. d
5. c
6. d
7. b
8. c
9. c
10. c
11. d
12. c
13. c
14. a
15. a
16. d

Case Study
1. b
2. d
3. Answer appears in online appendix

On the Test
1. b
2. a

Chapter 14
1. b
2. b
3. d
4. b
5. b
6. b
7. c
8. c
9. a
10. a
11. c
12. d
13. c
14. d
15. d
16. c

Case Study
1. a
2. d
3. Answer appears in online appendix

On the Test
1. b
2. c

Chapter 15
1. b
2. a
3. c
4. a
5. c
6. b
7. b
8. c
9. a
10. c
11. a
12. c
13. e
14. b
15. c
16. d
17. b
18. c
19.
IgG	bfgh
IgA	abc
IgD	bj
IgE	bi
IgM	deh

20. adej, fgk, bej,
 bcej, adej,
 bcej, fm, fklm,
 bdej, acej,
 fklm, cfi,
 fgk, fhk

Case Study

1. d
2. a
3. Answer appears
 in online appendix

On the Test

1. c
2. a, d

Chapter 16

1. d
2. d
3. d
4. c
5. b
6. c
7. b
8. a
9. d
10. d
11. d
12. a
13. b
14. d
15. b
16. a

Case Study

1. a
2. d
3. Answer appears
 in online appendix

On the Test

1. a
2. b

Chapter 17

1. b, a, b, c, a
2. c
3. b
4. c
5. a
6. a
7. d
8. c
9. d

Case Study

1. b, c
2. c
3. Answer appears
 in online appendix

On the Test

1. c
2. b

Chapter 18

1. d
2. a
3. c
4. b
5. c
6. b
7. c
8. b
9. c
10. c
11. a
12. a
13. d
14. a
15. f
16. h, j, d, l, m, a, f, i,
 e, k, b, c

Case Study

1. a
2. Answer appears
 in online appendix
3. Answer appears
 in online appendix

On the Test

1. a
2. c

Chapter 19

1. b
2. c
3. b
4. d
5. c
6. c
7. d
8. c
9. b
10. c
11. d
12. c
13. a
14. a

15. 4.5.8/ 4.5.7/
 1.2.8.10/
 2.3.8.11/
 4.5.8.9
16. a/d, b, c, b c, d, b,
 d, a

Case Study

1. d
2. c
3. Answer appears
 in online appendix

On the Test

1. a
2. b

Chapter 20

1. b
2. b
3. d
4. b
5. e
6. d
7. d
8. b
9. d
10. d
11. c
12. d
13. b
14. all but c
15. l, i, h, a, d,
 g, k, e, j, m,
 f, c, b

Case Study

1. a
2. d
3. Answer appears
 in online appendix

On the Test

1. b
2. a

Chapter 21

1. b
2. b
3. c
4. d
5. d
6. e
7. d
8. c

9. b
10. d
11. a
12. d
13. b
14. c
15. d
16. d
17. a
18. b
19. a, c, b, d, c/e, g, f,
 e, c, f, g, c
20. g, c, f, f, c, d, a,
 d, g, a, e, g, g

Case Study

1. d
2. e
3. Answer appears
 in online appendix

On the Test

1. e
2. b

Chapter 22

1. c
2. a
3. a
4. d
5. d
6. a
7. a
8. d
9. c
10. c
11. d
12. c
13. c
14. d
15. b
16. b, g, d, e, c, a, f

Case Study

1. b
2. a, d
3. Answer appears
 in online appendix

On the Test

1. d
2. d

Chapter 23

1. c

2. b
3. d
4. b
5. b
6. d
7. c
8. d
9. c
10. a
11. d
12. d
13. b
14. a
15. a
16. c
17. c
18. d
19. 1. f, P
 2. j, P
 3. k, H
 4. g, H
 5. h, P
 6. b, H
 7. i, H
 8. l, P
 9. a, P
 10. d, P
 11. m, H
 12. e, H
 13. c, H
20. c, d, i, g, b, a, h,
 j, f, e

Case Study

1. b
2. c
3. c

On the Test

1. c
2. c

Chapter 24

1. d
2. c
3. b
4. a
5. d
6. d
7. c
8. d
9. a
10. b
11. d
12. b

13. c
14. d
15. a
16. d
17. e/a, g, i, c, h, l,
 b/k, f/k, f, d, j

Case Study

1. a
2. e
3. Answer appears
 in online appendix

On the Test

1. d
2. d

Chapter 25

1. a
2. b
3. b
4. c
5. d
6. d
7. b
8. d
9. c
10. d
11. b
12. d
13. c
14. a, c, d, f; a, c, f;
 a, c, f; b, d, e, g;
 a, c, f; c, e, g; a,
 c, e; a, c, d, f
15. c, ad, b, ac, hg, c,
 af, hf, a, cij, h
16.
 a. Influenza,
 mumps, rubella,
 measles
 b. HIV
 c. Hepatitis A
 virus, polio,
 rotavirus
 d. western equine
 encephalitis
 virus
 e. rabies,
 hantavirus
 f. rotavirus,
 measles, polio,
 mumps, rubella,
 influenza

Case Study

1. d
2. a-G, b-M, c-M,
 d-G, e-G
3. Answer appears
 in online appendix

On the Test

1. c
2. b

Chapter 26

1. c
2. b
3. b
4. d
5. c
6. d
7. c
8. d
9. b
10. d

Case Study

1. c
2. d
3. Answer appears
 in online appendix

On the Test

1. d
2. a

Chapter 27

1. c
2. a
3. d
4. d
5. b
6. b
7. d
8. b
9. b
10. c

Case Study

1. b
2. b
3. Answer appears
 in online appendix

On the Test

1. a
2. c

abiogenesis The belief in spontaneous generation as a source of life.

abiotic Nonliving factors such as soil, water, temperature, and light that are studied when looking at an ecosystem.

ABO blood group system Developed by Karl Landsteiner in 1904; the identification of different blood groups based on differing isoantigen markers characteristic of each blood type.

abscess An inflamed, fibrous mass enclosing a core of pus.

abyssal zone The deepest region of the ocean; a sunless, high-pressure, cold, anaerobic habitat.

acid-fast A term referring to the property of mycobacteria to retain carbol fuchsin even in the presence of acid alcohol. The staining procedure is used to diagnose tuberculosis.

acidic A solution with a pH value below 7 on the pH scale.

acidic fermentation An anaerobic degradation of pyruvic acid that results in organic acid production.

acquired immunodeficiency syndrome See **AIDS.**

acquired immunodeficiency syndrome/AIDS The complex signs and symptoms of immune system destruction seen during the late phase of human immunodeficiency virus (HIV) infection.

acquired or adaptive immunity Refers to specific immunity developed by lymphocytes responding to antigens.

actin Fine protein fibers within cells that contribute to structure and support.

actinomycetes A group of filamentous, funguslike bacteria.

active immunity Immunity acquired through direct stimulation of the immune system by antigen.

active site The specific region on an apoenzyme that binds substrate. The site for reaction catalysis.

active transport Nutrient transport method that requires carrier proteins in the membranes of the living cells and the expenditure of energy.

acute Characterized by rapid onset and short duration.

acyclovir A synthetic purine analog that blocks DNA synthesis in certain viruses, particularly the herpes simplex viruses.

adapt/adaptation The act of successfully adjusting to a new environment, often made possible by random genetic changes that provide an advantage under changed environmental conditions.

adenine (A) A purine nitrogen base found in DNA and RNA that pairs with the pyrimidine thymine.

adenosine deaminase (ADA) deficiency An immunodeficiency disorder and one type of SCIDs that is caused by an inborn error in the metabolism of adenine. The accumulation of adenine destroys both B and T lymphocytes.

adenosine triphosphate (ATP) A nucleotide that is the primary source of energy for cells.

adenovirus Nonenveloped DNA virus that causes colds; transmissible via respiratory and ocular secretions.

adhesion The process by which microbes gain a stable foothold at the portal of entry; often involves a specific interaction between the molecules on the microbial surface and the receptors on the host cell.

adjuvant In immunology, a chemical vehicle that enhances antigenicity, presumably by prolonging antigen retention at the injection site.

adsorption A process of adhering one molecule onto the surface of another molecule.

aerobe A microorganism that lives and grows in the presence of free gaseous oxygen (O_2).

aerobic respiration Respiration in which the final electron acceptor in the electron transport chain is oxygen (O_2).

aerosol Airborne suspension of fine dust or moisture particles that contain live pathogens.

aflatoxin From *Aspergillus flavus* toxin, a mycotoxin that typically poisons moldy animal feed and can cause liver cancer in humans and other animals.

agammaglobulinemia The absence of functioning antibodies in serum. A related term, hypogammaglobulinemia, means there is a reduced level of antibodies, rather than a complete absence.

agar A polysaccharide found in seaweed and commonly used to prepare solid culture media.

agglutination The aggregation caused by antibodies when they cross-link cells or large particles into clumps that settle.

agranulocyte One form of leukocyte (white blood cell) having globular, nonlobed nuclei and lacking prominent cytoplasmic granules.

AIDS-defining illness A group of serious and life-threatening diseases that occur primarily in HIV-positive people. When a person acquires one of these illnesses, he or she is diagnosed with the advanced stage of HIV infection known as AIDS.

alcoholic fermentation An anaerobic degradation of pyruvic acid that results in alcohol production.

algae Photosynthetic, plantlike organisms that generally lack the complex structure of plants; they may be single-celled or multicellular and inhabit diverse habitats such as marine and freshwater environments, glaciers, and hot springs.

alkaline See **basic.**

allergen A substance that provokes an allergic response.

allergy The altered, usually exaggerated, immune response to an allergen; sometimes used interchangeably with hypersensitivity.

alloantigen Antigens that vary in exact composition among the members the same species, which is what causes incompatibilities in blood types.

allograft Relatively compatible tissue exchange between nonidentical members of the same species; also called homograft.

allosteric Pertaining to the altered activity of an enzyme due to the binding of a molecule to a region other than the enzyme's active site.

amastigote The rounded or ovoid nonflagellated form of the *Leishmania* parasite.

amensalism A relationship where the actions of one microbe cause harm to another microbe sharing the same space or nutrient source.

Ames test A method for detecting mutagenic and potentially carcinogenic agents based upon the genetic alteration of nutritionally defective bacteria.

amination The addition of an amine (—NH_2) group to a molecule.

amino acid The building block of protein. Amino acids exist in 20 naturally occurring forms that impart different characteristics to the various proteins they compose.

aminoglycoside A complex group of drugs derived from soil actinomycetes that impair ribosome function and have antibiotic potential. Example: streptomycin.

ammonification Phase of the nitrogen cycle in which ammonia is released from decomposing organic material.

amphibolism Pertaining to the metabolic pathways that serve multiple functions in the breakdown, synthesis, and conversion of metabolites.

amphipathic Relating to a compound that has contrasting characteristics, such as hydrophilic-hydrophobic or acid-base.

amphitrichous Having a single flagellum or a tuft of flagella at opposite poles of a microbial cell.

anabolism The energy-consuming process of incorporating nutrients into protoplasm through biosynthesis.

anaerobe A microorganism that grows best, or exclusively, in the absence of oxygen and that does not use oxygen in its metabolism.

anaerobic digesters Closed chambers used in a microbial process that converts organic sludge from waste treatment plants into useful fuels such as methane and hydrogen gases; also called bioreactors.

anaerobic respiration Respiration in which the final electron acceptor in the electron transport chain is an inorganic molecule containing sulfate, nitrate, nitrite, carbonate and other salts, rather than molecular oxygen gas.

analog In chemistry, a compound that closely resembles another in structure.

anamnestic response In immunology, an augmented response or memory related to a prior stimulation of the immune system by antigen. It boosts the levels of antibodies.

anaphylaxis An exaggerated systemic allergic reaction to antigen that leads to severe respiratory and cardiac complications.

anion A negatively charged ion.

anoxygenic Any reaction that does not produce oxygen; usually in reference to the type of photosynthesis occurring in anaerobic photosynthetic bacteria.

anthrax A zoonotic disease of herbivorous livestock. The anthrax bacillus is a facultative parasite and can infect humans in a number of ways. In its most virulent form, it can be fatal.

antibiotic A chemical substance produced by one microorganism that can inhibit or kill another microbe, even in minute amounts.

antibody A large protein molecule evoked in response to an antigen that interacts specifically with that antigen.

anticodon The triplet sequence in transfer RNA that is complementary to the triplet sequence of messenger RNA (the codon).

antigen Any cell, particle, or chemical that has properties that allow it to stimulate a specific immune response by B cells or T cells. See **immunogen.**

antigen binding site Specific regions at the ends of the antibody molecule that recognize specific antigens. These sites have numerous shapes to fit a wide variety of antigens.

antigen-presenting cell (APC) A macrophage or dendritic cell that ingests and degrades an antigen and subsequently places the antigenic determinant molecules on its surface for recognition by CD4 T lymphocytes.

antigenic drift Minor antigenic changes in the influenza virus due to mutations in the spikes' genes.

antigenic shift Major changes in the influenza virus due to recombination of viral strains from two different host species.

antigenicity The property of a substance to stimulate a specific immune response such as antibody formation.

antihistamine A drug that counters the action of histamine and is useful in allergy treatment.

antisepsis/antiseptic Use of a growth-inhibiting agent (antiseptic) on tissues to prevent infection.

antiserum Antibody-rich serum derived from people who have recovered from specific infections such as hepatitis; sometimes taken from the blood of animals deliberately immunized against an infectious or toxic antigen. Used in passive immune therapy.

antitoxin Globulin fraction of serum that neutralizes a specific toxin. Also refers to the specific antitoxin antibody itself.

apicomplexan A eukaryotic microorganism that possesses an apical complex, used to penetrate host cells. The most well-known apicomplexans are the *Plasmodium* parasites responsible for malaria.

apoenzyme The protein part of an enzyme, as opposed to the nonprotein or inorganic cofactors.

appendage Accessory structure that sprouts from the surface of bacteria. They can be divided into two major groups: those that provide motility and those that enable adhesion.

aquifer A subterranean water-bearing stratum of permeable rock, sand, or gravel.

arboviruses Arthropod-borne viruses including togaviruses, reoviruses, flaviviruses, and bunyaviruses. These viruses generally cause mild, undifferentiated fevers and occasionally cases of severe encephalitis and hemorrhagic fever.

archaea Prokaryotic single-celled organisms of primitive origin that have unusual anatomy, physiology, and genetics, and live in harsh habitats; when capitalized (**Archaea**), the term refers to one of the three domains of living organisms as proposed by Woese.

arthropod A phylum of invertebrate animals with jointed exoskeletons. Includes insects such as mosquitoes and arachnids such as ticks that may be vectors of infectious diseases.

Arthus reaction An immune complex phenomenon that develops after repeat injection. This localized inflammation results from aggregates of antigen and antibody that bind, complement, and attract neutrophils.

artificial immunity Specific protection acquired through medical means.

ART Short for antiretroviral therapy, the drug cocktail that is used as a treatment for HIV infection and AIDS.

ascospore A spore formed within a saclike cell (ascus) of Ascomycota following nuclear fusion and meiosis.

ascus Special fungal sac in which haploid spores are created.

asepsis A condition free of viable pathogenic microorganisms.

aseptic techniques Methods of handling microbial cultures, patient specimens, and other sources of microbes in a way that prevents infection of the handler and others who may be exposed.

asthma An allergic respiratory disease marked by extreme sensitivity to allergens.

asymptomatic An infection that produces no noticeable symptoms even though the microbe is active in the host tissue.

asymptomatic carrier A person with an inapparent infection who shows no symptoms of being infected yet is able to pass the disease agent on to others.

atmosphere That part of the biosphere that includes the gaseous envelope up to 14 miles above the earth's surface. It contains gases such as carbon dioxide, nitrogen, and oxygen.

atom The smallest particle of an element to retain all the properties of that element.

atomic number (AN) A measurement that reflects the number of protons in an atom of a particular element.

atomic weight The average of the mass numbers of all the isotopic forms for a particular element.

atopy Allergic reaction classified as type I, with a strong familial relationship; caused by allergens such as pollen, insect venom, food, and dander; involves IgE antibody; includes symptoms of hay fever, asthma, and skin rash.

ATP synthase A unique enzyme located in the mitochondrial cristae, bacterial cell membrane, and chloroplast grana that harnesses the flux of hydrogen ions to the synthesis of ATP.

attenuate To reduce the virulence of a pathogenic bacterium or virus by passing it through a nonnative host or by long-term subculture.

autoantibody An antibody formed by a person against his own self molecules, called autoantigens, that are part of his cells.

autoantigen Molecules that are inherently part of self but are perceived by the immune system as foreign.

autoclave A sterilization chamber that allows the use of steam under pressure to sterilize materials. The most common temperature/pressure combination for an autoclave is 121°C and 15 psi.

autograft Tissue or organ surgically transplanted to another site on the same subject.

autoimmune disease/autoimmunity Literally, an immune reaction that targets self. This pathologic condition arises from the production of antibodies against autoantigens, for example in rheumatoid arthritis and multiple sclerosis.

autotroph A microorganism that requires only inorganic nutrients and whose sole source of carbon is carbon dioxide.

axenic A sterile state such as a pure culture. An axenic animal is born and raised in a germ-free environment. See **gnotobiotic.**

axial filament A type of flagellum (called an endoflagellum) that lies in the periplasmic space of spirochetes and is responsible for locomotion; also called periplasmic flagellum.

azole Five-ringed compound used in antifungal therapy. They are usually recognized by their *-azole* suffix (e.g., ketoconazole, clotrimazole).

bacillus (plural, **bacilli**) Bacterial cell shape that is basically cylindrical (longer than it is wide).

back-mutation A mutation that counteracts an earlier mutation, resulting in the restoration of the original DNA sequence.

bacteremia The presence of viable bacteria in circulating blood.

bacteria (plural of *bacterium*) Category of prokaryotes with peptidoglycan in their cell walls and a single, circular chromosome. This group of small cells is widely distributed in the earth's habitats.

bacterial chromosome A circular body in bacteria that contains the primary genetic material; also called **nucleoid.**

bacterial meningitis Inflammation of the meninges as a result of bacterial infection.

bactericide An agent that kills bacterial vegetative cells.

bacteriophage A virus that specifically infects bacteria; phage means "to eat."

bacteriostatic Any process or agent that inhibits bacterial growth.

barophile A microorganism that thrives under high (usually hydrostatic) pressure.

basement membrane A thin layer (1–6 μm) of protein and polysaccharide found at the base of epithelial tissues.

basic A solution with a pH value above 7 on the pH scale.

basidiospore A sexual spore that arises from a basidium. Found in basidiomycota fungi.

basidium A reproductive cell created when the swollen terminal cell of a hypha develops filaments (sterigmata) that form spores.

basophil A motile polymorphonuclear leukocyte that binds IgE. The basophilic cytoplasmic granules contain mediators of anaphylaxis and atopy.

benign tumor A self-contained growth within an organ that does not spread into adjacent tissue.

benthic zone The sedimentary bottom region of a pond, lake, or ocean.

beta oxidation The degradation of long-chain fatty acids. Two-carbon fragments are formed as a result of enzymatic attack directed against the second or beta carbon of the hydrocarbon chain. Aided by coenzyme A, the fragments enter the tricarboxylic acid (TCA) cycle and are processed for ATP synthesis.

beta-lactamase An enzyme secreted by certain bacteria that cleaves the beta-lactam ring of penicillin and cephalosporin and thus provides for resistance against the antibiotic. See **penicillinase.**

binary fission The formation of two new cells of approximately equal size as the result of parent cell division.

binomial system Scientific method of assigning names to organisms that employs two names to identify every organism—genus name plus species name.

biochemistry The study of organic compounds produced by (or that are components of) living things. The four main categories of biochemicals are carbohydrates, lipids, proteins, and nucleic acid.

bioenergetics The study of the production and use of energy by cells.

bioethics The study of biological issues and how they relate to human conduct and moral judgment.

biofilm A complex aggregate of interacting microbial cells that adhere to each other and to surfaces by means of a polysaccharide matrix. Biofilms permit communication among participants, which facilitates their survival and adaptation.

biogenesis Belief that living things can only arise from others of the same kind.

biogeochemical cycle A process by which matter is converted from organic to inorganic form and returned to various nonliving reservoirs on earth (air, rocks, and water) where it becomes available for reuse by living things. Elements such as carbon, nitrogen, and phosphorus are constantly cycled in this manner.

bioinformatics A field that uses computer technology to manage and analyze large sets of biological data, including genome and protein sequences.

biological vector An animal that not only transports an infectious agent but plays a role in the life cycle of the pathogen, serving as a site in which it can multiply or complete its life cycle. It is usually an alternative host to the pathogen.

biomes Particular climate regions in a terrestrial realm.

bioremediation The use of microbes to reduce or degrade pollutants, industrial wastes, and household garbage.

biosphere Habitable regions comprising the aquatic (hydrospheric), soil-rock (lithospheric), and air (atmospheric) environments.

biotechnology The use of organisms (microbes, plants, animals) or their products in the commercial or industrial realm.

biotic Living factors such as parasites, food substrates, or other living or once-living organisms that are studied when looking at an ecosystem.

blocking antibody The IgG class of immunoglobulins that competes with IgE antibody for allergens, thus blocking the degranulation of basophils and mast cells.

blood cells Cellular components of the blood consisting of red blood cells, primarily responsible for the transport of oxygen and carbon dioxide, and white blood cells, primarily responsible for host defense and immune reactions.

bradykinin An active polypeptide that is a potent vasodilator released from IgE-coated mast cells during anaphylaxis.

broad spectrum A term to denote drugs that affect many different types of bacteria, both gram-positive and gram-negative, as well as atypical bacteria such as rickettsias and chlamydias.

brucellosis A zoonosis transmitted to humans from infected animals or animal products; causes a fluctuating pattern of severe fever in humans as well as muscle pain, weakness, headache, weight loss, and profuse sweating; also called **undulant fever.**

bubo The swelling of one or more lymph nodes due to inflammation.

bubonic plague The form of plague in which bacterial growth is primarily restricted to the lymph and is characterized by the appearance of a swollen lymph node referred to as a bubo.

budding See **exocytosis.**

bulbar poliomyelitis Complication of polio infection in which the brainstem, medulla, or cranial nerves are affected. Leads to loss of respiratory control and paralysis of the trunk and limbs.

calculus Dental deposit formed when plaque becomes mineralized with calcium and phosphate crystals; also called **tartar.**

Calvin cycle The recurrent photosynthetic pathway characterized by CO_2 fixation and glucose synthesis; also called the dark reactions.

cancer Any malignant neoplasm that invades surrounding tissue and can metastasize to other locations. A carcinoma is derived from epithelial tissue, and a sarcoma arises from proliferating mesodermal cells of connective tissue.

capsid The protein covering of a virus' nucleic acid core. Capsids exhibit symmetry due to the regular arrangement of subunits called capsomers. See **icosahedron.**

capsomer A subunit of the virus capsid shaped as a triangle or disc.

capsule In bacteria, the loose, gel-like covering or slime made chiefly of simple polysaccharides. This layer is protective and can be associated with virulence.

carbohydrate A compound containing primarily carbon, hydrogen, and oxygen in a 1:2:1 ratio.

carbon cycle That pathway taken by carbon from its abiotic source to its use by producers to form organic compounds (biotic), followed by the breakdown of biotic compounds and their release to a nonliving reservoir in the environment (mostly carbon dioxide in the atmosphere).

carbon fixation Reactions in photosynthesis that incorporate inorganic carbon dioxide into organic compounds such as sugars. This occurs during the Calvin cycle and uses energy generated by the light reactions. This process is responsible for the vast majority of productivity on earth.

carbuncle A deep staphylococcal abscess joining several neighboring hair follicles.

carotenoid Yellow, orange, or red pigments that are accessories that trap light for photosynthesis.

carrier In epidemiology, a person who asymptomatically harbors infectious agents and inconspicuously spreads them to others. In chemistry, a chemical that can accept an atom, chemical radical, or electron from one compound and pass it to another chemical.

caseous lesion Necrotic area of lung tubercle superficially resembling cheese. Typical of tuberculosis.

catabolism The chemical breakdown of complex compounds into simpler units to be used in cell metabolism.

catalyst A substance that alters the rate of a reaction without being consumed or permanently changed by it. In cells, enzymes are catalysts.

catalytic site The niche in an enzyme where the substrate is converted to the product (also active site).

cation A positively charged ion.

cecum The intestinal pocket that forms the first segment of the large intestine; also called the appendix.

cell An individual membrane-bound living entity; the smallest living unit capable of an independent existence.

cell-mediated immunity The type of immune responses brought about by T cells, such as cytotoxic, regulatory, and helper effects. An activated T cell interacts directly with antigen-bearing cells in order to bring about its end result.

cellulose A long, fibrous polymer composed of β-glucose; one of the most common substances on earth.

cephalosporins A group of antibiotics isolated from the fungus *Cephalosporium* that block the synthesis of the cell wall and can be used for a variety of infections.

cercaria The free-swimming larva of the schistosome trematode that emerges from the snail host and can penetrate human skin, causing schistosomiasis.

cestode The common name for tapeworms that parasitize humans and domestic animals.

chancre The primary sore of syphilis that forms at the site of penetration by *Treponema pallidum*. It begins as a hard, dull red, painless papule that erodes from the center.

chancroid A lesion that resembles a chancre but is soft and is caused by *Haemophilus ducreyi*.

chemical bond A link formed between molecules when two or more atoms share, donate, or accept electrons.

chemical mediators Small molecules that are released during inflammation and specific immune reactions that allow communication between the cells of the immune system and facilitate surveillance, recognition, and attack.

chemiosmosis The movement of ions across a semipermeable membrane.

chemiosmotic theory An explanation for ATP formation that is based on the formation of a proton (H^+) gradient across a membrane during electron transport. Movement of the protons back across an ATP synthase causes the formation of ATP.

chemoautotrophs An organism that relies upon inorganic chemicals for its energy and carbon dioxide for its carbon; also called a chemolithotroph.

chemokines Chemical mediators (cytokines) that stimulate the movement and migration of white blood cells.

chemostat A growth chamber with an outflow that is equal to the continuous inflow of nutrient media. This steady-state growth device is used to study such events as cell division, mutation rates, and enzyme regulation.

chemotaxis The tendency of cells to move in response to a chemical gradient (toward an attractant or to avoid adverse stimuli). In inflammation, it refers to the movement of blood cells in reaction to chemical signals.

chemotherapy The use of chemical substances or drugs to treat or prevent disease.

chemotroph An organism that oxidizes compounds to feed on nutrients.

chickenpox A papulo-pustular rash caused by infection by varicella-zoster virus.

chimera A product formed by the fusion of two different organisms.

chitin A polysaccharide similar to cellulose in chemical structure. This polymer makes up the horny substance of the exoskeletons of arthropods and certain fungi.

chlamydias Tiny gram–negative bacteria that are obligate parasites inside the vacuoles of host cells; members cause a type of STD and pneumonia.

chlorophyll A group of mostly green pigments that are used by photosynthetic eukaryotic organisms and cyanobacteria to trap light energy to use in making chemical bonds.

chloroplast An organelle containing chlorophyll that is found in photosynthetic eukaryotes.

cholesterol Best-known member of a group of lipids called steroids. Cholesterol is commonly found in cell membranes and animal hormones.

chromatin The genetic material of the nucleus. Chromatin is made up of nucleic acid and stains readily with certain dyes.

chromophore The chemical radical of a dye that is responsible for its color and reactivity.

chromosome The tightly coiled bodies within cells, composed of DNA, that are the primary locations for genetic material.

chronic infection An infection that persists over a long duration, with symptoms being mild or absent.

ciliates Eukaryotic microorganisms that use cilia as a means of motility.

cilium (plural, **cilia**) Eukaryotic structure similar to flagella that propels a protozoan through the environment.

class In the levels of classification, the division of organisms that follows phylum.

clonal selection theory A conceptual explanation for the development of lymphocyte specificity and variety during maturation of the immune system.

clone A colony of cells (or group of organisms) derived from a single cell (or single organism) by asexual reproduction. All units share identical characteristics. Also used as a verb to refer to the process of producing a genetically identical population of cells or genes.

cloning host An organism such as a bacterium or a yeast that receives and replicates a foreign piece of DNA inserted through genetic engineering techiques.

cluster of differentiation (CD) Receptors on mature T cells that serve in cell communication; react with MHC receptors for immune recognition by antigen processing cells.

coagulase A plasma-clotting enzyme secreted by *Staphylococcus aureus*. It contributes to virulence and is involved in forming a fibrin wall that surrounds staphylococcal lesions.

coagulase-negative staphylococci Opportunistic species that are usually part of the normal flora of the skin and mucous membranes. They cause infection when host defenses are low and lack many virulence factors such as coagulase.

coccobacillus An elongated coccus; a short, thick, oval-shaped bacterial rod.

coccus (plural, **cocci**) A spherical-shaped bacterial cell.

codon A specific sequence of three nucleotides in DNA or mRNA that constitutes the genetic code for a particular amino acid.

coenzyme A complex organic molecule, several of which are derived from vitamins (e.g., nicotinamide or niacin, riboflavin). A coenzyme operates in conjunction with an enzyme. Coenzymes serve as transient carriers of specific atoms or functional groups during metabolic reactions.

cofactor An enzyme accessory. It can be organic, such as coenzymes, or inorganic, such as Fe^{2+}, Mn^{2+}, Zn^{2+}, or other metallic ions.

cold sterilization The use of nonheating methods such as radiation or filtration to sterilize materials.

coliform A collective term that includes normal enteric bacteria that are gram-negative and lactose-fermenting.

colony A macroscopic cluster of cells appearing on a solid medium, each arising from the multiplication of a single cell.

colostrum The clear yellow early product of breast milk that is very high in secretory antibodies. Provides passive intestinal protection.

commensalism An unequal relationship described as one member (A) deriving benefit from another member (B), without harming or benefiting (B).

common (seed) warts Painless, elevated rough growths on the fingers or occasionally other parts of the body.

communicable infection Capable of being transmitted from one individual to another.

community The interacting mixture of populations in a given habitat.

competitive inhibition The blockage of microbial growth through a metabolic analog drug that inserts on the active site of an essential metabolic enzyme and prevents further action of that enzyme.

complement/complement fixation In immunology, protein components that act in a defined sequence (cascade) when set in motion either by an antigen-antibody complex or by factors from the lectin or alternative pathways. When complement adheres to a certain antibody or receptor, it is said to be fixed.

complementary DNA (cDNA) DNA created by using reverse transcriptase to synthesize DNA from RNA templates.

complex (nonsynthetic) medium Culture medium containing at least one component that is chemically undefined.

compound Molecule that is a combination of two or more different elements.

concentration The expression of the amount of a solute dissolved in a certain amount of solvent. It may be defined by weight, volume, or percentage.

condylomata acuminata Extensive, branched masses of genital warts caused by infection with human papillomavirus.

congenital rubella Transmission of the rubella virus to a fetus *in utero*. Injury to the fetus is generally much more serious than it is to the mother.

conidia Asexual fungal spores shed as free units from the tips of fertile hyphae.

conjugation In bacteria, the contact between donor and recipient cells associated with the transfer of genetic material such as plasmids. Can involve special (sex) pili. Also a form of sexual recombination in ciliated protozoans.

conjunctivitis Sometimes called "pinkeye." A *Haemophilus* infection of the subconjunctiva that is common among children, easily transmitted, and treated with antibiotic eyedrops.

constitutive enzyme An enzyme present in bacterial cells in constant amounts, regardless of the presence of substrate. Enzymes of the central catabolic pathways are typical examples.

consumer An organism that feeds on producers or other consumers. It gets all nutrients and energy from other organisms (also called **heterotroph**). May exist at several levels, such as primary (feeds on producers), and secondary (feeds on primary consumers).

contagious Very readily communicable; transmissible by direct contact with infected people and their fresh secretions or excretions.

contaminant An impurity; any undesirable material or organism. A culture into which unknown microbes have been introduced is contaminated.

convalescence Recovery; the period between the end of a disease and the complete restoration of health in a patient.

corepressor A molecule that combines with an inactive repressor to form an active repressor. The resultant combined molecule attaches to the operator gene site and inhibits the activity of structural genes in line with the operator.

covalent bond A chemical bond formed by the sharing of electrons between two atoms.

Creutzfeldt-Jakob disease (CJD) A spongiform encephalopathy caused by infection with a prion. The disease is marked by dementia, impaired senses, and uncontrollable muscle contractions.

CRISPR An acronym for clustered regularly interspaced short palindromic repeats.

CRISPR-Cas9 A system of specific DNA sequences (CRISPR) and bacterial enzymes (Cas9) that allow DNA to be cut and edited with great precision.

crista (plural, **cristae**) The infolded inner membrane of a mitochondrion that is the site of the respiratory chain and oxidative phosphorylation.

culture The visible accumulation of microorganisms in or on a nutrient medium. Also, the propagation of microorganisms with various media.

curd The coagulated milk protein used in cheese making.

cutaneous Second level of skin, including the stratum corneum and occasionally the upper dermis.

cutaneous anthrax The mildest form of anthrax, caused by the entrance of bacterial spores into small nicks or openings in the skin, their germination, and the formation of a dark necrotic lesion called an eschar.

cutaneous candidiasis A mycosis occurring in the skin and membranes of compromised patients and neonates as a result of infection by *Candida albicans*.

cyanobacteria Widespread and ecologically important photosynthetic bacteria; evidence indicates their role in the evolution of chloroplasts in eukaryotic cells.

cyst The resistant, dormant, but infectious form of protozoans. Can be important in spread of infectious agents such as *Entamoeba histolytica* and *Giardia lamblia*.

cysteine Sulfur-containing amino acid that is essential to the structure and specificity of proteins.

cytochrome A group of heme protein compounds whose chief role is in electron and/or hydrogen transport occurring in the last phase of aerobic respiration.

cytokine A chemical substance produced by white blood cells and tissue cells that regulates development, inflammation, and immunity.

cytopathic effect The degenerative changes in cells associated with virus infection. Example: the formation of multinucleate giant cells (Negri bodies), the prominent cytoplasmic inclusions of nerve cells infected by rabies virus.

cytoplasm Dense fluid encased by the cell membrane; the site of many of the cell's biochemical and synthetic activities.

cytosine (C) One of the nitrogen bases found in DNA and RNA, with a pyrimidine form.

cytoskeleton A fine intracellular network of fibers, filaments, and other strands that function in support and shape of cells.

cytotoxic/cytotoxicity Having the capacity to destroy specific cells. The cytotoxic class of T cells attacks cancer cells, virus-infected cells, and eukaryotic pathogens.

death phase A dramatic downturn in numbers occurs due to lack of nutrition, adverse environmental factors, and accumulation of wastes. A greater number of cells are dying in this phase.

debridement Trimming away devitalized tissue and foreign matter from a wound.

decomposer A consumer that feeds on organic matter from the bodies of dead organisms. These microorganisms feed from all levels of the food pyramid and are responsible for recycling elements (also called saprobes).

decomposition The breakdown of dead matter and wastes into simple compounds that can be directed back into the natural cycle of living things.

decontamination The removal or neutralization of an infectious, poisonous, or injurious agent from a site.

definitive host The organism in which a parasite develops into its adult or sexually mature stage; also called the **final host.**

degeneracy The property of the genetic code that allows an amino acid to be specified by several different codons.

degerm/degermation To physically remove surface oils, debris, and soil from skin and wounds to reduce the microbial load.

degranulation The release of cytoplasmic granules, as when cytokines are secreted from mast cell granules.

dehydration synthesis During the formation of a carbohydrate bond, the step in which one carbon molecule gives up its OH group and the other loses the H from its OH group, thereby producing a water molecule. This process is common to all polymerization reactions.

denature/denaturation The loss of normal characteristics (shape, configuration) resulting from some molecular alteration. Used in reference to loss of normal activity by proteins when their 3-D structure has been altered by heat or chemicals.

dendritic cell A large, antigen-processing cell characterized by long, branchlike extensions of the cell membrane.

denitrification The end of the nitrogen cycle when nitrogen compounds are returned to the reservoir in the air.

dental caries A mixed infection of the tooth surface that gradually destroys the enamel and may lead to destruction of the deeper tissue.

deoxyribonucleic acid (DNA) The nucleic acid often referred to as the "double helix." DNA carries the master plan for an organism's heredity.

deoxyribose A 5-carbon sugar that is an important component of DNA.

dermatophytoses Superficial mycoses such as athlete's foot and ringworm associated with certain fungi with an affinity for the skin, hair, and nails. These fungi are called **dermatophytes.**

desensitization/hyposensitization A therapeutic exposure to known allergens designed to build tolerance and eventually prevent allergic reaction. Hyposensitization is gaining in use because it emphasizes that the allergy is reduced, not completely removed.

desiccate/desiccated To dry thoroughly. To preserve by drying.

diabetes mellitus A disease involving compromise in insulin function. In one form, the pancreatic cells that produce insulin are destroyed by autoantibodies; and in another, the pancreas does not produce sufficient insulin.

diapedesis The migration of intact blood cells between endothelial cells of a blood vessel such as a venule.

differential medium A single substrate that discriminates between groups of microorganisms on the basis of differences in their appearance due to different chemical reactions.

differential stain A technique that utilizes two dyes to distinguish between different microbial groups or cell parts by color reaction.

diffusion The passive dispersal of molecules, ions, or microscopic particles propelled down a concentration gradient by spontaneous random motion to achieve a uniform distribution.

DiGeorge syndrome A genetic defect that causes the loss of thymus function; results in abnormally low or absent T cells and other developmental abnormalities.

dimer A molecule that is composed of two monomers bound together.

dimorphic In mycology, the tendency of some pathogens to alter their growth form from mold to yeast in response to rising temperature.

diphtheria Infection by *Corynebacterium diphtheriae*. It is transmitted by human carriers or contaminated milk, and the primary infection is in the upper respiratory tract. Several forms of this infection may be fatal if untreated. Vaccination on the recommended schedule can prevent infection.

diphtherotoxin Exotoxin responsible for the effects seen in diphtheria. The toxin affects the upper respiratory system, peripheral nervous system, and the heart.

diplococcus Spherical or oval-shaped bacteria, typically found in pairs.

diplomonads A group of eukaryotic microorganisms marked by simplified, poorly functioning mitochondria, requiring them to generate most of their energy anaerobically. The most well-known diplomonad is *Giardia.*

direct, or total, cell count 1. Counting total numbers of individual cells being viewed with magnification. 2. Counting isolated colonies of organisms growing on a plate of media as a way to determine population size.

disaccharide A sugar containing two monosaccharides. Example: sucrose (fructose + glucose).

disinfection/disinfectant The destruction of pathogenic nonsporulating microbes or their toxins, usually on inanimate surfaces. A disinfectant is a chemical used for this purpose.

division In the levels of classification, an alternative term for *phylum.*

DNA polymerase Enzyme responsible for the replication of DNA. Several versions of the enzyme exist, each completing a unique portion of the replication process.

DNA profiling, DNA fingerprinting A method of identifying patterns of specific genetic markers unique to an individual for the purpose of identification. Used in forensics, medicine, anthropology, and microbial identification

DNA sequencing A process of determining the exact order of nucleotides in a segment of DNA, ranging from small pieces to whole chromosomes or genomes. The newest technologies are rapid machine-based methods that use lasers, cameras, or microscopes to read fluorescent nucleotides on a strand of DNA.

DNA vaccine A newer vaccine preparation based on inserting DNA from pathogens into host cells to encourage them to express the foreign protein and stimulate immunity.

domain In the levels of classification, the broadest general category to which an organism is assigned. Members of a domain share only one or a few general characteristics.

droplet nuclei The dried residue of fine droplets produced by mucus and saliva sprayed while sneezing and coughing. Droplet nuclei are less than 5 μm in diameter (large enough to bear a single bacterium and small enough to remain airborne for a long time) and can be carried by air currents.

drug resistance An adaptive response in which microorganisms begin to tolerate an amount of drug that had previously been inhibitory.

dry heat Air with a low moisture content that has been heated from 160 to several thousand degrees Celsius.

dysentery Infectious diarrhea characterized by blood and mucus in the feces.

dyspnea Difficulty in breathing.

ecosystem A collection of organisms together with its surrounding physical and chemical factors existing in a given place and time.

eczema An acute or chronic allergy of the skin associated with itching and burning sensations. Typically, red, edematous, vesicular lesions erupt, leaving the skin scaly and sometimes hyperpigmented.

edema The accumulation of excess fluid in cells, tissues, or serous cavities; also called swelling.

electrolyte Any compound that ionizes in solution and conducts current in an electrical field.

electron A negatively charged subatomic particle that is distributed around the nucleus in an atom.

electrophoresis The separation of molecules by size and charge through exposure to an electrical current.

element A substance comprising only one kind of atom that cannot be degraded into two or more substances without losing its chemical characteristics.

ELISA Abbreviation for enzyme-linked immunosorbent assay, a very sensitive serological test used to detect antibodies in diseases such as AIDS. Two types are **indirect ELISA** and **capture ELISA.**

emerging disease Newly identified diseases that are becoming more prominent.

endemic disease A native disease that exists continuously in a geographic region. This pattern may reflect a vector or environmental source.

endergonic reaction A chemical reaction that occurs with the absorption and storage of surrounding energy. Antonym: **exergonic.**

endocytosis The process whereby solid and liquid materials are taken into the cell through membrane invagination and engulfment into a vesicle.

endoenzyme An intracellular enzyme that functions primarily within the cell compartment, as opposed to enzymes that are secreted.

endogenous Originating or produced within an organism or one of its parts.

endoplasmic reticulum (ER) An intracellular network of flattened sacs or tubules with or without ribosomes on their surfaces.

endospore A small, dormant, resistant derivative of a bacterial cell that germinates under favorable growth conditions into a vegetative cell. The bacterial genera *Bacillus* and *Clostridium* are typical spore-formers.

endosymbiosis The evolutionary process through which prokaryotic cells came together in a mutually beneficial association that gave rise to eukaryotic cells during billions of years of coevolution.

endotoxin A bacterial intracellular toxin that is not ordinarily released (as is exotoxin). Endotoxin is composed of a phospholipid-polysaccharide complex that is an integral part of gram-negative bacterial cell walls. Endotoxins can cause severe shock and fever.

energy of activation The minimum energy input necessary for reactants to form products in a chemical reaction.

energy pyramid An ecological model that shows the energy flow among the organisms in a community. It is structured like the food pyramid, but shows how energy is reduced from one trophic level to another.

enriched medium A nutrient medium supplemented with blood, serum, or some growth factor to promote the multiplication of fastidious microorganisms.

enterohemorrhagic E. coli (EHEC) A strain of *E. coli*, type 0157: H7, that secretes toxins that provoke secretory diarrhea and intestinal hemorrhage.

enteroinvasive Predisposed to invade the intestinal tissues.

enteropathogenic Pathogenic to the alimentary canal.

enterotoxigenic E. coli (ETEC) Strains of *E. coli* that produce toxins that attack the GI tract; effects are similar to cholera.

enterotoxin A bacterial toxin that specifically targets intestinal mucous membrane cells. Enterotoxigenic strains of *Escherichia coli* and *Staphylococcus aureus* are typical sources.

enveloped virus A virus whose nucleocapsid is enclosed by a membrane derived in part from the host cell. It usually contains exposed glycoprotein spikes specific for the virus.

enzyme A protein biocatalyst that facilitates metabolic reactions.

enzyme induction One of the controls on enzyme synthesis. This occurs when enzymes are synthesized only when suitable substrates are present.

enzyme repression The inhibition of enzyme synthesis by the end product of a catabolic pathway.

eosinophil A leukocyte whose cytoplasmic granules readily stain with red eosin dye. Eosinophils function primarily in the destruction of large parasites and in allergy and inflammation.

epidemic A sudden and simultaneous increase in the number of cases of a certain disease in a community.

epidemic parotitis (mumps) Disease caused by infection with *Paramyxovirus* and marked by swelling in and around the parotid salivary glands.

epidemiology The study of the factors affecting the prevalence and spread of disease within a community.

epimastigote The trypanosomal form found in the tsetse fly or reduviid bug vector. Its flagellum originates near the nucleus, extends along an undulating membrane, and emerges from the anterior end.

epitope The portion of a foreign cell or virus that is the precise stimulus for an immune response; also called the **antigenic determinant.**

Epstein-Barr virus (EBV) Herpesvirus linked to infectious mononucleosis, Burkitt lymphoma, and nasopharyngeal carcinoma.

erysipelas An acute, sharply defined inflammatory disease specifically caused by hemolytic *Streptococcus*. The eruption is limited to the skin but can be complicated by serious systemic symptoms.

erysipeloid An inflammation resembling erysipelas but caused by *Erysipelothrix*, a gram-positive rod. The self-limited cellulitis that appears at the site of an infected wound, usually the hand, comes from handling contaminated fish or meat.

erythrocytes (red blood cells) Blood cells involved in the transport of oxygen and carbon dioxide.

erythrogenic toxin An exotoxin produced by lysogenized group A strains of β-hemolytic streptococci that is responsible for the severe fever and rash of scarlet fever in the nonimmune individual; also called a pyrogenic toxin.

eschar A dark, sloughing scab that is the lesion of anthrax and certain rickettsioses.

essential nutrient Any ingredient such as a certain amino acid, fatty acid, vitamin, or mineral that cannot be formed by an organism and must be supplied in the diet; a growth factor.

ester bond A covalent bond formed by reacting carboxylic acid with an OH group:

$$(R\!-\!\overset{\overset{\textstyle O}{\|}}{C}\!-\!O\!-\!R')$$

Olive and corn oils, lard, and butter are examples of triacylglycerols—esters formed between glycerol and three fatty acids.

ethylene oxide (ETO) A potent, highly water-soluble gas invaluable for gaseous sterilization of heat-sensitive objects such as plastics, surgical and diagnostic appliances, and spices. Potential hazards are related to its carcinogenic, residual, and explosive nature. Ethylene oxide is rendered nonexplosive by mixing with 90% CO_2 or fluorocarbon.

etiologic agent The microbial cause of disease; the pathogen.

Eukarya One of the three domains (sometimes called superkingdoms) of living organisms, as proposed by Woese; contains all eukaryotic organisms.

eukaryotic cell A cell that differs from a prokaryotic cell chiefly by having a nuclear membrane (a well-defined nucleus), membrane-bounded subcellular organelles, and mitotic cell division.

eutrophication The process whereby dissolved nutrients resulting from natural seasonal enrichment or industrial pollution of water cause overgrowth of algae and cyanobacteria to the detriment of fish and other large aquatic inhabitants.

evolution Scientific principle that states that living things change gradually through hundreds of millions of years, and these changes are expressed in structural and functional adaptations in each organism. Evolution presumes that those traits that favor survival are preserved and passed on to following generations, and those traits that do not favor survival are lost.

exanthem An eruption or rash of the skin.

exergonic A chemical reaction associated with the release of energy to the surroundings. Antonym: **endergonic.**

exfoliative toxin A poisonous substance that causes superficial cells of an epithelium to detach and be shed. Example: staphylococcal exfoliatin; also called an epidermolytic toxin.

exocytosis The process that releases enveloped viruses from the membrane of the host's cytoplasm.

exoenzyme An extracellular enzyme chiefly used to hydrolyze nutrient macromolecules that cannot readily enter the cell. This enzyme is secreted into the environment, where it may function in saprobic decomposition of organic debris or support the invasion of tissues by pathogens.

exogenous Originating from outside the body.

exon A section of eukaryotic DNA coding for a corresponding portion of mRNA that is translated into proteins. Intervening stretches of DNA that are not expressed are called introns. During transcription, exons are separated from introns and are spliced together into a continuous mRNA transcript.

exotoxin A toxin (usually protein) that is secreted and acts upon a specific cellular target. Examples: botulin, tetanospasmin, diphtheria toxin, and erythrogenic toxin.

exponential Pertaining to the use of exponents, numbers that are typically written as superscripts to indicate how many times a factor is to be multiplied. Exponents are used in scientific notation to render large, cumbersome numbers into small, workable quantities.

extrapulmonary tuberculosis A condition in which tuberculosis bacilli have spread to organs other than the lungs.

extremophile Organism capable of living in harsh environments, such as extreme heat or cold.

facilitated diffusion The passive movement of a substance across a plasma membrane from an area of higher concentration to an area of lower concentration utilizing specialized carrier proteins.

facultative Pertaining to the capacity of microbes to adapt or adjust to variations; not obligate. Example: The presence of oxygen is not required for a facultative anaerobe to grow, even though it can use oxygen if it is present.

family In the levels of classification, a mid-level division of organisms that groups more closely related organisms than previous levels. An order is divided into families.

fastidious Requiring strict, narrow nutritional or environmental conditions for growth. Said of bacteria.

fecal coliforms Any species of gram-negative lactose-positive bacteria (primarily *Escherichia coli*) that live primarily in the intestinal tract and not the environment. Finding evidence of these bacteria in a water or food sample is substantial evidence of fecal contamination and potential for infection. See **coliform.**

fermentation The extraction of energy through anaerobic degradation of substrates into simpler, reduced metabolites. In large industrial processes, fermentation can mean any use of microbial metabolism to manufacture organic chemicals or other products.

fermentor A large tank used in industrial microbiology to grow mass quantities of microbes that can synthesize desired products. These devices are equipped with means to stir, monitor, and harvest products such as drugs, enzymes, and proteins in very large quantities.

fertility (F) factor Donor plasmid that allows synthesis of a pilus in bacterial conjugation. Presence of the factor is indicated by F^+, and lack of the factor is indicated by F^-.

filament A helical structure composed of proteins that is part of bacterial flagella.

fimbria, fimbriae Short, numerous surface appendages on some bacteria that provide adhesion but not locomotion.

final electron acceptor A molecule that receives the electrons (is reduced) at the end of a pathway where electrons are being transported. For example, in aerobic organisms, the final acceptor in the electron transport chain is O_2, whereas in organisms with anaerobic respiration, it is some other compound such as SO_2^{2-}, or NO_3^-.

flagellum (plural, **flagella**) A long appendage used to propel an organism through a fluid environment. Flagella of bacteria and eukaryotes are similar in general function but differ significantly in structure.

fluid mosaic model A conceptualization of the molecular architecture of cellular membranes as a bilipid layer containing proteins. Membrane proteins are embedded to some degree in this bilayer, where they float freely about.

fluorescence/fluorescent antibodies The property possessed by certain minerals and dyes to emit visible light when excited by ultraviolet radiation. One application is to combine a fluorescent dye with a specific antibody to detect the presence of an unknown antigen.

focal infection Occurs when an infectious agent breaks loose from a localized infection and is carried by the circulation to other tissues.

folliculitis An inflammatory reaction involving the formation of papules or pustules in clusters of hair follicles.

fomite Virtually any inanimate object an infected individual has contact with that can serve as a vehicle for the spread of disease.

food chain A simple straight-line feeding sequence among organisms in a community.

food fermentations Addition to and growth of known cultures of microorganisms in foods to produce desirable flavors, smells, or textures. Includes cheeses, breads, alcoholic beverages, and pickles.

food infection A form of food-borne illness associated with ingesting living pathogenic microbes that invade the intestine. The damage caused by microbes growing in the body cause the main symptoms, which are usually gastroenteritis (example is salmonellosis).

food intoxication A form of food-borne illness that is the result of ingesting microbial toxins given off by bacteria growing in the food. The toxins cause the main symptoms (example is botulism).

food poisoning Any form of illness acquired from ingesting foods; sources include microbes, chemicals, plants, and animals (also food-borne disease).

food web A complex network that traces all feeding interactions among organisms in a community (see **food chain**). This is considered to be a more accurate picture of food relationships in a community than a food chain.

formalin A 37% aqueous solution of formaldehyde gas; a potent chemical fixative and microbicide.

frameshift mutation An insertion or deletion mutation that changes the codon reading frame from the point of the mutation to the final codon. Almost always leads to a nonfunctional protein.

fructose One of the carbohydrates commonly referred to as sugars. Fructose is commonly fruit sugars.

functional group In chemistry, a particular molecular combination that reacts in predictable ways and confers particular properties on a compound. Examples: —COOH, —OH, —CHO.

fungicide A chemical that can kill fungal spores, hyphae, and yeast.

fungus/fungi Heterotrophic unicellular or multicellular eukaryotic organism that may take the form of a larger macroscopic organism, as in the case of mushrooms, or a smaller microscopic organism, as in the case of yeasts and molds.

furuncle A boil; a localized pyogenic infection arising from a hair follicle.

Gaia theory The concept that biotic and abiotic factors sustain suitable conditions for one another simply by their interactions. Named after the mythical Greek goddess of earth.

GALT Abbreviation for gut-associated lymphoid tissue. Includes **Peyer's patches.**

gamma globulin The fraction of plasma proteins high in immunoglobulins (antibodies). Preparations from pooled human plasma containing normal antibodies make useful passive immunizing agents against pertussis, polio, measles, and several other diseases.

gas gangrene Disease caused by a clostridial infection of soft tissue or wound. The name refers to the gas produced by the bacteria growing in the tissue. Unless treated early, it is fatal; also called **myonecrosis.**

gastroenteritis Inflammation of the lining of the stomach and intestine. May be caused by infection, intestinal disorders, or food poisoning.

gene A site on a chromosome that provides information for a certain cell function. A specific segment of DNA that contains the necessary code to make a protein or RNA molecule.

gene probe Short strand of single-stranded nucleic acid that hybridizes specifically with complementary stretches of nucleotides on test samples and thereby serves as a tagging and identification device.

gene therapy The introduction of normal functional genes into people with genetic diseases such as sickle-cell anemia and cystic fibrosis. This is usually accomplished by a virus vector.

generation time Time required for a complete fission cycle—from parent cell to two new daughter cells; also called **doubling time.**

genetic engineering/bioengineering A field involving deliberate alterations (recombinations) of the genomes of microbes, plants, and animals through special technological processes.

genetics The science that studies inheritance of biological characteristics.

genital warts A prevalent STD linked to some forms of cancer of the reproductive organs. Caused by infection with human papillomavirus.

genome The complete set of chromosomes and genes in an organism.

genotype The genetic makeup of an organism as inherited from parents. The genotype is ultimately responsible for an organism's phenotype, or expressed characteristics.

genus In the levels of classification, the second-most specific level. A family is divided into several genera.

germ theory of disease A theory first originating in the 1800s that proposed that microorganisms can be the cause of diseases. The concept is so well established in the present time that it is considered a fact.

germicide An agent lethal to non-endospore-forming pathogens.

giardiasis Infection by the *Giardia* flagellate. The most common mode of transmission is contaminated food and water. Symptoms include diarrhea, abdominal pain, and flatulence.

gingivitis Inflammation of the gum tissue in contact with the roots of the teeth.

glomerulonephritis An inflammatory autoimmune condition in response to streptococcal toxins.

gluconeogenesis The formation of glucose (or glycogen) from noncarbohydrate sources such as protein or fat; also called **glyconeogenesis.**

glucose One of the carbohydrates commonly referred to as sugars. Glucose is characterized by its 6-carbon structure.

glutaraldehyde A yellow acidic liquid used in antimicrobial control. Because glutaraldehyde kills spores, it is considered a sterilant.

glycan A polysaccharide.

glycerol A 3-carbon alcohol, with three OH groups that serve as binding sites.

glycocalyx A filamentous network of carbohydrate-rich molecules that coats cells.

glycogen A glucose polymer stored by cells.

glycolysis The energy-yielding breakdown of glucose to pyruvic or lactic acid (occurs in fermentation). It is often called anaerobic glycolysis because no molecular oxygen is consumed in the processes.

glycosidic bond A bond that joins monosaccharides to form disaccharides and polymers.

gnotobiotic Literally means known (gnoto) and life (bios). Referring to experiments performed on germ-free animals that have been inoculated with known species of microbes.

Golgi apparatus An organelle of eukaryotes that participates in packaging and secretion of molecules; also known as **Golgi complex.**

gonococcus Common name for *Neisseria gonorrhoeae,* the agent of gonorrhea.

graft versus host disease (GVHD) A condition associated with a bone marrow transplant in which T cells in the transplanted tissue mount an immune response against the recipient's (host) normal tissues.

graft/graft rejection Live tissues or organs taken from a donor and transplanted into a recipient to replace damaged or missing tissues such as skin, bone, blood vessels, heart, bone marrow. When the donor displays antigens that are recognized and trigger an immune attack, the grafted tissue or organ may be lost.

Gram stain A differential stain for bacteria useful in identification and taxonomy. Gram-positive organisms appear purple from crystal violet-mordant retention, whereas gram-negative organisms appear red after loss of crystal violet and absorbance of the safranin counterstain.

grana Discrete stacks of chlorophyll-containing thylakoids within chloroplasts.

granulocyte A mature leukocyte that contains noticeable granules in a Wright stain. Examples: neutrophils, eosinophils, and basophils.

granuloma A solid mass or nodule of inflammatory tissue containing modified macrophages and lymphocytes. Usually a chronic pathologic process of diseases such as tuberculosis or syphilis.

granzymes Cytotoxic enzymes produced by cytotoxic T cells and natural killer cells that participate in cell death.

Graves' disease A malfunction of the thyroid gland in which autoantibodies directed at thyroid cells stimulate an overproduction of thyroid hormone (hyperthyroidism).

greenhouse effect The capacity to retain solar energy by a blanket of atmospheric gases that redirects heat waves back toward the earth.

group translocation A form of active transport in which the substance being transported is altered during transfer across a plasma membrane.

growth curve A graphical representation of the change in population size over time. This graph has four periods known as lag phase, exponential or log phase, stationary phase, and death phase.

growth factor An organic compound such as a vitamin or amino acid that must be provided in the diet to facilitate growth. An essential nutrient.

guanine (G) The purine nitrogen base found in DNA and RNA that pairs with cytosine.

Guillain-Barré syndrome A neurological complication of influenza vaccination. Approximately 1 in 100,000 recipients of the vaccine will develop this autoimmune disorder, which is marked by varying degrees of weakness and sensory loss.

gumma A nodular, infectious granuloma characteristic of tertiary syphilis.

gyrase An enzyme that functions in packaging of DNA in bacterial chromosomes by preventing excess distortion of the molecule as it is coiling.

HLA (human leukocyte antigen) A gene complex coding for a series of glycoprotein receptors (also known as MHC molecules) found on all cells except red blood cells. This receptor complex plays a vital role in recognition of self by the immune system and in rejection of transplanted tissues.

habitat The environment to which an organism is adapted.

halogens A group of related chemicals with antimicrobial applications. The halogens most often used in disinfectants and antiseptics are chlorine and iodine.

halophile A microbe that needs a high concentration of salt for growth or one that tolerates high salt concentrations.

Hansen's disease A chronic progressive disease of the skin and nerves caused by a slow growing, strictly parasitic bacterium, *Mycobacterium leprae;* also known as **leprosy.**

hapten An incomplete or partial antigen. Although it constitutes the determinative group and can bind antigen, hapten cannot stimulate a full immune response without being carried by a larger protein molecule.

Hashimoto's thyroiditis An autoimmune disease of the thyroid gland that damages the thyroid follicle cells and results in decreased production of thyroid hormone (hypothyroidism).

hay fever A form of atopic allergy marked by seasonal acute inflammation of the conjunctiva and mucous membranes of the respiratory passages. Symptoms are itching, coughing, and runny nose.

health care–associated infection (HAI) An infection not present upon admission to a hospital, clinic, or care home, but incurred while being treated there.

helical Having a spiral or coiled shape. Said of certain virus capsids and bacteria.

helminth A term that designates parasitic worms such as roundworms and flatworms.

hemagglutinin (H) A molecule that causes red blood cells to clump or agglutinate. A major surface receptor on the influenza virus needed for entry.

hemolysin Any biological agent that is capable of destroying red blood cells and causing the release of hemoglobin. Many bacterial pathogens produce exotoxins that act as hemolysins.

hemolytic disease of the newborn Incompatible Rh factor between mother and fetus causes maternal antibodies to enter the fetus and trigger complement-mediated destruction of fetal RBCs (hemolysis).

hemolytic uremic syndrome (HUS) A kidney disease caused by infection with *E.coli* 0157:H7.

hemopoiesis The process by which the various types of blood cells are formed by stem cells in the bone marrow; also called **hematopoiesis**.

hepadnavirus Enveloped DNA viruses with a predisposition to affect the liver. Hepatitis B is the most serious form.

hepatitis Inflammation and necrosis of the liver, often the result of viral infection.

hepatitis A virus (HAV) Enterovirus spread by contaminated food responsible for short-term (infectious) hepatitis.

hepatitis B virus (HBV) Hepadnavirus that is the causative agent of serum hepatitis.

hepatitis C virus (HCV) A blood-borne RNA virus that is the third most common cause of hepatitis.

hepatocellular carcinoma A liver cancer associated with infection with hepatitis B virus.

herd immunity A collective acquired immunity in a population that reduces the incidence of a pathogen and makes it less likely that nonimmune individuals will contract and spread infection. One aim of vaccination is to induce herd immunity.

heredity Genetic inheritance.

hermaphroditic Containing the sex organs for both male and female in one individual.

herpes zoster A recurrent infection caused by latent chickenpox virus. Its manifestation on the skin tends to correspond to dermatomes and to occur in patches that "girdle" the trunk; also called **shingles.**

herpetic keratitis Corneal or conjunctival inflammation due to herpesvirus type 1.

heterotroph An organism that relies upon organic compounds for its carbon and energy needs.

hexose A 6-carbon sugar such as glucose and fructose.

hierarchies Levels of power. Arrangement in order of rank.

histamine A cytokine released when mast cells and basophils release their granules. An important mediator of allergy, its effects include smooth muscle contraction, increased vascular permeability, and increased mucus secretion.

histone Protein associated with eukaryotic DNA. These simple proteins serve as a scaffolding to compact and condense DNA into chromosomes, while also enhancing or preventing the expression of certain genes.

holoenzyme An enzyme complete with its apoenzyme and cofactors.

hops The ripe, dried fruits of the hop vine (*Humulus lupulus*) that is added to beer wort for flavoring.

host range The limitation imposed by the characteristics of the host cell on the type of virus that can successfully invade it.

human diploid cell vaccine (HDCV) A vaccine made using cell culture that is currently the vaccine of choice for preventing infection by rabies virus.

human herpesvirus-6 (HHV-6) The herpesvirus that causes roseola and may possibly be linked to chronic neurological diseases.

human immunodeficiency virus (HIV) A retrovirus that causes acquired immunodeficiency syndrome (AIDS).

human papillomavirus (HPV) A group of DNA viruses whose members are responsible for common, plantar, and genital warts.

humoral immunity Protective molecules (mainly antibodies) carried in the fluids of the body.

hybridization A process that matches complementary strands of nucleic acid (DNA-DNA, RNA-DNA, RNA-RNA). Used for locating specific sites or identifying exact sequences of nucleic acids.

hybridoma An artificial cell line that produces monoclonal antibodies. It is formed by fusing (hybridizing) a normal antibody-producing cell with a cancer cell, and it can produce pure antibody indefinitely.

hydrogen bond A weak chemical bond formed by the attraction of forces between molecules or atoms—in this case, hydrogen and either oxygen or nitrogen. In this type of bond, electrons are not shared, lost, or gained.

hydrologic cycle The continual circulation of water between hydrosphere, atmosphere, and lithosphere.

hydrolysis A process in which water is used to break bonds in molecules. Usually occurs in conjunction with an enzyme.

hydrophilic The property of attracting water. Molecules that attract water to their surface are called hydrophilic.

hydrophobic The property of repelling water. Molecules that repel water are called hydrophobic.

hydrosphere That part of the biosphere that encompasses water-containing environments such as oceans, lakes, and rivers.

hyperthermophile A microorganism that thrives at temperatures of 80°C or higher.

hypertonic A solution that, when compared to a reference solution, has a higher concentration of solute and less water; placed opposite a hypotonic solution, it will cause water to to diffuse more rapidly from the hypotonic solution, thus creating a greater osmotic pressure.

hyphae The tubular threads that make up filamentous fungi (molds). This web of branched and intertwining fibers is called a mycelium.

hypogammaglobulinemia An inborn disease in which the gamma globulin (antibody) fraction of serum is greatly reduced. The condition is associated with a high susceptibility to pyogenic infections.

hypothesis A tentative explanation of what has been observed or measured.

hypotonic A solution that, when compared with a reference solution, is less concentrated, i.e., has more water and less solute. When a membrane is placed between this solution and a hypertonic solution, water will move from the hypotonic side to the hypertonic side at a higher rate.

icosahedron A regular geometric figure having 20 surfaces that meet to form 12 corners. Some virions have capsids that resemble icosahedral crystals.

immune complex reaction Type III hypersensitivity of the immune system. It is characterized by the reaction of soluble antigen with antibody and the deposition of the resulting complexes in basement membranes of epithelial tissue.

immune surveillance The continual function of macrophages, cytotoxic T cells, and natural killer cells in identifying and destroying cancer cells within the body.

immune tolerance The ability of the immune system to remain nonreactive to normal cell molecules.

immunity An acquired resistance to an infectious agent due to prior contact with that agent.

immunoassays Extremely sensitive tests that permit rapid and accurate measurement of trace antigen or antibody.

immunocompetence The ability of the body to recognize and react with multiple foreign substances.

immunodeficiency Immune function is incompletely developed, suppressed, or destroyed.

immunogen Any antigen molecule that, after being processed by the immune system, will stimulate protective T and B cell responses.

immunoglobulin (IG) The chemical class of proteins to which antibodies belong.

immunology The study of internal body defenses that protect against infection. This includes phagocytosis, inflammation, and acquired immunities.

immunopathology A disease state initiated by incorrect or harmful immune responses. Some immune diseases are caused by overreactions (allergies), and others are due to the lack of a functional immune response (immunodeficiencies).

immunotherapy Preventing or treating infectious diseases by administering substances that produce artificial immunity. May be active or passive.

impetigo Contagious skin infection marked by pustules and vesicles; caused by *S. aureus* and *S. pyogenes*; also known as **pyoderma.**

IMViC Abbreviation for four identification tests: **i**ndole production, **m**ethyl red test, **V**oges-Proskauer test (**i** inserted to concoct a wordlike sound), and **c**itrate as a sole source of carbon. This test was originally developed to distinguish between *Enterobacter aerogenes* (associated with soil) and *Escherichia coli* (a fecal coliform).

in vitro Literally means "in glass," signifying a process or reaction occurring in an artificial environment, as in a test tube or culture medium.

in vivo Literally means "in a living being," signifying a process or reaction occurring in a living thing.

incidence In epidemiology, the number of new cases of a disease occurring during a time period.

incineration Destruction of microbes by subjecting them to extremes of dry heat. Microbes are reduced to ashes and gas by this process.

inclusion A relatively inert body in the cytoplasm such as storage granules, glycogen, fat, or some other aggregated metabolic product; also called **inclusion body.**

incubate To isolate a sample culture in a temperature-controlled environment to encourage growth.

incubation period The period of time from the initial contact with an infectious agent to the appearance of the first symptoms.

indicator bacteria In water analysis, any easily cultured bacteria that may be found in the intestine and can be used as an index of fecal contamination. The category includes coliforms and enterococci. Discovery of these bacteria in a sample means that pathogens may also be present.

induced mutation Any alteration in DNA that occurs as a consequence of exposure to chemical or physical mutagens.

inducible operon A system of gene regulation in which a gene is ordinarily repressed unless the substrate of the structural proteins is present and induces it to become active; otherwise, the operon is blocked and the RNA polymerase cannot transcribe.

induction Process by which an individual accumulates data or facts and then formulates a general hypothesis that accounts for those facts.

infection The entry, establishment, and multiplication of pathogenic organisms within a host.

infectious disease The state of damage or toxicity in the body caused by an infectious agent.

infectious dose The estimated number of microbial cells or units required to establish an infection.

inflammation A natural, nonspecific response to tissue injury that protects the host from further damage. It stimulates immune reactivity and blocks the spread of an infectious agent.

inoculation The implantation of microorganisms into or upon culture media.

inorganic chemical Molecule that is composed of elements other than the basic framework of carbon and hydrogen and that is usually much simpler chemically than organic molecules.

interferon (IFN) Naturally occurring polypeptide produced by fibroblasts and lymphocytes that can block viral replication and regulate a variety of immune reactions.

interleukin Protein secreted by leukocytes that regulate immune function.

intermediate host The organism in which the larval development of a parasite occurs.

intoxication Poisoning that results from the ingestion of a toxin and the subsequent effects of that toxin as it spread into body tissues.

intron A contracted version of "intragenic regions." These are segments on split genes of eukaryotes that do not code for polypeptide. They serve other functions. See **exon.**

iodophor A combination of iodine and an organic carrier that is a moderate-level disinfectant and antiseptic.

ionic bond A chemical bond in which electrons are transferred and not shared between atoms.

ionization The aqueous dissociation of an electrolyte into ions.

ionizing radiation Radiant energy consisting of short-wave electromagnetic rays (X-ray) or high-speed electrons that cause dislodgement of electrons on target molecules, which creates ions.

irradiation The application of radiant energy for diagnosis, therapy, disinfection, or sterilization.

irregular (in shape) Refers to bacteria that stain unevenly or display cell-to-cell variation in size and/or shape (pleomorphic) within a single species.

isograft Transplanted tissue from one monozygotic twin to the other; transplants between highly inbred animals that are genetically identical.

isolation The separation of microbial cells by serial dilution or mechanical dispersion on solid media to create discrete colonies.

isomer A compound with the same chemical formula as another compound, but a different arrangement of atoms in the molecule and different properties.

isotonic Solutions having the same osmotic pressure, such that, when separated by a semipermeable membrane, show no net movement of solvent in either direction.

isotope A version of an element that is virtually identical in all chemical properties to another version except that their atoms have slightly different atomic masses.

jaundice The yellowish pigmentation of skin, mucous membranes, sclera, deeper tissues, and excretions due to abnormal deposition of bile pigments. Jaundice is associated with liver infection, as with hepatitis B virus and leptospirosis.

Kaposi's sarcoma A malignant or benign neoplasm that appears as multiple hemorrhagic sites on the skin, lymph nodes, and viscera and apparently involves the metastasis of abnormal blood vessel cells. It is a clinical feature of AIDS.

keratoconjunctivitis Inflammation of the conjunctiva and cornea.

killed or inactivated vaccine A whole cell or intact virus preparation in which the microbes are dead or preserved and cannot multiply but are still capable of conferring immunity.

kingdom In the levels of classification, the second division from more general to more specific. Each domain is divided into kingdoms.

Koch's postulates A procedure to establish the specific cause of disease. In all cases of infection (1) The agent must be found; (2) inoculations of a pure culture must reproduce the same disease in animals; (3) the agent must again be present in the experimental animal; and (4) a pure culture must again be obtained.

Koplik's spots Tiny red blisters with central white specks on the mucosal lining of the cheeks. Symptomatic of measles.

Krebs cycle Metabolic cycle that is linked to glycolysis and receives acetyl groups generated when pyruvic acid is decarboxylated; it provides $NADH_1$, $FADH_2$, and ATP; also known as **TCA cycle** and **citric acid cycle**.

L form L-phase variants; wall-less forms of some bacteria that are induced by drugs or chemicals. These forms can be involved in infections.

labile In chemistry, molecules or compounds that are chemically unstable in the presence of environmental changes.

lactose One of the carbohydrates commonly referred to as sugars. Lactose is commonly found in milk.

lactose (lac) operon Control system that manages the regulation of lactose metabolism. It is composed of three DNA segments, including a regulator, a control locus, and a structural locus.

lag phase The early phase of population growth during which little sign of growth occurs. It is this period that readies the cells for the rapid expansion to come.

lager The maturation process of beer, which is allowed to take place in large vats at a reduced temperature.

lagging strand The newly forming DNA strand that is discontinuously replicated in short segments (Okazaki fragments) because the template cannot be continuously read by the DNA polymerase.

latency The state of being inactive and not multiplying. Example: a latent virus or latent infection.

leading strand The newly forming DNA strand that is replicated in a continuous fashion without fragments because it is oriented in the correct 3′ to 5′ direction for the DNA polymerase.

leaven To lighten food material by entrapping gas generated within it. Example: the rising of bread from the CO_2 produced by yeast or baking powder.

legionellosis/legionnaire's disease Pulmonary infection by *Legionella* bacteria. Gram-negative rods survive inside amoebas in aquatic habitats. Some conditions may be fatal.

lepromatous leprosy Severe, disfiguring leprosy characterized by widespread dissemination of the leprosy bacillus in deeper lesions.

lesion A wound, injury, or some other pathologic change in tissues.

leukocidin A heat-labile substance formed by some pyogenic cocci that impairs and sometimes lyses leukocytes.

leukocytes White blood cells. The primary infection-fighting blood cells.

leukocytosis An abnormally large number of leukocytes in the blood, which can be indicative of acute infection.

leukopenia A lower-than-normal leukocyte count in the blood, which can be indicative of blood infection or disease.

leukotriene An unsaturated fatty acid derivative of arachidonic acid. Leukotriene functions in chemotactic activity, smooth muscle contractility, mucus secretion, and capillary permeability.

lichen A group of organisms consisting of algae or cyanobacteria living together with fungi in a mutualistic relationship.

ligase An enzyme required to join nucleotides together to complete the final attachment of the ends of two fragments of DNA; this enzyme also works in DNA technology to attach sticky ends of DNA pieces during splicing.

light-dependent reaction The series of reactions in photosynthesis that are driven by the light energy (photons) absorbed by chlorophyll. They involve splitting of water into hydrogens and oxygen, transport of electrons by NADP, and ATP synthesis.

light-independent reaction The series of reactions in photosynthesis that can proceed with or without light. It is a cyclic system that uses ATP from the light reactions to incorporate or fix carbon dioxide into organic compounds, leading to the production of glucose and other carbohydrates (also called the **Calvin cycle**).

limnetic zone The deep-water region beyond the shoreline.

lipid A term used to describe a variety of substances that are not soluble in polar solvents such as water but will dissolve in nonpolar solvents such as benzene and chloroform. Lipids include triglycerides, phospholipids, steroids, and waxes.

lipopolysaccharide A molecular complex of lipid and carbohydrate found in the bacterial cell wall. The lipopolysaccharide (LPS) of gram-negative bacteria is an endotoxin with generalized pathologic effects such as fever.

listeriosis Infection with *Listeria monocytogenes,* usually due to eating contaminated dairy products, poultry, or meat. It is usually mild in healthy adults but can produce severe symptoms in neonates and immunocompromised adults.

lithosphere That part of the biosphere that encompasses the earth's crust, including rocks and minerals.

littoral zone The shallow region along a shoreline.

lobar pneumonia Infection involving whole segments (lobes) of the lungs, which may lead to consolidation and plugging of the alveoli and extreme difficulty in breathing.

localized infection An infection in which a microbe enters a specific tissue, infects it, and remains confined there.

locus (plural, **loci**) The specific site on a DNA molecule where a particular gene or sequence of nucleotides is located. In diploid organisms, the locus is occupied by two allele copies, one on each of the chromosome pairs.

logarithmic or log phase Maximum rate of cell division during which growth is geometric in its rate of increase; also called **exponential growth phase.**

lophotrichous Describing bacteria having a tuft of flagella at one or both poles.

lumen The cavity within a tubular organ.

lymphadenitis Inflammation of one or more lymph nodes; also called **lymphadenopathy.**

lymphatic or lymphoid system A system of vessels and organs that serve as sites for development of immune cells and immune reactions. It includes the spleen, thymus, lymph nodes, and GALT.

lymphocyte The second-most common form of white blood cells.

lyophilization Freeze-drying; the separation of a dissolved solid from the solvent by freezing the solution and evacuating the solvent under vacuum. A means of preserving the viability of cultures.

lysin A complement-fixing antibody that destroys specific targeted cells. Examples: hemolysin and bacteriolysin.

lysis The physical rupture or deterioration of a cell.

lysogeny The indefinite persistence of bacteriophage DNA in a host without bringing about the production of virions. A lysogenic cell can revert to a lytic cycle, the process that ends in lysis.

lysosome A cytoplasmic organelle containing lysozyme and other hydrolytic enzymes.

lysozyme An enzyme that attacks the bonds on bacterial peptidoglycan. It is a natural defense found in tears and saliva.

macromolecule Large, molecular compound assembled from smaller subunits, most notably biochemicals.

macronutrient A chemical substance required in large quantities (phosphate, for example).

macrophage A white blood cell derived from a monocyte that leaves the circulation and enters tissues. These cells are important in nonspecific phagocytosis and in regulating, stimulating, and cleaning up after immune responses.

macroscopic Visible to the naked eye.

major histocompatibility complex (MHC) See **HLA.**

major histocompatibility complex/human leukocyte antigen These alternative terms refer to a closely linked cluster of genes that program cell surface glycoprotein markers that control immune interactions between cells and are involved in immune recognition and some hypersensitives, transfusion reactions, and graft rejections.

malignant tumor Cancerous growth characterized by uncontrolled growth or abnormal cells within normal tissue.

malt The grain, usually barley, that is sprouted to obtain digestive enzymes and dried for making beer.

MALT (mucosal-associated lymphoid tissue) Active lymphocytes distributed within the mucosal surfaces of respiratory and other systems.

maltose One of the carbohydrates referred to as sugars. A fermentable sugar formed from starch.

Mantoux test An intradermal screening test for tuberculin hypersensitivity. A red, firm patch of skin at the injection site greater than 10 mm in diameter after 48 hours is a positive result that indicates current or prior exposure to the TB bacillus.

marker Any trait or factor of a cell, virus, or molecule that makes it distinct and recognizable. Example: a genetic marker.

mash In making beer, the malt grain is steeped in warm water, ground up, and fortified with carbohydrates to form mash.

mass number (MN) Measurement that reflects the number of protons and neutrons in an atom of a particular element.

mast cell A nonmotile connective tissue cell implanted along capillaries, especially in the lungs, skin, gastrointestinal tract, and genitourinary tract. Like a basophil, its granules store mediators of allergy.

matrix The dense ground substance between the cristae of a mitochondrion that serves as a site for metabolic reactions.

matter All tangible materials that occupy space and have mass.

maximum temperature The highest temperature at which an organism will grow.

mechanical vector An animal that transports an infectious agent but is not infected by it, such as houseflies whose feet become contaminated with feces.

medium (plural, **media**) A nutrient used to grow organisms outside of their natural habitats.

membrane, cell A molecular "skin" surrounding the cytoplasm of cells that functions in protection, transport, communication, and secretion.

memory cell A long-lived progeny of a sensitized lymphocyte that remains in circulation and is genetically programmed to react rapidly the next time it encounters its antigen.

meningitis An inflammation of the membranes (meninges) that surround and protect the brain.

merozoite The motile, infective stage of an apicomplexan parasite that comes from a liver or red blood cell undergoing multiple fission.

mesophile Microorganisms that grow at intermediate temperatures—usually between 20 and 40 degrees C.

messenger RNA (mRNA) A single-stranded transcript that is a copy of the DNA template that corresponds to a gene; it generally carries the genetic code for a protein.

metabolic analog A chemical, usually a drug, that mimics the natural substrate of an enzyme and vies for its active site. This reaction, called competitive inhibition, can block the metabolic pathway that requires that enzyme.

metabolism A general term designating the totality of chemical processes occurring in a cell.

metabolites Small organic molecules that are intermediates in the stepwise biosynthesis or breakdown of macromolecules.

metagenomics The analysis of genomes recovered from mixed environmental samples that provides information on the diversity of microbe types without isolating or culturing them.

methanogen Microbe that produces methane gas.

MIC Abbreviation for minimum inhibitory concentration. The lowest concentration of antibiotic needed to inhibit bacterial growth in a test system.

microaerophile An aerobic bacterium that requires oxygen at a concentration less than that in the atmosphere.

microbe See **microorganism.**

microbial loop A process occurring in natural aquatic habitats that maintains the cycling of nutrients from producers to consumers and back to producers. It is powered primarily by mineralizing and decomposing bacteria and protozoa.

microbiology A specialized area of biology that deals with living things ordinarily too small to be seen without magnification, including bacteria, archaea, fungi, protozoa, and viruses.

microbiota The native types of bacteria, fungi, and viruses that normally reside on the body. An older term is normal flora.

microfilaments Cellular cytoskeletal element formed by thin protein strands that attach to the cell membrane and form a network though the cytoplasm. Responsible for movement of cytoplasm.

micronutrient A chemical substance required in small quantities (trace metals, for example).

microorganism A living thing ordinarily too small to be seen without magnification; an organism of microscopic size.

microscopic Invisible to the naked eye.

microscopy Science that studies structure, magnification, lenses, and techniques related to use of a microscope.

microtubule Long, tubular structure made of protein that functions in the structure, shape, and movement of eukaryotic cells.

mineralization The process by which decomposers (bacteria and fungi) convert organic debris into inorganic and elemental form. It is part of the recycling process.

minimum inhibitory concentration (MIC) The smallest concentration of drug needed to visibly control microbial growth.

minimum temperature The lowest temperature at which an organism will grow.

miracidium The ciliated first-stage larva of a trematode. This form is infective for a corresponding intermediate host snail.

missense mutation A mutation in which a change in the DNA sequence results in a different amino acid being incorporated into a protein, with varying results.

mitochondrion (plural, **mitochondria**) A double-membrane organelle of eukaryotes that is the main site for aerobic respiration. It contains its own chromosome and ribosomes.

mitosis Somatic cell division that preserves the somatic chromosome number.

mixed acid fermentation An anaerobic degradation of pyruvic acid that results in more than one organic acid being produced (acetic acid, lactic acid, succinic acid, etc.).

mixed culture A container growing two or more different, known species of microbes.

mixed infection Occurs when several different pathogens interact simultaneously to produce an infection; also called a **synergistic infection.**

mixotroph An organism that may obtain energy autotrophically or heterotrophically.

moist heat Heat combined with some form of water, including hot water, boiling water, or steam, generally ranging from 60°C to 135°C.

molds The filamentous fungi. composed of elongate hyphae.

molecule A distinct chemical substance that results from the combination of two or more atoms.

molluscum contagiosum Poxvirus-caused disease that manifests itself by the appearance of small lesions on the face, trunk, and limbs. Often associated with sexual transmission.

monoclonal antibody (MAB) An antibody produced by a clone of lymphocytes that respond to a particular antigenic determinant and generate identical antibodies only to that determinant. See **hybridoma.**

monocyte A large mononuclear leukocyte normally found in the lymph nodes, spleen, bone marrow, and loose connective tissue. This type of cell makes up 3% to 7% of circulating leukocytes.

monomer A simple molecule that can be linked by chemical bonds to form larger molecules.

mononuclear phagocyte system A collection of monocytes and macrophages scattered throughout the extracellular spaces that function to engulf and degrade foreign cells and substances.

monosaccharide A simple sugar such as glucose that is a basic building block for more complex carbohydrates.

monotrichous Describing a microorganism that bears a single flagellum.

morbidity A diseased condition.

morphology The study of organismic structure.

mortality rate Total number of deaths in a population attributable to a particular disease.

most probable number (MNP) Coliform test used to detect the concentration of contaminants in water supplies.

motility Self-propulsion.

MRSA/methicillin-resistant *Staphylococcus* *aureus* This refers to a strain of *S. aureus* that resists not only methicillin but a wide variety of nonpenicillin drugs such as cephalosporins, gentamycin, tetracycline, and erythromycin. These "superbugs" are common in the hospital and are increasingly found in community settings.

multibacillary Containing many bacilli.

multinucleate giant cell A cytopathic effect that arises from the fusion of the cytoplasmic membranes of several infected cells. Characteristic of infection with paramyxoviruses.

mumps See **epidemic parotitis.**

must Juices expressed from crushed fruits that are used in fermentation for wine.

mutagen Any agent that induces a change in the composition of DNA. Examples: certain chemical substances, ultraviolet radiation, radioactive elements.

mutant strain A subspecies of microorganism that has undergone a mutation, causing expression of a trait that differs from other members of that species.

mutation A permanent inheritable alteration in the DNA sequence or content of a cell.

mutualism Organisms living in a close, mutually beneficial relationship.

mycelium The filamentous mass that makes up a mold. Composed of hyphae.

mycetoma A chronic fungal infection usually afflicting the feet, typified by swelling and multiple draining lesions. Example: maduromycosis or Madura foot.

mycoplasma Species of mycoplasma are among the smallest self-replicating microorganisms. Mycoplasma naturally lack a cell wall. Most species are parasites of animals and plants.

mycorrhizae Various species of fungi adapted in an intimate, mutualistic relationship to plant roots.

mycosis Any disease caused by a fungus.

mycotoxicosis Illness resulting from eating poisonous fungi.

myonecrosis Another name for **gas gangrene.**

nanobe Cell-like particle, found in sediments and other geologic deposits, that some scientists speculate are the smallest bacteria. Short for **nanobacteria.**

narrow spectrum Denotes drugs that are selective and limited in their effects. For example, they inhibit either gram-negative or gram-positive bacteria but not both.

nasopharyngeal carcinoma A malignancy of epithelial cells that occurs in older Chinese and African men and is associated with exposure to Epstein-Barr virus.

natural immunity Specific protection from disease acquired through normal, nonmedical life processes.

necrosis A pathologic process in which cells and tissues die and disintegrate.

necrotizing faciitis Severe invasive disease of skin, muscle, and connective tissue, usually caused by group A streptococci.

negative feedback Enzyme regulation of metabolism by the end product of a multienzyme system that blocks the action of a "pacemaker" enzyme at or near the beginning of the pathway.

negative stain A staining technique that renders the background opaque or colored and leaves the object unstained so that it is outlined as a colorless area.

nematode A common name for helminths called roundworms.

neoplasm A synonym for tumor.

neuraminidase A glycoprotein found in the envelope of influenza virus that facilitates release of new viruses from the host cell.

neurotropic Having an affinity for the nervous system. Most likely to affect the spinal cord.

neutralization In immunology, a type of antibody-antigen reaction which results in the blockage of a virus receptor or toxic protein by an antibody. In chemistry, the process of combining an acid and a base until they reach a balanced proportion, with a pH value close to 7.

neutron An electrically neutral particle in the nuclei of all atoms except hydrogen.

neutrophil A mature granulocyte present in peripheral circulation, exhibiting a multilobular nucleus and numerous cytoplasmic granules that retain a neutral stain. The neutrophil is an active phagocytic cell in bacterial infection.

niche In ecology, an organism's biological role in or contribution to its community.

nicotinamide adenine dinucleotide/NAD/NADH Abbreviations for the oxidized/reduced forms of nicotinamide adenine dinucleotide, an electron carrier. Nicotinamide is another name for the vitamin niacin.

nitrification Phase of the nitrogen cycle in which ammonium is oxidized.

nitrogen cycle The pathway followed by the element nitrogen as it circulates from inorganic sources in the nonliving environment to living things and back to the nonliving environment. The long-time reservoir is nitrogen gas in the atmosphere.

nitrogen fixation A process occurring in certain bacteria in which atmospheric N_2 gas is converted to a form (NH_4) usable by plants.

nitrogenous base A ringed compound of which pyrimidines and purines are types.

nomenclature A set system for scientifically naming organisms, enzymes, anatomical structures, etc.

noncoliforms Lactose-negative enteric bacteria in normal flora.

noncommunicable An infectious disease that is not established through transmission of an infectious agent via another infected host.

nonionizing radiation Method of microbial control, best exemplified by ultraviolet light, that causes the formation of abnormal bonds within the DNA of microbes, increasing the rate of mutation. The primary limitation of nonionizing radiation is its inability to penetrate beyond the surface of an object.

nonpolar A term used to describe an electrically neutral molecule formed by covalent bonds between atoms that have the same or similar electronegativity.

nonself Cells or molecules recognized by the immune system as containing foreign markers. Nonself can stimulate the immune system to react and eliminate the foreign substances.

nonsense codon A triplet of mRNA bases that does not specify an amino acid but signals the end of a polypeptide chain; also called **stop codon.**

nonsense mutation A mutation that changes an amino acid-based codon into a stop codon, leading to premature termination of a protein during translation.

Norwalk agent One of a group of Caliciviruses, Norwalk agent causes gastrointestinal distress and is commonly transmitted in schools, camps, cruise ships, and nursing homes.

nucleocapsid In viruses, the close physical combination of the nucleic acid with its protective covering.

nucleoid The undifferentiated space or region in the cytoplasm that contains the bacterial genetic material. It is naked and not enclosed in a membrane.

nucleolus A granular mass containing RNA that is contained within the nucleus of a eukaryotic cell.

nucleosome Structure in the packaging of eukaryotic DNA formed when the DNA strands wrap around histone proteins, forming an arrangement that looks like beads on a chain.

nucleotide The basic structural unit of DNA and RNA; each nucleotide consists of a phosphate, a sugar (ribose in RNA, deoxyribose in DNA), and a nitrogenous base such as adenine, guanine, cytosine, thymine (DNA only), or uracil (RNA only).

nucleus 1) In chemistry, the central core of an atom, composed of protons and neutrons. 2) In cell structure, a prominent spherical organelle that is encased by a double membrane or envelope; it is the site where the majority of a cell's DNA is housed.

numerical aperture (NA) In microscopy, a measure of the light passing from the object and into the objective to maximize optical clarity and resolution.

nutrient Any chemical substance that is acquired from the environment and used for metabolism and growth. Macronutrients are required in large amounts, and micronutrients in small amounts.

nutrition The acquisition of chemical substances by a cell or organism for use as an energy source or as building blocks of cellular structures.

obligate/strict Without alternative; restricted to a particular way of life. Example: An obligate parasite survives and grows only in a host; an obligate aerobe must have oxygen to grow; an obligate anaerobe is destroyed by oxygen.

Okazaki fragment In replication of DNA, a segment formed on the lagging strand where biosynthesis is conducted in a discontinuous manner as required by the DNA polymerase orientation.

oligodynamic action A chemical having antimicrobial activity in minuscule amounts. Example: Certain heavy metals are effective in a few parts per billion.

oligotrophic Nutrient-deficient ecosystem.

oncogene A naturally occurring type of gene that when activated can transform a normal cell into a cancer cell.

oncology The study of neoplasms, their cause, disease characteristics, and treatment.

oncogenic Causing the development of cancer.

onychomycosis A fungal infection of the nail and nailbed; also called **tinea unguium.**

operator In an operon sequence, the DNA segment where transcription of structural genes is initiated.

operon A genetic operational unit that regulates metabolism by controlling mRNA production. In sequence, the unit consists of a regulatory gene, inducer or repressor control sites, and structural genes.

opportunistic infection A situation where ordinarily nonpathogenic or weakly pathogenic microbes cause disease in an immunologically compromised host.

opportunistic pathogen A microbe that infects a host when the body's defense system is vulnerable, causing an **opportunistic infection.**

opsonization The process of stimulating phagocytosis by affixing molecules (opsonins such as antibodies and complement) to the surfaces of foreign cells or particles.

optimum temperature The temperature at which a species shows the most rapid growth rate.

orbital The pathway of electrons as they rotate around the nucleus of an atom.

order In the levels of classification, the division of organisms that follows class. Increasing similarity may be noticed among organisms assigned to the same order.

organelle A small component of eukaryotic cells that is bounded by a membrane and specialized in function.

organic chemicals Molecules that are structured with a basic framework of the elements carbon and hydrogen; usually these are larger than inorganic molecules and contain additional elements as well.

ornithosis Worldwide zoonosis carried in the latent state in wild and domesticated birds; caused by *Chlamydia psittacosis*.

osmophile A microorganism that thrives in a medium having high osmotic pressure.

osmosis The diffusion of water across a selectively permeable membrane in the direction towards lower water concentration and higher solute concentration.

osteomyelitis A focal infection of the internal structures of long bones, leading to pain and inflammation. Often caused by *Staphylococcus aureus*.

otitis media Acute infection of the middle ear, usually by the pneumococcus, that causes severe pain and drainage.

outer membrane (OM) A structure made of lipids in the outer layer of the cell wall of gram-negative bacteria.

oxidation In chemical reactions, the loss of electrons by one reactant. An oxidizing agent is a molecule that causes electron loss or removes electrons from a substrate.

oxidation-reduction reaction Redox reactions in which paired sets of molecules participate in electron transfers.

oxidative phosphorylation The synthesis of ATP using energy released during the electron transport phase of respiration.

oxygenic Any reaction that gives off oxygen; usually in reference to the result of photosynthesis in eukaryotes and cyanobacteria.

palindrome In the DNA code, a short segment of paired nitrogen bases that have the same sequence when read in opposite directions. Palindromes have significance as transposable elements, regulatory protein targets, and in DNA splicing. In ordinary language, a palindrome is a word, verse, number, or sentence that reads the same forward or backward.

palisade The characteristic bacterial arrangement resembling a row of fence posts created by cells snapping together.

pandemic An epidemic that has spread across a wide geographic area, including more than one continent or international border, and can extend to a worldwide occurrence.

papilloma Benign, squamous epithelial growth commonly referred to as a wart.

parabasalids A group of eukaryotic microorganisms marked by simplified, poorly functioning mitochondria, requiring them to generate most of their energy anaerobically. The most well-known parabasalid is *Trichomonas*.

parainfluenza A respiratory disease (croup) caused by infection with Paramyxovirus.

parasitism/parasite A close interaction in which one organism (the parasite) lives on or within another organism (the host), from which it obtains nutrients and receives protection. The parasite produces some degree of harm to the host.

parenteral Administering a substance into a body compartment other than through the gastrointestinal tract, such as via intravenous, subcutaneous, intramuscular, or intramedullary injection.

passive carrier Persons who mechanically transfer a pathogen without ever being infected by it, such as health care workers who don't wash their hands adequately between patients.

passive immunity Specific resistance that is acquired indirectly by donation of preformed immune substances (antibodies) produced in the body of another individual.

passive transport Nutrient transport method that follows basic physical laws and does not require direct energy input from the cell.

pasteurization Heat treatment of perishable fluids such as milk, fruit juices, or wine to destroy heat-sensitive vegetative cells, followed by rapid chilling to inhibit growth of survivors and germination of spores. It prevents infection and spoilage.

pathogen Any agent—usually a virus, bacterium, fungus, protozoan, or helminth—that infects body tissues and causes disease.

pathogen-associated molecular pattern (PAMP) Molecules on the surfaces of pathogenic microbes that are recognized by phagocytes and trigger immune responses against the microbes.

pathogenicity The capacity of microbes to cause disease.

paucibacillary Containing just a few bacilli.

pelvic inflammatory disease (PID) An infection of the uterus and fallopian tubes that has ascended from the lower reproductive tract. Caused by gonococci and chlamydias.

penicillin A large group of naturally occurring and synthetic antibiotics produced by *Penicillium* mold and active against the cell wall of bacteria.

penicillinase An enzyme that hydrolyzes penicillin; found in penicillin-resistant strains of bacteria.

pentose A monosaccharide with five carbon atoms per molecule. Examples: arabinose, ribose, and xylose.

peptide Molecule composed of short chains of amino acids, such as a dipeptide (two amino acids), a tripeptide (three), and a tetrapeptide (four).

peptide bond The covalent union between two amino acids that forms between the amine group of one and the carboxyl group of the other. The basic bond of proteins.

peptidoglycan A network of polysaccharide chains cross-linked by short peptides that forms the rigid part of bacterial cell walls. Gram-negative bacteria have a smaller amount of this rigid structure than do gram-positive bacteria.

perforin A protein secreted by cytotoxic and natural killer cells that attacks the cell membrane of infectious agents and forms pores.

period of invasion The period during a clinical infection when the infectious agent multiplies at high levels, exhibits its greatest toxicity, and becomes well established in the target tissues.

periplasmic space An open area between the cell wall and cell membrane in the cell envelopes of bacteria. Gram-negative bacteria have a a more extensive space than do gram-positive bacteria.

peritrichous In bacterial morphology, having flagella distributed over the entire cell.

pertussis Infection by *Bordetella pertussis*. A highly communicable disease that causes acute respiratory syndrome. Pertussis can be life-threatening in infants, but vaccination on the recommended schedule can prevent infection; also called **whooping cough.**

petechiae Minute hemorrhagic spots in the skin that range from pinpoint- to pinhead-size.

Peyer's patches Oblong lymphoid aggregates of the gut located chiefly in the wall of the terminal and small intestine. Along with the tonsils and appendix, Peyer's patches make up the gut-associated lymphoid tissue that responds to local invasion by infectious agents.

pH The symbol for the negative logarithm of the H ion concentration; p (power) or $[H^+]_{10}$. A system for rating acidity and alkalinity.

phage See **bacteriophage.**

phagocytosis A type of endocytosis in which the cell membrane actively engulfs large particles or cells into vesicles. A **phagocyte** is a cell specialized for doing this.

phagolysosome A body formed in a phagocyte, consisting of a union between a vesicle containing the ingested particle (the phagosome) and a vacuole of hydrolytic enzymes (the lysosome).

phenetic Based on phenotype, or expression of traits.

phenotype The observable characteristics of an organism produced by the expression of its genetic potential (genotype). Includes any morphological and physiological traits.

phlebotomine Pertains to a genus of very small midges or blood-sucking (phlebotomous) sand flies and to diseases associated with those vectors such as kala-azar, Oroya fever, and cutaneous leishmaniasis.

phosphate An acidic salt containing phosphorus and oxygen that is an essential inorganic component of DNA, RNA, and ATP.

phospholipid A class of lipids that compose a major structural component of cell membranes.

phosphorylation Process in which inorganic phosphate is added to a compound.

photic zone The aquatic stratum from the surface to the limits of solar light penetration.

photoautotroph An organism that utilizes light for its energy and carbon dioxide chiefly for its carbon needs.

photolysis Literally, splitting water with light. In photosynthesis, this step frees electrons and gives off O_2.

photon A subatomic particle released by electromagnetic sources such as radiant energy (sunlight). Photons are the ultimate source of energy for photosynthesis.

photophosphorylation The process of electron transport during photosynthesis that uses captured light energy to synthesize ATP from ADP and phosphate.

photosynthesis A process occurring in plants, algae, and some bacteria that traps the sun's energy and converts it to ATP in the cell. This energy is used to fix CO_2 into organic compounds.

phototroph A microbe that uses sunlight for energy and CO_2 as a carbon source.

phylogenetic A classification system based on evolutionary relationships; also called **phyletic.**

phylum In the levels of classification, the third level of classification from general to more specific. Each kingdom is divided into numerous phyla. Sometimes referred to as **division.**

physiology The study of the function of an organism.

pili (singular, **pilus**) Small, stiff filamentous appendages in gram-negative bacteria that function in DNA exchange during bacterial conjugation.

pinocytosis The engulfment, or endocytosis, of liquids by extensions of the cell membrane.

plague Zoonotic disease caused by infection with *Yersinia pestis*. The pathogen is spread by flea vectors and harbored by various rodents.

plankton/planktonic Minute animals and protozoa (zooplankton) or algae (phytoplankton) that float and drift in the limnetic zone of bodies of water.

plantar warts Deep, painful warts on the soles of the feet as a result of infection by human papillomavirus.

plaque In virus propagation methods, the clear zone of lysed cells in tissue culture or chick embryo membrane that corresponds to the area containing viruses. In dental application, the filamentous mass of microbes that adheres tenaciously to the tooth and predisposes to caries, calculus, or inflammation.

plasma The carrier fluid element of blood.

plasma cell A progeny of an activated B cell that actively produces and secretes antibodies against a specific microbe.

plasmid Extrachromosomal genetic unit characterized by several features. A plasmid is a double-stranded DNA that is smaller than and replicates independently of the cell chromosome; it bears genes that are not essential for cell growth; it can bear genes that code for adaptive traits; and it is transmissible to other bacteria.

plasmolysis The loss of water from a cell in a hypertonic solution. As water is lost, the cell shrinks or, in the case of cells with a cell wall, the cell membrane pulls away from the cell wall.

platelet Formed element in the blood that develops when megakaryocytes disintegrate. Platelets are involved in hemostasis and blood clotting.

pleomorphism Normal variability of cell shapes in a single species; bacteria having diverse shapes are called **pleomorphic.**

pneumococcus Common name for *Streptococcus pneumoniae,* the major cause of bacterial pneumonia.

pneumonia An inflammation of the lung leading to blockage of the respiratory tract that compromises breathing.

pneumonic plague The acute, frequently fatal form of pneumonia caused by *Yersinia pestis.*

point mutation A mutation affecting no more than a few nucleotides in a sequence of DNA.

polar Term to describe a molecule with an asymmetrical distribution of charges. Such a molecule has a negative pole and a positive pole.

polar flagellum Description of flagella that are attached at one or both ends of the cell.

poliomyelitis An acute enteroviral infection of the spinal cord that can cause neuromuscular paralysis.

polyclonal antibodies In reference to a collection of antibodies with mixed specificities that arose from more than one clone of B cells.

polymer A macromolecule made up of a chain of repeating units. Examples: starch, protein, and DNA.

polymerase An enzyme that produces polymers through catalyzing bond formation between building blocks (polymerization).

polymerase chain reaction (PCR) A technique that amplifies segments of DNA for testing. Using denaturation, primers, and heat-resistant DNA polymerase, the number can be increased several million-fold.

polymyxin A mixture of antibiotic polypeptides from *Bacillus polymyxa* that are particularly effective against gram-negative bacteria.

polypeptide A relatively large chain of amino acids linked by peptide bonds.

polyribosomal complex An assembly line for mass production of proteins composed of a chain of ribosomes involved in mRNA transcription.

polysaccharide A carbohydrate that can be hydrolyzed into a number of monosaccharides. Examples: cellulose, starch, and glycogen.

population A group of organisms of the same species living simultaneously in the same habitat. A group of different populations living together constitutes the community level.

porin Transmembrane proteins of the outer membrane of gram-negative cells that permit transport of small molecules into the periplasmic space but bar the penetration of larger molecules.

portal of entry Characteristic route of entry for an infectious agent; typically a cutaneous or membranous route.

portal of exit Characteristic route through which a pathogen departs from the host organism.

positive stain Technique in which dye affixes to a specimen and imparts color to it. It takes advantage of the ready binding of bacterial cells to dyes.

potable Describing water that is relatively clear, odor-free, and safe to drink.

pox The thick, elevated pustular eruptions of various viral infections; also spelled *pocks.*

poxvirus A group of large complex DNA viruses that create pox skin lesions. Agents of smallpox and molluscum contagiosum.

PreP Pre-exposure prophylaxis. Medication taken daily to reduce the risk of contracting HIV. Used by people at high risk of contracting the virus.

prevalence The total cumulative number of cases of a disease in a certain area and time period.

primary infection An initial infection in a previously healthy individual that is later complicated by an additional (secondary) infection.

primary pulmonary infection (PPI) Disease that results from the inhalation of fungal spores and their germination in the lungs. This may serve as a focus of infection that spreads throughout the body.

primary response The first response of the immune system when exposed to an antigen.

primary (1°) structure Initial protein organization described by type, number, and order of amino acids in the chain. The primary structure varies extensively from protein to protein.

primer Short segment of RNA that serves as binding sites for DNA polymerase to start adding nucleotides to the new strand of DNA.

prion A concocted word to denote "proteinaceous infectious agent"; a cytopathic protein associated with the slow-virus spongiform encephalopathies of humans and animals.

probes Small fragments of single-stranded DNA (or RNA) that are known to be complementary to a specific sequence of DNA being studied.

probiotic A microbe or mixture of microbes that may be used to balance the normal microbiota and improve gastrointestinal health.

prodromium A short period of nonspecific symptoms at the end of the period of incubation that is usually the earliest indication of an infection.

producer An organism that synthesizes complex organic compounds from simple inorganic molecules. Examples would be photosynthetic microbes and plants. These organisms are solely responsible for originating food pyramids and are the basis for life on earth (also called **autotroph**).

proglottid The egg-generating segment of a tapeworm that contains both male and female organs.

progressive multifocal leukoencephalopathy (PML) An uncommon, fatal complication of infection with JC virus (polyomavirus).

prokaryotic cell Small cell lacking special structures such as a nucleus and organelles. All prokaryotes are microorganisms.

promastigote A morphological variation of the trypanosome parasite responsible for leishmaniasis.

prophage A lysogenized bacteriophage; a phage that is latently incorporated into the host chromosome instead of undergoing viral replication and lysis.

prophylactic/prophylaxis Any device, method, or substance that prevents a disease from developing.

prostaglandin A hormonelike substance that regulates many body functions. Prostaglandin comes from a family of organic acids containing 5-carbon rings that are essential to the human diet.

protein Predominant organic molecule in cells, formed by long chains of amino acids.

proton An elementary particle that carries a positive charge. It is identical to the nucleus of the hydrogen atom.

proton motive force Energy that is created by the transfer of protons across a semipermeable membrane.

protoplast A bacterial cell whose cell wall is completely lacking and that is vulnerable to osmotic lysis.

protozoa A group of single-celled, eukaryotic organisms that feed on other cells and usually have a locomotor organelle.

pseudohypha A chain of easily separated, spherical to sausage-shaped yeast cells partitioned by constrictions rather than by septa.

pseudomembrane A tenacious, noncellular mucous exudate containing cellular debris that tightly blankets the mucosal surface in infections such as diphtheria and pseudomembranous enterocolitis.

pseudopod Appendage responsible for motility of protozoa such as amoebas; also called "false foot."

psychrophile A microorganism that thrives at low temperatures (0°C–20°C), with a temperature optimum of 0°C–15°C.

pulmonary Occurring in the lungs. Examples include pulmonary anthrax and pulmonary nocardiosis.

pulmonary anthrax The more severe form of anthrax, resulting from inhalation of spores and resulting in a wide range of pathological effects, including death.

pure culture A container growing a single species of microbe whose identity is known.

purine A nitrogen base that is an important encoding component of DNA and RNA. It is composed of a basic two-ring structure and is larger than a pyrimidine. The two most common purines are adenine and guanine.

pus The viscous, opaque, usually yellowish matter formed by an inflammatory infection. It consists of serum exudate, tissue debris, leukocytes, and microorganisms. *Purulent* refers to a puslike condition.

pyogenic Pus-forming; especially pertaining to the pyogenic cocci: pneumococci, streptococci, staphylococci, and neisseriae.

pyrimidine A nitrogen base that helps form the genetic code on DNA and RNA. It is composed of a single-ring structure and is smaller than a purine. Thymine, cytosine, and uracil are the most important pyrimidines.

pyrimidine dimer The union of two adjacent pyrimidines on the same DNA strand, brought about by exposure to ultraviolet light. It is a form of mutation.

pyrogen A substance that causes a rise in body temperature. It can come from infectious agents (exogenous) or from polymorphonuclear leukocytes and macrophages (endogenous pyrogens).

Q fever A disease first described in Queensland, Australia, initially dubbed Q for "query" to denote a fever of unknown origin. Q fever is now known to be caused by a rickettsial infection.

quaternary ammonium compounds See **quats.**

quaternary (4°) structure The most complex protein structure, characterized by the formation of large, multiunit proteins by more than one of the polypeptides. This structure is typical of antibodies and some enzymes that act in cell synthesis.

quats/quaternary ammonium compounds A family of surfactants called **quaternary ammonium compounds,** termed **quats** for short. These detergents are weakly microbicidal and are used as disinfectants, sanitizers, and preservatives.

quorum sensing A phenomenon occurring among microbes in a biofilm in which the members signal each other and coordinate their functions.

rabies The only rhabdovirus that infects humans. Zoonotic disease characterized by fatal meningoencephalitis.

radiation Electromagnetic waves or rays given off from an energy source. Includes gamma rays, X-rays, ultraviolet, visible light, and others.

rales An abnormal rattling sound heard when listening to lung sounds with a stethoscope.

reactant Molecule entering or starting a chemical reaction.

reactive oxygen intermediate (ROI) Any charged oxygen radical (e.g., superoxide ions, peroxide) given off during oxygen metabolism that can be toxic to microbial and other cells.

real image An image formed at the focal plane of a convex lens. In the compound light microscope, it is the image created by the objective lens.

recognition site (sequence) A sequence of nucleotides that is recognized by a protein, such as a restriction enzyme.

recombinant DNA technology A technology, associated with genetic engineering that deliberately modifies the genetic structure of an organism to create novel products, microbes, animals, plants, and viruses.

recombination A type of genetic transfer in which DNA from one organism is donated to another. The resultant cell is termed *recombinant.*

recycling A process that converts unusable organic matter from dead organisms back into their essential inorganic elements and returns them to their nonliving reservoirs to make them available again for living organisms. This is a common term that means the same as *mineralization* and *decomposition.*

redox Denoting an oxidation-reduction reaction.

reduction In chemistry, the gain of electrons. A reducing agent is one that causes the addition of electrons to a substrate.

reemerging disease Previously identified disease that is increasing in occurrence.

refraction In optics, the bending of light as it passes from one medium to another with a different index of refraction.

regular (in shape) Refers to bacteria with uniform staining properties and that are consistent in shape from cell to cell within a particular species.

regulator DNA segment that codes for a protein capable of repressing an operon.

rennin The enzyme casein coagulase, which is used to produce curd in the processing of milk and cheese.

reovirus Respiratory enteric orphan virus. Virus with a double-stranded RNA genome and both an inner capsid and an outer capsid. Not a significant human pathogen.

replication In DNA synthesis, the semiconservative mechanisms that ensure precise duplication of the parent DNA strands.

replication fork The Y-shaped point on a replicating DNA molecule where the DNA polymerase is synthesizing new strands of DNA.

reportable disease Any disease that needs regular and frequent monitoring of individual cases so that it can be managed and prevented. These are diseases that must be reported to health authorities by law.

repressible operon A system of gene regulation that is normally active but can be blocked when a build-up of the operon's product occurs; this causes transcription by the RNA polymerase to be stopped (i.e., repressed).

repressor The protein product of a repressor gene that combines with the operator and arrests the transcription and translation of structural genes.

reservoir In epidemiology, the natural host or habitat of a pathogen that is its long-term origin.

resident microbiota The deeper, more stable microflora that inhabit the skin and exposed mucous membranes, as opposed to the superficial, variable, transient population.

resistance (R) factor Plasmids, typically shared among bacteria by conjugation, that provide resistance to the effects of antibiotics.

resolving power The capacity of a microscope lens system to accurately distinguish between two separate entities that lie close to each other; also called **resolution.**

respiratory chain In cellular respiration, a series of electron-carrying molecules that transfers energy-rich electrons and protons to molecular oxygen. In transit, energy is extracted and conserved in the form of ATP.

respiratory syncytial virus (RSV) An RNA virus that infects the respiratory tract. RSV is the most prevalent cause of respiratory infection in newborns.

restriction endonuclease An enzyme present naturally in bacteria that cleaves specific locations (palindromes) on DNA. It is an important means of inactivating viral genomes, and it is also used in genetic engineering to splice genes.

reticuloendothelial system (RES) A network of fibers and phagocytic cells (macrophages) that permeates the tissues of all organs. Examples: Kupffer cells in liver sinusoids, alveolar phagocytes in the lung, and microglia in nervous tissue; also known as the **mononuclear phagocyte system.**

retrovirus A group of RNA viruses (including HIV) that have the mechanisms for converting their genome into a double strand of DNA that can be inserted on a host's chromosome.

reverse transcriptase (RT) The enzyme possessed by retroviruses that carries out the reversion of RNA to DNA—a form of reverse transcription.

Reye's syndrome A sudden, usually fatal neurological condition that occurs in children after a viral infection. Autopsy shows cerebral edema and marked fatty change in the liver and renal tubules.

Rh factor An isoantigen that can trigger hemolytic disease in newborns due to incompatibility between maternal and infant blood factors.

rhabdovirus Family of bullet-shaped viruses that includes rabies.

rheumatic fever Chronic group A streptococcus–associated syndrome that damages the heart valves.

rhinoviruses Picornaviruses associated with the common cold. Transmission is through human-to-human contact, and symptoms typically are short-lived. Most effective control is effective hand washing and care in handling nasal secretions.

rhizobia Bacteria that live in plant roots and supply supplemental nitrogen that boosts plant growth.

rhizosphere The zone of soil, complete with microbial inhabitants, in the immediate vicinity of plant roots.

ribonucleic acid (RNA) The nucleic acid responsible for carrying out the hereditary program transmitted by an organism's DNA.

ribose A 5-carbon monosaccharide found in RNA.

ribosome A bilobed macromolecular complex that coordinates the codons of mRNA with tRNA anticodons and, in so doing, constitutes the protein assembly site. It is composed of ribosomal RNA (rRNA) and protein.

ribozyme An RNA-containing catalyst that serves to cut and splice RNA during gene processing, protein synthesis, and other RNA-based functions.

rickettsias Medically important family of tiny, intracellular parasitic bacteria, commonly carried by ticks, lice, and fleas. Cause of Rocky Mountain spotted fever and typhus.

rifampin An antibiotic used primarily in the treatment of mycobacterial infection.

ringworm A superficial mycosis caused by various dermatophytic fungi. This common name is actually a misnomer.

RNA polymerase The enzyme that converts the genetic code provided by DNA into a complementary RNA molecule.

root nodules Small growths on the roots of legume plants that arise from a symbiotic association between the plant tissues and bacteria (Rhizobia). This association allows fixation of nitrogen gas from the air into a usable nitrogen source for the plant.

roseola Disease of infancy, usually self-limiting, caused by infection with human herpesvirus-6.

Rotavirus Virus with a double-stranded RNA genome and both an inner capsid and an outer capsid. Transmitted by fecal contamination, it is common in areas with poor sanitation. *Rotavirus* typically causes diarrheal disease and can be fatal.

rough endoplasmic reticulum (RER) Microscopic series of tunnels that originate in the outer membrane of the nuclear envelope and are used in transport and storage. Large numbers of ribosomes, partly attached to the membrane, give the rough appearance.

rubella Commonly known as German measles. Rubella is caused by *Rubivirus,* a member of the Togavirus family. Postnatal rubella is generally a mild condition; congenital rubella poses a risk of birth defects and results when virus passes from infected mother to fetus.

rubeola (red measles) Acute disease caused by infection with *Morbillivirus.*

S-layer A proteinaceous layer found as part of the cell envelope of most archaea and many bacterial species.

saccharide Scientific term for sugar. Refers to a simple carbohydrate with a sweet taste.

salmonelloses Illnesses caused by infection of the noncoliform *Salmonella* pathogens. The cause of typhoid fever, *Salmonella* food poisoning, and gastroenteritis.

salpingitis Inflammation of the fallopian tubes.

sanitize/sanitization To clean inanimate objects using soap and degerming agents so that they are safe and free of high levels of microorganisms.

saprobe A microbe that decomposes organic remains from dead organisms; also known as a **saprophyte** or **saprotroph.**

sarcina A cubical packet of 8, 16, or more cells; the cellular arrangement of the genus *Sarcina* in the Family Micrococcaceae.

saturation The complete occupation of the active site of a carrier protein or enzyme by the substrate.

scarlet fever Serious group A streptococcus infection that causes redness, shedding of the skin, and high fever.

schistosomiasis Infection by blood fluke, often as a result of contact with contaminated water in rivers

and streams. Symptoms include fever, chills, diarrhea, and cough. Infection may be chronic.

schizogony A process of multiple fission whereby first the nucleus divides several times, and subsequently the cytoplasm is subdivided for each new nucleus during cell division.

scientific method Principles and procedures for the systematic pursuit of knowledge, involving the recognition and formulation of a problem, the collection of data through observation and experimentation, and the formulation and testing of a hypothesis.

scolex The anterior end of a tapeworm characterized by hooks and/or suckers for attachment to the host.

secondary infection An infection that complicates a preexisting primary infection.

secondary response The rapid rise in antibody titer following a repeat exposure to an antigen that has been recognized from a previous exposure. This response is brought about by memory cells left behind after the primary exposure.

secondary (2°) structure Protein structure that occurs when the functional groups on the outer surface of the molecule interact by forming hydrogen bonds. These bonds cause the amino acid chain either to twist, forming a helix, or to pleat into an accordion pattern called a β-pleated sheet.

selectively toxic Property of an antimicrobic agent to be highly toxic against its target microbe while being far less toxic to other cells, particularly those of the host organism.

self Natural markers of the body that are recognized by the immune system and generally do not stimulate an immune response.

semiconservative replication In DNA replication, during the synthesis of new DNA strands (the daughter DNA), the parent strand template DNA is retained in the final molecule.

semisolid media Nutrient media with a firmness midway between that of a broth (a liquid medium) and an ordinary solid medium; motility media.

semisynthetic Antibiotics that have been isolated as natural products of bacteria, fungi, or other living sources, and are then chemically modified in the industrial setting to achieve a desired action.

sensitizing dose The initial effective exposure to an antigen or an allergen that stimulates an immune response but not symptoms.

sepsis The state of putrefaction; the presence of pathogenic organisms or their toxins in tissue or blood.

septic shock Blood infection resulting in a pathological state of low blood pressure accompanied by a reduced amount of blood circulating to vital organs. Endotoxins of all gram-negative bacteria can cause shock, but most clinical cases are due to gram-negative enteric rods.

septicemia Systemic infection associated with microorganisms multiplying in circulating blood.

septum (plural, **septa**) A partition or cellular cross wall, as in certain fungal hyphae.

sequela (plural, **sequelae**) A morbid complication that follows a disease.

serology The branch of immunology that deals with in vitro diagnostic testing of serum.

seropositive Showing the presence of specific antibodies in a serological test. Indicates ongoing or recent infection.

serotonin A vasoconstrictor that inhibits gastric secretion and stimulates smooth muscle.

serotyping The subdivision of a species or subspecies into an immunologic type, based upon antigenic characteristics.

serum The clear fluid expressed from clotted blood that contains dissolved nutrients, antibodies, and hormones but not cells or clotting factors.

serum sickness A type of immune complex disease in which immune complexes enter circulation; are carried throughout the body; and are deposited in the blood vessels of the kidney, heart, skin, and joints. The condition may become chronic.

severe acute respiratory syndrome (SARS) A severe respiratory disease caused by infection with a newly described coronavirus.

severe combined immunodeficiencies A collection of syndromes occurring in newborns caused by a genetic defect that knocks out both B- and T-cell types of immunity. There are several versions of this disease, termed **SCIDs** for short.

sewage Liquid runoff or wastewater from communities.

sexually transmitted disease (STD) An infection resulting from pathogens that enter the body via sexual intercourse or intimate, direct contact. Sometimes referred to as sexually transmitted infection (STI) because the disease state is not always apparent.

shigellosis An incapacitating dysentery caused by infection with *Shigella* bacteria.

shingles A skin condition occurring on the trunk or head that is caused by the reactivation of a latent varicella-zoster virus; also known as **herpes zoster.**

side effects Unintended, usually harmful consequences of chemotherapy, including damage to organs, allergy, and disruption of normal microbiota.

sign Any abnormality uncovered upon physical diagnosis that indicates the presence of disease. A sign is an objective assessment of disease, as opposed to a symptom, which is the subjective assessment perceived by the patient.

silent mutation A mutation that, because of the degeneracy of the genetic code, results in a nucleotide change in both the DNA and mRNA but not the resultant amino acid and, thus, not the protein.

simple stain Type of positive staining technique that uses a single dye to add color to cells so that they are easier to see. This technique tends to color all cells the same color.

smallpox Disease caused by infection with variola virus. Smallpox has been eradicated worldwide, and variola virus exists today only in a few government laboratories.

smooth endoplasmic reticulum (SER) A microscopic series of tunnels lacking ribosomes that functions in the nutrient processing function of a cell.

solution A mixture of one or more substances (solutes) that cannot be separated by filtration or ordinary settling.

solvent A dissolving medium.

somatic (O or cell wall) antigen One of the three major antigens commonly used to differentiate gram-negative enteric bacteria.

source The person, location, or object that supplies the pathogen in an infection. This is different from the reservoir, which is where the pathogen lives.

Southern blot A technique that separates fragments of DNA using electrophoresis and identifies them by hybridization.

species In the levels of classification, the most specific level of organization.

specificity Limited to a single, precise characteristic or action.

spheroplast A gram-negative cell whose peptidoglycan, when digested by lysozyme, remains intact but is osmotically vulnerable.

spike A receptor on the surface of certain enveloped viruses that facilitates specific attachment to the host cell.

spirillum (plural, **spirilla**) A type of bacterial cell with a rigid spiral shape and external flagella.

spirochete A coiled, spiral-shaped bacterium that has endoflagella and flexes as it moves.

spontaneous generation Early belief that living things arose from vital forces present in nonliving, or decomposing, matter.

spontaneous mutation A mutation in DNA caused by random mistakes in replication and not known to be influenced by any mutagenic agent. These mutations give rise to an organism's natural, or background, rate of mutation.

sporadic Description of a disease that exhibits new cases at irregular intervals in unpredictable geographic locales.

sporangium A fungal cell in which asexual spores are formed by multiple cell cleavage. This division results in sporangiospores.

spore A differentiated, specialized cell form that can be used for dissemination, for survival in times of adverse conditions, and/or for reproduction. Spores are usually unicellular and may develop into gametes or vegetative organisms.

sporicide A chemical agent capable of destroying bacterial endospores.

sporotrichosis A subcutaneous mycosis caused by *Sporothrix schenckii;* a common cause is the prick of a rose thorn.

sporozoite One of many minute elongated bodies generated by multiple division of the oocyst. It is the infectious form of the malarial parasite that is harbored in the salivary gland of the mosquito and inoculated into the victim during feeding.

sporulation The process of spore formation.

staphylococci (singular, **staphylcoccus**) Coccus-shaped bacteria arranged in irregular clusters due to their division in several different planes.

start codon The nucleotide codon AUG that codes for the first amino acid in protein sequences.

starter culture Pure cultures of bacteria, molds, or yeasts inoculated into substrates for bulk processing, as in the preparation of fermented foods, beverages, and pharmaceuticals.

stationary growth phase Survival mode in which cells either stop growing or grow very slowly and the population number evens out.

stem cells Undifferentiated cells found in the bone marrow and other organs that have the capacity to develop or differentiate into the lines of blood cells (pluripotential).

sterile Completely free of all microbial life forms, including spores and viruses.

sterilization Any process that completely removes or destroys all viable microorganisms, including viruses, from an object or habitat. Material so treated is sterile.

STORCH Acronym for common infections of the fetus and neonate. STORCH stands for syphilis, toxoplasmosis, other diseases (hepatitis B, AIDS, and chlamydiosis), rubella, cytomegalovirus, and herpes simplex virus.

strain In microbiology, a set of descendants cloned from a common ancestor that retain the original characteristics. Any deviation from the original is a different strain.

streptococci (singular, **streptococcus**) Coccus-shaped bacteria arranged in chains due to their division in one plane.

streptolysin A hemolysin produced by streptococci.

strict, or obligate, anaerobe An organism that does not use oxygen gas in metabolism and cannot survive in oxygen's presence.

stroma The matrix of the chloroplast that is the site of the dark reactions.

subacute endocarditis An infection of the heart lining due to invasion of the blood by oral streptococci.

subacute sclerosing panencephalitis (SSPE) A complication of measles infection in which progressive neurological degeneration of the cerebral cortex invariably leads to coma and death.

subcellular vaccine A vaccine against isolated microbial antigens rather than against the entire organism.

subclinical A period during an infection when no noticeable manifestations occur.

subculture To make a second-generation culture from a well-established colony of organisms.

subcutaneous The deepest level of the skin structure.

substrate The specific molecule upon which an enzyme acts.

subunit vaccine A vaccine preparation that contains only antigenic fragments such as surface receptors from the microbe. Usually in reference to virus vaccines.

sucrose One of the carbohydrates commonly referred to as sugars. Common table or cane sugar.

sulfonamide Antimicrobial drugs that interfere with the essential metabolic process of bacteria and some fungi; also known as **sulfa drugs.**

superantigens Microbial toxins and proteins that can activate T cells nonspecifically and often lead to an overpowering reaction such as toxic shock.

superficial mycosis A fungal infection located in hair, nails, and the epidermis of the skin.

superinfection An infection occurring during antimicrobic therapy that is caused by an overgrowth of drug-resistant microorganisms.

surfactant An agent that reduces surface tension and forms a water-soluble interface. Derived from **surf**ace-**act**ive agent. Examples: detergents, soaps, wetting agents, and dispersing agents.

sylvatic Denotes the natural presence of disease among wild animal populations. Examples: sylvatic (sylvan) plague and rabies.

symbiosis/symbionts An intimate association between two or more individuals that are termed symbionts; is sometimes used incorrectly as a synonym for mutualism.

symptom The subjective evidence of infection and disease as perceived by the patient.

syncytium A multinucleated protoplasmic mass formed by consolidation of individual cells.

syndrome The collection of signs and symptoms that, taken together, paint a portrait of the disease.

synergism The coordinated or correlated action by two or more drugs or microbes that results in a heightened response or greater activity.

syntrophy (cross-feeding) A relationship between two organisms where metabolic products produced by one are usable by the other.

syphilis A sexually transmitted bacterial disease caused by the spirochete *Treponema pallidum.*

systemic infection *Systemic* means occurring throughout the body; said of infections that invade many compartments and organs via the circulation.

T helper cell/helper T cell A class of thymus-stimulated lymphocytes that facilitate various immune activities such as assisting the activation of B cells and macrophages; also called **T**$_H$ or **helper T cell.**

T-even phages A group of related bacterial viruses (T-2, T-4, and T-6) that infect *Escherichia coli* bacteria.

taxa Taxonomic categories.

taxonomy The formal system for organizing, classifying, and naming living things.

temperate phage A bacteriophage that enters into a less virulent state by becoming incorporated into the host genome as a prophage instead of in the vegetative or lytic form that eventually destroys the cell.

template The strand in a double-stranded DNA molecule that is used as a model to synthesize a complementary strand of DNA or RNA during replication or transcription.

teratogenic Causing abnormal fetal development.

tertiary (3°) structure Protein structure that results from additional bonds forming between functional groups in a secondary structure, creating a three-dimensional mass.

tetanospasmin The neurotoxin of *Clostridium tetani,* the agent of tetanus. Its chief action is directed upon the inhibitory synapses of the anterior horn motor neurons.

tetanus A neuromuscular disease caused by infection with *Clostridium tetani.* Usual portals of entry include puncture wounds, burns, umbilical stumps, frostbite sites, and crushed body parts. Vaccination repeated at the recommended times can prevent infection; also called **lockjaw.**

tetracyclines A group of broad-spectrum antibiotics with a complex 4-ring structure.

tetrad Group of four.

theory A collection of statements, propositions, or concepts that explains or accounts for a natural event.

therapeutic index (TI) The ratio of the toxic dose to the effective therapeutic dose that is used to assess the safety and reliability of the drug.

thermal death point The lowest temperature that achieves sterilization in a given quantity of broth culture upon a 10-minute exposure. Examples: 55°C for *Escherichia coli,* 60°C for *Mycobacterium tuberculosis,* and 120°C for spores.

thermal death time The least time required to kill all cells of a culture at a specified temperature.

thermal dimorphism A property of certain fungal pathogens of converting from hyphal to yeast form in response to increased temperature.

thermocline A temperature buffer zone in a large body of water that separates the warmer water (the epilimnion) from the colder water (the hypolimnion).

thermoduric Resistant to the harmful effects of high temperature.

thermophile A microorganism that thrives at temperatures between 50°C and 80°C.

thrush *Candida albicans* infection of the oral cavity.

thylakoid Vesicle of a chloroplast formed by elaborate folding of the inner membrane to form "discs." Solar energy trapped in the thylakoids is used in photosynthesis.

thymine (T) One of the nitrogen bases found in DNA but not in RNA. Thymine is a pyrimidine that pairs with adenine.

thymus Butterfly-shaped organ near the tip of the sternum that is the site of T-cell maturation.

tincture A medicinal substance dissolved in an alcoholic solvent.

tinea Ringworm; a fungal infection of the hair, skin, or nails.

tinea versicolor A condition of the skin appearing as mottled and discolored pigmentation as a result of infection by the yeast *Malassezia furfur.*

titer In immunochemistry, a measure of antibody levels in a patient's serum or specimen, as determined by agglutination methods.

toll-like receptors (TLRs) Small surface receptors on phagocytes that are specialized to bind and react to pathogens.

topoisomerase Enzyme that can add or remove DNA twists and thus regulate the degree of supercoiling.

toxemia An abnormality associated with certain infectious diseases. Toxemia is caused by toxins or other noxious substances released by microorganisms circulating in the blood.

toxic shock syndrome Toxemia caused by *Staphylococcus aureus* and associated with the use of tampons.

toxigenicity The tendency for a pathogen to produce toxins. It is an important factor in bacterial virulence.

toxin A specific chemical product of microbes, plants, and some animals that is poisonous to other organisms.

toxinosis Disease whose adverse effects are primarily due to the production and release of toxins.

toxoid A toxin that has been rendered nontoxic but is still capable of eliciting the formation of protective antitoxin antibodies; used in vaccines.

trace elements Micronutrients (zinc, nickel, and manganese) that occur in small amounts and are involved in enzyme function and maintenance of protein structure.

transcription mRNA synthesis; the process by which a strand of RNA is produced against a DNA template.

transduction The transfer of genetic material from one bacterium to another by means of a bacteriophage vector.

transfection Introduction of genetic material into an animal or plant cell using a viral or bacterial vector.

transfer RNA (tRNA) A transcript of DNA that specializes in converting RNA language into protein language.

transformation In microbial genetics, the transfer of genetic material contained in "naked" DNA fragments from a donor cell to a competent recipient cell.

transfusion Infusion of whole blood, red blood cells, or platelets directly into a patient's circulation.

transgenic organisms/genetically modified organisms (GMOs) Cells or organisms into which foreign DNA has been introduced. Includes recombinant plants, animals, and microbes created through genetic engineering.

transient In normal microbiota, the assortment of superficial microbes whose numbers and types vary depending upon recent exposure. The deeper-lying residents constitute a more stable population.

translation Also termed protein synthesis; the process of decoding a messenger RNA code into a polypeptide.

transmissible spongiform encephalopathies (TSEs) Progressive brain infections caused by unusual pathogens called prions, leading to loss of brain structure and function.

transposon A DNA segment with an insertion sequence at each end, enabling it to migrate to another plasmid, to the bacterial chromosome, or to a bacteriophage.

trematode A fluke or flatworm parasite of vertebrates.

trichomoniasis Sexually transmitted disease caused by infection by the trichomonads, a group of protozoa. Symptoms include urinary pain and frequency and foul-smelling vaginal discharge in females or recurring urethritis with a thin milky discharge in males.

triglyceride A type of lipid composed of a glycerol molecule bound to three fatty acids.

triplet A grouping of three nucleotides that serves as the genetic code for protein synthesis. Synonymous with codon.

trophozoite A vegetative protozoan (feeding form) as opposed to a resting (cyst) form.

tropism The property of a virus to favor or be restricted to a specific type of tissue.

true pathogen A microbe capable of causing infection and disease in healthy persons with normal immune defenses.

trypomastigote The infective morphological stage transmitted by the tsetse fly or the reduviid bug in African trypanosomiasis and Chagas disease.

tubercle In tuberculosis, the granulomatous well-defined lung lesion that can serve as a focus for latent infection.

tuberculin reaction A diagnostic test in which an intradermal injection of a purified protein (tuberculin) extract from *M. tuberculosis* elicits an immune response, seen as a small red bump, in those persons previously exposed to tuberculosis.

tuberculoid leprosy A superficial form of leprosy characterized by asymmetrical, shallow skin lesions containing few bacterial cells.

tularemia Infection by *Francisella tularensis*. A zoonotic disease of mammals common to the Northern Hemisphere. Occasionally called rabbit fever. Portal of entry and symptoms are varied.

turbid Cloudy appearance of nutrient solution in a test tube due to growth of microbe population.

turgid Swollen.

tyndallization Fractional (intermittent) sterilization designed to destroy spores indirectly. A preparation is exposed to flowing steam for an hour, followed by incubation to permit spore germination. The resultant new vegetative cells are destroyed by repeated steaming and incubation.

typhoid fever A form of salmonelloses. It is highly contagious. Primary symptoms include fever, diarrhea, and abdominal pain. Typhoid fever can be fatal if untreated.

typhus Rickettsia infection characterized by high fever, chills, frontal headache, muscular pain, and a generalized rash within 7 days of infection. In more severe cases, a personality change, low urine output, hypotension, and gangrene can cause complications. Mortality is high in older adults.

ubiquitous, ubiquity The state of being everywhere at the same time; omnipresent. Said of microbes that are known to live in the vast majority of the habitats on earth.

ultraviolet (UV) radiation Radiation with an effective wavelength from 240 nm to 260 nm. UV radiation induces mutations readily but has very poor penetrating power.

undulant fever See **brucellosis.**

universal donor In blood grouping and transfusion, blood whose erythrocytes bear no A or B antigens and so may be given to any person in an emergency.

universal precautions (UPs) Centers for Disease Control and Prevention guidelines for health care workers regarding the prevention of disease transmission when handling patients and body substances.

uracil (U) The only nitrogen base existing in RNA but not in DNA. It is a pyrimidine and the mate of adenine during transcription.

urban plague Plague passed to humans through contact with domestic animals or other humans.

vaccination The process of inoculation with a selected microbial antigen (vaccine) in order to stimulate an immunity to that microbe.

vaccine Originally used in reference to inoculation with the cowpox or vaccinia virus to protect against smallpox. In general, the term now pertains to injection of whole microbes (killed or attenuated), toxoids, or parts of microbes as a prevention or cure for disease.

vacuole In the cell, membrane-bounded sac containing fluids or solid particles to be digested, excreted, or stored.

valence The combining power of an atom based upon the number of electrons it can either take on or give up.

van der Waals forces Weak interactions between regions of a molecule (especially proteins) that play a significant role in determining the final shape of the molecule.

variable (V) region The antigen-binding fragment of an immunoglobulin molecule, consisting of a combination of heavy and light chains whose molecular conformation is specific for the antigen.

varicella See **chickenpox.**

varicella-zoster virus Herpesvirus responsible for the diseases chickenpox and shingles.

variolation A hazardous, outmoded process of deliberately introducing smallpox material scraped from a victim into the nonimmune subject in the hope of inducing resistance.

VDRL A flocculation test that detects syphilis antibodies. An important screening test. The abbreviation stands for **V**enereal **D**isease **R**esearch **L**aboratory.

vector An animal that transmits infectious agents from one host to another, often a biting or piercing arthropod such as the tick, mosquito, or fly, but it can also include birds and mammals. Vectors convey infectious agents mechanically by simple contact or biologically, with the parasite developing in the vector.

vector₂ A genetic element such as a plasmid or a bacteriophage used to introduce genetic material into a cloning host as a part of recombinant DNA technology.

vehicle An inanimate material (solid object, liquid, or air) that serves as a transmission agent for pathogens.

verruca A flesh-colored wart. This self-limited tumor arises from accumulations of growing epithelial cells. Example: papilloma warts.

vesicle A blister characterized by a thin-skinned, elevated, superficial pocket inflated with serum.

viable but nonculturable (VBNC) A description of organisms that have such a low metabolic rate that they do not normally divide and cannot be detected through culture-based means.

vibrio A curved, rod-shaped bacterial cell.

viremia The presence of viruses in the bloodstream.

virion An elementary virus particle in its complete morphological and thus infectious form. A virion consists of the nucleic acid core surrounded by a capsid, which can be enclosed in an envelope.

viroid An infectious agent that, unlike a virion, lacks a capsid and consists of a closed circular RNA molecule. Although known viroids are all plant pathogens, it is conceivable that animal versions exist.

virtual image In optics, an image formed by diverging light rays; in the compound light microscope, the second, magnified visual impression formed by the ocular from the real image formed by the objective.

virucide A chemical agent that inactivates viruses, especially on living tissue.

virulence In infection, the relative capacity of a pathogen to invade and harm host cells.

virulence factor A product of microbes such as an enzyme or toxin that increases the microbe's invasiveness or pathogenicity.

virus Microscopic, acellular agent composed of nucleic acid surrounded by a protein coat.

vitamins Components of coenzymes critical to nutrition and the metabolic function of coenzyme complexes.

vulvovaginal candidiasis (VC) Vaginal STD caused by *Candida albicans* and often associated with disruption of the normal vaginal flora.

wart An epidermal tumor caused by papillomaviruses; also called a **verruca.**

Western blot test A procedure for separating and identifying antigen or antibody mixtures by two-dimensional electrophoresis in polyacrylamide gel, followed by immune labeling.

wheal/flare A welt; marked, slightly red, usually itchy bumps on the skin that change in size and shape as they spread. It is surrounded by a red patch (the flare). The reaction is triggered by cutaneous contact or intradermal injection of allergens in sensitive individuals.

whey The residual fluid from milk coagulation that separates from the solidified curd.

white piedra A fungus disease of hair, especially of the scalp, face, and genitals, caused by *Trichosporon beigelii*. The infection is associated with soft, mucilaginous, white-to-light-brown nodules that form within and on the hair shafts.

whitlow A deep inflammation of the finger or toe, especially near the tip or around the nail. Whitlow is a painful herpes simplex virus infection that can last several weeks and is most common among health care personnel who come in contact with the virus in patients.

whole blood A liquid connective tissue consisting of blood cells suspended in plasma.

whooping cough See **pertussis.**

Widal test An agglutination test for diagnosing typhoid fever and determining the antibody titer.

wild type The natural, nonmutated form of a genetic trait.

wort The clear fluid derived from soaked mash that is fermented for beer.

xenograft The transfer of a tissue or an organ from an animal of one species to a recipient of another species.

yaws A tropical disease caused by *Treponema pertenue* that produces granulomatous ulcers on the extremities and occasionally on bone but does not produce central nervous system or cardiovascular complications.

yeasts Single-celled, budding fungi.

yellow fever Best-known arboviral disease. Yellow fever is transmitted by mosquitoes. Its symptoms include fever, headache, and muscle pain that can proceed to oral hemorrhage, nosebleeds, vomiting, jaundice, and liver and kidney damage.

zoonosis An infectious disease indigenous to animals that humans can acquire through direct or indirect contact with infected animals.

zooplankton The collection of nonphotosynthetic microorganisms (protozoa, tiny animals) that float in the upper regions of aquatic habitat and together with phytoplankton comprise the plankton.

zygospore A thick-walled sexual spore produced by the zygomycete fungi. It develops from the union of two hyphae, each bearing nuclei of opposite mating types.

Note: In this index entries followed by a lowercase f refer to figures, entries followed by a lowercase t refer to tables, and entries printed in **boldface** type indicate definitions or introductory discussions.